D1491894

technical mathematics with calculus

McGraw-Hill Book Company
NEW YORK • ST. LOUIS • SAN FRANCISCO
LONDON • TORONTO • SYDNEY

technical mathematics with calculus

SECOND EDITION

harold s. rice

SENIOR HEAD, DEPARTMENT OF MATHEMATICS, WENTWORTH INSTITUTE

raymond m. knight

CHAIRMAN, MATHEMATICS DEPARTMENT, HUDSON VALLEY COMMUNITY COLLEGE

technical
mathematics
with calculus

Printed in the United States of America.

Library of Congress Catalog Card Number: 65-17496
52191

567890 HDBP 754321069

preface

Every textbook should have a definable purpose and point of view. In this edition, as in the first, the authors intend to help students of engineering learn how to use the techniques of mathematics as a professional tool. The point of view, therefore, is still that mathematics is an engineer's tool, one that can be used to learn, to work, and to communicate. The authors are well aware that there are other values of mathematics. Those, however important and worthwhile they are, are definitely subordinate to the central theme of this text.

The authors are also well aware that there are many functions and many techniques that are not even hinted at in this volume. They have been omitted intentionally because experience has shown that these functions and techniques are not ordinarily encountered by the beginning engineer and engineering technician. The authors feel very strongly that the classroom time and the textbook space can much more properly be devoted to building skills in the use of more elementary techniques rather than to discussing the more theoretical aspects of mathematics, which the student will probably not use until he has acquired considerable experience in his chosen field.

This text is the outgrowth of years of classwork with students at Wentworth Institute and Hudson Valley Community College, who are high school graduates who have had at least a year or two of algebra. Although they expect to enter industry and work closely with craftsmen, they must also be at ease in the more precise atmosphere of engineering. With today's and tomorrow's needs in mind, the general approach of this edition has been modernized; and the problems, which now include space-technology topics, have been revised with great care. The level of rigor itself has also been raised, especially in the calculus sections. In Chap. 6, "Functions and Graphs," the graphic analysis of word problems emphasizes the slope concept, and in Chap. 7, "Systems of Linear Equations," the treatment of determinants has been enlarged. Chapter 11, "Exponential Functions," has been rearranged to make it easier to teach. The chapters dealing with the binomial theorem and with common and natural logarithms (Chaps. 9, 10, and 11) have been relocated in this edition to support the presentation of curve sketching. In this latter topic, the advantages of the "take-apart-and-put-together" techniques are demonstrated. This technique not only deals with the addition and subtraction of ordinates but shows the advantage of taking products, quotients, reciprocals, squares, and square roots of ordinates. The treatment of curve sketching, together with an increased emphasis on the application of slopes in Chap. 6, should help the student make a strong start in calculus. The large number of calculus applications to physics and the engineering sciences should be valuable for supplementing an algebra-based approach in these areas.

The topics have been broken down into nine teaching units and four appendixes, as follows:

*Unit One	Slide Rule and Review of Geometry
*Unit Two	Basic Algebra and Analytic Geometry of the Straight Line
Unit Three	More Advanced Algebra and Logarithms
Unit Four	Curve Sketching, Nonlinear Empirical Equations
*Unit Five	Numerical Trigonometry of the Right Triangle
Unit Six	Introduction to Analytical Trigonometry
Unit Seven	Oblique Triangles and Applications of Numerical Trigonometry
Unit Eight	Analytical Trigonometry
Unit Nine	An Introduction to Calculus
*Appendix A	Treatment of Measured Data
*Appendix B	Computation Aids and Approximations
*Appendix C	Interpolation
*Appendix D	Solution of Higher-degree Equations

The starred units can be used in any order.

Unit One is a mature review of geometry built around a study of the slide rule.

Unit Two is a rather thorough review of basic algebra. As a review, it has been handled somewhat differently from a unit intended to introduce algebra.

Unit Three continues where Unit Two leaves off. This section is not a review; it assumes that the student is studying these topics for the first time.

Unit Four, discussed above, is a completely revised introduction and discussion of these two important topics.

Unit Five is an elementary treatment of numerical trigonometry designed for the beginning student. This unit may be assigned on the opening day of school if desired.

Unit Six introduces analytical trigonometry from the point of view of the electricity student and the more analytically inclined mechanics student.

Unit Seven continues the study of numerical trigonometry and emphasizes the oblique triangle and trigonometric applications. The section of Chap. 10, "Logarithms," on the use of logarithms in computation may be assigned in preparation for Unit Seven without the earlier part of Unit Five.

Unit Eight is intended for electricity students, but Chap. 21, "Trigonometric Formulas, Identities, and Equations," would apply as well for mechanics and building construction students.

Unit Nine is an introduction to the techniques of elementary calculus. The intention of the authors here is to introduce those techniques of calculus which will be useful to the engineering student in the pursuit of his major subjects. It is written for the student engineer and the student engineering technician. It is definitely not written for the physics major.

The authors, in their courses, devote about a year and a half to the material in this book; but in courses that give a greater proportion of time to shopwork, the material may occupy two full years.

Thanks are due to the authors' colleagues for their continued interest and constructive criticisms. The authors are also grateful to the users of the first edition who have taken the trouble to write to us their thoughts for an improved second edition.

In particular, the authors wish to express their appreciation to Mr. Barclay V. Huiell of Voorhees Technical Institute for his valuable suggestions as to problem material; to Mr. John W. Cell, author of *Engineering Problems Illustrating Mathematics,* for permission to adapt problem material from his book; and to Miss Florence Pasquini for checking many of the solutions to problems in the calculus section.

Harold S. Rice

Raymond M. Knight

contents

unit one
slide rule and review of arithmetic and geometry

unit two
basic algebra and analytic geometry of the straight line

unit seven
oblique triangles and applications of numerical trigonometry

unit eight
analytical trigonometry

unit one slide rule and review of geometry

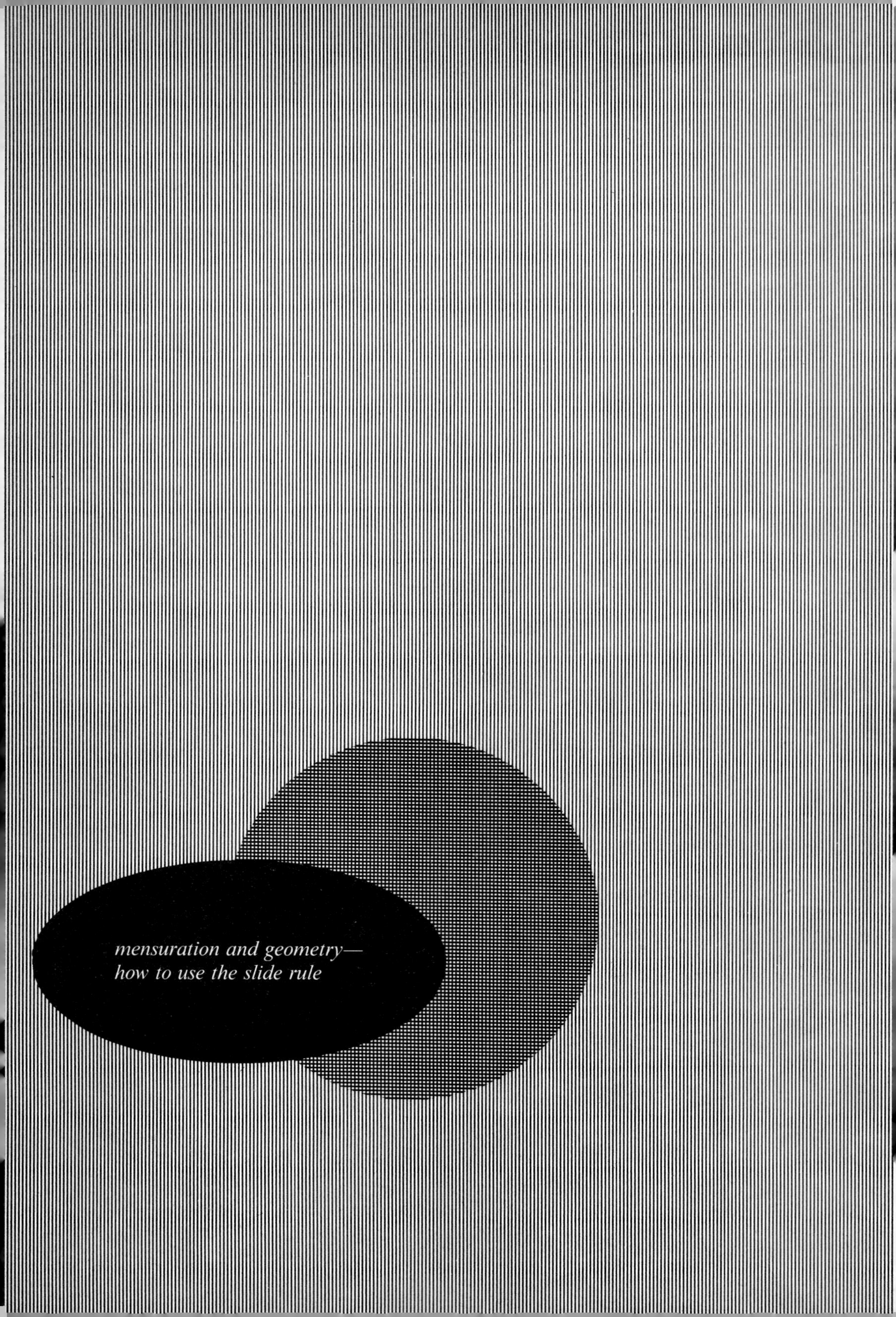
mensuration and geometry—
how to use the slide rule

1

the slide rule

From time to time we shall review some of the methods whereby much of the drudgery of computation may be eliminated and the effectiveness of work increased. These methods include the use of the slide rule, tables, approximations, and graph paper, to name a few. In this chapter we shall obtain practice in the use of the first of these.

1·1 Scope of the slide rule

It is essential to have a clear idea of what can and what cannot be done on a slide rule. The slide rule is an instrument used for processes of multiplication, division, proportion, and calculation of simple powers and roots. Further discussion of the slide rule will be found in Secs. 10·32, 10·33, and 16·21 to 16·23, but this chapter will deal only with the processes named above. Addition and subtraction cannot be performed on the slide rule. One of the most frequently asked questions is, "Is slide-rule computation good enough?" The answer depends upon the nature of the problem. Many experimental data are accurate to no more than three significant figures. In such cases slide-rule computation is sufficiently accurate. Even in problems requiring more precise methods, the slide rule is accurate enough to detect gross errors and to estimate the order of magnitude of the answer.

The slide rule will not think for you. Like an automobile, it will take you to your destination if you provide the proper direction.

There are many types of slide rules, but our discussion will be limited to the general technique of operation common to most basic 10-in. rules. (More versatile slide rules feature inverted and folded scales as well as log-log scales. Instruction in their use is given in the manual provided with the rule. Almost as many operations can be performed on the basic rule as on the rule having additional scales. The chief advantage of the latter lies in its greater ease of operation.) Additional practice in using the slide rule may be gained by solving many of the problems in Chap. 3.

1·2 Description of the slide rule

The slide rule consists of three parts (see Fig. 1·1): the *slide,* or central sliding part; the *body,* or the upper and lower bars between which the slide operates; and the *indicator,* which is the movable glass plate marked with a hairline.

The mark associated with the numeral 1 at an end of a scale is called the *index* of the scale. Two positions on two different scales are said to be *opposite* if the hairline can be made to cover both simultaneously.

In order to perform the operations mentioned in Sec. 1·1, we need use only the C, D, A, B, and K scales. The C and D scales are identical. The A and B scales are identical with each other, and the distance between two successive integers is one-half the distance between the same two integers on the C and D scales. The K scale is compressed even further, so that the distance between any two integers is one-third the distance between the same two integers on scales C and D.

The C and D scales are divided into nine principal divisions by *primary marks* bearing the large numbers 1, 2, 3, . . . , 8, 9, 1. The space between any two primary marks is divided into ten parts by *secondary marks.* These are not numbered, except between the primary marks 1

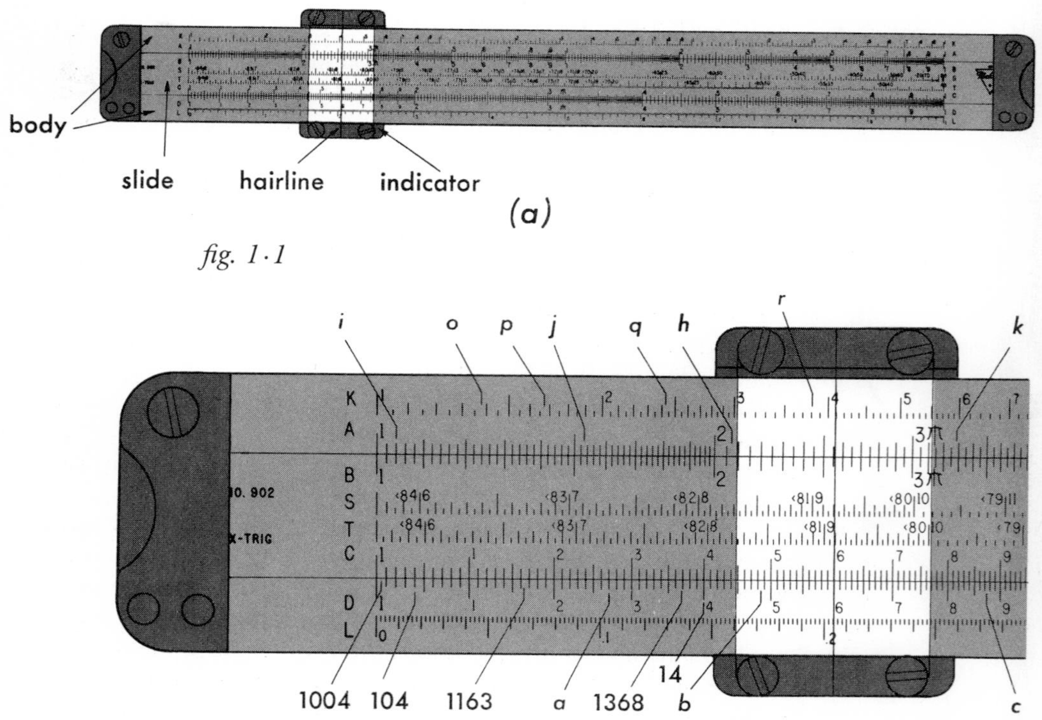

(a)

fig. 1·1

(b)

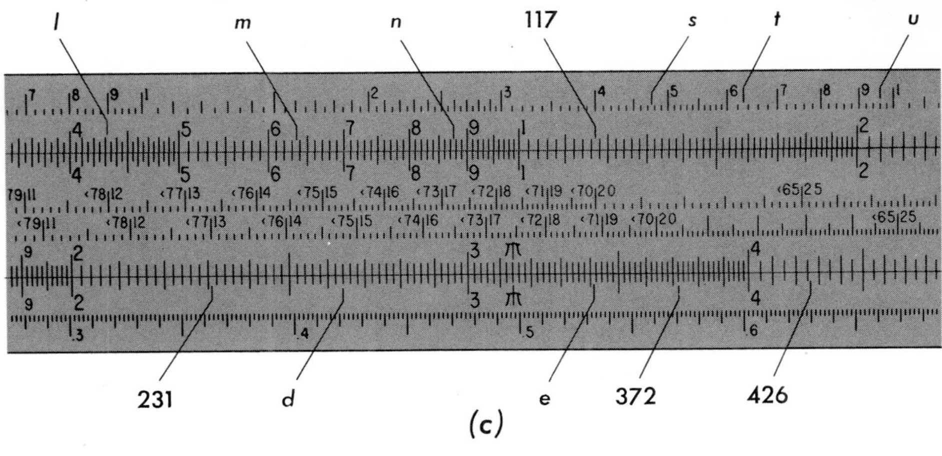

(c)

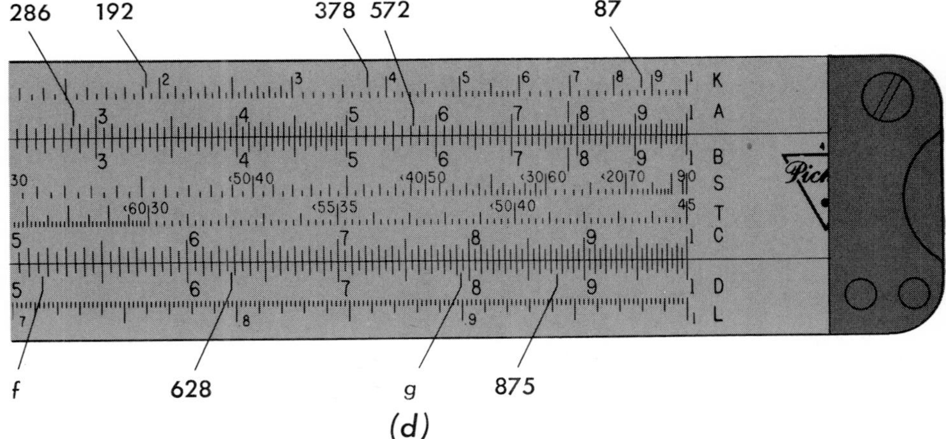

(d)

and 2, where they bear the small numerals 1 through 9. The space between two successive secondary marks is divided into two, five, or ten spaces by unnumbered *tertiary marks.*

The A and B scales each have two identical portions. Each portion is divided into nine principal divisions by numbered primary marks. Unnumbered secondary marks further divide each principal division, and still finer division is supplied by tertiary marks between the primary marks numbered 1 and 5.

The K scale is divided into three identical portions. They are divided much as the A and B scales are, but more coarsely.

1·3 Location of numbers on the scales; accuracy of the slide rule

It must be remembered that the decimal point plays no part in locating a number on the C and D scales. The first significant digit is located by reference to the primary marks, the second by reference to the secondary marks, and the third by reference to the tertiary marks or to some point between tertiary marks, according to the portion of the scale being used. By estimating fractions of a graduation, a fourth digit may be located for numbers occurring between primary marks 1 and 2 on the C and D scales. This means that the maximum accuracy ordinarily available with a 10-in. slide rule is 1 part in 1,000. Location of actual numbers will be best illustrated by referring to the examples in Fig. 1·1*b* to *d*.

EXERCISE 1

Read as closely as possible the points indicated in Fig. 1·1*b* to *d*.

D scale: *a b c d e f g*
A scale: *h i j k l m n*
K scale: *o p q r s t u*

1·4 Multiplication

Either the C and D scales or the A and B scales may be used. Ordinarily the C and D scales are preferable, since their larger-scale divisions make for greater accuracy. Their use is illustrated in Fig. 1·2 and in the following example.

example 1 Multiply 8 by 5.

Set the right index of C opposite 8 on the D scale. Move the indicator so the hairline covers 5 on the C scale. Directly below this 5 will be found the "slide-rule product" 4 on the D scale. The student must locate the decimal point himself, and common sense indicates that the answer is 40, not 4.

It will be appreciated that the same setting would be used for multiplying 80 by 50, 8,000 by 0.5, 0.08 by 500, etc.

fig. 1·2

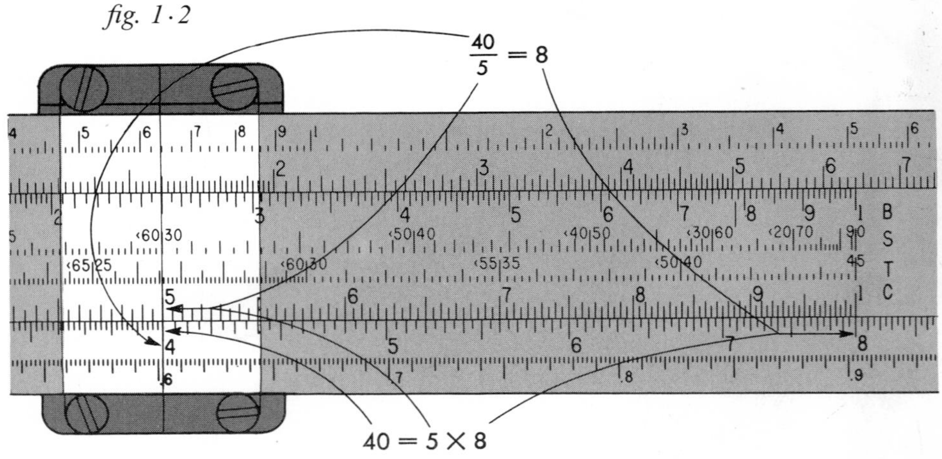

If we were to try to use the above setting of the right index to multiply 8 by 12, a reading would be impossible, as the 12 on the C scale is located beyond the end of the D scale. In this case we would set the *left* index of the C scale over 8 on the D scale and locate on the D scale our answer 96, immediately under 12 on the C scale. It will be useful to remember that when the product of the first significant figures in multiplicand and multiplier is less than 10, the student should use the left index; when it is greater than 10, he should use the right index.

When multiplying more than two numbers, use the hairline to mark the position of the product of the first two. Without reading this product, use it as the multiplicand for the next multiplication.

If the magnitude of the product is not immediately obvious, a rough mental check will suffice.

example 2 The slide-rule product of 1,440 × 37.5 × 0.08125 is 439. It is evident that our product is approximately 1,500 × 40 × 0.08, or 4,800. Hence the answer must be 4,390.

To multiply two numbers:

1. *Set the proper index of C opposite either factor on the D scale.*
2. *Place the hairline over the other factor on the C scale, and read the significant digits of the product under the hairline on the D scale.*
3. *Determine the position of the decimal point by a rough mental estimate.*
4. *In the above steps, C and D may be replaced by B and A, respectively.*

EXERCISE 2

Perform the following multiplications, retaining in the product as many significant figures as you think are justified:

1. 4.00 × 17.00
2. 7.50 × 1.20
3. 3.30 × 9.0
4. 64.0 × 0.375
5. 288 × 382
6. 321 × 1,069
7. 728 × 1,218
8. 617 × 1,645
9. 1,006 × 902
10. 1,258 × 1,562
11. 862 × 482
12. 66.2 × 10.3
13. 1.475 × 1,520
14. 0.981 × 0.693
15. 329 × 0.00352
16. 0.342 × 1.306
17. 8.14 × 0.0309
18. 2.46 × 330,000 × 3.14
19. 3.1 × 920 × 0.486 × 1,520
20. 0.1038 × 0.0063 × 28 × 9.82
21. 512 × 62.5 × 0.0027 × 87
22. 0.1047 × 0.00774 × 0.349 × 0.0562

1·5 Division

Since division is the inverse of multiplication, Fig. 1·2 may be used to illustrate division as well as multiplication. In this example we have the setting for 40 ÷ 5 = 8.

To divide one number by another:

1. *Bring the divisor on the C scale opposite the dividend on the D scale by means of the hairline.*
2. *Opposite the index of the C scale, read the significant figures of the quotient on the D scale. If desired, the indicator may be used to aid in this reading.*
3. *Determine the position of the decimal point by a rough mental estimate.*
4. *C and D may be replaced by B and A, respectively, as in multiplication.*

EXERCISE 3

Perform the following divisions, retaining in the quotient as many significant figures as you think are justified:

1. 18.00 ÷ 50.0	2. 25.0 ÷ 3.00	3. 750 ÷ 5.50
4. 12.8 ÷ 72	5. 69.8 ÷ 4.78	6. 197.2 ÷ 858
7. 0.924 ÷ 21.0	8. 17.5 ÷ 1,646	9. 1 ÷ 37.5
10. 0.0752 ÷ 0.000718	11. 0.1804 ÷ 363	12. 1 ÷ 2.73
13. 0.1875 ÷ 0.078125	14. 0.005632 ÷ 18.432	

1·6 Location of decimal point in scientific notation

Use of scientific notation makes work with very large or very small numbers easier and reduces the likelihood of error.

example 3 Multiply 538,000 by 0.00377.

In scientific notation, we have roughly $(5 \times 10^5) \times (4 \times 10^{-3})$. This product may be written $5 \times 4 \times 10^2 = 2 \times 10^3$. Since the product of 5.38 and 3.77 on the slide rule is 203 (before locating the decimal point), our answer must be 2.03×10^3, or 2,030.

example 4 Divide 538,000 by 0.00377.

In scientific notation, we have roughly $(5 \times 10^5)/(4 \times 10^{-3}) = 1.2 \times 10^8$. Since the slide-rule reading is 1,427, our answer must be 1.427×10^8, or 142,700,000.

1·7 Combined multiplication and division

The easiest method of computing the quotient of two products is to alternate between division and multiplication. If we do all the multiplying first, then all the dividing, more moves are required, with greater chance of error.

example 5 Evaluate

$$\frac{825 \times 184}{227 \times 316}$$

Divide 825 by 227 in the usual way. The quotient will be found on the D scale under the C index. However, we do not read the value, since it serves merely as the multiplicand for 184. Without moving the slide, we move the indicator so that the hairline covers 184 on the C scale. The product will be found on the D scale under the hairline. Since this product is to be divided by 316, we do not read the value, nor do we move the hairline, but we move the slide so that 316 is under the hairline. Directly beneath the C index read approximately 2115. The answer is 2.115, with the last figure in doubt.

Sometimes the slide must be moved so that one C index is moved to the spot formerly occupied by the other C index (as marked with the hairline). This situation might have been avoided, with some sacrifice of accuracy, by using the A and B scales.

EXERCISE 4

Perform the following computations, expressing the answer in scientific notation. Retain in the answer as many significant figures as conditions justify.

1. $2.4 \times 6.5 \times 10.37$
2. $1{,}476 \times 37.8 \times 54.0$
3. $0.00842 \times 0.295 \times 6.1875$
4. $67.1 \times 0.000418 \times 3.0$
5. $32.00 \times 5.000 \times 1.900 \times 0.4000$
6. $\dfrac{1}{0.00532 \times 0.0612}$
7. $\dfrac{1.28 \times 3.56}{74.4}$
8. $\dfrac{15.8 \times 1.35}{0.031}$
9. $\dfrac{21.3 \times 0.054}{97.4 \times 3.80}$
10. $\dfrac{1{,}927}{412 \times 0.00592 \times 483}$
11. $\dfrac{24.6 \times 0.359}{296 \times 4.61 \times 98.7}$
12. $\dfrac{560{,}000 \times 0.0045 \times 12{,}500}{1{,}050{,}000 \times 0.072}$

1·8 Proportion

Proportions may usually be solved with only one setting of the slide. Observe in Fig. 1·3 that when 8 on the C scale is opposite 64 on the D scale, we find 5 opposite 4. This setting could therefore illustrate the solution of the proportion $5/x = 8/6.4$, in which we set 8 opposite 64 and, opposite 5, read $x = 4$. Note that all other pairs of numbers that are opposite each other have the same ratio (e.g., $^{60}/_{48}$, $^{70}/_{56}$, $^{75}/_{60}$, $^{90}/_{72}$).

To solve a proportion, locate the numbers on the C and D scales in the same relative position as in the proportion $a/b = c/d$ (or $c/d = a/b$ if the setting for a falls to the right of the setting for c). When the C and D scales cannot accommodate the simultaneous settings of a over b and c over d, the A and B scales may be used.

Of course we can solve for x, obtaining $x = (5)(6.4)/8$, and, using the principle of Sec. 1·7, again obtain $x = 4$.

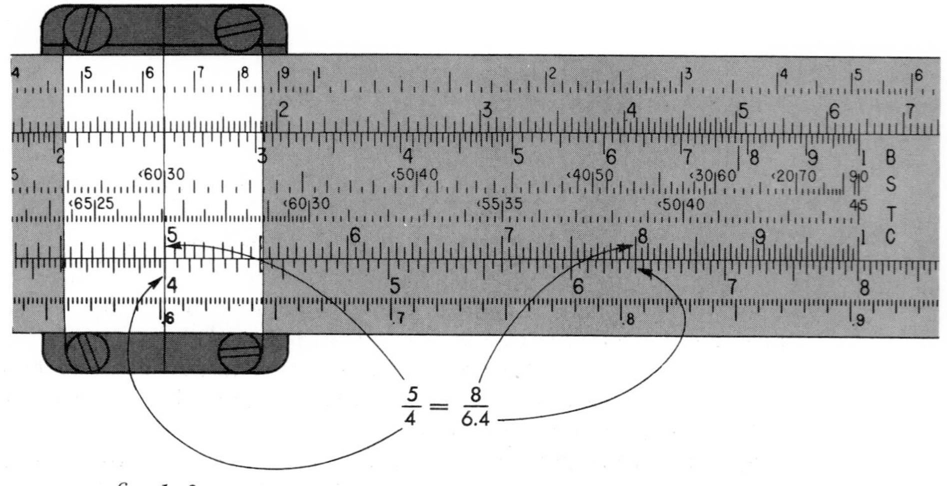

fig. 1·3

EXERCISE 5

In the following proportions, calculate x to three significant figures:

1. $\frac{x}{8.5} = \frac{32}{28.9}$
2. $\frac{x}{21.5} = \frac{89}{79}$
3. $\frac{372}{x} = \frac{637}{9.31}$
4. $\frac{8.2}{377} = \frac{0.323}{x}$
5. $\frac{18.3}{63.6} = \frac{x}{29}$
6. $\frac{267}{8.75} = \frac{x}{192}$
7. $\frac{0.716}{x} = \frac{10.1}{168}$
8. $\frac{795}{0.109} = \frac{42.3}{x}$

1·9 Squares and square roots

To find the square of a number, set the hairline of the indicator over that number on the D scale, and under the hairline read the square of that number on the A scale. We can also read from the C to the B scale in the same way. Figure 1·4 shows that $4^2 = 16$ (D to A scale), that $5^2 = 25$ (C to B scale), and that $8^2 = 64$ (right C index reading to right B index setting).

Figure 1·5 illustrates that $(1.428)^2 = 2.04$ and that $(2.53)^2 = 6.4$.

example 6 Find 6^2.

Set the hairline over 6 on the D scale. Read 36 under the hairline on the A scale.

example 7 Find $(8.62)^2$.

Set the hairline over 8.62 on the D scale. Read 74.3 under the hairline on the A scale.

example 8 Find $(71{,}700)^2$.

On the A scale read 514 directly above the 717 on the D scale. Since $(71{,}700)^2 = (7.17 \times 10^4)^2$, the answer must be $51.4 \times 10^{4\times 2} = 51.4 \times 10^8 = 5{,}140{,}000{,}000$.

example 9 Find $(0.00386)^2$.

On the A scale read 149 directly above the 386 on the D scale. Since $(0.00386)^2 = (3.86 \times 10^{-3})^2$, the answer must be $14.9 \times 10^{-3\times 2} = 14.9 \times 10^{-6} = 0.0000149$.

fig. 1·4

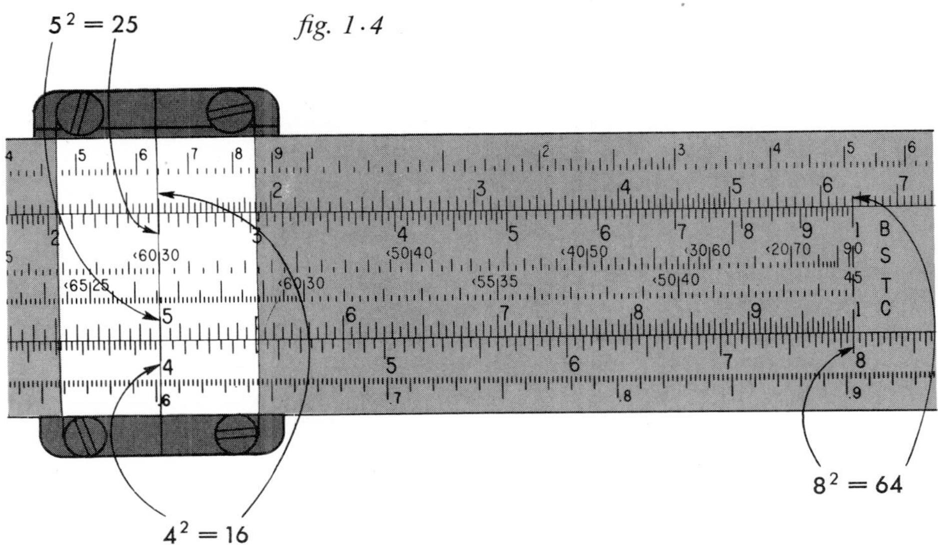

fig. 1·5

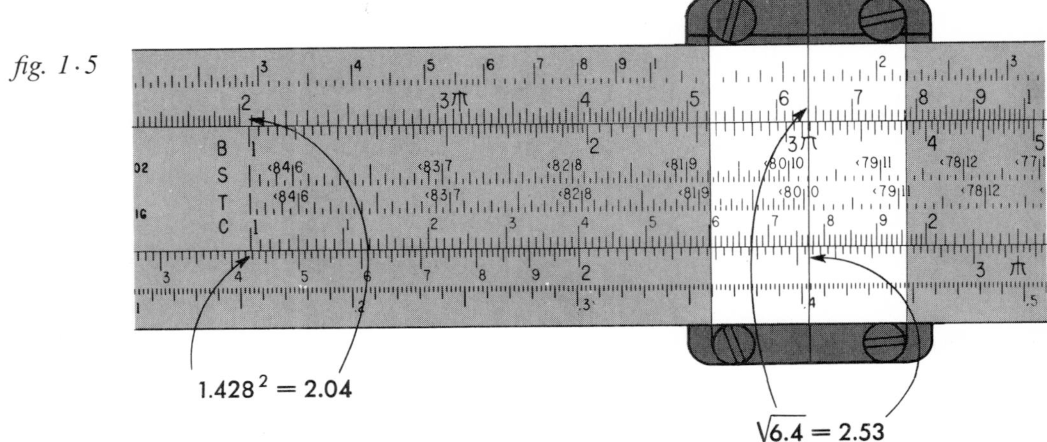

The process of obtaining square roots is the reverse of that used in calculating squares. Therefore Figs. 1·4 and 1·5 may be used to show that $\sqrt{16} = 4$, $\sqrt{25} = 5$, $\sqrt{64} = 8$, $\sqrt{2.04} = 1.428$, and $\sqrt{6.4} = 2.53$. We may indeed use Fig. 1·4 to read $\sqrt{64} = 8$; but if we had not had the operation of squaring 8 to guide us, we might have made an unfortunate choice in working from the 64 on the left half of the A scale; i.e., we might have read 253 directly below on the D scale. A quick check will show that 2.53 is the square root of 6.4. (This procedure is opposite to that of squaring 2.53, an operation originally illustrated in Fig. 1·5.)

It is evident that in reversing the procedure for squaring we must first determine which half of the A scale to choose as a starting point. There are a number of ways of making this choice. Perhaps the simplest is that used in the examples in Sec. 2·1. The procedure is as follows: Write down the number whose square root is to be found. Indicate the grouping of the digits as for longhand extraction of square root. Write in their proper positions the decimal point and the first significant digit in the square root. Select that half of the A scale which lies above the first significant figure (just determined) on the D scale.

example 10 Find $\sqrt{6{,}870{,}000.}$

Indicating the grouping, the decimal point, and the first significant figure, we write

$$\begin{array}{l} \;\;2 \\ \sqrt{6\ 87\ 00\ 00.} \end{array}$$

It is apparent that we read from 687 on the *left* half of the A scale, since we find 2 on the D scale under that half. Accordingly we read from 687 on the left half of the A scale directly below to 262 on the D scale. This indicates that the square root of 6,870,000 will be written

$$\begin{array}{l} \;\;2\ \ 6\ \ 2\ \ 0. \\ \sqrt{6\ 87\ 00\ 00.} \end{array}$$

example 11 Find $\sqrt{0.0000687.}$

A rough indication of the answer is found by proceeding as before and writing

$$\begin{array}{l} \;\;0.\ \ 0\ \ 0\ \ 8 \\ \sqrt{0.\ 00\ 00\ 68\ 7} \end{array}$$

In this case we evidently read down from the 687 on the *right* half of the A scale. We read 829 on the D scale, and the answer is clearly 0.00829.

1·10 Cubes and cube roots

To find the cube of a number, set the hairline over that number on the D scale and read its cube on the K scale under the hairline.

example 12 Find $(6.35)^3$.

Set the hairline over 6.35 on the D scale. Read 256 under the hairline on the K scale.

example 13 Find $(0.0439)^3$.

Read 846 on the K scale directly opposite 439 on the D scale. Since $(0.0439)^3 = (4.39 \times 10^{-2})^3$, the answer must be $84.6 \times 10^{-2\times 3} = 84.6 \times 10^{-6} = 0.0000846$.

To find a cube root, we reverse the procedure for cubing and work from the K scale to the D scale. When working from the A scale to the D scale, we had to choose between two sections. On the K scale we must choose the proper section out of three. The process is exactly comparable to that used in finding a square root. Figures 1·6 to 1·8 show the settings for 4^3, 8^3, and 16^3, and therefore the settings for $\sqrt[3]{64}$, $\sqrt[3]{512}$, and $\sqrt[3]{4{,}100}$.

example 14 Find $\sqrt[3]{0.0000048}$.

Indicating the grouping, the decimal point, and the first significant figure, we write

$$\begin{array}{l}\;\;\,0.\;0\quad\;\;1\\ \sqrt[3]{0.000\;004\;8}\end{array}$$

fig. 1·6

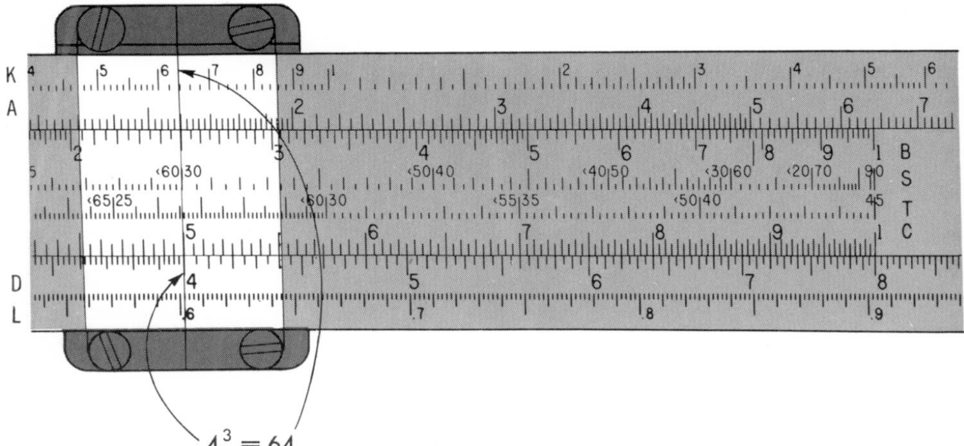

Evidently we work from the *left* third of the K scale, since it lies opposite the 1+ on the D scale. Therefore, we read from 48 on the left third of the K scale directly to 1,687 on the D scale. This indicates that the cube root of 0.0000048 will be written

$$\begin{array}{l} 0.\ 0\quad 1\ \ 6\ 8\ 7 \\ \sqrt[3]{0.000\ 004\ 8} \end{array}$$

example 15 Find $\sqrt[3]{58{,}500{,}000}$.

Proceeding as before, we write

$$\begin{array}{l} \quad 3 \\ \sqrt[3]{58\ 500\ 000.} \end{array}$$

fig. 1·7

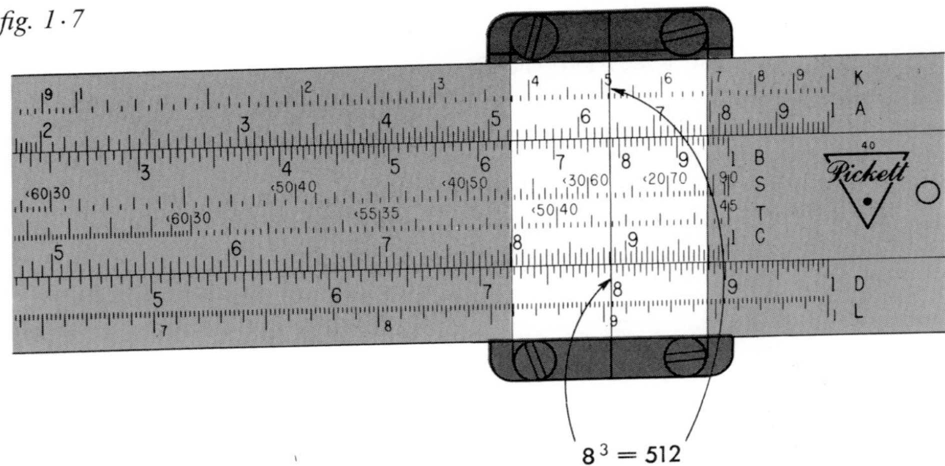

fig. 1·8

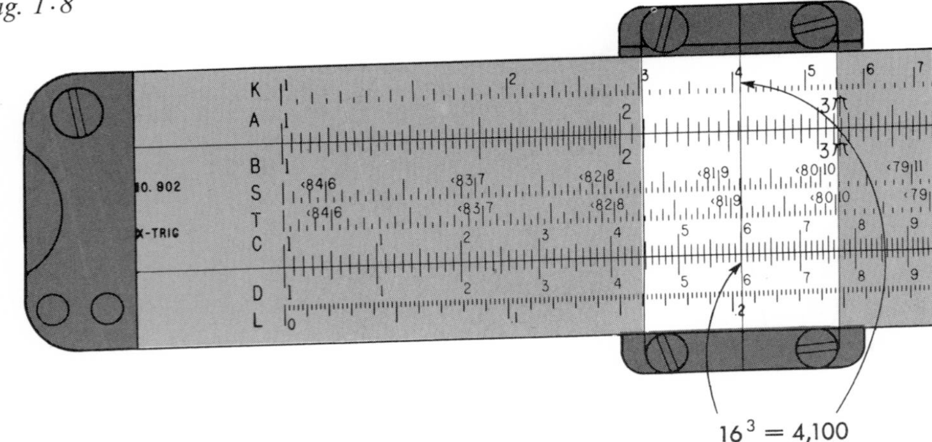

and find that the *middle* third of the K scale lies opposite the 3 on the D scale. Reading, therefore, from 585 in the middle section of the K scale, we find 388 on the D scale directly opposite. Hence the answer must be 388.

EXERCISE 6

Evaluate the following as accurately as the slide rule will allow:

1. $(18.00)^2$
2. $(2{,}730)^2$
3. $(6.05)^2$
4. $(34.5)^2$
5. $(167.8)^2$
6. $(0.854)^2$
7. $(0.1054)^2$
8. $(0.00782)^2$
9. $(517.23)^2$
10. $(0.030448)^2$
11. $(63 \times 426)^2$
12. $(9.1 \times 0.0119)^2$
13. $(0.027 \times 1.72 \times 7.95)^2$
14. $(5.1 \times 0.438 \times 14.12)^2$
15. $\left(\frac{1{,}647}{658}\right)^2$
16. $\left(\frac{69.8}{858}\right)^2$
17. $\left(\frac{852}{658}\right)^2$
18. $\left(\frac{61.4 \times 0.673}{2.16}\right)^2$
19. $\left(\frac{582 \times 1.104}{37.2 \times 8}\right)^2$
20. $\sqrt{49.2}$
21. $\sqrt{0.00702}$
22. $\sqrt{2{,}980}$
23. $\sqrt{0.837}$
24. $\sqrt{17{,}840}$
25. $\sqrt{0.0542}$
26. $\sqrt{0.000347}$
27. $\sqrt{45{,}897}$
28. $\sqrt{103.6}$
29. $\sqrt{7{,}080{,}000}$
30. $\sqrt{\frac{1.316}{0.016}}$
31. $\sqrt{\frac{1{,}127 \times 5.47}{21 \times 0.0025}}$
32. $\sqrt{\frac{11.26}{0.787 \times 24.8}}$
33. $(11.9)^3$
34. $(1.33)^3$
35. $(0.157)^3$
36. $(118.5)^3$
37. $(23.19)^3$
38. $(0.0342)^3$
39. $(478)^3$
40. $(6.375)^3$
41. $(783)^3$
42. $(0.0876)^3$
43. $(15.45 \times 0.132)^3$
44. $(8.75 \times 0.037)^3$
45. $\left(\frac{10.12}{17.58}\right)^3$
46. $\left(\frac{48.8}{4.21}\right)^3$
47. $\sqrt[3]{13.5}$
48. $\sqrt[3]{0.0474}$
49. $\sqrt[3]{76{,}215}$
50. $\sqrt[3]{2.85}$
51. $\sqrt[3]{9{,}384{,}260}$
52. $\sqrt[3]{0.00625}$
53. $\sqrt[3]{652 \times 0.725}$
54. $\sqrt[3]{1.447 \times 0.0298}$
55. $\sqrt[3]{\frac{8{,}747}{0.212}}$
56. $\sqrt[3]{\frac{158.5}{255}}$

1·11 Circumference and area of a circle

Since the problem of finding the circumference of a circle is simply one of finding the product of a given diameter and 3.14, we follow the usual procedure for multiplication.

To find the area of a circle when the radius is given, set the index of C opposite the radius on the D scale. Place the hairline over π on the B scale. The answer is found under the hairline on the A scale. Figure 1·9 shows that the area of a circle of radius 17.44 in. is about 956 sq in.

To find the area of a circle when the diameter is given, set the index of C opposite the diameter on the D scale. Place the hairline over $\pi/4$ or 0.785 on the B scale. The area is found under the hairline on the A scale. Figure 1·10 shows that the area of a 9.03-in.-diameter circle is 64.0 sq in.

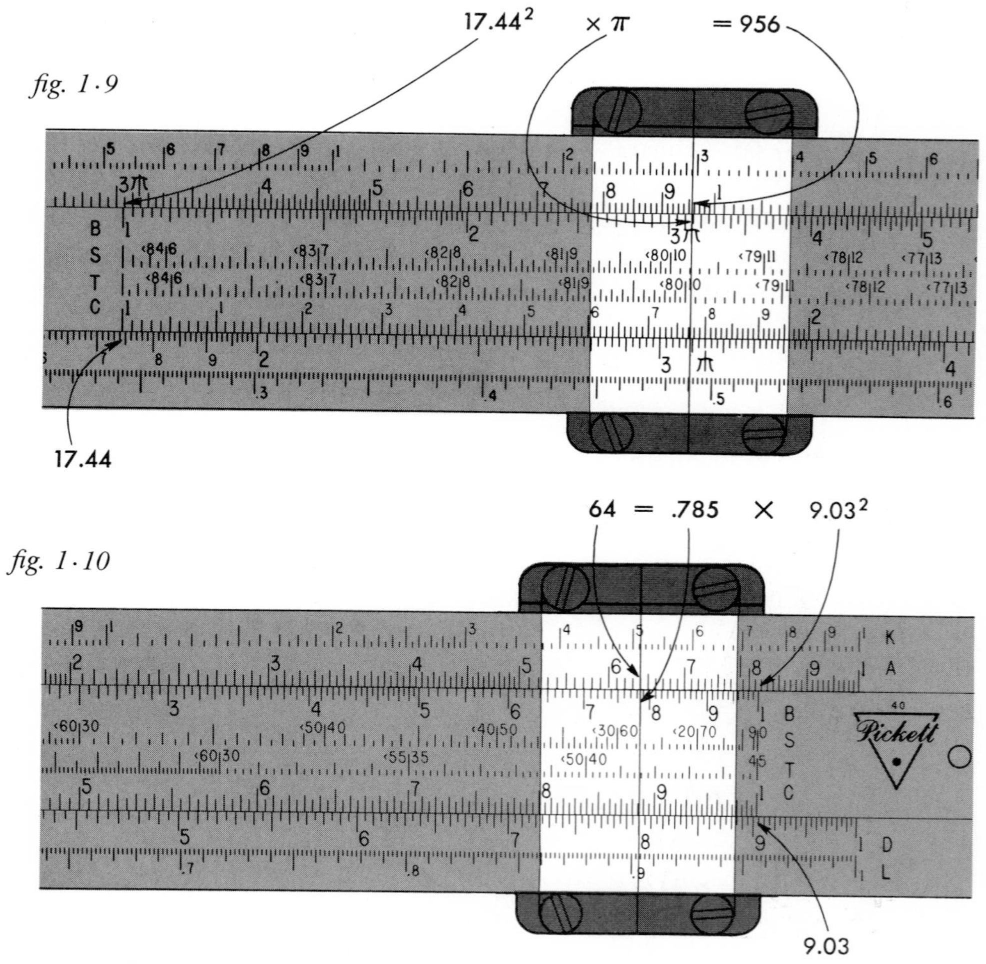

fig. 1·9

fig. 1·10

EXERCISE 7

Make a copy of the following table of circles and fill in the blanks:

	Radius	*Diameter*	*Circumference*	*Area*
1.	6.3 miles	-----------	-----------	-----------
2.	5¼ in.	-----------	-----------	-----------
3.	78 ft	-----------	-----------	-----------
4.	9/16 in.	-----------	-----------	-----------
5.	-----------	11.2 yd	-----------	-----------
6.	-----------	31.6 ft	-----------	-----------
7.	-----------	⅞ in.	-----------	-----------
8.	-----------	14½ in.	-----------	-----------
9.	-----------	-----------	8.43 in.	-----------
10.	-----------	-----------	26.7 ft	-----------
11.	-----------	-----------	-----------	10.00 sq in.
12.	-----------	-----------	-----------	63.8 sq ft

1·12 General suggestions for slide-rule operation

As the student becomes skillful in the use of the slide rule, he will acquire various tricks of the trade which will make this tool even more effective. A few suggestions are outlined in the following paragraphs.

Before setting numbers on the slide rule, cancel or combine simple numbers to reduce the number of moves required.

example 16

$$\frac{2 \times 43 \times 3}{17 \times 61} = \frac{6 \times 43}{17 \times 61}$$

A move is saved.

example 17

$$\frac{60 \times 105}{5 \times 2 \times 97} = \frac{6 \times 105}{97}$$

Two moves are saved.

Increased accuracy in slide-rule division is possible through the calculation of the first few significant figures by long division.

example 18 Divide 483 by 617, obtaining five significant figures in the quotient.

We may obtain the first two significant figures by long division and the next three by slide rule.

By slide rule 174 ÷ 617 yields the digits 282. Hence our answer is 0.78282.

$$\begin{array}{r|l} & .78 \\ \hline 617 & 483.00 \\ & 431\ 9 \\ \hline & 51\ 10 \\ & 49\ 36 \\ \hline & 174 \end{array}$$

In cases in which the dividend differs but little from the divisor, greatly improved accuracy may be obtained as indicated by the following example.

example 19 Divide 732.00 by 741.00.

$$\frac{732}{741} = \frac{741 - 9}{741} = 1 - \frac{9}{741}$$

By slide rule, $9 \div 741 = 0.01215$. Hence

$$\frac{732.00}{741.00} = 1 - 0.01215 = 0.98785$$

A similar device is useful when multiplying by a number having a value near unity.

example 20 Multiply 0.99756 by 610.95.

$$(0.99756)(610.95) = (1 - 0.00244)(610.95) = 610.95 - 1.49 = 609.46$$

Preliminary rearrangement of formulas is often helpful, as in logarithmic computation (see Sec. 10·31).

As an alternative to the factoring method, it is suggested that the familiar formulas of the Pythagorean theorem be modified before use on the slide rule, as indicated below:

$a = \sqrt{c^2 - b^2}$	becomes	$a = b\sqrt{(c/b)^2 - 1}$	
$b = \sqrt{c^2 - a^2}$	becomes	$b = a\sqrt{(c/a)^2 - 1}$	
$c = \sqrt{a^2 + b^2}$	becomes	$c = b\sqrt{(a/b)^2 + 1}$	$(a > b)$
		$c = a\sqrt{(b/a)^2 + 1}$	$(b > a)$

With the subtraction or addition of 1 done mentally, a minimum of moves is required.

fig. 1·11

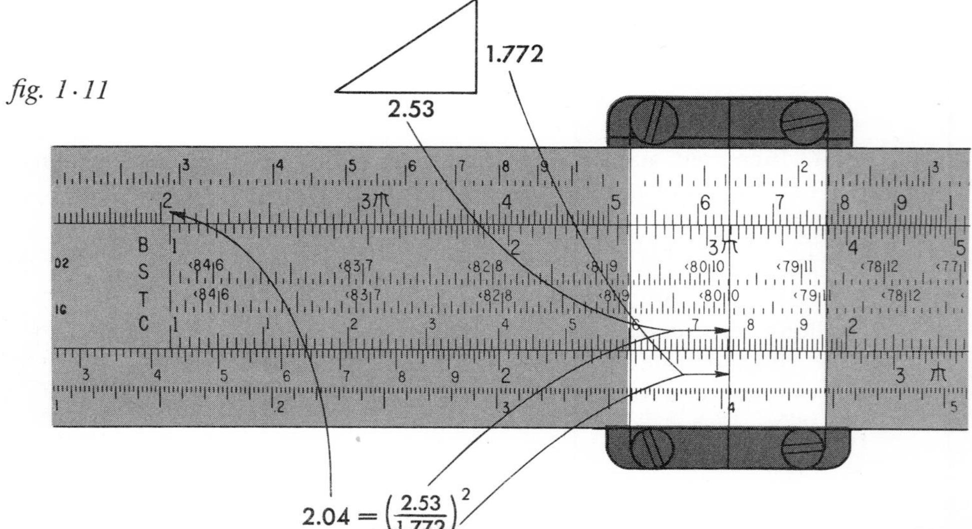

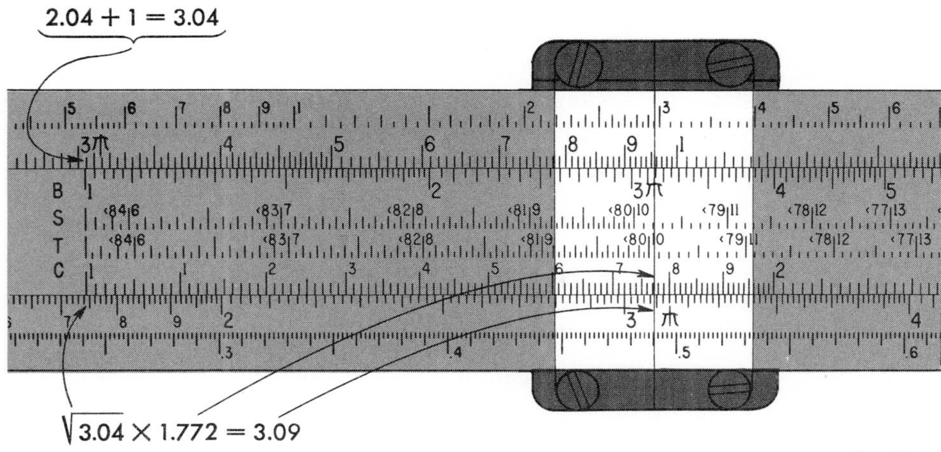

fig. 1·12

example 21 Find the hypotenuse of a right triangle whose sides are 2.53 and 1.772.

Letting 2.53, the larger side, be represented by a, and 1.772 by b, and referring to Fig. 1·11, we have the setting for obtaining $(2.53/1.772)^2$, which is seen to be 2.04. Adding 1 mentally to obtain 3.04, or $(a/b)^2 + 1$, we then refer to Fig. 1·12, which shows the setting for $1.772\sqrt{3.04}$, which we read on the D scale as approximately 3.09.

EXERCISE 8

Compute the missing sides in the following right triangles in which c is the hypotenuse:

	a	b	c
1.	38	47	
2.	7.52	10.36	
3.	523	408	
4.	1⅞ in.	2¾ in.	
5.	9.85	25.6	
6.		0.0645	0.0892
7.		12.33	20.7
8.		3⅛ in.	4¼ in.
9.	5,670		7,030
10.	0.1525		0.291
11.	4⅞ in.		5½ in.

In finding the hypotenuse of a right triangle containing a small acute angle, the approximation $c \approx a + (b^2/2a)$, where b is the smallest side, is useful (see Sec. B·16). The smaller b becomes in relation to a, the closer the approximation. Where b is as large as $0.2a$, c, as calculated by the approximation, will be about 0.02 per cent too large.

EXERCISE 9

Find c, evaluating $b^2/2a$ to three significant figures by slide rule.

	a	b
1.	52	3
2.	109	4
3.	15 in.	⅜ in.
4.	213	7
5.	1.75	0.08

An interesting application of proportion to gear ratios is as follows: Suppose we must have a gear ratio of approximately 1/0.7933, the number of teeth on each gear not to exceed 100. Referring to Fig. 1·13, in which 1 is set opposite 0.7933, we read (in addition to the pair 92 over 73 indicated by the hairline) the following pairs of integers which are approximately matched: 97 over 77, 87 over 69, 63 over 50, and 58 over 46 (58 over 46 is a variation of 87 over 69 and would not be considered an independent pair). These results indicate in a rough way the number of teeth in gears giving us the ratio 1:0.7933. The decimal values and accuracies of these ratios are tabulated below.

$$\frac{77}{97} = 0.7938, \text{ or } 0.06 \text{ per cent too large}$$

$$\frac{73}{92} = 0.7935, \text{ or } 0.02 \text{ per cent too large}$$

$$\frac{69}{87} = 0.7931, \text{ or } 0.02 \text{ per cent too small}$$

$$\frac{50}{63} = 0.7936, \text{ or } 0.04 \text{ per cent too large}$$

fig. 1·13

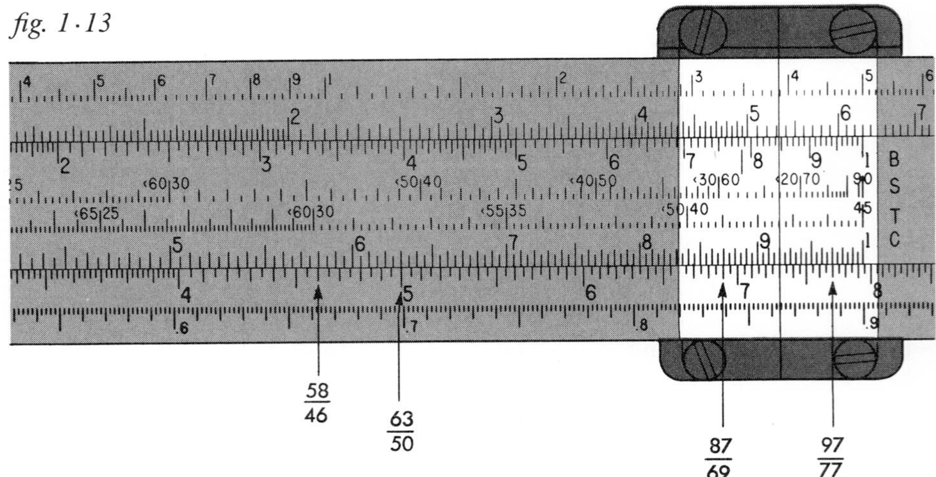

More precise results can be obtained by using logarithms or continued fractions.

EXERCISE 10

Determine for each of the following ratios all independent pairs of integers, less than 100, whose ratio does not differ from the given value by more than 0.05 per cent:

1. 1.369:1
2. 1.841:1
3. 2.073:1
4. 1.5847:1
5. 0.881:1
6. 0.82367:1
7. 0.763:1
8. 0.6833:1

2

tables and interpolation

To the average student the utility of the numerical tables is limited to direct readings. In this chapter we shall show how the usefulness of the tables can be extended by appropriate shifting of decimal points and by interpolation, which need not be a hit-or-miss affair. Suggestions for its orderly application will be made.

In this chapter and in Chap. 3 any commonly used handbook of tables may be referred to. For example, see the later editions of Burington's "Handbook of Mathematical Tables and Formulas," McGraw-Hill Book Company; Hudson's "Engineer's Manual," John Wiley & Sons, Inc.; "Standard Mathematical Tables," Chemical Rubber Publishing Co.

2·1 Extending the range of the tables

The table of squares may be extended beyond the given range by shifting the decimal point twice as many places in the square of the number as in the number itself, for $[x(10)^n]^2 = x^2(10)^{2n}$.

example 1 Find $(7{,}650)^2$.

In most tables we shall have to use 765, since 7,650 is beyond the scope of the table. Looking up $(765)^2$, we find 585,225. Therefore, $(7{,}650)^2 = 58{,}522{,}500$.

example 2 Find $(1.38)^2$.

Looking up $(138)^2$, we find 19,044. Therefore, $(1.38)^2 = 1.9044$.

NOTE: *The same method applies to finding the areas of circles, since the area varies as the square of the diameter.*

example 3 Find the area of a 2¾-in. circle.

Looking up the area of a circle of diameter 275, we find 59,396. Therefore, the area of a 2.75-in. circle is 5.9396 sq in.

The table of cubes may be extended by shifting the decimal point 3 times as many places in the cube of the number as in the number itself, for $[x(10)^n]^3 = x^3[10]^{3n}$.

example 4 Find $(3.17)^3$.

Looking up $(317)^3$, we find 31,855,013. Therefore, $(3.17)^3 =$ 31.855013.

example 5 Find $(0.431)^3$.

Looking up $(431)^3$, we find 80,062,991. Therefore, $(0.431)^3 =$ 0.080062991.

The use of the square-root table is governed by a rule similar to those just given. That is, we move the decimal point half as many places in the square root of the number as in the number itself. This is shown by the identity $\sqrt{x(10)^{2n}} = \sqrt{x}(10)^n$. For example,

$$\sqrt{5{,}090{,}000} = \sqrt{(509)(10{,}000)} = 100\sqrt{509}$$

The operation of this rule will be better understood by the following procedure:

Indicate the grouping of the digits of the number as for longhand extraction of square root. Write in their proper positions the decimal point and the first significant digit in the square root. Determine the subsequent digits as found in the square root of the tabulated number having the same grouping as the original number. Fill in these digits in proper sequence after the first significant digit already located.

example 6 Find $\sqrt{5{,}090{,}000}$.

Indicating the grouping and the decimal point and first significant digit in the answer, we write

$$\begin{array}{l} 2\ \ \ \ \ \ \ \ \ \ \ \ \ \ \ . \\ \sqrt{5\ 09\ 00\ 00.} \end{array}$$

The first group, or "key group," is 5, whose square root is 2+. It is apparent that the tabulated number having the same digits and grouping is 509, of which the square root is 22.56103. This indicates that $\sqrt{5{,}090{,}000}$ will be written as follows:

$$\begin{array}{l} \ \ 2\ \ 2\ \ 5\ \ 6.\ 103 \\ \sqrt{5\ 09\ 00\ 00.} \end{array}$$

example 7 Find $\sqrt{0.00509}$.

Our first indication of the answer is given by the grouping

$$\begin{array}{l} \;\;0.\;0\;\;\;7 \\ \sqrt{0.00\;50\;90} \end{array}$$

In this example, the first group containing significant figures is 50, whose square root is 7+. Thus the grouping is seen to correspond to that of 5,090, of which the square root is 71.34424. Hence the square root of 0.00509 must be 0.07134424.

The procedure for extending the range of the cube-root table is analogous to that used with the square-root table. That is, we move the decimal point one-third as many places in the cube root of the number as in the number itself. This is shown by the identity $\sqrt[3]{x(10)^{3n}} = \sqrt[3]{x}(10)^n$.

example 8 Find $\sqrt[3]{356{,}000}$.

Indicating the grouping, the decimal point, and the first significant digit in the answer, we write

$$\begin{array}{l} \;\;\;\;7\;\;\;\;\;\;. \\ \sqrt{356\;000.} \end{array}$$

The tabulated number having the same digits and grouping as 356,000 is 356, of which the cube root is 7.087341. Thus the cube root of 356,000 will be

$$\begin{array}{l} \;\;\;\;7\;\;\;0\;.87341 \\ \sqrt{356\;000.} \end{array}$$

example 9 Find $\sqrt[3]{0.0356}$.

Grouping, we get

$$\begin{array}{l} \;\;0.\;3 \\ \sqrt{0.035\;600} \end{array}$$

and the corresponding tabulated number is 35,600, of which the cube root is 32.89652. Hence we find

$$\begin{array}{l} \;\;0.\;3\;\;\;2\;\;8\;9\;6\;5\;2 \\ \sqrt{0.035\;600} \end{array}$$

example 10 Find $\sqrt[3]{0.00000356}$.

Grouping, we get

$$\begin{array}{l} \;\;0.\;0\;\;\;\;1 \\ \sqrt{0.000\;003\;560} \end{array}$$

Since the corresponding tabulated number is 3,560, of which the cube root is 15.26921, the desired cube root is

$$\frac{0.\ 0 \quad 1\ \ 5\ 2\ 6\ 9\ 2\ 1}{\sqrt{0.000\ 003\ 560}}$$

which may be rounded off as desired.

2·2 Interpolation between two points

Interpolation between two points assumes a linear relationship over the range between the points. Graphically, a chord replaces the curve connecting the points, and the interpolation error increases with the departure of the chord from the curve. The departure of the chord increases with the curvature of the graph and the distance between the points (see Fig. 2·1). Since Δy is a relatively small (compared to y) additive factor and rarely exceeds three significant figures, slide-rule computation of interpolation is accurate enough for usual cases. (Δx and Δy, read "delta x" and "delta y," represent *changes* in x and y.)

Figure 2·1 shows that linear interpolation is based on similar triangles and that we may write

$$\frac{\Delta y}{y_2 - y_1} = \frac{\Delta x}{x_2 - x_1}$$

or

$$\Delta y = \frac{\Delta x}{x_2 - x_1}(y_2 - y_1) \tag{1}$$

fig. 2·1

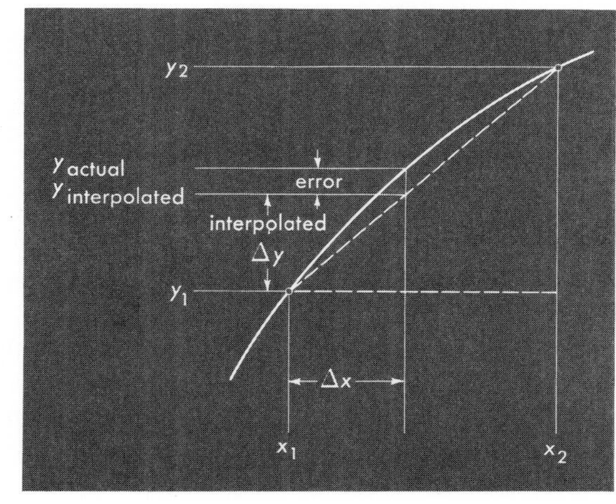

A linear equation is characterized by a constant ratio between Δy, the changes in y, and Δx, the corresponding changes in x.

Let us take, for example, the equation $y = 0.8x + 2$ and list some of the pairs of values of x and y satisfying this equation. We note that

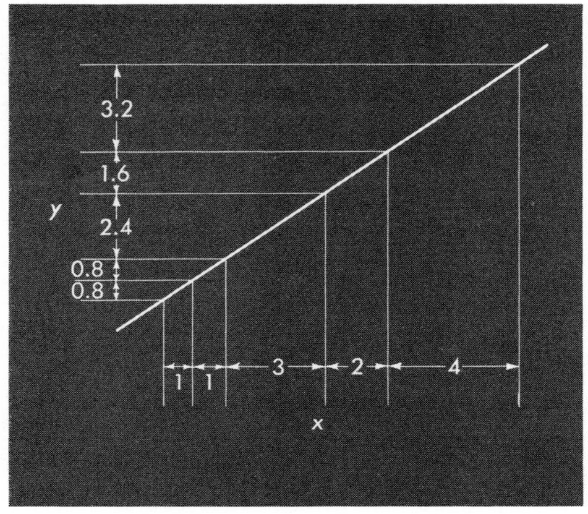

fig. 2·2

the ratio between the values of Δy and the corresponding values of Δx is constant. This is shown graphically in Fig. 2·2.

Δx	x	y	Δy	$\Delta y/\Delta x$
	0	2		
1			0.8	0.8
	1	2.8		
1			0.8	0.8
	2	3.6		
3			2.4	0.8
	5	6.0		
2			1.6	0.8
	7	7.6		
4			3.2	0.8
	11	10.8		

When we interpolate, we shall assume a linear relationship over a range between the two points.

2·3 Other helpful devices

Frequently interpolation may be avoided by judicious use of factoring; e.g., $\sqrt{1,328} = \sqrt{4(332)} = 2\sqrt{332} = 2(18.2209) = 36.4418$.

The student should not overlook the advantages of rationalization in extracting roots of fractions. For example, $\sqrt{2/3}$ is much more conveniently found by evaluating $\frac{1}{3}\sqrt{6} = \frac{1}{3}(2.4495) = 0.8165$ than by finding $\sqrt{0.666667}$. These operations with radicals are explained in Chap. 8.

Square roots, for instance, may at times be found with increased accuracy by working backward from the table of squares. This is true if the table of square roots is given only to four or five significant figures or so.

example 11 Find the square root of 174,126.

x	$y(=\sqrt{x})$
174,000	417.13
174,126	?
175,000	418.33

By interpolation, $\sqrt{174{,}126} = 417.28$. Working backward from the table of squares,

$$\begin{array}{cccc} \Delta x & x & y(=x^2) & \Delta y \\ 1\left\{\begin{array}{c} \\ \\ \end{array}\right. & \begin{array}{c} 417 \\ ? \end{array} & \begin{array}{c} 173{,}889 \\ 174{,}126 \end{array}\Big\} & 237 \Big\} \; 835 \\ 1\left\{\begin{array}{c} \\ \\ \end{array}\right. & \begin{array}{c} 418 \\ 419 \end{array} & \begin{array}{c} 174{,}724 \\ 175{,}561 \end{array} & \Big\} \; 837 \end{array}$$

Interpolating by either of two similar processes, we obtain

$$417 + \frac{237}{835}(1) = 417.284 \qquad \text{or} \qquad 417 + \frac{237}{2(417)} = 417.284$$

(See Sec. B·16.)

It should be observed that the nearly constant ratio $\Delta y/\Delta x$, together with the exact values of both x and y, makes it possible to obtain three extra digits by interpolation instead of the usual one.

Circumferences by addition of parts

Since $\pi(a + b) = \pi a + \pi b$, we may consider that the sum of the circumferences of two circles is equal to the circumference of a circle whose diameter is equal to the sum of the diameters of the first two circles.

example 12 Find the circumference of a 5 7/16-in. circle.

Divide 5.4375 into groups of not more than three significant figures each to avoid interpolation.

N	πN
5.4	16.96460
0.0375	0.11781
5.4375	17.08241

In most cases two or more superfluous digits will have to be rounded off to be consistent with the accuracy of the data of the problem, but interpolation will have been avoided.

It should be noted in passing that the method of "addition of parts" is applicable to any linear relation between two variables having a common zero, e.g., degrees to radians and inches to centimeters.

The use of the table of multiples of π is by no means limited to circumferences. For example, the area of an ellipse whose semiaxes are 6 and 8 is found by looking up the circumference of a circle of diameter 48. The circumference table is also useful in the calculation of surface speeds of drills, grinding wheels, pulleys, etc. In electrical engineering, multiples of π are involved in calculations of electromagnetic effects, capacitance, and inductance.

The reciprocal table may be used to evaluate fractions.

example 13 What decimal part of a foot is 7/16 in.?

$$7/16 \div 12 = 7/16 \times 1/12 = 7/192 = 7(1/192) = 7(0.0052083) = 0.03646$$

Further suggestions for interpolation will be found in Appendix C.

EXERCISE 1

Find (a) x^2, (b) $\sqrt{x}$, (c) x^3, (d) $\sqrt[3]{x}$, (e) $1/x$, (f) πx, and (g) $(\pi/4)x^2$ for each of the values of x listed below. Consider that the accuracy of x is known to justify five significant figures in the answers. Problems 10 to 13 may be solved as directed by the instructor.

1. 972	2. 97.2	3. 9.72	4. 0.972
5. 0.0972	6. 0.00972	7. 2¾	8. 17½
9. ⅝	10. 43.35	11. 7.8125	12. 0.1756
13. 0.082167			

3
applications in geometry

A working knowledge of geometry is essential for solving many practical problems. When data are unavailable, the engineer, technician, or machinist is compelled to obtain his information indirectly. The word *geometry* means earth measurement—a science in which many dimensions are either inaccessible or too large for direct measurement. We assume that you have already learned some geometry; so in this chapter we are dealing chiefly with applications. A list of some of the more important facts in geometry appears on pages 42–45, and in the problems below, reference is made to them in brackets. For additional theorems or formulas see any standard geometry text or mathematical tables.

A glance at the problems in this chapter might lead to the impression that many different theorems and formulas are involved in their solution. However, in the majority of cases, one uses essentially only such familiar relationships as those dealing with similar figures, properties of the circle, and the Pythagorean theorem. It might be added that it is usually a good idea to draw a radius to any point of tangency on a circle. If two or more circles are involved, it is often helpful to draw their line of centers.

Many times it is a good idea to construct a scale drawing. The drawing will emphasize the relationships among the data and indicate the approximate answer. If the problem can be laid out to scale, it can be solved.

You should watch for situations involving parallel lines cut by a transversal. You should also be alert for possible angle bisectors. Equal angles so formed may suggest the construction of either congruent or similar triangles.

It is suggested that you solve the problems in this chapter by slide rule as far as possible. You will gain skill in its use, and the drudgery of longhand computation will be reduced.

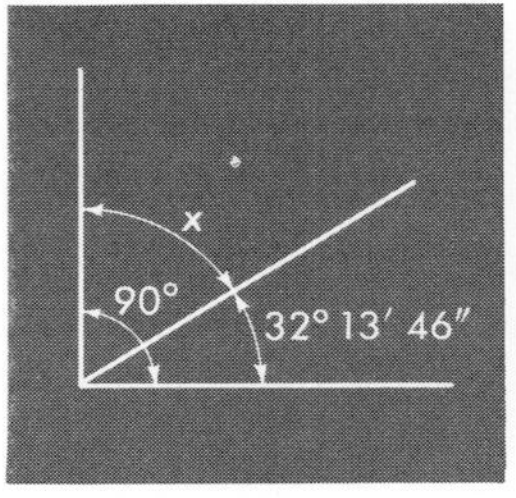

fig. 3·1

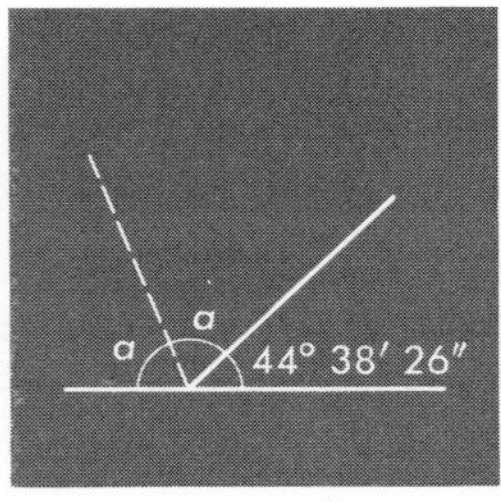

fig. 3·2

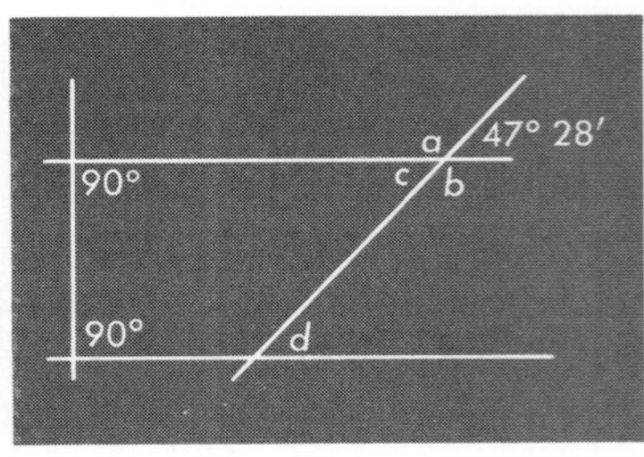

fig. 3·3

Examine each problem critically. Are the given data of the type considered reliable? Are any unreasonable or unwarranted assumptions involved? Answers should be calculated to a point deemed consistent with data given.

EXERCISE 1

1. Find angle x in Fig. 3·1.
2. Find angle a in Fig. 3·2.
3. Find angles a, b, c, and d in Fig. 3·3.
4. Find x and y in Fig. 3·4. [46, 48]
5. An exterior angle of a triangle is 73°. One opposite interior angle is 39°. Find the other opposite interior angle. [15]
6. Find angle a in Fig. 3·5.
7. Find angles a and b in Fig. 3·6. [13]
8. Two angles of a triangle are 41°30′ and 97°. The included side is 4.75. Find the shorter missing side. [7]
9. The altitude to the hypotenuse of a right triangle divides the hypotenuse into segments 3.70 and 8.43 in. long. Find the altitude. [52]
10. Find to the nearest 0.1 sq in. the area of a triangle whose sides are 19, 28, and 39 in. [56]
11. If the angles of a triangle are in the ratio 1:2:3, find the angles and the ratio of the longest side to the shortest side. [14]
12. Find the area of a square whose diagonal is 30 in.

fig. 3·4

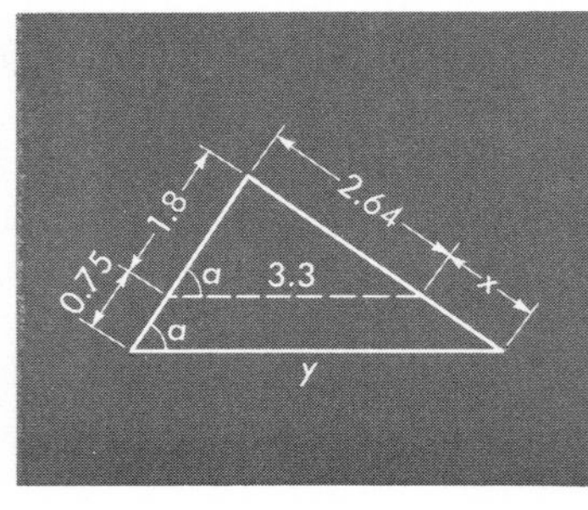

fig. 3·5

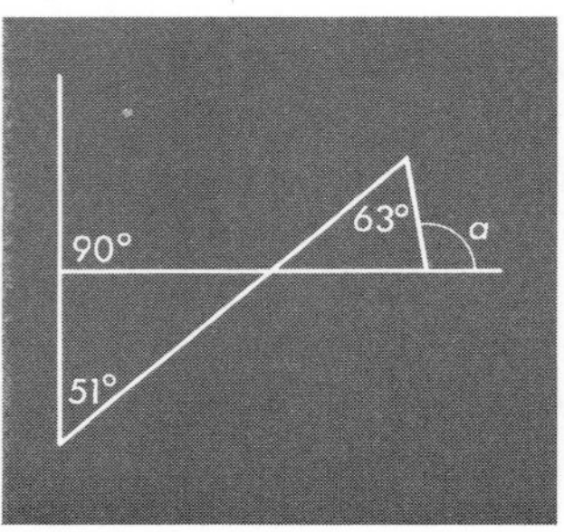

fig. 3·6

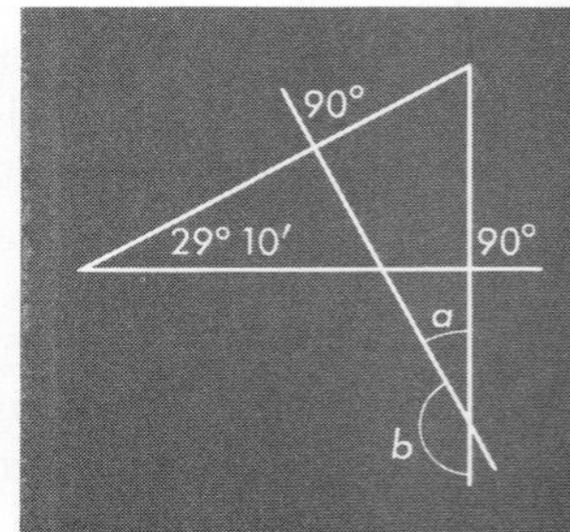

13. Two sides of a triangle are 13 and 15 in., and the altitude upon the third side is 12 in. Find the third side and the area. [53]
14. Find the area of a 51°24′ sector of a 15-in. circle.
15. Find the length of one side and the area of a rhombus whose diagonals are 15 and 22 in. [53]
16. Find the tensile strength of a hexagonal brass bar ⅝ in. across flats. Assume 1 sq in. will support 30,000 lb.
17. A circle is inscribed in a triangle whose vertex angle is 48°14′. Find the angle formed at the center of the circle by lines drawn to the extremities of the base. [37]
18. What diameter hole should be drilled clear through a ⅜-in. plate of cast iron to remove 2 oz? The density of cast iron is 0.26 lb per cu in.
19. Three circular ducts whose diameters are 4, 4½ and 5½ in. are supplied by a single larger duct. Find its diameter to the nearest 1/16 in.
20. A ¼-in. wire is wound around a 1½-in. cylinder with a lead of ⅝ in. How much wire is required for 12 turns? (Compute the length of the center line of the wire.) [53]
21. Find the area of the three-cornered section enclosed by three mutually tangent 15-in. circles.
22. The base angles of a trapezoid are 60 and 45°. The upper base is 15, and the leg adjacent to the 60° angle is 10. Find the area of the trapezoid. [57]
23. Find the angle between the bisectors of the two angles of a trapezoid which are formed by the bases and one nonparallel side. [14]
24. Find the angle between the bisectors of the acute angles of a right triangle. [14]
25. Two consecutive angles of a quadrilateral are 83 and 105°. Find the angle between the bisectors of the other two angles. [23]
26. Find the angles a and b in Fig. 3·7. [35, 37]
27. Find the angle a in Fig. 3·8. [7]
28. The diagonals of a quadrilateral are 16 and 22 in. and are perpendicular to each other. Find the area of the quadrilateral.
29. Two sides of a parallelogram are 10 and 12 in. long, and the included angle is 135°. Find the length of the longer diagonal.

fig. 3·7 *fig. 3·8*

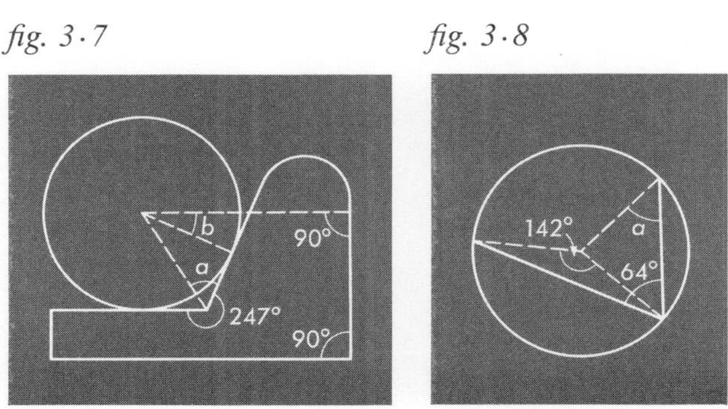

30. In an isosceles trapezoid the parallel sides are 11 and 19 in. long, and the diagonals are each 17 in. long. Find its area.
31. The lengths of the sides of a triangle are 3, 4, and 5. What is the ratio of the areas of the two smaller triangles into which it is divided by a perpendicular drawn to the longest side from the opposite vertex? [52]
32. An equilateral triangle and a regular hexagon are inscribed in the same circle. Find the ratio between the areas of hexagon and triangle.
33. A counterweight on a 60-in. driving wheel is in the form of a segment subtending a central angle of 60°. Find the weight if it is 4 in. thick and made of cast iron (density 0.26 lb per cu in.).
34. Find the area of a segment 3½ in. high in a circle 18 in. in diameter [see Eq. (1), Sec. B·17]. The smaller h is in relation to the other quantities, the closer is the approximation in the formulas used.
35. Two circles of radii 3 and 9 in. are externally tangent to each other. Find the length of the common external tangent (i.e., of a line whose extremities are externally tangent to these circles at points other than the point of their mutual tangency). [35, 39]
36. A pyramid is 5 in. square on the base and 7 in. high. Find the volume, total area, and lateral edge.
37. The eight corners of a rectangular solid 3 by 4 by 12 in. all lie in the surface of a sphere. Find the surface of the sphere in terms of π.
38. Find the total surface and volume of a cone whose height and base diameter are 17 and 20 in., respectively.
39. Find the volume and lateral surface of the frustum of a cone having base diameters of 13 and 22 in. and a height of 20 in.
40. The frustum of a cone is 5¼ in. high. The diameters of its bases are 8¾ and 12½ in. Find the height of the original cone. [65]
41. In Fig. 3·9 two cuts are made approximately 11 in. from each corner of a 30-in. square to make a regular duodecagon (12 sides). What distance should be measured when working with a 14-in. square? How many degrees are there in angle a? [26, 51]
42. The scale ratio of a certain aerial photograph is 1:25,000. What is the area in acres of a town if the area in the photograph is 34.23 sq in.? [58]

fig. 3·9

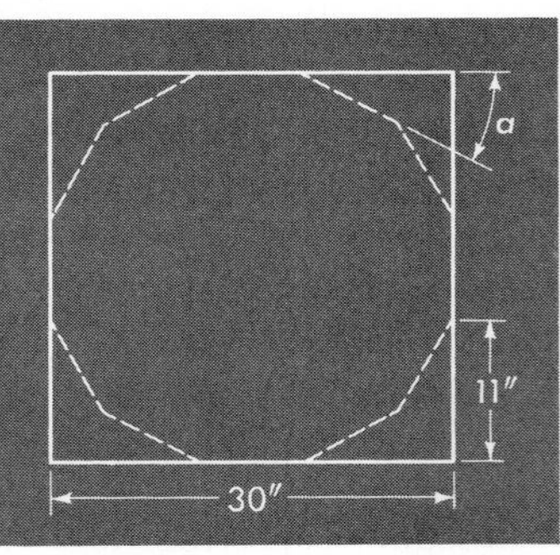

fig. 3·10

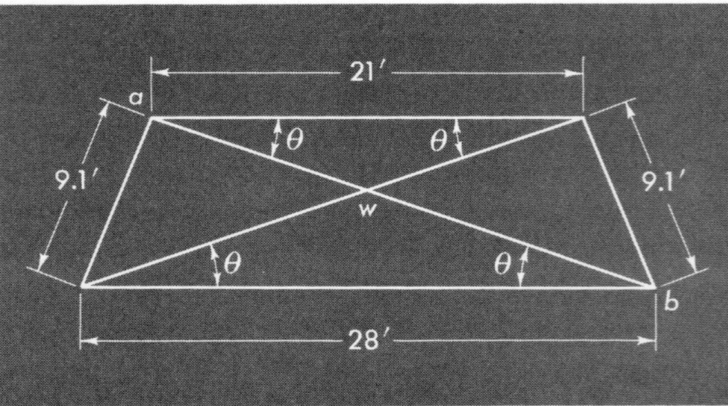

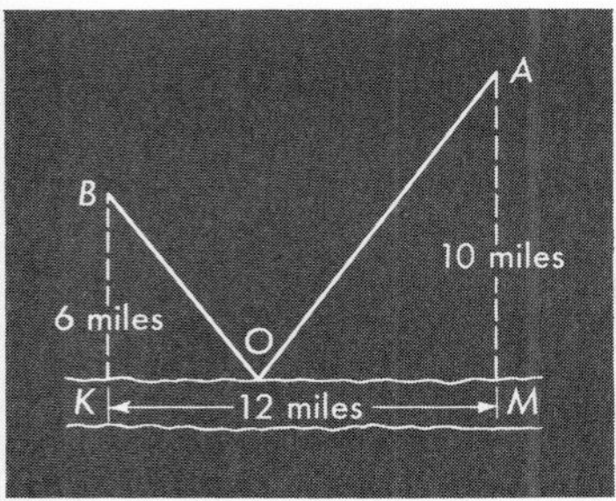

fig. 3·11

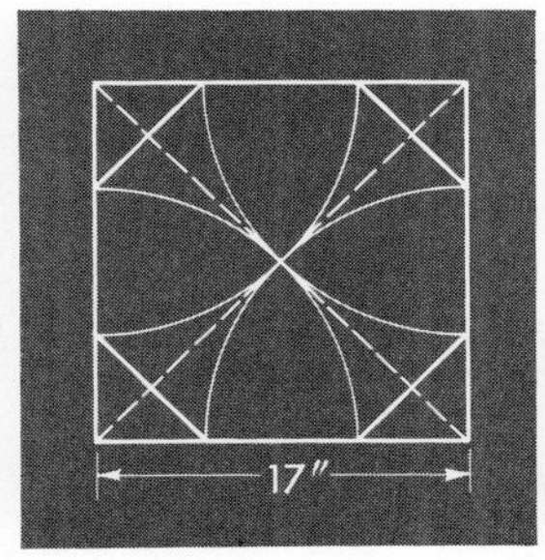

fig. 3·12

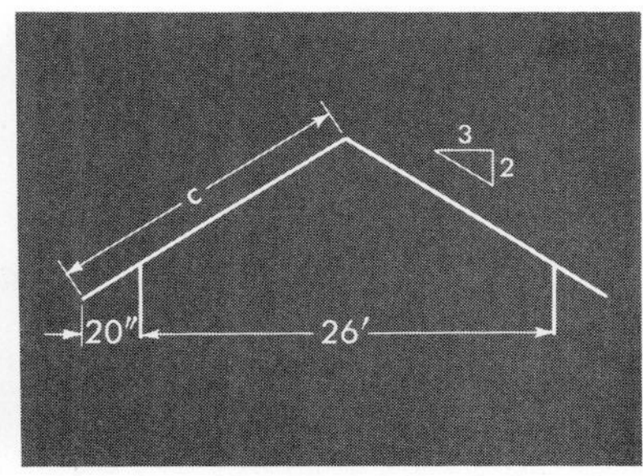

fig. 3·13

43. What is the area of an orchard which appears in the photograph of Prob. 42 as a square 0.1 in. on a side?
44. A lean-to roof is 22 ft long. The rafters are 13 ft long, with a ⅔ pitch (2 in. rise in every 3 in. horizontally). If all the rain which falls on the roof is collected, how many gallons will have been collected after a rainfall of 0.82 in.?
45. In Fig. 3·10 find the length of a cross brace *ab* and the distance *aw* of the rivet from one end. [17]
46. A pumping station at *O* on a river is to deliver water to *A* and to *B*. When angle *KOB* equals angle *AOM*, the total length of piping is a minimum. Find this length in Fig. 3·11. [18]
47. A regular octagon may be cut from a square by the method shown in Fig. 3·12. Find the length of a side of the octagon.
48. Find the length of a common rafter *c* in the gable roof shown in Fig. 3·13.
49. A plot of land has the shape of a quadrilateral whose sides, in order, are 3,470, 1,980, 2,540, and 3,720 ft. If the last two sides form a right angle, find the area of the plot in acres. [56]
50. Find the altitude to the longest side of a triangle whose sides are 8, 12, and 15 in. [55, 56]
51. Find the fraction of the large circle occupied by the seven small circles in Fig. 3·14. [58—applies to any two similar figures.]

fig. 3·14

fig. 3·16

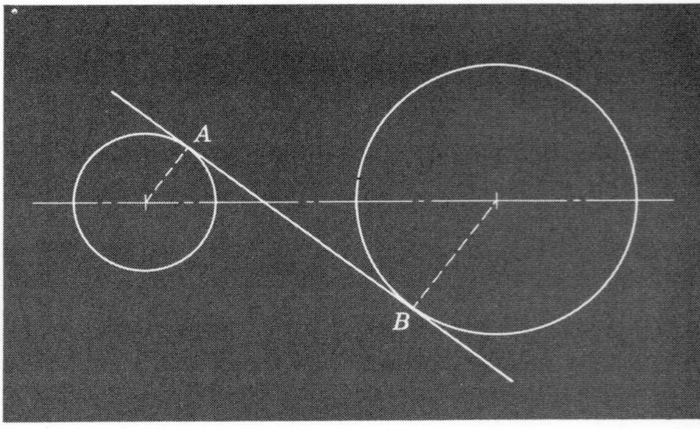

fig. 3·15

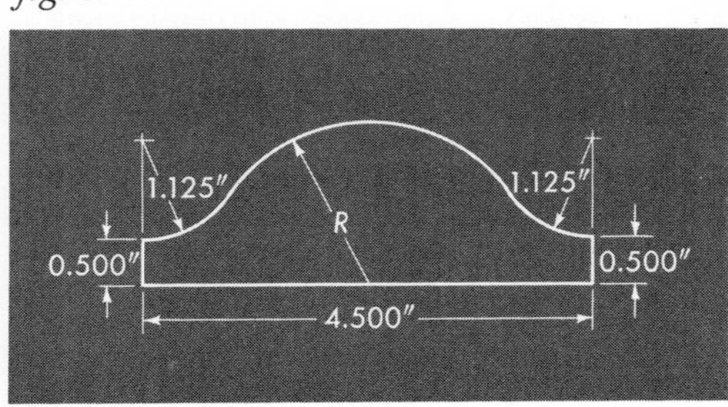

52. Two 10-in. pulleys are connected by a belt which crosses itself at an angle of 60°. Find the length of the belt.
53. Find *R* in Fig. 3·15. [39]
54. In Fig. 3·16 the centers of a 6-in. circle and a 12-in. circle are 15 in. apart. How long is *AB*?
55. Find the angle α in Fig. 3·17. [41]
56. A circular pool 65 ft in diameter is surrounded by a walk having an area of 600 sq ft. Find the width of the walk to the nearest ½ in.
57. A horizontal cylindrical tank 30 in. in diameter contains 400 gal when full. How many gallons remain when the depth of liquid is 8 in.? (See Prob. 34, this exercise.)
58. Find the length of stock needed for the piece shown in Fig. 3·18. (Find the length of the center line.)
59. A 12,000-gal cylindrical tank is to be installed in a factory. Because of headroom the height is restricted to 15 ft. What should be the diameter of the tank to the nearest inch?
60. (a) If a number of plants are to be set out 8 in. apart each way in a 9½-ft-diameter circular flower bed, how many plants are needed?
    (b) If the plants were set out on 8-in. equilateral-triangular centers, how many would be required?

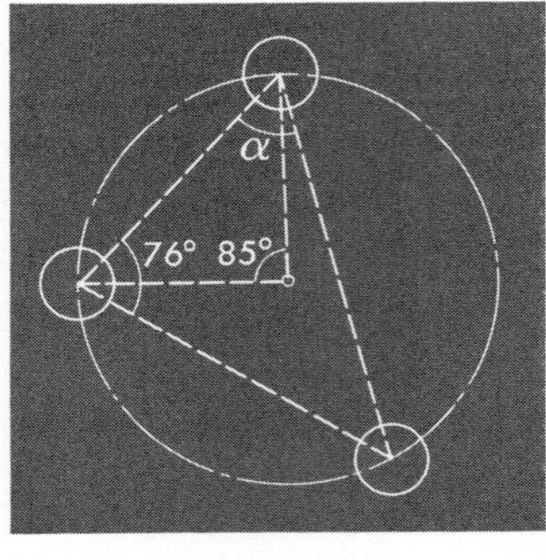

fig. 3·17

fig. 3·18

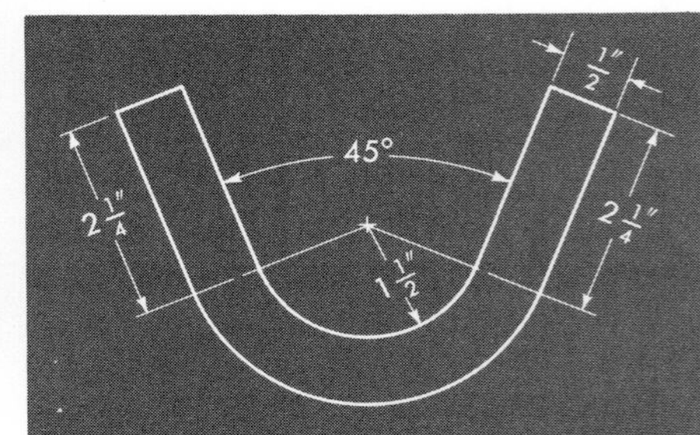

61. Using the approximate formula $l = \pi(D + d)/2 + 2a$, where l is the length of an open belt connecting two pulleys whose diameters D and d differ only slightly and whose center-to-center distance is a, find the length of belting required for a 12-in. and a 16-in. pulley 5 ft apart (a, l, D, and d are expressed in like units).
62. When an open belt connects two pulleys of radically different sizes, the formula in Prob. 61 will give a better approximation if modified to the following:

$$l = 2\sqrt{\left(\frac{D-d}{2}\right)^2 + a^2} + \pi\frac{D+d}{2}$$

Find l when D is 18, d is 5, and a is 30 in.
63. If water is flowing through an 8-in. pipe with an average linear rate of 0.35 fps, find the rate of flow in gallons per minute.
64. What is the linear rate of flow in Prob. 63 when water is passing through a ¾-in.-diameter metering orifice?
65. Find the diameter of the flywheel, a fragment of which is shown in Fig. 3·19. [54]
66. How large a cylindrical tank can be placed in a triangular plot 42 by 50 by 55 ft? Show that the radius r of the inscribed circle $= A/s$, where A is the area of the triangle. [56]
67. Find, in terms of s, the area of the regular dodecagon shown in Fig. 3·20.
68. Find the percentage error in taking the area of the square as equal to that of the circle in Fig. 3·21.
69. A 3-in.-diameter piston ring should have an end clearance of 0.010 to 0.015 in. If the end clearance was 0.010 in. when the ring was installed, how much could the diameter increase with wear before the clearance exceeded 0.015 in.?
70. A strip of metal 12 in. wide is bent along the center line to form a V trough. What angle between the sides would correspond to the maximum water capacity of the trough? [55]

fig. 3·19

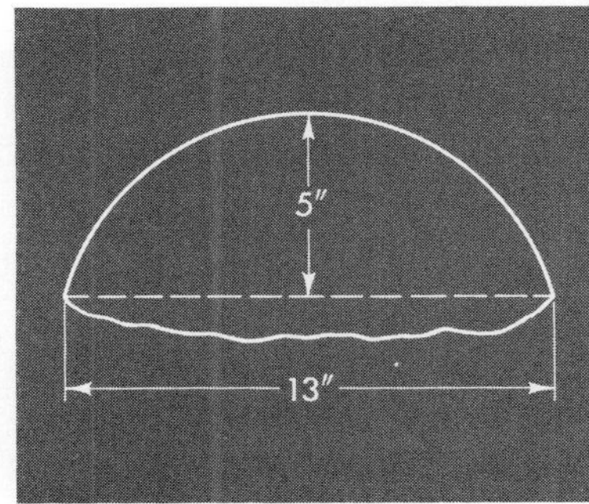

fig. 3·20

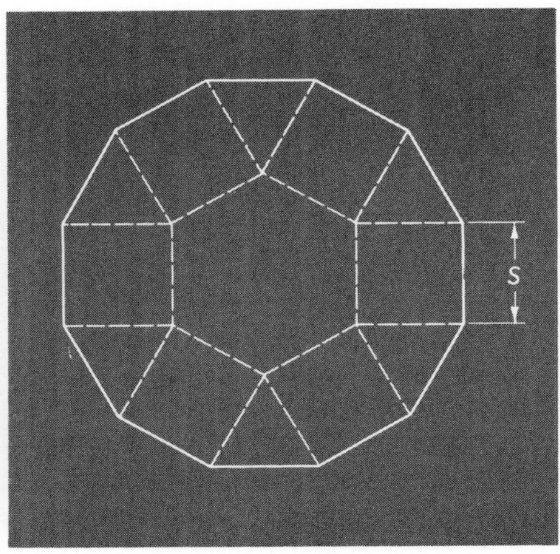

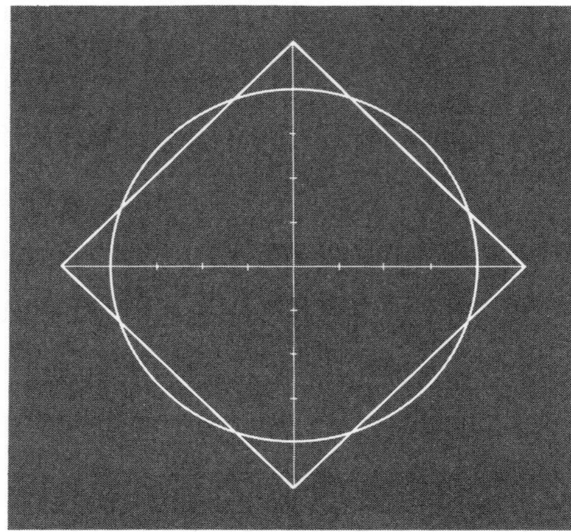

fig. 3·21

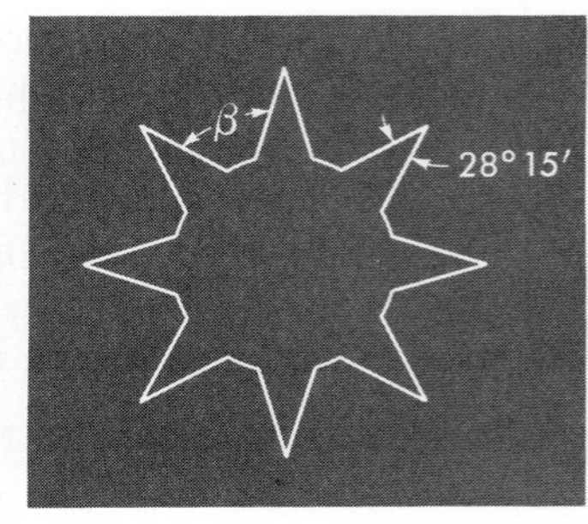

fig. 3·22

71. The following data were obtained in finding the diameter of the bore in a capillary glass tube: weight of empty tube, 14.603 g; weight of tube containing a thread of mercury 11¼ in. long, 16.385 g. Find the diameter of the bore to the nearest 0.001 in. if 1 g = 0.0353 oz and 1 cu in. of mercury weighs 7.84 oz.
72. Find the volume of a square pyramid with edges 7 in. long.
73. Find the altitude to one of the equal sides of an isosceles triangle whose sides are 5, 5, and 6.
74. A regular hexagonal pyramid has a base edge 10 in. long. If the lateral faces are inclined 60° to the base, find the altitude of the pyramid.
75. An empty rectangular swimming pool is 2 ft deep at one end, and the bottom slopes uniformly to a depth of 10 ft at the other end. After cleaning, the pool is being refilled at a constant rate. If after 2½ hr the water is 2 ft deep at the deep end, how much longer will it take to fill the pool?
76. Find angle β in Fig. 3·22.

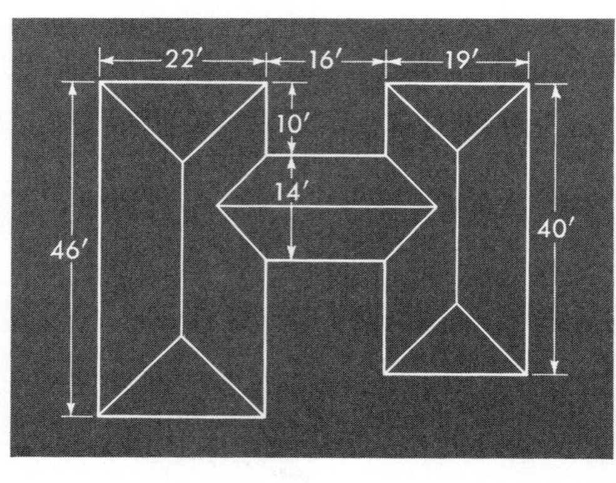

fig. 3·23

fig. 3·24

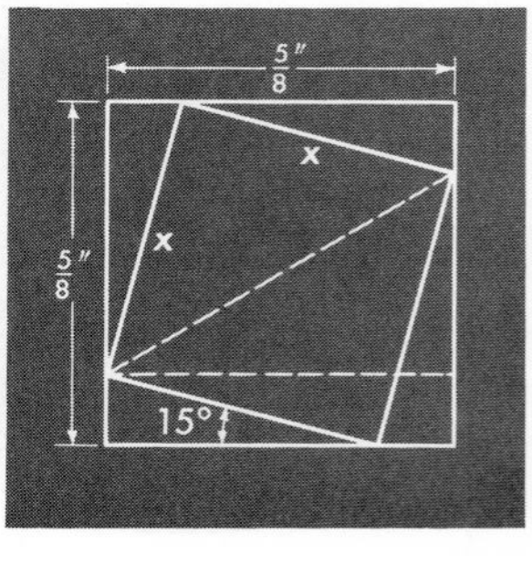

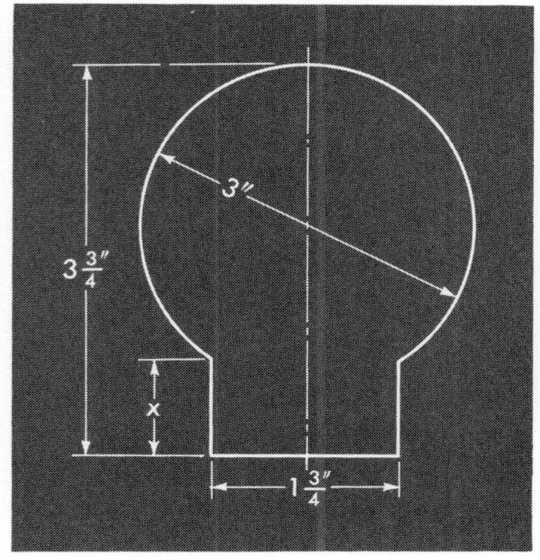

fig. 3·25

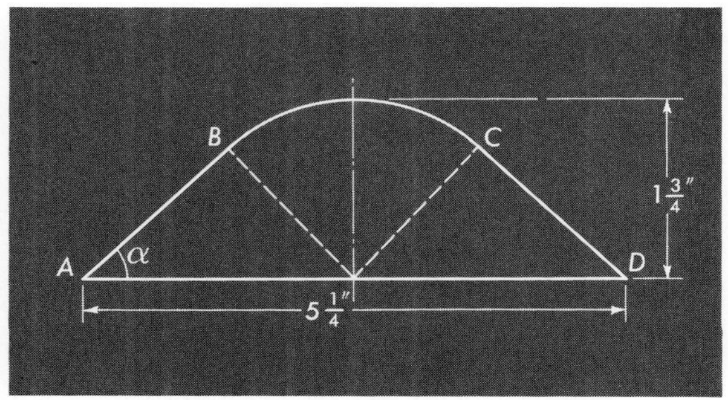

fig. 3·26

77. A farmer traced the map of his farm on a sheet of No. 4 zinc and cut out the outline of his map. Then, to the same scale (1 in. = 50 ft), he cut out a 4-in. square. The 4-in. square weighed ½ oz, while the zinc map weighed 3 lb 10½ oz. How many acres were there in the farm?
78. The U. S. Coast and Geodetic Survey maps have a scale of about 1 in. to the mile. It is desired to measure areas on one of these maps by laying a grid made of celluloid over the area to be measured. The lines on the grid form squares. What should be the spacing of the rulings if each square represents 100 acres?
79. Find the roof area, the top view of which is given in Fig. 3·23, if all parts of the roof have a ¾ pitch (3-in. rise in every 4 in. taken horizontally).
80. A wrench is to have a total play of 30° in a ⅝-in.-square socket. Find the size of the wrench (Fig. 3·24).
81. Find x in Fig. 3·25. [53]
82. Using 3,960 miles as the radius of the earth, find the length in miles of 1′ longitude (a) at 45°N; (b) at 60°N.
83. In Fig. 3·26 find angle α if the total length $ABCD$ = 6.426 in.
84. Find the distance x in Fig. 3·27. [53]
85. Find the angle β in Fig. 3·28. (There are 21 teeth.)

fig. 3·27

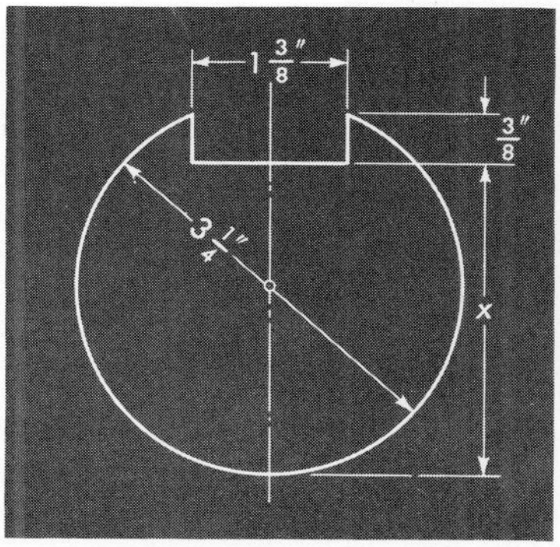

fig. 3·28

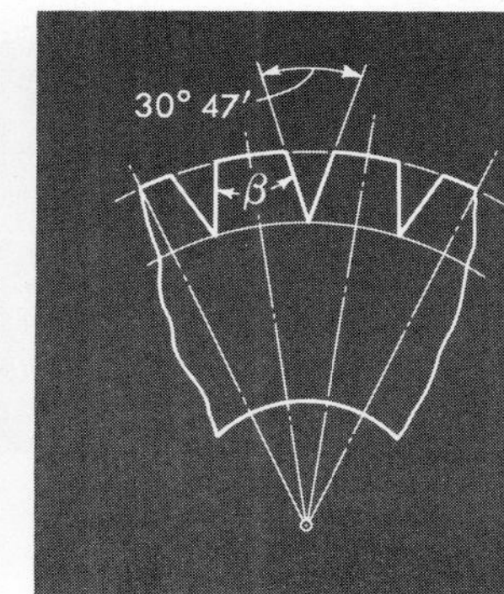

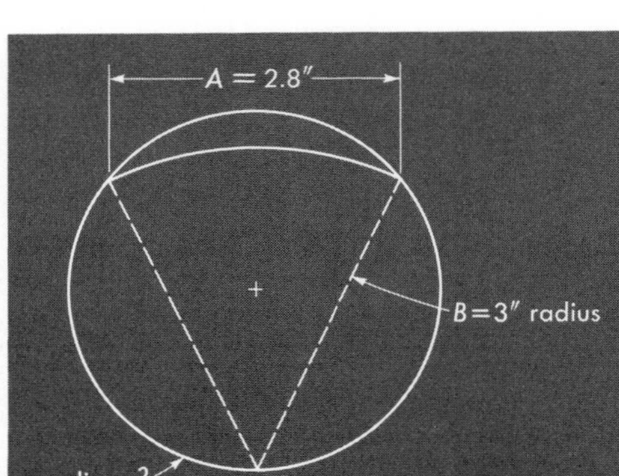

fig. 3·29

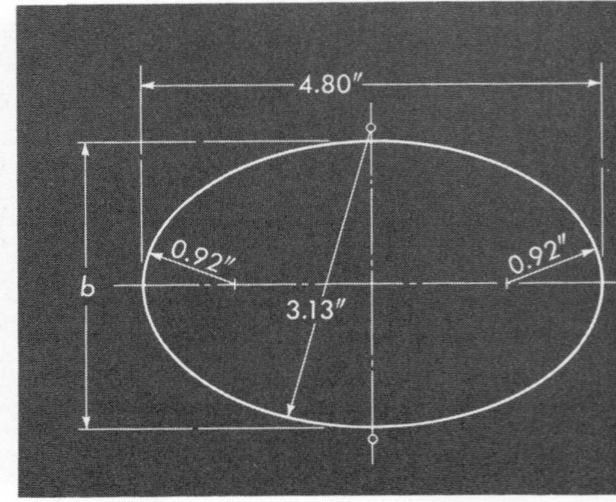

fig. 3·30

86. Find the diameter of the circle in Fig. 3·29. (This occurs in caliper measurement of inside diameters. See also Prob. 57, page 286.) [54]
87. Find the short diameter *b* in the approximate ellipse in Fig. 3·30.
88. Two 15-in. pulleys connected by an open belt are 10 ft apart (center to center). If the belt splice passes a given point 125 times per minute, find the speed (revolutions per minute) of one of the pulleys.
89. A roll of paper 4 ft 6 in. in diameter is wound on a 6-in. hub. Find the length of the paper in the roll if the sheet is 0.0080 in. thick. What assumption is made here?
90. In Fig. 3·31 the speed of the upper pulley is 450 rpm. Find the speed of the lower pulley when the idler belt is in the position shown. What is the extreme range of speeds possible in the lower pulley?
91. On one side of a river is a rectangular playground 100 ft wide measured back from the riverbank. An observer on the opposite bank

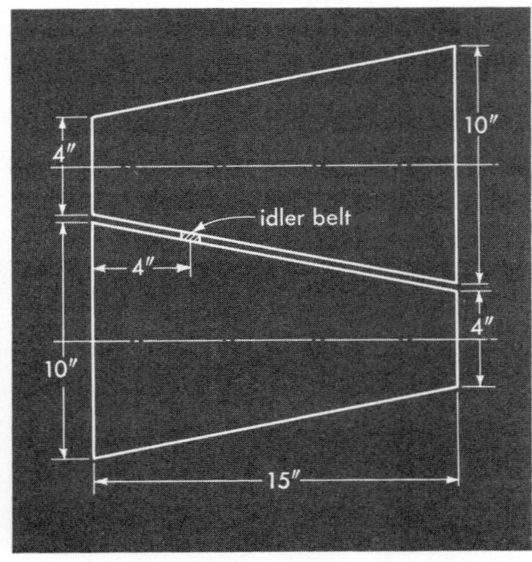

fig. 3·31

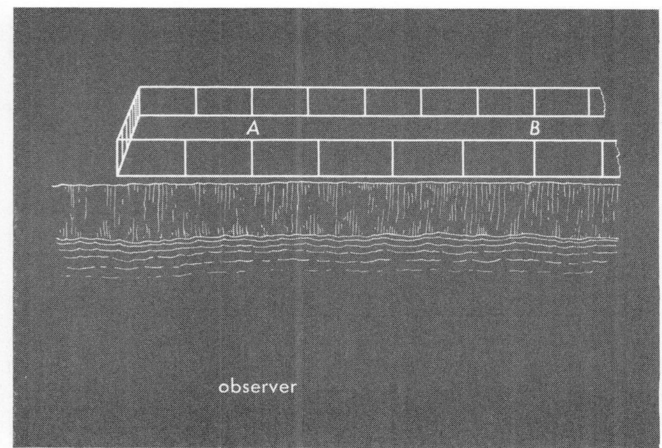

fig. 3·32

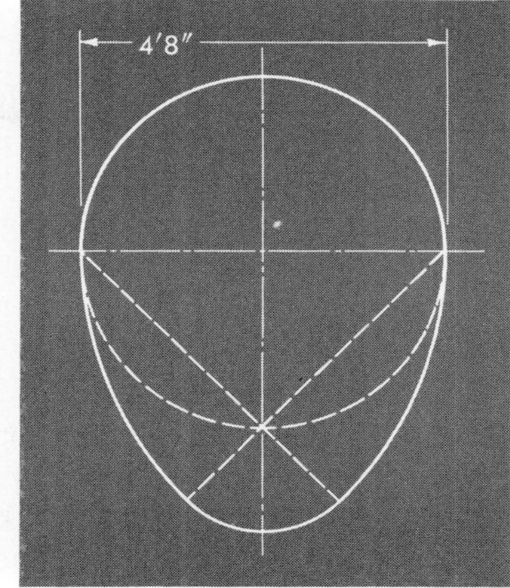

fig. 3·33

notices that the fence posts of the sides parallel to the riverbank line up at A and B, as illustrated in Fig. 3·32. Assuming the fence posts to be uniformly spaced, find the width of the river. [17]

92. A cone is to have an altitude of 10 in. and a base diameter of 8 in. Find the radius and central angle of its development sector.
93. Find the cross section of the storm sewer illustrated in Fig. 3·33.
94. A semicircular piece of copper having a 6-in. radius is rolled into a cone by bringing the two radii together. Find the capacity of the cone in cubic inches.
95. Find m in Fig. 3·34. [17, 35]
96. A slab of granite is being moved on logs 6 in. in diameter. How far will the slab advance when a log revolves once?
97. Find the area of the arch in Fig. 3·35.

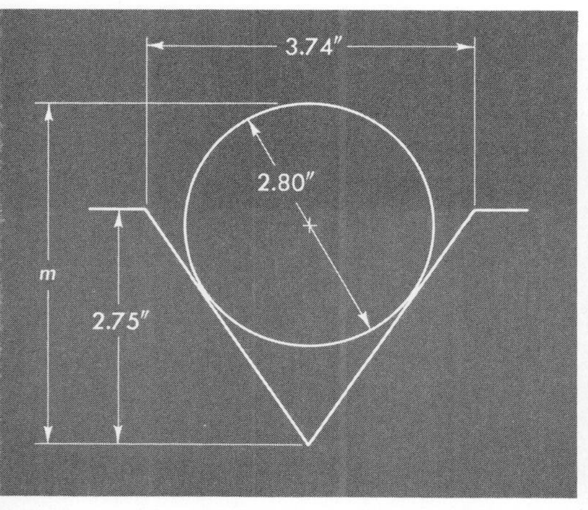

fig. 3·34

fig. 3·35

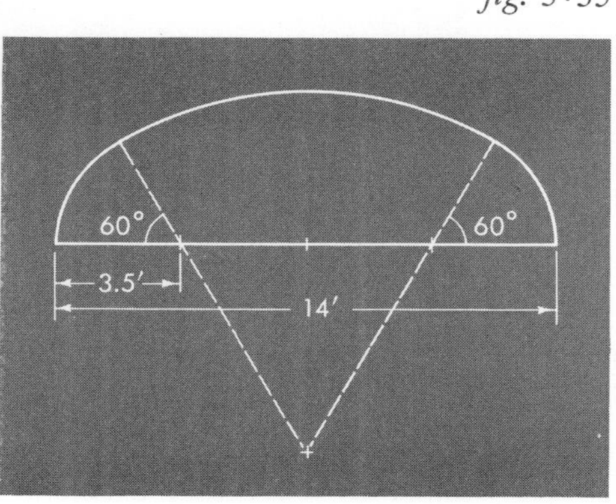

98. Find the percentage error in taking $4PM$ as equal to the circumference of the circle in Fig. 3·36. Assume the radius is 1. Would the final answer be affected by assuming a different value for the radius?
99. Two 12-in. circles have their centers 6 in. apart. What is the area of the portion common to both?
100. Find the weight supported by a hollow copper sphere completely submerged in water. The average diameter of the sphere is 4 in., and the metal is 0.04 in. thick. The densities of copper and water are 0.317 and 0.0361 lb per cu in., respectively.
101. A horizontal 300-gal cylindrical tank has a diameter of 40 in. A gauge is to be made by locating depth marks corresponding to 50, 100, 150, 200, and 250 gal. How far from the bottom of the gauge should each of these marks be located? Use Eq. (1), Sec. B·17, to determine volumes corresponding to various depths. From these values plot a graph of volume against depth. Read off the depths corresponding to the given volumes.
102. A hollow bronze sphere is 11 in. in diameter and weighs 52 lb. The wall thickness is assumed to be uniform and is to be determined without mutilating the sphere. Assume the density of bronze is 0.30 lb per cu in. How might we test for uniformity of wall thickness?
103. A picture AB on a vertical wall (Fig. 3·37) is viewed from eye level CE. Find the distance CD corresponding to the maximum subtended angle ADB (best angle for viewing). [41]
104. As an auto traveled at constant speed, a point P on the tread of the tire traveled through space with varying speed, as shown by values taken at intervals during one revolution of the wheel.

Time, sec	0	0.02	0.04	0.06	0.08	0.10	0.12	0.14	0.16
Speed, fps	0	38	69.5	91.5	99	91.5	69.5	38	0

Find the speed of the car and the diameter of the wheel.

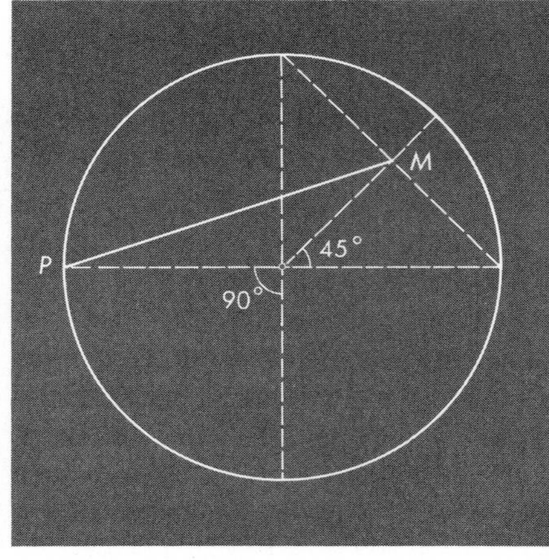

fig. 3·36

fig. 3·

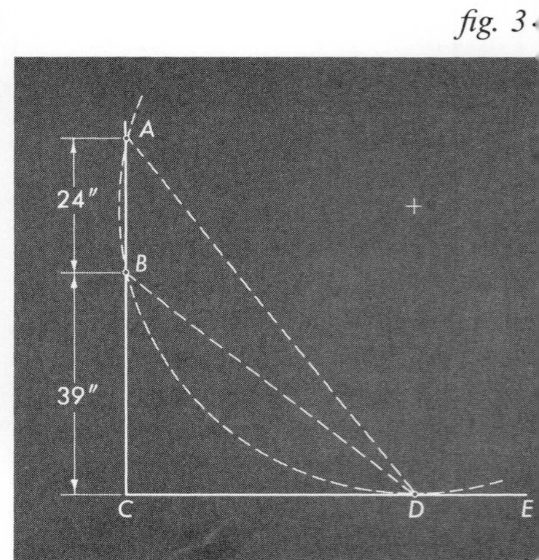

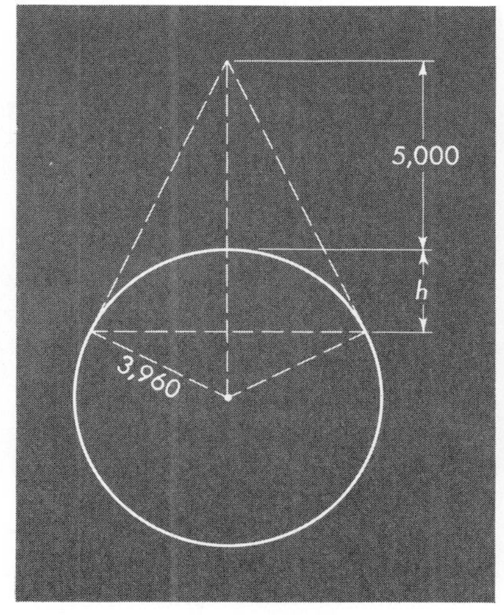

fig. 3·38

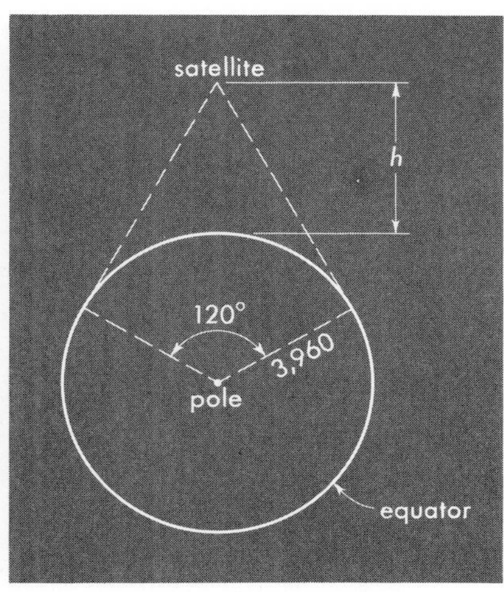

fig. 3·39

105. An artificial earth satellite is 5,000 miles above the earth's surface. If the radius of the earth is 3,960 miles, what fraction of the earth's surface can the satellite "see"? (Area of curved surface of spherical segment or zone $= 2\pi rh$, where $r =$ radius of sphere, and $h =$ height of segment or zone.) (Fig. 3·38)
106. If three satellites having equatorial orbits are evenly spaced what must be their altitude so that a satellite is visible from any part of the equator? (Fig. 3·39)
107. Assuming similar coverage at 60° N latitude, what would the altitude in Prob. 106 become? (Hint: In Fig. 3·40 draw lines *PT* and *PS*.)

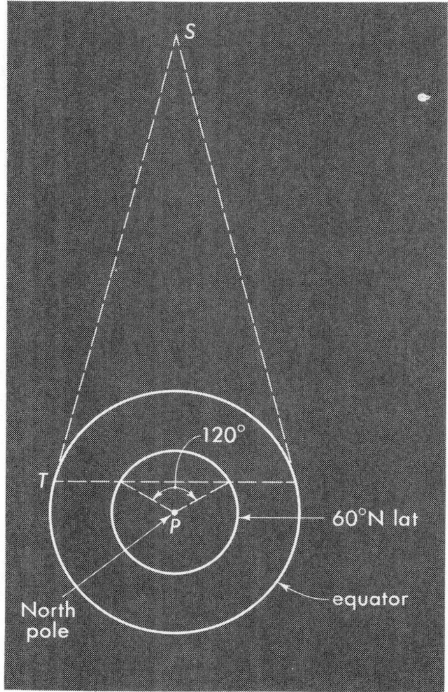

fig. 3·40

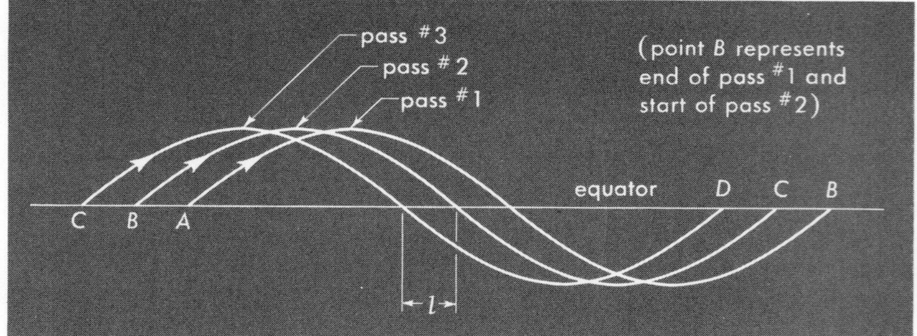

fig. 3·41

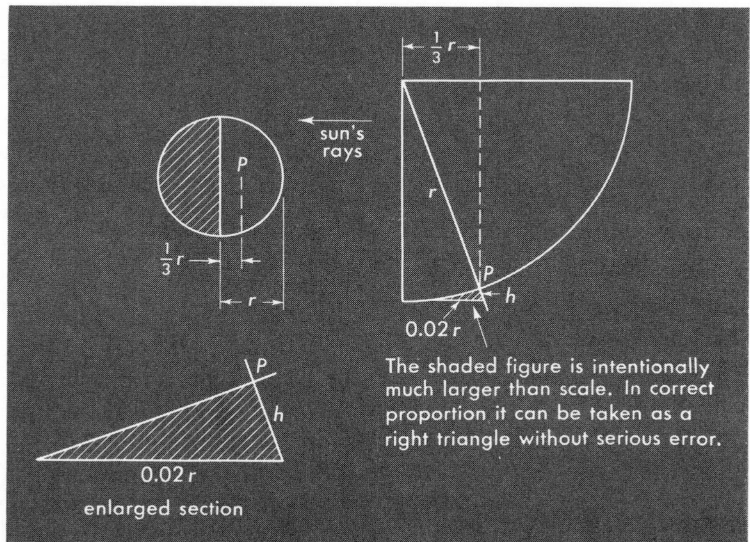

fig. 3·42

108. Given the period of one pass of satellite Faith 7 = 88 min and the diameter of the earth = 7,920 miles, find the distance l in Fig. 3·41 between two successive north-south equatorial crossings. (The displacement results from the rotation of the earth during this interval.)

109. The shadow of a mountain on the moon at first quarter is observed at point P, located at about one-third of a radius from the center of the disk. The length of the shadow is approximately 0.02 times the radius of the moon. What is the height of the mountain if the moon's diameter is 2,160 miles? (Fig. 3·42)

Facts in geometry

1. If one straight line intersects another straight line, the opposite or vertical angles are equal.

2. Two triangles are congruent if two sides and the included angle of one are equal, respectively, to two sides and the included angle of the other.
3. Two triangles are congruent if two angles and the included side of one are equal, respectively, to two angles and the included side of the other.
4. Two triangles are congruent if the three sides of one are equal, respectively, to the three sides of the other.
5. Two right triangles are congruent if the hypotenuse and an acute angle of one are equal to the hypotenuse and an acute angle of the other.
6. Two right triangles are congruent if the hypotenuse and a leg of one are equal to the hypotenuse and a leg of the other.
7. In an isosceles triangle the angles opposite the equal sides are equal.
8. The perpendicular bisector of a line is the locus of all points equidistant from the extremities of the line.
9. The bisector of an angle is the locus of all points equidistant from the sides of the angle.
10. If two parallel straight lines are cut by a transversal, the alternate interior angles are equal.
11. If two parallel lines are cut by a transversal, the exterior-interior angles on the same side of the transversal are equal.
12. Two angles whose sides are parallel, each to each, are either equal or supplementary.
13. Two angles whose sides are perpendicular, each to each, are either equal or supplementary.
14. The sum of the angles of a triangle is equal to $180°$.
15. An exterior angle of a triangle is equal to the sum of the two opposite interior angles.
16. In a right triangle the sum of the two acute angles equals $90°$.
17. If two angles of one triangle equal two angles of another triangle, their third angles are equal and the triangles are similar.
18. If two right triangles have an acute angle of one equal to an acute angle of the other, they are similar.
19. Two triangles are congruent if two angles and a side of one are equal to two angles and the corresponding side of the second.
20. Two right triangles are congruent if a leg and an acute angle of one are equal to the corresponding leg and acute angle of the other.
21. The opposite sides of a parallelogram are equal; the opposite angles are also equal.
22. The diagonals of a parallelogram bisect each other.
23. The sum of the interior angles of a polygon of n sides is equal to $(n - 2)180°$.
24. Each interior angle of a regular polygon of n sides is equal to $[(n - 2)/n]180°$.
25. The sum of the exterior angles of a polygon formed by producing its sides in succession at one extremity equals $360°$.
26. Each exterior angle of a regular polygon of n sides is equal to $360°/n$.

27. If three or more parallels intercept equal parts on one transversal, they intercept equal parts on every transversal.
28. The line which joins the midpoints of two sides of a triangle is parallel to the third side and is equal to one-half the third side.
29. The line which joins the midpoints of the legs of a trapezoid is parallel to the bases and equal to their arithmetic mean.
30. The intersection of the bisectors of the angles of a triangle determines the center of the inscribed circle.
31. The intersection of the perpendicular bisectors of the sides of a triangle determines the center of the circumscribed circle.
32. The medians of a triangle intersect at a point which cuts off two-thirds of each median from its vertex.
33. In the same circle, or in equal circles, equal central angles subtend equal arcs and equal chords.
34. A diameter perpendicular to a chord bisects the chord and the arc subtended by the chord.
35. A radius drawn to the point of contact is perpendicular to a tangent to a circle.
36. Through three points not in the same straight line, one circle, and only one, can be drawn.
37. The two tangents drawn to a circle from an outside point are equal and make equal angles with a line drawn from the point to the center of the circle.
38. If two circles intersect, their line of centers is perpendicular to their common chord at its midpoint.
39. If two circles are tangent to each other, the line of centers passes through the point of contact.
40. The number of degrees in a central angle equals the number of degrees in its intercepted arc.
41. An inscribed angle is measured by one-half its intercepted arc.
42. An angle inscribed in a semicircle is a right angle.
43. An angle formed by two chords intersecting within a circle is measured by one-half the sum of the intercepted arcs.
44. An angle formed by a tangent and a chord drawn from the point of contact is measured by one-half the intercepted arc.
45. An angle formed by two secants, by two tangents, or by a secant and a tangent meeting outside the circle is measured by one-half the difference between the intercepted arcs.
46. A line parallel to one side of a triangle and meeting the other two sides divides these sides proportionally.
47. If two lines are cut by a number of parallels, the corresponding segments are proportional.
48. If two triangles are similar, their corresponding sides are in proportion.
49. In any triangle the bisector of an angle divides the opposite side into segments which are proportional to the other two sides.

50. If three or more lines pass through the same point and intersect two parallel lines, they intercept proportional segments on the parallel lines.
51. In two similar polygons any two corresponding dimensions are to each other as any other two corresponding dimensions; also the perimeters are to each other as any two corresponding dimensions.
52. The altitude to the hypotenuse of a right triangle forms two right triangles which are similar to each other and to the whole right triangle and is a mean proportional between the segments of the hypotenuse.
53. In a right triangle the square of the hypotenuse is equal to the sum of the squares of the legs.
54. If two chords in a circle intersect, the product of the segments of one chord is equal to the product of the segments of the other chord.
55. The area of a triangle is equal to one-half the product of its base and its altitude.
56. The area of a triangle equals $\sqrt{s(s - a)(s - b)(s - c)}$, where a, b, and c are the sides and $s = \frac{1}{2}(a + b + c)$.
57. The area of a trapezoid is equal to the altitude multiplied by the average of the bases.
58. The areas of two similar polygons are to each other as the squares of any two corresponding dimensions.
59. A circle may be circumscribed about, and a circle may be inscribed in, any regular polygon.
60. The area of a regular polygon is equal to one-half the product of its perimeter and its apothem.
61. Of isoperimetric polygons having the same number of sides, the regular polygon has the greatest area.
62. Of all polygons equivalent in area and having the same number of sides, the regular polygon has the smallest perimeter.
63. The volumes of two similar solid figures are to each other as the cubes of corresponding dimensions.
64. The surfaces of two similar solid figures are to each other as the squares of corresponding dimensions.
65. Pyramidal or conic sections parallel to the base are figures similar to the base. Corresponding dimensions in two sections are proportional to the distances of the sections from the vertex, and corresponding areas are proportional to the squares of these distances.
66. The intersection of a plane with the surface of a sphere is a circle. If the plane passes through the center of the sphere, the intersection is called a great circle.
67. The shortest distance between two points on a spherical surface is along the great circle connecting the points.
68. The area (curved surface) of a spherical segment or zone is equal to $2\pi Rh$, where R is the radius of the sphere, and h is the height of the segment or zone.

unit two

basic algebra and analytic geometry of the straight line

algebra which the student should know already, but which he may have forgotten—slopes and other properties of the straight line—a prelude to calculus

4

introduction to algebra

In this chapter we shall attempt to set forth some of the first principles of algebra. Their mastery is essential to the successful handling of the more involved applications in later chapters.

Mathematics differs from some other studies in that it is built layer upon layer. Once a particular mathematical operation is learned, it will be used repeatedly in subsequent operations. In fact, a study of a later operation would be futile without the support of the thoroughly mastered rudiments. By way of analogy it might be pointed out that the construction of the foundation of a house must precede that of the first floor. The foundation supports the superstructure for all time—unlike a scaffolding, which is removed after it has served its purpose.

4·1 Explicit and literal numbers

In arithmetic we represent numbers by *explicit* number symbols such as 3, 8, and 0, whereas in algebra we also make use of various letters of the alphabet to designate general numbers. Such number symbols as a, r, x, and y will be called *literal* numbers. For example we use the letter r to represent the number of units of length in the radius of a circle. Its value changes for different circles. It may be 5 yd, 8 miles, or any number of length units of any denomination, but in a general way it represents the radius of a circle. When we see the general formula $C = 2\pi r$ for the circumference of a circle, we do not think of a circle of any particular size, but rather of circles in general.

The set of numbers used in elementary algebra is called the set of *real* numbers, in contrast with *imaginary* numbers which we shall consider at a later stage.

Real algebraic numbers may be positive, negative, or zero, whereas arithmetic numbers do not include negative values. A number written without a sign is understood to be positive; thus the number 5 is understood to be $+5$.

Real numbers may also be classified as *rational* or *irrational*. The former can be expressed as the ratio of two integers, e.g., ⅔, 5, ⅞. The latter as has been proved, $\sqrt{2}$, $\sqrt[3]{6}$, π, for example, cannot be so expressed.

4·2 Absolute values

Positive and negative signs are used to convey the idea of measuring in opposite directions from a zero value or reference point. For example, $+12°$ and $-7°$ refer to 12° *above* and 7° *below* 0°, respectively. Likewise, if $+140$ lb designates a *lifting* force of 140 lb, then -38 lb refers to a dead *weight* of 38 lb. Further, if $+\$4$ denotes a *credit* of \$4, then $-\$6$ represents a *debit* of \$6. The velocity of a guided missile might be $+3{,}400$ fps on the upward trajectory, and a little later a similar velocity on the descent would be referred to as $-3{,}400$ fps. However, if we simply wish to designate the rate of motion without specifying sense or direction (that is, the *speed*), we write $|3{,}400|$ fps, which is called the *absolute value* of either $+3{,}400$ or $-3{,}400$ fps.

Accordingly we adopt the following definitions:

For any real number a
$|a| = a$ if $a \geq 0$ (equal to or greater than zero)
$|a| = -a$ if $a < 0$

Thus the absolute value of a number is never negative.

It is evident that although $-15 < +10$ (-15 is less than $+10$) $|-15| > |+10|$ (the absolute value of -15 is greater than the absolute value of $+10$).

example 1 Point A is 15 miles south of point B. Point C is 10 miles north of point B. We say that A is farther from B than C is, regardless of direction.

4·3 Some properties of the set of real numbers

Fundamental laws of addition and multiplication

I. $a + b = b + a$ Commutative law of addition
II. $ab = ba$ Commutative law of multiplication
III. $a + (b + c) = (a + b) + c$ Associative law of addition
IV. $a(bc) = (ab)c$ Associative law of multiplication
V. $a(b + c) = ab + ac$ Distributive law

Also by the above laws, $a(b + c) = (b + c)a = ba + ca = a(c + b) = ac + ab$

We shall refer to these laws in Appendix B where rules for simplifying computation are given.

4·4 Addition

The operation of addition of signed numbers may well be illustrated by the balancing of credits and debits.

For example,

$(+7) + (+8) = +15$	(Adding credits of \$7 and \$8 results in a total credit of \$15)
$(-3) + (-1) = -4$	(Adding debits of \$3 and \$1 gives us a total debit of \$4)
$(-4) + (+7) = +3$	(Adding a debit of \$4 and a credit of \$7 gives us a net credit of \$3)
$(-9) + (+2) = -7$	(Adding a debit of \$9 and a credit of \$2 results in a net debit of \$7)

From the above it will be seen that the following rules are valid:

To add two numbers of the same sign, add their absolute values and prefix the sum by their common sign.

To add two numbers of opposite sign, find the difference of their absolute values and prefix the result by the sign of the number having the greater absolute value.

To find the sum, or net value, of several numbers of both positive and negative sign, add all the positive numbers and all the negative numbers and find the algebraic sum according to the preceding rule.

example 2 Add 5, -3, -6, $+2$, -1, $+7$, and -8.

Applying the commutative law of addition, we find that we are adding 5, $+2$, $+7$ and -3, -6, -1, -8, or $+14$ and -18, which equal -4.

4·5 Subtraction

Subtraction of two numbers is performed by reversing the sign of the subtrahend and proceeding as with the addition of signed numbers.

That is, if a and b are real numbers the quantity $(a - b)$ is defined such that

$$a - b = a + (-b)$$

Now the rules for addition stated in the preceding section will hold.

Examples of this rule follow:

$$(+8) - (+5) = (+8) + (-5) = +3$$
$$(+4) - (+9) = (+4) + (-9) = -5$$
$$(-7) - (-3) = (-7) + (+3) = -4$$
$$(-2) - (-9) = (-2) + (+9) = +7$$
$$(-5) - (+6) = (-5) + (-6) = -11$$
$$(+7) - (-3) = (+7) + (+3) = +10$$

Note that in the second example it is possible to subtract a larger number from a smaller. Consider the embarrassing situation of the bank depositor who, although he has only a \$4 balance, draws a check of \$9 and is therefore \$5 overdrawn!

In the last example a man may figure that he is \$7 to the good after taking account of all his debits and credits. If, after taking stock, an outstanding debt of \$3 is canceled (subtract $-\$3$), or \$3 in cash is received (add $+\$3$), the result is the same in either case—his net worth is \$10. Note that the minus sign functions in two capacities; (1) to denote the operation of subtraction (2) to designate a negative quantity.

example 3 $8 - 5 = 3$ could designate either (1) or (2) but $8 + (-5) = 3$ or $-5 + 8 = 3$ definitely refers to the quantity -5.

4·6 Multiplication

The multiplication of signed numbers is governed by the following rules:

1. *The product of two numbers of like sign is positive.*
   In other words, the product of two positive real numbers or the product of two negative real numbers is the product of their absolute values.
2. *The product of two numbers of opposite sign is negative.*
   That is, the product of a positive real number and a negative real number is the negative of the product of their absolute values.
3. *The continued product of three or more numbers is positive if there is an even number of negative numbers, and negative if there is an odd number of negative numbers.*

To this rule we may add a corollary:

Even powers of both positive and negative numbers are positive. Odd powers of positive numbers are positive, and odd powers of negative numbers are negative. (See Sec. 4·10.)

example 4 (a) The product of $+2$ and $+3$ is $+6$.
(b) The product of $+2$ and -3 is -6.
(c) The product of -2 and $+3$ is -6.
(d) The product of -2 and -3 is $+6$.

These examples may be illustrated by the following commonplace situations:

(a) The temperature is rising at the rate of 2° an hour. At this rate it will be 6° warmer in 3 hr.
(b) At the same rate it was 6° colder 3 hr ago.

(c) The temperature is falling at the rate of 2° an hour. At this rate it will be 6° colder 3 hr from now.
(d) At the rate in (c), it was 6° warmer 3 hr ago.

4. *Changing the sign of a quantity is equivalent to multiplying that quantity by −1.*
5. *The product of zero and any number is equal to zero.*
6. *If the product of two or more quantities is zero, at least one of the quantities is zero.*

4·7 Division

The rules of sign governing division resemble those for multiplication, since dividing by a number x is equivalent to multiplying by the fraction $1/x$ (the reciprocal of x).

In addition to the foregoing, the following principles apply to division:

1. *A number cannot be divided by zero. Such a quotient is undefined.*

For example, assume $5 \div 0 = n$. Then $5 = n \times 0$. But this is impossible since $n \times 0 = 0$.

2. *The value of a fraction is unchanged if both numerator and denominator are multiplied, or divided, by the same number.*
3. *Changing the sign of either the numerator or denominator of a fraction reverses the sign of the fraction. Reversing the sign of both numerator and denominator does not change the sign of the fraction.*
4. *Division of zero by zero is indeterminate.*

For example, assume $0 \div 0 = n$. Then $0 = 0 \times n$. But $0 \times n = 0$ whatever the value of n; hence n is indeterminate.

4·8 Signs of operation

The signs $+$, $-$, $\times$, $\div$, and $\sqrt{}$ have the same meaning as in arithmetic. However, the sign $\times$ is not commonly used in algebra. For example, multiplication of a by b is customarily written $a \cdot b$, or simply ab. Thus abc has the same meaning as $a \times b \times c$. If we wish to multiply the expression $a + b$ by the expression $x + y$, we write $(a + b)(x + y)$, the absence of any connecting sign indicating multiplication.

EXERCISE 1

1. Find the sum of each of the following pairs of numbers:

(a) $+8, +5$ (b) $+7, -2$ (c) $+4, +10$ (d) $+6, -9$
(e) $-3, -11$ (f) $-12, -8$ (g) $-9, +13$ (h) $-11, +4$

2. Subtract the second number from the first in each pair of numbers in Prob. 1.

3. Apply the commutative law to add:

(a) $8 + 2 - 3 - 4 + 6 - 1 - 9 + 5$
(b) $-3 + 7 + 2 - 6 - 5 + 1 - 8$
(c) $4 + 10 - 3 + 7 - 6 - 9 + 2$

4. Find each of the following products:

(a) $(8)(5)$ (b) $(-6)(7)$ (c) $(-12)(-4)$
(d) $(9)(-6)$ (e) $(2)(-3)(4)$ (f) $(-5)(3)(-4)$
(g) $(-3)(-6)(2)(-1)$

5. Perform the indicated operations:

(a) $20 \div 5$ (b) $24 \div (-8)$ (c) $(-30) \div 6$
(d) $(-35) \div (-7)$ (e) $\dfrac{-28}{(-7)(3)}$ (f) $\dfrac{(36)(15)}{-81}$
(g) $\dfrac{(42)(-35)}{(-49)(-18)}$

4·9 Algebraic expression

An *algebraic expression* is a collection of number symbols combined through one or more of the operations of addition, subtraction, multiplication, division, and extraction of roots.

In an algebraic expression, a term is an indicated product of a finite number of factors. Thus, in the expression $ab - ac + bcxy$, the terms are ab, $-ac$, and $bcxy$.

An algebraic expression containing only one term is called a *monomial,* e.g., bcm or $-ax$. An expression containing two terms is called a *binomial,* e.g., $mn + xyz$; one containing three terms is called a *trinomial,* e.g., $k - hn + w$. In general, expressions containing more than one term are called *polynomials,* or *multinomials.* A polynomial may also be defined as an algebraic expression in which the operations are limited to addition, subtraction, and multiplication. A *coefficient* is the multiplier of a term. When two or more quantities are multiplied together to form a product, each of the quantities is called a factor of the product. In the term $5xyz$, 5, x, y, and z are called factors of the expression. Usually the numerical part of the term is regarded as the coefficient, although any one or more of the factors could be taken as the coefficient of the remaining factors. Thus, 5 would usually be considered the coefficient but by the associative law, $5y$ could be considered the coefficient of xz. When the expression contains no numerical coefficient, a coefficient of 1 is understood. Thus bcm is the same as $1bcm$.

An *exponent* is a figure or letter placed to the right of and somewhat above a quantity called the *base* to indicate how many times the base is to be taken as a factor. Thus a^4 means $a \cdot a \cdot a \cdot a$ and is read "a fourth" or "a to the fourth *power*."

It is important to maintain a clear distinction between coefficient and exponent: $3x$ means $x + x + x$, whereas x^3 means $x \cdot x \cdot x$.

When a quantity is written without an exponent, the exponent 1 is understood. Thus y means y^1.

Monomials having a common literal part can be combined by combining the coefficients and affixing the common literal part. If the monomials are unlike, the operations can only be indicated.

example 5 Express the sum of $5cd^2$, cd^2, $-2cd^2$.

By the distributive law $5cd^2 + cd^2 - 2cd^2 = (5 + 1 - 2)cd^2 = 4cd^2$

example 6

$$\begin{array}{l} 7xy \\ 5x^2 \\ \underline{-2y^2 \qquad\qquad\qquad} \\ 7xy + 5x^2 - 2y^2 \end{array}$$

EXERCISE 2

Write the expressions in Probs. 1 to 8 in the most concise form possible by using coefficients and exponents. Use the commutative and associative laws where applicable.

1. $a + a + a - a + a$
2. $x - x - x + x - x - x$
3. $y \cdot y \cdot y \cdot y$
4. $a \cdot a \cdot b \cdot b \cdot b$
5. $4x \cdot y \cdot y \cdot z \cdot z \cdot z$
6. $(a + c)(a + c)(a + c)$
7. $w(xw)w(xw)$
8. $a(ab)(abc)(bc)c$

Find the numerical values in Probs. 9 to 30 if $a = 3$, $b = 4$, $c = -5$, and $x = 1$.

9. $a + b$
10. $2c - a$
11. $7(2a - c)$
12. $3a^2bc$
13. $4a^2 - b^2$
14. $(a + c)^2$
15. $b^2 - x^2$
16. $(3a - b)^3$
17. $(a + b)(a + b)$
18. $a + b(a + b)$
19. $(a + b)a + b$
20. $a + ba + b$
21. $(2a - b + c)^2$
22. $(c + b)^3x$
23. $\sqrt{a^2 + b^2}$
24. $\sqrt{(3a)^2 - b^2 - x^2}$
25. $\dfrac{4a + b}{c + 3x}$
26. $\dfrac{4a}{c} + \dfrac{b}{3x}$
27. $(4b + 3c - x)^4$
28. $\left(\dfrac{4a + 2b}{3x - c}\right)^2$
29. $3abc^2$
30. $(3abc)^2$

Perform the indicated additions in Probs. 31 to 42.

31. $\begin{array}{r} 7x \\ 5x \\ \underline{-x} \end{array}$

32. $\begin{array}{r} -11ab \\ 4ab \\ ab \\ -2ab \\ \underline{8ab} \end{array}$

33. $\begin{array}{r} 9mn \\ -2mn \\ -mn \\ \underline{7mn} \end{array}$

34. $\begin{array}{r} 6cd \\ -4cd \\ 7cd \\ \underline{-8cd} \end{array}$

35. $\begin{array}{r} 5x + 4y \\ \underline{x + 5y} \end{array}$

36. $\begin{array}{r} -3a + 2c \\ \underline{4a - 3c} \end{array}$

37. $\begin{array}{l} 6m + 10p \\ \underline{6m - \ \ 2p} \end{array}$

38. $\begin{array}{l} 4x^2 - 2xy + \ \ y^2 \\ \underline{5x^2 + 3xy - 2y^2} \end{array}$

39. $\begin{array}{l} 3k^2 - 2km + \ \ m^2 \\ \underline{k^2 \qquad\qquad + 4m^2} \end{array}$

40. $\begin{array}{l} 2p^2 \qquad\qquad - 3q^2 \\ \underline{5p^2 + 4pq - 2q^2} \end{array}$

41. $\begin{array}{l} 4x - 2y \\ \underline{5x \qquad - 3z} \end{array}$

42. $\begin{array}{l} 10c^2 + cm - 3m^2 \\ \underline{\ \ 3c^2 + cm - 4m^2} \end{array}$

43–50. In Probs. 35 to 42 subtract the second expression from the first.

51. From the sum of $a^2 - 2a + 3$ and $2a^2 - a + 5$ subtract $4a^2 - 4a + 7$.

52. From $8c^2 - 2c + 11$ subtract the sum of $c^2 - 4c + 6$ and $5c^2 + 3c + 5$.

53. Subtract the sum of $9x^2 - xy$ and $3x^2 + xy - 2y^2$ from $6x^2 - 3xy - y^2$.

4 · 10 Some fundamental rules of exponents

The following laws relate to positive integral exponents, but in Chap. 8 it will be shown that they are valid for fractional and negative exponents as well.

I. Products $a^m \cdot a^n = a^{m+n}$

example 7 $c^2 \cdot c^3 = c^{2+3} = c^5$ because

$$c^2 \cdot c^3 = (c \cdot c)(c \cdot c \cdot c) = c \cdot c \cdot c \cdot c \cdot c = c^5$$

example 8 $a \cdot a^2 \cdot a^5 = a^1 \cdot a^2 \cdot a^5 = a^{1+2+5} = a^8$

IIa. Powers $(a^m)^n = a^{mn}$

example 9 $(y^2)^3 = y^{2\times 3} = y^6$ because

$$(y^2)^3 = y^2 \cdot y^2 \cdot y^2 = (y \cdot y)(y \cdot y)(y \cdot y) = y \cdot y \cdot y \cdot y \cdot y \cdot y = y^6$$

IIb. $(ab)^n = a^n b^n$

example 10 $(ab)^5 = (ab)(ab)(ab)(ab)(ab)$
$= (a \cdot a \cdot a \cdot a \cdot a)(b \cdot b \cdot b \cdot b \cdot b) = a^5b^5$

IIc. $\left(\frac{a}{b}\right)^n = \frac{a^n}{b^n}$

example 11 $\left(\frac{a}{b}\right)^4 = \left(\frac{a}{b}\right)\left(\frac{a}{b}\right)\left(\frac{a}{b}\right)\left(\frac{a}{b}\right) = \frac{a \cdot a \cdot a \cdot a}{b \cdot b \cdot b \cdot b} = \frac{a^4}{b^4}$

III. Quotients $\frac{a^m}{a^n} = a^{m-n}$ $(m > n, a \neq 0)$ [Read "m is greater than n, a is not equal to zero."]

example 12 $x^5 \div x^3 = x^{5-3} = x^2$ because

$$x^5 \div x^3 = \frac{\cancel{x} \cdot \cancel{x} \cdot \cancel{x} \cdot x \cdot x}{\cancel{x} \cdot \cancel{x} \cdot \cancel{x}} = x \cdot x = x^2$$

A further definition will be given [Eq. (3), Sec. 8 · 1] to cover cases in which the power of the numerator is less than that of the denominator.

EXERCISE 3

Perform the indicated operations:

1. $x^2 \cdot x^4$	2. $c^3 \cdot c^5$	3. $y^6 \cdot y$
4. $k^3 \cdot k^4 \cdot k^2$	5. $a \cdot a^2 \cdot a^3 \cdot a^4$	6. $(b^2)^4$
7. $(m^5)^3$	8. $(3a)^2$	9. $(5x^3)^2$
10. $(-4c^2)^3$	11. $(-2b^4)^6$	12. $-(-5w^4)^3$
13. $x^7 \div x^4$	14. $h^{12} \div h^3$	15. $y^6 \div y$
16. $(-a)^5 \div a^2$	17. $(-b)^6 \div (-b)^5$	18. $(-b)^6 \div (-b^4)$

4 · 11 Symbols of grouping

Parentheses, ( ), brackets, [ ], or braces, { } indicate that the expression which they enclose is to be treated as a unit. The less frequently used vinculum, $\overline{}$, written over an expression, has the same meaning.

example 13 $5 + (2 + 7) = 5 + 9 = 14$

example 14 $8 - (3 + 10) = 8 - 13 = -5$

example 15 $6 - \overline{7 - 2} = 6 - 5 = 1$

example 16 $4(5 + 2) = 4(7) = 28$. Note that we might write (by the distributive law)

$$4(5 + 2) = 4(5) + 4(2) = 20 + 8 = 28$$

The following remarks concerning parentheses will be understood to apply equally well to brackets and braces.

Parentheses are useful in enclosing expressions to be multiplied:

example 17 $5(-4)$ means 5 times -4, or -20.

example 18 To multiply the expression $a + 3$ by the expression $a - 5$, we write $(a + 3)(a - 5)$ (read "the quantity $a + 3$ times the quantity $a - 5$"). If $a = 9$, then $(9 + 3)(9 - 5) = (12)(4) = 48$.

Parentheses can be used to avoid ambiguity regarding the order of application of the fundamental operations.

example 19 Does the expression $14 - 6 \div 2$ mean that 8 is to be divided by 2 or that 3 is to be subtracted from 14?

There is a rule stating that multiplication and division take precedence over addition and subtraction. However, such sloppiness is indefensible when the intent is easily clarified by the use of parentheses. If written $(14 - 6) \div 2 = 8 \div 2 = 4$ in one case or $14 - (6 \div 2) = 14 - 3 = 11$ in the other, the meaning is no longer questionable.

To insert or remove parentheses preceded by a plus sign, rewrite the affected quantities with their respective signs unchanged.

example 20 $8 + (3 - 4) = 8 + 3 - 4 = 7$

To insert or remove parentheses preceded by a minus sign, rewrite the affected quantities with their respective signs reversed.

example 21 $11 - (7 - 2) = 11 - 7 + 2 = 6$

The last example may be illustrated by the following common situation: A man with \$11 in his possession buys a \$7 article and returns for credit a \$2 article.

If the purchase and refund were made at the same counter, the \$2 refund would probably be applied at the time of purchase, so that $11 - (7 - 2) = 11 - 5 = 6$; i.e., only \$5 would change hands. If, on the other hand, the refund were made in another department after the \$7 purchase, we would write $11 - 7 + 2 = 6$. (In either case the customer still has \$6 in cash.)

Note that if we started with the expression $11 - 7 + 2$ and wished to enclose the last two quantities with a pair of parentheses preceded by a minus sign, we should have to write $11 - 7 + 2 = 11 - (7 - 2)$, since we have already seen that $11 - (7 - 2) = 11 - 7 + 2$, and the operation must be reversible.

When one set of grouping symbols is contained within another, the innermost set is removed first.

example 22 Perform the indicated operations and apply the commutative and distributive laws in the following expression: $3x + 2 - [2y + 5 - (6y - 2x + 3)]$.

Beginning with the inner group and performing the indicated multiplications with due attention to signs, we obtain

$$3x + 2 - [2y + 5 - 6y + 2x - 3] = 3x + 2 - 2y - 5 + 6y - 2x + 3 = x + 4y$$

EXERCISE 4

In Probs. 1 to 10, simplify by removing the symbols of grouping as in Example 22.

1. $3a + 4b + (2a - b)$
2. $5a - 3c - (2a - 4c)$
3. $4x - 7y - (3x - 4y) + x + 3y$
4. $6u + 5 - (3v + 4w - 2) - 2u + 4v$
5. $8m - [4n - (-3m + 3n) + m]$
6. $a - \{2x + [3a - 5x - (4a + x)] - 2a\}$
7. $-7b + \{6c - [2b - c + (8c - 4b) + b]\}$
8. $\{8c + 3k - [5c + 2k]\} - \{3c + k - [7c - (c - 4k)]\}$
9. $11ab - 3a^2b - [5ab^2 - (6ab + 2a^2b) + ab] + 3ab^2$
10. $\{4x^2 - xy + [y^2 - 2xy] - x^2\} - \{3x^2 - [y^2 - (2xy + x^2) + xy]\}$

In Probs. 11 to 16, enclose the last three terms in parentheses preceded by (a) a minus sign and (b) a plus sign.

11. $5a + 2b - 4c + m - x$
12. $2a^2 + 3ab - 7b^2 + 4b$
13. $7mn + 3m^2 - 4n^2 - 8m + 5n + 2mn$
14. $6c^2 + 5cd + d^2 - 2m^2$
15. $9w^2 + 5y^3 - 2w^2y - 3wy^2 + w^3$
16. $-7x^2 - 5xy - 2y^2 + 4yz - z^2$

4·12 Multiplying by a monomial

To multiply a monomial by a monomial, multiply the product of the numerical coefficients by the product of the literal factors, making use of the law of exponents where it applies. Determine and apply the proper sign.

example 23 Find the indicated product:

$$(-3axy^2)(5a^3x^2) \qquad \text{ANS.: } -15a^4x^3y^2$$

To multiply a polynomial by a monomial, multiply each term of the polynomial by the monomial and write the sum of the products.

example 24 $4x^2y(5a^2x - 7b^2y) = 20a^2x^3y - 28b^2x^2y^2$ (by the distributive law)

EXERCISE 5

Perform the following multiplications:

1. $(8mn)(4mx)$
2. $(-3h^2x)(6hx^2)$
3. $(9abc)(-4bcd)$
4. $(-2ck^2x)(-7c^2x^5)$
5. $(a^2m)(m^2x)(ax^2)$
6. $(3ac^2d)(-4cd^3)(-2a^4cd^2)$
7. $(-9a^2b^3c^4)(-4a^3b^4m^5)(-2b^4c^5m^6)$
8. $5(4h - 6k)$
9. $-3y(6m - 5t)$
10. $4ax(5ay + 9mx)$
11. $6a^2b(5a^2 - 7ab - 9b^2)$
12. $-2xy^2(1 - 2x + 3x^2 - 4x^3)$
13. $(-3hk)(-2hk^3)(4a^3h^2 - 11bk)$
14. $\frac{2}{3}ab^2c^3(12ax - 21by)$

4 · 13 Multiplying one polynomial by another polynomial

In order to multiply one polynomial by another, arrange the terms in descending powers of one of the letters involved. Multiply the first polynomial by the successive terms of the second, arranging like terms of the product in columns, and add.

example 25 Multiply $10x - 2x^3 + x^4 - 1$ by $x^2 + 2 + 6x^3$.

Arranging in descending powers of x,

$$\begin{array}{rrrrrrrrl}
x^4 & -\ 2x^3 & & & +\ 10x & -\ 1 & & & \\
6x^3 & +\ x^2 & +\ 2 & & & & & & \\
\hline
6x^7 - 12x^6 & & +\ 60x^4 & -\ 6x^3 & & & & & \text{(multiplying by } 6x^3) \\
+\ x^6 - 2x^5 & & & +\ 10x^3 & -\ x^2 & & & & \text{(multiplying by } x^2) \\
& & +\ 2x^4 & -\ 4x^3 & & +\ 20x & -\ 2 & & \text{(multiplying by 2)} \\
\hline
6x^7 - 11x^6 - 2x^5 & & +\ 62x^4 & & -\ x^2 & +\ 20x & -\ 2 & &
\end{array}$$

The answer may be checked with reasonable certainty by substituting some simple number for x. Substitution of the number 1 should be avoided since any power of 1 is also 1.

Let us check by letting $x = 2$; then

$$x^4 - 2x^3 + 10x - 1 = (2)^4 - 2(2)^3 + 10(2) - 1$$
$$= 16 - 16 + 20 - 1 = 19$$

and $$6x^3 + x^2 + 2 = 6(2)^3 + (2)^2 + 2 = 48 + 4 + 2 = 54$$
$$(19)(54) = 1{,}026$$

$$6x^7 - 11x^6 - 2x^5 + 62x^4 - x^2 + 20x - 2$$
$$= 6(2)^7 - 11(2)^6 - 2(2)^5 + 62(2)^4 - (2)^2 + 20(2) - 2$$
$$= 768 - 704 - 64 + 992 - 4 + 40 - 2 = 1{,}026$$

EXERCISE 6

Perform the following multiplications:

1. $(a + b)(c + d)$
2. $(m + x)(m - y)$
3. $(h + k)(h - k)$
4. $(y^4 - y^2)(y^5 + y^3)$
5. $(2m + 5w)(3m - 7w)$
6. $(4x - 6y)(6x + 9y)$

7. $(4x - 2y - 13)(6x + 3y)$
8. $(3p^2 + 4pq + 5q^2)(2p - 3q)$
9. $(b - x - y)(b + x + y)$
10. $(c + d - 5)(c - d + 4)$
11. $(n^2 + 2n + 4)(n - 2)$
12. $(a^2 - 5ab + b^2)(a^2 + 5ab - b^2)$
13. $(x^4 - x^3 + 4x^2 - x + 1)(x + 1)$
14. $(c^3 + 2c^2 - 9c - 18)(c - 2)$

4·14 Removing parentheses used to indicate multiplication

In removing parentheses used to indicate multiplication, the usual rules of multiplication apply.

example 26 Simplify the expression

$$3 + 2\{5 - 4x[1 - 6(x + 2)]\}$$

[Note that 1 and $-6(x + 2)$ do not make -5 of any one thing.]

Performing the indicated multiplications, beginning with the innermost group, we obtain

$$\begin{aligned} 3 + 2[5 - 4x(1 - 6x - 12)] &= 3 + 2(5 - 4x + 24x^2 + 48x) \\ &= 3 + 10 - 8x + 48x^2 + 96x \\ &= 13 + 88x + 48x^2 \end{aligned}$$

EXERCISE 7

Simplify the following expressions:

1. $1 - 2\{1 + 3[1 - 4(1 - 5x)]\}$
2. $a - \{[b - c] - [a + b - c - 2(a - b + c)]\}$
3. $5\{4[3(2 + x)]\} - 5\{-4[-3(2 - x)]\}$
4. $y^2 - y\{y + z[x(y - z) + y(z - x) + z(x - y)]\}$

EXERCISE 8

In the following problems, in cases in which the result can be expressed in more than one way, the use of the letter representing the smaller dimension is preferred.

1–4. Express in the simplest possible form the perimeter of each of the following figures:

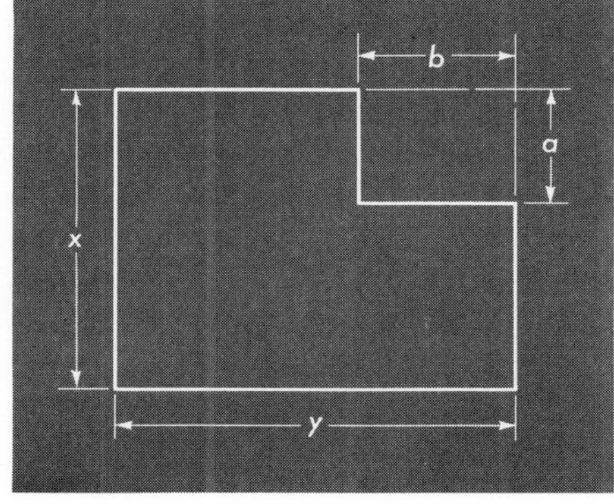

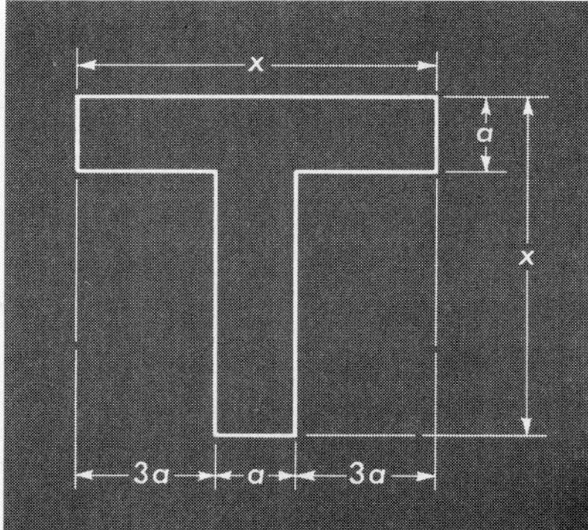

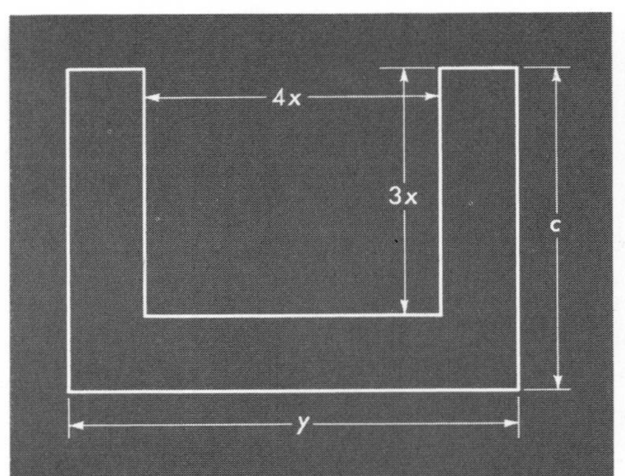

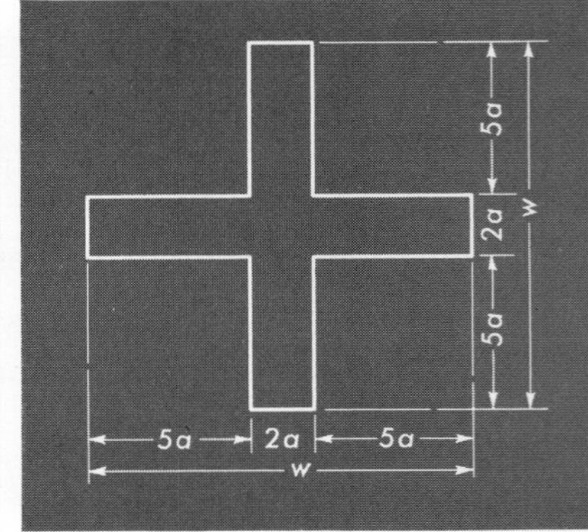

5–8. Express in the simplest possible form the area of each of Probs. 1 to 4, inclusive.
9. Find the area of the form in Fig. 4·1.
10. Find the area of overlap in Fig. 4·2.
11. Find the outer surface and volume of the open-top box shown in Fig. 4·3.
12. Find in terms a and b the distance x in Fig. 4·4.
13. Find in terms of D and d the wall thickness t in Fig. 4·5.
14. Find in Fig. 4·6 the values of x and y in terms of a and b.

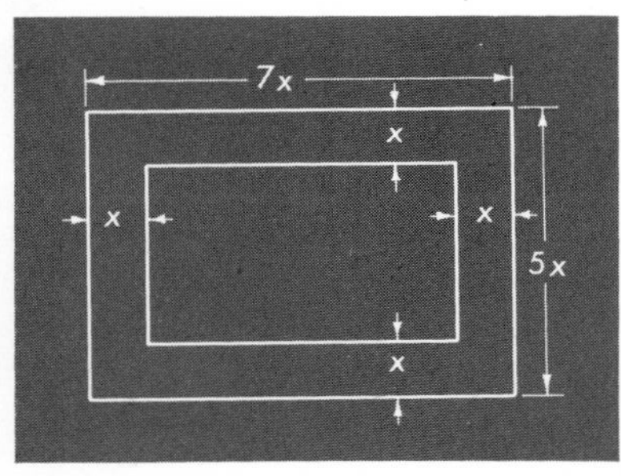

fig. 4·1

fig. 4·2

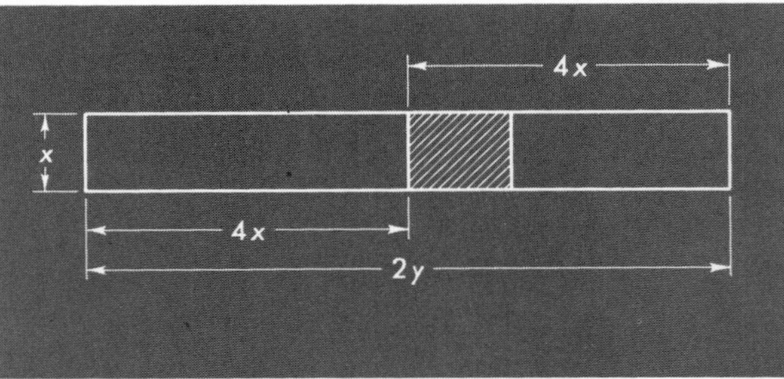

fig. 4·3

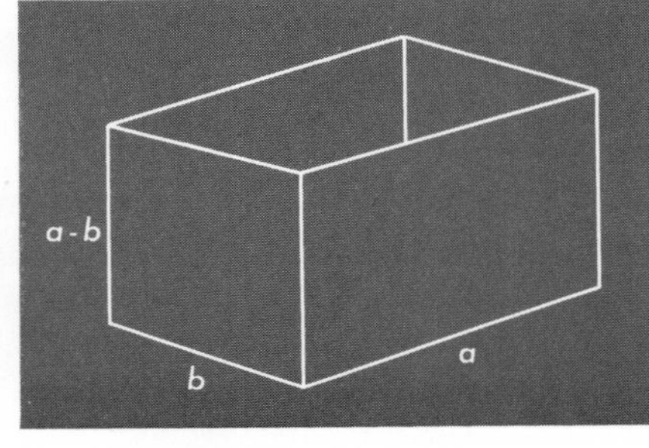

fig. 4·4

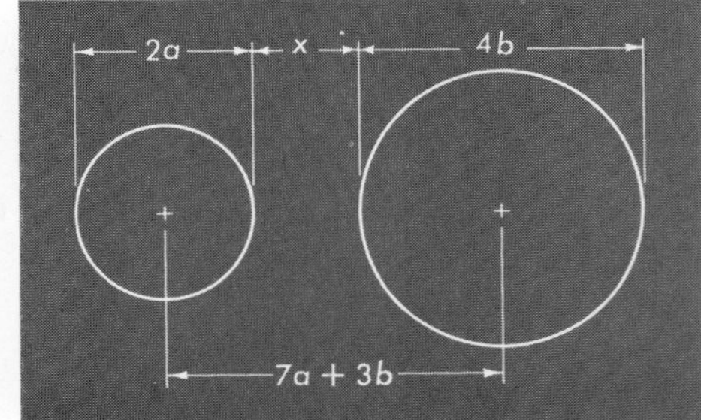

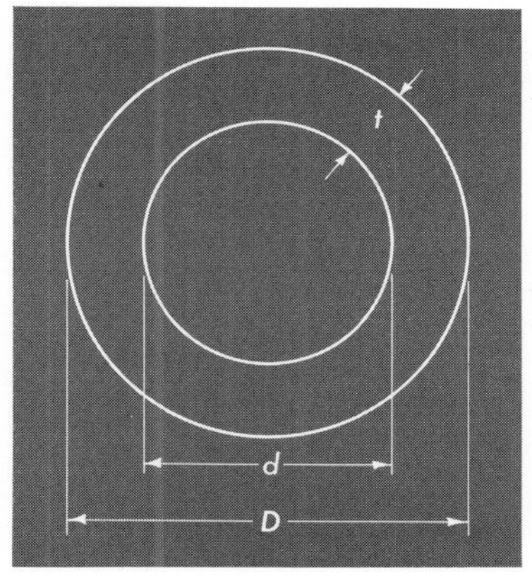

fig. 4·5

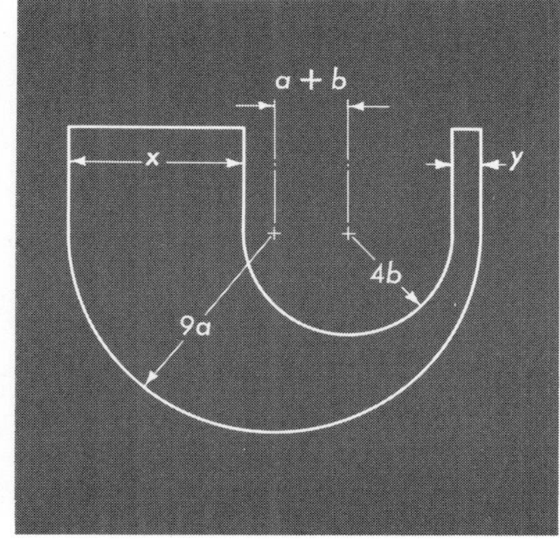

fig. 4·6

4·15 Dividing one monomial by another monomial

To divide one monomial by another monomial, divide the coefficient of the dividend by the coefficient of the divisor, apply the rule of exponents to the literal factors, and prefix the proper sign.

example 27 Divide $-20x^3yz^2$ by $-5xyz$.

Regarding the problem as a cancellation (that is, we divide like factors out of numerator and denominator), we write

$$\frac{-\overset{4}{\cancel{20}}\cancel{x}\cdot x\cdot x\cdot \cancel{y}\cdot z\cdot \cancel{z}}{-\cancel{5}\cancel{x}\quad \cancel{y}\quad \cancel{z}} = 4x^2z$$

example 28 Divide $-12a^2bc^3$ by $16a^3cx^2$.

Cancellation gives us

$$\frac{-\overset{3}{\cancel{12}}\cancel{a}\cdot \cancel{a}\cdot b\cdot \cancel{c}\cdot c\cdot c}{\underset{4}{\cancel{16}}\cancel{a}\cdot \cancel{a}\cdot a\cdot \cancel{c}\cdot x\cdot x} = -\frac{3bc^2}{4ax^2}$$

To divide a polynomial by a monomial, divide each term of the polynomial by the monomial and write the sum of the quotients.

example 29

$$(24c^4x - 21c^2x^2 + 18cx^2) \div (-6c^2x) = -4c^2 + \frac{7x}{2} - \frac{3x}{c}$$

EXERCISE 9

Obtain the following quotients:

1. $15c^3 \div 5c^2$
2. $-24h^3 \div 8h$
3. $35c^3d^2 \div (-7cd^2)$
4. $-42ab^2c^3 \div (-3ac^2)$
5. $12x^{12} \div 3x^3$
6. $-12ab^2m^3 \div 18a^3bm^2$

7. $40x^2y^3z \div 5wxz^3$
8. $-28a^4h^2k^3 \div (-20a^3h^3n^3)$
9. $(6ab - 8ac) \div 2a$
10. $(12c^2y + 20cw) \div 4c$
11. $(16km^2 - 24k^2m) \div (-8km)$
12. $(6xy - 30x^2y - 6xy^2) \div 6xy$
13. $(\pi r^2h + 2\pi rh) \div \pi rh$
14. $(35xy^4 - 20x^2y^3) \div 10xy^4$
15. $(20hk^3r^4 + 30h^2k^2r^2 - 21h^3k^2r^2) \div 12h^2k^2r^3$
16. $(10a^3bc - 12ab^2c^2 + 16ab^4) \div 8a^2b^2c^2$

4·16 Division of a polynomial by a polynomial

Division of a polynomial by a polynomial is governed by essentially the same rules as long division in arithmetic.

example 30 Divide $3x^2 + 8x + 9$ by $x + 2$.

$$\begin{array}{r|l} & 3x + 2 \\ \hline x + 2 & 3x^2 + 8x + 9 \\ & 3x^2 + 6x \\ \hline & \quad 2x + 9 \\ & \quad 2x + 4 \\ \hline & \qquad 5 \end{array}$$

ANS.: $3x + 2 + \dfrac{5}{x + 2}$

If we let $x = 10$, we obtain the very similar long division in arithmetic.

$$\begin{array}{r|l} & 32 \\ \hline 12 & 389 \\ & 36 \\ \hline & \ 29 \\ & \ 24 \\ \hline & \ \ 5 \end{array}$$

ANS.: $32\frac{5}{12}$

In each case we note that

$$\text{Quotient} = \frac{\text{Dividend}}{\text{Divisor}} = \text{Integral portion} + \frac{\text{remainder}}{\text{divisor}}$$

Therefore we proceed to divide one polynomial by another as follows:

1. *Arrange each polynomial in either descending or ascending powers of some letter common to each expression.*
2. *Divide the first term of the dividend by the first term of the divisor to find the first term of the quotient.*
3. *Multiply the entire divisor by the first term of the quotient and subtract the result from the dividend.*
4. *Consider the remainder obtained in step 3 as a new dividend and repeat steps 2 and 3, continuing the process until there is either no remainder or a remainder whose first term cannot be evenly divided by the first term of the divisor.*

example 31 Divide $8x - 13x^2 + 6x^3 - 12$ by $2x - 3$.

Rearranging, we obtain

$$\begin{array}{r|l} & 3x^2 - 2x + 1 \\ \hline 2x - 3 & 6x^3 - 13x^2 + 8x - 12 \\ & 6x^3 - 9x^2 \\ \hline & \quad - 4x^2 + 8x \\ & \quad - 4x^2 + 6x \\ \hline & \qquad\qquad 2x - 12 \\ & \qquad\qquad 2x - 3 \\ \hline & \qquad\qquad\quad - 9 \end{array}$$

ANS.: $3x^2 - 2x + 1 - \dfrac{9}{2x - 3}$

Note that while remainders in arithmetical division are always positive, they may be either positive or negative in algebraic division.

To check, (integral portion)(divisor) + remainder = dividend. In this illustration,

$$(3x^2 - 2x + 1)(2x - 3) - 9 = 6x^3 - 13x^2 + 8x - 12$$

A check may also be obtained which is usually valid as in multiplication by numerical substitution (avoiding the use of 0 and 1, or any value of x which makes the divisor equal zero).

Occasionally the dividend will be lacking one or more intermediate powers of a letter. In this case space should be left where such gaps occur.

example 32 Divide $36x^4 - 25x^2 + 4$ by $3x - 2$.

It will be noted that there are no x^3 and x terms in the dividend. Hence we arrange as follows:

$$\begin{array}{r|l} & 12x^3 + 8x^2 - 3x - 2 \\ \hline 3x - 2 & 36x^4 \qquad\quad - 25x^2 \qquad + 4 \\ & 36x^4 - 24x^3 \\ \hline & \quad + 24x^3 - 25x^2 \\ & \quad\;\; 24x^3 - 16x^2 \\ \hline & \qquad\qquad - 9x^2 \\ & \qquad\qquad - 9x^2 + 6x \\ \hline & \qquad\qquad\qquad - 6x + 4 \\ & \qquad\qquad\qquad - 6x + 4 \\ \hline \end{array}$$

EXERCISE 10

Divide:

1. $a^2 + 11a + 24$ by $a + 3$
2. $c^3 - 2c^2 - 2c + 1$ by $1 + c$
3. $8m^2 - 22mw + 15w^2$ by $2m - 3w$
4. $16z^4 - 1$ by $2z - 1$
5. $6k^6 - 48$ by $3k^2 - 6$
6. $8q^2 - q - 19q^3 + 15q^4 - 1$ by $5q^2 - 3q - 1$

7. $h^6 - 2h^3 + 1$ by $h^2 + h + 1$
8. $y^5 - 2y^4 - 13y^2 + 17y + 5$ by $3y + 1 + y^3 - 4y^2$
9. $64x^6 - 1$ by $2x - 1$
10. 1 by $1 + x$ (to 4 terms)
11. 1 by $x + 1$ (to 4 terms)
12. $\dfrac{x^3}{2x + 1}$ (see Example 29)

4·17 Special products or expansions

The following special products should be verified by the student and memorized both as literal formulas and as equivalent descriptive sentences.

$$a(x + y + z) = ax + ay + az \qquad \text{(see distributive law)} \tag{1}$$

For example: $3ab^2(5ax - 8b) = 15a^2b^2x - 24ab^3$

$$(x + y)(x - y) = x^2 - y^2 \tag{2}$$

For example: $(3cm^2 + 4x)(3cm^2 - 4x) = 9c^2m^4 - 16x^2$

$$(x + y)^2 = x^2 + 2xy + y^2 \tag{3}$$

For example: $(5ab + 4w)^2 = 25a^2b^2 + 40abw + 16w^2$

$$(x - y)^2 = x^2 - 2xy + y^2 \tag{4}$$

For example: $(2ax - 7x^2y)^2 = 4a^2x^2 - 28ax^3y + 49x^4y^2$

$$(x + a)(x + b) = x^2 + (a + b)x + ab \tag{5}$$

For example:
$$\begin{aligned}(x + 5)(x - 2) &= x^2 + (5 - 2)x - 10\\ &= x^2 + 3x - 10\end{aligned}$$

$$(ax + b)(cx + d) = acx^2 + (ad + bc)x + bd \tag{6}$$

For example:
$$\begin{aligned}(3x + 8)(2x - 7) &= 6x^2 + (-21 + 16)x - 56\\ &= 6x^2 - 5x - 56\end{aligned}$$

$$(a + b)(c + d) = ac + ad + bc + bd \tag{7}$$

For example:
$$\begin{aligned}(3e - 2k)(2m + 5n) &= 3e(2m + 5n) - 2k(2m + 5n)\\ &= 6em + 15en - 4km - 10kn\end{aligned}$$

$$(x - y)(x^2 + xy + y^2) = x^3 - y^3 \tag{8}$$

For example: $(a - 3b)(a^2 + 3ab + 9b^2) = a^3 - 27b^3$

$$(x + y)(x^2 - xy + y^2) = x^3 + y^3 \tag{9}$$

For example: $(2c + m)(4c^2 - 2cm + m^2) = 8c^3 + m^3$

$$(a + b + c)^2 = a^2 + b^2 + c^2 + 2ab + 2ac + 2bc \qquad (10)$$

For example: $(2x - 3y + 5z)^2 = 4x^2 + 9y^2 + 25z^2 - 12xy + 20xz - 30yz$

There are additional special products which have not been listed above, as they arise too infrequently to be memorized. Some of these are as follows:

$$(x - y)(x^{n-1} + x^{n-2}y + \cdots + xy^{n-2} + y^{n-1}) = x^n - y^n \qquad (11)$$

$$(x + y)(x^{n-1} - x^{n-2}y + \cdots + xy^{n-2} - y^{n-1}) = x^n - y^n \qquad (12)$$

(for even values of n only)

$$(x + y)(x^{n-1} - x^{n-2}y + \cdots - xy^{n-2} + y^{n-1}) = x^n + y^n \qquad (13)$$

(for odd values of n only)

$$(x + y)^3 = x^3 + 3x^2y + 3xy^2 + y^3 \qquad (14)$$

$$(x - y)^3 = x^3 - 3x^2y + 3xy^2 - y^3 \qquad (15)$$

$$(x^2 + xy + y^2)(x^2 - xy + y^2) = x^4 + x^2y^2 + y^4 \qquad (16)$$

EXERCISE 11

Obtain the following special products as far as possible as an oral exercise:

1. $4xy(5a - 7b)$
2. $-5m^2x(3bm - 8cx)$
3. $2ab^2c(3ax - 4by + 7cz)$
4. $-8hk(-2ah^2 - 9b^2k)$
5. $(x - 3)(x + 3)$
6. $(7 - c)(7 + c)$
7. $(8k - 3m)(8k + 3m)$
8. $(5c^2 - 4n)(5c^2 + 4n)$
9. $(9pq - 7r)(9pq + 7r)$
10. $(c + 7)^2$
11. $(8 + n)^2$
12. $(3a + 1)^2$
13. $(4b + 3)^2$
14. $(6c + 5k)^2$
15. $(12am + 7y)^2$
16. $(m - 6)^2$
17. $(6 - m)^2$
18. $(h - 8)^2$
19. $(5x - 1)^2$
20. $(1 - 4c)^2$
21. $(7t - 9)^2$
22. $(11w - 4)^2$
23. $(5h - 12n)^2$
24. $(d + 3)(d + 4)$
25. $(m + 7)(m - 3)$
26. $(y + 2)(y - 9)$
27. $(a - 4)(a - 11)$
28. $(x + 1)(x + 6)$
29. $(z - 4)(z - 12)$
30. $(2b + 3)(3b + 1)$
31. $(4c - 1)(2c + 5)$
32. $(5m + 3)(4m - 7)$
33. $(6x - 1)(5x - 2)$

4·18 Factoring

Factoring is the inverse of multiplication such as is illustrated by the problems in Exercise 11. We shall now start with a given product and determine what numbers or factors were multiplied to give this product. We are interested in determining any monomial factors and any prime polynomial factors, i.e., polynomial factors which are divisible by no rational integral expression except themselves or 1.

By reversing each of the expansion rules in Sec. 4·17, we obtain rules for factoring. Each example, upon interchange of right and left members of the identity, becomes an example of factoring.

In the factoring out of a common monomial factor of a polynomial, each literal factor of the monomial is taken the least number of times that it occurs in any one of the terms of the original polynomial.

example 33 Factor $18ab^4x^3 - 30a^2b^2c$.

We obtain (by the distributive law)

$$6ab^2(3b^2x^3 - 5ac)$$

since 6 is the highest common factor of 18 and 30, and the lowest power of a in any term is 1 and of b is 2, with c and x missing entirely from one term each.

HINT ON FACTORING: If an expression appears to be of the type illustrated in Eq. (6), Sec. 4·17, after removing any monomial factor, test out the various factor combinations of the coefficients. We might go further and state that the factoring of any polynomial is simplified by first removing any monomial factors.

example 34 Factor $12x^2 + x - 6$.

Writing the factors in a general form, we have

$$(ax + b)(cx - d)$$

We note that ac must equal 12, $(b)(-d)$ must equal -6, and $bc - ad$ must equal 1. Two possible factors *might* be $(6x - 2)$ and $(2x + 3)$. Instead of actually multiplying, all we need to do is to write $\begin{matrix} 6 - 2 \\ 2 + 3 \end{matrix}$, representing the coefficients and constants arranged for multiplication. A glance at the cross products (6)(3) and (2)(−2) whose sum is 18 − 4 or 14 shows that this is not the answer. A more careful inspection would have eliminated this choice as a possibility, since $6x - 2$ contains a factor of 2, whereas $12x^2 + x - 6$ does not. It will be seen from the arrangement $\begin{matrix} 3 - 2 \\ 4 + 3 \end{matrix}$ that $(3x - 2)$ and $(4x + 3)$ are the required factors (see Note, page 275).

EXERCISE 12

Factor out the common monomial factor from each of the following:

1. $15x - 18y$
2. $16x + 40y$
3. $30ab - 42km$
4. $ax + ay$
5. $a^2 - ac$
6. $12xy - 20x^2$
7. $abc + bcm + cmx$
8. $a^2b^2 + a^2b + ab^2$
9. $42ax^2y - 24bx^3y^2 + 18cx^4y$
10. $15ab^2c^2 - 12a^2bc^2 + 8a^2b^2c$
11. $10a^2x^2 - 15abxy + 20b^2y^2$
12. $30ax^2y + 48bxy^2 - 36cxyz$
13. The expression $ab - ac$ may be written $a(b - c)$. Make use of this identity to state whether or not 63,549 and 63,574 have any common factors.

EXERCISE 13

Factor completely:

1. $x^2 - 4$
2. $c^2 - 25$
3. $36 - y^2$
4. $16z^2 - 1$
5. $49m^2 - 1$
6. $4a^2 - 9b^2$
7. $25d^2 - 64m^2$
8. $36 - 121a^2b^2$
9. $100y^2z^2 - 49c^2d^2$
10. $121k^4 - 1$
11. $16n^8 - 1$
12. $16 - 81x^{12}$
13. $(25)^2 - (24)^2$
14. $(10\frac{1}{2})^2 - (8\frac{1}{2})^2$
15. Show that $(97)^2$ may be calculated at sight by writing

$$(97)^2 = (97 + 3)(97 - 3) + 3^2 = 9{,}409$$

(see Sec. B·6).

16. Show that the number 391 may be expressed as the difference between two squares and, as such, is factorable. Find the factors.
17. If n is any positive integer greater than unity, show that $n^3 - n$ is always divisible by 6.
18. Show that the difference between the squares of two consecutive odd integers must be divisible by 8.

EXERCISE 14

Find the missing terms needed to make the following expressions take the form of the trinomial squares $x^2 + 2xy + y^2$ or $x^2 - 2xy + y^2$. Insert only positive quantities within the parentheses.

1. $x^2 + (\quad) + 25$
2. $y^2 + (\quad) + 81$
3. $z^2 - (\quad) + 49$
4. $m^2 - (\quad) + 144$
5. $4a^2 + (\quad) + 1$
6. $36c^2 - (\quad) + 1$
7. $9n^2 + (\quad) + 25$
8. $16 - (\quad) + 121k^2$
9. $64b^2 - (\quad) + 25h^2$
10. $d^2 + 4d + (\quad)$
11. $p^2 - 10p + (\quad)$
12. $a^2 + 6ab + (\quad)$
13. $c^2 - 14cq + (\quad)$
14. $4w^2 - 28w + (\quad)$
15. $9m^2 + 30mx + (\quad)$
16. $25t^2 - 50tr + (\quad)$

EXERCISE 15

Factor each of the following trinomial squares:

1. $x^2 - 4x + 4$
2. $b^2 + 10b + 25$
3. $36 - 12m + m^2$
4. $4y^2 - 20y + 25$
5. $9 + 42z + 49z^2$
6. $16c^2 + 24cd + 9d^2$
7. $64a^2 - 80an + 25n^2$
8. $49a^2b^2 - 112abc + 64c^2$
9. $81m^4 - 72m^2p + 16p^2$
10. $121x^2 + 154xyz^2 + 49y^2z^4$

EXERCISE 16

Factor each of the following expressions:

1. $y^2 + 7y + 12$
2. $a^2 + 9a + 20$
3. $m^2 - 12m + 35$
4. $c^2 - 15c + 36$
5. $x^2 + 19x + 48$
6. $b^2 - 2b - 24$

7. $h^2 + h - 30$
8. $w^2 - 11w - 42$
9. $k^4 + k^2 - 72$
10. $z^6 - 3z^3 - 108$
11. $x^2 + 21xy + 54y^2$
12. $y^2 - 25yz + 66z^2$
13. $2a^2 + 3a + 1$
14. $3c^2 + 10c + 3$
15. $4m^2 - 11m + 6$
16. $7k^2 - 16k + 4$
17. $8b^2 + 18b + 9$
18. $17n^2 + 6n - 11$
19. $54h^2 - 15h - 50$
20. $48x^2 + 14x - 45$

example 35 Factor:

$$3a^2x^4 - 15a^2x^2 + 12a^2 = 3a^2(x^4 - 5x^2 + 4)$$
$$= 3a^2(x^2 - 4)(x^2 - 1)$$
$$= 3a^2(x + 2)(x - 2)(x + 1)(x - 1)$$

EXERCISE 17

In the following miscellaneous expressions first determine whether any factors exist. If an expression is factorable, it is suggested that any monomial factor be removed first. Factor completely into prime factors.

1. $9ac + 15bc$
2. $2c^3 - 32c^2 + 128c$
3. $4a^2 - 100$
4. $4m^2 - 20m + 100$
5. $6b^2 - 18b + 12$
6. $4y^3 - 8y^2 - 32y$
7. $16k^2 + 36$
8. $9am^2 - 30am + 9a$
9. $9h^2 - 34h + 25$
10. $100z^2 - 60z + 36$
11. $81x^4 - 16$
12. $35a^2b^2 - 80a^2b + 20a^2$
13. $4y^2 - 30y + 36$
14. $24h^2 + 12h - 36$
15. $36t^2 + 120t + 100$
16. $16rx^2 - 30rx + 9r$
17. $9m^2 - 12m + 16$
18. $6c^2 - c + 4$
19. $a^3y^3 + 8$
20. $a^2 + 2ab + 3ac + 6bc$
21. $x^2 + 4y^2 + z^2 + 4xy + 2xz + 4yz$
22. $x^3 - \frac{1}{8}$
23. $x^3 - x + x^2 - 1$
24. $27 - m^3$
25. $3ax + 3ay - bx - by$
26. $a^2 + 4b^2 + 9c^2 - 4ab - 6ac + 12bc$
27. $bm^3 - bn^3$
28. $y^3 - y + 4y^2 - 4$
29. $25c^2 + 9d^2 + f^2 + 30cd - 10cf - 6df$
30. $x^6 + 7x^3 - 8$
31. Given the right triangle in which the legs are $p^2 - q^2$ and $2pq$, determine the expression for the hypotenuse. Determine the three sides of each of the following right triangles: (a) $p = 5, q = 2$; (b) $p = 7, q = 4$; (c) $p = 8, q = 3$. What special property do these right triangles have in common?

4·19 Properties of fractions

The basic properties of algebraic fractions resemble those of arithmetical fractions.

1. *If both numerator and denominator of a fraction are multiplied or divided by the same number (other than zero), the value of the fraction remains unchanged.*

2. *Multiplying the numerator or dividing the denominator of a fraction by a given number multiplies the fraction by that quantity.*
3. *Dividing the numerator or multiplying the denominator of a fraction by a given number divides the fraction by that quantity.*
4. *If an even number of factors in a fraction are multiplied by (−1), the sign of the fraction remains unchanged. If an odd number of factors are multiplied by (−1), the sign before the fraction must be reversed* (see Sec. 4·6).

example 36 The rule just expressed states in effect that we must introduce an even number of (−1)'s as a multiplier. Given the expression

$$\frac{(a-3)(a+2)}{a-8}$$

the following modifications are all equivalent:

$$-\frac{(\mathbf{3-a})(a+2)}{a-8} \qquad -\frac{(a-3)(\mathbf{-a-2})}{a-8} \qquad -\frac{(a-3)(a+2)}{\mathbf{8-a}}$$

$$\frac{(\mathbf{3-a})(\mathbf{-a-2})}{a-8} \qquad \frac{(\mathbf{3-a})(a+2)}{\mathbf{8-a}} \qquad \frac{(a-3)(\mathbf{-a-2})}{\mathbf{8-a}}$$

$$-\frac{(\mathbf{3-a})(\mathbf{-a-2})}{\mathbf{8-a}}$$

In several of the modifications the binomial $a - 3$ in the original expression was multiplied by (−1) to give us $3 - a$, which is called the *negative* of $a - 3$ (and vice versa).

The original expression with its minimum of minus signs is usually preferred because of its simplicity.

To reduce a fraction to its lowest terms, express the numerator and denominator as products of their prime factors and cancel all factors common to both.

example 37

$$\frac{3a+6b}{a^2+3ab+2b^2} = \frac{3\cancel{(a+2b)}}{(a+b)\cancel{(a+2b)}} = \frac{3}{a+b}$$

example 38

$$\frac{a^2+a-12}{9-a^2} = \frac{(a-3)(a+4)}{(3-a)(3+a)}$$

Multiplying by −1 in two places, we obtain

$$-\frac{\cancel{(a-3)}(a+4)}{\cancel{(a-3)}(3+a)} = -\frac{a+4}{a+3}$$

Note that any quantity canceled must be a factor of the entire numerator and denominator.

example 39 $3bx/(a + b)$ does *not* equal $3x/a$, for b is not a factor of $a + b$; here we have *subtracted* b instead of dividing.

example 40

$$\frac{3bx}{ab+bc} = \frac{3\not{b}x}{\not{b}(a+c)} = \frac{3x}{a+c}$$

EXERCISE 18

Express each of the following negative fractions as an equivalent fraction containing a minimum of negative signs:

1. $-\frac{y}{5}$
2. $-\frac{3}{-a}$
3. $-\frac{-x}{-2}$
4. $-\frac{1}{1-x}$
5. $-\frac{c-3}{4}$
6. $-\frac{m+8}{7}$
7. $-\frac{a-1}{a+1}$
8. $-\frac{1+k}{k-1}$
9. $-\frac{-b-c}{a-c}$
10. $-\frac{1}{(a-b)(a-c)}$
11. $-\frac{x-y}{(x-z)(y+z)}$
12. $-\frac{(k-m)^2}{h-k}$
13. $-\frac{(c-d)^3}{p+r}$
14. $-\frac{(a+b)(b-c)}{(b+c)(c-d)}$

EXERCISE 19

Reduce the following fractions to lowest terms where possible, using a minimum of negative signs in your answer:

1. $\frac{xy}{wx+xz}$
2. $\frac{a}{a^2+a}$
3. $\frac{am+an}{ab-ac}$
4. $\frac{8a-12b}{16a+24b}$
5. $\frac{a+b}{a^2+2ab+b^2}$
6. $\frac{k-m}{k^2-m^2}$
7. $\frac{2a+4b}{a^2-4b^2}$
8. $\frac{x^2-4x+4}{x^2-4}$
9. $\frac{6a+9b}{4a^2-9b^2}$
10. $\frac{2m^2-4m}{m^2+4m-12}$
11. $\frac{9-a^2}{3a^2-9a}$
12. $\frac{a^2+3a+2}{a^2+2a+1}$
13. $\frac{x^2-8x+16}{x^2-4}$
14. $\frac{5cm^3-20c^3m}{10cm^2-10c^2m-20c^3}$
15. $\frac{8a^2-16ab+8b^2}{4b^2-4a^2}$
16. $\frac{6x^2-12xy+18xz}{9mx+27mz-18my}$
17. $\frac{18x^2-24x+32}{9x^3-16x}$
18. $\frac{4c^2-17c+4}{12-3c}$
19. $\frac{(b-2c)^3}{2c^2+3bc-2b^2}$
20. $\frac{3x^2-10xy+3y^2}{6y^2-18xy}$

4·20 Least common multiple

The *least common multiple* (LCM) of several algebraic expressions is the product of all the factors of the various expressions, each factor being taken the greatest number of times that it occurs in any one of the given expressions. In other words the least common multiple is the smallest quantity which is divisible by all the several algebraic expressions.

example 41 Find the LCM of $6ax - 9x^2$, $8a^4 - 18a^2x^2$, and $16a^3 + 48a^2x + 36ax^2$.

The factors of each are $3x(2a - 3x)$, $2a^2(2a - 3x)(2a + 3x)$, and $4a(2a + 3x)^2$. The LCM of 3, 2, and 4 is 12; hence the required LCM is $12a^2x(2a - 3x)(2a + 3x)^2$, each factor appearing to the highest power to which it occurs in any one expression.

4·21 Addition and subtraction of fractions

These operations in algebra are entirely comparable to the corresponding arithmetical procedures.

To add or subtract fractions:

1. *Reduce to lowest terms any fractions which may be so reduced.*
2. *Find the least common denominator, which is the LCM of all the denominators.*
3. *For each fraction, divide the least common denominator (LCD) by its own denominator and multiply both numerator and denominator by this quotient.*
4. *Write the new numerators obtained in step 3 over a single denominator (LCD). Each polynomial numerator is placed in parentheses preceded by the sign of the fraction from which it originated.*
5. *Remove the grouping signs, collect terms, and reduce the resulting fraction to lowest terms.*

example 42 Simplify the expression

$$\frac{a}{b} + \frac{c}{b}$$

By the distributive law

$$\frac{a}{b} + \frac{c}{b} = \frac{1}{b}(a) + \frac{1}{b}(c) = \frac{1}{b}(a + c) = \frac{a + c}{b}$$

example 43

$$\frac{a}{b} + \frac{c}{d} = \frac{ad}{bd} + \frac{bc}{bd} = \frac{1}{bd}(ad + bc) = \frac{ad + bc}{bd}$$

example 44 Simplify

$$\frac{2x^2 - 1}{6x^2} - \frac{2x - 5}{10x} - \frac{2}{15}$$

The LCM of the denominators is $30x^2$. Hence by step 3 we obtain

$$\frac{5(2x^2 - 1)}{30x^2} - \frac{3x(2x - 5)}{30x^2} - \frac{4x^2}{30x^2}$$

and by step 4

$$\frac{5(2x^2 - 1) - 3x(2x - 5) - 4x^2}{30x^2} = \frac{10x^2 - 5 - 6x^2 + 15x - 4x^2}{30x^2}$$
$$= \frac{15x - 5}{30x^2}$$
$$= \frac{3x - 1}{6x^2}$$

example 45 Add

$$\frac{5x}{2x + 4} + \frac{3x - 1}{x^2 - 4}$$

The factors of the denominators are $2(x + 2)$ and $(x - 2)(x + 2)$. Hence the LCM (and LCD) is $2(x - 2)(x + 2)$. By step 3 we obtain

$$\frac{5x(x - 2)}{2(x - 2)(x + 2)} + \frac{2(3x - 1)}{2(x - 2)(x + 2)}$$

and by step 4

$$\frac{5x(x - 2) + 2(3x - 1)}{2(x - 2)(x + 2)} = \frac{5x^2 - 10x + 6x - 2}{2(x - 2)(x + 2)} = \frac{5x^2 - 4x - 2}{2(x - 2)(x + 2)}$$

example 46 Combine

$$\frac{3x^2 - 4}{x^2 - 10x + 25} + \frac{7x - 9}{20 - 4x} + 2$$

Factoring denominators,

$$\frac{3x^2 - 4}{(x - 5)^2} + \frac{7x - 9}{4(5 - x)} + \frac{2}{1}$$

(Note that we may write integral expressions such as 2 as $2/1$.) If we write the fraction

$$+\frac{7x - 9}{4(5 - x)} \qquad \text{as} \qquad -\frac{7x - 9}{4(x - 5)}$$

we obtain a common factor $x - 5$. Therefore, the LCD is $4(x - 5)^2$, and we obtain

$$\frac{4(3x^2 - 4)}{4(x - 5)^2} - \frac{(x - 5)(7x - 9)}{4(x - 5)^2} + \frac{8(x - 5)^2}{4(x - 5)^2}$$
$$= \frac{4(3x^2 - 4) - (x - 5)(7x - 9) + 8(x - 5)^2}{4(x - 5)^2}$$
$$= \frac{12x^2 - 16 - (7x^2 - 44x + 45) + 8(x^2 - 10x + 25)}{4(x - 5)^2}$$
$$= \frac{12x^2 - 16 - 7x^2 + 44x - 45 + 8x^2 - 80x + 200}{4(x - 5)^2}$$
$$= \frac{13x^2 - 36x + 139}{4(x - 5)^2}$$

example 47 Occasionally, two fractions that have the same denominator or one denominator the negative of the other may first be combined to advantage.

Simplify:

$$
\begin{aligned}
1 + \frac{2a}{2a-1} + \frac{8a^2-4}{1-4a^2} - \frac{2}{4a^2-1} &= 1 + \frac{2a}{2a-1} - \frac{8a^2-4}{4a^2-1} - \frac{2}{4a^2-1} \\
&= 1 + \frac{2a}{2a-1} - \frac{8a^2-2}{4a^2-1} \\
&= 1 + \frac{2a}{2a-1} - 2 \\
&= \frac{2a}{2a-1} - \frac{2a-1}{2a-1} = \frac{1}{2a-1}
\end{aligned}
$$

EXERCISE 20

Simplify each of the following:

1. $\frac{7x}{10} - \frac{x}{6}$
2. $\frac{5w}{8y} - \frac{7w}{12y}$
3. $\frac{x}{yz} + \frac{y}{xz} + \frac{z}{xy}$
4. $\frac{3x-2y}{6} - \frac{5x+y}{10}$
5. $\frac{7a+b}{8} + \frac{5a-4b}{12} - \frac{-2a+3b}{9}$
6. $\frac{7x-3a^2y}{6a^2b} - \frac{3x-4by}{8b^2}$
7. $\frac{2a+3b-c}{4ab} - \frac{a-2b+3c}{6bc} + \frac{-3a-b+2c}{8ac}$
8. $\frac{1}{a+b} - \frac{1}{a+c}$
9. $\frac{m+5}{5} - \frac{m+6}{6}$
10. $\frac{x+y}{x-y} - \frac{x-y}{x+y}$
11. $a - \frac{c^2}{a}$
12. $\frac{4}{5a} - 3$
13. $b + 2 + \frac{1}{b}$
14. $\frac{6}{k+3} + k - 2$
15. $\frac{a-2b}{a^2-b^2} + \frac{2}{a-b}$
16. $\frac{k+2m}{k^2-9m^2} + \frac{4}{3m-k}$
17. $\frac{x-5}{x-6} + \frac{2x-8}{x^2-10x+24}$
18. $y^2 + y + 1 + \frac{1}{y-1}$
19. $\frac{2-c}{c^2+c-6} - \frac{5}{9-c^2} - \frac{4-c}{c^2-7c+12}$
20. $\frac{a+b}{(b-c)(c-a)} - \frac{b+c}{(a-c)(a-b)} + \frac{a+c}{(a-b)(b-c)}$
21. $\frac{3}{c-d} + \frac{4d}{(c-d)^2} - \frac{5d^2}{(c-d)^3}$
22. $\frac{1}{a-b} - \frac{2b}{a^2-ab} + \frac{b^2}{a^3-a^2b}$

4·22 Multiplying two or more fractions

To multiply two or more fractions involving polynomials, write the indicated product of all the factors of the numerators over the indicated product of all the factors of the denominators. Cancel out all common factors of the result.

example 48

$$\frac{24a^2 - 54b^2}{35x^2y} \cdot \frac{28xy^2}{30a^2 + 15ab - 90b^2}$$

$$= \frac{6\cancel{(2a - 3b)}(2a + 3b)}{35x^2y} \cdot \frac{28xy^2}{15\cancel{(2a - 3b)}(a + 2b)}$$

$$= \frac{8y(2a + 3b)}{25x(a + 2b)}$$

4·23 Dividing one fraction by another

To divide one fraction by another, multiply the first fraction by the reciprocal of the second and proceed as in Sec. 4·22.

example 49

$$\frac{k^2 + 9km + 18m^2}{k^2 - 9km + 20m^2} \div \frac{k^2 + 6km + 9m^2}{km^2 - 4m^3}$$

$$= \frac{k^2 + 9km + 18m^2}{k^2 - 9km + 20m^2} \cdot \frac{km^2 - 4m^3}{k^2 + 6km + 9m^2}$$

$$= \frac{(k + 6m)\cancel{(k + 3m)}}{\cancel{(k - 4m)}(k - 5m)} \cdot \frac{m^2\cancel{(k - 4m)}}{\cancel{(k + 3m)}(k + 3m)}$$

$$= \frac{m^2(k + 6m)}{(k - 5m)(k + 3m)}$$

EXERCISE 21

Carry out the indicated operations:

1. $\frac{a^2 - b^2}{16} \cdot \frac{12}{a - b}$
2. $\frac{x^2 + 2x + 1}{18cw^3} \cdot \frac{12c^3w}{x^2 - 1}$
3. $\frac{x^2 - x + 12}{abc} \cdot \frac{bcd}{x^2 + x - 6}$
4. $\frac{6x + 12y}{10a + 5} \cdot \frac{100a^2 - 25}{9x^2 - 81y^2}$
5. $\frac{a^2 + 2ab + b^2}{a^2 - b^2} \cdot \frac{a^2 - 2ab + b^2}{a^2 - b^2}$
6. $\frac{x + 3y}{2a + 1} \cdot \frac{1 - 4a^2}{x^2 - 9y^2}$
7. $\frac{m^2 + 2mn + n^2}{4m^2 + 4mn} \cdot \frac{6m^2}{n^2 - m^2}$
8. $\frac{x^2 + x - 2}{7b^2x^2 - 14b^2x + 7b^2} \cdot \frac{14abx - 28ab}{1 - 2x + x^2}$
9. $\frac{a + 2}{15} \div \frac{a^2 - 4}{10a}$
10. $\frac{a - b}{x + y} \div \frac{x - y}{a + b}$
11. $\frac{4a - 6x}{9ay} \div \frac{9x - 6a}{12y^2}$
12. $\frac{15ax^2}{x^2 - 9} \div \frac{25a^2bx}{x^2 + x - 12}$
13. $\frac{14xy^2z}{4x^2 - 9} \div \frac{10x^2y}{6x + 9}$
14. $\frac{3c^2 - 12cm + 12m^2}{2c^2 + 2c - 12} \div \frac{6c^2 - 24m^2}{8ac + 24a}$
15. $\frac{a^2 - 25}{4a - 8} \cdot \frac{8 - 2a^2}{5a^2 + 5a - 10} \div \frac{5 + a}{15a^2 - 15}$

16. $\dfrac{4x^2 - 20x + 9}{4x^2 - 15x + 9} \cdot \dfrac{5x - 15}{4x - 18} \div (12x^2 - 3)$

17. $\dfrac{1}{b}(a + bx)^2 - \dfrac{a}{b}(a + bx)$

18. $\dfrac{1}{b^2}\left[\dfrac{b}{(a + bx)^2} - \dfrac{ab}{(a + bx)^3}\right]$

19. $\dfrac{1}{ad - bc}\left(\dfrac{d}{c + dx} - \dfrac{b}{a + bx}\right)$

20. $\dfrac{b}{a(a + bx)^2} + \dfrac{1}{a^2}\left(\dfrac{b}{a + bx} - \dfrac{1}{x}\right)$

21. $\dfrac{1}{b^3}\left[\dfrac{b}{(a + bx)^2} - \dfrac{2ab}{(a + bx)^3} + \dfrac{a^2b}{(a + bx)^4}\right]$

22. What is the value of $(1 - \frac{1}{4})(1 - \frac{1}{5})(1 - \frac{1}{6}) \cdots (1 - \frac{1}{30})$?

4·24 Complex fractions

A complex fraction is a fraction whose numerator or denominator or both contain fractions.

example 50

$$\frac{\dfrac{a^2}{b^2} - 1}{\dfrac{a}{b} + 1}$$

is a complex fraction. For convenience we shall refer to $a^2/b^2 - 1$ as the primary numerator and $a/b + 1$ as the primary denominator, while b^2 and b will be known as *secondary denominators.*

To simplify a complex fraction reduce the primary numerator and the primary denominator each to a single fraction and divide the primary numerator by the primary denominator.

example 51 Simplify

$$\frac{4 - \dfrac{4}{a} + \dfrac{1}{a^2}}{1 - \dfrac{1}{4a^2}}$$

Simplifying the primary numerator, we obtain

$$4 - \frac{4}{a} + \frac{1}{a^2} = \frac{4a^2}{a^2} - \frac{4a}{a^2} + \frac{1}{a^2} = \frac{4a^2 - 4a + 1}{a^2} = \frac{(2a - 1)^2}{a^2}$$

Simplifying the primary denominator, we have

$$1 - \frac{1}{4a^2} = \frac{4a^2}{4a^2} - \frac{1}{4a^2} = \frac{4a^2 - 1}{4a^2} = \frac{(2a + 1)(2a - 1)}{4a^2}$$

Then

$$\frac{(2a - 1)^2}{a^2} \div \frac{(2a + 1)(2a - 1)}{4a^2} = \frac{\cancel{(2a - 1)}(2a - 1)}{\cancel{a^2}} \cdot \frac{4\cancel{a^2}}{(2a + 1)\cancel{(2a - 1)}}$$

$$= \frac{4(2a - 1)}{2a + 1}$$

This operation can often be performed more easily and quickly by finding the LCM of the *secondary* denominators. Multiply the *primary* numerator and denominator by the LCM just found and reduce to lowest terms.

Using the same complex fraction

$$\frac{4 - \frac{4}{a} + \frac{1}{a^2}}{1 - \frac{1}{4a^2}}$$

as in the preceding illustration, we note the LCM of the secondary denominators is $4a^2$. We then write

$$\frac{4a^2\left(4 - \frac{4}{a} + \frac{1}{a^2}\right)}{4a^2\left(1 - \frac{1}{4a^2}\right)} = \frac{16a^2 - 16a + 4}{4a^2 - 1} = \frac{4(4a^2 - 4a + 1)}{(2a + 1)(2a - 1)}$$

$$= \frac{4(2a - 1)(2a - 1)}{(2a + 1)(2a - 1)} = \frac{4(2a - 1)}{2a + 1}$$

The short method often makes it possible to simplify less involved complex fractions at sight; e.g.,

$$\frac{x - \frac{1}{x}}{1 + \frac{1}{x}} = \frac{x\left(x - \frac{1}{x}\right)}{x\left(1 + \frac{1}{x}\right)} = \frac{x^2 - 1}{x + 1} = x - 1$$

A special type of complex fraction is the continued fraction, which is typified by the expression

$$\frac{1}{1 + \frac{2}{1 + \frac{1}{1 + \frac{3}{x}}}}$$

Simplification is best effected by starting with the end fraction.

$$\frac{1}{1 + \frac{2}{1 + \frac{1}{1 + \frac{3}{x}}}} = \frac{1}{1 + \frac{2}{1 + \frac{x}{x + 3}}} = \frac{1}{1 + \frac{2}{\frac{2x + 3}{x + 3}}} = \frac{1}{1 + \frac{2x + 6}{2x + 3}}$$

$$= \frac{1}{\frac{4x + 9}{2x + 3}} = \frac{2x + 3}{4x + 9}$$

EXERCISE 22

Simplify the following complex fractions:

1. $\dfrac{\frac{1}{x} - \frac{1}{y}}{\frac{1}{x} + \frac{1}{y}}$

2. $\dfrac{\frac{1}{x} + \frac{1}{y}}{\frac{1}{z}}$

3. $\dfrac{\frac{c}{d} - \frac{d}{c}}{c - d}$

4. $\dfrac{m+w}{\dfrac{1}{m}+\dfrac{1}{w}}$

5. $\dfrac{\dfrac{1}{h}-\dfrac{1}{k}}{\dfrac{h-k}{hk}}$

6. $\dfrac{\dfrac{b}{c}+\dfrac{b}{d}}{\dfrac{b}{cd}}$

7. $\dfrac{q-\dfrac{1}{q}}{1+\dfrac{1}{q}}$

8. $\dfrac{\dfrac{a^2-x^2}{a}}{\dfrac{a+x}{a^2}}$

9. $\dfrac{1-\dfrac{1}{r}}{r-2+\dfrac{1}{r}}$

10. $\dfrac{b+\dfrac{b}{c-1}}{\dfrac{c}{c-1}}$

11. $\dfrac{\dfrac{m}{1+m}-\dfrac{1-m}{m}}{\dfrac{m}{1+m}+\dfrac{1-m}{m}}$

12. $\dfrac{a-\dfrac{ab}{b-a}}{\dfrac{a^2}{a^2-b^2}-1}$

13. $1-\cfrac{1}{1-\cfrac{1}{1-\cfrac{1}{x}}}$

14. $1+\cfrac{1}{2+\cfrac{1}{3+\cfrac{1}{4+\cfrac{5}{x}}}}$

4·25 Continued fractions

The expressions appearing in Probs. 13 and 14 of Exercise 22 are called continued fractions. They appear in the development of certain types of approximations and in the design of electrical networks. One application is the determination of one or more fractions which are approximately equivalent to a more complicated fraction. The process is illustrated in the following example. It will be seen that each divisor serves as the next dividend, and each remainder serves as the next divisor.

example 52 Determine by means of a continued fraction some possible fractional approximations to the fraction $285/384$.

```
                                1
                          285 | 384
                                285    2
                                 99 | 285
                                      198    1
                                       87 | 99
                                            87    7
                                            12 | 87
                                                 84    4
Greatest common factor ---------------------> (3) | 12
                                                    12
```

This rather odd-appearing process is actually a condensation of the following:

$$\frac{285}{384} = \cfrac{1}{\cfrac{384}{285}} = \cfrac{1}{1 + \cfrac{99}{285}} = \cfrac{1}{1 + \cfrac{1}{\cfrac{285}{99}}} = \cfrac{1}{1 + \cfrac{1}{2 + \cfrac{87}{99}}}$$

$$= \cfrac{1}{1 + \cfrac{1}{2 + \cfrac{1}{\cfrac{99}{87}}}} = \cfrac{1}{1 + \cfrac{1}{2 + \cfrac{1}{1 + \cfrac{12}{87}}}} = \cfrac{1}{1 + \cfrac{1}{2 + \cfrac{1}{1 + \cfrac{1}{\cfrac{87}{12}}}}}$$

$$= \cfrac{1}{1 + \cfrac{1}{2 + \cfrac{1}{1 + \cfrac{1}{7 + \cfrac{3}{12}}}}} = \cfrac{1}{1 + \cfrac{1}{2 + \cfrac{1}{1 + \cfrac{1}{7 + \cfrac{1}{\cfrac{12}{3}}}}}}$$

$$= \cfrac{1}{1 + \cfrac{1}{2 + \cfrac{1}{1 + \cfrac{1}{7 + \cfrac{1}{4}}}}}$$

$1/1 = 1,00000$

$2/3 = 0.66667$

$3/4 = 0.75000$

$23/31 = 0.74194$

$95/128 = 0.74219$

We see that, as the process is continued, the value of the approximation alternately decreases and increases, but each fraction is a successively closer approximation to the original. When the process is concluded, as indicated by a division with no remainder, we obtain a fraction equal to or equivalent to the original. In this example we finally obtain the fraction $95/128$, the reduced equivalent of $285/384$.

Observe that the final divisor, 3, is the highest common factor (HCF) of 285 and 384. When the determination of the HCF is the objective, the operation is known as the Euclidean algorithm.

EXERCISE 23

1. Find the HCF of 391 and 437.
2. Use continued fractions to obtain a better fractional equivalent for π than $22/7$.
   Hint: Take $\pi = 3.141593$ and express it as $3{,}141{,}593/1{,}000{,}000$.
3. We wish to select two gears producing a speed ratio of 2.679 : 1 within an error of 0.1 per cent. Develop a continued fraction to determine a suitable pair of gears, each having no more than 100 teeth. Assume gears having any number of teeth from 10 to 100 are available.
4. A system of equations solved by determinants (Sec. 7·16) yielded a root $x = 221/323$. Reduce this fraction to lowest terms.

5 linear equations in one unknown

In this chapter we shall continue with the study of the "language" of algebra. We shall see how it is developed from our ordinary "language" and thus makes possible the solution of "word" problems.

5·1 Equations

An *equation* is a statement that two expressions represent the same number. The two expressions are called the *members* or *sides* of the equation. However, an equation containing one or more unknowns is not only a statement of fact; it also proposes a problem.

The equation $x + 5 = 13$ states the fact that 13 is 5 more than some number x, as yet unknown. The equation also proposes the problem of finding what number x is. If 13 is 5 more than x, it follows that x is 5 less than 13, or $x = 13 - 5 = 8$, and the problem is solved.

To *solve* an equation, then, we find a numerical value for the letter which makes the equation a true sentence.

To put the same idea somewhat more formally, we might say that the equation

$$x + 5 = 13 \tag{1}$$

has been converted to the equation

$$x = 13 - 5$$

or

$$x = 8 \tag{2}$$

by subtracting 5 from both members.

If we had subtracted, say, 2 from each member of Eq. (1), we would have obtained the equation

$$x + 5 - 2 = 13 - 2$$

or

$$x + 3 = 11 \tag{3}$$

However, in solving Eq. (1) we chose to subtract 5, instead of 2, from each number because 5 and only 5, when so used, will make x appear alone on one side. The process of adding or subtracting the same quantity from both members of an equation is known as *transposition.*

Consider now the equation

$$x - 2 = 6 \tag{4}$$

The statement of fact is that 6 is 2 less than some as yet unknown number x. The proposed problem is to find what number x is. If 6 is 2 less than x, it follows that x is 2 more than 6, or

$$x = 6 + 2 = 8$$

More formally, if we add 2 to both sides of the equation, we obtain

$$x - 2 + 2 = 6 + 2$$

$$x = 8 \tag{5}$$

The equation

$$\frac{x}{4} = 2 \tag{6}$$

states that 2 is one-fourth of x and implies the question, "What is x?" If one-fourth of a single x is 2, then one whole x must be 4 times 2, or 8. In other words, we can multiply both members of Eq. (6) by 4 and obtain

$$4\frac{x}{4} = (4)(2)$$

$$x = 8$$

Finally, let us consider the equation

$$3x = 24 \tag{7}$$

This equation states that 24 is equal to 3 times a certain number x, whose value is at present unknown. It also implies the question, "What is x?" If 3 x's are equal to 24, then a single x must be equal to one-third of 24, or 8. We can obtain the same result by dividing both sides of the equation by 3.

$$3x \div 3 = 24 \div 3$$

$$x = 8$$

Equations may be classified into equivalent, identical, or conditional types. Two or more equations are *equivalent* if their respective members become equal when the same value (or values) of the unknown letter is used in each case.

Thus Eqs. (1), (3), (4), (6), and (7) are equivalent equations. Each may be obtained from any of the others by one or more of the processes of subtraction, addition, multiplication, and division illustrated above. In each case a true statement results when 8 is substituted for x.

An *identical* equivalent equation is a statement of equality holding true for all permissible values of the unknown letter. [A permissible value is one for which all of the expressions appearing in the equation are defined. As an example, in the equation $(x^2 - 1)/(x - 1) = x + 1$, the value $x = 1$ is not permissible, the left-hand member being undefined, since this value leads to division by zero which is impossible.] Thus $x^2 - 9 = (x + 3)(x - 3)$ is an identical equation. It is often written $x^2 - 9 \equiv (x + 3)(x - 3)$, the sign $\equiv$ being read "is identically equal to."

A *conditional* equation holds true for one or more but not all permissible values of the unknown letter. Thus each of the equivalent equations referred to above is also a conditional equation. Most of the equations with which we shall deal will be conditional equations.

An equation is said to be satisfied by certain values of the letter or unknown if, on substitution of these values for the unknown, the members of the equation become obviously equal. A *solution* of an equation consists of the values of the unknowns (called *roots*) which satisfy the equation.

5·2 Operations on equations

Summarizing Sec. 5·1, we may state that both sides of an equation may be increased, decreased, multiplied, or divided by the same quantity without destroying the equality. (Division by zero is excluded.)

However, it should be remembered that multiplying or dividing both numbers of an equation by an expression containing the variable may not lead to an equivalent equation (Prob. 36, Exercise 1; also Sec. 12·12). Raising both members to the same power may result in a nonequivalent equation. (In curve sketching we find that $y = \sqrt{25 - x^2}$ is not equivalent to $y^2 = 25 - x^2$). All "solutions" should be checked against the original equation.

5·3 Degree of an equation

The *degree of a term* in an equation is obtained by adding the exponents of the unknown literal quantities in that term. The *degree of an equation* corresponds to the term of highest degree occurring in the equation. For example, if x and y are unknown, all other letters being considered as known quantities, the following equations are of the first degree: $3x - 4 = b^2 + x$, $x + y = 7$. Second-degree equations may be exemplified by

$$x^2 - 3x + xy - y = 10 \qquad y^2 + 2y = x - 3$$

A typical third-degree equation is $x^2 - x^2y = y + 6$.

A first-degree equation is usually called a *linear equation.* We shall see why in the next chapter.

We may transpose a term from one side of the equation to the other if we change its sign. This is equivalent to a process of subtraction [see Eqs. (1) and (2), Sec. 5·1]. Thus in the equation $6x - 5 = 13$ we may transpose the -5 from left to right, obtaining $6x = 13 + 5$, or $6x = 18$. We have actually subtracted -5 from each member of the equation.

5·4 To solve a linear equation

1. *If fractions occur in the equation, first make sure that they are in their lowest terms. Usually it will be best to clear the equation of fractions by multiplying both members by the LCD.*
2. *Remove any parentheses.*
3. *Transpose all terms containing the unknown to one side of the equation and all other terms to the other side.*
4. *Apply the distributive law by collecting like terms and expressing in a factored form the collection of terms containing the unknown.*
5. *Divide each member of the equation by the coefficient of the unknown.*
6. *Check the solution by substituting it for the unknown in the original equation.*

example 1 Solve the equation

$$\frac{3x}{4} + \frac{1}{6} = 2x - \frac{7}{3}$$

Multiplying by the LCD, 12, we obtain

$$9x + 2 = 24x - 28$$

Transposing terms containing x to the right and other terms to the left (the reverse procedure might have been followed but would have resulted in a greater number of negative values), we have

$$2 + 28 = 24x - 9x$$

Combining like terms,

$$30 = 15x$$

Dividing by 15,

$$30/15 = 2 = x$$

Substituting 2 for x in the original equation produces the identity $5/3 = 5/3$.

example 2 Solve the equation

$$\frac{8}{x-4} - \frac{6}{x-3} = \frac{2}{x-6}$$

Multiplying by the LCD,

$$(x-4)(x-3)(x-6)$$

$$8(x-3)(x-6)-6(x-4)(x-6)=2(x-4)(x-3)$$

Removing parentheses,

$$8x^2-72x+144-6x^2+60x-144=2x^2-14x+24$$

Transposing,

$$8x^2-6x^2-2x^2-72x+60x+14x=24-144+144$$

Collecting like terms,

$$2x=24$$

Dividing by 2,

$$x=12$$

example 3 Solve for x the equation

$$3(3x-a)+2a=a(ax-3)+6$$

(This is called a *literal equation,* since in addition to the unknown x it contains a letter a, considered here as a known quantity.)

Removing parentheses,

$$9x-3a+2a=a^2x-3a+6$$

Transposing,

$$-3a+2a+3a-6=a^2x-9x$$

Collecting like terms,

$$2a-6=x(a^2-9)$$

Dividing by a^2-9,

$$\frac{2a-6}{a^2-9}=\frac{2}{a+3}=x$$

We may check by substituting $2/(a+3)$ for x in the original equation, but such a check in a literal equation is apt to entail more work than the original solution. A reasonably certain check may be obtained by assigning to a some arbitrary simple numerical value. We should avoid using 1 or 0 or any number which will make any denominator equal to zero.

In this illustration, if we let $a=-2$, then $x=2$. Substituting in the original equation,

$$3[(3)(2)-(-2)]+2(-2)=(-2)[(-2)(2)-3]+6$$

or

$$3(6+2)-4=(-2)(-4-3)+6$$

or

$$20=20$$

EXERCISE 1

Solve the following linear equations. When more than one letter appears, consider the last letter (in alphabetical order) as the unknown quantity and all other letters as known quantities.

1. $13x - 8 = 8x + 2$
2. $9x - 1 = 2x + 6$
3. $7x + 4 = x - 8$
4. $5 - 2x = x + 20$
5. $2 - 3x + 7 = 8x + 3 - x$
6. $11x + 3 - 4x = 16 - 2x + 2$
7. $5y - (3y - 2) = 10$
8. $7 - (8x + 1) = 18$
9. $6(w + 5) - 12 = 3(3w - 1) + 4w$
10. $26 - 5(3 - 2z) = z - 4(z + 9)$
11. $(r + 1)^2 = r^2 + 9$
12. $(2x - 3)^2 = 4x^2 - 15$
13. $(x - 2)^3 = x^2(x - 6)$
14. $(y + 1)(y - 2) = y^2 + 5$
15. $(z + 1)(z + 5) = (z + 2)(z + 3)$
16. $(2w + 1)(3w + 1) = (6w - 1)(w + 2)$
17. $\frac{x}{3} + \frac{x}{4} = \frac{7}{2}$
18. $\frac{5}{8}x - 1 = 1 + \frac{7}{10}x$
19. $\frac{x}{10} + \frac{x}{12} + \frac{x}{15} = x - 6$
20. $\frac{1}{6}(x - 2) = \frac{1}{8}(x + 1)$
21. $\frac{1}{8}(1 - y) - \frac{1}{10}(2 - y) - \frac{1}{12}(3 + y) = 0$
22. $0.2x = 46 - 0.03x$
23. $0.103 - 0.1x = 0.02x - 0.13x + 0.11$
24. $\frac{2}{x} + \frac{3}{x} = 10$
25. $\frac{4}{w} + 3 = 4 - \frac{3}{w}$
26. $\frac{1}{4y} - \frac{1}{6y} = \frac{1}{8}$
27. $\frac{3}{5x} - \frac{1}{2x} = \frac{1}{40}$
28. $\frac{8}{x + 4} = \frac{6}{x - 4}$
29. $\frac{5}{3y + 2} = \frac{7}{5y - 2}$
30. $\frac{4}{7z + 3} = \frac{3}{6z + 2}$
31. $\frac{4x - 3}{2x + 6} = \frac{6x - 2}{3x + 11}$
32. $\frac{6y - 3}{3y + 2} = \frac{2y + 1}{y + 2}$
33. $\frac{4}{5x + 5} - \frac{7}{10x + 10} = \frac{1}{20}$
34. $\frac{8}{x - 2} - \frac{5}{x - 11} = \frac{3}{x - 5}$
35. $\frac{7}{x + 1} - \frac{4}{x - 1} = \frac{3}{x + 5}$
36. $\frac{2x}{x^2 - 4} - \frac{4}{x^2 - 4} = \frac{2}{2x - 3}$
37. $\frac{2}{1 - 2w} + \frac{2}{7 - 2w} = 1 - \frac{4w^2 - 1}{4w^2 - 16w + 7}$
38. $ax + b = c$
39. $t - sx = r$
40. $6abx = 9a^3b^2c$
41. $\frac{x}{a} = \frac{a}{4}$
42. $\frac{b}{y} = \frac{c}{d}$
43. $\frac{m}{x} = k$
44. $\frac{c}{x} = a + 1$
45. $ax + bx = 3a + 3b$

46. $mx - h = hx - m$

47. $2mx + n^2 = 2nx + m^2$

48. $3ay = 5by + 2$

49. $ax + 2 = bx + 8$

50. $b(x + 1) = c$

51. $\frac{x}{c} - a = b$

52. $\frac{x}{a} + \frac{x}{b} = a^2 - b^2$

53. $\frac{a}{x} = b + c$

54. $\frac{m + n}{x} = m^2 + mn$

55. $(a - b)x - a^2 = (a + b)x$

56. $c(1 + w) + d(1 + w) = w(c + d + 1)$

57. $b(b - 2y) + c(c - 2y) + 2bc = 0$

58. $mn(z^2 - 1) = (m + nz)(n + mz)$

59. $(p - y)(y + q) - r(y + r) = (r - y)(y + r) + pq$

60. $\frac{ax}{b} + \frac{bx}{a} = 1$

61. $\frac{c + x}{m} = \frac{x}{c + m}$

62. $a^2 = \frac{a + c}{x} + c^2$

63. $\frac{w - c}{w - d} = \frac{c^2}{d^2}$

64. $\frac{by^2}{c - ay} + b + \frac{by}{a} = 0$

65. $\frac{m}{n - p} + \frac{n - p}{z} = \frac{m}{n + p} + \frac{n + p}{z}$

66. By inspection determine the number of roots in (a) the equation

$$y + \frac{3}{y - 5} = -5 + \frac{3}{y - 5}$$

(b) the equation

$$y + \frac{3}{y - 5} = 5 + \frac{3}{y - 5}$$

5·5 Formulas

Perhaps the most common occurrence of the literal equation is the formula. In most mathematical or engineering handbooks will be found a number of formulas for determining length, area, volume, etc. Frequently it will be desirable to transform a formula or solve for one of the factors previously regarded as a known quantity. For example, the volume of a cone is expressed by the formula $V = \pi r^2 h/3$, in which it is assumed that the radius r and the height h are known and the volume V is to be found. Should there be repeated occasions when the volume and radius are known and the height is to be found, we should solve the formula for h. Following the usual procedure for solving literal linear equations, we obtain $h = 3V/\pi r^2$.

In Exercise 2 the transformed version of the formula should be left in the most convenient form for computation. Few specific directions can be offered, but it is suggested that a number of constants related to each other by multiplication or division may well be combined into a single constant. Furthermore, a multiplying constant is usually more easily handled than a dividing constant. The student's most reliable guide is his imagination. If he will regard himself as the user of the formula he has produced, he will so arrange it that it requires a minimum of effort for actual computation.

If we consider the recently discussed formula $h = 3V/\pi r^2$, we see that possible variations are

(a) $$h = \frac{3}{\pi}\cdot\frac{V}{r^2} = \frac{0.9549V}{r^2}$$

(b) $$h = \frac{V}{(\pi/3)r^2} = \frac{V}{1.047r^2}$$

If a table of areas of circles is available, the original form would probably be best; otherwise Eq. (a) would be preferable. On the other hand it is doubtful that Eq. (b) would be a good choice under any circumstances.

EXERCISE 2

Solve the following formulas for the letter indicated. Leave your answer in the most convenient form for computation, and be prepared to justify your choice. The formulas are identified in the right-hand column.

		Solve for	*Description of formula*
1.	$Q = \frac{WL}{T}$	T	Latent heat of vaporization
2.	$X = \frac{1}{2\pi fC}$	C	Reactance of a capacitor
3.	$I = \frac{E - e}{R}$	e	Current flowing through armature of generator
4.	$V = \frac{V_t + V_0}{2}$	V_0	Average speed of uniformly accelerating body
5.	$\frac{E}{e} = \frac{R + r}{r}$	r	Voltage drop
6.	$T = \frac{1}{a} + t$ $\left(\text{first solve for } \frac{1}{a}\right)$	a	Temperature-conversion formula
7.	$C = \frac{Kab}{b - a}$	a	
8.	$S = \frac{rl - a}{r - 1}$	a,r	Geometric progression
9.	$\rho = \frac{m}{d - L} - \frac{m}{d + L}$	m	
10.	$\frac{e}{x} = C(e - b) + \frac{b}{x}$	x	
11.	$Q = 0.000477EIT$	T	Electrical equivalent of heat
12.	$d = \frac{1}{2}at^2 - \frac{1}{2}a(t - 1)^2$	t	Distance covered by falling body

	Equation	Solve for	Application
13.	$C = \frac{5}{9}(F - 32)$	F	Centigrade-Fahrenheit temperature conversion
14.	$A = \frac{m}{t}(p + t)$	t	Thickness of pipe
15.	$H = \frac{0.4\pi NI}{L}$	I	Magnetic intensity
16.	$M = 10.5C + 35.2\left(W - \frac{C}{8}\right)$	C	Theoretical amount of air required to burn solid fuel
17.	$\frac{1}{x} + \frac{1}{nx} = \frac{1}{f}$	x	Photographic enlargement
18.	$S = \left(\frac{\pi d^2}{2} + \frac{\pi dl}{r}\right) \div \frac{\pi d^2 l}{4rc}$	r	Exposed surface of cylinders
19.	$S = T - \frac{1.299}{N}$	N	Tap-size drill for U. S. standard thread
20.	$W = \frac{2PR}{R - r}$	R	Differential pulley
21.	$\frac{1}{R} = \frac{1}{r_1} + \frac{1}{r_2}$	R	Parallel resistances
22.	$I = \frac{E}{r + \frac{R}{n}}$	n	Current produced by cells in parallel
23.	$T = T_1\left(1 - \frac{n-1}{n} \cdot \frac{h}{h_0}\right)$	n	
24.	$x - y = xy$	y	
25.	$V = \frac{h}{6}(B + 4M + b)$	M	Prismoidal formula
26.	$wf = \left(\frac{w}{k} - 1\right)\frac{1}{k}$	w	
27.	$V_1 = V_0(1 + 0.00365t)$	t	Expansion of gases

5·6 Mathematical operations with dimensional units

In setting up equations derived from physical problems, it must be remembered that each side of the equation must reduce to like units or dimensions; i.e., the equation must be dimensionally correct. Operations with dimensional symbols are subject to the usual laws of algebra. Some common examples are listed below:

Length × length = area	$(\text{ft})(\text{ft}) = \text{ft}^2$
Length × length × length = volume	$(\text{ft})(\text{ft})(\text{ft}) = \text{ft}^3$
Area × length = volume	$\text{ft}^2 \times \text{ft} = \text{ft}^3$
$\frac{\text{Weight}}{\text{Volume}} = \text{density}$	$\text{lb} \div \text{ft}^3 = \frac{\text{lb}}{\text{ft}^3}$

$\dfrac{\text{Distance}}{\text{Time}} = \text{average velocity}$	$\text{ft} \div \text{sec} = \dfrac{\text{ft}}{\text{sec}}$
$\dfrac{\text{Change in velocity}}{\text{Time}} = \text{average acceleration}$	$\dfrac{\text{ft}}{\text{sec}} \div \text{sec} = \dfrac{\text{ft}}{\text{sec}^2}$
$\dfrac{\text{Force}}{\text{Area}} = \text{pressure}$	$\text{lb} \div \text{ft}^2 = \dfrac{\text{lb}}{\text{ft}^2}$
Density × height = pressure	$\dfrac{\text{lb}}{\text{ft}^3} \times \text{ft} = \dfrac{\text{lb}}{\text{ft}^2}$
Mass (absolute units) × acceleration = force	$\dfrac{\text{lb}}{\text{ft/sec}^2} \times \dfrac{\text{ft}}{\text{sec}^2} = \text{lb}$
Pressure × volume = work	$\dfrac{\text{lb}}{\text{ft}^2} \times \text{ft}^3 = (\text{ft})(\text{lb})$
Distance × force = work	$\text{ft} \times \text{lb} = (\text{ft})(\text{lb})$
Power × time = work	$\dfrac{(\text{ft})(\text{lb})}{\text{sec}} \times \text{sec} = (\text{ft})(\text{lb})$
$\dfrac{\text{Work}}{\text{Time}} = \text{power}$	$(\text{ft})(\text{lb}) \div \text{sec} = \dfrac{(\text{ft})(\text{lb})}{\text{sec}}$
Force (absolute units) × time = momentum	$\dfrac{(\text{ft})(\text{lb})}{\text{sec}^2} \times \text{sec} = \dfrac{(\text{ft})(\text{lb})}{\text{sec}}$
Height × weight = potential energy	$\text{ft} \times \text{lb} = (\text{ft})(\text{lb})$
Weight × (velocity)^2 ÷ gravitational constant = kinetic energy	$\text{lb} \times \left(\dfrac{\text{ft}}{\text{sec}}\right)^2 \div \dfrac{\text{ft}}{\text{sec}^2} = \text{lb} \times \dfrac{\text{ft}^2}{\text{sec}^2} \times \dfrac{\text{sec}^2}{\text{ft}} = (\text{ft})(\text{lb})$

5·7 Analysis of a formula

Whenever a formula is developed or applied for the first time, it is instructive to subject it to a few screening tests. The most common of these are the test for dimensional soundness and the test for applicability to special conditions.

The application of these tests can be illustrated to advantage by referring to a formula such as that given in Prob. 41, Exercise 5, Chap. 15, for the volume of the frustum of a cone. The formula is

$$V = \tfrac{1}{3}\pi h(r_1^2 + r_1r_2 + r_2^2)$$

If the indicated multiplication is carried out, the terms will be hr_1^2, hr_1r_2, and hr_2^2—all third-degree terms in a length unit. Such terms are, therefore, expressions of volume (Sec. 6·6), and the formula is dimensionally sound.

If we assume $r_1 = r_2$, as would be the case in a cylinder, we obtain

$$V = \tfrac{1}{3}\pi h(r_1^2 + r_1r_1 + r_1^2)$$

or $$V = \pi r_1^2 h$$

the formula for the volume of a cylinder.

If we assume $r_1 = 0$, as in a cone, we obtain

$$V = \tfrac{1}{3}\pi h r_2^2$$

the formula for the volume of a cone.

If we take $h = 0$, the entire expression assumes the value zero, as is to be expected.

5·8 Dimensional units in conversions

Dimensional units, properly handled, will not only check the dimensional soundness of a formula; they will also indicate what steps are necessary to make a required conversion.

example 4 It costs \$30 per hr to run a boat when sailing at 10 mph. Find the operating cost in dollars per mile.

$$\frac{\$30}{1\text{ hr}} \div \frac{10\text{ miles}}{1\text{ hr}} = \frac{\overset{3}{\cancel{\$30}}}{1\ \cancel{\text{hr}}} \times \frac{1\ \cancel{\text{hr}}}{\underset{1}{\cancel{10}}\text{ miles}} = \$3\text{ per mile}$$

example 5 The density of mercury is 13.6 g per cu cm. Express the density in lb per cu in.

$$\frac{13.6\text{ g}}{\text{cm}^3} = \frac{13.6\ \cancel{\text{g}}}{1\ \cancel{\text{cm}^3}} \times \frac{1\text{ lb}}{454\ \cancel{\text{g}}} \times \frac{(2.54)^3\ \cancel{\text{cm}^3}}{1\text{ in.}^3} = 0.492\text{ lb/cu in.}$$

example 6 The velocity of a ripple v cm/sec is given approximately by the equation $v = \sqrt{2\pi T/l\rho}$, where T = surface tension of the liquid, l = wavelength of the ripple (cm), and ρ = density of the liquid (g/cm³). Determine the units of T in the centimeter-gram-second (cgs) system.

If $v = \sqrt{2\pi T/l\rho}$, then

$$T = \frac{v^2 l\rho}{2\pi} = \frac{\cancel{\text{cm}^2}}{\text{sec}^2}\cdot\cancel{\text{cm}}\cdot\frac{\text{g}}{\cancel{\text{cm}^3}} = \frac{\text{g}}{\text{sec}^2} \quad (2\pi\text{ has no units}).$$

EXERCISE 3

Check the dimensional soundness of the formulas in the following:

1. Prob. 62, Chap. 3. 2. Prob. 4, Exercise 19, Chap. 10.
3. Geometric Fact 56, Chap. 3. 4. Eq. (1), Sec. B·17. 5. Eq. (11), Sec. B·17.
6. $V = \tfrac{1}{3}h(A_1 + \sqrt{A_1A_2} + A_2)$, where V = volume of a frustum (cu in.), h = height (in.), A_1 and A_2 are the areas of the upper and lower bases, respectively (sq in.).

EXERCISE 4

In this exercise t = time, h = height, v = velocity, g = gravitational constant, F = force, m = mass, a = acceleration, and ρ = density (all in cgs units unless specified otherwise). Also 1 in. = 2.54 cm and 1 lb = 454 g.

1. Express a speed of 60 mph as ft per sec.
2. If force equals mass $\times$ acceleration, find the units of force in the cgs system.
3. The density of iron is 450 lb per cu ft. Express the density in g per cm^3.
4. Confirm the dimensional soundness of the formula $v = \sqrt{2gh}$ for the velocity of a freely falling body.
5. Pressure equals force per unit area. What are the cgs units of pressure?
6. If a liquid of density ρ rises to a height h cm in a tube of internal radius r, the surface tension is given by $T = rh\rho g/k$. What are the cgs units of T? (k is a constant having no dimension.)
7. Flow of liquid through a tube is given by $v = pr^4/8lk$, where v = volume rate of flow, r = radius, l = length, k = coefficient of viscosity, p = pressure difference. Find the cgs units of this coefficient.
8. What are the units of coefficient of friction k if $k = F/W$, where W is the weight of an object, and F is the force barely sufficient to keep it moving?
9. What are the units of hydrostatic pressure if $P = h\rho g$?

5·9 Suggestions for the solution of applied problems involving linear equations

There is no pat formula for the solution of "word" problems. One should not feel discouraged if he finds this section of the work difficult, for this is a common reaction. This situation is due largely to the fact that the translation of a verbal or descriptive problem (commonly called a "word" problem) involves a minimum of dependence on mechanical rules. Such translation requires some exercise of ingenuity and of the skill that comes only with experience. If this seems a bleak outlook, it should be remembered that these remarks apply equally well to carpentry, machine design, music, painting, etc. The feeling of accomplishment in solving the more interesting applied problems is not experienced by those content merely to follow mechanical procedures.

While a rigid, ironclad procedure cannot be offered, a few general suggestions which have proved helpful can be outlined.

1. *Read the problem through once to get the general idea.*
2. *Carefully reread the problem, noting what is given and what is wanted.*
3. *A rough graphical representation will often suggest relationships leading to a solution* (see Sec. 7·9).
4. *Represent the unknown quantity by some appropriate symbol, such as* v *for velocity,* t *for time,* w *for weight.*

The symbol should be quantitative: it should refer to the number of units in the unknown; e.g., "Let t represent the time for the trip in hours"; "Let w represent the weight of copper in pounds." Be explicit.

All related quantities should be expressed in consistent units. For example, if it has been decided to express a velocity in miles per hour, all distances must be expressed in miles and all times must be expressed in hours.

1. *Try to discover two expressions which are equal. Form them into an equation and check dimensionality.*
2. *Solve the equation and check the solution against the original worded statement,* not *the equation you derived from it.*

Numerous laws of mathematics, natural sciences, etc., such as the following, may serve as the basis of equality:

The sum of the parts equals the whole.

Distance equals rate times time.

Weight equals volume times density.

Number of units times the unit cost equals the total cost.

Principal times the rate of interest times the time equals the interest.

Amount of material times the fraction of a particular ingredient equals the amount of ingredient.

Square of the hypotenuse of a right triangle equals the sum of the squares of the legs.

example 7 A tourist, having 4½ hr at his disposal, rides out into the country on a bus averaging 19 mph. He plans to walk back at 3½ mph. How far can he ride without arriving late at his starting point?

The one-way distance is required. The total time and the outgoing and return rates are given. Let d = number of miles one way. We know that distance = rate × time, or distance/rate = time. We can set up an equation:

$$\text{Outbound time} + \text{return time} = \text{total time}$$

$$\underset{\text{(outbound)}}{\frac{\text{Distance}}{\text{Rate}}} + \underset{\text{(return)}}{\frac{\text{distance}}{\text{rate}}} = \text{total time}$$

$$\frac{d}{19} + \frac{d}{3\frac{1}{2}} = 4\tfrac{1}{2}$$

Then

$$3\tfrac{1}{2}d + 19d = (19)(3\tfrac{1}{2})(4\tfrac{1}{2})$$

$$22\tfrac{1}{2}d = 299\tfrac{1}{4}$$

$$d = 13.3 \text{ miles}$$

Checking against the original statement,

$$\frac{13.3}{19} = 0.7 \text{ hr outbound}$$

$$\frac{13.3}{3.5} = \underline{3.8} \text{ hr return}$$

$$4.5 \text{ hr total}$$

example 8 How much 80 per cent antifreeze (alcohol) must be added to 5 qt of 30 per cent antifreeze to raise the strength to 65 per cent?

We wish to know the amount of 80 per cent antifreeze needed. We are given the concentrations of the initial solutions and the final mixture and the amount of the weaker solution. Let $n =$ the number of quarts of 80 per cent solution required. Then $n + 5 =$ number of quarts of mixture finally obtained. We can set up an equation saying that quarts of pure alcohol in the 5 qt of the 30 per cent solution plus the quarts of pure alcohol in the n qt of 80 per cent solution taken equals the quarts of pure alcohol in the $(n + 5)$ qt of 65 per cent final mixture. Hence

$$(0.30)(5) + 0.80n = 0.65(n + 5)$$
$$1.5 + 0.8n = 0.65n + 3.25$$
$$0.15n = 1.75$$
$$n = \frac{1.75}{0.15} = 11\tfrac{2}{3} \text{ qt of 80 per cent antifreeze required}$$

CHECK: $0.80 \times 11\tfrac{2}{3} = 9\tfrac{1}{3}$ qt pure alcohol in 80 per cent solution
$0.30 \times 5 = 1\tfrac{1}{2}$ qt pure alcohol in 30 per cent solution
Total $= 10\tfrac{5}{6}$ qt pure alcohol in mixture
$0.65 \times 16\tfrac{2}{3} = 10\tfrac{5}{6}$ qt pure alcohol in mixture (check)

EXERCISE 5

Set up linear equations in terms of one unknown for the following problems. Do not solve.

1. The difference between two numbers is 7. Their sum is 53. Find the numbers.
2. One number is $1\tfrac{1}{2}$ times as large as another. The sum of the numbers is 35. Find the numbers.
3. The sum of two numbers is 45. The quotient obtained by dividing the larger by the smaller is 2, with a remainder of 3. Find the numbers.
4. Separate 22 into two parts such that one part is 3 times the other.
5. Find the angles of a triangle if the first angle is $2\tfrac{1}{2}$ times the second and the third angle is $\tfrac{1}{4}$ of the second.
6. Find three consecutive numbers whose sum is 72.
7. Find four consecutive even numbers whose sum is 68.
8. Find five consecutive odd numbers whose sum is 85.
9. One side of a right triangle is 8 in., and the hypotenuse is 2 in. longer than the other side. Find the sides of the triangle.
10. The difference between the squares of two consecutive numbers is 37. Find the numbers.
11. The denominator of a fraction exceeds the numerator by 8. The reduced value is $\tfrac{7}{9}$. What is the fraction?
12. The reduced value of a fraction is $\tfrac{2}{3}$. If 16 is added to both numerator and denominator, the reduced value of the new fraction is $\tfrac{10}{13}$. What was the original fraction?

13. The reduced value of a fraction is $\frac{4}{5}$. If 21 is deducted from both numerator and denominator, the reduced value of the new fraction is $\frac{1}{3}$. Find the original fraction.
14. The length of a rectangle exceeds the width by 14 ft. The perimeter is 160 ft. Find the dimensions.
15. The circumference of a circle exceeds its diameter by 13. Find the diameter.
16. The hypotenuse of a 45° right triangle exceeds one of the equal sides by 9. Find one of the equal sides.
17. The perimeter of an isosceles triangle is 50 in. The base is 11 in. longer than one of the equal sides. Find the sides of the triangle.
18. The side of an equilateral triangle exceeds the altitude by 5. Find a side of the triangle.
19. Ten boys agreed to buy a canoe, dividing the expense equally. Two more boys joined the group, reducing the share of each by $1.50. How much did the canoe cost?
20. A boy worked 16 days for a certain amount of money. Had he received $0.50 a day more, he could have earned his money in 1 day less time. Find his daily wages.
21. A man bought 30 acres of land for $1,280. Part of the land cost $40 an acre; the rest cost $50 an acre. How much land was sold at $40 an acre?
22. A sum of money consists of dimes and quarters. There are 9 more dimes than quarters. If the total value is $10, find the number of dimes.
23. A man invested $7,000, part at $2\frac{1}{4}$ per cent and the rest at 3 per cent. If the interest for one year was $174, find the amount invested at 3 per cent.
24. How much solder containing 50 per cent tin and how much type metal containing 15 per cent tin must be mixed to make 80 lb of solder containing 40 per cent tin?
25. A 12-qt cooling system is filled with 25 per cent antifreeze. How many quarts must be drawn off and replaced with pure antifreeze to raise the strength to 45 per cent?
26. Two trains leave opposite terminals of a 200-mile line at the same time. If the rates are 40 and 35 mph, respectively, when will they meet?
27. A group of bicyclists maintains an average rate of 12 mph. One hour and 45 min after they leave, a motorist sets out to overtake them. If his rate is 40 mph, how long will he take?

EXERCISE 6

Solve the following problems and check against the original statement.

1–8. Solve Probs. 1, 2, 4 to 7, 11, and 22 in Exercise 5.

9. In a municipal election a total of 82,347 votes were cast for two nominees, *A* and *B*. If *A* received 6,051 votes more than *B*, find the number of votes each contestant received.

10. The difference between the squares of two consecutive odd numbers is 48. Find the numbers.
11. A pile of dimes and quarters has a value of $4.60. There are three more quarters than dimes. How many quarters are there?
12. A grocer estimated that his supply of sugar would last 30 days. Because he sold 20 lb per day more than he expected, it lasted only 24 days. How many pounds did he have?
13. The reduced value of a certain fraction is ⅔, and its denominator exceeds its numerator by 4. Find the fraction.
14. A circle of what diameter has numerically the same diameter in inches as it has area in square inches?
15. At a high-school game the price of admission was $0.25 for each adult and $0.10 for each child. If the turnstile showed 397 persons at the game and the gate receipts were $56.80, how many adults attended?
16. In the formula $N = 0.907(D/d - 0.94)^2 + 3.7$, N is the number of wires of diameter d that can be contained in a conduit of diameter D. What must be the ratio of conduit diameter to wire diameter in order that the conduit may hold 100 wires?
17. A bonus of $30,000 is to be distributed among 500 employees of a factory. There are 50 men with 20 years' service, 100 men with 10 years' service, and 350 men with 5 years' service. Each 20-year man is to receive twice as much as a 10-year man, and each 10-year man is to receive twice as much as a 5-year man. How much should each of the 5-year, 10-year, and 20-year men receive?
18. A farmer bought 100 acres of land for $3,880. Part cost $50 an acre; the rest $18 an acre. Find the number of acres bought at each price.
19. Find the height of a segment whose width is 24 in. if the diameter of the circle is 40 in.
20. A man can clear a wood lot in 6 days, while his son could do it alone in 12 days. How long would the job take if they worked together?
21. A tank can be filled by two pipes in 6 min, while the first pipe alone would require 10 min. How long would it take the second pipe alone to fill the tank?
22. How much time would be required to fill the tank in Prob. 21 if the first pipe operated as an inlet and the second pipe as an outlet? The tank is being used for leaching purposes.
23. A job can be completed by A in 1½ hr, by B in 2⅓ hr, and by C in 3 hr. Find the time required when all are working together.
24. How many gallons of water must be mixed with 500 gal of 96 per cent sulfuric acid to reduce the strength to 80 per cent?
25. A uniform 20-in. bar weighing 1 lb is in equilibrium when a 3-lb weight is suspended from one end, and a 2-lb weight from the other. Find the position of the point of support.
26. A bar of metal contains 20 per cent silver, and a second bar 12 per cent. How many ounces of each must be taken to make a 40-oz bar containing 14½ per cent silver?

27. Find the length of one of the equal sides and the area of an isosceles right triangle having a perimeter of 20 ft.
28. The area of a 4-ft walk surrounding a circular pond is 1,496 sq ft. Using $\pi = 22/7$, find the diameter of the pond.
29. A length of rope hangs from the top of a flagpole to the ground. Six feet of rope lies coiled up on the ground. It is found that the free end of the rope can be brought out 30 ft from the base of the pole and yet be touched to the ground. How high is the flagpole?
30. Eight thousand dollars is invested, some at 6½ and the rest at 4½ per cent. How much must be invested at 6½ per cent to ensure a total annual income of $420?
31. How much high-speed tool steel containing 18 per cent tungsten and how much steel containing 12 per cent tungsten should be mixed to make 3,000 lb containing 14.6 per cent tungsten?
32. What will be the final temperature when 42 lb of water at 135°F is mixed with 70 lb of water at 60°F? In problems of heat exchange involving no change of state, weight × specific heat × temperature change for the warm body = weight × specific heat × temperature change for the cooler body.
33. A bookrack is to be 44 in. high overall. The stock is ⅞ in. thick. There are to be five shelf spaces, each one having ¾ in. more vertical space than the one above it. Find the height of each shelf space. (There are to be six thicknesses of stock.)
34. If the equation $C = \frac{5}{9}(F - 32)$ represents the relationship between the centigrade and Fahrenheit readings for any temperature, find the temperature at which the two will be equal.
35. A machine having an initial value of $1,450 depreciates in value each year $50 less than during the preceding year. At the end of the sixth year it has a value of $190. What is its value at the end of the first year?
36. A 39¾-in.-diameter iron tire is to be shrunk onto a 40-in. wheel. If the linear coefficient of expansion of iron is 0.000006 per degree Fahrenheit, to what temperature must the tire be heated from 70°F to fit on the wheel?
37. A poorly compensated watch, when carried vertically in the pocket, gains 11 sec in 9 hr and, when laid down horizontally, loses 28 sec in 13 hr. How many hours out of 24 in the horizontal position would result in no net gain or loss in a 24-hr period?
38. An isosceles triangle has a perimeter of 32 in.; the altitude to the base is 8 in. Find the length of one of the equal sides.
39. A group of men pay $1.75 each toward the expenses of a luncheon. An excess of $1.25 results. If each had paid out $1.50 there would have been $2.50 lacking. How many men were there?
40. An oval running track has semicircular ends and straight sides. The overall length is three times the width. If one lap is 600 ft, find the length and width of the oval.
41. A guy rope runs from the top of a derrick to a stake 7 ft from the base.

If the rope is lengthened 15 ft, it will reach a stake 32 ft from the base. Find the height of the derrick.

42. Fifty pounds of high-grade solder spatters containing 50 per cent lead and 50 per cent tin are to be melted with some type metal containing 90 per cent lead and 10 per cent tin. The resulting alloy is to be a low-grade solder containing 75 per cent lead and 25 per cent tin. How many pounds of type metal will be needed?
43. A utility company petitioned to change its rate on electrical energy from a straight 5½ cents per kilowatthour to 4¼ cents per kilowatt-hour plus 75 cents per month service charge. What monthly cost would be unaffected by the change in rate?
44. A man pays an income tax of $118.06 on an income which is taxed as follows: 1 per cent on all income over $1,500, plus 3 per cent on all income over $2,500, plus 5 per cent on all income over $4,000. What is his income?
45. A stick of wood is to be cut into four equal sections for braces, as shown in Fig. 5·1. Find x and y, making no allowance for saw kerfs.
46. How many gallons of 35 per cent antifreeze solution must be added to 3 gal of 80 per cent antifreeze solution to reduce the strength to 60 per cent?
47. A dairyman has 1,000 qt of milk containing 4.8 per cent butterfat, but the city in which he sells his milk requires only 4 per cent butterfat. How many quarts of cream testing 20 per cent butterfat may be separated from the milk and still satisfy the legal minimum requirement?
48. Find the diameter of the circle shown in Fig. 5·2.
49. Three equal circles are externally tangent, each to each. A belt passed around these three circles is 60 in. long. Find, in terms of π, the radius of a circle.
50. The outbound trip of a bus was made at 24 mph, while the return trip was made at 30 mph. Find the one-way distance if the total running time was 4½ hr.

fig. 5·1

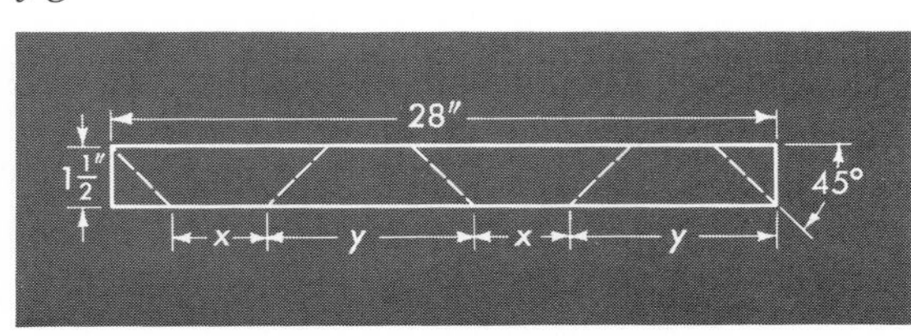

fig. 5·2

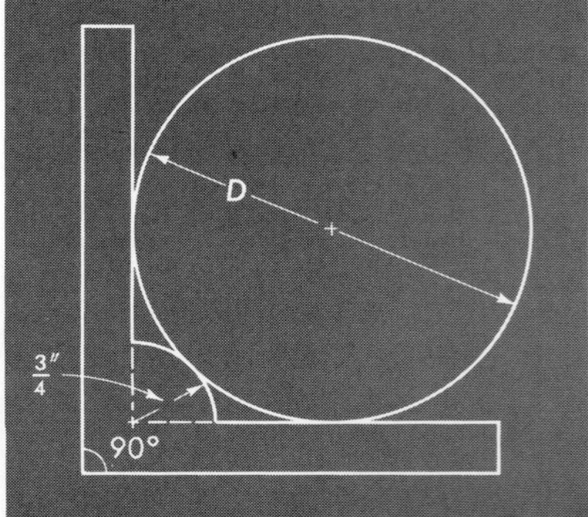

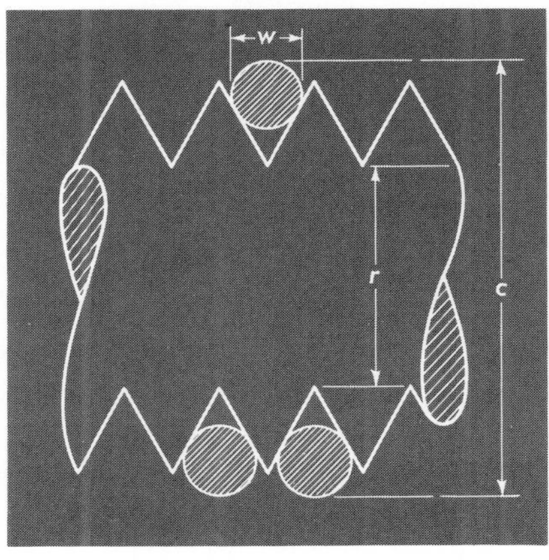

fig. 5·3

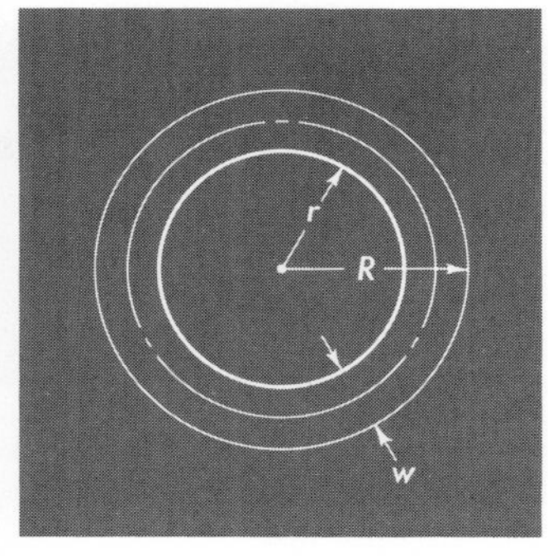

fig. 5·4

51. Position B is 5 miles due east of position A. An enemy battery is firing due north of A. The sound of the firing reaches A 2.5 sec before it reaches B. Find the distance of the battery from A if sound travels at 1,100 fps.
52. The indicated airspeed of a Piper Cub plane is 120 mph. If a 40-mph west wind is blowing, how far west can the plane fly and still return to the airport 2¼ hr after taking off?
53. A man has 4½ hr at his disposal. He can ride out on a bus at 16 mph and walk back at 3½ mph. How far can he ride and still be able to return to his starting point within the allotted time?
54. At two stations A and B on a railroad line, the prices of soft coal are \$16.50 and \$17 per ton, respectively. If the distance between A and B is 180 miles and coal can be shipped for ½ cent per ton per mile, find the location on the line between A and B at which it will be immaterial to a consumer whether he buys from A or from B.
55. A and B have a pile of 825 pieces to stamp. A works alone for 1½ hr, during which time he stamps 105 pieces. Then he is joined by B, and together they finish the job in 4 hr more. At the rate of \$0.016 a piece, how much should each man receive?
56. A plane has an airspeed of 300 mph. It flies directly into a head wind for 48 min and returns along the same route in 42 min. Find the wind speed.
57. The explosion of a floating mine was heard 8 sec sooner through the water than through the air. If the speed of sound is 4,800 fps through the water and 1,125 fps through the air, how far away was the explosion?
58. Using the three-wire system for determining the root diameter r of a 60° sharp-V thread, develop a formula for r in terms of c and w (Fig. 5·3).
59. Show that the annular area in Fig. 5·4 equals the length of the center line times the width w.

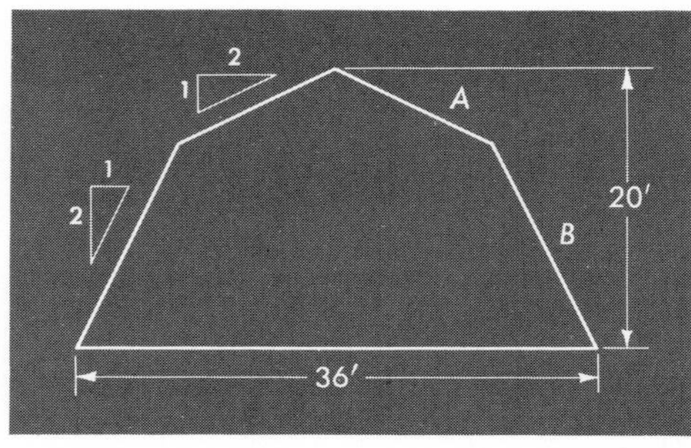

fig. 5·5

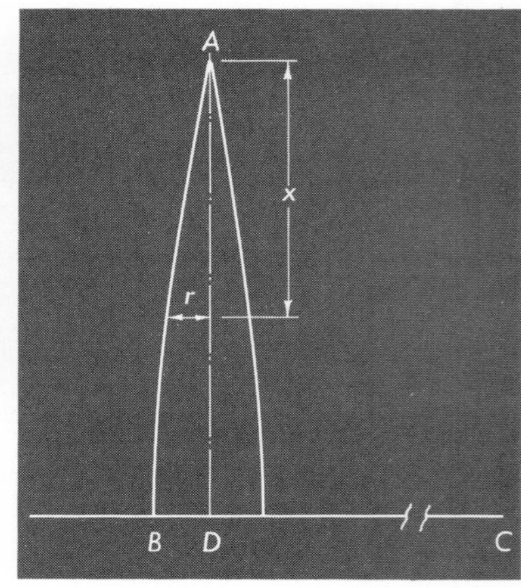

fig. 5·6

60. In order to measure the flow of chlorine which would corrode an ordinary mechanical meter, pure oxygen is "bled" into the stream of chlorine gas at the rate of 5.3 cubic feet per minute (cfpm). If the chlorine, before dilution, contained 2.8 per cent oxygen, and afterward contained 12.1 per cent oxygen, find the original flow of chlorine gas in cubic feet per minute.
61. In the gambrel roof in Fig. 5·5 the upper set of rafters has a ½ pitch, and the lower set a pitch of 2. Find the lengths of A and B.
62. A manufacturer wishes to make a competitive line of copper-coated iron wire which he can sell for $0.27 per pound and make a gross profit of 50 per cent above the cost of materials. If copper costs $0.32 per pound and iron costs $0.12 per pound, find the percentage of copper in the wire.
63. A 4-in. circle is inscribed in a right triangle ABC. The circle is tangent to the hypotenuse AB at point D. If $AD = 8$ in., find BC.
64. The profile AB of the nose of an experimental rocket in Fig. 5·6 is an arc of a circle whose center C is on the line BC. If AD is 24 ft and

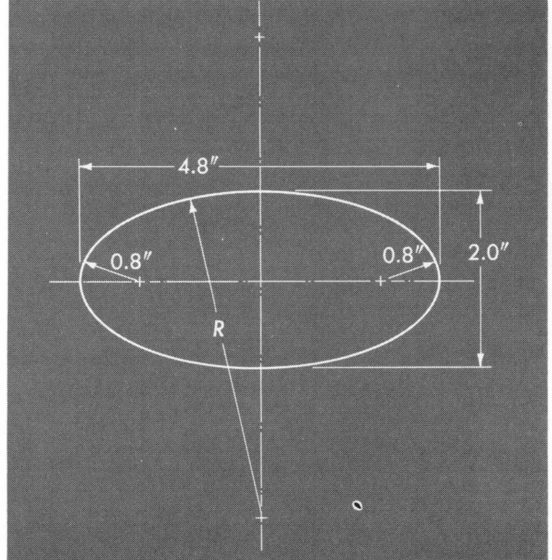

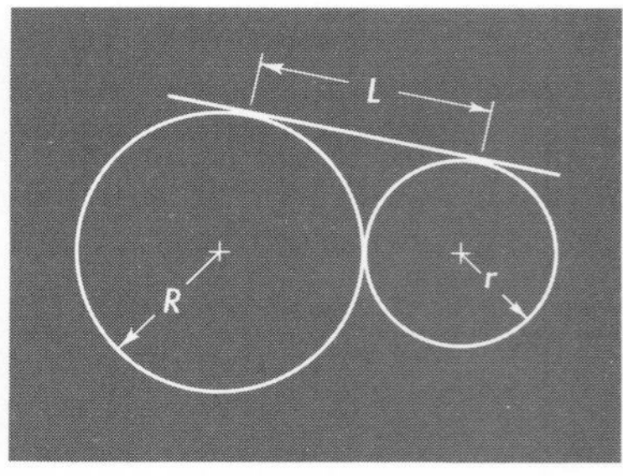

fig. 5·8

fig. 5·7

BD is 2½ ft, find the radius r of the cross section at distances x from the nose tip, making x successively 6 ft, 12 ft, and 18 ft.

65. Find the radius R used in the construction of the approximate ellipse shown in Fig. 5·7.
66. In Fig. 5·8 show that $L = 2\sqrt{Rr}$.
67. Given a square $ABCD$, in which $AB = 3½$ in.; a circle is drawn passing through vertex C and tangent to AB and AD. Find the diameter of the circle.
68. In Fig. 5·9 derive an expression for h in terms of the other dimensions.
69. In Fig. 5·10 derive an expression for w in terms of the other dimensions.
70. In order to weigh a uniform bar of iron 8 ft long, a 5-lb weight was hung 8 in. from one end, whereupon the bar was found to balance 45½ in. from that end. Find the weight of the bar.
71. A planer has a ratio of cutting speed to return speed of 1:2.75. Find the cutting speed in feet per second for a 5-ft stroke when the planer is making 15 cycles every 2 min.
72. A valve operates off a camshaft turning at a speed of 1,200 rpm. What is the travel of the valve if it opens at the rate of 2 fps and closes at the rate of 10 fps?
73. A man, aged 50, has savings, etc., valued at $24,500. He considers that this amount will increase by $1,000 each year while he is employed. After retirement he will be obliged to reduce the principal by $1,800 each year. At what age can he retire so that the principal will not be exhausted before he reaches age 85?
74. A contractor must finish a job in 35 days. Only one steam shovel can be used on the job at a time. The contractor owns a shovel that can do the job in 40 days and can rent, for $50 a day, a second shovel that can do the job in 20 days. What is the smallest amount the contractor will have to pay for renting the shovel?
75. A range burner uses up a 54-gal drum of fuel oil in 31 days. The drum is filled the first of the month; after 10 days a water heater is also started, and the oil lasts 8 days longer. How many gallons did the heater use per day?

fig. 5·9 *fig. 5·10*

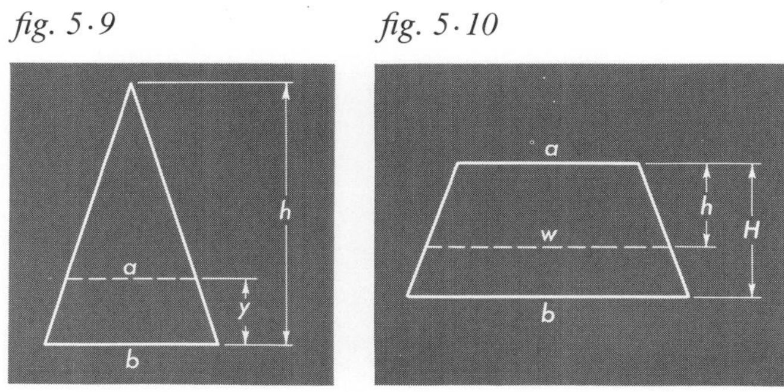

76. A contractor agrees to put in a concrete foundation within a certain time limit. He is to receive \$28 per day worked, plus \$40 for each day by which completion of the job precedes the time limit. He finished the job in two-thirds of the time allowed and received \$576. What was the time limit?
77. A man may retire at age 62 with social-security benefits of \$102 a month for the rest of his life, or he may retire at age 65 with benefits of \$126 a month. At what age will the total benefits from each plan be equal?
78. An excavation job could be done by a steam shovel alone in 12 days or by a gang of laborers alone in 28 days. After being used a certain time, the shovel was disabled, and the work was then completed by the men, who worked 2 days less than the time of steam-shovel operation. How long was the shovel used?
79. A circle of diameter D is inscribed in a 45° right triangle with leg S. Derive a formula for D in terms of S.
80. Find the diameters of the circles in Fig. 5·11.
81. A number is composed of six digits, of which the first is 1. When the number is multiplied by 3, the order of digits remains the same except that the 1 is transposed to the units place. What is the number?
82. A square is inscribed in a triangle. Show that $s = ab/(a + b)$ (see Fig. 5·12).
83. Using the formula for the length of a pulley belt in Prob. 61, page 35, find the missing diameters of the step-cone pulleys in Fig. 5·13 so that the same belt may be used in each of the three positions.
84. A closed manometer tube is shown in Fig. 5·14. A length of air column AB is sealed off at atmospheric pressure with mercury. More mercury is then poured into the open arm at D, with new levels at C and D. Find, to the nearest 0.1 in. of mercury, the original atmospheric pressure.

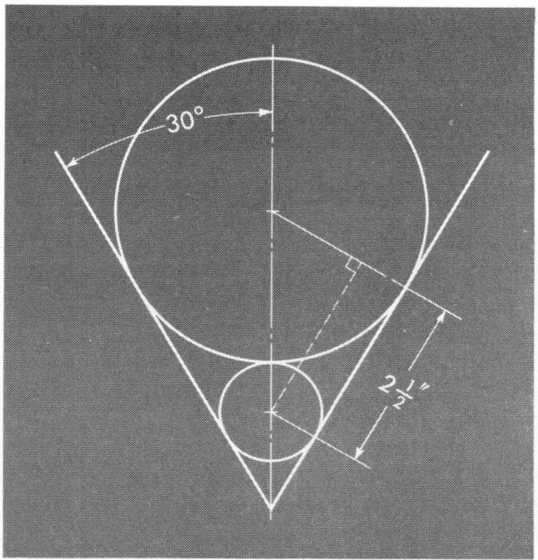

fig. 5·11

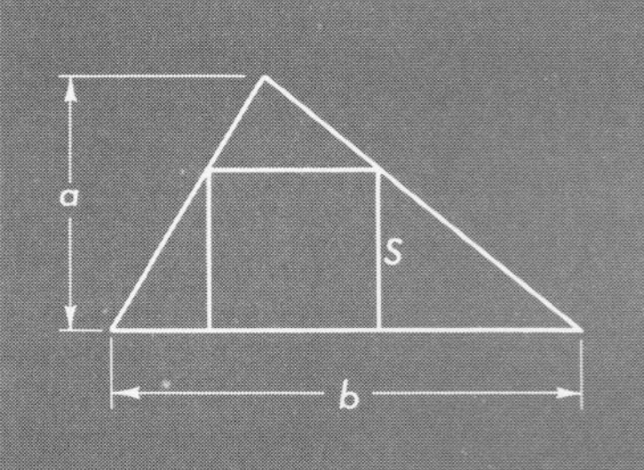

fig. 5·12

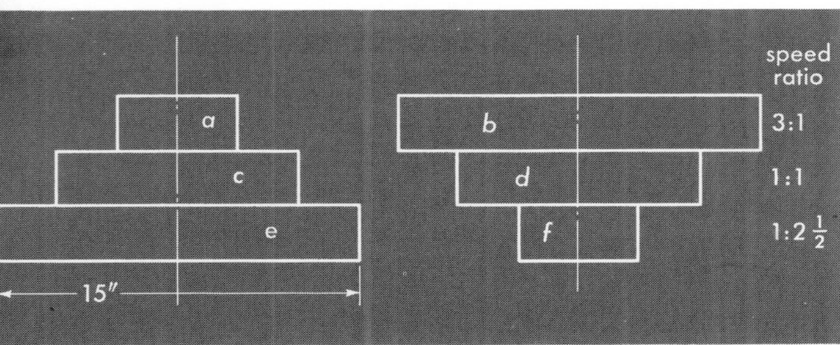

fig. 5·13

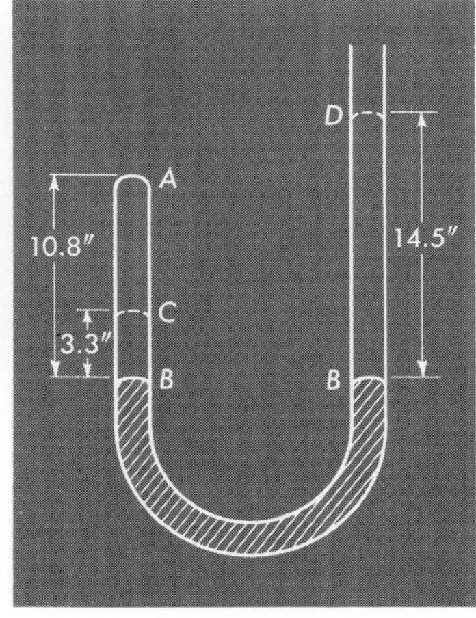

fig. 5·14

85. A man pays 25 cents per gallon for gasoline. He gets 16 miles per gallon from his car. He can have his engine overhauled for \$110, after which he can expect to get 22 miles per gallon of gasoline and save 30 cents per hundred miles on oil. After how many miles will he recover the cost of overhauling?
86. In Prob. 103, page 40, show that $CD = \sqrt{(AC)(BC)}$.
87. A family has 1 qt of milk delivered daily. The bill for the month of November was \$7.56. It is known that the price advanced 2 cents per quart at some time before the middle of the month. What was the price per quart before the increase? When did the increase become effective? Prices are in integral cents.
88. In Fig. 5·15 the stars photograph as traces (arcs) in a time exposure of the night sky. Estimate the length of exposure by scaling any measurements you think necessary. Polaris is off the photo.

fig. 5·15

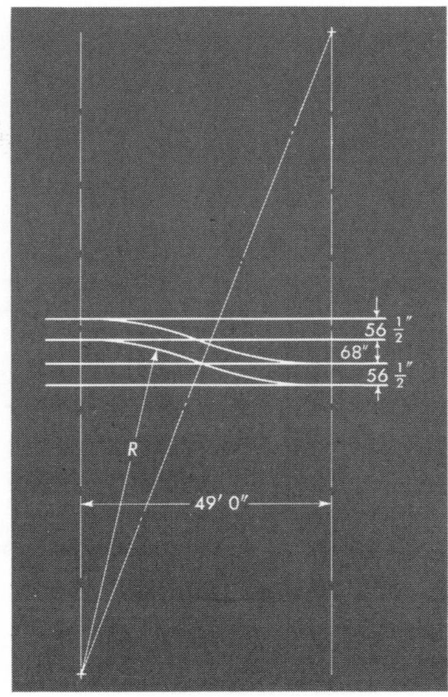

fig. 5·16

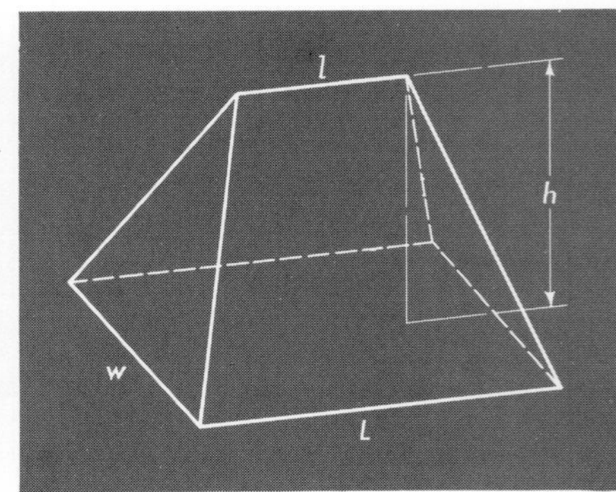

fig. 5·17

89. A 6-ft offset in a pipe line consists of two equal reverse arcs. If the offset is accomplished in a distance of 10 ft (measured parallel to the straight pipe), find the radius of curvature of an arc.
90. A crossover in a double-track railroad line (Fig. 5·16) consists of two equal reverse arcs. Find the radius of curvature R of the inner rail.
91. The volume of a prismoid is given by $V = \frac{1}{6}h(b + 4M + B)$, where h = height and b, M, and B are the areas of the upper base, midsection, and lower base respectively. Applying this formula to the wedge in Fig. 5·17, develop a formula for V in terms of w, h, l, and L.
92. A cone of base diameter d and slant height S is developed from a sector of central angle θ. Derive a formula for θ (in degrees) in terms of d and S.
93. A circle of diameter D is inscribed in a right triangle. Show that $D = a + b - c$, where c is the hypotenuse.
94. A bus went up a hill at 25 mph and returned at 40 mph. What was the average speed for the round trip?
95. What is the smallest positive number which can at the same time represent the sum of (a) three consecutive positive integers, (b) four consecutive positive integers, and (c) five consecutive positive integers?

6

functions and graphs

A graph or curve is a forceful way of representing data and portraying the relation between them. In this chapter, suggestions will be given for effective graphical presentation of data.

The graphical methods of analysis are stressed because they afford an easy approach to the understanding of fundamental concepts of calculus and because they are important in their own right.

In the second part of this chapter, which deals with the properties of a straight line, we shall see how the more direct methods of algebra may be applied to the solution of geometrical problems. This offspring of algebra and geometry is called *analytic geometry*.

The last part of the chapter describes the techniques of analyzing linear experimental data.

6·1 Variable quantities and constants

A *variable quantity* is one that is free to change during the course of a problem. The change may take place according to some simple law, or it may be the result of a combination of influences too complex to be represented by a formula.

Variable quantities are often represented by the last letters of the alphabet, x, y, and z. Usually it is desirable to use letters suggestive of the unit represented, such as v for volume, t for time, and w for weight.

A *constant* is a quantity that does not change in value during the course of a problem. Some quantities, such as $\sqrt{2}$, -7, and π, are inherently constant. Other constants, usually represented by the first few letters of the alphabet, a, b, c, etc., retain their values without change throughout a particular problem, but may vary from one problem to another.

For example, when using the formula $W = DV$ to compute the weights of various volumes of cast iron, weight and volume are variable quantities, and density is a constant.

6·2 Sets and functions

In connection with the relationships to be described, we shall refer to "sets." We shall define a set as a collection of objects having some property in common. A function is a set of ordered pairs of numbers, for example (x, y), such that for each value of the first variable x, there corresponds a unique value of the second variable y. Since the value of the variable y is considered to depend upon the value of the variable x, we refer to y as the dependent variable, and to x as the independent variable, and we say that y is the value of a function of x.

In each of the following illustrations it will be noted that the dependent variable is mentioned before the independent variable.

Rate of growth of vegetation depends upon the temperature.
Time of high tide depends upon the position of the moon.
Price of an article depends upon supply and demand.
Flow of electric current through a fixed resistance depends upon the voltage.
Postage to a given destination depends upon the weight of the package.

The *domain* of the function is the set of numbers from which specific values of x may be chosen. The *range* of the function is the set of y values then determined. Unless otherwise expressed or implied, both the range and the domain of the function involved will be the largest possible set of real numbers.

We observe that there are three important aspects of the discussion of functions so far.

1. The set of x values or the *domain* of the function
2. The set of y values or the *range* of the function
3. Some type of association between y and x such that a unique value of y can be determined if x is given

There are four ways by which the type of association between y and x can be described. They are:

1. By a worded statement: The circumference of a circle is the product of π and the diameter.
2. By an equation: $y = 5x^2$.
3. By a table of values enumerating convenient, corresponding values for the variables involved in an equation.
4. By a graph of the function. The graph of a function is the set of points whose coordinates represent respectively the set of ordered pairs of numbers which constitutes the function. This is discussed in

greater detail in Sec. 6·5. The primary meaning of the word "function" was given above. However, it is commonly used in a slightly different sense. Thus if

$$A = \pi r^2$$

We often say that A is a function of r. In this sense the word "function" is identified with the dependent variable rather than with an ordered pair of numbers.

6·3 Functional notation

When, for any reason, the exact relation between variables is not to be expressed, a general form is used. Thus, instead of writing $A = \pi r^2$, we might use the more general form $A = f(r)$, which states that A is a function of r without giving the exact relation. It is read, "A is a function of r" or, more simply, "A equals f of r."

Suppose that y is some function of x. We may then write $y = f(x)$. Then $f(6)$ is the value of y when $x = 6$; likewise $f(-1)$ is the value y assumes when $x = -1$; and so on. In general, $f(a)$ is the value of y which results when a is substituted for x in the expression for $f(x)$.

It should be remembered that $f(x)$ does not mean f times x; in fact, f does not represent a number. In the expression $y = f(x)$, f simply indicates that a functional relationship exists between y and x.

example 1 Suppose that $y = x^2 - 3x - 4$. We may then write

$$y = f(x) = x^2 - 3x - 4$$

Then, when $x = 5$,

$$y = f(5) = (5)^2 - 3(5) - 4 = 6$$

Also, when $x = -6$,

$$y = f(-6) = (-6)^2 - 3(-6) - 4 = 50$$

EXERCISE 1

If $y = 3x^2 - 2x - 5$, find

1. $f(0)$ 2. $f(-1)$ 3. $f(\frac{2}{3})$ 4. $f(a + 1)$ 5. $f(4) - f(-2)$

If $y = 12x/(16 - x^2)$, find

6. $f(-2)$ 7. $f(5)$ 8. $f(\frac{1}{2})$ 9. $f(3a - 4)$ 10. $f(2a) - f(a)$

6·4 Rectangular coordinates

To form a *rectangular system of coordinates* we draw a horizontal line $X'X$ and a vertical line $Y'Y$. Their point of intersection O is called the *origin*. $X'X$ is called the X axis, and $Y'Y$ is called the Y axis.

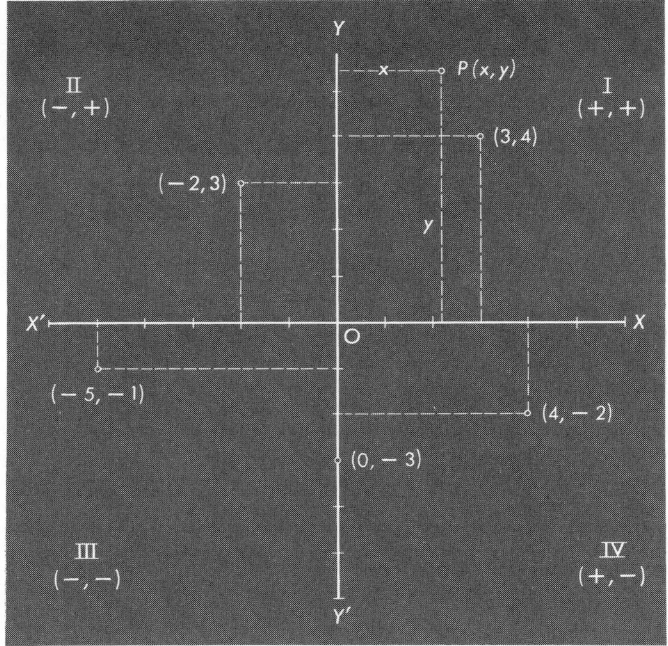

fig. 6·1

The location of any point in the plane of the coordinate axes may be expressed by stating its distance and direction from each of the two axes. Distances above $X'X$ and distances to the right of $Y'Y$ are positive, whereas distances below $X'X$ and distances to the left of $Y'Y$ are negative.

The distance of a point measured to the right or left of the Y axis is called the *abscissa,* or X coordinate, of the point. The distance of a point from the X axis (upward or downward) is called the *ordinate,* or Y coordinate, of the point. In Fig. 6·1, point P is said to have the *coordinates* (x,y) and may be referred to as the point (x,y). In the same figure, points $(3,4)$, $(4,-2)$, $(0,-3)$, $(-5,-1)$, and $(-2,3)$ are also designated. It should be noted that the coordinates are enclosed in parentheses and separated by a comma and that the abscissa is always written first (hence the term "ordered pair"). It will also be seen that the axes divide the plane into four quadrants, numbered as shown. The signs of the coordinates of points in each quadrant are also indicated.

The position of any point can be determined if its coordinates are known, and conversely the coordinates of a point appearing on the plane can be determined by measurement.

EXERCISE 2

Locate the points having the coordinates given below.

1. $(2,5)$	2. $(4,\sqrt{3})$	3. $(-2,6)$	4. $(-\sqrt{2},3)$
5. $(8,-3)$	6. $(7,-4)$	7. $(-3,-5)$	8. $(-6,-2)$
9. $(0,5)$	10. $(-\frac{5}{2},0)$	11. $(0,0)$	12. $(1\frac{1}{2},-\frac{2}{3})$

EXERCISE 3

Identify the closed figures formed by plotting the given points and joining in order with straight lines.

1. (5,2), (5,−4), (−1,−4), (−1,2)
2. (0,4), (7,4), (7,−1), (0,−1)
3. (3,2), (8,0), (0,−9)
4. (2,4), (5,−3), (−1,−3)
5. (−1,6), (5,2), (−1,2)
6. (5,5), (7,−3), (−4,−3), (−6,5)
7. (1,3), (4,2), (6,8)
8. (5,3), (12,4), (7,9), (0,8)

6·5 Graph of a function

When we sketch the graph of a function, we say that we "graph the function."

Suppose that we are given some function $y = f(x)$. The first step in graphing the function is to make a table listing a number of different values of x and opposite them to write the corresponding values of y. We take these pairs of corresponding values of x and y as the coordinates of points which we plot. These points all lie on the graph of $y = f(x)$. Accordingly, we may define the *graph,* or *locus,* of a function as consisting of a system of points whose coordinates satisfy the relation $y = f(x)$.

A *linear function* of x is a first-degree polynomial in x having the form $ax + b$, where a and b are constants. The graph of such a function is always a straight line; hence the name linear function.

example 2 Graph the function $y = f(x) = \frac{2}{3}x - 4$.

Form a table of arbitrarily chosen values of x together with the corresponding values of $f(x)$, i.e., of y.

x	−6	−3	0	1½	3	5	8	12
y	−8	−6	−4	−3	−2	−⅔	1⅓	4

In Fig. 6·2 the points (−6, −8), (−3, −6), etc., are plotted, and a smooth line is drawn through these points.

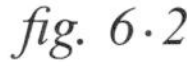
fig. 6·2

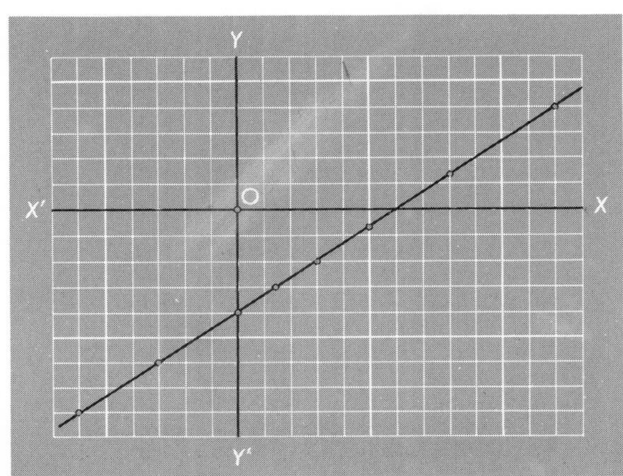

It is evident that we might plot any number of points whose coordinates satisfy the equation $y = \frac{2}{3}x - 4$. We infer, then, that we have a straight line which may be extended indefinitely in either direction. Theoretically, two points are sufficient to determine a straight line. However, in graphing any linear function, we should compute a minimum of three values of the function. For the sake of accuracy, these points should be located some distance apart. Any points not lying on the same straight line should be checked for errors.

For a given section of coordinate paper the position of the axes and the number of units assigned to a division on the paper should be chosen so as to make the desired portion of the graph as large as possible.

In general, if a function of x is defined by a formula, its graph is a smooth curve or, in some cases, two or more disconnected smooth curves. The term "smooth curve" is used in a broad sense to denote a line which may be straight or curved but which does not show any abrupt change in direction. For greater clarity it may be desirable to use different scales on the X and Y axes. Perhaps the most common example of an independent variable is time. Time units, with rare exceptions, are scaled horizontally.

example 3 Graph the function $y = f(x) = 2x^3 - 8x^2 - 11$.

Form a table listing arbitrary values of x and corresponding values of y:

x	6	5	4	3	2	1	0	−1	−2	−3
y	133	39	−11	−29	−27	−17	−11	−21	−59	−137

From the plotting in Fig. 6·3 it will be noticed that, in order to open up the curve, the same distance that represents 20 vertical units is used

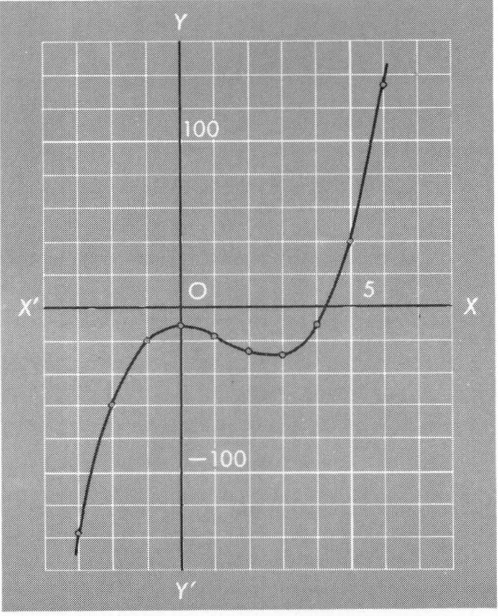

fig. 6·3

to represent 1 horizontal unit. Note that, although the curve continues indefinitely above and below the portion shown, we have included only the interesting part of the graph.

That part of a curve which is higher than points immediately adjacent to it on either side is called a *relative-maximum* point. In our illustration it occurs at $x = 0$, for which the corresponding maximum value of the function is -11. On the other hand, that part of the curve which is lower than points immediately adjacent to it on either side is called a *relative-minimum* point. In the illustration it occurs at $x = 8/3$, for which the corresponding minimum value of the function is about -30.

It is good practice to see that each division on the axes corresponds to one, two, or five times an integral power of 10, as is the case with the scales of a slide rule.

EXERCISE 4

Plot the graphs of the following equations in which $y = f(x)$, indicating any intersections with the axes:

1. $y = x$
2. $y = 3x$
3. $y = \frac{1}{2}x$
4. $y = -x$
5. $y = -2x$
6. $y = -\frac{1}{3}x$
7. $y = 2$
8. $y = -3$
9. $x = 4$
10. $x = -2\frac{1}{2}$
11. $y = x + 3$
12. $y = 2x - 1$
13. $y = \frac{1}{2}x + 2$
14. $y = -x^2$
15. $y = \frac{1}{2}x^2 - 8$
16. $x = 0$
17. $y = 0$

6·6 Slope of a straight line

Referring to Fig. 6·4, draw any straight line not parallel to the axes. Let P and Q be any two points on the line; denote the coordinates of P by (x_1, y_1), and the coordinates of Q by (x_2, y_2).

The steepness or slope of the line is then expressed by the equation

$$m = \frac{y_2 - y_1}{x_2 - x_1} \quad \textbf{(1)}$$

fig. 6·4

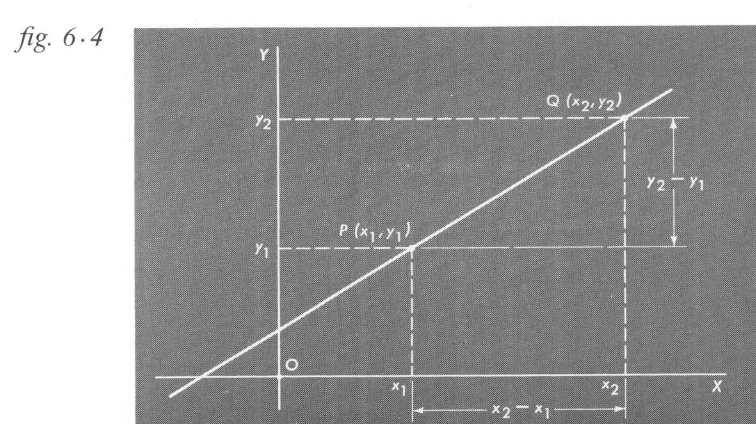

provided $x_2 - x_1 \neq 0$ or $x_2 \neq x_1$. Hence the *slope* of the straight line passing through two given points is equal to the difference of the ordinates of the points divided by the difference of their abscissas taken in the same order.

It is apparent from the rule just stated that the slope of a line could also be expressed by the fraction $(y_1 - y_2)/(x_1 - x_2)$. This is, of course, in agreement with the law of signs as applied to fractions.

example 4 Find the slope of the line passing through $(-3,5)$ and $(9,11)$ (Fig. 6·5).

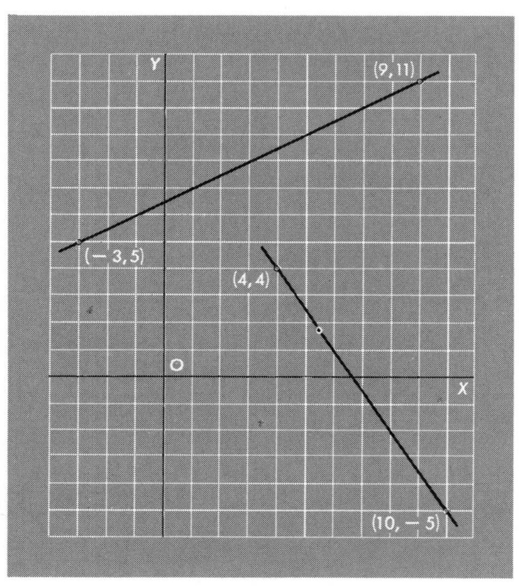

fig. 6·5

Referring to Eq. (1), we may consider $x_1 = -3$, $x_2 = 9$, $y_1 = 5$, $y_2 = 11$. The slope is therefore

$$\frac{11-5}{9-(-3)} = \frac{6}{12} = \frac{1}{2}$$

example 5 Find the slope of the line passing through $(4,4)$ and $(10,-5)$ (Fig. 6·5).

Taking $x_1 = 4$, $x_2 = 10$, $y_1 = 4$, and $y_2 = -5$, we have

$$\text{Slope} = \frac{-5-4}{10-4} = \frac{-9}{6} = -\frac{3}{2}$$

The following characteristics of slope may be cited:

1. *A line sloping upward to the right has a positive slope; a line sloping downward to the right has a negative slope.*
2. *The slope of a horizontal line is zero.*

3. *The slope of a vertical line is undefined* (since $x_2 - x_1 = 0$ and division by zero is undefined.)
4. *If we move a point to the right along a straight line, the slope corresponds to the progress made in a vertical direction when the point has advanced one unit horizontally.* Thus if the point rises 1½ units while at the same time moving one unit to the right, the slope of the line is 1½; if the point falls ⅘ of a unit while advancing one unit to the right, the slope is −⅘. Scale units are to be used in all cases.

EXERCISE 5

Find the slope of the straight line passing through the following points:

1. (−2,1) and (4,3)
2. (1,−3) and (4,3)
3. (0,4) and (8,−2)
4. (−2,5) and (3,0)
5. Origin and (4,10)
6. (−3,−1) and (5,−1)
7. What is the slope of (a) a 30° line, (b) a 45° line, (c) a 60° line, (d) a 120° line, (e) a 135° line, and (f) a 150° line? Assume equal X and Y scales.

If three points $P(x_1,y_1)$, $Q(x_2,y_2)$, and $R(x_3,y_3)$ lie in a straight line (Fig. 6·6), the slope of PQ must be equal to that of QR. Hence, by Eq. (1) for three points lying in a straight line,

$$\frac{y_3 - y_2}{x_3 - x_2} = \frac{y_2 - y_1}{x_2 - x_1} \tag{2}$$

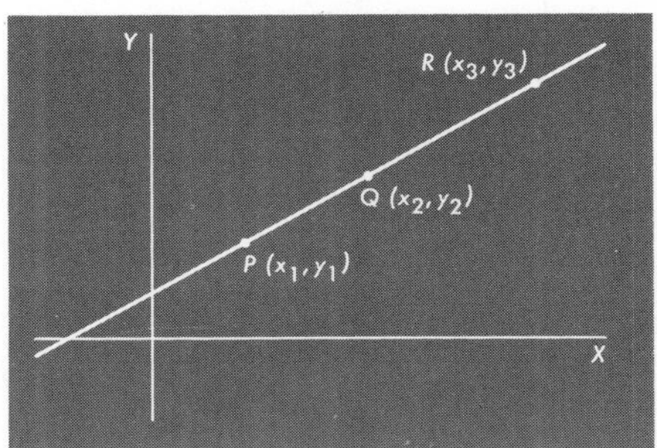

fig. 6·6

The student will recognize that this is the type of straight-line equation which forms the basis of interpolation.

6·7 Rate of change of linear functions

It will be noted that Eq. (1) for slope expresses the *ratio* of the *change in* y to the *change in* x. We may then extend Eq. (1) to read $m = \dfrac{y_2 - y_1}{x_2 - x_1} = \dfrac{\Delta y}{\Delta x}$ (read "delta" y over "delta" x)

The delta concept of rates of change is of utmost importance in the study of calculus.

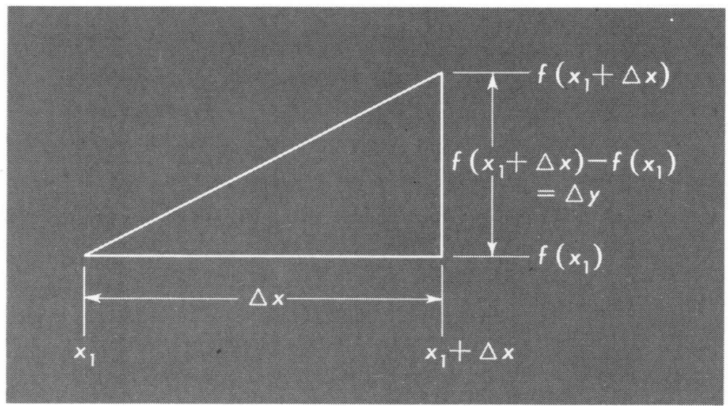

fig. 6·7

To express the concepts of Sec. 6·6 in functional notation, we shall find the rate of change in the value of a linear function by starting with a definite value of the independent variable, for example x, to which we shall assign the value x_1 and let x change by a certain amount Δx (Fig. 6·7). Then the rate of change in the value of this function is

$$\text{Rate of change in } f(x) = \frac{f(x_1 + \Delta x) - f(x_1)}{\Delta x} \tag{3}$$

We shall agree that $+\Delta x$ denotes an increase in the value of x and that $-\Delta x$ denotes a decrease in the value of x.

If we let

$$\Delta y = f(x_1 + \Delta x) - f(x_1)$$

then the rate of change in $f(x)$ with respect to x, or, what amounts to the same thing, the rate of change in y with respect to x is

$$\frac{\Delta y}{\Delta x} = \frac{f(x_1 + \Delta x) - f(x_1)}{\Delta x} \tag{4}$$

By comparing Eq. (4) above with Eq. (1) in Sec. 6·6 we note that the rate of change in the value of a linear function is numerically equal to the slope of the graph of that linear function.

example 6 For the linear function represented in Fig. 6·2, find $f(x_1)$ and $f(x_1 + \Delta x)$ by direct reading of the graph when $x_1 = 3$ and $\Delta x = 6$. Also find the rate of change of this function.

By reading the graph, $f(x_1) = f(3) = -2$ and $f(x_1 + \Delta x) = f(3 + 6) = +2$.

$$\frac{f(x_1 + \Delta x) - f(x_1)}{\Delta x} = \frac{\Delta y}{\Delta x} = \frac{2 - (-2)}{6} = \frac{2}{3}$$

In this example we could, with equal logic, have reasoned that as x decreases by 6 units, then y decreases by 4 units and $\frac{\Delta y}{\Delta x} = \frac{-4}{-6} = \frac{2}{3}$.

However it is usually more convenient to deal consistently with increasing abscissas.

example 7 If a straight line passes through the points $(-5, -16)$ and $(+10, +20)$, how much does y change when x increases by 0.005?

$$\text{Slope} = m = \frac{20 - (-16)}{10 - (-5)} = \frac{20 + 16}{10 + 5} = \frac{36}{15} = \frac{12}{5} = +2.4$$

In other words,

$$\frac{\Delta y}{\Delta x} = +\frac{12}{5} = +2.4$$

In this example Δx is given to be 0.005 and we are required to find Δy. Therefore

$$\frac{\Delta y}{0.005} = 2.4$$

$$\Delta y = 2.4 \times 0.005 = 0.012$$

EXERCISE 6

1. For the linear function displayed in Fig. 6·8 find $f(x_1 + \Delta x)$ by direct reading of the graph. Also calculate the rate of change of $f(x)$ per unit increase of x when (a) $x_1 = 9$, $\Delta x = 6$; (b) $x_1 = 21$, $\Delta x = 12$; (c) $x_1 = 27$, $\Delta x = 15$. (d) How much does y change when x increases by 0.012? (This graph shows the expansion at constant pressure of a gas occupying 91 ml at 0°C and warming to 45°C. Can you attribute any physical significance to the value of the slope?)

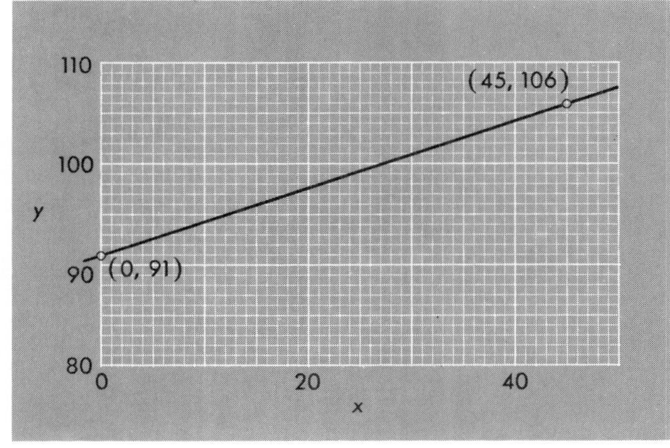

fig. 6·8

2. As in Prob. 1, find the rate of change of the function in Fig. 6·9 when (a) $x_1 = 4$, $\Delta x = 3$; (b) $x_1 = 12$, $\Delta x = 5$; (c) $x_1 = 20$, $\Delta x = 8$. (d) How much does y change when x increases by 0.04? (Figure 6·9 represents the "straight-line" depreciation of a machine over a period of 30 yr.)

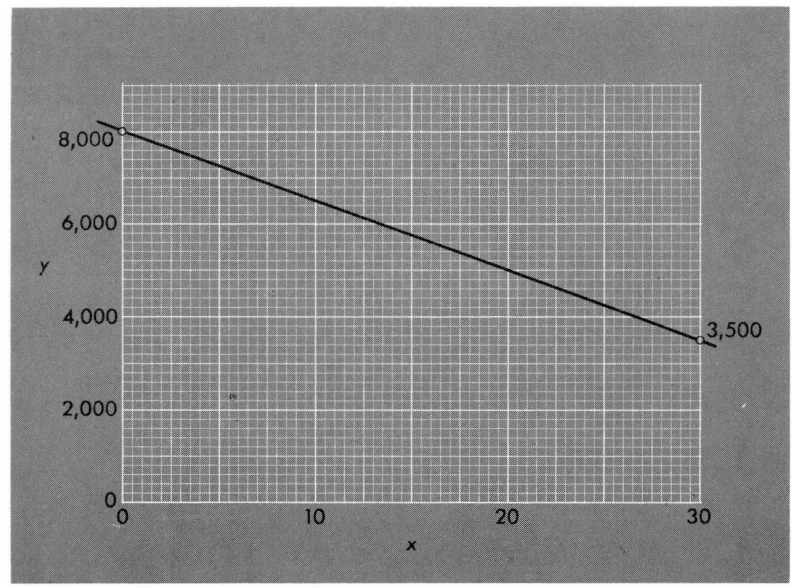

fig. 6·9

6·8 Determination of a straight line

A straight line may be determined (1) if the slope of the line and a point on the line are known or (2) if two points on the line are known.

Slope-point form

According to Sec. 6·6, the slope of the straight line in Fig. 6·10 is

$$m = \frac{y - y_1}{x - x_1} \tag{5}$$

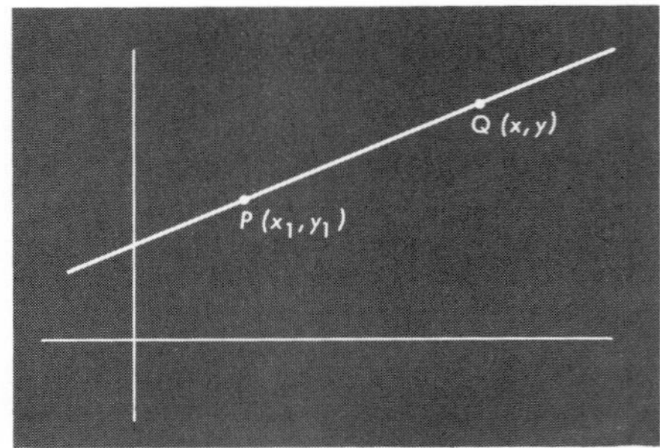

fig. 6·10

where the coordinates (x_1, y_1) of the fixed point P are given and $Q(x, y)$ is any variable point on the line.

Rearranging Eq. (5), we obtain the slope-point form:

$$y - y_1 = m(x - x_1) \tag{6}$$

example 8 Find the equation of the straight line having a slope of ⅔ and passing through point (4,5).

Substituting $y_1 = 5$, $m = \frac{2}{3}$, and $x_1 = 4$ in Eq. (4), we obtain

$$y - 5 = \tfrac{2}{3}(x - 4)$$

whence $$3y - 15 = 2x - 8 \qquad \text{or} \qquad 3y - 2x = 7$$

A familiar example of this relationship is found in the equation $r_1 - r_2 = k(t_1 - t_2)$ which states that the change in electrical resistance of a conductor is proportional to the temperature change.

Slope-intercept form

If we substitute in Eq. (6), above, the coordinates of point P (Fig. 6·11), we obtain

$$y - b = m(x - 0)$$

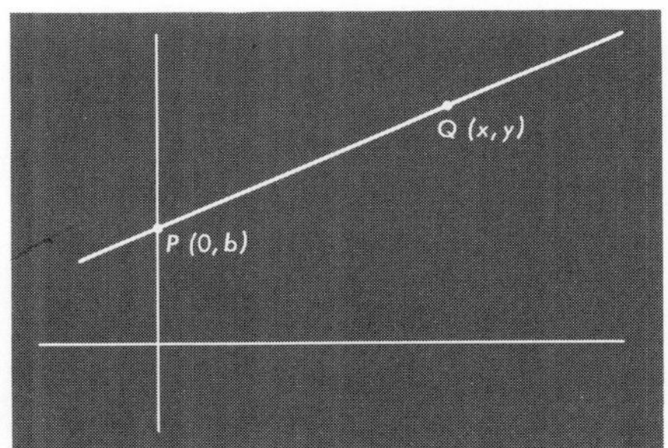

fig. 6·11

or, rearranging, we have the slope-intercept form:

$$y = mx + b \qquad \textbf{(7)}$$

Equation (7) is the most widely used of the various straight-line equations. (For applications see Sec. 6·15.) Moreover, it can be used in most of the situations normally calling for Eqs. (6), (8*b*), and (9).

NOTE: *The ordinate of the point of intersection of a straight line with the* Y *axis is called the* y *intercept. The abscissa of its point of intersection with the* X *axis is called the* x *intercept.*

example 9 Find the slope and y intercept of the line whose equation is

$$3x + 2y = 8$$

Solving the equation for y, we obtain

$$y = -\tfrac{3}{2}x + 4$$

Hence the line has a slope of $-\frac{3}{2}$ and a y intercept of 4.

A common example of the slope-intercept form occurs in the equation $l_1 = kW + l$ which states that in a spring balance the length of the relaxed spring is extended by k length units per W units of weight applied, producing a length l_1 under tension.

If the student has any doubt that the graph of $y = mx + b$ is a straight line, he may be reassured by noting the similarity to a flight of stairs. If we tabulate a series of values as in plotting a graph, we obtain the following table:

Δx		1		1		1		1		1		
x	0		1		2		3		4		5	. . .
y	b		$m + b$		$2m + b$		$3m + b$		$4m + b$		$5m + b$	. . .
Δy		m		m		m		m		m		

The change in x from point to point has been represented by Δx. The change in y from point to point has been represented by Δy.

It will be noted that when x increases uniformly in steps of 1, y also increases uniformly, but in steps of m. The ratio of vertical progress to horizontal progress is, therefore, uniform, and the slope is everywhere equal to m. Referring to Fig. 6·12, we may draw an analogy to a flight of steps, each tread being equal to 1, and each riser equal to m.

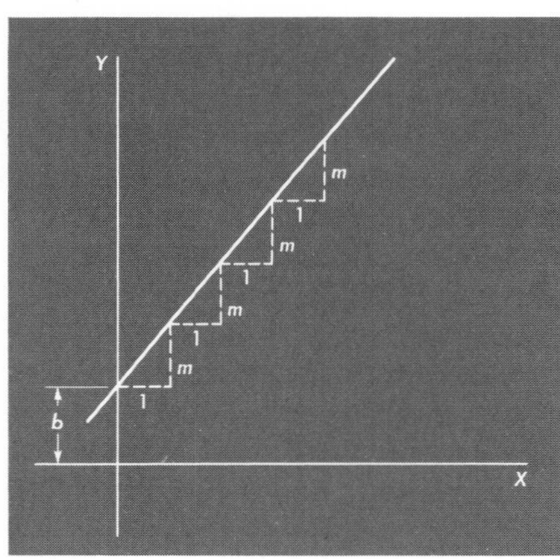

fig. 6·12

Two-point form

If we have given the coordinates (x_2,y_2) and (x_1,y_1) of the fixed points P_2 and P_1, and if $P(x,y)$ is any variable point on the line (Fig. 6·13), we may eliminate m from Eqs. (1) and (6) by substituting $(y_2 - y_1)/(x_2 - x_1)$ for m in the formula

$$y - y_1 = m(x - x_1)$$

obtaining

$$y - y_1 = \frac{y_2 - y_1}{x_2 - x_1}(x - x_1) \qquad \textbf{(8a)}$$

fig. 6·13

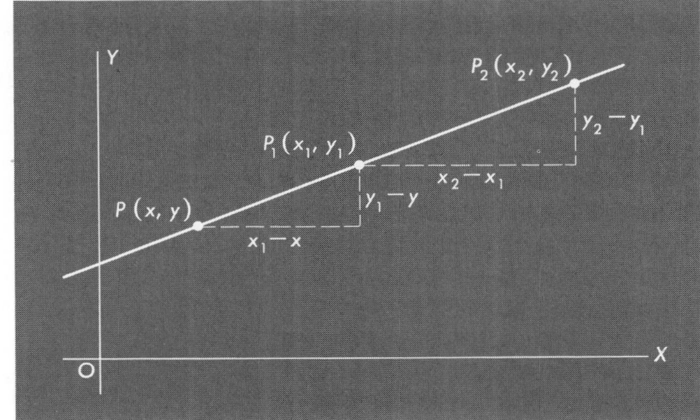

A more easily remembered form is

$$\frac{y - y_1}{x - x_1} = \frac{y_2 - y_1}{x_2 - x_1} \tag{8b}$$

Referring to the similar right triangles in Fig. 6·13, it is evident that

$$\frac{y_1 - y}{x_1 - x} = \frac{y_2 - y_1}{x_2 - x_1}$$

which is equivalent to Eq. (8*b*).

This is called the *two-point form* of a straight-line equation [note the similarity to Eq. (2)].

example 10 Find the equation of the straight line passing through the points (−2,3) and (6,9).

Here we have $x_1 = -2$, $y_1 = 3$, $x_2 = 6$, and $y_2 = 9$. Substituting in Eq. (8*a*),

$$y - 3 = \frac{9 - 3}{6 - (-2)}[x - (-2)]$$

or

$$y - 3 = \frac{6}{8}(x + 2)$$

Multiplying by 4,

$$4y - 12 = 3(x + 2)$$

or

$$4y - 3x = 18$$

which is the desired equation.

An everyday example of the operation of this formula is found with a slight rearrangement by writing

$$\frac{l - l_1}{t - t_1} = \frac{l_2 - l_1}{t_2 - t_1}$$

which states that the linear expansion of a metal rod obeys the law that changes in length are proportional to changes in temperature.

Intercept form

One of the most convenient ways of plotting the graph of a linear equation is to find the intercepts on the X and Y axes and draw a straight line through them.

To derive the intercept form we shall rearrange Eq. (8*a*) in the form

$$\frac{y - y_1}{x - x_1} = \frac{y_2 - y_1}{x_2 - x_1}$$

From Fig. 6·14, $x_1 = 0$, $y_1 = b$, $x_2 = a$, and $y_2 = 0$. Hence we obtain (on substituting)

$$\frac{y - b}{x - 0} = \frac{0 - b}{a - 0}$$

or

$$\frac{y - b}{x} = \frac{-b}{a}$$

or

$$a(y - b) = -bx$$

or

$$bx + ay = ab$$

Dividing through by ab, we have

$$\frac{x}{a} + \frac{y}{b} = 1 \tag{9}$$

This is known as the *intercept form* of the linear equation.

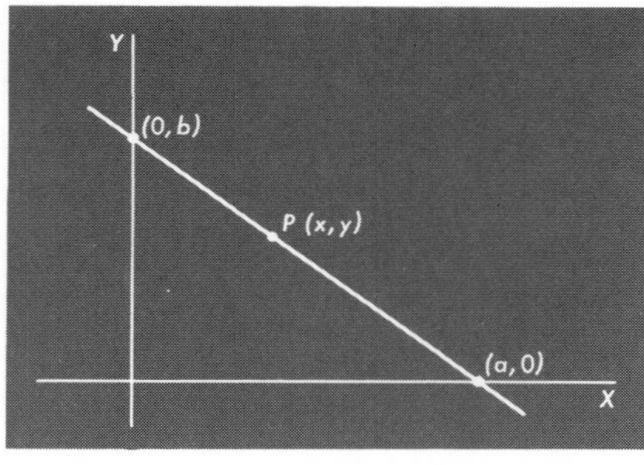

fig. 6·14

example 11 Find the equation of the line having an x intercept of -4 and a y intercept of 10.

Substituting $a = -4$ and $b = 10$ in Eq. (9), we obtain

$$\frac{x}{-4} + \frac{y}{10} = 1$$

Multiplying by -20, we have

$$5x - 2y = -20$$

which is the required equation.

example 12 Find the intercepts of the line $3x - 4y = 12$.

Dividing through by 12, we have

$$\frac{x}{4} - \frac{y}{3} = 1 \qquad \text{or} \qquad \frac{x}{4} + \frac{y}{-3} = 1$$

Hence $a = 4 = x$ intercept, and $b = -3 = y$ intercept.

A more direct method consists of replacing x and y in turn by zero. When $x = 0$, $-4y = 12$ or $y = -3$ (y intercept). When $y = 0$, $3x = 12$ or $x = 4$ (x intercept).

EXERCISE 7

Write the equations for lines passing through the given point P and having the slope indicated (see Fig. 6·15, where $\angle A$ is given in degrees):

1. $P(4,6)$; $m = \frac{1}{2}$
2. $P(-2,3)$; $m = 1$
3. $P(5,-1)$; $m = 2$
4. $P(-3,-2)$; $m = -\frac{2}{3}$
5. $P(3,7)$; $\angle A = 45°$
6. $P(-3,6)$; $\angle A = 30°$
7. $P(2,-5)$; $\angle A = 60°$
8. $P(0,0)$; $\angle A = 135°$
9. $P(2,7)$; horizontal
10. $P(4,-3)$; vertical

(In Probs. 5 through 8, assume equal x and y scale moduli.)

Convert each of the following equations to the slope-intercept form $y = mx + b$, finding the slope and y intercept in each case:

11. $x + y = 8$
12. $2x - y = 6$
13. $x - 3y = 12$
14. $2x + 3y = 6$
15. $4y - x = 10$
16. $3x - 4y - 6 = 0$
17. $7x - 5y + 14 = 0$
18. $\frac{1}{2}x - \frac{1}{3}y = 1$
19. $4y = 6$

Find the equation of the line passing through each of the following given pairs of points, leaving the answer in the form $Ax + By = C$, where A and B are integers:

20. (3,1), (5,3)
21. (3,2), (6,3)
22. (1,−1), (3,3)
23. (2,−4), (−6,2)
24. (0,0), (−4,−6)
25. (3,0), (−5,2)
26. (6,3), (−4,−2)
27. (−2,5), (4,5)

fig. 6·15

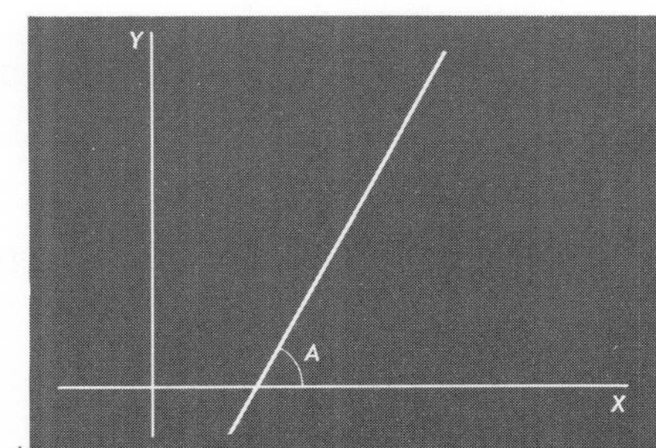

Find the equations of the lines having the following given intercepts:

28. x intercept: 3; y intercept: -6
29. x intercept: -4; y intercept: 2
30. x intercept: 10; y intercept: 4
31. x intercept: -9; y intercept: -6
32. x intercept: 6; y intercept: -10
33. x intercept: -8; y intercept: 6
34. x intercept: 8; y intercept: 14
35. x intercept: -15; y intercept: -10

6·9 Lines parallel to the axes

If a line is parallel to the X axis, its slope m is equal to zero, for, by Eq. (1), $m = (y_2 - y_1)/(x_2 - x_1)$, or $m = 0/(x_2 - x_1) = 0$ (since $y_2 = y_1$). Substituting $m = 0$ in $y = mx + b$, we obtain $y = b$. This is reasonable, for it indicates that everywhere on the line the ordinate is b. Hence the line is parallel to the X axis and b units above it or below it, according to the sign of b.

Since a line parallel to the Y axis is vertical, it has no finite slope, and the form $y = mx + b$ does not apply, for $x_2 = x_1$ and, by Eq. (1), $m = (y_2 - y_1)/(x_2 - x_1)$, or $m = (y_2 - y_1)/0$; since division by zero is not allowed, m is undefined. Moreover, it should be clear that a vertical line a units to the right or left of the Y axis must have the equation $x = a$, where a may be either positive or negative.

It follows that every line comprising the grid of a sheet of graph paper has a unique equation (e.g., each horizontal line and each vertical line in Fig. 6·5 is represented by its own distinct equation).

6·10 Lines passing through the origin

If the line $y = mx + b$ passes through the origin, the y intercept, b, must equal zero, and the equation cannot have a constant term.

example 13 Show that the line passing through the points (12,8) and (9,6) also passes through the origin.

Substituting $x_1 = 9$, $y_1 = 6$, $x_2 = 12$, and $y_2 = 8$ in Eq. (8*a*), we obtain

$$y - 6 = \frac{8 - 6}{12 - 9}(x - 9)$$

$$y - 6 = \tfrac{2}{3}(x - 9)$$

$$3(y - 6) = 2(x - 9)$$

$$3y - 18 = 2x - 18$$

$$3y - 2x = 0$$

Since the values $x = 0$, $y = 0$ satisfy the equation (that is, $b = 0$), the line must pass through the origin.

6·11 Parallel lines

If two lines are parallel, their slopes are equal. The comparison is most conveniently made by reducing both equations to the slope-intercept form, $y = mx + b$ [Eq. (7)].

6·12 Perpendicular lines

In Fig. 6·16 let AC and CD be two perpendicular lines, where $C(b,c)$ is their common point and $A(a,0)$ and $D(d,0)$ are their x intercepts. Let $B(b,0)$ be the foot of the perpendicular CB drawn from C to AD.

Since the altitude to the hypotenuse of a right triangle is a mean proportional between the segments of the hypotenuse, we may write

$$\overline{CB^2} = \overline{AB} \cdot \overline{BD}$$

Expressed in terms of the coordinates, this relationship becomes

$$c^2 = (b - a)(d - b) \tag{10}$$

The slope m_1 of AC is $(c - 0)/(b - a)$ or

$$m_1 = \frac{c}{b - a}$$

The slope m_2 of CD is $(c - 0)/(b - d)$ or

$$m_2 = \frac{c}{b - d}$$

Multiplying the values of the two slopes by each other, we obtain

$$m_1 m_2 = \frac{c^2}{(b - a)(b - d)} = -1$$

from Eq. (10) or

$$m_1 = -\frac{1}{m_2} \tag{11}$$

Hence the slopes of perpendicular lines are negative reciprocals (see also Sec. 21·6).

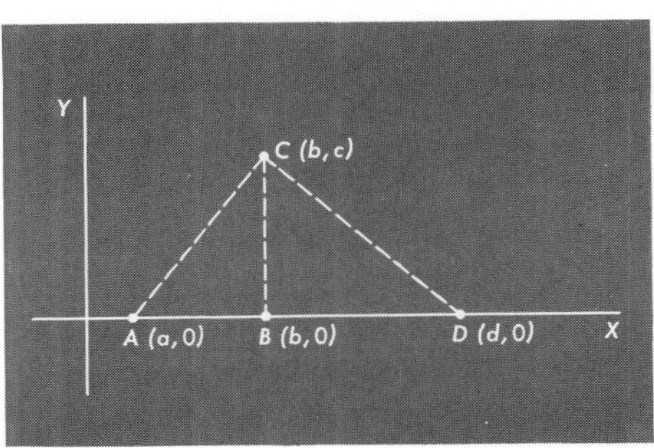

fig. 6·16

6·13 Distance between two points

Given the points $P_1(x_1, y_1)$ and $P_2(x_2, y_2)$ in Fig. 6·17, locate the point $Q(x_1, y_2)$ and draw lines P_1P_2, P_1Q, and P_2Q. Then in right triangle P_1P_2Q,

$$\overline{P_1P_2}^2 = \overline{P_1Q}^2 + \overline{P_2Q}^2$$

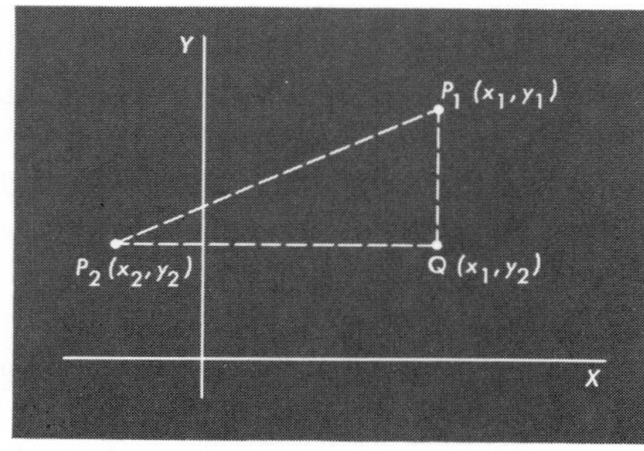

fig. 6·17

In terms of the coordinates this becomes

$$\overline{P_1P_2}^2 = (y_1 - y_2)^2 + (x_1 - x_2)^2$$

The distance between P_1 and P_2 is then

$$P_1P_2 = \sqrt{(y_1 - y_2)^2 + (x_1 - x_2)^2} \qquad \textbf{(12)}$$

This rule is valid regardless of the quadrants in which P_1 and P_2 are located, provided only that due regard is paid to signs when evaluating $y_1 - y_2$ and $x_1 - x_2$.

In short, we find the absolute values of P_1Q and P_2Q and determine the hypotenuse P_2P_1 of the triangle in the usual way.

Obviously, in cases where $y_1 = y_2$ or $x_1 = x_2$, we have a horizontal line or a vertical line, respectively, and the answer follows by inspection.

EXERCISE 8

1. Given the equation $3x - 4y = 24$, corresponding to the general equation $Ax + By = C$, modify only one quantity at a time (A, B, or C) to make the line (a) pass through the origin; (b) vertical; (c) horizontal; (d) parallel to $6x - y = 11$; and (e) perpendicular to $8x - 12y = 13$.
2. Given the equation $5x + 8y = 20$, proceed as in Prob. 1 to make the line (a) pass through the origin; (b) vertical; (c) horizontal; (d) parallel to $15x - 10y = 23$; and (e) perpendicular to $4x - 15y = 17$.

Find the distance between P_1 and P_2 in Probs. 3–10:

3. $P_1(2,5)$; $P_2(2,11)$
4. $P_1(3,-4)$; $P_2(3,3)$
5. $P_1(-4,7)$; $P_2(5,7)$
6. $P_1(6,1)$; $P_2(0,9)$
7. $P_1(1,5)$; $P_2(4,9)$
8. $P_1(-2,6)$; $P_2(3,9)$
9. $P_1(8,-4)$; $P_2(-1,-6)$
10. $P_1(7,-8)$; $P_2(3,-5)$

11. Referring to Eq. (2) and Fig. 6·6, if point Q were located midway between points P and R, prove that the midpoint of line segment PR is located at $x_2 = (x_1 + x_3)/2$, $y_2 = (y_1 + y_3)/2$.
12. Without plotting, determine what kind of figure is enclosed by the lines $x + y = -3$, $x - y = 3$, and $y = 3$.
13. What points on the line $2x + 3y = 6$ are equidistant from the axes?
14. Write the equation for the line passing through the origin and perpendicular to the line $y = \frac{3}{2}x - 4$.
15. Write the equation for the line parallel to the line $2x + 3y = 9$ and having its x intercept $= 7$.
16. Find the distance between the lines $y = 2x + 3$ and $y = 2x + 8$.
17. Given points $A(2,7)$ and $B(14,3)$, what is the equation for the perpendicular bisector of the line segment AB?
18. Find the distance from the point (6,7) to the line $3x + 4y = 30$.

6·14 Area of a triangle

The area of the triangle PQR (Fig. 6·18) is evidently equal to the area of triangle PQM plus the area of the trapezoid $MQRN$ minus the area of the triangle PRN.

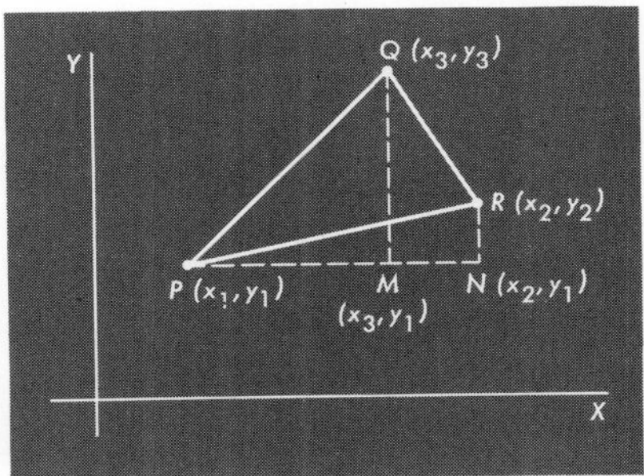

fig. 6·18

In terms of the coordinates we have:

$$\text{Area of } PQM = \tfrac{1}{2}(x_3 - x_1)(y_3 - y_1)$$
$$\text{Area of } MQRN = \tfrac{1}{2}(x_2 - x_3)[(y_2 - y_1) + (y_3 - y_1)]$$
$$\text{Area of } PRN = \tfrac{1}{2}(x_2 - x_1)(y_2 - y_1)$$

(The order of points must be counterclockwise.) Therefore

$$\begin{aligned}
\text{Area of } PRQ &= PQM + MQRN - PRN \\
&= \tfrac{1}{2}(x_3 - x_1)(y_3 - y_1) + \tfrac{1}{2}(x_2 - x_3)[(y_2 - y_1) + (y_3 - y_1)] \\
&\qquad - \tfrac{1}{2}(x_2 - x_1)(y_2 - y_1) \\
&= \tfrac{1}{2}(x_3y_3 - x_1y_3 - x_3y_1 + x_1y_1 + x_2y_2 - x_3y_2 - 2x_2y_1 \\
&\qquad + 2x_3y_1 + x_2y_3 - x_3y_3 - x_2y_2 + x_1y_2 + x_2y_1 - x_1y_1) \\
&= \tfrac{1}{2}(-x_1y_3 - x_3y_2 - x_2y_1 + x_3y_1 + x_2y_3 + x_1y_2) \\
&= \tfrac{1}{2}[x_1(y_2 - y_3) + x_2(y_3 - y_1) + x_3(y_1 - y_2)] \qquad \textbf{(13)}
\end{aligned}$$

If any of the vertices lie outside the first quadrant, proper attention must be paid to signs. (For an application of this principle to surveying see Sec. 19·7.)

example 14 Find the area of the triangle in Fig. 6·19.

From the figure we write

$$x_1 = -3 \qquad y_1 = -5 \qquad x_2 = 17 \qquad y_2 = 2 \qquad x_3 = 3 \qquad y_3 = 8$$

Substituting in Eq. (13),

$$\begin{aligned}\text{Area of } \Delta PQR &= \tfrac{1}{2}\{(-3)(2-8) + 17[8-(-5)] + 3(-5-2)\}\\ &= \tfrac{1}{2}(18 + 221 - 21)\\ &= 109\end{aligned}$$

A simple method of computing the area of the triangle in Example 14 without memorizing a formula consists in enclosing the triangle in a rectangle and subtracting from the area of the rectangle the combined area of the three smaller right triangles that are formed. From Fig. 6·19, the dimensions may be shown as in Fig. 6·20.

$$\begin{aligned}\text{Area of triangle I} &= \text{area of rectangle} - (\text{area of triangles II + III + IV})\\ &= (13)(20) - \tfrac{1}{2}[(6)(13) + (14)(6) + (7)(20)]\\ &= 260 - \tfrac{1}{2}(302)\\ &= 109\end{aligned}$$

The area of a polygon of n sides may be found in like manner by first dividing by diagonals into $n - 2$ triangles.

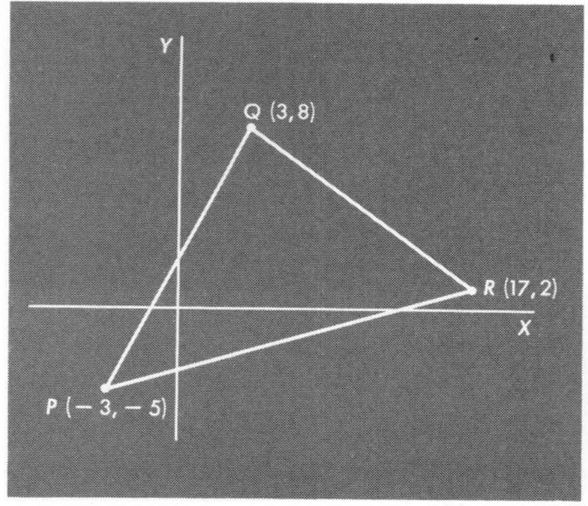

fig. 6·19

fig. 6·20

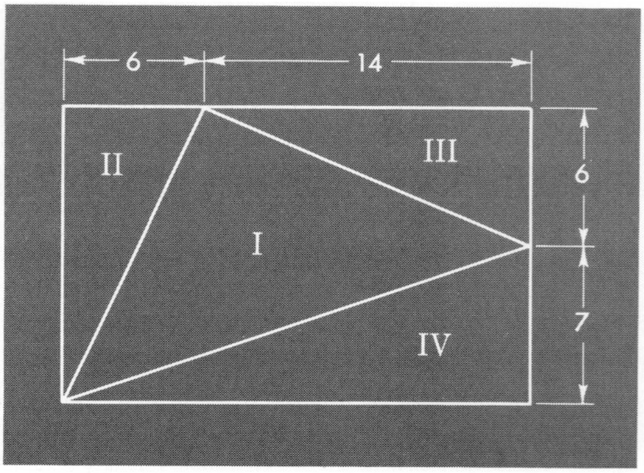

EXERCISE 9

Find the area of the triangles represented by the following vertices:

1. (0,0), (0,8), (12,0)
2. $(-2,-5)$, $(-4,4)$, (7,1)
3. $(-5,-3)$, (2,3), $(9,-7)$
4. $(-5,6)$, (3,8), $(4,-4)$
5. $(-5,0)$, (0,7), $(8,-4)$
6. (1,4), (10,5), $(3,-4)$
7. Prove that the triangle in Prob. 5 is isosceles.

Find the areas of the polygons formed by joining the following points in the order given:

8. $(-2,2)$, (2,6), (8,3), $(5,-3)$
9. $(0,-4)$, (3,4), (12,0), $(10,-3)$
10. $(-3,-1)$, (0,8), (12,4), $(9,-5)$
11. $(-2,-4)$, $(-3,3)$, (4,6), (7,2), $(4,-3)$
12. Prove that the figure in Prob. 10 is a rectangle.

6·15 Application to "word" problems

There are some 20 to 25 problems in Exercise 6, Chap. 5, which lend themselves well to graphical treatment, making use of the slope and intercept concepts of this chapter.

Perhaps the reader's first reaction is that we have here a means of scaling an answer from a graph drawn accurately to scale. Although this is true, the objective is the setting up of equations, based on dimensions and relations appearing in a rough freehand sketch. The problems illustrated below have been selected as typical examples.

Problem 37, Exercise 6 (Fig. 6·21). Draw a line OA with a slope of $^{11}\!/_{9}$ sec per hr. Draw from the 24-hr point line BC with a slope of $-^{28}\!/_{13}$ sec per hr. Drop the perpendicular DE dividing the 24 hr into $24 - h$ vertical hours and h horizontal hours.

Algebraically, since $\Delta y = m\,\Delta x$, the gain in $24 - h$ hr in the vertical position is $DE = {}^{11}\!/_{9}(24 - h)$. The loss in h hr in a horizontal position is $DE = -^{28}\!/_{13}h$. Since the net gain or loss is zero, we have ${}^{11}\!/_{9}(24 - h) + (-^{28}\!/_{13}h) = 0$. ANS.: $h = 8.7$ hr

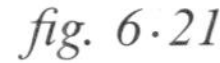

fig. 6·21

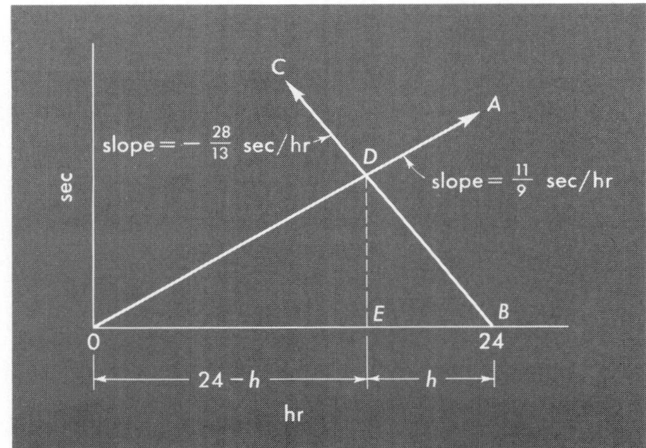

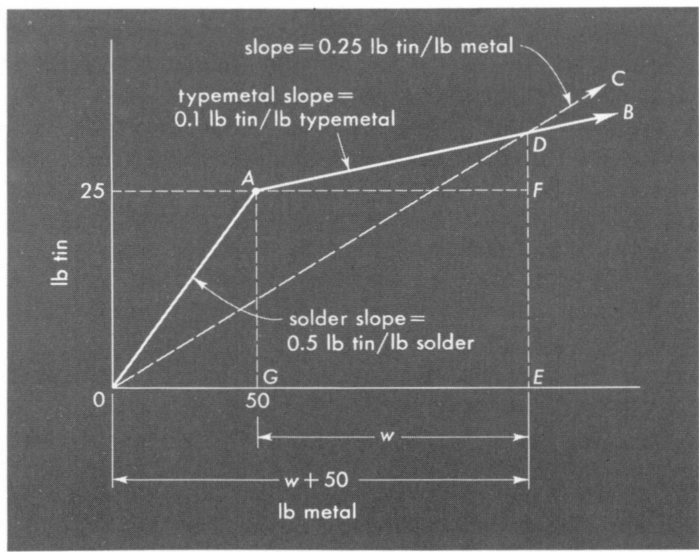

fig. 6·22

Problem 42, Exercise 6 (Fig. 6·22). Locate point A at (50,25). Draw line OA. From A draw line AB with a slope of 0.1 lb tin per lb metal. Draw line OC with a slope of 0.25 lb tin per lb metal. From the intersection point D of lines OB and OC drop the perpendicular DE. Since D is on the 25 per cent line, it must represent an alloy containing 25 per cent tin. Drop the perpendicular AG. This length represents 25 lb, which is the weight of tin in 50 lb of solder. DF is the weight of tin in w lb of type metal, or $DF = 0.1w$. (Since $\Delta y = m\,\Delta x$) Total tin $= AG + DF = 25 + 0.1w$. Total tin also $= DE = 0.25(w + 50)$. Therefore $25 + 0.1w = 0.25(w + 50)$. ANS.: $w = 83\frac{1}{3}$ lb

Problem 43, Exercise 6 (Fig. 6·23). From point $A = 75$ draw line AB with a slope of $4\frac{1}{4}$ cents per kilowatthour. From the slope-intercept equation (7) the equation for this line must be $c = 4\frac{1}{4}k + 75$. Draw line OC with a slope of $5\frac{1}{2}$ cents per kilowatthour. The equation for this line is evidently $c = 5\frac{1}{2}k$. At the intersection point D we have $c = 4\frac{1}{4}k + 75 = 5\frac{1}{2}k$. ANS.: $k = 60$ kwhr

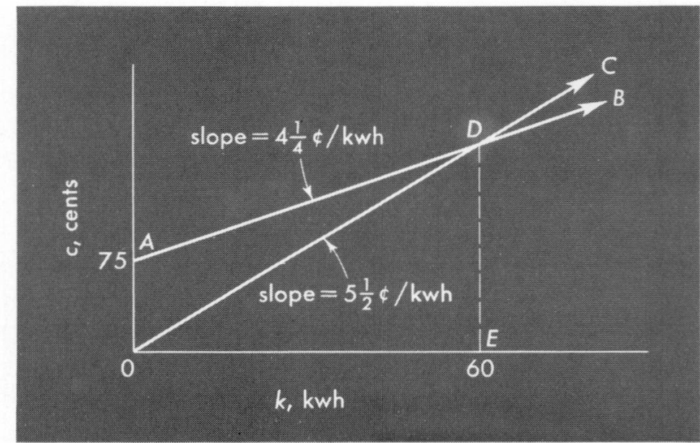

fig. 6·23

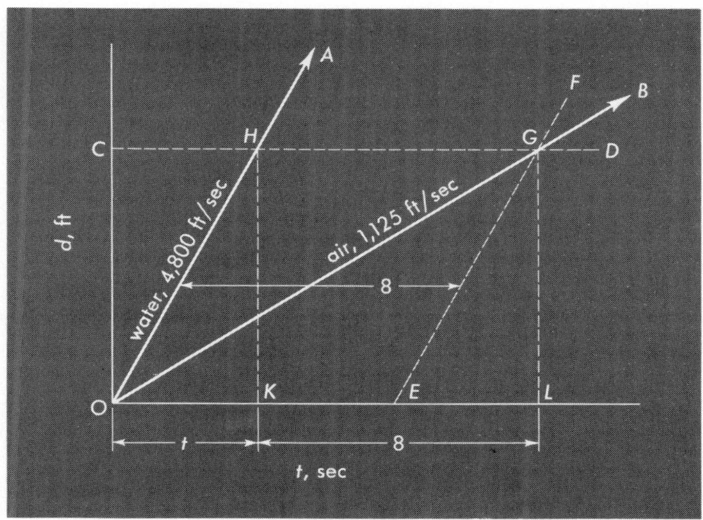

fig. 6·24

Problem 57, Exercise 6 (Fig. 6·24). Draw line OA with a slope of 4,800 fps, representing the progress of sound through water. Similarly draw OB with a slope of 1,125 fps for passage through the air. Where the horizontal distance between OA and $OB = 8$, draw the horizontal line CD. (This is more conveniently done by locating point E at $t = 8$, and drawing EF parallel to OA cutting OB at G.) Drop perpendiculars HK and GL. Then the time for passage through the air is $d/1{,}125$ (since $\Delta x = \Delta y/m$). Similarly the time through water is $d/4{,}800$. But $d/1{,}125 - d/4{,}800 = 8$. ANS.: $d = 11{,}750$ ft

Problem 61, Exercise 6 (Fig. 6·25). Draw line OA with slope $= 2$. Locate point C at (18,20). From C draw CB with slope $= \frac{1}{2}$ intersecting OA at D. Draw horizontal line DE from D and vertical line DF from

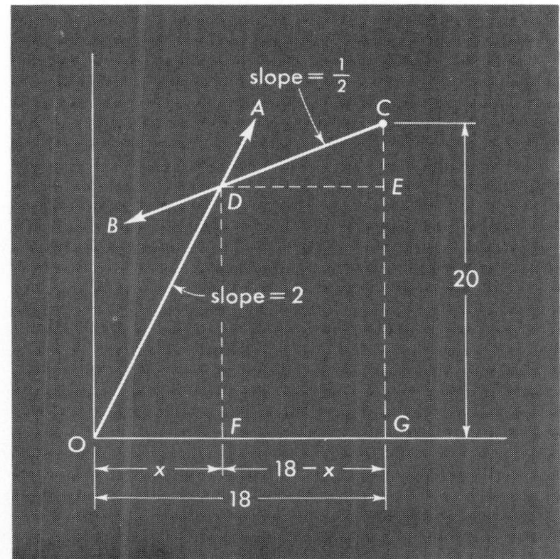

fig. 6·25

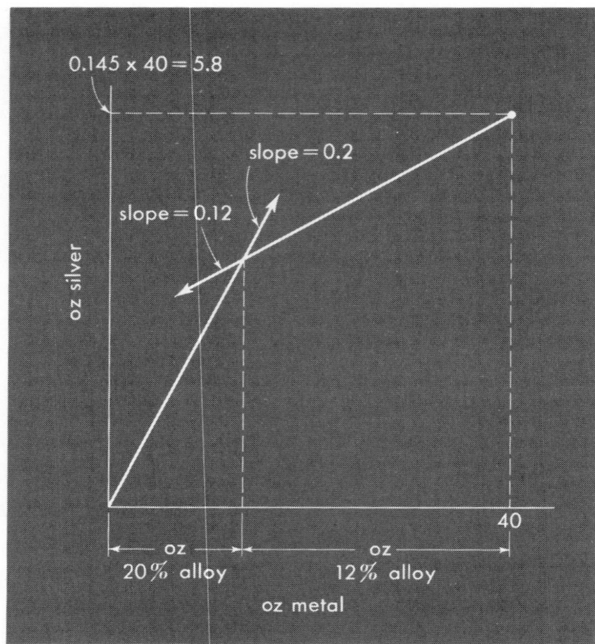

fig. 6·26

D. Then $DF = 2x$, $(\Delta y = m\,\Delta x)$ and $CE = \frac{1}{2}(18 - x)$. But $DF + CE = CG$ or $2x + \frac{1}{2}(18 - x) = 20$, from which $x = 7\frac{1}{3}$ ft, and the rest of the solution follows readily. (Note the similar Fig. 6·26 used in solving Prob. 26.)

6·16 Evaluation of Constants in the Equation $y = mx + b$

If a straight line has already been drawn such as the line segment AB in Fig. 6·27, we may determine the equation by either inspection or algebraic means. By inspection we would select two arbitrary points on the line, such as $C(4,2)$ and $D(16,-1)$. It can be seen that

$$\frac{\Delta y}{\Delta x} = \frac{-1 - 2}{16 - 4} = -\frac{1}{4} = m.$$

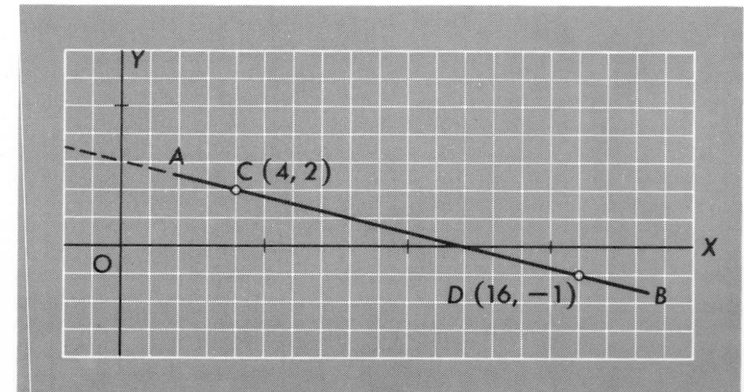

fig. 6·27

If the line is extended to cut the y axis, we read the y intercept $= 3$. Therefore the equation is $y = -\frac{1}{4}x + 3$. (Does the x intercept confirm this equation?)

If the information is presented as a graph in which the y axis in not shown, or if the data appear in a table, we can resort to any one of at least three algebraic methods.

1. Determine the slope (a) by inspection as above if a graph, (b) by the method of the constant ratio $\Delta y/\Delta x$ if a table (Sec. 2·2). Substitute the value of the slope just found and the coordinates of a given point into the equation $y = mx + b$. If we choose point $C(4,2)$ we obtain $2 = -\frac{1}{4}(4) + b$, or $b = 3$. Hence the equation is $y = -\frac{1}{4}x + 3$.
2. Using the two-point formula (8*a*) and substituting the coordinates of point C $(x_1 = 4, y_1 = 2)$ and point D $(x_2 = 16, y_2 = -1)$, we have

$$y - 2 = \frac{-1 - 2}{16 - 4}(x - 4)$$

$$y - 2 = -\tfrac{1}{4}(x - 4) \qquad \text{or} \qquad y = -\tfrac{1}{4}x + 3$$

3. Solve a pair of simultaneous equations as described in Chap. 7. If, as we have seen, a straight line can be represented by the equation $y = mx + b$, we can insert the coordinates of any two points on the line and solve for the constants m and b.

Thus, from point C, $y_1 = mx_1 + b$ or $\quad 2 = m(4) + b$

From point D, $y_2 = mx_2 + b$ or $\quad -1 = m(16) + b$

Subtracting $\quad 3 = -12m \quad$ or $m = -\frac{1}{4}$

By substitution we obtain $b = 3$.

EXERCISE 10

Determine the equation for each line in Fig. 6·28 in the form $y = mx + b$. Where possible confirm your answer by determining the x intercept by inspection.

1. Line A 2. Line B 3. Line C 4. Line D
5. Line E 6. Line F 7. Line G

6·17 Linear empirical equations

The underlying relationship between the variables in a set of experimental data is often more clearly revealed if expressed in the form of an equation. Because of the limitations of measured data such an equation is called empirical. An *empirical formula* is one whose reliability is based upon a limited number of observations and is not necessarily supported by any established theory or law. It is based upon immediate experience rather than logical or mathematical conclusions. The term

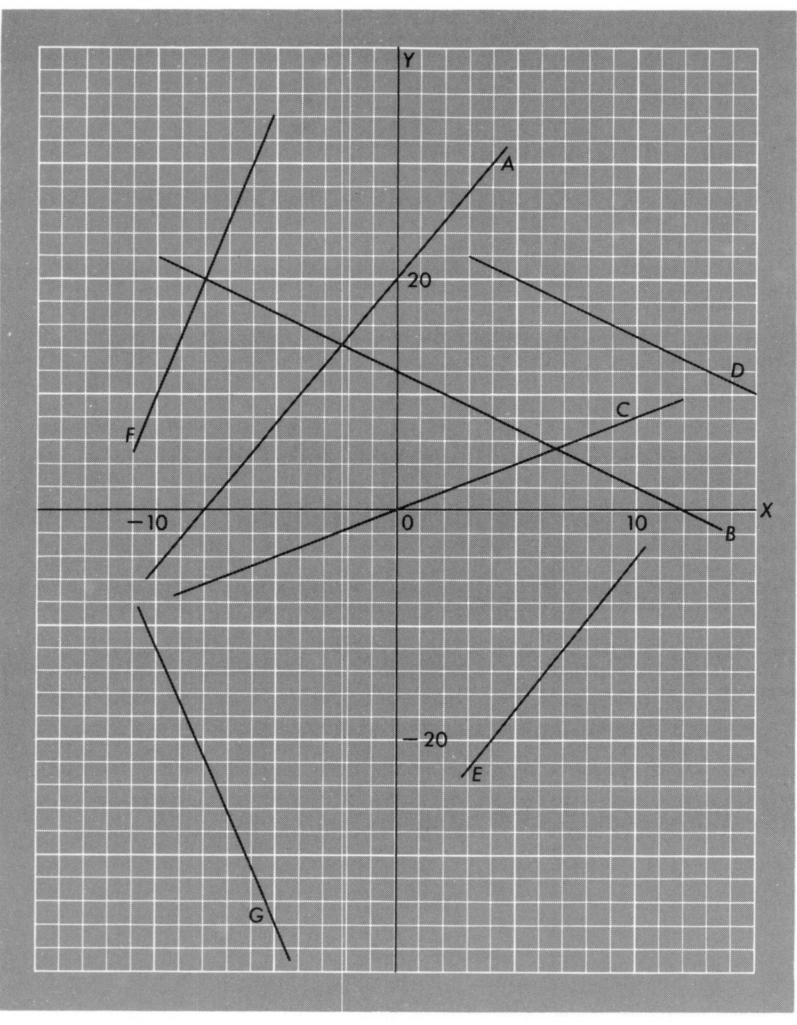

fig. 6·28

is not applied in a derogatory sense since many currently accepted scientific laws have been the outgrowth of empirical equations.

It is common observation that experimentally obtained data rarely fall exactly on a straight line when plotted, even though the general relationship appears to be linear. In such cases the constants of the most suitable linear equation may be derived by a variety of methods. One method consists of simply drawing a straight line through two representative points visually selected. This is done when the data are so rough that extreme refinements would be a waste of time and might even be misleading. The method of least squares is indicated when the data are sufficiently refined to warrant expenditure of considerable time. The method of averages represents a fair compromise between these two extremes. In this chapter we shall limit our discussion of derivation of constants to the method of averages.

example 15 The following data were obtained on the amount of fuel oil (G gal per 24 hr) required to heat a house at various outdoor temperatures ($T°$ = 24 hr average). In order to avoid complicating factors, only clear, relatively calm days were chosen.

ΔT	T	G	ΔG	$\Delta G/\Delta T$
	9	13.0		
9			−2.0	−0.22
	18	11.0		
7			−1.8	−0.26
	25	9.2		
10			−2.2	−0.22
	35	7.0		
11			−2.5	−0.23
	46	4.5		
13			−2.8	−0.22
	59	1.7		

To satisfy ourselves as to the degree of linearity we may plot these data or determine the constancy of the ratio $\Delta G/\Delta T$. These ratios have been tabulated above and indicate a fairly close, but not exact, correspondence to linearity.

In view of the approximate nature of the relationship we shall use the *method of averages.* This method requires that the data be divided into two groups as nearly equal as possible and the values averaged. Hence we obtain

$$T_1 = \text{average of first three } T\text{'s} = \frac{9 + 18 + 25}{3} = 17.3$$

$$T_2 = \text{average of last three } T\text{'s} = \frac{35 + 46 + 59}{3} = 46.7$$

$$G_1 = \text{average of first three } G\text{'s} = \frac{13.0 + 11.0 + 9.2}{3} = 11.1$$

$$G_2 = \text{average of last three } G\text{'s} = \frac{7.0 + 4.5 + 1.7}{3} = 4.4$$

Substituting these values in the equation $G = mT + b$, we obtain

$$11.1 = m(17.3) + b$$
$$4.4 = m(46.7) + b$$

Completing the solution as in Sec. 6·16, we have

$$m = -0.228 \qquad \text{and} \qquad b = 15.0$$

or

$$G = -0.228T + 15.0$$

According to our equation, when the outdoor temperature is 0°F the fuel consumption is 15.0 gal per 24 hr and decreases by 0.228 gal for each degree rise in temperature.

The same result might have been obtained without the operation of division by writing an equation based on the sum of the first three pairs of values and an equation based on the sum of the second three pairs of values. The resulting equations are:

$$33.2 = m(52) + 3b$$
$$13.2 = m(140) + 3b$$

Completing the solution as above, we have

$$m = -0.227 \qquad \text{and} \qquad b = 15.0$$

It will be noted in the above examples that we have solved for the dependent variable in terms of the independent variable. Although this is the usual practice, it is occasionally preferable to solve for the independent variable. Problem 8 in the following exercise illustrates this point. In this case the initial reading of the instrument is in terms of the dependent variable (temperature). Then we proceed to determine the corresponding independent variable (concentration of alcohol).

Other examples of this reversal of common procedure are conversion of voltage reading to temperature when checking a thermocouple; conversion of a manometer reading of pressure difference to rate of fluid flow; computation of wind speed from rpm of an anemometer; etc. (see Sec. 6·2).

EXERCISE 11

1. Show, without plotting, that the points in the following table fall exactly in a straight line.

x	20	28	34	44	48
y	50	38	29	14	8

(a) Derive the equation for y in terms of x.
(b) Find y when $x = 100$.
(c) Find x when $y = -13$.
(d) At what value is $x = y$?
(e) How could your answer in d be obtained graphically?

2. Show, without plotting, that the following points fall exactly in a straight line.

x	-10	15	65	165	240
y	-5	-3	1	9	15

(a) Derive the equation for y in terms of x.
(b) Find the x intercept.
(c) Find y when $x = 40$.

3. Calculate, by the method of averages, the empirical linear equation best fitting the following data:

x	8	18	29	37	48	51	62	68
y	18	25	32	36	44	45	52	56

When $x = 55$ what is the probable value of y?

4. Find the empirical equation, as in Prob. 3, for the following data:

x	−11	1	9	12	19	25	34	45
y	−3	5	10	12	17	22	28	35

Derive the empirical linear equations best representing the data in the following tables. Indicate whether the linear relationship is exact or approximate. If approximate, use the method of averages.

5. The following readings were taken in calibrating a spring where W is the load in pounds and d is the extension in inches. Derive an equation expressing W as a function of d.

W	3.0	5.0	7.0	8.5	11.0	12.0
d	0.20	0.45	0.80	1.0	1.3	1.5

6. The barometer reading in inches of mercury (P) varies with the altitude above sea level in feet (h) as follows:

h	200	500	1,200	1,800	2,500	3,200
P	29.72	29.36	28.58	27.93	27.20	26.48

What linear equation best describes h as a function of P within the range of the data? What is the sea-level pressure?

7. The following prices were quoted for printing a quantity of booklets where N is the number of booklets and C is the cost (dollars) of the lot.

N	100	250	500	800	1,200
C	30	45	70	100	140

Derive a formula for C in terms of N. What is the significance of the constants?

8. The boiling point (t°C) of dilute alcohol solutions is related to the weight per cent concentration of alcohol (p) as shown in the following table:

p	0	2	4	7	10
t	100	97.2	95.2	92.5	90.3

What formula will indicate approximately the alcoholic content when the boiling point is known? It is required that the values $p = 0$, $t = 100$ satisfy the equation. (Base your equation on two points, the first being $p = 0$, $t = 100$, the other point being the average of the other four.)

9. The boiling point of water (t°C) is related to the atmospheric pressure (P mm) as follows:

P	777	766	760	750	740.4	731.4	723.3
t	100.62	100.22	100.00	99.63	99.27	98.93	98.62

It is required that the equation shall be satisfied by the values $P = 760$, $t = 100$ and that it shall represent the best fit for the remaining data.

Derive an equation for P in terms of t.

Derive an equation for t in terms of P.

10. The speed of revolution of an anemometer (R rpm) was checked against the wind speed (V mph) to yield the following calibration data:

V	5.0	11.0	17.0	20.0	25.0	30.0	33.0	37.0
R	50	120	190	230	300	360	410	470

Derive a linear equation for V in terms of R. What is the significance of the constants?

11. The resistance R_t of a nickel wire at various centigrade temperatures (t) is shown in the following table:

t	10	25	45	70
R_t	50.4	55.2	61.6	69.6

Derive an equation of the form $R_t = R_{20}[1 + a(t - 20)]$, where R_{20} is the resistance at 20°C.

What is the nature of a?

12. The velocity of sound in air (meters per second) at any centigrade temperature (t) is given by the formula

$$V = 331.7\sqrt{1 + \frac{t}{273}}$$

Evaluate V at $t = -30, -20, -10, 0, 10, 20, 30, 40$ and derive a linear formula for V to best fit these points.

6·18 Area under a straight-line graph

The phrase "area under a graph" refers to the area between the graph and the x axis (see Figs. 6·29 and 6·30).

The region C in Fig. 6·29 is the area under the graph between $x = +15$ and $x = +35$. The region D in Fig. 6·30 is the area "under" the graph between $x = +2.5$ and $x = +10$. The region E in Fig. 6·31 is the area "under" the graph between $x = +5$ and $x = +20$.

In the case of a straight line (and in this case only), the area under the graph is either a triangle, a trapezoid, or a rectangle.

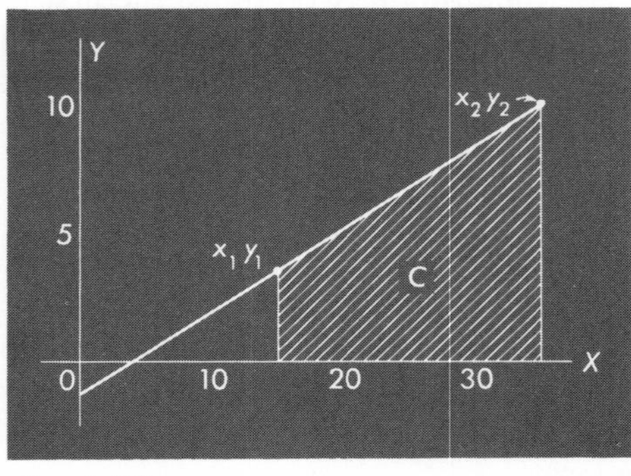

fig. 6·29

fig. 6·30

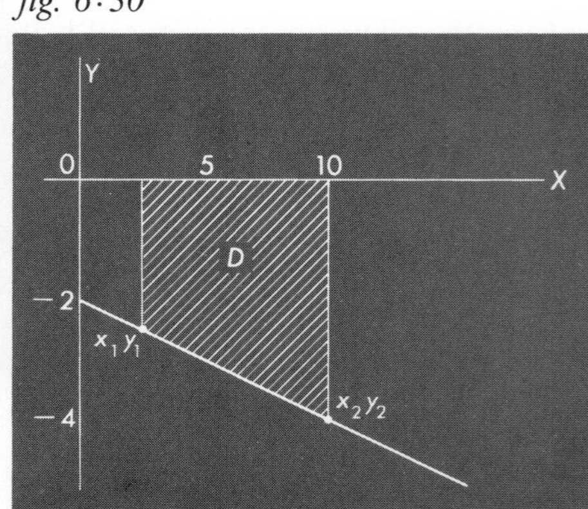

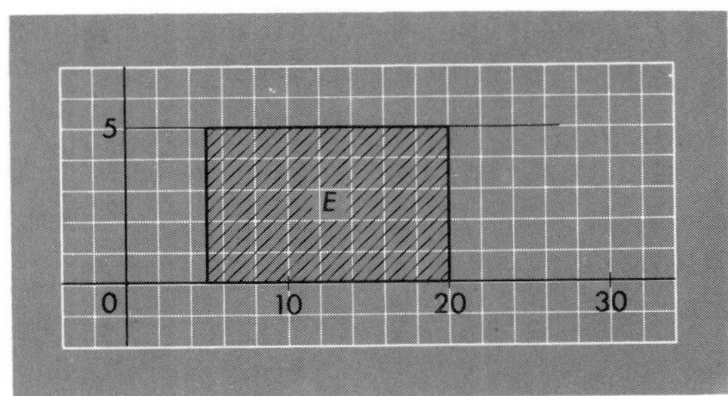

fig. 6·31

In Fig. 6·29

$$A_C = \frac{y_2 + y_1}{2}(x_2 - x_1) \tag{14}$$

In Fig. 6·30 the area under the graph is also

$$A_D = \frac{y_2 + y_1}{2}(x_2 - x_1) \tag{15}$$

(Geometric Fact No. 57, page 45.)

By reading the graph,

$$A_C = \frac{10.0 + 3.5}{2}(35 - 15) = 135.0$$

It is important to observe that we use the scale of the graph in calculating the area:

$$A_D = \frac{-4 + (-2.5)}{2}(10.0 - 2.5) = -24.375$$

In this case the signs of the ordinates lead to a negative area. In the case of a practical problem the negative sign attached to the area may or may not be significant. We shall retain such negative signs, at least for the present.

The quantity $(y_2 + y_1)/2$ is the arithmetic average of y_1 and y_2. The symbol $\bar{y}$ is adopted to mean "average y." It is read "bar y" or "average y" or "average ordinate." In general

$$\bar{y} = \frac{y_2 + y_1}{2} \tag{16}$$

and

$$A = \bar{y}(x_2 - x_1) \tag{17}$$

where A = area under graph between ordinates erected at x_2 and x_1
$\bar{y}$ = average ordinate between x_2 and x_1

If we define the quantity $x_2 - x_1$ as the *base* of the area, we can define average ordinate as "that ordinate which, multiplied by the base, equals the area under the graph."

Dimensionally, the area under the graph is the product of the dimension of the average ordinate and the dimension of the abscissa.

If the dimension of the average ordinate is *force* and the dimension of the abscissa is *distance*, then the dimension of the area under the graph is

$$\text{Force} \times \text{distance} = \text{work}$$

provided the force is in the direction of motion.

If the dimension of the average ordinate is *speed* and the dimension of the abscissa is *time*, then the dimension of the area under the graph is

$$\text{Speed} \times \text{time} = \text{distance}$$

If the dimension of the average ordinate is *area* and the dimension of the abscissa is *length*, then the dimension of the area under the graph is

$$\text{Area} \times \text{length} = \text{volume}$$

For example, let us consider a coiled spring elongated by a variable force F.

Let the elongation caused by the force be e. We shall let F be measured in pounds and e in inches. A graph of the elongation related to F is shown in Fig. 6·32. Actually F is the independent variable and e is the

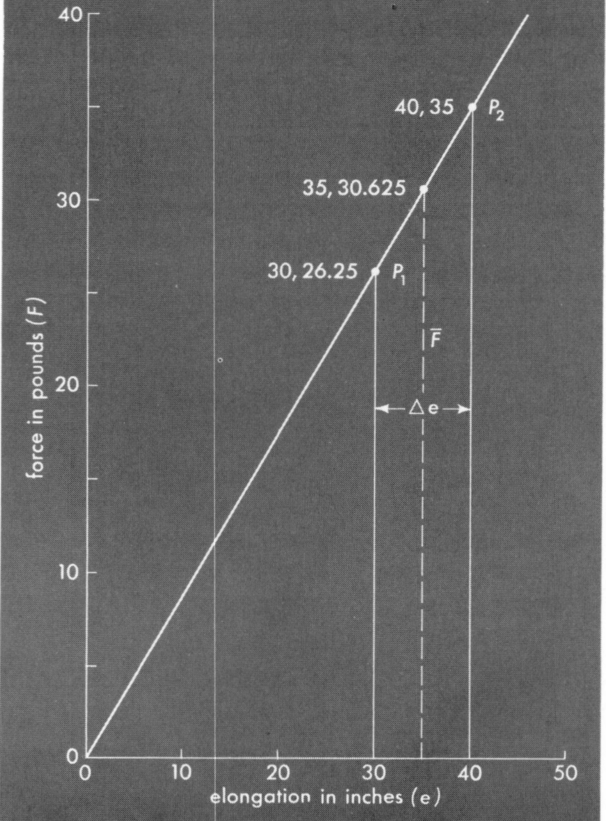

fig. 6·32

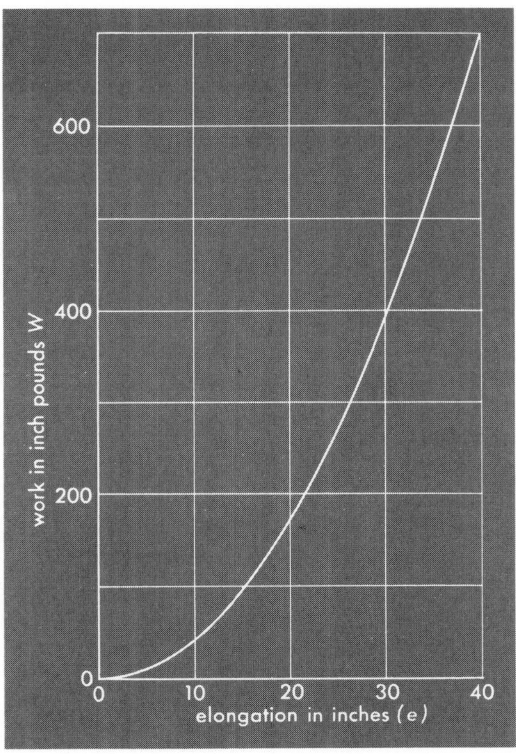

fig. 6·33

dependent variable. Nevertheless, it will be more convenient to plot F vertically and e horizontally.

The slope of this line is

$$m = \frac{35 - 0}{40 - 0} = 0.875 \text{ lb/in.}$$

It follows that the equation for this line is $F = 0.875e$ (Sec. 6·10).

example 16 Find the work done in elongating the spring from 30 to 40 in. (see Fig. 6·32).

The force exerted for a 30-in. elongation is read from the graph to be 26.25 lb. The force exerted for a 40-in. elongation is read from the graph to be 35 lb. The *average* force is

$$\bar{F} = \frac{35 + 26.25}{2} = \frac{61.25}{2} = 30.625 \text{ lb}$$

Note that more simply $\bar{F}$ = the ordinate at $(e_1 + e_2)/2$ $(e = 35)$.

$$\text{Work} = 30.625 \times 10 = 306.25 \text{ in.-lb}$$

This is precisely the area under the quadrilateral $P_2P_1(30,0)$ $(40,0)$ in terms of the scale of the graph (see Fig. 6·32).

Suppose we are required to plot a curve of the work done to reach any elongation between 0 and 40 in. (see Fig. 6·33). We can proceed as follows.

By direct reading of the graph in Fig. 6·32 we find that the average force between $e = 0$ and $e = 10$ is

$$\bar{F}_{0-10} = 4.38 \text{ lb} \qquad (\bar{F} = \text{force at } e = 5)$$

It might be argued that we cannot read F this closely, but knowing that $F = 0.875e$, it follows that $\bar{F} = 0.875(5) = 4.38$ lb.

The elongation over this interval is 10 in. The work done over this interval is therefore

$$W_{0-10} = 4.38 \times 10 = 43.8 \text{ in.-lb}$$

Similarly, by direct reading of the graph, we find that the average force between $e = 0$ and $e = 20$ is

$$\bar{F}_{0-20} = 8.75 \text{ lb} \qquad (\bar{F} = \text{force at } e = 10)$$

The elongation over this interval is 20 in. The work done in this interval is therefore

$$W_{0-20} = 8.75 \times 20 = 175 \text{ in.-lb}$$

In the same way additional data could be calculated for plotting the work versus elongation graph shown in Fig. 6·33.

EXERCISE 12

The relation between the force and the corresponding elongation of a spring is illustrated by Fig. 6·34.

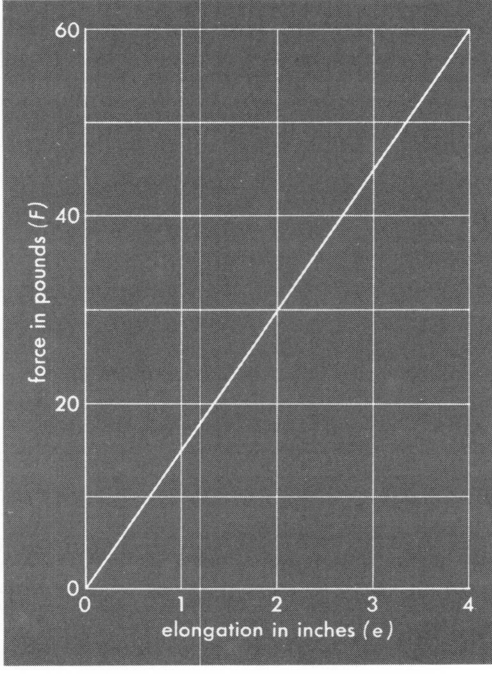

fig. 6·34

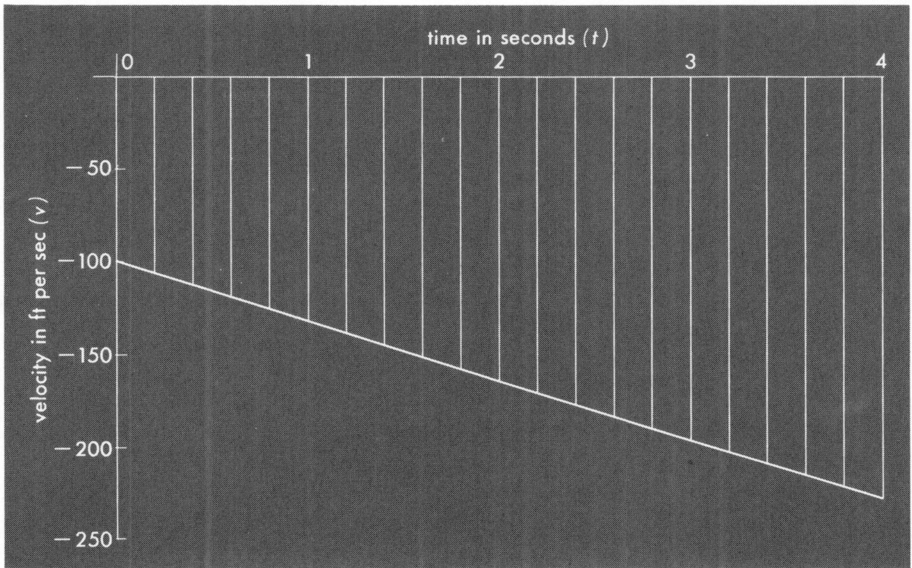

fig. 6·35

1. (a) Find the average force over the interval between $e = 1$ and $e = 3$. (b) Find the work done in elongating the spring over this interval.
2. Plot a curve of work done versus elongation between $e = 0$ in. and $e = 4$ in.
3. The pressure on a certain piston is related to the volume between the piston and cylinder head by the equation

$$p = 900V + 3{,}000 \text{ lb/sq ft}$$

The work done in compressing the volume from 1 to 0.5 cu ft is equal to the area between the given curve, the V axis, from $V = 0.5$ to $V = 1$. Determine this area.

4. The specific heat of mercury c at a temperature of T°C is given by $c = 0.03346 - 0.000{,}009{,}2T$ cal per degree centigrade (at constant pressure). Sketch and determine the area between the straight line, the horizontal T axis, and $T = 0°$ to $T = 50°$. This area is equivalent to the heat required to raise the temperature of 1 g of mercury from 0 to 50°C.

6·19 Calculation of distance from a speed-time graph

If we have given a graph of the speed versus time for a moving object, we can calculate the distance covered in a way exactly analogous to the calculation of work from a force-distance plot (see Sec. 6·18).

Figure 6·35 shows the graph of speed for a freely falling body with an initial downward velocity of 100 fps.

The area between the graph and the t axis is proportional to the distance covered.

It will be noted that this area carries a negative sign. The reason is that velocities in a downward direction are conventionally negative.

The area under this graph is the product of a negative velocity and a positive time interval. This product is a negative distance (see Fig. 6·30 and Sec. 6·18).

EXERCISE 13

1. Find the distance the object falls for each strip in Fig. 6·35.
2. Plot the distance the object falls versus time.
3. Plot a curve of altitude versus time. The object was thrown downward from a height of 800 ft.
4. When does the object hit the ground?

7

systems of linear equations

Technical students constantly deal with formulas and equations. In engineering, technology, business statistics, etc., systems of linear equations are frequently encountered. In this chapter we shall discuss graphical and algebraic methods (including determinants) for solving such equations.

7·1 Graphical solution of a system of two equations

A solution of two *simultaneous equations* in two unknowns, x and y, is a pair of corresponding values of x and y which simultaneously satisfies both equations.

example 1 Solve graphically:

$$x + y = 1 \tag{1}$$
$$x - 2y = 7 \tag{2}$$

In Fig. 7·1, AB is the graph of Eq. (1), and CD is the graph of Eq. (2). All points on AB have coordinates satisfying Eq. (1), and all points on CD have coordinates satisfying Eq. (2); therefore intersection point P has coordinates satisfying the two equations *simultaneously*. Since two straight lines can intersect in but one point, P is the only point having the property of a common solution. In this example the coordinates of P are $(3, -2)$; therefore $(x = 3, y = -2)$ is the only solution of this system of equations.

If the graphs of the equations are parallel lines, there is no solution and the equations are termed *inconsistent*.

example 2 Given the system of equations

$$3x - 5y = 6 \tag{3}$$
$$6x - 10y = 10 \tag{4}$$

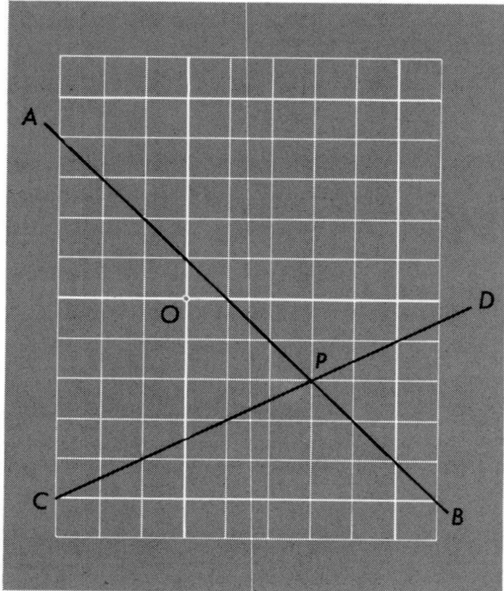

fig. 7·1

The graphs of these two equations are parallel lines, each having a slope of $3/5$; since the lines cannot intersect, the equations have no common solution. This conclusion might have been reached without plotting, since on dividing Eq. (4) by 2 we have $3x - 5y = 5$. Since the expression $3x - 5y$ cannot, at the same time, be equal to 6 and to 5, there are no values of x and y satisfying both equations simultaneously.

If the graphs of the two equations are the same line, any solution of one equation is also a solution of the other, and the system has an unlimited number of solutions. Such equations are known as *dependent* or equivalent equations. (See Sec. 5·1.)

example 3 Given the system

$$2x - 5y = 4 \tag{5}$$
$$6x - 15y = 12 \tag{6}$$

Since Eq. (6) is reducible to Eq. (5) by division by 3, the equations are not independent but are equivalent.

It will be appreciated that graphical solutions are only approximate; when we have to estimate fractional scale divisions, the approximation is rougher.

EXERCISE 1

In the following problems determine whether each pair of equations is inconsistent or dependent or possesses one common solution. In the last case solve graphically, estimating fractional answers to the nearest 0.1.

1. $x + y = 8$, $x - y = 2$
2. $x + y = -4$, $x - y = 8$
3. $2x - y = 3$, $2x - 3y = 11$
4. $3x - y = 4$, $2y - 6x = -8$
5. $2x + 5y = 8$, $3x - 2y = -7$
6. $4x - 6y = 8$, $6x - 9y = 14$
7. $2x = 7y$, $6x - 5y = 16$
8. $3x + 2y = 12$, $3y - 2x = 4$
9. $4x - 3y = 10$, $6y - 8x = -20$
10. $5x - 8y = 0$, $7y - 4x = 3$
11. $2x - y = 5$, $x + y = 2$
12. $8x - 12y = 10$, $18y - 12x = 15$
13. $12x + 5y = 0$, $8x - 10y = 8$
14. $2x - 7y + 9 = 0$, $5x + 3y - 6 = 0$

7·2 Algebraic methods of solution

Algebraic methods of solving systems of simultaneous equations depend on eliminating one of the unknowns. There are four common methods of solution: addition or subtraction, substitution, comparison, and determinants.

7·3 Elimination by addition or subtraction

example 4 Solve for x and y:

$$4x - 7y = 29 \qquad (7)$$
$$6x + 5y = -3 \qquad (8)$$

Multiplying Eq. (7) by 3,

$$12x - 21y = 87 \qquad (9)$$

Multiplying Eq. (8) by 2,

$$12x + 10y = -6 \qquad (10)$$

Subtracting Eq. (10) from Eq. (9),

$$-31y = 93 \qquad (11)$$

Dividing Eq. (11) by -31,

$$y = -3 \qquad (12)$$

Substituting -3 for y in Eq. (7),

$$4x + 21 = 29$$

or

$$x = 2 \qquad (13)$$

Check by substituting $x = 2$ and $y = -3$ in Eq. (8).

$$12 - 15 = -3 \qquad \text{(check)}$$

The above procedure may be summarized as follows:

To solve a system of linear equations by elimination by addition or subtraction:

1. *Multiply both members of both equations, if necessary, by numbers which will cause the coefficients of one of the unknowns to have the same absolute value in both equations.*
2. *To eliminate this unknown, the two equations obtained in step 1 are added if the matched coefficients have opposite signs. They are subtracted if they have like signs.*
3. *Solve the equation formed in step 2 for the unknown contained in it. Substitute the result in one of the original equations to obtain the other unknown.*
4. *Check by substituting the values of the unknowns in the original equation not used in step 3.*

NOTE: *If both members of an equation contain a common factor, it may be advisable to divide through by that factor.*

Clear of any fractions before eliminating an unknown (see exception, Sec. 7·7).

It will usually be preferable to eliminate the unknown whose coefficients have the smaller LCM.

7·4 Elimination by substitution

example 5 Solve for x and y:

$$7x - 3y = 10 \tag{14}$$
$$5x - 2y = 8 \tag{15}$$

Solve Eq. (15) for y:

$$5x - 8 = 2y \tag{16}$$

or

$$y = \frac{5x - 8}{2} \tag{16}$$

Substitute $(5x - 8)/2$ for y in Eq. (14):

$$7x - 3\left(\frac{5x - 8}{2}\right) = 10 \tag{17}$$

Solve Eq. (17) for x, first eliminating fractions:

$$14x - 3(5x - 8) = 20$$
$$14x - 15x + 24 = 20$$
$$x = 4$$

Substitute $x = 4$ in Eq. (16):

$$y = \frac{(5)(4) - 8}{2}$$

or

$$y = 6$$

Hence the solution of the system is $x = 4$, $y = 6$.

Check by substituting $x = 4$ and $y = 6$ in Eq. (14):

$$(7)(4) - (3)(6) = 10 \qquad 28 - 18 = 10$$

To solve a system of two linear equations by elimination by substitution:

1. *Solve one equation for one unknown (preferably the unknown having the simplest coefficient) in terms of the other.*
2. *The expression obtained in step 1 is to be substituted for the equivalent unknown in the other equation.*
3. *Solve the equation obtained in step 2 for the second unknown.*
4. *Substitute the value of the second unknown in the expression obtained in step 1, and solve for the first unknown.*
5. *Check by substituting values of both unknowns in the original equation not used in step 1.*

7·5 Elimination by comparison

example 6 Solve the following for x and y:

$$4x + 7y = 3 \tag{18}$$
$$6x - 5y = 20 \tag{19}$$

Solving Eq. (18) for x,

$$x = \frac{3 - 7y}{4} \tag{20}$$

Solving Eq. (19) for x,

$$x = \frac{5y + 20}{6} \tag{21}$$

Equating Eqs. (20) and (21),

$$\frac{3 - 7y}{4} = \frac{5y + 20}{6}$$

$$\begin{aligned} 3(3 - 7y) &= 2(5y + 20) \\ 9 - 21y &= 10y + 40 \\ -31y &= 31 \\ y &= -1 \end{aligned}$$

Complete the solution as in elimination by addition or subtraction, obtaining $x = 2\frac{1}{2}$.

NOTE: *The method of addition or subtraction is the most generally useful, especially when the coefficients of one unknown have the same absolute value in both equations.*

The method of substitution is most convenient to apply when the unknown which is to be expressed in terms of the other has a coefficient of one.

There is seldom a case of solution by comparison which could not have been done at least as easily by either of the first two methods.

EXERCISE 2

Solve the following systems of equations by the most convenient method:

1. $3x - 2y = 4$, $x = y$
2. $9x - 5y = 42$, $x + y = 0$
3. $8y - 5x = 18$, $x - y = 0$
4. $7x - 5y = 161$, $x = 4y$
5. $9x + 8y = 77$, $x - y = 1$
6. $3x - 2y = 10$, $x - y = 1$
7. $8x - 5y = 58$, $x + y = 4$
8. $6x - 10y = 4$, $x + y = 14$
9. $2x + y = 5$, $x + 2y = 19$
10. $4x + 5y = 30$, $6x + y = 19$
11. $x + y = 13$, $x - y = 5$
12. $5x + 2z = 61$, $3x - 2z = 43$
13. $11y - 4z = 41$, $7y + 2z = 42$
14. $5w + 6y = 17$, $3w - 2y = 27$
15. $9x - 13w = -3$, $6x - 7w = 3$
16. $12x - 11z = -5$, $9x + 4z = 33$
17. $7x - 3y = 41$, $4x + 5y = 10$
18. $9w + 8z = 15$, $5w + 7z = 16$
19. $11x - 3y + 34 = 0$, $8x + 10y - 24 = 0$
20. $13y + 5z - 33 = 0$, $7y - 9z - 47 = 0$
21. $3(x + y) = 33$, $5(x - y) = 25$
22. $4(x + z) = 22$, $6(x - z) = 15$
23. $0.5x + 0.4w = 0.26$, $0.7x + 0.3w = 0.26$
24. $0.3x + 0.4y = 14.5$, $0.4x + 0.3y = 13.5$
25. $\frac{x}{4} + 4y = 28$, $7x - \frac{y}{5} = 36$
26. $\frac{x}{3} - 4y = -58$, $5x - \frac{y}{6} = 27\frac{1}{2}$
27. $\frac{w+3}{2} + 5z = 9$, $\frac{z+9}{10} - \frac{w-2}{3} = 0$
28. $\frac{x-2}{10} + 3y = 8$, $\frac{x+2}{6} - \frac{y-7}{9} = 2$

Solve Probs. 29 and 30 by slide rule to whatever degree of accuracy is possible.

29. $0.103x + 0.950y = 10.47$, $1.068x - 2.74y = 19.63$
30. $5.95x + 5.17y = 3.39$, $4.62x - 12.3y = 5.56$

NOTE: *In slide-rule solution, instead of finding the LCM of 5.95 and 4.62, we would usually prefer to eliminate an unknown, say* x, *by dividing the first equation through by 5.95 and the second by 4.62.*

7·6 Literal linear equations

A system involving letters other than the unknowns is usually best solved by finding each unknown independently by elimination by addition or subtraction.

example 7 Solve for x and y:

$$mx + ny = 2(m^2 - n^2) \tag{22}$$
$$x - y = m + n \tag{23}$$

Multiply Eq. (23) by n:

$$nx - ny = mn + n^2 \tag{24}$$

Add Eqs. (22) and (24):

$$\begin{array}{rcl} mx + ny &=& 2m^2 \qquad\quad - 2n^2 \\ nx - ny &=& \qquad\quad mn + n^2 \\ \hline mx + nx &=& 2m^2 + mn - n^2 \end{array} \tag{25}$$

Factor Eq. (25):

$$x(m + n) = (m + n)(2m - n) \tag{26}$$

Divide Eq. (26) through by $m + n$:

$$x = 2m - n$$

Multiply Eq. (23) by m:

$$mx - my = m^2 + mn \tag{27}$$

Subtract Eq. (27) from Eq. (22):

$$\begin{array}{rcl} mx + ny &=& 2m^2 \qquad\quad - 2n^2 \\ mx - my &=& m^2 + mn \\ \hline ny + my &=& m^2 - mn - 2n^2 \end{array} \tag{28}$$

Factor Eq. (28):

$$y(n + m) = (m + n)(m - 2n) \tag{29}$$

Divide Eq. (29) through by $m + n$:

$$y = m - 2n$$

But note that y is more easily found here by substitution. Rewriting Eq. (23) as $x - m - n = y$ and substituting $x = 2m - n$, we find at once that $2m - n - m - n = m - 2n = y$.

If answers are at all involved, checking may best be done by numerical substitution, as in Example 3, Sec. 5·4.

7·7 Equations linear in the reciprocals of the unknowns

Equations of the type $a/x + b/y = c$ are usually best solved without removing the unknowns from the denominators.

example 8 Solve the system

$$\frac{9}{x} - \frac{15}{y} = 1 \tag{30}$$

$$\frac{14}{x} + \frac{20}{y} = 3 \tag{31}$$

Multiply Eq. (30) by 4:

$$\frac{36}{x} - \frac{60}{y} = 4 \tag{32}$$

Multiply Eq. (31) by 3:

$$\frac{42}{x} + \frac{60}{y} = 9 \tag{33}$$

Add Eqs. (32) and (33):

$$\frac{78}{x} = 13$$

$$78 = 13x$$

or

$$x = 6$$

Substitute $x = 6$ in Eq. (30):

$$\frac{9}{6} - \frac{15}{y} = 1$$

$$-\frac{15}{y} = -\frac{1}{2}$$

$$y = 30$$

The solution of the system is $x = 6, y = 30$.

example 9 Solve the system

$$\frac{3}{8x} - \frac{1}{2y} = 2 \tag{34}$$

$$\frac{5}{6x} - \frac{5}{3y} = -8\frac{1}{3} \tag{35}$$

Multiply Eq. (34) by 10:

$$\frac{15}{4x} - \frac{5}{y} = 20 \tag{36}$$

Multiply Eq. (35) by 3:

$$\frac{5}{2x} - \frac{5}{y} = -25 \tag{37}$$

Subtract Eq. (37) from Eq. (36):

$$\frac{15}{4x} - \frac{5}{2x} = 45 \tag{38}$$

Multiply Eq. (38) by $4x$:

$$15 - 10 = 180x$$
$$x = 1/36$$

Substitute $x = 1/36$ in Eq. (34):

$$\frac{3}{8(1/36)} - \frac{1}{2y} = 2$$
$$\frac{27}{2} - \frac{1}{2y} = 2$$
$$-\frac{1}{2y} = -\frac{23}{2}$$
$$y = \frac{1}{23}$$

Hence the solution of the system is $x = 1/36$, $y = 1/23$.

EXERCISE 3

Solve the following systems for x, y, z, or w, as the case may be.

1. $3x + y = 4c$
 $x - y = 4d$
2. $x + y = 5a$
 $2x - 3y = 5b$
3. $2x - 3y = a + 4b$
 $x + 2y = 4a - 5b$
4. $5x - 4y = 6c - 15d$
 $3x + y = 7c - 9d$
5. $ax + 2by = 4$
 $2ax - 6by = 3$
6. $12ax - 5by = -16$
 $6ax + 7by = 30$
7. $2ax + by = 10c$
 $ax - 3by = -9c$
8. $3ax - 4by = 18ab$
 $2ax + by = ab$
9. $bx + cy = 2bc$
 $cx + by = b^2 + c^2$
10. $ax - by = 2a^2 - 6ab + 2b^2$
 $bx + ay = 3a^2 - 3b^2$
11. $2nx + 2my = m^2 + n^2$
 $4nx - mx + my = mn + 2n^2$
12. $ax + 2cy = 5ac$
 $\frac{2x}{c} - \frac{y}{a} = \frac{-5}{ac}$
13. $\frac{1}{x} + \frac{1}{y} = 6$
 $\frac{1}{x} - \frac{1}{y} = 4$
14. $\frac{3}{x} - \frac{2}{y} = 10$
 $\frac{4}{x} + \frac{1}{y} = 28$
15. $\frac{10}{x} + \frac{6}{y} = 7$
 $\frac{14}{x} - \frac{9}{y} = 4$
16. $\frac{15}{x} + \frac{14}{w} = 5$
 $\frac{25}{x} - \frac{6}{w} = 1$
17. $\frac{1}{2x} + \frac{1}{3y} = 12$
 $\frac{1}{4x} + \frac{1}{9y} = 5$
18. $\frac{5}{6x} - \frac{3}{4z} = 6$
 $\frac{7}{9x} + \frac{1}{6z} = 7\frac{1}{3}$

7·8 Linear equations in more than two unknowns

Like a system in two unknowns, a system of linear equations in more than two unknowns may have a solution or may be dependent or inconsistent. Only the first case will be considered here. For a system to have a unique solution, it must have as many independent equations as unknowns.

example 10 Solve for x, y, and z:

$$6x - 5y - 2z = 2 \tag{39}$$
$$4x + y + 3z = 10 \tag{40}$$
$$5x + 3y + 7z = 13 \tag{41}$$

Multiply Eq. (40) by 5:

Add Eq. (39):

$$\begin{array}{r} 20x + 5y + 15z = 50 \\ 6x - 5y - 2z = 2 \\ \hline 26x \qquad + 13z = 52 \end{array} \tag{42}$$

Multiply Eq. (40) by 3:

Subtract Eq. (41):

$$\begin{array}{r} 12x + 3y + 9z = 30 \\ 5x + 3y + 7z = 13 \\ \hline 7x \qquad + 2z = 17 \end{array} \tag{43}$$

Note that Eq. (42) may be divided throughout by 13. Therefore we will obtain smaller coefficients in Eq. (42) by multiplying by $2/13$ rather than by 2.

Subtract Eq. (43):

$$\begin{array}{r} 4x + 2z = 8 \\ 7x + 2z = 17 \\ \hline -3x \qquad = -9 \\ x = 3 \end{array} \tag{44}$$

Substitute $x = 3$ in Eq. (43):

$$(7)(3) + 2z = 17$$
$$z = -2$$

Substitute $x = 3$ and $z = -2$ in Eq. (40):

$$(4)(3) + y + 3(-2) = 10$$
$$y = 4$$

Check the solution by substituting the values of x, y, and z in Eq. (39) or (41).

The procedure for solving a system of three linear equations in three unknowns may be summarized as follows:

1. *Select the unknown most easily eliminated and eliminate this unknown from one pair of equations.*
2. *Eliminate the same unknown from one of the equations just used and the third equation.*

3. *Solve the two equations so obtained as in Sec. 7·2.*
4. *Substitute the two values found in step 3 in the simplest of the original equations and solve for the third unknown.*
5. *Check by substituting the values of the unknowns in the two original equations not used in step 4.*

Simultaneous linear equations in more than three unknowns may be solved by an extension of the above method, but a more effective method will be explained in Secs. 7·12 to 7·14.

EXERCISE 4

Solve the following systems of equations:

1. $x + y = 7$
   $x + z = 8$
   $y + z = 9$

2. $x + y = 4$
   $x + z = 7$
   $y + z = 1$

3. $x + y + z = 8$
   $x - y + z = 2$
   $x + y - z = 12$

4. $x - y - z = 1$
   $x + y - z = 6$
   $x - y + z = -1$

Suggestion for Probs. 5 and 6: Add the equations and divide the sum through by the common factor.

5. $2x + y + z = 7$
   $x + 2y + z = 15$
   $x + y + 2z = 18$

6. $x + y + 3z = 9$
   $x + 3y + z = 7/3$
   $3x + y + z = 7$

7. $2x + 3y - 4z = 11$
   $3x - 5y + z = -3$
   $6x + 2y - 7z = 18$

8. $7x + 4y - 3z = -15$
   $5x - 6y + 2z = 41$
   $x - 10y - 9z = -8$

9. $6x - 8y + 3z = -5$
   $9x + 20y - 4z = 25$
   $15x + 12y + 7z = 12$

10. $10x + 9y + 7z = 32$
    $11x - 6y - 8z = 20$
    $-9x + 12y + 10z = -22$

7·9 Graphical solutions of simultaneous linear equations

Two-component mixture problems may be solved approximately and quickly by means of the graphical procedure outlined in Appendix B, Sec. B·19.

Distance, time, and rate linear problems are especially adaptable to graphical solution. Time, the independent variable, is usually the abscissa, and distance, the dependent variable, the ordinate.

example 11 A westbound New York Central express leaves Albany at 1 P.M. and maintains an average speed of 50 mph; an eastbound train leaves Buffalo at 1:30 P.M. and maintains an average speed of 40 mph. If the

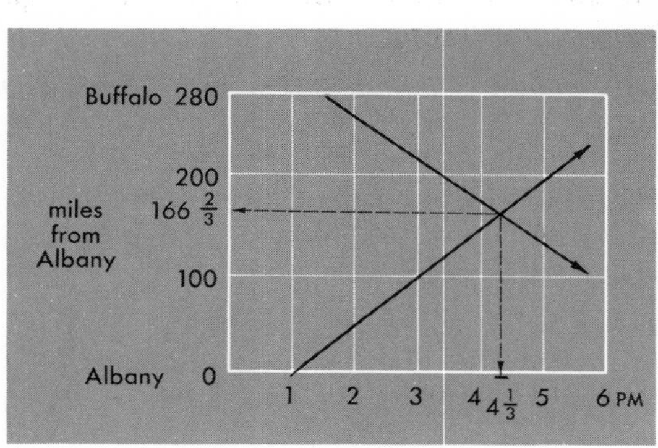

fig. 7·2

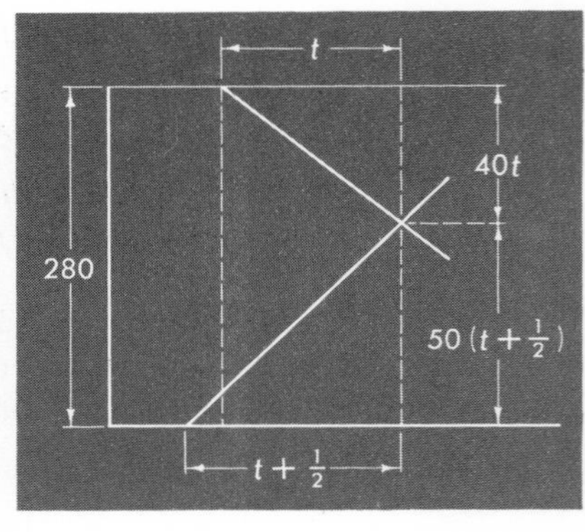

fig. 7·3

distance from Albany to Buffalo is 280 miles, when and where will they pass?

Reading answers from Fig. 7·2, we find that the trains pass at 4:20 P.M. at a point 166⅔ miles west of Albany and 113⅓ miles east of Buffalo. A rough sketch of the graphical solution may be used to indicate the relationships upon which to base an algebraic solution. By dimensioning the sketch (Fig. 7·3), which need not be drawn to scale, we obtain an equation $280 = 40t + 50(t + \frac{1}{2})$ (the whole equals the sum of the parts).

example 12 A Pennsylvania local leaves New York City for Philadelphia at 9:30 A.M. and maintains an average speed of 30 mph. An express leaves New York for Philadelphia at 10:15 A.M. and maintains an average speed of 40 mph for the first 10 miles, after which the average speed is 60 mph. When and where will the express overtake the local?

Figure 7·4 indicates that the express overtakes the local at 11:10 A.M. at a point 50 miles out of New York City.

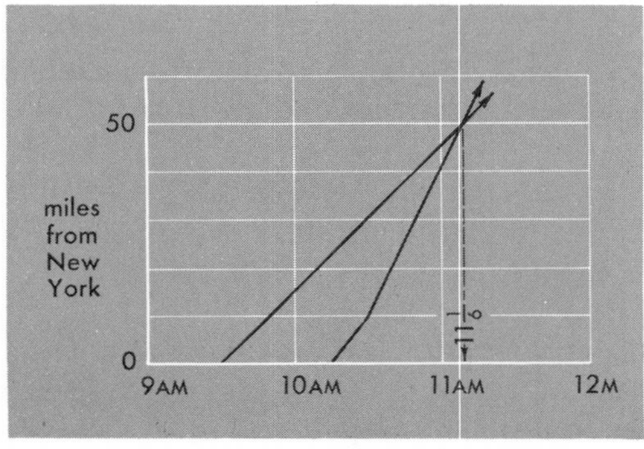

fig. 7·4

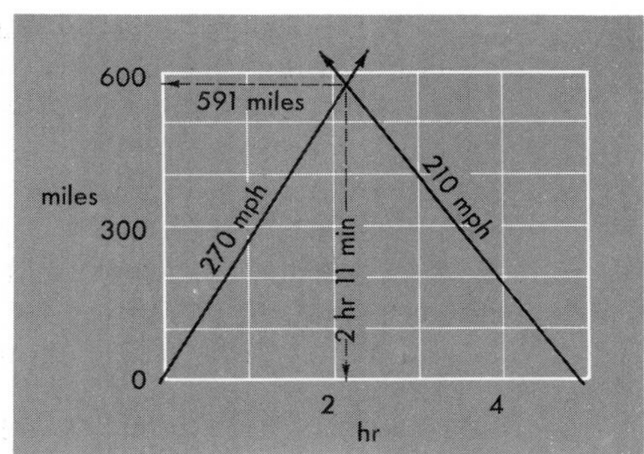

fig. 7·5

example 13 A plane has enough fuel for 5 hr of flying at a cruising speed of 240 mph. If a 30-mph west wind is blowing, how far east can the plane fly and return to the airport before the fuel is exhausted? (That is, find the "point of no return.") When must the pilot reverse his course?

Figure 7·5 shows that the point of no return is reached in about 2 hr 11 min at about 591 miles from the airport.

example 14 A time-honored problem is that of the motorcycle courier who starts from the rear of a troop column, rides to the head of the column, and immediately returns to the rear. How far did the courier ride if the column is 6 miles long and marching at 4 mph? The speed of the motorcycle is 30 mph. How long was the courier riding?

According to Fig. 7·6, the courier traveled about 12.2 miles (6.9 miles to the head of the column and 5.3 miles to the rear). The total time was about 0.4 hr, or 24 min.

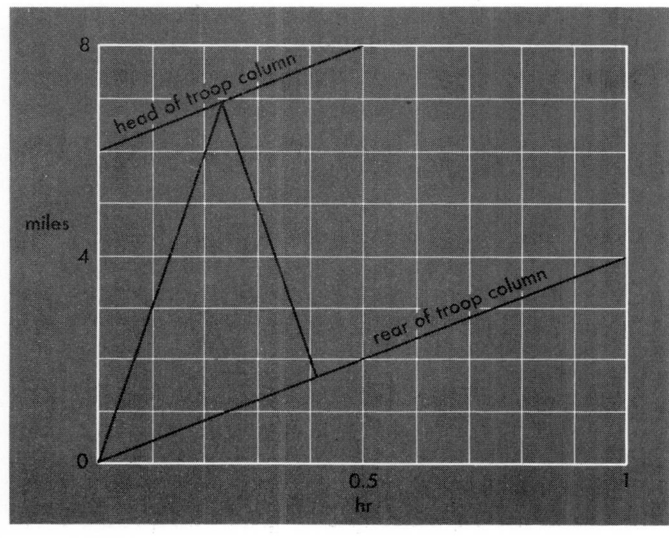

fig. 7·6

This problem is a good example of the opportunity offered by maintaining the proper relative values while changing other conditions.

In this illustration let us consider rates of the cyclist relative to that of the troop column. It is evident the cyclist is riding at 30 − 4, or 26, mph relative to the troop column while riding to the head of the column, and 30 + 4, or 34, mph relative to the column while riding to the rear. If the 6-mile column were stationary, then our problem would be to find the total time for the cyclist to advance 6 miles at 26 mph and return at 34 mph. The solution is obvious:

$$\frac{6}{34} + \frac{6}{26} = 0.1765 \text{ hr} + 0.231 \text{ hr, or } 0.408 \text{ hr}$$

and confirms the answer already obtained by graphical means.

EXERCISE 5

Solve the following using two or more unknowns:

1. The sum of two numbers is 53 and their difference is 15. Find the numbers.
2. A fraction reduces to ⅔ if 2 is added to its numerator. It reduces to ½ if 1 is added to its denominator. What is the fraction?
3. A boat travels 60 miles upstream in 10 hr, making the return trip downstream in 8 hr. Find the rate of the current and of the boat in still water.
4. Two planes are 60 miles apart. If flying toward each other, they will pass in 5 min. If they are headed in the same direction the faster plane will overtake the slower in 45 min. What are their speeds?
5. If the width of a rectangle is increased by 2 ft, and the length by 12 ft, the area will be increased by 480 sq ft. If the width is increased by 12 ft, and the length by 2 ft, the area will be increased by 660 sq ft. Find the dimensions of the original rectangle.
6. A plumber and his helper together receive $40.80, the plumber working 5 hr and the helper 6 hr. At another time the plumber works 8 hr and the helper 7½ hr, and they receive together $59.40. What are the hourly wages of each?
7. Three men and 6 boys can do in 2 days what 1 man and 8 boys can do in 3 days. Find the time required for 1 man alone and for 1 boy alone to do the work.
8. Six men and 5 boys take 2 days to do what 9 men and 15 boys can do in 1 day. If the labor cost for the job is $252, find the daily wage for a man and for a boy.
9. Three disks A, B, and C are externally tangent each to each. If the center-to-center distances AB, AC, and BC are 6¾, 6¼, and 8½ in., respectively, find the diameters.
10. Find the diameters of the disks in Fig. 7·7.
11. The resistance R_t of a nickel wire at any centigrade temperature t is

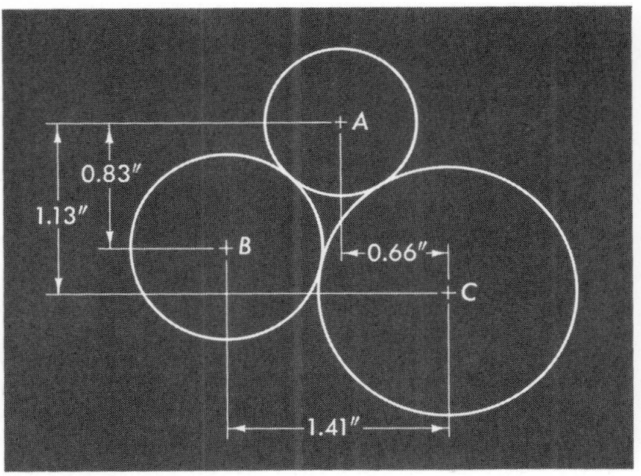

fig. 7·7

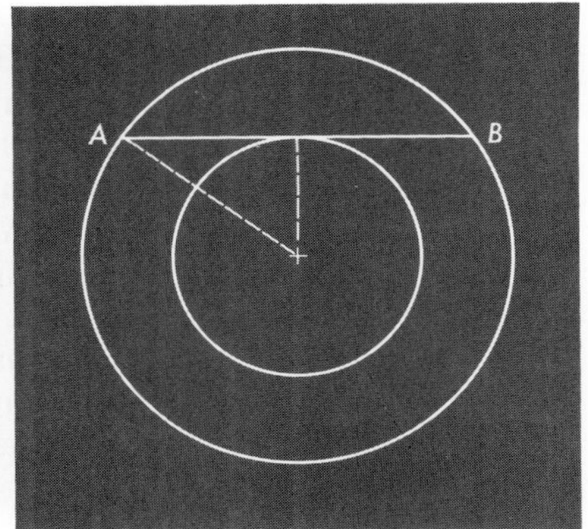

fig. 7·8

equal to $R_0(1 + at)$, where R_0 is the resistance at 0°C and a is the temperature coefficient of resistance. If the resistance at 20°C is 26.82 ohms, and at 32°C is 28.10 ohms, find a and R_0.

12. Express the area of the ring in Fig. 7·8 in terms of AB. Given a regular 6-in. pentagon, find the difference between the areas of the circumscribed and inscribed circles. How does your answer compare with that obtained by taking a 6-in. heptagon?
13. Two stations A and B on the same railroad line are on opposite sides of a mountain pass. A is 10 miles east of the divide, and B is 15 miles west of the divide. The grade is the same on both sides. If the running time from A to B is 44 min and the running time from B to A is 50 min, find the upgrade and downgrade speeds.
14. A gas company charges $\$a$ service charge plus $\$b$ a thousand cubic feet. Find a and b if 12,000 cu ft of gas cost \$1.46 and 20,000 cu ft cost \$2.10.
15. A small firm has a taxable income of \$390,000. The state tax is 10 per cent of that portion remaining after the federal tax is paid. The federal tax is 25 per cent of that portion remaining after the state tax is paid. What are the state and federal taxes?
16. A New York Central passenger train running between New York City and Albany can make up 20 min time lost in starting by averaging 6 mph faster than usual. If on another occasion, by giving another train the right of way, it reduces its average speed by 8 mph and will finish its run 36 min late, find the distance and usual running time from New York to Albany.
17. A man ordered a number of pamphlets from a job printer. The printer made a fixed charge for each order plus a certain amount for each pamphlet. The total cost amounted to \$42. Several months later the customer placed a somewhat larger order for additional pamphlets. This order cost \$54. Had the customer been able to anticipate his needs

and ordered all the pamphlets at one time, they would have cost only \$84. How much was the fixed charge? If the second order contained 80 more pamphlets than the first, find the number of pamphlets in each order and the unit cost.

18. A marksman fires at a target 480 yd away. He hears the bullet strike 2.4 sec after he fires. An observer standing 420 yd from the target and 240 yd from the marksman hears the bullet strike 1.6 sec after he hears the report of the rifle. Find the velocities of sound and of the bullet, assuming each to be uniform.
19. The difference between two quantities equals their product. Their sum less their product equals the smaller divided by the larger. What are the numbers?
20. The product of two quantities equals their difference. Their product plus their sum equals the larger divided by three times the smaller. Find the numbers.
21. A traveler has 400 lb of baggage, for which he must pay \$4.50 transportation because of excess over the weight carried without charge. If a friend takes charge of part of the baggage, the traveler will pay \$1.80 and the friend \$1.20 for excess above the weight carried free. How much baggage is allowed to go free on one ticket?
22. Two workmen, A and B, were employed at different wages. Over a given pay period, A received \$24 more than B. If A had been idle two days while B worked the entire period, they would have received equal amounts. If B had been idle two days with A working the entire period, A would have received \$45 more than B. How long was a pay period and what was the daily wage of each man?
23. In a race of 100 yd, A beats B by ⅕ sec. In the second trial, A gives B a start of 4 yd and B wins by ⅕ sec. Find the time required for A and B each to run 100 yd.
24. Two cars are traveling in the same direction around a 1-mile circular race track. The faster car overtakes the slower car every 3 min. When the cars are traveling in opposite directions, they pass each other every 18 sec. Find their speeds.
25. In balancing the equation for the combustion of methyl alcohol, the coefficients a, b, and c must be determined in the equation

$$a\mathrm{CH_3OH} + b\mathrm{O_2} \rightarrow c\mathrm{H_2O} + a\mathrm{CO_2}$$

According to a hydrogen balance,

$$4a = 2c$$

An oxygen balance requires that

$$a + 2b = c + 2a$$

Find the smallest integral values of a, b, and c satisfying the above equations.

26. The solution of copper in nitric acid proceeds according to the equation

$$a\text{Cu} + 2b\text{HNO}_3 \rightarrow a\text{Cu(NO}_3)_2 + c\text{NO} + b\text{H}_2\text{O}$$

The nitrogen balance requires that

$$2b = 2a + c$$

The oxygen balance requires that

$$6b = 6a + c + b$$

Find the smallest integral values of a, b, and c satisfying the above equations.

27. If the sum of two numbers is represented by S and their product is represented by P, express the sum of the cubes of these numbers in terms of S and P.

7 · 10 Determinants

Simultaneous linear equations containing three or more unknowns may entail considerable computation in their solution. A common example may be found in the application of Kirchhoff's laws to the determination of the current and voltage in various parts of an electrical network. Expressions called *determinants* are particularly useful in facilitating such solutions.

7 · 11 Determinants of the second order

If a_1, b_1, a_2, and b_2 represent any numbers, the arrangement

$$\begin{vmatrix} a_1 & b_1 \\ a_2 & b_2 \end{vmatrix}$$

is called a *determinant of the second order,* in which a_1, b_1, a_2, and b_2 are the *elements.*

The value of the determinant

$$\begin{vmatrix} a_1 & b_1 \\ a_2 & b_2 \end{vmatrix}$$

is, by definition, equal to

$$a_1b_2 - a_2b_1 \tag{45}$$

example 15 Find the value of $\begin{vmatrix} 4 & 5 \\ 3 & 7 \end{vmatrix}$.

By Eq. (45),

$$\begin{vmatrix} 4 & 5 \\ 3 & 7 \end{vmatrix} = (4)(7) - (3)(5) = 28 - 15 = 13$$

example 16 Evaluate $\begin{vmatrix} 6 & 3 \\ -2 & 5 \end{vmatrix}$.

$$\begin{vmatrix} 6 & 3 \\ -2 & 5 \end{vmatrix} = (6)(5) - (-2)(3) = 30 + 6 = 36$$

example 17 Evaluate $\begin{vmatrix} 7 & x \\ 5 & -y \end{vmatrix}$.

$$\begin{vmatrix} 7 & x \\ 5 & -y \end{vmatrix} = (7)(-y) - (5)(x) = -7y - 5x$$

EXERCISE 6

Evaluate the following determinants:

1. $\begin{vmatrix} 3 & 5 \\ 5 & 8 \end{vmatrix}$
2. $\begin{vmatrix} 3 & a \\ 4 & b \end{vmatrix}$
3. $\begin{vmatrix} 4 & -6 \\ 2 & 5 \end{vmatrix}$
4. $\begin{vmatrix} 7 & -x \\ 6 & y \end{vmatrix}$
5. $\begin{vmatrix} 9a & 5b \\ 4b & a \end{vmatrix}$
6. $\begin{vmatrix} 6x & -7x \\ 5y & -6y \end{vmatrix}$

7·12 Solution of simultaneous linear equations by determinants

Given the system of linear equations in x and y

$$\begin{aligned} a_1x + b_1y &= k_1 \\ a_2x + b_2y &= k_2 \end{aligned} \tag{46}$$

the solution can be shown to be

$$x = \frac{k_1b_2 - k_2b_1}{a_1b_2 - a_2b_1} \qquad y = \frac{a_1k_2 - a_2k_1}{a_1b_2 - a_2b_1} \tag{47}$$

provided $a_1b_2 - a_2b_1$ is not equal to zero.

In determinant notation we can write

$$k_1b_2 - k_2b_1 = \begin{vmatrix} k_1 & b_1 \\ k_2 & b_2 \end{vmatrix} \qquad a_1k_2 - a_2k_1 = \begin{vmatrix} a_1 & k_1 \\ a_2 & k_2 \end{vmatrix}$$

and

$$a_1b_2 - a_2b_1 = \begin{vmatrix} a_1 & b_1 \\ a_2 & b_2 \end{vmatrix}$$

We can, therefore, write the solution of Eq. (47) in the form

$$x = \frac{\begin{vmatrix} k_1 & b_1 \\ k_2 & b_2 \end{vmatrix}}{\begin{vmatrix} a_1 & b_1 \\ a_2 & b_2 \end{vmatrix}} \qquad y = \frac{\begin{vmatrix} a_1 & k_1 \\ a_2 & k_2 \end{vmatrix}}{\begin{vmatrix} a_1 & b_1 \\ a_2 & b_2 \end{vmatrix}} \qquad \text{if} \qquad \begin{vmatrix} a_1 & b_1 \\ a_2 & b_2 \end{vmatrix} \neq 0 \tag{48}$$

The solution [Eq. (48)] is, therefore, a general formula applicable to any system [Eq. (46)] of two simultaneous linear equations in two unknowns when arranged in standard form. (This equation has been numbered in boldface to indicate its importance.) A system of linear equations is said to be in *standard form* when, as in Eq. (46), the terms containing the unknowns are in the left-hand members and in the same order in both equations, and the right-hand members contain only constants.

It will be noted that both denominators of Eq. (48) are the same. This determinant

$$\begin{vmatrix} a_1 & b_1 \\ a_2 & b_2 \end{vmatrix}$$

is called the *determinant of the system.* Its elements are the coefficients of the unknown quantities arranged in the same relative position as in the system of equations when the equations are arranged in standard form.

The numerator of the fraction which expresses the value of x differs from the denominator in that the constants k_1 and k_2 replace a_1 and a_2, the coefficients of x; and the numerator of the fraction which expresses the value of y differs from the denominator in that the constants k_1 and k_2 replace b_1 and b_2, the coefficients of y. This procedure may be summarized in *Cramer's rule:*

Arrange the given equations in standard form. In the solution, the value of an unknown is given by a fraction whose denominator is the determinant of the system and whose numerator is the same determinant except that the coefficients of the unknown have been replaced by the constants k_1 *and* k_2.

example 18 Solve by determinants

$$4x + 7y = -19$$
$$5x - 3y = 35$$

We have

$$a_1 = 4 \qquad b_1 = 7 \qquad k_1 = -19$$
$$a_2 = 5 \qquad b_2 = -3 \qquad k_2 = 35$$

Hence

$$x = \frac{\begin{vmatrix} -19 & 7 \\ 35 & -3 \end{vmatrix}}{\begin{vmatrix} 4 & 7 \\ 5 & -3 \end{vmatrix}} = \frac{57 - 245}{-12 - 35} = \frac{-188}{-47} = 4$$

$$y = \frac{\begin{vmatrix} 4 & -19 \\ 5 & 35 \end{vmatrix}}{\begin{vmatrix} 4 & 7 \\ 5 & -3 \end{vmatrix}} = \frac{140 + 95}{-12 - 35} = \frac{235}{-47} = -5$$

example 19 Solve by determinants

$$x - y = m - n$$
$$mx - ny = 2m^2 - 2n^2$$

Here

$$a_1 = 1 \qquad b_1 = -1 \qquad k_1 = m - n$$
$$a_2 = m \qquad b_2 = -n \qquad k_2 = 2m^2 - 2n^2$$

Hence

$$x = \frac{\begin{vmatrix} m-n & -1 \\ 2m^2-2n^2 & -n \end{vmatrix}}{\begin{vmatrix} 1 & -1 \\ m & -n \end{vmatrix}} = \frac{-mn + n^2 + 2m^2 - 2n^2}{-n+m}$$

$$= \frac{2m^2 - mn - n^2}{m-n} = 2m + n$$

$$y = \frac{\begin{vmatrix} 1 & m-n \\ m & 2m^2-2n^2 \end{vmatrix}}{\begin{vmatrix} 1 & -1 \\ m & -n \end{vmatrix}} = \frac{2m^2 - 2n^2 - m^2 + mn}{-n+m}$$

$$= \frac{m^2 + mn - 2n^2}{m-n} = m + 2n$$

If the equations $a_1x + b_1y = k_1$ and $a_2x + b_2y = k_2$ have not just one simultaneous solution, they are either inconsistent or dependent. Graphically, this means that the lines are either parallel or coincident. In either case the slopes are equal, and $-(a_1/b_1) = -(a_2/b_2)$ or $a_1b_2 - a_2b_1 = 0$. If the two lines coincide, their y intercepts are equal, or $k_1/b_1 = k_2/b_2$; that is, $k_1b_2 - k_2b_1 = 0$.

These facts may be summarized as follows:

If $a_1b_2 - a_2b_1 \neq 0$	*The equations have just one unique simultaneous solution.*
If $a_1b_2 - a_2b_1 = 0$ and $k_1b_2 - k_2b_1 \neq 0$	*The equations are inconsistent and have no solution.*
If $a_1b_2 - a_2b_1 = 0$ and $k_1b_2 - k_2b_1 = 0$	*The equations are dependent and have an infinite number of solutions.*

EXERCISE 7

In the following systems, use determinants to ascertain whether the equations are inconsistent, dependent, or have a unique common solution. Determine any common solutions.

1. $2x - 3y = 5$
   $4x - 6y = 8$

2. $3x - 7y = 1$
   $6x + 5y = 40$

3. $6x + 9y = 15$
   $8x + 12y = 20$

4. $3x - 4y - 15 = 0$
   $7x + 2y - 52 = 0$

5. $4x + 15y = 7a$
   $10x - 9y = 2a$

6. $\dfrac{2x - y}{3} = 5$
   $\dfrac{11x + 2y}{5} = 6$

7. $ax + by = (a - b)^2$
   $ax - by = a^2 - b^2$

8. $bx + ay = 2ab$
   $ax + by = a^2 + b^2$

9. $17x + 11y = 13$
   $7x - 9y = 73$

7·13 Determinants of the third order

If a_1, b_1, c_1, a_2, b_2, c_2, a_3, b_3, and c_3 represent any numbers, the arrangement

$$\begin{vmatrix} a_1 & b_1 & c_1 \\ a_2 & b_2 & c_2 \\ a_3 & b_3 & c_3 \end{vmatrix}$$

is called a *determinant of the third order*. By definition its value may be written

$$\begin{vmatrix} a_1 & b_1 & c_1 \\ a_2 & b_2 & c_2 \\ a_3 & b_3 & c_3 \end{vmatrix} = a_1b_2c_3 + a_2b_3c_1 + a_3b_1c_2 - a_3b_2c_1 - a_2b_1c_3 - a_1b_3c_2$$

There are various ways of evaluating a determinant of the third order. If the student does not expect to use determinants of higher order than the third, the following is an easily remembered rule:

1. *Repeat the first and second columns of the determinant at the right of the determinant.*
2. *Form the products of the numbers in each full diagonal running downward to the right.*
3. *Form the products of the numbers in each full diagonal running upward to the right.*
4. *Subtract the algebraic sum of the products in step 3 from the algebraic sum of the products in step 2.*

This method is valid for a determinant of the third order, *but not for one of any higher order.*

The arrangement is illustrated below.

$$\begin{matrix} & & & - & - & - \\ \mathbf{a_1} & \mathbf{b_1} & \mathbf{c_1} & a_1 & b_1 & \\ \mathbf{a_2} & \mathbf{b_2} & \mathbf{c_2} & a_2 & b_2 & \\ \mathbf{a_3} & \mathbf{b_3} & \mathbf{c_3} & a_3 & b_3 & \\ & & & + & + & + \end{matrix} = a_1b_2c_3 + a_2b_3c_1 + a_3b_1c_2 - a_3b_2c_1 - a_2b_1c_3 - a_1b_3c_2$$

example 20 Evaluate the third-order determinant

$$\begin{vmatrix} 8 & -2 & 3 \\ 5 & -4 & 1 \\ -6 & 7 & 2 \end{vmatrix}$$

Arranging as described, we write

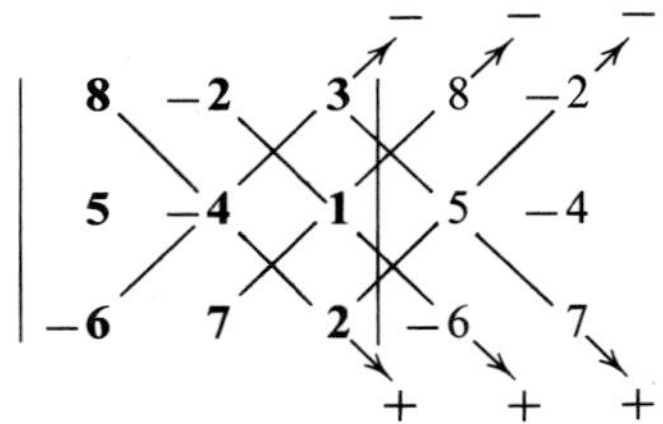

and obtain

$$(8)(-4)(2) + (-2)(1)(-6) + (3)(5)(7) - (-6)(-4)(3) - (7)(1)(8) - (2)(5)(-2)$$
$$= -64 + 12 + 105 - 72 - 56 + 20$$
$$= -55$$

7·14 Method of minors applied to determinants of any order

The utility of the diagonal method described above is limited to third-order determinants. For the solution of determinants of any order whatever, the method of minors is applicable. The expansion of a third-order determinant may be written

$$\begin{vmatrix} a_1 & b_1 & c_1 \\ a_2 & b_2 & c_2 \\ a_3 & b_3 & c_3 \end{vmatrix} = a_1\begin{vmatrix} b_2 & c_2 \\ b_3 & c_3 \end{vmatrix} - a_2\begin{vmatrix} b_1 & c_1 \\ b_3 & c_3 \end{vmatrix} + a_3\begin{vmatrix} b_1 & c_1 \\ b_2 & c_2 \end{vmatrix} \tag{49}$$

The first of the second-order determinants is formed by removing from the third-order determinant the row and column containing the element a_1, the second by removing the row and column containing the element a_2, and the third by removing the row and column containing the element a_3.

The determinant that remains after removing the row and column containing a particular element is called the *minor* of that element. Thus in Eq. (49),

$$\begin{vmatrix} b_1 & c_1 \\ b_3 & c_3 \end{vmatrix}$$

is the minor of a_2, and a_2 is called the *cofactor* of this minor.

In Eq. (49) the third-order determinant has been expanded by minors of the first column. Other definitive equations which are algebraically equivalent could be written in place of Eq. (49). For example, by methods discussed in Sec. 7·11, Eq. (49) is equivalent to

$$a_1(b_2c_3 - b_3c_2) - a_2(b_1c_3 - b_3c_1) + a_3(b_1c_2 - b_2c_1)$$

or

$$a_1b_2c_3 - a_1b_3c_2 - a_2b_1c_3 + a_2b_3c_1 + a_3b_1c_2 - a_3b_2c_1 \tag{50}$$

Equation (50) can be regrouped in a variety of ways; for example,

$$a_1(b_2c_3 - b_3c_2) - b_1(a_2c_3 - a_3c_2) + c_1(a_2b_3 - a_3b_2)$$

which is equivalent to

$$a_1\begin{vmatrix} b_2 & c_2 \\ b_3 & c_3 \end{vmatrix} - b_1\begin{vmatrix} a_2 & c_2 \\ a_3 & c_3 \end{vmatrix} + c_1\begin{vmatrix} a_2 & b_2 \\ a_3 & b_3 \end{vmatrix} \tag{51}$$

Therefore Eq. (51), in which we have expanded the determinant by minors of the first row, is equivalent to the third-order determinant in Eq. (49).

Equation (50) could also be regrouped to give

$$a_3(b_1c_2 - b_2c_1) - b_3(a_1c_2 - a_2c_1) + c_3(a_1b_2 - a_2b_1)$$

which is equivalent to

$$a_3\begin{vmatrix} b_1 & c_1 \\ b_2 & c_2 \end{vmatrix} - b_3\begin{vmatrix} a_1 & c_1 \\ a_2 & c_2 \end{vmatrix} + c_3\begin{vmatrix} a_1 & b_1 \\ a_2 & b_2 \end{vmatrix} \tag{52}$$

Therefore Eq. (52), in which we have expanded by minors of the third row, is also equivalent to the third-order determinant in Eq. (49). Other equivalent defining equations can be developed by the student from Eq. (50).

When a determinant is expanded by minors, the signs can be determined as follows:

Add the number of the column and the number of the row in which an element lies. If the sum is even, that element is preceded by a plus sign; if the sum is odd, by a minus sign. Thus in Eq. (49) the coefficient of the second group is preceded by a minus sign, since a_2 is in the first column and the second row.

The general procedure of expansion by minors is applicable to determinants of fourth or higher order. Thus a fourth-order determinant will have as minors of its elements four determinants of the third order. Each of these third-order determinants will expand into three second-order determinants. In this way a fourth-order determinant expands into 12 second-order determinants, a fifth-order determinant into 60 of the second order, and so on.

If one of the elements of a determinant is zero, the work may be simplified by using minors of the elements in the same row or column (see Example 22).

example 21 Evaluate the determinant

$$\begin{vmatrix} 8 & -2 & 3 \\ 5 & -4 & 1 \\ -6 & 7 & 2 \end{vmatrix}$$

Expanding by minors of the third column (we might have chosen any column or any row), we obtain

$$\begin{vmatrix} 8 & -2 & 3 \\ 5 & -4 & 1 \\ -6 & 7 & 2 \end{vmatrix} = 3\begin{vmatrix} 5 & -4 \\ -6 & 7 \end{vmatrix} - 1\begin{vmatrix} 8 & -2 \\ -6 & 7 \end{vmatrix} + 2\begin{vmatrix} 8 & -2 \\ 5 & -4 \end{vmatrix}$$

$$= 3[(5)(7) - (-6)(-4)] - 1[(8)(7) - (-6)(-2)] + 2[(8)(-4) - (5)(-2)]$$

$$= 3(35 - 24) - 1(56 - 12) + 2(-32 + 10) = 33 - 44 - 44 = -55$$

example 22 Evaluate the determinant

$$\begin{vmatrix} 3 & 0 & -2 & 1 \\ 4 & -5 & 2 & -3 \\ -1 & 6 & 0 & -4 \\ 7 & 1 & -6 & 5 \end{vmatrix}$$

Expanding by minors of the first row (since it contains a zero),

$$3\begin{vmatrix} -5 & 2 & -3 \\ 6 & 0 & -4 \\ 1 & -6 & 5 \end{vmatrix} - 0\begin{vmatrix} 4 & 2 & -3 \\ -1 & 0 & -4 \\ 7 & -6 & 5 \end{vmatrix} + (-2)\begin{vmatrix} 4 & -5 & -3 \\ -1 & 6 & -4 \\ 7 & 1 & 5 \end{vmatrix} - 1\begin{vmatrix} 4 & -5 & 2 \\ -1 & 6 & 0 \\ 7 & 1 & -6 \end{vmatrix}$$

Taking minors of the second row of the first determinant, since it contains a zero, the first term equals

$$3\left\{-6\begin{vmatrix} 2 & -3 \\ -6 & 5 \end{vmatrix} + 0\begin{vmatrix} -5 & -3 \\ 1 & 5 \end{vmatrix} - (-4)\begin{vmatrix} -5 & 2 \\ 1 & -6 \end{vmatrix}\right\}$$
$$= 3[-6(10 - 18) + 0 + 4(30 - 2)] = 3(48 + 112) = 480$$

The value of the second term is zero.

Taking minors of the first row, the third term equals

$$-2\left\{4\begin{vmatrix} 6 & -4 \\ 1 & 5 \end{vmatrix} - (-5)\begin{vmatrix} -1 & -4 \\ 7 & 5 \end{vmatrix} + (-3)\begin{vmatrix} -1 & 6 \\ 7 & 1 \end{vmatrix}\right\}$$
$$= -2[4(30 + 4) + 5(-5 + 28) - 3(-1 - 42)]$$
$$= -2(136 + 115 + 129) = -760$$

Taking minors of the second row, the fourth term equals

$$-1\left\{-(-1)\begin{vmatrix} -5 & 2 \\ 1 & -6 \end{vmatrix} + 6\begin{vmatrix} 4 & 2 \\ 7 & -6 \end{vmatrix} - 0\begin{vmatrix} 4 & -5 \\ 7 & 1 \end{vmatrix}\right\}$$
$$= -1[30 - 2 + 6(-24 - 14) - 0] = -1(28 - 228) = 200$$

Hence the value of the fourth-order determinant is

$$480 - 0 - 760 + 200 = -80$$

7·15 Simplifying determinants

The following theorem is of considerable importance in reducing the labor of evaluating determinants.

THEOREM: *The value of a determinant is not changed if all the elements in any column or row are multiplied by the same number and either added to or subtracted from the corresponding elements in another column or row.*

The proof of this theorem may be found in texts on college algebra. We shall not prove it formally, but we shall illustrate its use.

By reference to Eq. (49), it is evident that if one of the cofactors a_1, a_2, or a_3 is zero, then the product of it and its associated minor will also be zero, and no particular arithmetical work is involved in evaluating the product.

Frequently, we can, by the use of the above theorem, take a given determinant and from it write an equal determinant in which one or more elements in a row or column are zero. If we then choose our minors from this row or column, we know without further calculation that the products of these zero cofactors and their associated minors are zero.

By this method let us evaluate the third-order determinant given in Example 21.

Multiply the third column by 5 and subtract from the first column, obtaining

$$\begin{vmatrix} -7 & -2 & 3 \\ 0 & -4 & 1 \\ -16 & 7 & 2 \end{vmatrix}$$

Multiply the third column by 4 and add to the second column, obtaining

$$\begin{vmatrix} -7 & 10 & 3 \\ 0 & 0 & 1 \\ -16 & 15 & 2 \end{vmatrix}$$

This determinant may be expressed as

$$-1\begin{vmatrix} -7 & 10 \\ -16 & 15 \end{vmatrix} = -1(-105 + 160) = -55$$

Note that in this problem we were fortunately able to retain the cofactor 1, which reduced the arithmetical labor also.

As another example let us simplify the fourth-order determinant given in Example 22.

Multiply the fourth column by 3 and subtract from the first column, obtaining

$$\begin{vmatrix} 0 & 0 & -2 & 1 \\ 13 & -5 & 2 & -3 \\ 11 & 6 & 0 & -4 \\ -8 & 1 & -6 & 5 \end{vmatrix}$$

Multiply the fourth column by 2 and add to the third column, obtaining

$$\begin{vmatrix} 0 & 0 & 0 & 1 \\ 13 & -5 & -4 & -3 \\ 11 & 6 & -8 & -4 \\ -8 & 1 & 4 & 5 \end{vmatrix}$$

This reduces to

$$-1\begin{vmatrix} 13 & -5 & -4 \\ 11 & 6 & -8 \\ -8 & 1 & 4 \end{vmatrix}$$

Multiply the second column by 8 and add to the first column, obtaining

$$-1\begin{vmatrix} -27 & -5 & -4 \\ 59 & 6 & -8 \\ 0 & 1 & 4 \end{vmatrix}$$

Multiply the second column by 4 and subtract from the third column, obtaining

$$-1\begin{vmatrix} -27 & -5 & 16 \\ 59 & 6 & -32 \\ 0 & 1 & 0 \end{vmatrix}$$

This reduces to

$$(-1)(-1)\begin{vmatrix} -27 & 16 \\ 59 & -32 \end{vmatrix} = (-27)(-32) - (59)(16) = -80$$

EXERCISE 8

Evaluate each of the following determinants as directed by the instructor:

1. $\begin{vmatrix} 2 & -1 & 3 \\ 4 & 5 & -2 \\ 1 & -3 & 1 \end{vmatrix}$

2. $\begin{vmatrix} 5 & 4 & 3 \\ 0 & 6 & 2 \\ 1 & 1 & 7 \end{vmatrix}$

3. $\begin{vmatrix} 4 & 0 & -2 \\ 7 & 8 & 3 \\ -5 & 0 & 1 \end{vmatrix}$

4. $\begin{vmatrix} 8 & 7 & -6 \\ 2 & 1 & 4 \\ 3 & -1 & 0 \end{vmatrix}$

5. $\begin{vmatrix} 6 & 2 & 1 \\ -3 & 4 & -5 \\ 3 & -1 & 2 \end{vmatrix}$

6. $\begin{vmatrix} 7 & 0 & -2 \\ -3 & 1 & 4 \\ 6 & 3 & 5 \end{vmatrix}$

7. $\begin{vmatrix} 4 & -4 & a \\ 3 & 5 & a \\ 2 & -1 & a \end{vmatrix}$

8. $\begin{vmatrix} 11 & 2 & -3 \\ -10 & 1 & 4 \\ 9 & 5 & 3 \end{vmatrix}$

9. $\begin{vmatrix} 2 & 3 & a+b \\ 1 & -4 & b+c \\ 5 & -1 & a+c \end{vmatrix}$

10. $\begin{vmatrix} m & -2 & 3 \\ 4 & 2 & 5 \\ 1 & -1 & m \end{vmatrix}$

11. $\begin{vmatrix} 1 & 2 & 0 & 5 \\ 3 & 0 & 7 & 4 \\ 0 & -6 & 1 & -1 \\ 4 & 3 & 0 & -2 \end{vmatrix}$

12. $\begin{vmatrix} 7 & 2 & 5 & -1 \\ 4 & 3 & 6 & 1 \\ 8 & 0 & 9 & -2 \\ -3 & 4 & 2 & 1 \end{vmatrix}$

13. $\begin{vmatrix} 5 & 2 & -3 & 8 \\ 4 & -1 & 0 & -2 \\ 0 & 3 & -4 & 1 \\ 6 & 0 & 3 & 5 \end{vmatrix}$
14. $\begin{vmatrix} 6 & 4 & 0 & -1 \\ 1 & 3 & -5 & m \\ 2 & 0 & -4 & 0 \\ 7 & -3 & 1 & -2m \end{vmatrix}$

15. Show that the equivalent of Eq. (13), p. 125, in determinant form is

$$A = \frac{1}{2}\begin{vmatrix} x_1 & y_1 & 1 \\ x_2 & y_2 & 1 \\ x_3 & y_3 & 1 \end{vmatrix}$$

16. Show that the equivalent of Eq. (8*b*), p. 119, in determinant form is

$$\begin{vmatrix} x & y & 1 \\ x_1 & y_1 & 1 \\ x_2 & y_2 & 1 \end{vmatrix} = 0$$

7·16 Determinant formulas for the solution of linear equations in three unknowns

The application of Cramer's rule to the solution of a system of three linear equations in three unknowns is entirely comparable to that used in the solution of two simultaneous equations in two unknowns.

In solving the system

$$\begin{aligned} a_1x + b_1y + c_1z &= k_1 \\ a_2x + b_2y + c_2z &= k_2 \\ a_3x + b_3y + c_3z &= k_3 \end{aligned}$$

we obtain, by a method entirely analogous to that used in Sec. 7·12,

$$x = \frac{\begin{vmatrix} k_1 & b_1 & c_1 \\ k_2 & b_2 & c_2 \\ k_3 & b_3 & c_3 \end{vmatrix}}{\begin{vmatrix} a_1 & b_1 & c_1 \\ a_2 & b_2 & c_2 \\ a_3 & b_3 & c_3 \end{vmatrix}} \qquad y = \frac{\begin{vmatrix} a_1 & k_1 & c_1 \\ a_2 & k_2 & c_2 \\ a_3 & k_3 & c_3 \end{vmatrix}}{\begin{vmatrix} a_1 & b_1 & c_1 \\ a_2 & b_2 & c_2 \\ a_3 & b_3 & c_3 \end{vmatrix}} \qquad z = \frac{\begin{vmatrix} a_1 & b_1 & k_1 \\ a_2 & b_2 & k_2 \\ a_3 & b_3 & k_3 \end{vmatrix}}{\begin{vmatrix} a_1 & b_1 & c_1 \\ a_2 & b_2 & c_2 \\ a_3 & b_3 & c_3 \end{vmatrix}} \tag{53}$$

As in second-order determinants, the common denominator is called the *determinant of the system.*

As in the case of two equations in two unknowns, if the determinant of the system equals zero, the equations are either inconsistent, with no solution, or dependent, with infinitely many solutions.

example 23 Use determinants to solve the system

$$\begin{aligned} 10x + 3y - 6z &= -9 \\ 7x + 5y + 4z &= 12 \\ 8x - 2y - 9z &= -2 \end{aligned}$$

We note the following values:

$$\begin{array}{llll} a_1 = 10 & b_1 = 3 & c_1 = -6 & k_1 = -9 \\ a_2 = 7 & b_2 = 5 & c_2 = 4 & k_2 = 12 \\ a_3 = 8 & b_3 = -2 & c_3 = -9 & k_3 = -2 \end{array}$$

Hence

$$x = \frac{\begin{vmatrix} -9 & 3 & -6 \\ 12 & 5 & 4 \\ -2 & -2 & -9 \end{vmatrix}}{\begin{vmatrix} 10 & 3 & -6 \\ 7 & 5 & 4 \\ 8 & -2 & -9 \end{vmatrix}}$$

Expanding each determinant by minors of the first row,

$$x = \frac{(-9)\begin{vmatrix} 5 & 4 \\ -2 & -9 \end{vmatrix} - (3)\begin{vmatrix} 12 & 4 \\ -2 & -9 \end{vmatrix} + (-6)\begin{vmatrix} 12 & 5 \\ -2 & -2 \end{vmatrix}}{(10)\begin{vmatrix} 5 & 4 \\ -2 & -9 \end{vmatrix} - (3)\begin{vmatrix} 7 & 4 \\ 8 & -9 \end{vmatrix} + (-6)\begin{vmatrix} 7 & 5 \\ 8 & -2 \end{vmatrix}}$$

$$x = \frac{-9[(5)(-9) - (-2)(4)] - 3[(12)(-9) - (-2)(4)] - 6[(12)(-2) - (-2)(5)]}{10[(5)(-9) - (-2)(4)] - 3[(7)(-9) - (8)(4)] - 6[(7)(-2) - (8)(5)]}$$

$$x = \frac{-9(-45 + 8) - 3(-108 + 8) - 6(-24 + 10)}{10(-45 + 8) - 3(-63 - 32) - 6(-14 - 40)}$$

$$= \frac{333 + 300 + 84}{-370 + 285 + 324} = \frac{717}{239} = 3$$

By a similar method y and z can be calculated, giving

$$y = \frac{\begin{vmatrix} 10 & -9 & -6 \\ 7 & 12 & 4 \\ 8 & -2 & -9 \end{vmatrix}}{\begin{vmatrix} 10 & 3 & -6 \\ 7 & 5 & 4 \\ 8 & -2 & -9 \end{vmatrix}} = -5 \qquad z = \frac{\begin{vmatrix} 10 & 3 & -9 \\ 7 & 5 & 12 \\ 8 & -2 & -2 \end{vmatrix}}{\begin{vmatrix} 10 & 3 & -6 \\ 7 & 5 & 4 \\ 8 & -2 & -9 \end{vmatrix}} = 4$$

EXERCISE 9

Solve the following systems of simultaneous linear equations by determinants:

1. $\begin{aligned} x + 2y + z &= 20 \\ 3x - y + 2z &= 22 \\ 2x + y - 4z &= 7 \end{aligned}$

2. $\begin{aligned} 4x + 7y + 2z &= 21 \\ 5x + 8y - 3z &= 16 \\ -3x - 5y + 9z &= 5 \end{aligned}$

3. $\begin{aligned} 5x + 2y &= -17 \\ 3x + 7z &= 23 \\ 4y + 6z &= 36 \end{aligned}$

4. $\begin{aligned} 3x + 5y - 4z &= 9a \\ 2x - 3y + 4z &= 7b \\ -6x + y + 3z &= b - a \end{aligned}$

Suggestion for Prob. 6: Let $a = 1/x$, $b = 1/y$, $c = 1/z$, and solve for a, b, and c.

5. $\begin{aligned} -7x + y + 4z &= -16a \\ x + y - 4z &= -\ 8b \\ -x + 7y - 4z &= 16c \end{aligned}$

6. $\begin{aligned} \frac{1}{x} - \frac{1}{y} + \frac{2}{z} &= 7 \\ \frac{2}{x} + \frac{2}{y} - \frac{3}{z} &= -2 \\ -\frac{3}{x} + \frac{1}{y} + \frac{1}{z} &= 1 \end{aligned}$

7. $\begin{aligned} x - 2y - 3z + 4w &= -4 \\ 3x \qquad - z + 2w &= 16 \\ 5y + 2z - 3w &= 20 \\ 4x + y \qquad - 7w &= 10 \end{aligned}$

8. $\begin{aligned} x + 2y + 3z \qquad &= 11 \\ -x \qquad + 2z + 3w &= 9 \\ 2x - 3y \qquad - w &= -23 \\ y - z + 2w &= -1 \end{aligned}$

Problems in Exercises 2 through 5 may be worked by determinants as directed by the instructor.

7·17 Application of simultaneous linear equations to Kirchhoff's law

Figure 7·9 is an idealized diagram of considerable importance if batteries are operated in parallel. Ordinarily, in such problems the given circuit parameters are the resistances R_1, R_2, and R_3 and the battery voltages E_1 and E_2. The problem is to solve for the currents I_1 and I_2. The arrows next to the resistors indicate the direction in which the current is assumed to flow. Should either I_1 or I_2 come out negative, it simply means that the assumed direction of current flow was wrong, but if the solution is otherwise correct the absolute value of the current will be correct.

The basic equations for the solution of this and similar problems are

$$E_1 = R_1I_1 + R_3(I_1 + I_2) \tag{54}$$
$$E_2 = R_2I_2 + R_3(I_1 + I_2) \tag{55}$$

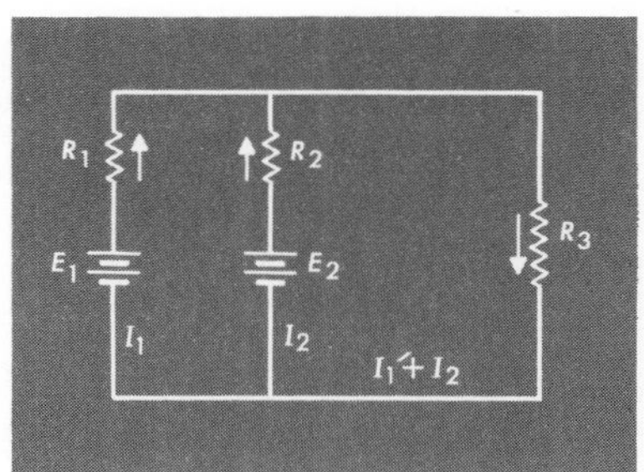

fig. 7·9

EXERCISE 10

1. Find I_1 and I_2 when the circuit parameters are as follows:

	R_1	R_2	R_3	E_1	E_2
(a)	0.05	0.10	0.75	4.5	5.2
(b)	1.50	2.30	0.50	32.0	35.5
(c)	0.10	0.01	5.00	6.0	7.5

2. (a) Solve Eq. (54) for I_1 and find under what conditions I_1 must be negative.
(b) Solve Eq. (55) for I_2 and find under what conditions I_2 must be negative.
3. If $E_1 = 5$, $E_2 = 6$, and $R_3 = 10$, find the value of R_2 so that $I_1 = 0$.
4. Show that if

$$\frac{R_2}{R_3} + 1 = \frac{E_2}{E_1}$$

then $I_1 = 0$. [Refer to Eqs. (54) and (55).]

Figure 7·10 illustrates a "bridge" circuit which is widely used for electrical measurements as well as other applications.

We shall assume that the known quantities are E, R_1, R_2, R_3, R_4, and R_5. Having been given these quantities, we shall solve for I_1, I_2, and I_3. As in the previous group of problems, the arrows next to the resistors indicate the assumed direction of current flow. Should either I_1, I_2, or I_3 come out to be negative, it means that the actual direction of current flow is exactly opposite to the assumed direction. This will not affect the absolute value of the current.

fig. 7·10

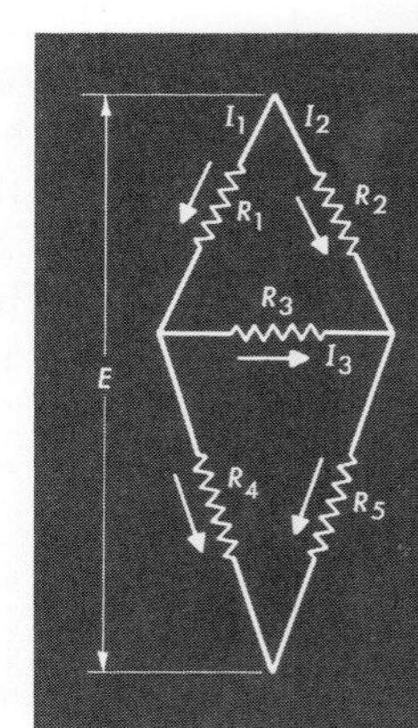

The basic equations involved are the following:

$$E = R_1I_1 + R_4(I_1 - I_3)$$
$$E = R_2I_2 + R_5(I_2 + I_3)$$
$$E = R_1I_1 + R_3I_3 + R_5(I_3 + I_2)$$

EXERCISE 11

1. Find I_1, I_2, and I_3 from the following data:

	E	R_1	R_2	R_3	R_4	R_5
(a)	10	2	3	4	5	6
(b)	5	1	5	3	8	4
(c)	1	2	6	9	5	3
(d)	2	5	9	5	3	8
(e)	25	6	9	2	5	8

2. If $I_3 = 0$, show that $R_1/R_4 = R_2/R_5$.
3. Show that Eq. (13), page 125 may be expressed by a determinant.

EXERCISE 12

Solve the following, using determinants.

1. There are three bars of metal, *A*, *B*, and *C*, having the following weight composition: *A* contains 6 parts gold, 2 parts silver, and 1 part copper; *B*, 3 parts gold, 4 parts silver, and 2 parts copper; *C*, 1 part gold, 3 parts silver, and 5 parts copper. How many ounces of each must be taken to make 28 oz of alloy containing equal parts of gold, silver, and copper?
2. The following table gives the weight composition of three alloys *A*, *B*, and *C*.

	Copper, %	*Tin, %*	*Zinc, %*
A	80	10	10
B	20	40	40
C	50	. . .	50

How many pounds each of *A*, *B*, and *C* must be mixed to produce 600 lb of an alloy containing 60 per cent copper, 10 per cent tin, and 30 per cent zinc?

3. A man wishes to apply to his garden 50 lb of a fertilizer containing 5 per cent phosphorus and 12 per cent nitrogen. He has available brand A containing 4 per cent phosphorus and 10 per cent nitrogen, brand B containing 7 per cent phosphorus and 11 per cent nitrogen, and brand C containing negligible phosphorus and 18 per cent nitrogen. How much of each brand should be taken?
4. A waste mixed acid left over from nitrating is composed of 61.8 per cent sulfuric acid, 20.1 per cent nitric acid, and 18.1 per cent water. It is required to make a mixture of 1,000 lb containing 60 per cent sulfuric acid, 23 per cent nitric acid, and 17 per cent water. Solutions of sulfuric acid (98 per cent) and nitric acid (90 per cent) are available. How many pounds each of waste acid, sulfuric acid, and nitric acid must be taken if no additional water is used?
5. A beam AF weighing 400 lb per ft is supported at points A, B, C, D, E, and F. $AB = 5$ ft, $BC = 6$ ft, $CD = 7$ ft, $DE = 5$ ft, and $EF = 4$ ft. To determine the load carried by each support, the following equations must be solved for W_2, W_3, W_4, and W_5:

$$\begin{aligned} 11W_2 + 3W_3 &= -\ 34{,}100 \\ 6W_2 + 26W_3 + 7W_4 &= -118{,}000 \\ 7W_3 + 24W_4 + 5W_5 &= -\ 93{,}600 \\ 5W_4 + 16W_5 &= -\ 37{,}800 \end{aligned}$$

6. A girder AE weighing p lb per ft is supported at five equally spaced points A, B, C, D, and E. $AB = d$ ft. To determine how much of the

load each support bears, solve the following equations for W_2, W_3, and W_4 in terms of p and d. ($W_1 = W_5 = 0$.)

$$W_1 + 4W_2 + W_3 = -\frac{pd^2}{2}$$

$$W_2 + 4W_3 + W_4 = -\frac{pd^2}{2}$$

$$W_3 + 4W_4 + W_5 = -\frac{pd^2}{2}$$

7. Fifty people wish to reach a place 27½ miles away. The only available transportation is a bus having a capacity of 30 people and a speed of 35 mph. The party is divided into two roughly equal groups, which start at the same time. The first group starts on foot, walking at an average rate of 4 mph. The second group rides on the bus a certain distance and then walks the rest of the way at an average rate of 3 mph. The bus returns to meet the first group and to carry it the rest of the way. How far should each group walk in order that all may arrive at their destination at the same time? How many hours are required for the transfer?

unit three more advanced algebra and logarithms

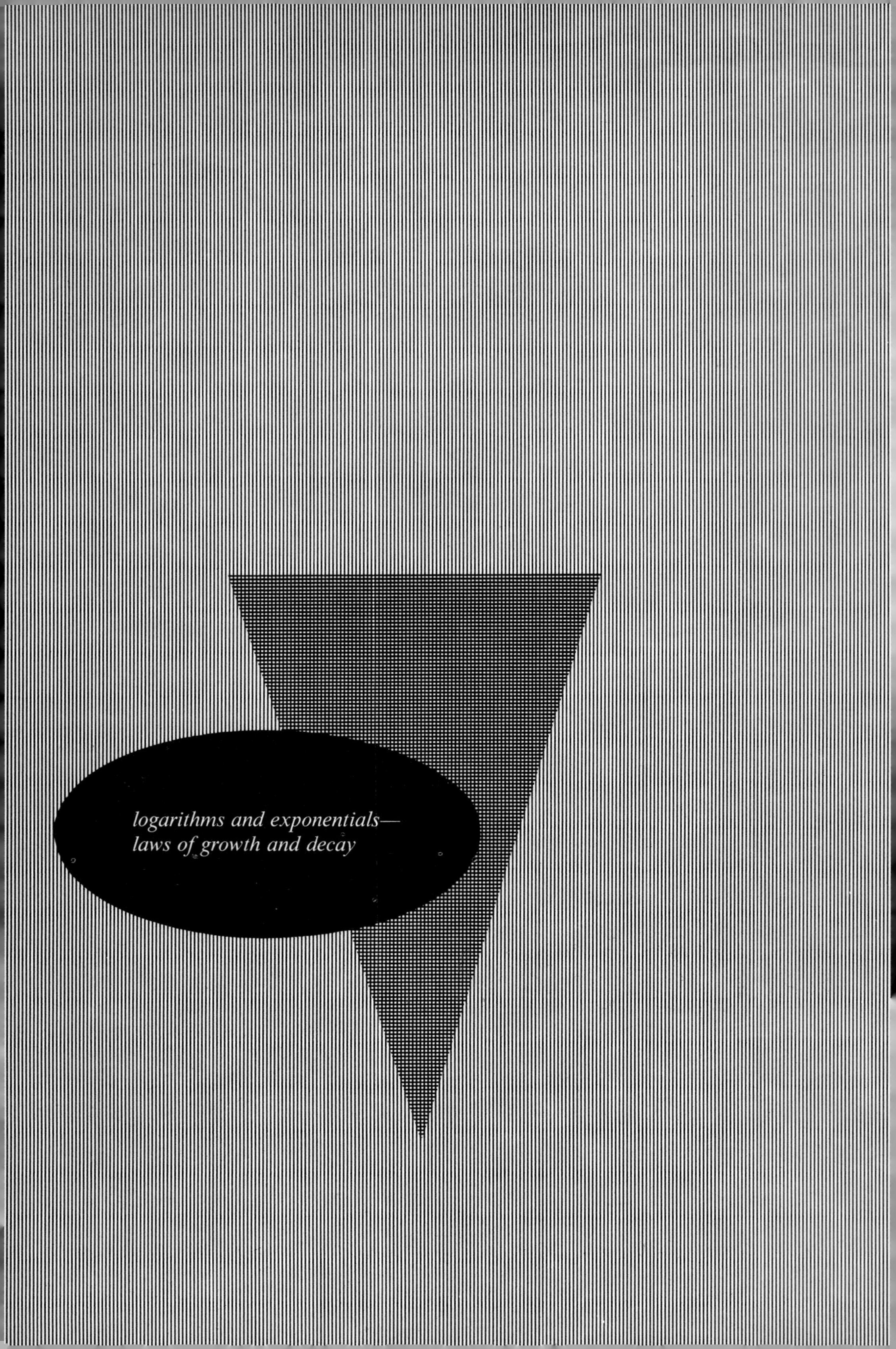
logarithms and exponentials—
laws of growth and decay

8
exponents and radicals

In Chap. 4 we discussed positive integral exponents. In this chapter we shall extend our study to cover negative, zero, and fractional exponents and the equivalent radical notation.

Fractional exponents and radicals find frequent application in engineering and mathematics.

8·1 Laws of positive integral exponents

We recall from Sec. 4·9 that a positive integral exponent of a number indicates how many times that number is to be taken as a factor. Thus

$$a^1 = a \qquad a^2 = a \cdot a \qquad a^3 = a \cdot a \cdot a$$

and in general,

$$a^n = a \cdot a \cdot a \cdots a \qquad n \text{ factors}$$

a^n is read "the nth power of a," or "a to the nth power." The quantity a is called the base and n the exponent (of the power).

The following relationships are either set forth in Sec. 4·10 or can easily be demonstrated, where m and n are assumed to be positive integers and a and b are any real numbers other than zero. The term *real number* is used here to distinguish between the kind of number which we have been using in ordinary practice and a new kind of number which we shall introduce in Secs. 8·14 and 8·15.

$$a^m \cdot a^n = a^{m+n} \tag{1}$$

For example:

$$x^7 \cdot x^5 = x^{12} \quad \text{and} \quad 2^3 \cdot 2^4 = 2^7 = 128$$

$$(a^m)^n = a^{mn} \tag{2}$$

For example:

$$(x^2)^3 = x^6 \quad \text{and} \quad (3^2)^3 = 3^6 = 729$$

$$\frac{a^m}{a^n} = a^{m-n} \quad \text{if } m > n \quad \text{or} \quad \frac{1}{a^{n-m}} \quad \text{if } n > m \tag{3}$$

For example:

$$\frac{x^8}{x^5} = x^3 \qquad \frac{x^5}{x^8} = \frac{1}{x^3} \quad \text{and} \quad \frac{5^7}{5^4} = 5^3 = 125 \qquad \frac{5^6}{5^8} = \frac{1}{5^2} = \frac{1}{25}$$

$$(ab)^n = a^n b^n \tag{4}$$

For example:

$$(2x^2)^3 = (2)^3(x^2)^3 = 8x^6 \quad \text{and} \quad (3xy^3)^4 = 3^4x^4(y^3)^4 = 81x^4y^{12}$$

$$\left(\frac{a}{b}\right)^n = \frac{a^n}{b^n} \tag{5}$$

[Note that $(1/a)^n$ may be written $1/a^n$.]

For example:

$$\left(\frac{3}{5}\right)^4 = \frac{3^4}{5^4} = \frac{81}{625} \quad \text{and} \quad \left(\frac{4x^2}{3y^3}\right)^3 = \frac{4^3(x^2)^3}{3^3(y^3)^3} = \frac{64x^6}{27y^9}$$

An even power of any number is positive; an odd power of any number has the same sign as the number. (6)

For example:

$$(-2)^4 = 16 \qquad (-2)^5 = -32 \qquad (2)^4 = 16 \qquad (2)^5 = 32$$

EXERCISE 1

Carry out the indicated operations according to the laws of exponents.

1. $x^4 \cdot x^2$
2. $y \cdot y^6$
3. $b^x \cdot b^3$
4. $c^4 \cdot c^n$
5. $3^2 \cdot 3^3$
6. $a^x \cdot a^{1-x}$
7. $a^{2y} \cdot a^{3y}$
8. $(-2)^4$
9. $(-1)(-4)^2$
10. $-(-5)^2$
11. $(-2x)^3$
12. $-(2x)^3$
13. $-(-2x)^3$
14. $(a^2)^5$
15. $(y^3)^4$
16. $(-x^3)^2$
17. $(a^n)^2$
18. $(a^2)^n$
19. $(a^n)^n$
20. $(-5x^4)^2$
21. $(5/3)^2$
22. $(-3/4)^3$
23. $(2/3 x)^5$
24. $(-3/2 x)^3$
25. $(0.2x)^3$
26. $(-0.3x^2)^4$
27. $(a^nb^2)^3$
28. $(a^2b^3)^n$
29. $(4x^2y^n)^n$
30. $(-2x^3)(-2x)^3$
31. $xy^4(xy)^4$
32. $\frac{x^7}{x^4}$
33. $\frac{a^5}{a^3}$
34. $\frac{b^8}{b}$
35. $\frac{y^2}{y^6}$
36. $\frac{x^3}{x^8}$
37. $\frac{a}{a^5}$
38. $\frac{a^2b^3}{b^5}$
39. $\frac{x^3y^3}{x^2y^4}$
40. $\frac{x^5}{x^7y^3}$

41. $\dfrac{(6x^3)^2}{(4x^2)^3}$ 42. $\dfrac{(8a^2b^3)^2}{(6ab^2)^3}$ 43. $\dfrac{(xy^2)^n}{(x^ny)^2}$ 44. $\dfrac{a^nb^{n+3}}{a^{n+1}b^{n+2}}$

45. $\dfrac{10ab^3}{15(ab)^3}$ 46. $\dfrac{0.6ab^2}{(0.2ab)^2}$ 47. $\dfrac{(ab^2c^3)^n}{(a^nb^nc^n)^2}$ 48. $\dfrac{(3)^{4m}}{(9)^{2m}}$

49. $\dfrac{4^4 + 4^4 + 4^4 + 4^4}{2^4}$ 50. $2^n + 2^n + 2^n + 2^n$

8·2 Roots and radicals

If $a^n = b$, where n is a positive integer, not only is b equal to the nth power of a, but by definition a is said to be an nth root of b. If $n = 2$, a is a square root of b; if $n = 3$, a is a cube root of b; and so on.

example 1 Since $2^3 = 8$, 2 is a cube root of 8.

example 2 Since $(-2)^3 = -8$, -2 is a cube root of -8.

example 3 Since $(-3)^2 = 9$, and $3^2 = 9$, both -3 and 3 are square roots of 9.

example 4 Since $2^5 = 32$, 2 is a fifth root of 32.

From the above examples it is apparent that a number may have more than one nth root. On the other hand we have, at this point, no method at all for finding an *even* root of a *negative* number. That is, we have no method for finding a square root, fourth, sixth, eighth, etc., root of any negative number. For example, we can find the square root of $+25$, and we know that there are two such roots. They are $+5$ and -5. However, we have, at the moment, no method for finding two *equal* factors which will multiply and give -25. The fact that $(-5)(+5) = -25$ has no bearing on the problem, because -5 and $+5$ are not equal factors.

We shall deal with the problem of finding even roots of negative numbers in Sec. 8·14, and we shall present some extremely important applications of these methods in Chap. 23.

For the present we shall exclude from the discussion any consideration of even roots of negative numbers.

This brings us to the definition of principal root.

8·3 Principal roots

The nth root of the quantity b is written $\sqrt[n]{b}$, except that when $n = 2$, we simply write $\sqrt{b}$. However, without further definition, this symbol may be somewhat ambiguous. For example, does $\sqrt{9}$ mean $+3$ or -3? The answer is found in the concept of *principal root*.

Excluding even roots of negative numbers, which we are not ready to handle yet, the principal root of a number has the same sign as the number itself. Thus: $\sqrt{+16} = +4$, and $+4$ is the principal square root of $+16$; $\sqrt[3]{-8} = -2$, and the principal cube root of -8 is -2; $\sqrt[3]{+8} = +2$, and the principal cube root of $+8$ is $+2$.

example 5 $\sqrt{9} = 3$. Note that $\sqrt{9}$ is not equal to -3 even though -3 is one of the square roots of 9. When we wish to designate the negative square root of 9, we write $-\sqrt{9}$, so that $-\sqrt{9} = -3$ and $\sqrt{9} = 3$.

example 6 $\sqrt{36} = 6$, since $6^2 = 36$.

example 7 $\sqrt[3]{-125} = -5$, since $(-5)^3 = -125$.

example 8 $\sqrt[4]{16} = 2$, since $2^4 = 16$.

example 9 $\sqrt[5]{243} = 3$, since $3^5 = 243$.

example 10 $\sqrt{9/25} = 3/5$, since $(3/5)^2 = 9/25$.

example 11 $\sqrt[3]{8x^6y^9} = 2x^2y^3$, since $(2x^2y^3)^3 = 8x^6y^9$.

These examples illustrate the following rules:

If b is positive and n is even or odd, $\sqrt[n]{b}$ is positive. (7)
If b is negative and n is odd, $\sqrt[n]{b}$ is negative. (8)
If b is negative and n is even, no real root exists. (9)

In the notation $\sqrt[n]{b}$, the symbol $\sqrt{\ }$ is called the *radical* sign, n is the *index* of the root, and b is the *radicand*. Where n does not appear, as in $\sqrt{b}$, the square root of b is understood.

EXERCISE 2

In Probs. 1 to 8, write in radical form the principal roots of the numbers indicated and find their values.

1. The cube root of -8
2. The cube root of 8
3. The fourth root of 81
4. The fifth root of -32
5. The square root of $1/25$
6. The sixth root of $1/64$
7. The square root of 49
8. The cube root of $27/125$

Find the principal value of each of the following:

9. $\sqrt{25}$
10. $\sqrt{121}$
11. $\sqrt{64}$
12. $\sqrt{225}$
13. $\sqrt[3]{27}$
14. $\sqrt[3]{64}$
15. $\sqrt{144}$
16. $\sqrt[3]{-27}$
17. $\sqrt[4]{16}$
18. $\sqrt[3]{1}$
19. $\sqrt[3]{-1}$
20. $\sqrt[5]{32}$
21. $\sqrt{0.04}$
22. $\sqrt[3]{0.125}$
23. $\sqrt{1600}$
24. $\sqrt{9/49}$
25. $\sqrt[3]{-27/125}$
26. $\sqrt[3]{1/8}$
27. $\sqrt{4a^2b^4c^6}$
28. $\sqrt[3]{8m^6n^9}$

29. $\sqrt[4]{\dfrac{a^4x^8}{c^{12}}}$

30. $\sqrt[5]{\dfrac{-x^{10}y^{20}}{32}}$

31. $\sqrt{0.0169x^{16}}$

32. $\sqrt[3]{0.008a^{27}}$

8·4 Rational and irrational numbers

In Sec. 4·1 the distinction between rational and irrational numbers was brought out. A real *rational* number can be expressed as the *ratio* of one integer to another. *Irrational* numbers are numbers that cannot be so expressed.

An example of an irrational number is $\sqrt{2}$. There exists a real number, approximately 1.414, which, when squared, equals 2. But this number ($\sqrt{2}$), though real, cannot be expressed by an integer or the ratio of two integers. Other examples of real but irrational numbers are $\sqrt[3]{5}$, $\sqrt{6}$, $\sqrt[5]{-7}$, and π.

8·5 Fractional exponents

So far we have considered only positive integral values of n. We shall require that the rules for positive integral exponents shall apply to negative, fractional, and zero exponents and thus see what significance we must, as a consequence, attribute to these kinds of exponents.

At present the expression a^2 indicates that a is taken twice as a factor, but it is meaningless to say that $a^{1/2}$ indicates that a is taken one-half a time. However, if we require that Sec. 4·9 hold, we may write

$$a^{1/2} \cdot a^{1/2} = a^{1/2+1/2} = a^1 = a$$

Evidently, then, $a^{1/2}$ is one of two equal factors of a, and hence

$$a^{1/2} = \sqrt{a}$$

Similarly, $a^{1/3}$ assumes a definite meaning if we write

$$a^{1/3} \cdot a^{1/3} \cdot a^{1/3} = a^{1/3+1/3+1/3} = a^1 = a$$

The expression $a^{1/3}$ is one of three equal factors of a, and hence

$$a^{1/3} = \sqrt[3]{a}$$

In general, if n is a positive integer,

$$a^{1/n} \cdot a^{1/n} \cdot a^{1/n} \cdots a^{1/n} \quad (n \text{ factors}) = a^{n/n} = a^1 = a$$

Therefore,

$$a^{1/n} = \sqrt[n]{a} \tag{10}$$

In a corresponding way we can define an expression like $a^{3/4}$ by writing

$$a^{3/4} \cdot a^{3/4} \cdot a^{3/4} \cdot a^{3/4} = a^{3/4+3/4+3/4+3/4} = a^3$$

or $$a^{3/4} = \sqrt[4]{a^3}$$

In general, if m and n are positive integers and a is a real number,

$$a^{m/n} \cdot a^{m/n} \cdot a^{m/n} \cdot \cdot \cdot a^{m/n} \quad (n \text{ factors}) = a^{mn/n} = a^m$$

Hence $$a^{m/n} = \sqrt[n]{a^m} = \left(\sqrt[n]{a}\,\right)^m \tag{11}$$

We conclude from the foregoing that a fractional exponent is equivalent to a radical. The numerator m indicates a power, and the denominator n a root. It is understood in this discussion that $a^{m/n}$ will be defined as the principal nth root of a^m. Unless it is specified, we shall exclude the case in which a is negative and n is an even integer.

8·6 Zero exponent

If a is any number except zero, we can define the symbol a^0 by writing

$$a^0 = 1 \qquad a \neq 0 \tag{12}$$

This interpretation is entirely consistent, since by Sec. 4·9

$$\frac{a^m}{a^m} = 1$$

But by Eq. (3), Sec. 8·1,

$$\frac{a^m}{a^m} = a^{m-m} = a^0$$

Hence the two results must be equivalent.

8·7 Negative exponents

We may define the symbol a^{-n} as follows:

$$a^{-n} = \frac{1}{a^n} \tag{13}$$

and $$a^n = \frac{1}{a^{-n}}$$

This conclusion follows from Eq. (3), Sec. 8·1, if we let $m = 0$.

$$\frac{a^m}{a^n} = a^{m-n}$$

And if $m = 0$,

$$\frac{1}{a^n} = \frac{a^0}{a^n} = a^{0-n} = a^{-n}$$

Note that from Eq. (13) any *factor* (not any term) of the numerator or denominator of a fraction may be transferred to the denominator or numerator, as the case may be, by reversing the sign of its exponent.

example 12 $$16^{3/4} = \sqrt[4]{16^3} \quad \text{or more conveniently} \quad (\sqrt[4]{16})^3 = 2^3 = 8$$

example 13 $27^{2/3} = \sqrt[3]{27^2}$ or more conveniently $(\sqrt[3]{27})^2 = 3^2 = 9$

example 14 $12^0 = 1$

example 15 $x^0 = 1 \qquad x \neq 0$

example 16 $(4x - 7)^0 = 1 \qquad x \neq 7/4$

example 17 $3x^{-2} = \dfrac{3}{x^2}$ $\left(\text{note that we do not obtain } \dfrac{1}{9x^2}\right)$

example 18 $$(3x)^{-2} = \frac{1}{(3x)^2} = \frac{1}{9x^2}$$

example 19 $$8^{-2/3} = \frac{1}{8^{2/3}} = \frac{1}{(\sqrt[3]{8})^2} = \frac{1}{2^2} = \frac{1}{4}$$

example 20 $$\frac{5x^3y^2}{z^4} = 5x^3y^2z^{-4}$$

example 21 $$\frac{4a^3c}{by^4} = 4a^3b^{-1}cy^{-4}$$

example 22 $$\frac{1}{x^{-1} - y^{-1}} = \frac{1}{1/x - 1/y} = \frac{1}{(y - x)/xy} = \frac{xy}{y - x}$$

(A simple solution at sight depends upon multiplying numerator and denominator by xy. See Sec. 4·24.)

EXERCISE 3

Find the value of each expression.

1. $16^{1/4}$
2. $36^{1/2}$
3. 5^{-2}
4. 7^{-1}
5. $(-3)^{-3}$
6. $(49)^{-1/2}$
7. $(2/3)^{-3}$
8. $(1/32)^{1/5}$
9. $(-1/32)^{-1/5}$
10. $(0.09)^{1/2}$
11. $(0.16)^{-1/2}$
12. $\dfrac{3a^0 - b^0}{a^0 + (3b)^0}$
13. $(-3)^4$
14. $-(-3)^4$
15. $(-3)^{-4}$
16. $-(3)^{-4}$
17. 10^{-3}
18. $(-1/6)^{-1}$
19. $4^{-1} + 2^{-2}$
20. $(0.001)^{-1/3}$
21. $(-8)^{5/3}$
22. $(-27)^{4/3}$
23. $(8^{-1} - 4^{-1})^{1/3}$
24. $(-27/64)^{-2/3}$

Write each expression without negative or zero exponents and simplify.

25. $x^{2/3} \cdot x^{1/2}$
26. $y^5 \cdot y^{-5}$
27. $(16x^{16})^{1/2}$
28. $(3x^{4/3})^3$
29. $(-5^{1/2}x^{3/4}y)^4$
30. $(2^{1/3}x^{1/4}y^{1/6})^{12}$
31. $-(-3a^{0.4}b^{0.6})^5$
32. $4^{-2}ab^{-3}c$
33. $\dfrac{3x^{-3}y^2}{6^{-1}z^{-2}}$
34. $\dfrac{3^{-1}x^6}{8y^{-3}}$
35. $\dfrac{x^0y^{-1}}{x^2w^{-4}}$
36. $\left(\dfrac{10^{-3}a^6}{90}\right)^{1/2}$

37. $(x^{1/2} - x^{-1/2})^2$
38. $(m^{1/2} + n^{1/2})(m^{1/2} - n^{1/2})$
39. $(a^{1/2} - 3a^{-1/2})(a^{1/2} + 3a^{-1/2})$
40. $(x^{3/2} + x^{1/2})^4$

Evaluate, simplify, or solve as indicated:

41. $\dfrac{2^{n+4} + 2^n + 2^n}{2(2^{n+3} - 2^{n+1})}$
42. $(a^{-1} - b^{-1})(a - b)^{-1}$
43. If $3^{x+y} = 9$ and $9^{x-y} = 3$, solve for x and y.
44. If $4^{n+3} - 120 = 4^{n+1}$, solve for n.
45. $\dfrac{x^{-1} - y^{-1}}{x^{-3} - y^{-3}}$
46. If $9^x + 9^{x-1} = 30$, solve for x.

Write the following expressions without denominators, using negative exponents where necessary.

47. $\dfrac{a}{b^3}$
48. $\dfrac{1}{xy}$
49. $\dfrac{z^2}{4^2}$
50. $\dfrac{3k}{ab^2}$
51. $\dfrac{x^{1/2}y^2}{x^{1/3}y^{5/2}}$
52. $\left(\dfrac{a^{1/2}b^{1/3}}{x^2}\right)^{-6}$
53. $\left(\dfrac{a^3x^{-1}}{2by^{-2}}\right)^{-3}$
54. $\left(\dfrac{64x^{1/3}}{y^{2/3}z^{1/2}}\right)^{1/6}$

Write the following expressions in radical notation.

55. $x^{1/2}$
56. $y^{3/2}$
57. $a^{-1/2}$
58. $8x^{2/3}$
59. $x^{3/4}y^{1/4}$
60. $(4xy^2)^{1/3}$
61. $(5x^2)^{-1/3}$
62. $(a^3b^2)^{1/6}$

Using fractional exponents, write the following expressions without radicals.

63. $\sqrt{a^3}$
64. $\sqrt[3]{x^2y}$
65. $\sqrt[4]{x + y}$
66. $\sqrt[6]{a^3b^2}$
67. $\sqrt[4]{a^2b^4c^6}$
68. $\sqrt{9ab^2c^3}$
69. $\sqrt[3]{\dfrac{a^2}{8x^6}}$
70. $\sqrt{16x^2y^3z^4}$

8·8 Laws of radicals

The following laws of radicals follow directly from the laws of exponents:

$$(\sqrt[n]{a})^n = |a| \tag{14}$$

NOTE: It is often stated that $\sqrt[n]{a^n}$ also equals a, but since this rule fails when n is even and a is negative (see Example 48b, page 196) it is better stated $\sqrt[n]{a^n} = |a|$.

$$\sqrt[n]{ab} = \sqrt[n]{a} \cdot \sqrt[n]{b} \tag{15}$$

$$\sqrt[n]{\frac{a}{b}} = \frac{\sqrt[n]{a}}{\sqrt[n]{b}} \tag{16}$$

$$(\sqrt[n]{a})^m = \sqrt[n]{a^m} = a^{m/n} \tag{17}$$

These laws are valid if we assume (1) that m and n are positive integers and (2) that the radical represents a real number. We are now in a position to write radicals in a number of equivalent ways. Application of Eq. (14) is illustrated in the following example:

example 23

$$(\sqrt[3]{x^2})^3 = x^2$$

To remove factors from the radicand, apply Eq. (15) and remove from the radicand any factor which is a perfect nth power.

example 24

$$\sqrt{45} = \sqrt{(3)(3)(5)} = \sqrt{(3)^2(5)} = \sqrt{3^2} \cdot \sqrt{5} = 3\sqrt{5}$$

example 25

$$\sqrt{4a^2x^2 - 36a^2y^2} = \sqrt{4a^2(x^2 - 9y^2)} = \sqrt{4a^2} \cdot \sqrt{x^2 - 9y^2}$$
$$= 2a\sqrt{x^2 - 9y^2}$$

example 26

$$\sqrt[3]{48x^4y^6z^8} = \sqrt[3]{(2)(2)(2)(2)(3)x^4y^6z^8}$$
$$= \sqrt[3]{(2)^3x^3y^6z^6(2)(3)xz^2}$$
$$= \sqrt[3]{(2)^3x^3y^6z^6} \cdot \sqrt[3]{(2)(3)xz^2} = 2xy^2z^2\sqrt[3]{6xz^2}$$

Note that this example is worked very conveniently by shifting temporarily to exponential notation.

$$\sqrt[3]{48x^4y^6z^8} = [(2)^4(3)x^4y^6z^8]^{1/3} = (2)^{4/3}(3)^{1/3}x^{4/3}y^{6/3}z^{8/3}$$

In any case in which an exponent is an improper fraction, divide the expression involved into two factors, one raised to an integral power, the other raised to a power expressed by an exponent in the form of a proper fraction. Thus, from the above example, we obtain

$$2^1 \cdot 2^{1/3} \cdot 3^{1/3}x^1 \cdot x^{1/3} \cdot y^2 \cdot z^2 \cdot z^{2/3}$$

Rearranging, we obtain

$$(2xy^2z^2)(2^{1/3} \cdot 3^{1/3}x^{1/3}z^{2/3}) = 2xy^2z^2(2 \cdot 3xz^2)^{1/3} = 2xy^2z^2\sqrt[3]{6xz^2}$$

Exponential notation is often useful in simplifying certain types of radicals involving literal powers and roots.

example 27 Rationalize $\sqrt[n-3]{a^{2n-1}}$.

In exponential notation this becomes $a^{(2n-1)/(n-3)}$.

But
$$\frac{2n-1}{n-3} = 2 + \frac{5}{n-3}$$

Therefore
$$a^{(2n-1)/(n-3)} = a^{2+5/(n-3)} = a^2 \cdot a^{5/(n-3)} = a^2\sqrt[n-3]{a^5}$$

EXERCISE 4

Simplify the following expressions by removing factors from the radicands:

1. $\sqrt{8}$
2. $\sqrt{12}$
3. $\sqrt{40}$
4. $\sqrt{54}$
5. $5\sqrt{18}$
6. $2\sqrt{27}$
7. $3\sqrt{32}$
8. $4\sqrt{63}$
9. $\sqrt[3]{24}$
10. $\sqrt[3]{-32}$
11. $5\sqrt[3]{54}$
12. $7\sqrt[3]{192}$
13. $\sqrt[3]{-250}$
14. $4\sqrt[3]{135}$
15. $5\sqrt[4]{96}$
16. $3\sqrt[5]{96}$
17. $\sqrt{x^7}$
18. $a^2\sqrt{c^9}$
19. $\sqrt{x^3y^3}$
20. $a\sqrt{a^2b}$
21. $\sqrt{12x^3y^5}$
22. $\sqrt{50a^3b^6c^9}$
23. $\sqrt{ax^2 + bx^2}$
24. $\sqrt{a^2b^2 + a^2c^2}$
25. $\sqrt{4m^2 - 16n^2}$
26. $\sqrt{18x^3 - 27x^2y}$
27. $\sqrt[n]{a^{n+1}}$
28. $\sqrt[n-1]{a^n}$
29. $\sqrt[n+1]{a^{n+3}}$
30. $\sqrt[n-1]{a^{2n}}$
31. $\sqrt[n+1]{a^{2n+3}}$
32. $\sqrt[n-2]{a^{2n-3}}$
33. $\sqrt[3]{x^6y^{6+a}}$
34. $\sqrt[4]{x^9y^{10+a}}$
35. $\sqrt[3n]{x^{8n}y^{6n}}$
36. $\sqrt[3k-1]{x^{6k}}$

In Probs. 37 to 42, simplify the radicals as before; then compute their values by using a table of square roots and cube roots.

37. $\sqrt{5300}$
38. $\sqrt{0.000105}$
39. $\sqrt{1375}$
40. $\sqrt{1648}$
41. $\sqrt[3]{6032}$
42. $\sqrt[3]{1875}$

Any quantity multiplying a radical may be introduced under the radical sign by raising to a power corresponding to the index of the radical.

example 28

$$5\sqrt{2} = \sqrt{5^2}\cdot\sqrt{2} = \sqrt{(25)(2)} = \sqrt{50}$$

example 29

$$3ab^2\sqrt[3]{2a^2b} = \sqrt[3]{(3ab^2)^3}\cdot\sqrt[3]{2a^2b} = \sqrt[3]{(27a^3b^6)(2a^2b)}$$
$$= \sqrt[3]{54a^5b^7}$$

8·9 Rationalizing the denominator in a radical

This term refers to the elimination of fractions within a radical. The procedure is desirable in that it usually simplifies numerical computations.

To rationalize the denominator of a radical having an index n, multiply numerator and denominator of the fraction by the smallest quantity which will make the denominator a perfect nth power. Extract the nth root of the denominator [see Eq. (16)].

example 30

$$\sqrt{\frac{3}{7}} = \sqrt{\frac{3}{7}\cdot\frac{7}{7}} = \sqrt{\frac{21}{49}} = \frac{\sqrt{21}}{\sqrt{49}} = \frac{\sqrt{21}}{\sqrt{7^2}} = \frac{\sqrt{21}}{7}$$

example 31

$$\sqrt{\frac{c^3}{x^3}} = \sqrt{\frac{c^3\cdot x}{x^3\cdot x}} = \frac{\sqrt{c^3x}}{\sqrt{x^4}} = \frac{c\sqrt{cx}}{x^2}$$

example 32

$$\sqrt[3]{\frac{5m^4}{16a^2x^4}} = \sqrt[3]{\frac{5m^4\cdot 4ax^2}{16a^2x^4\cdot 4ax^2}} = \frac{\sqrt[3]{20am^4x^2}}{\sqrt[3]{64a^3x^6}} = \frac{m\sqrt[3]{20amx^2}}{4ax^2}$$

example 33 $$\sqrt{\frac{xy}{x+y}} = \sqrt{\frac{xy}{x+y}\cdot\frac{x+y}{x+y}} = \frac{\sqrt{xy(x+y)}}{\sqrt{(x+y)^2}} = \frac{\sqrt{xy(x+y)}}{x+y}$$

example 34 $$\sqrt{\frac{a}{b}-\frac{b}{a}} = \sqrt{\frac{a^2-b^2}{ab}} = \sqrt{\frac{ab(a^2-b^2)}{a^2b^2}} = \frac{\sqrt{ab(a^2-b^2)}}{\sqrt{a^2b^2}}$$
$$= \frac{\sqrt{ab(a^2-b^2)}}{ab}$$

Note that, without rationalizing the denominator, we should have to evaluate an expression such as $\sqrt{3/7}$ by writing

$$\sqrt{3/7} = \sqrt{0.42857} = 0.6547$$

or
$$\frac{\sqrt{3}}{\sqrt{7}} = \frac{1.732}{2.646} = 0.6547$$

It can readily be appreciated how much easier and faster it is to rationalize and evaluate $\sqrt{21}/7 = 4.5826/7 = 0.6547$. Tables are assumed to be used in all cases.

EXERCISE 5

In the following expressions, rationalize the denominators and remove any perfect powers from the radicands. Where possible, use tables to compute the decimal values of Probs. 1 to 17.

1. $\sqrt{1/2}$	2. $\sqrt{2/3}$	3. $6\sqrt{1/8}$	4. $9\sqrt{1/12}$
5. $6\sqrt{1/15}$	6. $15\sqrt{5/18}$	7. $\sqrt[3]{1/2}$	8. $\sqrt[3]{1/4}$
9. $8\sqrt[3]{1/16}$	10. $10\sqrt[3]{1/25}$	11. $6\sqrt[4]{1/27}$	12. $6\sqrt[4]{1/8}$
13. $\frac{1}{2}\sqrt{8/3}$	14. $\sqrt{25/32}$	15. $4\sqrt{27/80}$	16. $\sqrt[3]{16/9}$
17. $\frac{1}{3}\sqrt[3]{36/25}$	18. $\sqrt{\frac{1}{a}}$	19. $\sqrt{\frac{1}{x^3}}$	20. $x\sqrt{\frac{1}{x^5}}$
21. $\sqrt[3]{\frac{1}{a^2}}$	22. $ab\sqrt[3]{\frac{1}{a^4}}$	23. $\sqrt[3]{\frac{m}{mx^2}}$	24. $\sqrt{\frac{3x}{2y}}$
25. $\sqrt{\frac{8a^3b}{27c^3}}$	26. $\frac{a}{b}\sqrt[3]{\frac{1}{ab}}$	27. $\sqrt{\frac{a-b}{a+b}}$	
28. $\sqrt{x-2+\frac{1}{x}}$	29. $\sqrt[n]{\frac{1}{x}}$	30. $\sqrt[n+1]{\frac{1}{c^n}}$	
31. $\sqrt{\frac{1}{a^{2n+1}}}$	32. $\sqrt[3]{\frac{1}{x^{3n-1}}}$	33. $\sqrt[8]{\frac{3^7+3^7+3^7}{4^7+4^7+4^7+4^7}}$	

It should be remembered that rationalization is not always desirable. In evaluating Prob. 27 above by a desk calculator, given numerical values for a and b, there would be no advantage in using the "simplified" form $\frac{\sqrt{a^2-b^2}}{a+b}$.

8·10 Reduction of the order of a radical

The order (index) of a radical can be reduced if the radicand can be expressed as a perfect power whose exponent contains a factor which is also contained in the index of the radical.

To reduce the order of a radical:

1. *Express the radicand as a perfect power of some rational number.*
2. *Transform the radical to equivalent fractional-exponent notation.*
3. *Reduce the fractional exponent to lowest terms.*
4. *Convert back to radical form.*

example 35 Reduce the order of $\sqrt[6]{8a^3b^3}$.

$$\sqrt[6]{8a^3b^3} = \sqrt[6]{(2ab)^3} = (2ab)^{3/6} = (2ab)^{1/2} = \sqrt{2ab}$$

In general, a radical may be said to be simplified if the procedures of the preceding sections have been carried out where applicable. That is, it contains no negative or fractional exponents, the denominator of the radicand has been rationalized, all possible factors have been removed from the radicand, and the order is as small as possible.

EXERCISE 6

Simplify each of the following:

1. $\sqrt[4]{25}$	2. $\sqrt[4]{49}$	3. $\sqrt[6]{16}$	4. $\sqrt[6]{36}$
5. $\sqrt[6]{x^3y^3}$	6. $\sqrt[4]{49x^2y^4}$	7. $\sqrt[6]{25x^4y^6z^8}$	8. $\sqrt[10]{x^6y^8}$
9. $\sqrt[2n]{x^n}$	10. $\sqrt[3n]{b^3}$	11. $\sqrt[6]{1/4}$	12. $\sqrt[4]{1/25}$
13. $\sqrt[6]{\frac{1}{c^2}}$	14. $\sqrt[6]{\frac{1}{x^3}}$		

8·11 Addition and subtraction of radicals

Two radicals are said to be the *same* if they have the same radicand and the same index. Multiples of the same radical can be added or subtracted by combining their coefficients. In order to add or subtract expressions containing radicals, simplify each radical and collect and combine all multiples of the same radical. Addition of radicals which remain unlike after simplification can only be indicated. The decimal value of numerical problems can be computed approximately by the use of tables.

example 36 Add $\sqrt{96} - 3\sqrt{2/3} + 1/2\sqrt{150} - 2\sqrt{3/8}$.

Simplifying each radical,

$$4\sqrt{6} - \sqrt{6} + 5/2\sqrt{6} - 1/2\sqrt{6}$$

By the distributive law,

$$(4 - 1 + 5/2 - 1/2)\sqrt{6} = 5\sqrt{6}$$

example 37 Add $\sqrt{5x} - \sqrt{5/x} + 2\sqrt{x/5} - \sqrt[6]{25x^2}$.

Simplifying each radical,

$$\sqrt{5x} - \frac{1}{x}\sqrt{5x} + \frac{2}{5}\sqrt{5x} - \sqrt[3]{5x}$$

Adding coefficients of like radicals,

$$\left(1 - \frac{1}{x} + \frac{2}{5}\right)\sqrt{5x} - \sqrt[3]{5x} = \left(\frac{7x - 5}{5x}\right)\sqrt{5x} - \sqrt[3]{5x}$$

EXERCISE 7

Simplify and combine where possible.

1. $\sqrt{2} + 6\sqrt{2}$
2. $3\sqrt{2} - \sqrt{18}$
3. $3\sqrt{75} - 2\sqrt{27} + \sqrt{48}$
4. $\sqrt{40} - 2\sqrt{90} + \sqrt{2/5}$
5. $\sqrt{98} + \frac{1}{3}\sqrt{72} - 2\sqrt{1/8}$
6. $3\sqrt{20} - \sqrt[4]{25} - \frac{2}{3}\sqrt{180}$
7. $3\sqrt{28} + 4\sqrt{1/7} + \sqrt{112}$
8. $\sqrt{60} - \sqrt{3/5} - \sqrt{5/27}$
9. $\frac{1}{2}\sqrt{24} + 3\sqrt{2/3} - 2\sqrt{3/2}$
10. $3\sqrt[3]{6} + 2\sqrt[3]{48} - 4\sqrt[6]{36}$
11. $2\sqrt{28} - 4\sqrt{63} + 14\sqrt{1/7}$
12. $5\sqrt[3]{108} - 2\sqrt[3]{32} - 4\sqrt[3]{1/2}$
13. $\sqrt{x} + \sqrt{x^3} + \sqrt{x^5}$
14. $\sqrt{12x} - \sqrt{75x^3} + \sqrt{\frac{3}{x}}$
15. $\sqrt{\frac{x+y}{x-y}} - \sqrt{\frac{x-y}{x+y}}$
16. $\sqrt{\frac{x+2}{x-1}} - \sqrt{\frac{x-1}{x+2}}$
17. $\sqrt{(a+b)^3} - \sqrt{a+b}$
18. $\sqrt{x^5} - 4\sqrt{x^3} + 4\sqrt{x}$
19. $\sqrt{18} - \sqrt{1/3} + \sqrt{12} - \sqrt{1/8}$
20. $\sqrt{12x^4 + 48x^3 + 48x^2} - \sqrt{12x^4 + 12x^3 + 3x^2}$
21. $\sqrt{\frac{a}{b} - 3} + 2\sqrt{1 - \frac{3b}{a}} - \frac{3}{a}\sqrt{a^3b^2 - 3a^2b^3}$

8·12 Multiplication and division of radicals

A radical may ordinarily be multiplied or divided by another radical of the same order by using the formulas

$$\sqrt[n]{a} \cdot \sqrt[n]{b} = \sqrt[n]{ab}$$

and

$$\frac{\sqrt[n]{a}}{\sqrt[n]{b}} = \sqrt[n]{\frac{a}{b}}$$

When radicals of different orders are multiplied or divided, they must first be reduced to radicals of the same order. (The common index is usually the LCM of the original indices.)

example 38 Multiply $\sqrt[3]{4x^2y^2}$ by $\sqrt[3]{12a^2x^2}$.

$$\sqrt[3]{4x^2y^2} \cdot \sqrt[3]{12a^2x^2} = \sqrt[3]{48a^2x^4y^2} = \sqrt[3]{(8x^3)(6a^2xy^2)} = 2x\sqrt[3]{6a^2xy^2}$$

example 39 Divide $\sqrt[4]{8a^3c^2}$ by $\sqrt[4]{54ac^3}$.

$$\frac{\sqrt[4]{8a^3c^2}}{\sqrt[4]{54ac^3}} = \sqrt[4]{\frac{8a^3c^2}{54ac^3}} = \sqrt[4]{\frac{4a^2}{27c}} = \sqrt[4]{\frac{4a^2}{27c} \cdot \frac{3c^3}{3c^3}} = \frac{1}{3c}\sqrt[4]{12a^2c^3}$$

example 40 Multiply $2\sqrt{6} - \sqrt{3}$ by $3\sqrt{3} - \sqrt{2}$.

$$\begin{array}{l} \quad 2\sqrt{6} - \sqrt{3} \\ 3\sqrt{3} - \sqrt{2} \\ \hline 6\sqrt{18} - 3(3) - 2\sqrt{12} + \sqrt{6} = 18\sqrt{2} - 9 - 4\sqrt{3} + \sqrt{6} \end{array}$$

example 41 Multiply $\sqrt{2}$ by $\sqrt[3]{4}$.

$$\sqrt{2} \cdot \sqrt[3]{4} = \sqrt[6]{8} \cdot \sqrt[6]{16} = \sqrt[6]{128} = 2\sqrt[6]{2}$$

example 42 Divide $\sqrt[3]{9}$ by $\sqrt{3}$.

$$\sqrt[3]{9} \div \sqrt{3} = \sqrt[6]{81} \div \sqrt[6]{27} = \sqrt[6]{81/27} = \sqrt[6]{3}$$

Alternative solution:

$$\begin{aligned} \sqrt[3]{9} \div \sqrt{3} &= \sqrt[3]{3^2} \div \sqrt{3} \\ &= 3^{2/3} \div 3^{1/2} \\ &= 3^{2/3-1/2} \\ &= 3^{1/6} = \sqrt[6]{3} \end{aligned}$$

8·13 Division by an irrational binomial

In one important case of division of radicals, the divisor is a binomial, in which one or both terms contain a second-degree radical. The division is effected by rationalizing the binomial divisor. This is done by multiplying the numerator and denominator of the fraction by the *conjugate* of the denominator, i.e., the denominator with the sign between its terms reversed. Simplify the new numerator and denominator. Similar methods can be applied to other special forms. This method will be extremely important in complex numbers and vector division (see Secs. 8·16 and 23·16).

example 43 Rationalize the denominator of

$$\frac{12}{5 - \sqrt{7}}$$

Multiplying numerator and denominator by the conjugate of $5 - \sqrt{7}$, we obtain

$$\frac{12}{5-\sqrt{7}} = \frac{12(5+\sqrt{7})}{(5-\sqrt{7})(5+\sqrt{7})}$$

$$\frac{12(5+\sqrt{7})}{5^2-(\sqrt{7})^2} = \frac{12(5+\sqrt{7})}{25-7} = \frac{12(5+\sqrt{7})}{18} = \frac{2(5+\sqrt{7})}{3}$$

example 44 Rationalize the denominator of

$$\frac{\sqrt{6}+3\sqrt{2}}{3\sqrt{6}+2\sqrt{3}}$$

Multiplying numerator and denominator by $3\sqrt{6}-2\sqrt{3}$,

$$\begin{aligned}\frac{\sqrt{6}+3\sqrt{2}}{3\sqrt{6}+2\sqrt{3}} &= \frac{(\sqrt{6}+3\sqrt{2})(3\sqrt{6}-2\sqrt{3})}{(3\sqrt{6}+2\sqrt{3})(3\sqrt{6}-2\sqrt{3})}\\ &= \frac{(3)(6)-2\sqrt{18}+9\sqrt{12}-6\sqrt{6}}{(3\sqrt{6})^2-(2\sqrt{3})^2}\\ &= \frac{18-6\sqrt{2}+18\sqrt{3}-6\sqrt{6}}{54-12}\\ &= \frac{6(3-\sqrt{2}+3\sqrt{3}-\sqrt{6})}{42}\\ &= \frac{3-\sqrt{2}+3\sqrt{3}-\sqrt{6}}{7}\end{aligned}$$

example 45 Rationalize the denominator of

$$\frac{\sqrt{a+1}-\sqrt{a-1}}{\sqrt{a+1}+\sqrt{a-1}}$$

Multiplying numerator and denominator by $\sqrt{a+1}-\sqrt{a-1}$,

$$\begin{aligned}\frac{(\sqrt{a+1}-\sqrt{a-1})(\sqrt{a+1}-\sqrt{a-1})}{(\sqrt{a+1}+\sqrt{a-1})(\sqrt{a+1}-\sqrt{a-1})} &= \frac{a+1-2\sqrt{a^2-1}+a-1}{(a+1)-(a-1)}\\ &= \frac{2a-2\sqrt{a^2-1}}{2} = a-\sqrt{a^2-1}\end{aligned}$$

EXERCISE 8

Perform the indicated operations and simplify the results. Where possible, use tables to compute the decimal values of answers containing no literal expressions.

1. $\sqrt{2}\cdot\sqrt{3}$
2. $\sqrt{3}\cdot\sqrt{6}$
3. $\sqrt{7}\cdot\sqrt{14}$
4. $3\sqrt{2}\cdot\sqrt{10}$
5. $2\sqrt{11}\cdot 3\sqrt{11}$
6. $4\sqrt{15}\cdot\sqrt{21}$
7. $\sqrt{6a}\cdot\sqrt{2ab}$
8. $2\sqrt{xy}\cdot\sqrt{yz}$
9. $\sqrt{abc}\cdot\sqrt{bcd}$
10. $\sqrt[3]{4}\cdot\sqrt[3]{6}$
11. $\sqrt[3]{18}\cdot\sqrt[3]{15}$
12. $\sqrt[3]{xy^2z}\cdot\sqrt[3]{x^2yz}$
13. $\sqrt[3]{4}\cdot\sqrt{6}$
14. $\sqrt[3]{9}\cdot\sqrt{3}$
15. $\sqrt[4]{8}\cdot\sqrt{2}$
16. $\sqrt[4]{27}\cdot\sqrt{3}$
17. $(\sqrt{10}+\sqrt{3})(\sqrt{10}-\sqrt{3})$
18. $(7+\sqrt{5})(7-\sqrt{5})$
19. $(5-3\sqrt{2})(5+3\sqrt{2})$
20. $(5\sqrt{6}-2\sqrt{10})(5\sqrt{6}+2\sqrt{10})$
21. $(\sqrt{6}-\sqrt{3})^2$

22. $(7 - 2\sqrt{5})^2$

23. $(\sqrt{3} + \sqrt{2})(3\sqrt{3} - 2\sqrt{2})$

24. $(2\sqrt{6} - \sqrt{3})(\sqrt{6} + 3\sqrt{2})$

25. $(\sqrt{6} + 2\sqrt{10})(2\sqrt{15} - \sqrt{6})$

26. $\dfrac{\sqrt{6}}{\sqrt{2}}$

27. $\dfrac{\sqrt{35}}{\sqrt{15}}$

28. $\dfrac{5\sqrt{22}}{\sqrt{11}}$

29. $\dfrac{6\sqrt{3}}{\sqrt{15}}$

30. $\dfrac{\sqrt{ab}}{\sqrt{ac}}$

31. $\dfrac{\sqrt{21xy}}{\sqrt{14yz}}$

32. $\dfrac{\sqrt[3]{4}}{\sqrt{2}}$

33. $\dfrac{\sqrt{6}}{\sqrt[3]{3}}$

34. $\dfrac{\sqrt[4]{a^3}}{\sqrt[4]{a}}$

35. $\dfrac{\sqrt[4]{27}}{\sqrt{3}}$

36. $\dfrac{\sqrt{2}}{\sqrt[4]{8}}$

37. $\dfrac{6}{\sqrt{7} - 2}$

38. $\dfrac{10}{\sqrt{13} - 3}$

39. $\dfrac{24}{10 - \sqrt{28}}$

40. $\dfrac{15}{\sqrt{17} - \sqrt{7}}$

41. $\dfrac{21}{2\sqrt{5} - \sqrt{6}}$

42. $\dfrac{\sqrt{6}}{2\sqrt{3} - \sqrt{2}}$

43. $\dfrac{\sqrt{10}}{3\sqrt{5} + 2\sqrt{2}}$

44. $\dfrac{3\sqrt{2} - \sqrt{3}}{2\sqrt{3} + \sqrt{2}}$

45. $\dfrac{4\sqrt{5} + 3\sqrt{3}}{3\sqrt{5} - 2\sqrt{3}}$

46. $\dfrac{\sqrt{a - b}}{\sqrt{a} - \sqrt{b}}$

47. $\dfrac{\sqrt{xy} + \sqrt{yz}}{\sqrt{xyz}}$

48. $\dfrac{a - x}{\sqrt{a} + \sqrt{x}}$

49. $\dfrac{x}{\sqrt{x^2 - a^2}} + \dfrac{a^2x}{\sqrt{(x^2 - a^2)^3}}$

50. $\dfrac{1}{15}\left[(3x^2 - 2a^2)(3x)\sqrt{a^2 + x^2} + 6x\sqrt{(a^2 + x^2)^3}\right]$

51. $\dfrac{1}{x + \sqrt{x^2 + a^2}}\left(\dfrac{x}{\sqrt{x^2 + a^2}} + 1\right)$

52. $-\dfrac{2}{3b^2}\left[(2a - bx)\dfrac{b}{2\sqrt{a + bx}} - b\sqrt{a + bx}\right]$

53. $\dfrac{2}{3a^2}\left[a(ax + b)^{1/2} + (ax - 2b)\dfrac{1}{2}(ax + b)^{-1/2}(a)\right]$

54. $\dfrac{2}{\sqrt{b}}\,\dfrac{1}{1 + (ax - b)/b}\,\dfrac{1}{2}\left(\dfrac{ax - b}{b}\right)^{-1/2}\left(\dfrac{a}{b}\right)$

55. Show that $\dfrac{\sqrt{3 + x} - \sqrt{3}}{x}$ approaches $\dfrac{1}{2\sqrt{3}}$ as x approaches zero.

56. If $\dfrac{p_2}{p_1} = \left(\dfrac{2}{k + 1}\right)^{k/(k-1)}$, show that $\left[\left(\dfrac{p_2}{p_1}\right)^{2/k} - \left(\dfrac{p_2}{p_1}\right)^{(k+1)/k}\right]^{1/2} \equiv \left(\dfrac{2}{k + 1}\right)^{1/(k-1)}$ $\sqrt{\dfrac{k - 1}{k + 1}}$. This simplification arises in a derivation for the theory of flow in a nozzle in thermodynamics. (Hint: First square both sides of the identity.)

57. Determine x, y, and z in terms of n so that the following will be an identity:

$$\frac{W}{LT^2} \equiv (L)^x\left(\frac{W}{L^3}\right)^y\left(\frac{W}{LT}\right)^z\left(\frac{L}{T}\right)^n$$

This problem arises in fluid mechanics, as a result of a study of pipe friction.

8·14 Imaginary numbers

Classical mathematicians (i.e., ancient Greek mathematicians) knew only the kind of numbers which we use in enumeration and in the ordinary elementary mathematical calculations. The letters which we have used thus far in algebra represent this kind of number.

The nomenclature and symbolism of our Western mathematics are dominated by the conventions of classical mathematics. Yet the Western mind has created a technology which makes demands on its mathematical symbolism not anticipated by the originators of this symbolism.

Thus, nomenclature which, from a classical point of view, is characteristically descriptive may, in the light of present usage, be ambiguous or even definitely misleading.

The words *imaginary* and *real,* as used to distinguish between two kinds of numbers, are an illustration of the ambiguity resulting from our unfortunate attempt to make classical mathematical symbols convey a meaning which they were never intended to convey. All numbers are imaginary to the extent that they are all creations of the human mind and have no physical existence. All numbers are real to the extent that they represent ideas and may be used as aids in consolidating familiar ideas and developing new ones.

Within the limits prescribed by classical mathematics, an even root of a negative number is an impossibility. That is, $\sqrt{-25}$ does not exist, for, again within the limits of classical mathematics, there are no two equal numbers which will multiply and yield -25 as a product. However, a symbolism has been developed to cover this situation. We have come to let the symbol j (sometimes i) be defined in such a way that

$$j^2 = -1 \tag{18}$$

Then

$$j = \sqrt{-1} \tag{19}$$

Now, following Eq. (15), where $a = -1$, $b = 25$, and $n = 2$,

$$\sqrt{-25} = \sqrt{-1 \times 25} = \sqrt{-1} \times \sqrt{25} = \sqrt{-1} \times 5 \tag{20}$$

or substituting Eq. (19) in Eq. (20),

$$\sqrt{-25} = j \times 5 \tag{21}$$

At this point the conservatives are willing to retreat slightly and concede that we can after all find the square root of a negative number, but that the result is "imaginary."

Actually, $\sqrt{-1}$ is an extremely useful number. True, it has no use in measuring some physical quantities like bushels of apples or in banking or in many other fields where mathematics is used. Yet, as we shall discover in Chap. 23, the number $\sqrt{-1}$ is a natural device for measuring vectors so important in alternating-current-circuit problems.

We shall use the traditional terms *real* and *imaginary* to designate each of two different kinds of numbers, but we shall bear in mind that these terms, as used in this connection, are not descriptive of everyday usage.

By definition, an *imaginary number* is a symbol in the form

$$\sqrt[n]{-b} \tag{22}$$

where n is an even integer and b is a positive real number.

By definition, a *real number* is the kind of number useful in enumeration, arithmetic, and the simple calculations.

The *imaginary unit* is, by definition, $\sqrt{-1}$. This we shall denote by the letter j, since that is the more common designation in works on engineering. Strictly mathematical texts usually use the letter i.

8·15 Operations with imaginary numbers

As a general policy, we shall require that imaginary numbers obey the same basic laws of operation that real numbers obey. Then we shall determine what meaning we may in consequence assign to these operations and hence what practical use they may be made to serve.

The imaginary unit

As was illustrated in Eq. (21), an imaginary number in the form $\sqrt{-b}$ can be written

$$\sqrt{-b} = \sqrt{-1} \times \sqrt{b} = j\sqrt{b} \tag{23}$$

Thus the square root of any negative number can be indicated as the product of the imaginary unit j and the principal root of the absolute value of the number under the radical.

Powers of j

By definition,

$$j^2 = -1$$

Then it follows from the basic rules of algebra that

$$\begin{aligned}
j^0 &= 1 \\
j^1 &= j \\
j^2 &= -1 \\
j^3 &= j^2 \times j = -j \\
j^4 &= j^2 \times j^2 = 1 \\
j^5 &= j^4 \times j = j \\
j^6 &= j^4 \times j^2 = -1
\end{aligned}$$

In general, where n is any integer,

$$j^{4n} = +1 \tag{24}$$
$$j^{4n+1} = +j \tag{25}$$
$$j^{4n+2} = -1 \tag{26}$$
$$j^{4n+3} = -j \tag{27}$$

By use of Eqs. (24) through (27), any power of j may be determined at a glance. Observe that any real, integral power of j must be either unity or j or their negatives.

EXERCISE 9

Find the value of

1. j^{10} 2. j^{6} 3. j^{15} 4. j^{985} 5. j^{-25}

Addition and subtraction of imaginary numbers

Imaginary numbers may be added and subtracted according to the rules of algebra already discussed.

example 46 Add $\sqrt{-9}$ and $\sqrt{-49}$.

$$\sqrt{-9} = j\sqrt{9} = j3$$
$$\sqrt{-49} = j\sqrt{49} = j7$$
$$\sqrt{-9} + \sqrt{-49} = j3 + j7 = j10$$

NOTE: An alternative expression is $3j + 7j = 10j$.

example 47 Subtract $\sqrt{-25}$ from $\sqrt{-121}$.

$$\sqrt{-25} = j\sqrt{25} = j5$$
$$\sqrt{-121} = j\sqrt{121} = j11$$
$$\sqrt{-121} - \sqrt{-25} = j11 - j5 = j6$$

Multiplication of imaginary numbers

Multiplication of imaginary numbers can be accomplished as illustrated below.

example 48a Multiply $\sqrt{-5}$ by $\sqrt{-7}$.

Both $\sqrt{-5}$ and $\sqrt{-7}$ are imaginary numbers and consequently must be changed to the form $j\sqrt{b}$ before multiplying.

$$\sqrt{-5} = j\sqrt{5}$$
$$\sqrt{-7} = j\sqrt{7}$$
$$\sqrt{-5} \times \sqrt{-7} = j\sqrt{5} \times j\sqrt{7} = j^2\sqrt{35} = -\sqrt{35}$$

If we had ignored the fact that $\sqrt{-5}$ and $\sqrt{-7}$ are imaginary numbers, we would have been inclined to write, according to Eq. (15),

$$\sqrt{-5} \times \sqrt{-7} = \sqrt{(-5)(-7)} = \sqrt{35}$$

which is incorrect.

example 48b $(\sqrt{-5})^2 = (j\sqrt{5})^2 = j^2(\sqrt{5})^2 = (-1)(5) = -5$
(See Rule 14*a*)
Note that if we write $\sqrt{(-5)^2}$, we obtain $\sqrt{25} = 5$, which is wrong.

example 49 Multiply $\sqrt{-5}$, $\sqrt{-7}$, and $\sqrt{-15}$.

$$\sqrt{-5} = j\sqrt{5}$$
$$\sqrt{-7} = j\sqrt{7}$$
$$\sqrt{-15} = j\sqrt{15}$$
$$\sqrt{-5} \times \sqrt{-7} \times \sqrt{-15} = j\sqrt{5} \times j\sqrt{7} \times j\sqrt{15}$$
$$= j^3\sqrt{5} \times \sqrt{7} \times \sqrt{15} = j^3\sqrt{525} = j^3 5\sqrt{21} = -j5\sqrt{21}$$

example 50 Multiply $3\sqrt{-6} + 2\sqrt{-5}$ by $3\sqrt{-3} - 7\sqrt{-11}$.

$$3\sqrt{-6} = j3\sqrt{6}$$
$$2\sqrt{-5} = j2\sqrt{5}$$
$$3\sqrt{-3} = j3\sqrt{3}$$
$$7\sqrt{-11} = j7\sqrt{11}$$

$$\begin{array}{l} j3\sqrt{6} + j2\sqrt{5} \\ \underline{j3\sqrt{3} - j7\sqrt{11}} \\ j^2 9\sqrt{18} + j^2 6\sqrt{15} - j^2 21\sqrt{66} - j^2 14\sqrt{55} \end{array}$$

Substituting for j^2 its numerical value, we obtain

$$-9\sqrt{18} - 6\sqrt{15} + 21\sqrt{66} + 14\sqrt{55}$$

Evaluating the radicals, we obtain

$$(-9 \times 4.243) - (6 \times 3.873) + (21 \times 8.124) + (14 \times 7.416)$$
$$= -38.187 - 23.238 + 170.604 + 103.824 = 213.00$$

Division of imaginary numbers

example 51 Divide $\sqrt{-30}$ by $\sqrt{-15}$.

$$\frac{\sqrt{-30}}{\sqrt{-15}} = \frac{j\sqrt{30}}{j\sqrt{15}} = \frac{\sqrt{30}}{\sqrt{15}} = \sqrt{2}$$

EXERCISE 10

Simplify:

1. $\sqrt{-27} + \sqrt{-147} - \sqrt{12}$
2. $\sqrt{-150} - \sqrt{-54} + \sqrt{216}$
3. $\sqrt{-18} + \sqrt{-72} - \sqrt{128} + \sqrt{32}$
4. $\sqrt{-63} - \sqrt{-567} + \sqrt{112}$
5. $\sqrt{-80} + \sqrt{-20} + \sqrt{-320} - \sqrt{-245}$
6. $\sqrt{-128} + \sqrt{-72} - \sqrt{-800} + \sqrt{-392}$
7. $\sqrt{-196} - \sqrt{-64} + \sqrt{-80} + \sqrt{80}$
8. $\sqrt{-192} + \sqrt{-12} - \sqrt{-48} + \sqrt{-256}$
9. $\sqrt{-32} - \sqrt{-392} + \sqrt{-128}$
10. $\sqrt{-3} \times \sqrt{-3}$
11. $\sqrt{-25y^4} \times \sqrt{-9x^2}$
12. $(-4\sqrt{-4})(-3\sqrt{-9})$
13. $-\sqrt{-27a^2} \times \sqrt{-75b^2}$
14. $j\sqrt{3} \times j\sqrt{5}$
15. $-j\sqrt{7} \times j\sqrt{15}$
16. $-j\sqrt{2} \times (-j\sqrt{5})$
17. $j5 \times j8$
18. $j5 \times (-j8)$
19. $(-j2) \times (-j3)$
20. $(2\sqrt{-5} - 3\sqrt{-2})(2\sqrt{-5} + 3\sqrt{-2})$
21. $(\sqrt{-2} + \sqrt{-3})^2$
22. $\sqrt{-5} \times \sqrt{-7} \times \sqrt{-2}$
23. $\sqrt{-3} \times \sqrt{-10} \times \sqrt{-5}$
24. $\sqrt{-15} \times \sqrt{-5} \times \sqrt{-3}$
25. $(\sqrt{-5} + \sqrt{-3})(\sqrt{-6} - \sqrt{-2})$
26. $(\sqrt{-2} + \sqrt{-5})(\sqrt{-7} + \sqrt{-6})(\sqrt{-4} - \sqrt{-9})$
27. $(\sqrt{-12} + \sqrt{-11})(\sqrt{-3} + \sqrt{-15})(\sqrt{-10} - \sqrt{-19})$
28. $\sqrt{-144} \div \sqrt{-100}$
29. $\sqrt{-294} \div \sqrt{-54}$
30. $j3 \div j^2 5$
31. $\sqrt{-160} \div \sqrt{8}$
32. $\sqrt{-320} \div \sqrt{-128}$
33. $\sqrt{-63} \div \sqrt{-18}$
34. $\sqrt{96} \div \sqrt{-32}$
35. $\sqrt{48} \div \sqrt{96}$
36. $(\sqrt{-392} \div \sqrt{-49}) \times \sqrt{196}$
37. $(\sqrt{-128} \div \sqrt{-80})(\sqrt{32} \div \sqrt{-16})$

8·16 Complex numbers

A *complex number* is an expression in the form $a + jb$, where a and b are real numbers and $j = \sqrt{-1}$.

Complex numbers are used extensively in the solution of alternating-current-circuit problems and will be discussed further in Chap. 23. For the present, we shall concentrate on the purely manipulative techniques involving complex numbers, leaving the applications until we have had a chance to cover more advanced algebra and trigonometry.

Notice that in the general form of a complex number $a + jb$, if $a = 0$, we have a pure imaginary number. If $b = 0$, we have a real number.

Addition of complex numbers

example 52 Add the complex numbers $2 + j6$, $3 - j5$, and $4 + j2$.

$$\begin{array}{r} 2 + j6 \\ 3 - j5 \\ \underline{4 + j2} \\ 9 + j3 \end{array}$$

Subtraction of complex numbers

example 53 Subtract $5 + j9$ from $8 + j4$.

$$\begin{array}{r} 8 + j4 \\ \underline{5 + j9} \\ 3 - j5 \end{array}$$

example 54 Subtract $8 - j5$ from $3 + j2$.

$$\begin{array}{r} 3 + j2 \\ \underline{8 - j5} \\ -5 + j7 \end{array}$$

Multiplication of complex numbers

Complex numbers are multiplied according to procedures already described in Sec. 4·13. After multiplication, any powers of j except the first are replaced by their equivalents (see Sec. 8·15).

example 55 Multiply $2 + j7$ by $3 - j6$.

$$\begin{array}{l} 2 + j7 \\ \underline{3 - j6} \\ 6 + j21 - j12 - j^2 42 \end{array}$$

Since $j^2 = -1$, the product can be written

$$6 + j21 - j12 + 42$$

or

$$48 + j9$$

example 56 Find the product of the general complex numbers $(a + jb)$ and $(c + jd)$ (also see Sec. 23·15). The multiplication is performed exactly as is the multiplication of any two binomials.

$$\begin{array}{l} a + jb \\ \underline{c + jd} \\ ac + jbc + jad + j^2 bd \end{array} \qquad (28)$$

By definition, $j^2 = -1$; therefore expression (28) becomes

$$ac + jbc + jad - bd \tag{29}$$

Grouping real and imaginary numbers, expression (29) becomes

$$(ac - bd) + j(bc + ad)$$

Division of complex numbers

In division of complex numbers we use the principle of rationalization described in Sec. 8·13.

example 57 Divide $5 + j8$ by $2 - j7$.

The problem can be arranged as

$$\frac{5 + j8}{2 - j7}$$

If we multiply the denominator by the conjugate of the denominator, i.e., by $(2 + j7)$ (see Sec. 8·13), we obtain

$$(2 - j7)(2 + j7) = 4 + 49 = 53$$

Thus it is a basic principle of complex numbers that the *product of a complex number and its conjugate is a real number.*

In the present problem we can multiply both numerator and denominator by the conjugate of the denominator and obtain a fraction with a complex numerator and a real denominator.

$$\frac{(5 + j8)(2 + j7)}{(2 - j7)(2 + j7)} = \frac{(5 + j8)(2 + j7)}{53}$$

The numerator can now be multiplied in the usual way.

$$\begin{array}{r} 5 + j8 \\ \underline{2 + j7} \\ 10 + j16 + j35 + j^2 56 \\ 10 + j16 + j35 - 56 \\ -46 + j51 \end{array}$$

The original fraction is now

$$\frac{-46 + j51}{53}$$

If it is desired to separate the number into its real and imaginary parts, it can be written

$$-\frac{46}{53} + j\frac{51}{53}$$

or

$$-0.868 + j0.962$$

example 58 Divide the complex number $(a + jb)$ by the complex number $(c + jd)$.

Rewriting the problem in the form of a fraction,

$$\frac{a + jb}{c + jd} \tag{30}$$

Multiplying numerator and denominator of expression (30) by $c - jd$, which is called the *complex conjugate* of $c + jd$ (see Sec. 8·13),

$$\frac{a + jb}{c + jd} = \frac{(a + jb)(c - jd)}{(c + jd)(c - jd)} \tag{31}$$

Performing the indicated multiplication to obtain the numerator of Eq. (31),

$$\begin{array}{r} a + jb \\ c - jd \\ \hline ac + jbc - jad - j^2bd \end{array}$$

Since by definition $j^2 = -1$, the above product becomes

$$ac + jbc - jad + bd$$

or, after simplification, the numerator of Eq. (31) becomes

$$(ac + bd) + j(bc - ad)$$

Performing the indicated multiplication to obtain the denominator of Eq. (31),

$$\begin{array}{r} c + jd \\ c - jd \\ \hline c^2 + jcd - jcd - j^2d^2 \end{array} \tag{32}$$

Simplifying expression (32), we obtain

$$c^2 + d^2$$

Equation (31) can now be written

$$\frac{a + jb}{c + jd} = \frac{(ac + bd) + j(bc - ad)}{c^2 + d^2}$$

or

$$\frac{a + jb}{c + jd} = \frac{ac + bd}{c^2 + d^2} + j\frac{bc - ad}{c^2 + d^2}$$

EXERCISE 11

Multiply the following:

1. $(2 + j3)(7 + j5)$
2. $(-3 - j6)(2 + j8)$
3. $(2 + j7)(4 - j5)(3 + j10)$
4. $(3 + j5)(3 - j5)$
5. $-(2 + j7)(2 - j7)$
6. $(5 + \sqrt{-6})(3 - \sqrt{-8})(2 + \sqrt{-5})$
7. $(2 + j5)^5$
8. $(1.4 + j3.6)(0.7 + j9.1)$
9. $(-0.42 - j2.7)(0.63 + j4.2)$
10. $(-8.6 + j3.6)(4.7 + j5.1)$
11. $\left(-\frac{1}{2} + j\frac{\sqrt{3}}{2}\right)^3$

Divide the following:

12. $\dfrac{1}{1 + j}$

13. $\dfrac{3 + j6}{4 - j8}$

14. $\dfrac{2 - j9}{3 + j5}$

15. $\dfrac{1 + j}{2j^5}$

16. $\sqrt{4^{-2}} \div \sqrt{0.625}$

17. $(3 - \sqrt{-5}) \div (3 + \sqrt{-5})$

18. $\dfrac{1}{4 + 2\sqrt{-3} - \sqrt{-7}}$

19. $\dfrac{1}{\sqrt{-2} - 1}$

20. $\dfrac{2\sqrt{-5} + 5\sqrt{-2}}{2\sqrt{-5} - 5\sqrt{-2}}$

21. $\dfrac{\sqrt{5} - \sqrt{-5}}{\sqrt{2} + \sqrt{-2}}$

22. $\dfrac{3 + j2}{j}$

23. $\dfrac{j}{5 - 3j}$

24. $\left(\dfrac{2 + 6j}{2 - 7j}\right)^2$

Simplify:

25. $\dfrac{(2 + 6j)(3 - 7j)}{(5 - 2j) + (6 - 4j)}$

26. $\dfrac{(1 + 7j)(2 - 3j)}{(4 - 6j) - (3 - 5j)}$

27. $\dfrac{(1.8 - 3.2j)(0.8 + 0.6j)}{(1.8 - 3.2j) + (0.8 + 0.6j)}$

28. $\dfrac{(2 + 3j)(6 - 4j)}{(2 + 3j) + (6 - 4j)}$

29. $\dfrac{(7.6 - 4.2j)(3.8 + 5.6j)}{(7.6 - 4.2j) - (3.8 + 5.6j)}$

30. $\dfrac{(10.5 - 31.6j)(24 + 15j)}{(10.5 - 31.6j) + (24 + 15j)}$

9
the binomial theorem

The binomial theorem and the progressions find application in the ready calculation of any power or root of a number and serve as the basis of derivation of many formulas and tables used in financial transactions. The binomial theorem is at the very foundation of probability and statistics, for the normal curve of distribution is based on this theorem. These expressions introduce us to the series and the sequence. A *sequence* is a succession of quantities arranged in a definite order or pattern. A *series* is the indicated sum of the quantities comprising a sequence.

9 · 1 The binomial theorem

The binomial theorem enables us to expand any power of a binomial into a series of terms. Powers of binomials occur frequently, and the application of the theorem can effect a substantial saving in time and labor. An important application of the binomial expansion will be made in Chap. 23, in which we shall use it to develop equations occurring in alternating-current theory. The binomial expansion is also the basis of several useful approximations (see Sec. B · 16).

9 · 2 Expansion of a positive integral power of a binomial

By actual multiplication the student may verify that

$$
\begin{aligned}
(a + b)^0 &= 1 \\
(a + b)^1 &= a + b \\
(a + b)^2 &= a^2 + 2ab + b^2 \\
(a + b)^3 &= a^3 + 3a^2b + 3ab^2 + b^3 \\
(a + b)^4 &= a^4 + 4a^3b + 6a^2b^2 + 4ab^3 + b^4
\end{aligned}
$$

We see from the foregoing that the expansion of the general expression $(a + b)^n$ has the following properties:

1. *The expansion contains* n + 1 *terms.*
2. *The first term is* a^n, *and in each successive term the exponent of* a *decreases by 1.*
3. *The second term is* $na^{n-1}b$, *and in each successive term the exponent of* b *increases by 1, making the last term* b^n.
4. *In any term the sum of the exponents of* a *and* b *is* n.
5. *The coefficients of terms equidistant from the ends are equal.*
6. *If the coefficient of any term is multiplied by the exponent of* a *in that term, and the product divided by the number of that term, the result is the coefficient of the next term.*

Application of the above rules leads to the following formula:

$$(a + b)^n = a^n + na^{n-1}b + \frac{n(n-1)}{2!}a^{n-2}b^2 + \frac{n(n-1)(n-2)}{3!}a^{n-3}b^3 + \cdots + b^n \qquad \textbf{(1)}$$

The notation $r!$ is read "factorial r" and denotes the product of the first r integers. Thus $3! = 1 \cdot 2 \cdot 3$; $5! = 1 \cdot 2 \cdot 3 \cdot 4 \cdot 5$; etc.

In this text we shall assume without proof that the theorem holds not only for all positive integers but also for all rational numbers, negative as well as fractional. When n is negative or fractional, we obtain an unending, or infinite, series, of which we compute as many terms as desired.

If we arrange in rows the coefficients of the expansion of a positive integral power of a binomial, we obtain the following arrangement, known as *Pascal's triangle.*

$n = 0$							1						
$n = 1$						1		1					
$n = 2$					1		2		1				
$n = 3$				1		3		3		1			
$n = 4$			1		4		6		4		1		
$n = 5$		1		5		10		10		5		1	
$n = 6$	1		6		15		20		15		6		1

It will be seen that the first and last coefficient in each row is 1 and that the second and next-to-the-last coefficients equal n. Any other coefficients may be obtained by adding the two nearest coefficients in the row above.

example 1 Expand $(2x + 3y)^4$.

Substituting $2x$ for a, $3y$ for b, and 4 for n in Eq. (1), we obtain

$$(2x + 3y)^4 = (2x)^4 + 4(2x)^3(3y) + \frac{4 \cdot 3}{2!}(2x)^2(3y)^2 + \frac{4 \cdot 3 \cdot 2}{3!}(2x)(3y)^3 + \frac{4 \cdot 3 \cdot 2 \cdot 1}{4!}(3y)^4 \qquad (2)$$

$$(2x + 3y)^4 = (2x)^4 + 4(2x)^3(3y) + 6(2x)^2(3y)^2 + 4(2x)(3y)^3 + (3y)^4 \qquad (3)$$
$$= 16x^4 + 96x^3y + 216x^2y^2 + 216xy^3 + 81y^4$$

Note that if we had referred to Pascal's triangle, we could have written Eq. (3) directly. However, Pascal's triangle is not applicable to expansions of negative and fractional powers.

example 2 Expand $\left(3x - \frac{1}{2x^2}\right)^6$.

Substituting $3x$ for a, $-\frac{1}{2}x^2$ for b, and 6 for n in Eq. (1), we obtain

$$\left[3x + \left(-\frac{1}{2x^2}\right)\right]^6 = (3x)^6 + 6(3x)^5\left(-\frac{1}{2x^2}\right) + \frac{6 \cdot 5}{2!}(3x)^4\left(-\frac{1}{2x^2}\right)^2$$
$$+ \frac{6 \cdot 5 \cdot 4}{3!}(3x)^3\left(-\frac{1}{2x^2}\right)^3 + \frac{6 \cdot 5 \cdot 4 \cdot 3}{4!}(3x)^2\left(-\frac{1}{2x^2}\right)^4$$
$$+ \frac{6 \cdot 5 \cdot 4 \cdot 3 \cdot 2}{5!}(3x)\left(-\frac{1}{2x^2}\right)^5 + \frac{6 \cdot 5 \cdot 4 \cdot 3 \cdot 2 \cdot 1}{6!}\left(-\frac{1}{2x^2}\right)^6$$
$$= 729x^6 - 729x^3 + \frac{1{,}215}{4} - \frac{135}{2x^3} + \frac{135}{16x^6} - \frac{9}{16x^9} + \frac{1}{64x^{12}}$$

Two significant points are brought out by Example 2. (1) If the terms of the binomial are at all complicated, each term should be enclosed in parentheses, with the proper coefficients and exponents as required by the binomial rule, after which the expansion may be computed. (2) If the terms of the binomial are opposite in sign and n is a positive integer, the terms of the expansion will alternate in sign, since odd powers of a negative quantity are negative, and even powers are positive.

EXERCISE 1

Expand each expression by the binomial theorem.

1. $(x + 3y)^4$
2. $(2m + k)^3$
3. $\left(w^2 + \frac{1}{2}x\right)^4$
4. $\left(\frac{2}{3}x - 6\right)^4$
5. $\left(4x + \frac{1}{2x}\right)^5$
6. $\left(\frac{2}{3}x - \frac{3}{4}y\right)^4$
7. $\left(\frac{x}{y} + \frac{y}{z}\right)^6$
8. $\left(\sqrt{x} - \frac{1}{\sqrt{x}}\right)^6$
9. $(100 - 2)^3$

9·3 The general term of the binomial expansion

In the binomial theorem [Eq. (1)] the term containing b^r, i.e., the $(r + 1)$st term, is

$$\frac{n(n-1)(n-2)\cdots(n-r+1)}{r!}a^{n-r}b^r \qquad \textbf{(4)}$$

There are several types of computation, notably in probabilities, in which it is necessary to calculate one particular term. With the foregoing formula, any term of an expansion can be found without deriving all the preceding terms.

example 3 Find the term involving y^5 in the expansion of $(x + y)^8$.

Substituting $n = 8$, $r = 5$, $a = x$, and $b = y$, we have, from expression (4),

$$\frac{8 \cdot 7 \cdot 6 \cdot 5 \cdot 4}{5 \cdot 4 \cdot 3 \cdot 2 \cdot 1} x^3y^5 = 56x^3y^5$$

example 4 Find the term not containing x in the expansion of $\left(x^2 - \frac{1}{2x}\right)^6$.

According to the conditions, $(x^2)^{6-r}(-\frac{1}{2}x^{-1})^r$ must produce a term containing no x, that is x^0. Therefore we may write

$$2(6 - r) + (-1)r = 0$$

or

$$r = 4$$

Hence we have

$$\frac{6 \cdot 5 \cdot 4 \cdot 3}{4 \cdot 3 \cdot 2 \cdot 1}(x^2)^{6-4}\left(-\frac{1}{2x}\right)^4 = 15x^4\frac{1}{16x^4} = \frac{15}{16}$$

EXERCISE 2

Write the specified term in each of the following without calculating the preceding terms:

1. $(x + y)^9$; term in y^6
2. $(5 - x)^7$; term in x^4
3. $(w + 3z)^8$; term in w^5
4. $(2x - 3)^6$; term in x^4
5. $(x/2 - 2y/3)^{10}$; fourth term
6. $(3x/4 + y/3)^8$; fifth term
7. $(3x - 4y)^6$; middle term
8. $(5m + 2w)^4$; middle term
9. $(2/x + 3x)^8$; term containing no x
10. $(x - 3/x^2)^9$; term containing no x

9·4 Computation of powers and roots

Many powers and roots may be found by calculating as many terms in the series as needed to give the required accuracy. The smaller the second term in the binomial relative to the first, the fewer terms will be required. In computing a root, i.e., a fractional power, the first term of the binomial should be a perfect power of the order corresponding to the index of the root.

example 5 Find $\sqrt[6]{1.04}$ to six significant figures.

Arranging in a form suitable for expansion, we have $(1 + 0.04)^{1/6}$. Substituting in the formula $a = 1$, $b = 0.04$, and $n = \frac{1}{6}$, we obtain

$$(1)^{1/6} + \tfrac{1}{6}(1)^{-5/6}(0.04) + \frac{(\frac{1}{6})(-\frac{5}{6})(1)^{-11/6}(0.04)^2}{2!}$$

$$+ \frac{(\frac{1}{6})(-\frac{5}{6})(-\frac{11}{6})(1)^{-17/6}(0.04)^3}{3!} + \cdots = 1 + 0.006667$$

$$-0.000111 + 0.000003 \cdots \text{(negligible terms)} = 1.00656$$

We note that the terms in the foregoing series become rapidly smaller. The series is said to converge rapidly, and relatively few terms are needed.

example 6 Find $1/(0.985)^3$ to six significant figures.

Our problem is evidently to expand $(1 - 0.015)^{-3}$. Substituting in the formula $a = 1$, $b = -0.015$, and $n = -3$, we write

$$(1)^{-3} + (-3)(1)^{-4}(-0.015) + \frac{(-3)(-4)(1)^{-5}(-0.015)^2}{2!}$$

$$+ \frac{(-3)(-4)(-5)(1)^{-6}(-0.015)^3}{3!} + \cdots = 1 + 0.045$$

$$+ 0.00135 + 0.00003375 + \cdots \text{(negligible terms)} = 1.04638$$

example 7 Find $\sqrt[3]{200}$ correct to six significant figures.

Since the perfect cube nearest to 200 is 216, our problem is to evaluate $(216 - 16)^{1/3}$. The expansion will be

$$(216)^{1/3} + \tfrac{1}{3}(216)^{-2/3}(-16) + \frac{(\frac{1}{3})(-\frac{2}{3})(216)^{-5/3}(-16)^2}{2!}$$

$$+ \frac{(\frac{1}{3})(-\frac{2}{3})(-\frac{5}{3})(216)^{-8/3}(-16)^3}{3!} + \cdots = 6 - 0.14815$$

$$- 0.00366 - 0.00015 - \cdots = 5.84804$$

EXERCISE 3

In Probs. 1 to 6 compute the first four terms in each expansion. (Confirm answers to Probs. 1 and 6 by division.)

1. $(1 + y)^{-1}$
2. $(a^2 + b)^{1/2}$
3. $(1 - x)^{-1/4}$
4. $(x^2 + 2)^{-1/2}$
5. $(a^3 + b)^{1/3}$
6. $(2w + 5)^{-2}$

(For Probs. 2 and 5, see also Table B·2.)

In Probs. 7 to 15 compute each value to five significant figures, using no tables.

7. $\sqrt{50}$
8. $\sqrt{35}$
9. $\sqrt{1.5}$
10. $\sqrt[3]{9}$
11. $\sqrt[3]{60}$
12. $\sqrt[3]{120}$
13. $\sqrt[5]{35}$
14. $1/\sqrt{5}$
15. $(25)^{2/3}$

More challenging problems may be selected from the applications in Probs. 16 to 22.

16. Engineering courses, such as thermodynamics or fluid mechanics, frequently require the computation of such quantities as $(1.045)^{1.41}$, $(0.976)^{1.28}$, $(0.917)^{0.938}$, and $(0.994)^{-1.26}$. Although these can be computed directly by use of a log-log slide rule, the use of the binomial theorem is just as rapid. Moreover, the accuracy by use of the slide rule is limited, whereas that by use of the binomial theorem is not. Compute the values of each of the preceding quantities, correct to the nearest third decimal.
17. In 1879 the American engineers Fteley and Stearns proposed the formula

$$Q = 3.31BH^{3/2}\left(1 + \frac{3h}{2H}\right)^{3/2} + 0.007B$$

for the quantity of water that would flow each second over a certain type of weir. Expand the binomial to two terms and simplify the equation. Then determine $K = Q/(BH^{3/2})$.
18. (Taken from a text in ceramics.) If b is small, show that an approximate formula for $a = (100)[1 - \sqrt[3]{1 - (b/100)}]$ is $a = b/3$.
19. (Taken from a text on principles of flight of airplanes.) Expand the square root in $Q_g = W[1 - \sqrt{1 - (Q/W)}]$ to three terms and simplify. W is the maximum gross weight of plane and fuel, Q is the maximum fuel load, and Q_g is the permissible quantity of fuel that may be consumed on the outward flight toward an objective.
20. A study of a certain type of meter in fluid mechanics starts with the equation

$$V_1 = \left\{2g\frac{k}{k-1}\frac{p_1}{w_1}\left[\left(\frac{p_2}{p_1}\right)^{(k-1)/k} - 1\right]\right\}^{1/2}$$

Show that this equation may be written successively in the following forms:

$$\frac{p_2}{p_1} = \left[\frac{w_1(k-1)}{p_1k}\frac{V_1^2}{2g} + 1\right]^{k/(k-1)}$$

$$\frac{p_2}{p_1} - 1 = \left[1 + \frac{w_1(k-1)}{p_1k}\frac{V_1^2}{2g}\right]^{k/(k-1)} - 1$$

$$p_2 - p_1 = p_1\left\{\left[1 + \frac{w_1(k-1)}{p_1k}\frac{V_1^2}{2g}\right]^{k/(k-1)} - 1\right\}$$

$$= \frac{w_1V_1^2}{2g}\left(1 + \frac{w_1}{2p_1k}\frac{V_1^2}{2g} + \cdots\right)$$

21. A derivation in fluid mechanics for the quantity of flow of water through a vertical rectangular orifice requires the expansion by the binomial theorem of the two binomial quantities in the following equation and simplification to obtain the second equation. Perform the intermediate steps.

$$q = \frac{2cb}{3}(2g)^{1/2}\left[\left(h + \frac{d}{2}\right)^{3/2} - \left(h - \frac{d}{2}\right)^{3/2}\right]$$

$$= (bcd)(2gh)^{1/2}\left(1 - \frac{d^2}{96h^2} - \frac{d^4}{2{,}048h^4} - \cdots\right)$$

22. The following thermodynamic equation occurs in the study of flow of a gas out of a nozzle:

$$V_{s2} = 223.7\left\{cT_1\left[1 - \left(\frac{p_2}{p_1}\right)^{(k-1)/k}\right]\right\}^{1/2}$$

(a) Evaluate $(p_2/p_1)^{(k-1)/k}$ by the binomial theorem if

(1) $\left(\frac{p_2}{p_1}\right) = 0.940$ and $k = 1.25$

(2) $\left(\frac{p_2}{p_1}\right) = 0.980$ and $k = 1.40$

(b) Write $(p_2/p_1)^{(k-1)/k}$ in the form

$$\left(1 - \frac{p_1 - p_2}{p_1}\right)^{(k-1)/k}$$

and expand to three terms by aid of the binomial theorem. Then simplify $1 - (p_2/p_1)^{(k-1)/k}$ to

$$\frac{k-1}{k}\left[\frac{p_1 - p_2}{p_1} + \frac{1}{2k}\left(\frac{p_1 - p_2}{p_1}\right)^2 + \cdots\right]$$

10
logarithms

One of the most effective devices for saving time and effort in mathematical computations when a desk calculator is not available is the logarithm. By means of logarithms, processes of multiplication and division are replaced by addition and subtraction, and those of raising to a power and extracting a root are replaced by multiplication and division. In fact, some mathematical operations, previously difficult, admit of ready solution by logarithms.

10·1 Definition of a logarithm

Given the equation $x = b^y$, the following assertions may be made:

1. If b is any positive number other than unity, then for every real value of y there exists one and only one positive number x, defined by the equation $x = b^y$.
2. Conversely, for every positive value of x there exists a unique number y such that $x = b^y$.

If $x = b^y$, then y is called the logarithm of x to the base b and is written

$$y = \log_b x \tag{1}$$

Substituting $\log_b x$ for y in the equation $x = b^y$, we have $x = b^{\log_b x}$ from which it follows that *the logarithm of a number is the exponent indicating the power to which it is necessary to raise the base to equal the given number.*

The above assertions imply that

1. For any given logarithm y to a given base there exists a unique number x corresponding to that logarithm.
2. Every positive number x has a unique logarithm for any given positive base other than unity.

10·2 Graphical representation

The graph shown in Fig. 10·1 is at once the graph for $x = b^y$ and $y = \log_b x$, since the two equations are equivalent. Here $b > 1$.

The shape of this curve remains substantially unchanged for all values of $b > 1$. The Y axis is an asymptote, with y approaching $-\infty$ as x approaches zero. The only intercept is $x = 1, y = 0$. y continually increases with increasing values of x. No portion of the curve exists for which x is negative, for there is no negative quantity representing a power of a positive number.

If we consider the equations $x = b^y$ or $y = \log_b x$, in which the base $b = 3$, Table 10·1 may be used for the purpose of plotting the graph in Fig. 10·1.

table 10·1

x	$\frac{1}{27}$	$\frac{1}{9}$	$\frac{1}{3}$	1	3	9	27	81
y	-3	-2	-1	0	1	2	3	4

It will be noted that the series of y values forms an arithmetic progression, whereas the corresponding values of x form a geometric progression.

By determining the means between the existing terms, we obtain

y	4	3.5	3	2.5	2	1.5	1	0.5	0	etc.
x	81	46.8	27	15.6	9	5.20	3	1.73	1	etc.

Repeating the process, we obtain

y	4	3.75	3.5	3.25	3	2.75	2.5	2.25	2	etc.
x	81	61.7	46.8	35.6	27	20.6	15.6	11.8	9	etc.

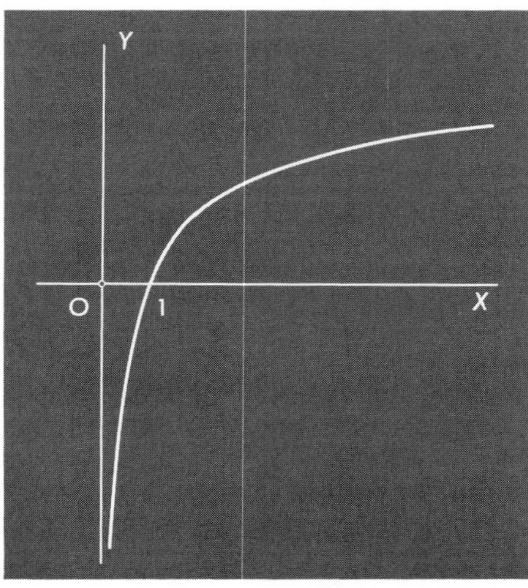

fig. 10·1

A continuation of this process would enable us to plot the graph in Fig. 10·1 as accurately as we wish.

10·3 Formation of a table of logarithms

From Fig. 10·1 it is possible to read and tabulate approximate values of y corresponding to assigned values of x. A portion of such a table is reproduced as Table 10·2.

table 10·2

x	1	2	3	4	5	6	7	8	9
y	0	0.63	1.00	1.26	1.46	1.63	1.77	1.89	2.00
x	10	11	12	. . .	24	. . .	27	. . .	60
y	2.09	2.18	2.26	. . .	2.89	. . .	3.00	. . .	3.72

This table, when sufficiently extended, becomes a table of logarithms to the base 3.

We may make use of this table to multiply or divide, remembering to observe the usual laws of exponents.

examples Multiply 2×5.

$$2 = 3^{0.63} \qquad \text{and} \qquad 5 = 3^{1.46}$$

Therefore,

$$2 \times 5 = 3^{0.63} \times 3^{1.46} = 3^{2.09} = 10$$

Multiply 3×8. Since $8 = 3^{1.89}$, we obtain

$$3 \times 8 = 3^1 \times 3^{1.89} = 3^{2.89} = 24$$

Divide 60 by 12.

$$60 = 3^{3.72} \qquad \text{and} \qquad 12 = 3^{2.26}$$
$$60 \div 12 = 3^{3.72} \div 3^{2.26} = 3^{1.46} = 5$$

Divide 24 by 6.

$$24 = 3^{2.89} \qquad \text{and} \qquad 6 = 3^{1.63}$$
$$24 \div 6 = 3^{2.89} \div 3^{1.63} = 3^{1.26} = 4$$

10·4 Use of exponents in determining logarithms

From the preceding discussion it can be seen that an exponential relationship may be expressed as a logarithm, and vice versa.

examples

$$3^2 = 9 \text{ is equivalent to } \log_3 9 = 2$$
$$5^3 = 125 \text{ is equivalent to } \log_5 125 = 3$$
$$4^{-1} = \tfrac{1}{4} \text{ is equivalent to } \log_4 \tfrac{1}{4} = -1$$
$$5^{-2} = \tfrac{1}{25} \text{ is equivalent to } \log_5 \tfrac{1}{25} = -2$$
$$49^{1/2} = 7 \text{ is equivalent to } \log_{49} 7 = \tfrac{1}{2}$$
$$15^0 = 1 \text{ is equivalent to } \log_{15} 1 = 0$$

Since any number other than zero raised to the zero power equals 1, it follows that the logarithm of 1 to any base equals zero.

EXERCISE 1

In Probs. 1 to 9 write each exponential expression in logarithmic notation.

1. (a) $2^3 = 8$ (b) $2^{-6} = 1/64$ (c) $7^{-2} = 1/49$
2. (a) $3^5 = 243$ (b) $10^{-2} = 0.01$ (c) $(1/6)^2 = 1/36$
3. (a) $5^4 = 625$ (b) $3^{-3} = 1/27$ (c) $(2/3)^3 = 8/27$
4. (a) $2^5 = 32$ (b) $7^0 = 1$ (c) $b^0 = 1$
5. (a) $3^{-4} = 1/81$ (b) $6^2 = 36$ (c) $(1/5)^{-2} = 25$
6. (a) $4^{1/2} = 2$ (b) $8^{1/3} = 2$ (c) $9^{3/2} = 27$
7. (a) $16^{3/4} = 8$ (b) $25^{1/2} = 5$ (c) $27^{2/3} = 9$
8. (a) $125^{2/3} = 25$ (b) $32^{3/5} = 8$ (c) $b^1 = b$
9. (a) $27^{-1/3} = 1/3$ (b) $16^{-5/4} = 1/32$ (c) $36^{-3/2} = 1/216$

Let it be required to find the value of $\log_7 49$. Setting $\log_7 49 = y$, we paraphrase the question by asking ourselves what power of 7 equals 49. Since $7^2 = 49$, it is apparent that $\log_7 49 = 2$.

EXERCISE 2

Find the values of the following logarithms:

1. (a) $\log_5 25$ (b) $\log_2 8$ (c) $\log_3 81$
2. (a) $\log_4 8$ (b) $\log_8 16$ (c) $\log_{16} 8$
3. (a) $\log_9 27$ (b) $\log_{27} 81$ (c) $\log_{125} 25$
4. (a) $\log_7 \sqrt{7}$ (b) $\log_{12} 1$ (c) $\log_3 1/3$
5. (a) $\log_2 1/8$ (b) $\log_{10} 0.001$ (c) $\log_4 1/32$
6. (a) $\log_{125} 5$ (b) $\log_{16} 4$ (c) $\log_{16} \sqrt{4}$

Another version of the logarithmic relationship is exemplified by the equation $\log_5 x = 3$. Here we wish to know what number is equal to the third power of 5. Since $5^3 = 125$, we have $\log_5 125 = 3$.

It may be required to find the base of a logarithmic equation. For example, $\log_b 16 = 4$. This is read "log 16 to what base equals 4?" In other words, what number b, raised to the fourth power, equals 16? The answer is evidently 2. Hence $\log_2 16 = 4$.

EXERCISE 3

Find the value of x in Probs. 1 to 4.

1. (a) $\log_2 x = 3$ (b) $\log_5 x = 2$ (c) $\log_3 x = 4$
2. (a) $\log_5 x = 0$ (b) $\log_6 x = -1$ (c) $\log_8 x = 4/3$
3. (a) $\log_{10} x = 2$ (b) $\log_3 x = -2$ (c) $\log_{27} x = 2/3$
4. (a) $\log_{16} x = 3/4$ (b) $\log_8 x = -2/3$ (c) $\log_{25} x = -1/2$

In Probs. 5 to 10 find the value of the base b.

5. (a) $\log_b 9 = 2$ (b) $\log_b 8 = 3$ (c) $\log_b 4 = 2/3$
6. (a) $\log_b 1{,}000 = 3$ (b) $\log_b 25 = 2$ (c) $\log_b 3 = 1/2$
7. (a) $\log_b 15 = 1$ (b) $\log_b 1 = 0$ (c) $\log_b 1/4 = -2$
8. (a) $\log_b 1/27 = -3/2$ (b) $\log_b 1/25 = -2/3$ (c) $\log_b 7 = -1/2$
9. (a) $\log_b 9 = -2/3$ (b) $\log_b 0.01 = 2$ (c) $\log_b 1/16 = -4/3$
10. (a) $\log_b 1{,}000 = 3/2$ (b) $\log_b 6 = -1/2$ (c) $\log_b 1/64 = -6$

10·5 Properties of logarithms

Since logarithms are exponents, the rules relating to the use of logarithms resemble the laws of exponents.

The most common relationships are the following:

$$\log_b PQ = \log_b P + \log_b Q \tag{2}$$

$$\log_b \left(\frac{P}{Q}\right) = \log_b P - \log_b Q \tag{3}$$

$$\log_b P^n = n \log_b P \tag{4}$$

$$\log_b \sqrt[n]{P} = \frac{1}{n} \log_b P \tag{5}$$

$$\log_b 1 = 0 \tag{6}$$

$$\log_b \left(\frac{1}{P}\right) = -\log_b P \tag{7}$$

These rules may be readily derived.

10·6 Multiplication

Let $P = b^c$ or $\log_b P = c$

and $Q = b^d$ or $\log_b Q = d$

Then $PQ = b^c \cdot b^d = b^{c+d}$

In logarithmic notation, this becomes

$$\log_b PQ = c + d$$

But $c + d = \log_b P + \log_b Q$

Therefore $\log_b PQ = \log_b P + \log_b Q$

The logarithm of a product is equal to the sum of the logarithms of the separate factors.

10·7 Division

Let $P = b^c$ or $\log_b P = c$

and $Q = b^d$ or $\log_b Q = d$

Then $$\frac{P}{Q} = \frac{b^c}{b^d} = b^{c-d}$$

In logarithmic notation, this becomes

$$\log_b \frac{P}{Q} = c - d$$

But $$c - d = \log_b P - \log_b Q$$

Therefore $$\log_b \frac{P}{Q} = \log_b P - \log_b Q$$

The logarithm of a quotient is equal to the logarithm of the numerator minus the logarithm of the denominator.

10·8 Powers

If $$Q = b^c$$

then $$\log_b Q = c$$

Also $$Q^n = b^{cn}$$

which in logarithmic notation is

$$\log_b Q^n = cn$$

But $$c = \log_b Q$$

Therefore $$\log_b Q^n = n \log_b Q$$

The logarithm of a power of a number is equal to the exponent times the logarithm of the number.

10·9 Roots

This is a form of the power rule, for if we write

$$\log_b \sqrt[n]{Q} \text{ as } \log_b Q^{1/n}$$

we obtain $$\log_b Q^{1/n} = \frac{1}{n} \log_b Q$$

Therefore $$\log_b \sqrt[n]{Q} = \frac{1}{n} \log_b Q$$

The logarithm of a root of a number is the logarithm of that number divided by the index of the root.

10·10 Logarithm of unity

This is also a special case of the power rule in which $n = 0$.

$$\log_b 1 = \log_b Q^0 = 0 \log_b Q = 0$$

The logarithm of unity to any base is zero.

10·11 Logarithm of the base

Returning to Eq. (1), we note that if $x = b^y$, then $y = \log_b x$. If we replace x by b and y by 1, we obtain $b = b^1$ and $1 = \log_b b$.

The logarithm of a number referred to itself as a base is unity.

10·12 Reciprocal

This is another variation of the power law. In this case $n = -1$.

$$\log_b \frac{1}{Q} = \log_b Q^{-1} = (-1)\log_b Q = -\log_b Q$$

The logarithm of the reciprocal of a number is the negative logarithm of that number.

10·13 Change of base

At times it is necessary to change from one base to another, especially when dealing with sound levels, mechanical shock, and transient electric currents. The formula is

$$\log_a Q = \frac{1}{\log_b a} \log_b Q \qquad \textbf{(8)}$$

Since a and b are both constants, $\log_b a$ is also a constant. Hence, if only a table to the base b is available, *the logarithm of a number to the base* b *can be converted to the logarithm of the same number to the base* a *by dividing the former by the constant log*$_b$ a.

The proof of the statement follows:

Let $$Q = a^x$$

so that $$\log_a Q = x \qquad (9)$$

Also if $$Q = a^x$$

then $$\log_b Q = \log_b a^x = x \log_b a$$

or $$x = \frac{1}{\log_b a} \log_b Q \qquad (10)$$

Then, from Eqs. (9) and (10),

$$\log_a Q = \frac{1}{\log_b a} \log_b Q$$

10·14 Systems of logarithms

From the problems in Exercises 1 through 3 it is evident that any positive number, except 1, can be used as a base for a system of logarithms. The number 1 cannot be used as a base because 1, when raised to any power whatever, is still equal to 1.

There are two systems of logarithms in general use: the system of common logarithms to the base 10, and the system of natural logarithms to the base *e*, or 2.71828· · · . Natural logarithms will be discussed further in Chap. 11.

The system of common logarithms is most convenient for general computation because it is best suited to the decimal system. Hereafter, unless otherwise indicated, the word *logarithm* will be understood to mean common logarithm. When the base is not expressed, the base 10 is understood. Thus $\log 3 = 0.47712$ means $\log_{10} 3 = 0.47712$.

From the laws of exponents we know that $10^0 = 1$, $10^1 = 10$, $10^2 = 100$, $10^3 = 1{,}000$, $10^4 = 10{,}000$, $10^5 = 100{,}000$, etc.

In logarithmic notation the above equations become $\log_{10} 1 = 0$, $\log_{10} 10 = 1$, $\log_{10} 100 = 2$, $\log_{10} 1{,}000 = 3$, $\log_{10} 10{,}000 = 4$, $\log_{10} 100{,}000 = 5$, etc.

10·15 Graphical derivation of table

If we use 10 for the base instead of the general value *b*, we obtain the graph shown in Fig. 10·2. This, then, is the graph of $x = 10^y$ or $y = \log_{10} x$. It is apparent that when $y = 0$, $x = 1$. When $y = 1/3$, $x = 10^{1/3}$ or $\sqrt[3]{10}$ or 2.154. When $y = 1/2$, $x = 10^{1/2}$ or $\sqrt{10}$ or 3.162. When $y = 1$, $x = 10$, etc.

For any given value of *y*, there is only one value of *x*; and conversely, for any given positive value of *x*, there is only one value of *y* (Sec. 10·1). Thus any positive number *x* may be expressed as a power

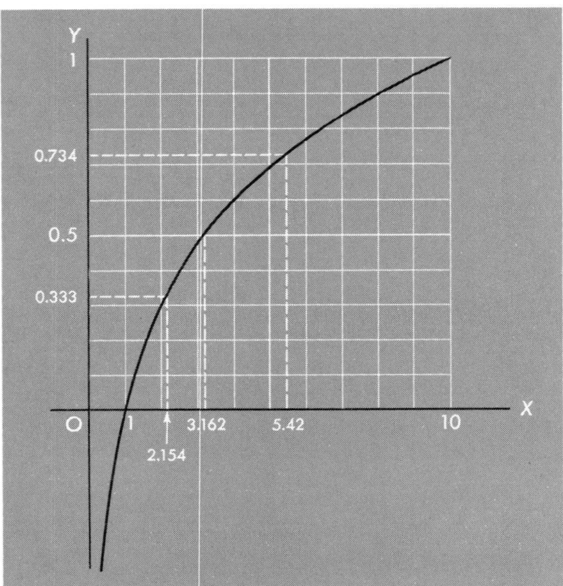

fig. 10·2

of 10, just as we have considered 2.154 as the 0.333 power of 10 and 3.162 as the 0.500 power of 10.

If this curve were drawn to a large enough scale, we should be able to read that when $x = 5.42$, $y = 0.734$ (approximately). Evidently, then, $10^{0.734} = 5.42$, or $\log_{10} 5.42 = 0.734$.

10·16 Characteristic and mantissa

If we know that $10^{0.734} = 5.42$ or that $\log_{10} 5.42 = 0.734$, we can write the logarithms of 5.42 times a power of 10. Thus

$$\log 54.2 = \log (10 \times 5.42) = \log 10 + \log 5.42 = 1 + 0.734$$
$$\log 542 = \log (100 \times 5.42) = \log 100 + \log 5.42 = 2 + 0.734$$
$$\log 5{,}420 = \log (1{,}000 \times 5.42) = \log 1{,}000 + \log 5.42 = 3 + 0.734$$
$$\log 0.542 = \log (0.1 \times 5.42) = \log 0.1 + \log 5.42 = -1 + 0.734$$
$$\log 0.0542 = \log (0.01 \times 5.42) = \log 0.01 + \log 5.42 = -2 + 0.734$$
$$\log 0.00542 = \log (0.001 \times 5.42) = \log 0.001 + \log 5.42 = -3 + 0.734$$

Each logarithm will be seen to consist of a whole number and a decimal value. *The whole number is called the characteristic, and the decimal value is called the mantissa.* The mantissa is usually an unending decimal which, by more advanced mathematics, may be computed to as many places as desired.

It will be noted that the mantissa depends only on a given sequence of digits, in this case 542. All numbers having a given sequence of digits will have the same mantissa. On the other hand the characteristic is seen to be related to the position of the decimal point.

The relationships set forth in the beginning of this section are summarized in Table 10·3.

table 10·3

		Characteristic		*Mantissa*	*Common method of writing logarithm*
log 5,420	=	3	+	0.734	3.734
log 542	=	2	+	0.734	2.734
log 54.2	=	1	+	0.734	1.734
log 5.42	=	0	+	0.734	0.734
log 0.542	=	−1	+	0.734	0.734 − 1
log 0.0542	=	−2	+	0.734	0.734 − 2
log 0.00542	=	−3	+	0.734	0.734 − 3

From this table it will be evident that *for numbers larger than 1 the characteristic of the logarithm is positive and one less than the number of digits at the left of the decimal point in the number. If the number is smaller than 1, the characteristic is negative and corresponds to the position of the first significant figure.* For example, in the number

0.00542 the first significant digit is in the third place to the right of the decimal point; therefore the characteristic of the logarithm is -3.

By common agreement the mantissa in a logarithm table (and elsewhere except as noted below) is always considered to be positive.

Alternative conventions of writing logarithms containing negative characteristics are illustrated below. For the most part we shall confine ourselves in this text to the first form.

$0.734 - 1$	$9.734 - 10$	$\bar{1}.734$	-0.266
$0.734 - 2$	$8.734 - 10$	$\bar{2}.734$	-1.266
$0.734 - 3$	$7.734 - 10$	$\bar{3}.734$	-2.266

The notation in the extreme right-hand column is used only under special conditions (Secs. 10·26 and 10·30).

If the number is expressed in scientific notation (A·3), the characteristic corresponds to the power of 10, as illustrated in Table 10·4.

table 10·4

Number	*Scientific notation*	*Logarithm*
5,420	5.42×10^3	3.734
542	5.42×10^2	2.734
54.2	5.42×10^1	1.734
5.42	5.42×10^0	0.734
0.542	5.42×10^{-1}	$0.734 - 1$
0.0542	5.42×10^{-2}	$0.734 - 2$
0.00542	5.42×10^{-3}	$0.734 - 3$

A table of mantissas, or logarithms of numbers between 1 and 10, will be seen to be sufficient to determine the logarithm of any positive number, the proper positive or negative characteristic being supplied by inspection when the logarithms of numbers greater than 10 or less than 1 are written.

10·17 The antilogarithm of an expression

The antilogarithm of an expression is the number whose logarithm is the given expression. For example, to find the antilogarithm of 1.734 is to find the number whose logarithm is 1.734, i.e., 54.2.

EXERCISE 4

1. Complete the following table:

	Number	*Scientific notation*	*Logarithm*
(a)	8.61	$8.61\ (\times 10^0)$	0.935
(b)	861	8.61×10^2	2.935
(c)	0.0861	8.61×10^{-2}	$0.935 - 2$

	Number	Scientific notation	Logarithm
(d)	8,610		
(e)		8.61×10^5	
(f)			4.935
(g)	0.00861		
(h)		8.61×10^{-1}	
(i)			$0.935 - 4$
(j)	8,610,000		
(k)		8.61×10^8	
(l)			$0.935 - 3$

Given log 3.54 = 0.549 and log 7.98 = 0.902 in Probs. 2 to 4, find the logarithms of the given numbers. In Probs. 5 to 7 find the antilogarithms of the given logarithms.

2.	(a) 35.4	(b) 798	(c) 79,800
3.	(a) 0.0354	(b) 0.354	(c) 7,980
4.	(a) 0.00798	(b) 3,540,000	(c) 0.000354
5.	(a) 2.549	(b) 1.902	(c) 8.902 − 10
6.	(a) 0.902 − 3	(b) 4.549	(c) 0.549 − 1
7.	(a) 6.549 − 10	(b) 3.902	(c) 0.549 − 3

10·18 Role of logarithms in rough approximation

The order of magnitude of a quantity (or the power of 10 to which it corresponds) may be readily approximated by logarithms.

example 1 Given only that log 2 = 0.301 and log 3 = 0.477, find the position of the first significant digit of N if $N = 6^7$.

Applying Eq. (2), Sec. 10·5,

$$\log 6 = \log 2 + \log 3 = 0.778$$

By Eq. (4), Sec. 10·5,

$$\log 6^7 = 7 \log 6 = 5.446$$

Since the characteristic equals 5, there must be 5 + 1 or 6 digits to the left of the decimal point (Sec. 10·16); hence the first significant digit is in the sixth place to the left of the decimal point.

example 2 Repeat Example 1 for $N = (0.45)^8$.

$$4.5 = \frac{(3)(3)}{2}$$

$$\log \frac{(3)(3)}{2} = 2 \log 3 - \log 2 = 0.653 \qquad \text{[Eqs. (1) and (3), Sec. 10·5]}$$

Therefore

$$\log 0.45 = 0.653 - 1 \qquad \text{(Sec. 10·16)}$$
$$\log (0.45)^8 = 8 \log 0.45 \qquad \text{[Eq. (4), Sec. 10·5]}$$
$$8(0.653 - 1) = 5.224 - 8 = 0.224 - 3$$

By Sec. 10·16 a characteristic of -3 indicates that the first significant digit of $(0.45)^8$ is in the third place to the right of the decimal point.

EXERCISE 5

Given only that $\log 2 = 0.301$ and $\log 3 = 0.477$, determine the order of magnitude (position of the first significant figure) of the following.

1. 2^{14}	2. 6^{10}	3. $(0.8)^{20}$	4. 30^9
5. 5^{13}	6. $(0.15)^8$	7. 3^{11}	8. $(200)^6$
9. $(0.02)^8$	10. $(0.5)^{12}$	11. 9^9	12. $(1.5)^{15}$

10·19 Using a table of logarithms

A portion of a five-place table of logarithms is reproduced in Table 10·5.

From this table we find that the mantissa of the logarithm of 3,124 is 0.49471. We have obtained this value by reading in from the number representing the first three digits, 312, and under the fourth digit, 4. Two space-saving conventions will be noted: The decimal point is not shown; neither are the first two digits, 49, of the mantissa shown.

Another space-saving device is revealed if it is required to look up the mantissa of the logarithm of 3,168. Reading opposite 316 and under 8, we find *079. The asterisk tells us that we have moved from mantissas 0.49 · · · to mantissas 0.50 · · ·. Therefore this particular mantissa is 0.50079.

Since $3{,}168 = 3.168 \times 10^3$, the characteristic of the logarithm is seen to be 3, and the complete logarithm of 3,168 is 3.50079.

EXERCISE 6

Referring to Table 10·5, determine the complete logarithms (characteristic and mantissa) of the following numbers:

1. 3,103	2. 313.6	3. 310	4. 3.190
5. 31,160	6. 318,200	7. 3.152	8. 3,167
9. 3,100,000	10. 31.63	11. 31	12. 3.1

In looking up the logarithm of a number smaller than unity, we may first express the number in scientific notation and then determine the mantissa and characteristic from the respective first and second parts of that number.

table 10·5

N	0	1	2	3	4	5	6	7	8	9
310	49136	150	164	178	192	206	220	234	248	262
311	276	290	304	318	332	346	360	374	388	402
312	415	429	443	457	471	485	499	513	527	541
313	554	568	582	596	610	624	638	651	665	679
314	693	707	721	734	748	762	776	790	803	817
315	831	845	859	872	886	900	914	927	941	955
316	969	982	996	*010	*024	*037	*051	*065	*079	*092
317	50106	120	133	147	161	174	188	202	215	229
318	243	256	270	284	297	311	325	338	352	365
319	379	393	406	420	433	447	461	474	488	501
320	515	529	542	556	569	583	596	610	623	637

example 3 Use Table 10·5 to read the logarithm of 0.003148. In scientific notation this becomes 3.148×10^{-3}. Therefore by inspection the characteristic is -3, and, from the table, the mantissa is 0.49803. Hence the logarithm of 0.003148 is $0.49803 - 3$.

EXERCISE 7

Referring to Table 10·5, determine the logarithms of the numbers in Probs. 1 to 12.

1. 0.003122 2. 0.03196 3. 0.3144 4. 0.00031
5. 0.03167 6. 0.0000315 7. 0.3171 8. 0.003185
9. 0.00000319 10. 0.3111 11. 0.03105 12. 0.003162

Referring to Table 10·5, determine the numbers corresponding to the logarithms (i.e., find the antilogarithms) in Probs. 13 to 24.

13. 1.49178 14. 2.49374 15. 3.50065
16. 0.50092 − 2 17. 0.50515 − 3 18. 0.50284 − 1
19. 4.50569 20. 0.50243 21. 5.49290
22. 0.50325 − 4 23. 1.50010 24. 0.49996 − 1

EXERCISE 8

Referring to a five-place log table, look up the logarithms of the numbers in Probs. 1 to 3.

1. (a) 1,234 (b) 100.3 (c) 0.01234 (d) 37.05 (e) 398.4
2. (a) 79,020 (b) 0.3076 (c) 3,000 (d) 0.005006 (e) 1,003,000
3. (a) 179.7 (b) 0.1042 (c) 0.01090 (d) 709.3 (e) 0.0007065

Find the numbers corresponding to the logarithms in Probs. 4 to 6.

4. (a) 3.75051 (b) 0.56038 − 2 (c) 1.55096 (d) 0.00043 (e) 0.93997 − 1

5. (a) 7.93475 − 10 (b) 0.06333 (c) 5.60206
(d) 2.96440 (e) 4.76005

6. (a) 1.21537 (b) 3.61794 (c) 0.27161 − 4
(d) 5.99502 (e) 2.47012

10·20 Interpolation

It is often necessary to find the logarithm of a number which does not appear in the table. If we are satisfied to use the logarithm of the nearest number, we reduce the accuracy of a five-place table to that of a four-place table. It is not necessary to sacrifice this extra degree of accuracy if we resort to interpolation. In a five-place table interpolation will determine for us the fifth digit in the mantissa, but not a sixth. Perhaps this process is best illustrated by an example.

example 4 Find, by interpolation, log 25.813.

First find the mantissas of 25,810 and 25,820. These are 41179 and 41196, respectively (decimal points are disregarded for the time being). The *tabular difference* between the mantissas is 17, whereas the difference between 25,810 and 25,820 is 10. It is evident that the given number 25,813 is 0.3 of the way from 25,810 to 25,820. Therefore the desired mantissa must be about 0.3 of the way from 41179 to 41196. 0.3 of 17 is 5.1, which is rounded off to 5. 41179 + 5 is 41184. Therefore the mantissa is 0.41184, and by inspection the characteristic is 1. Hence log 25.813 = 1.41184.

The interpolation may be arranged as follows:

Write down the bracketing numbers and their mantissas, leaving space for the intermediate number and its mantissa. Annex a cipher as a fifth digit to each bracketing number and write in the given number. Indicate the differences or proportional parts.

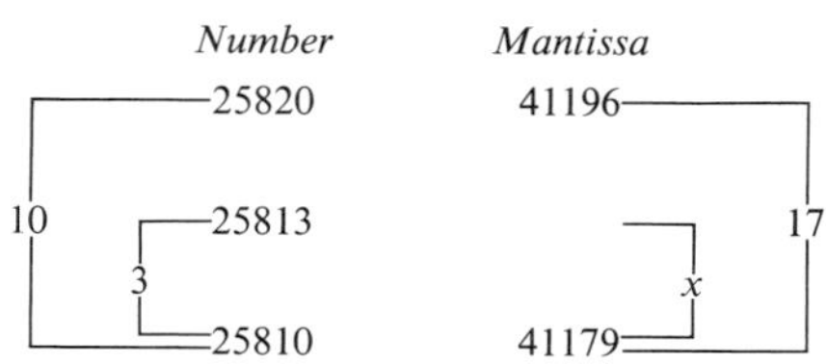

By proportion, $3/10 = x/17$; $x = 5.1$, by mental calculation or slide rule. Observe that since the mantissas are unending decimals and are rounded off to five digits, there would be no point in adding 41179. and 5.1 and calling the result 41184.1. Hence we calculate x only to the nearest whole number.

In most tables there are included tables of proportional parts in which x in the above proportion may be looked up. This is simply a table of tenths of the tabular difference, which is 17 in this example. Usually, mental computation is the quickest way to determine the proportional part x.

	17
1	1.7
2	3.4
3	5.1
etc.	

If the given number contains more than five significant figures and the tabular difference is 15 or more, round off to six significant figures and proceed as in the following example.

example 5 Find log 232.464973.

Rounding off to six digits, we get 232.465.

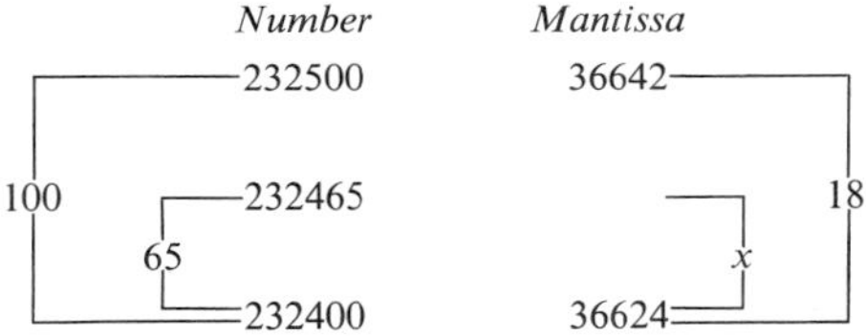

By proportion, $65/100 = x/18$; $x = 11.7$, which we call 12. Therefore, the mantissa is $36624 + 12$, or 0.36636. The complete logarithm is 2.36636.

The process of interpolation as applied to antilogarithms is simply the reverse of that used in looking up logarithms.

example 6 Find antilog 3.54859.

We do not find 54859 in the table of mantissas, but we do find the bracketing mantissas 54851 and 54864. These correspond to the numbers 3,536 and 3,537, respectively. The operation is illustrated below:

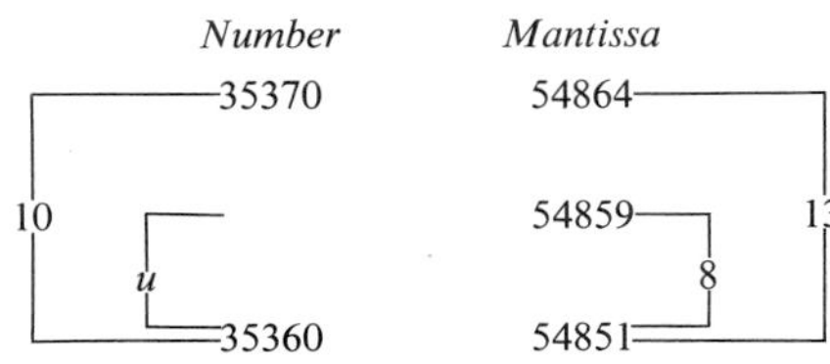

By proportion, $u/10 = 8/13$; $u = 6.2$, which we call 6. Therefore the digits of the number are 35,360 + 6, or 35,366. The characteristic 3 determines the number to be 3,536.6.

If we choose to use the proportional-parts table, we scan the values listed under 13 until we come to the value nearest 8. This is 7.8, which corresponds to 6 (0.6 of 13).

	13
—	—
5	6.5
6	7.8
7	9.1
—	—

Note that if the difference x is less than 1 part out of 20, interpolation is omitted, since if $x < 1$, $(x/20)(10) < 0.5$ or less than 5 in the sixth place.

In this case, simply the nearest mantissa is taken.

example 7 Find the antilogarithm of 1.21565.

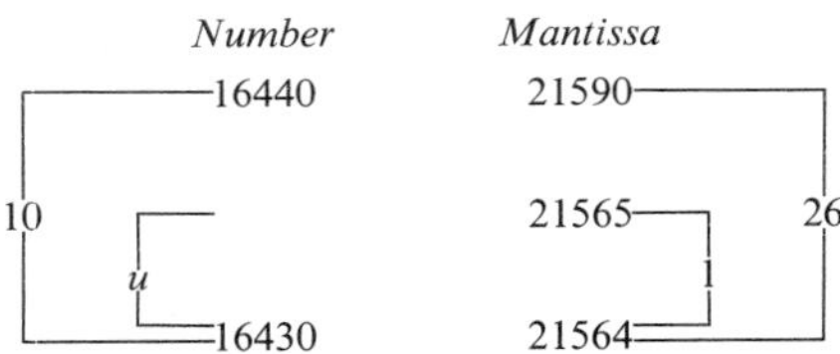

$u/10 = 1/26$; $u = 0.4$, which is less than 0.5; 21564. + 0.4 = 21564. Therefore we ignore interpolation and take the nearest mantissa, 21564. Thus we get antilog 1.21565 = 16.430.

Interpolation may sometimes be facilitated by approaching our answer from the upper value instead of the lower.

example 8 Find log 0.012148.

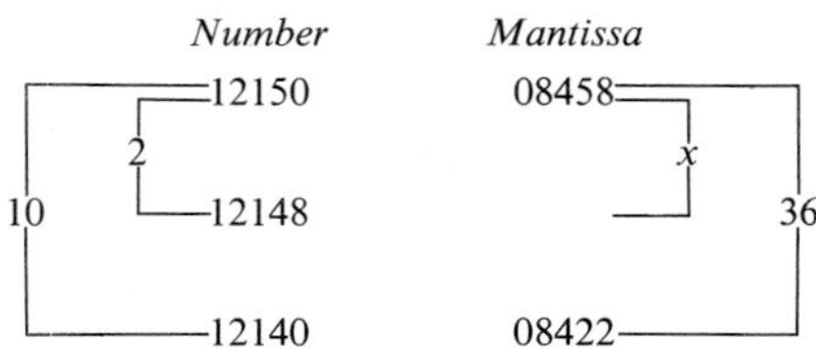

Here we write $x/36 = 2/10$; $x = 7.2$ or 7; 08458 − 7 = 08451.

This is somewhat easier than the equivalent operation:

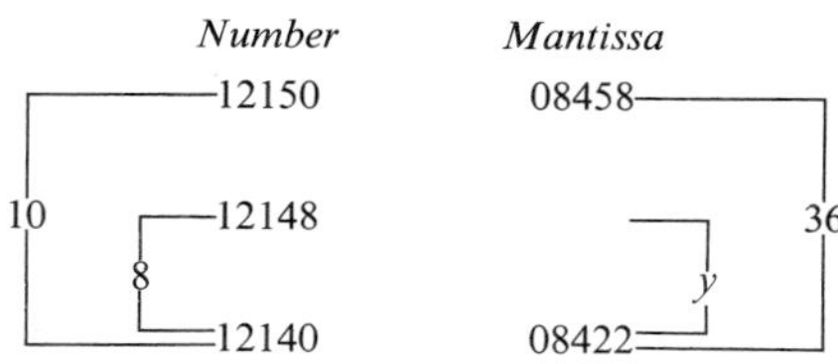

$y/36 = 8/10$; $y = 28.8$ or 29; $08422 + 29 = 08451$.
In either case the complete logarithm is $0.08451 - 2$.

EXERCISE 9

Using a five-place log table, look up the logarithms of the numbers in Probs. 1 to 3, obtaining the last digit by interpolation.

1. (a) 268.18 (b) 0.0043356 (c) 21.355 (d) 9.2354 (e) 4.1497
2. (a) 68.173 (b) 0.030689 (c) 55,071 (d) 0.13309 (e) 8,585.4
3. (a) 11,958 (b) 37.596 (c) 0.00079364 (d) 2,090.2 (e) 118,210,000

Find to five significant figures the numbers whose logarithms are given in Probs. 4 to 6. Obtain the fifth significant figure by interpolation.

4. (a) 3.20756 (b) $0.29577 - 1$ (c) 1.79652 (d) 4.38896 (e) 2.59460
5. (a) $0.00309 - 3$ (b) 0.47562 (c) $0.89964 - 4$ (d) $0.69250 - 2$ (e) 5.14521
6. (a) $0.01997 - 4$ (b) 1.27461 (c) 5.93376 (d) 2.00215 (e) $0.37965 - 1$

10·21 Computation using logarithms

In carrying out computations involving logarithms, we shall make use of the equations set forth in Sec. 10·5.

10·22 Multiplication by the use of logarithms

According to Eq. (2), the logarithm of a product equals the sum of the logarithms of the separate factors.

example 9 Find the product (238.24)(0.072495)(9.5668) = N.

From the tables,

$$\begin{aligned} \log 238.24 &= 2.37701 \\ \log 0.072495 &= 0.86031 - 2 \\ \log 9.5668 &= 0.98077 \\ \hline \log N &= 4.21809 - 2 \\ &= 2.21809 \\ N &= 165.23 \end{aligned}$$

If a computation involves negative quantities, they should be treated as though they were positive, since a negative number does not have a logarithm. The sign of the answer can be determined by inspection after completion of the computation.

EXERCISE 10

Using logarithms, perform the following computations to five significant figures:

1. 47.690 × 32.410 × 76.480 × 1.9320
2. 3.7596 × 159.06
3. 10.365 × 0.42659
4. (2,586.0)(−169.20)(1.4230)(−0.96000)
5. 73.650 × 9.9000 × 0.99990 × 1.0010 × 0.013090
6. (70.603)(0.55146)(0.00021300)(1.4020)(40.326)(−743.01)
7. 25.726 × 5.0789 × 2,188.5 × 5.2525 × 4,660.1
8. 2,208.6 × 0.043680 × 2,781,200,000 × 0.000016976
9. 0.0018746 × 15.856 × 2,650.0 × 2.0460 × 50,620,000
10. 3.6492 × 1,006.4 × 0.00037964 × 0.0017960 × 36.592

10·23 Division by the use of logarithms

From Eq. (3) we find that the logarithm of a quotient equals the logarithm of the numerator minus the logarithm of the denominator.

example 10 Evaluate 845.67/0.68332 = N.

$$\begin{aligned} \log 845.67 &= 2.92720 \\ \log 0.68332 &= 0.83462 - 1 \\ \hline \log N &= 2.09258 + 1 \\ &= 3.09258 \\ N &= 1237.6 \end{aligned}$$

If the denominator is larger than the numerator, we must devise some way to subtract a larger logarithm from a smaller one. This can be accomplished by adding enough to the characteristic of the logarithm of the numerator to make it larger than the logarithm of the denominator. To compensate for the increase in the characteristic, a like amount is written in as a negative characteristic of the logarithm of the numerator.

example 11 Evaluate $37.844/510.36 = N$.

$$\begin{aligned} \log 37.844 &= 1.57800 \\ \log 510.36 &= 2.70788 \end{aligned}$$

If we increase the characteristic in 1.57800 by 2, it will be larger than 2.70788. A compensating characteristic, -2, is appended.

$$\begin{aligned} \log 37.844 &= 3.57800 - 2 \\ \log 510.36 &= 2.70788 \\ \hline \log N &= 0.87012 - 2 \\ N &= 0.074152 \end{aligned}$$

EXERCISE 11

Use logarithms to compute the following quotients to five significant figures:

1. $(3{,}796.0) \div (-472.00)$
2. $7{,}943.2 \div 25.793$
3. $7.5437 \div 97.604$
4. $0.047920 \div 6.3951$
5. $4{,}605.2 \div 56{,}517$
6. $99.976 \div 10.532$
7. $1{,}000.1 \div 3{,}576.5$
8. $0.37960 \div 0.020710$
9. $12.147 \div 0.00049630$
10. $-5{,}076.0 \div 0.043297$
11. $1 \div 53.827$
12. $1 \div 0.082941$

10·24 Combined multiplication and division

This is simply a combination of Eqs. (2) and (3) for multiplication and division.

example 12 Evaluate $75.282\pi/(6.754)(0.38949)(0.01217) = N$.

$$\begin{aligned} \log 75.282 &= 1.87669 \\ \log 3.1416 &= 0.49715 \\ \hline \log \text{num.} &= 2.37384 \qquad \rightarrow 2.37384 \\ \log 6.754 &= 0.82956 \\ \log 0.38949 &= 0.59050 - 1 \\ \log 0.01217 &= 0.08529 - 2 \\ \hline \log \text{den.} &= 1.50535 - 3 \rightarrow \underline{1.50535 - 3} \\ & \qquad\qquad\qquad\quad 0.86849 + 3 \\ \log N &= 3.86849 \\ N &= 7387.3 \qquad \text{or better} \qquad N = 7387 \end{aligned}$$

10·25 Cologarithms

The *cologarithm* of a number is the logarithm of the reciprocal of the number. It is therefore equal to the negative of the logarithm of the number.

$$\operatorname{colog} N = \log\left(\frac{1}{N}\right) = -\log N \tag{11}$$

It is evident that division by a given number may be accomplished by adding the cologarithm instead of subtracting the logarithm. A combined multiplication and division problem may therefore be evaluated by adding up only one column of logarithms.

A separate table of cologarithms is not usually available, but by subtracting the logarithm from zero the student can write down the cologarithm at sight without writing down the logarithm. This is easily accomplished by subtracting each figure of the mantissa from 9 except the last, which is subtracted from 10.

example 13 Find colog 66.32.

$$\begin{array}{ll} \log 1 & = 2.00000 - 2 \\ \log 66.32 & = 1.82164 \\ \hline \operatorname{colog} 66.32 & = 0.17836 - 2 \end{array}$$

example 14 Find colog 0.7042.

$$\begin{array}{ll} \log 1 & = 1.00000 - 1 \\ \log 0.7042 & = 0.84770 - 1 \\ \hline \operatorname{colog} 0.7042 & = 0.15230 \end{array}$$

Note that the zero value of log 1 in each case is written in such a way as to avoid a split characteristic in the colog.

example 15 Evaluate the expression in Example 12, using cologs.

$$\begin{array}{rl} \log 75.282 & = 1.87669 \\ \log 3.1416 & = 0.49715 \\ \operatorname{colog} 6.754 & = 0.17044 - 1 \\ \operatorname{colog} 0.38949 & = 0.40950 \\ \operatorname{colog} 0.01217 & = 1.91471 \\ \cline{2-2} & 4.86849 - 1 \\ \log N & = 3.86849 \\ N & = 7387.3 \end{array}$$

EXERCISE 12

Evaluate the following to five significant figures:

1. $\dfrac{576.43 \times 976.52 \times 1.4962}{3.7425 \times 0.0096520 \times 0.017360}$

2. $\dfrac{57.040 \times 25.936 \times 0.48352}{764.32 \times 97.630 \times 0.0079860}$

3. $\dfrac{601.47 \times 93.276 \times 2.5037 \times 79.631}{927.43 \times 26.485 \times 0.0017930 \times 62.000}$

4. $\dfrac{10.243 \times 1.5006 \times 0.96016 \times 9.1207}{59.329 \times 3.8421 \times 0.027532 \times 0.50008}$

10·26 Raising to a power

According to Eq. (4), the logarithm of the power of a number is found by multiplying the logarithm of the number by the exponent.

example 16 Evaluate $(1.8653)^8 = N$.

$$\begin{aligned} \log 1.8653 &= 0.27075 \\ &\underline{8} \\ \log N &= 2.16600 \\ N &= 146.56 \end{aligned}$$

example 17 Evaluate $(5.167)^{-2.8} = N$.

$$(5.167)^{-2.8} = \frac{1}{(5.167)^{2.8}} \qquad \text{(law of exponents)}$$

$$\begin{aligned} \log 5.167 &= 0.71324 \\ &\underline{2.8} \\ &570592 \\ &\underline{142648} \\ \log (5.167)^{2.8} &= 1.997072 \end{aligned}$$

$$\begin{aligned} \log 1 &= 2.00000 - 2 \\ \log (5.167)^{2.8} &= 1.99707 \\ \hline \log N &= 0.00293 - 2 \\ N &= 0.010068 \end{aligned}$$

Alternative solution: $-2.8 \log 5.167 = (-2.8)(0.71324) = -1.99707$. Adding,

$$\begin{aligned} \log 1 = 0 = &2.00000 - 2 \\ &\underline{-1.99707} \\ &0.00293 - 2 \\ N = &0.010068 \end{aligned}$$

-1.99707 means that we have not only -1, but also -0.99707. Since mantissas in the table are positive, we must convert to a positive mantissa by a device such as that illustrated.

example 18 Evaluate $(0.17528)^{1.75} = N$.

$$\begin{array}{rl} \log 0.17528 = & 0.24373 - 1 \\ & \underline{\quad 1.75 \quad} \\ & 121865 \\ & 170611 \\ & \underline{24373} \\ & 0.4265275 - 1.75 \end{array}$$

Note that the entire logarithm, both mantissa and characteristic, is multiplied by 1.75.

Add zero in a form to make the characteristic a whole number.

$$\begin{array}{rl} & 0.42653 - 1.75 \\ & \underline{+0.25 \quad - 0.25} \quad (=0) \\ \log N = & 0.67653 - 2 \\ N = & 0.047482 \end{array}$$

example 19 Evaluate $(0.4627)^{-3.2}$.

$$(0.4627)^{-3.2} = \frac{1}{(0.4627)^{3.2}} = \left(\frac{1}{0.4627}\right)^{3.2}$$

$$\begin{array}{rl} \log 1 = & 1.00000 - 1 \\ \log 0.4627 = & \underline{0.66530 - 1} \\ & 0.33470 \\ & \underline{\quad 3.2} \\ & 66940 \\ & \underline{100410} \\ \log N = & 1.07104 \\ N = & 11.777 \end{array}$$

Alternative solution: $\log 0.4627 = 0.66530 - 1$.

Multiply entire logarithm by

$$\begin{array}{rl} & 0.66530 - 1 \\ & \underline{\qquad -3.2} \\ & 133060 \\ & \underline{199590} \\ & -2.12896 + 3.2 \end{array}$$

Combine:

$$\begin{array}{rl} & +3.20000 \\ & \underline{-2.12896} \\ \log N = & 1.07104 \\ N = & 11.777 \end{array}$$

EXERCISE 13

Use logarithms to evaluate the following to five significant figures. Consider all values good to five significant figures.

1. (a) $(4.875)^5$ (b) $(-11.83)^3$ (c) $(0.6432)^4$
2. (a) $(0.09458)^3$ (b) $(0.14732)^2$ (c) $(-0.25713)^4$
3. (a) $(23.805)^{-1}$ (b) $(7.432)^{-2}$ (c) $(16.031)^{-3}$

4. (a) $(17.584)^{3/2}$ (b) $(405.76)^{2/3}$ (c) $(1807.4)^{2/5}$
5. (a) $(0.6432)^{2.2}$ (b) $(0.09473)^{-1.8}$ (c) $(2.75)^{2.75}$
6. (a) $(0.16223)^{3/4}$ (b) $(0.074962)^{4/5}$ (c) $(0.25814)^{5/2}$
7. (a) $(70.58)^{0.2}$ (b) $(13.625)^{1.3}$ (c) $(48.461)^{-0.3}$
8. (a) $(14.83)^{-1.62}$ (b) $(0.3447)^{-2.22}$ (c) $(0.0962)^{3.15}$

10·27 Extracting roots

Referring to Eq. (5), Sec. 10·5, we read that the logarithm of the root of a number equals the logarithm of that number divided by the index of the root.

example 20 Evaluate $\sqrt[4]{737.12} = N$.

$$\log 737.12 = 2.86754$$
$$\log N = \frac{2.86754}{4}$$
$$= 0.71688$$
$$N = 5.2106$$

example 21 Evaluate $\sqrt[3]{0.00028864} = N$.

$$\log 0.00028864 = 0.46036 - 4$$

If we were to divide the entire logarithm by 3 as it stands, the characteristic -4 would give us the awkward -1.33333. To avoid this, we add at the left, and subtract at the right, a quantity which will make the characteristic divisible by 3. The simplest such number is 2.

$$\begin{aligned} \log 0.00028864 &= 0.46036 - 4 \\ & +2 - 2 \\ & 3/\underline{2.46036 - 6} \\ \log N &= 0.82012 - 2 \\ N &= 0.066087 \end{aligned}$$

EXERCISE 14

Evaluate the following expressions, considering all values accurate to five significant figures:

1. (a) $\sqrt[3]{972}$ (b) $\sqrt[3]{97.2}$ (c) $\sqrt[3]{9.72}$
2. (a) $\sqrt[3]{0.972}$ (b) $\sqrt[3]{0.0972}$ (c) $\sqrt[3]{0.00972}$
3. (a) $\sqrt{73.464}$ (b) $\sqrt[3]{168.15}$ (c) $\sqrt[4]{3051.8}$
4. (a) $\sqrt{0.082167}$ (b) $\sqrt[3]{0.22469}$ (c) $\sqrt[4]{0.000058274}$
5. $(8.527)^3 \times (0.7161)^2$
6. $\sqrt{58.43} \times (6.710)^2$
7. $(185.2 \times 0.071828)^3$
8. $\sqrt{97.422 \times 4.7881}$
9. $\sqrt{\dfrac{219.6}{0.005733}}$
10. $\sqrt[3]{\dfrac{52.482}{371.05 \times 0.18061}}$

11. $\sqrt[3]{\dfrac{3 \times 0.28617}{4\pi}}$

12. $[\pi(0.07112)(8.859)]^2$

13. $\sqrt[3]{\dfrac{(427.5)^2}{(13.482)^5}}$

14. $\sqrt[6]{\left(\dfrac{27.42}{0.03966}\right)^5}$

15. $\sqrt[5]{-381.72}$

16. $\sqrt[3]{\dfrac{-17.477}{(-0.84991)^2}}$

17. $\left(\dfrac{64.66}{-1009}\right)^{2/3}$

18. $\sqrt[4]{\dfrac{1}{8.3567}}$

10·28 Logarithmic computation of expressions involving addition and subtraction

Since numbers cannot be added or subtracted by logarithms, we must convert to antilogarithms before performing such an operation.

example 22 Evaluate $\sqrt{(a^5 + 1)/(a^5 - 1)} = N$, where $a = 1.0037$.

$$\log 1.0037 = 0.0016039 \qquad \text{(seven-place table)}$$
$$\underline{\qquad\qquad 5}$$
$$\log (1.0037)^5 = 0.0080195$$
$$(1.0037)^5 = 1.01864 \qquad \text{(seven-place table)}$$
$$\sqrt{\frac{1.01864 + 1}{1.01864 - 1}} = \sqrt{\frac{2.01864}{0.01864}}$$

$$\log 2.0186 = 0.30505$$

Subtract:

$$\log 0.01864 = \underline{0.27045 - 2}$$
$$0.03460 + 2$$
$$2\underline{/2.03460}$$
$$\log N = 1.01730$$
$$N = 10.41$$

Note that although we have been able to find $(1.0037)^5$ to six figures using a seven-place table, after we subtract 1 we get a denominator 0.01864 having only four significant figures. Therefore, we can retain only four significant figures in our answer. This situation points up the need of extra accuracy in reading logarithms of numbers near unity. The mantissas of such numbers may have only two or three significant figures when taken from a five-place table.

EXERCISE 15

Use logarithms to compute the value of the following to five significant figures:

1. $\sqrt{(8.3150)^2 - (5.0240)^2}$

2. $\sqrt{(11.964)^2 + (4.4857)^2}$

3. $\sqrt[3]{(4.1150)^3 + (6.3820)^3}$

4. $\sqrt[5]{(1.4860)^7 - 20.000}$

5. $\sqrt[3]{\dfrac{(1.3890)^3 + 1}{(1.3890)^3 - 1}}$

The short problems in Exercises 16 and 17 may be used to test the student's understanding of the properties of logarithms without spending the time usually required in consulting tables.

EXERCISE 16

Transform the equations in Probs. 1 to 4 into exponential form.

1. $\log_b (a - x) = c$
2. $\log_b (x^2 + 3) - \log_b (2x + 1) = k$
3. $2 \log_b (3x - 2) = a + c$
4. $\log_b y = \sqrt{2x + 5}$
5. If $\log \sqrt{x} = 0.35$, find $\log x^2$.
6. If $\log_b bx = 5$, find $\log_b x$.
7. If $\log 1/x = 1/4$, find $\log x$.
8. If $\log x^2 = 16$, find $\log x$.
9. If $\log (x^2 - 9) - \log (x + 3) = 0$, find x.

Rewrite the expressions in Probs. 10 to 12 without exponents or radicals.

10. (a) $\log x^5$ (b) $\log 3x^2$ (c) $\log \dfrac{5}{x^2}$
11. (a) $\log \sqrt[3]{x}$ (b) $\log \dfrac{1}{x^3}$ (c) $\log \dfrac{1}{2\sqrt{x}}$
12. (a) $\log \dfrac{x^5}{8}$ (b) $\log_b bx^2$ (c) $\log_b \dfrac{2x^3}{b^2}$

Convert the expressions in Probs. 13 and 14 to single positive logarithms whose coefficient is 1.

13. (a) $6 \log x$ (b) $2 \log x - \log 3$ (c) $\dfrac{\log_b x}{2} + 1$
14. (a) $3 - \log_b x$ (b) $\frac{1}{2} (\log x + \log 2)$ (c) $-10 \log x$
15. A student wrote $\log (N + 2) + \log N = \log (2N + 2)$. This is true only for what positive value of N?
16. What is the value of $\log_5 0.04$?
17. If $\log (p/q) + \log (q/r) - \log (r/p) - 2 \log (p/r) = \log x$, what is x?
18. If $S = P(1 + r)^{-n}$, solve for n.

EXERCISE 17

Given only that $\log 2 = 0.301$ and $\log 3 = 0.477$, find the following without using tables:

1. (a) $\log 2{,}000$ (b) $\log 0.03$ (c) $\log \sqrt{30}$
2. (a) $\log 1/16$ (b) $\log (3)^7$ (c) $\log 6$
3. (a) $\log 1$ (b) $\log 20$ (c) $\log 5$
4. (a) $\log 1.5$ (b) $\log 8$ (c) $\log 0.0003$
5. (a) $\log \sqrt{15}$ (b) $\log \sqrt[3]{60}$ (c) $\log 3\frac{1}{3}$
6. (a) $\log 39 - \log 13$ (b) $\log (1/3)^4$ (c) $\log \sqrt[5]{1/2}$
7. (a) $\log \sqrt[4]{1/3}$ (b) $\log \sqrt[3]{0.0002}$ (c) $\log (24)^{1.65}$
8. (a) $\log 46 - \log 23$ (b) antilog 3.477 (c) antilog 0.301 − 3
9. (a) antilog 2.301 (b) antilog 0.176 − 2 (c) antilog 3.01
10. (a) antilog 1.778 (b) antilog 7.778 − 10 (c) antilog 0.0477

10·29 Accuracy in logarithmic computations

The student should bear in mind that in multiplication and division the accuracy of the result is determined by the least accurate individual factor. If several six-digit numbers are to be multiplied by a number of four significant figures, all the individual factors should be rounded off to four significant figures, since the answer will be limited to this degree of accuracy. Consequently, a four-place table of logarithms will suffice. By the same token, if the utmost accuracy is to be secured from a combination of numbers of seven significant figures, a table to at least seven places must be used.

10·30 Exponential equations

An equation in which the unknown appears in the exponent is called an exponential equation. An example of the simplest of this type is $2^x = 8$. Here x is obviously equal to 3, since $2^3 = 8$.

In equations in which the result cannot be determined by inspection, we must take logarithms of both sides of the equation and obtain the final solution by ordinary algebraic methods.

example 23 Solve the following equation for x:

$$32^x = 512$$

Since we might have written $(2^5)^x = 2^9$, it is quite obvious from inspection that $5x = 9$ and that $x = 1.8$. However, we wish to assure ourselves that the logarithmic method is valid. Therefore we shall take the logarithm of each member, obtaining

$$\log 32^x = \log 512$$

Then

$$x \log 32 = \log 512$$
$$1.50515x = 2.70927$$

In order to avoid confusion, it is suggested that the student consider this equation as an ordinary linear equation, which it is. Had this equation appeared in the section of elementary algebra devoted to linear equations in one unknown, there would be no doubt as to the method of solving for x. The possible origin of the equation did not affect the procedure there; neither does it in this case. Accordingly,

$$x = \frac{2.70927}{1.50515} = 1.8000$$

If only two- or three-place accuracy is desired, this division may be performed on the slide rule.

example 24 Solve the equation $9^{2x-7} = 27^{x-3}$ for x.

Since in this example both 9 and 27 are powers of the same number, 3, we might proceed by inspection without tables:

$$9^{2x-7} = 27^{x-3}$$

But $$9 = 3^2 \quad \text{and} \quad 27 = 3^3$$

Therefore $$(3^2)^{2x-7} = (3^3)^{x-3}$$
$$3^{4x-14} = 3^{3x-9}$$

It is evident that $4x - 14$ must equal $3x - 9$; therefore $x = 5$.

Alternative solution: Taking logarithms of each member, we obtain

$$\log 9^{2x-7} = \log 27^{x-3}$$
$$(2x - 7) \log 9 = (x - 3) \log 27$$
$$(2x - 7)(0.95424) = (x - 3)(1.43136)$$

Here again we have an ordinary linear equation and proceed accordingly. Carrying out the indicated multiplication,

$$1.90848x - 6.67968 = 1.43136x - 4.29408$$
$$0.47712x = 2.38560$$
$$x = \frac{2.38560}{0.47712} = 5.0000$$

In some cases a few preliminary steps are necessary to obtain one term on each side of the equation before taking logarithms.

In Examples 25 and 26 below we cannot solve by inspection, and we must use the general logarithmic method.

example 25 Solve for x the equation $\dfrac{(1.05)^x - 1}{0.05} = 18$.

$$(1.05)^x - 1 = (0.05)(18) = 0.9$$
$$(1.05)^x = 1.9$$

Proceed as before.

Some equations in which the value of the exponent ultimately proves to be negative depend for their solution upon the deliberate conversion of the mantissa of a logarithm to the negative form (Sec. 10·16).

example 26 Solve for x the equation $6^x = 0.0208$.

Taking logarithms of both sides,

$$x \log 6 = \log 0.0208$$

Then $$x(0.77815) = 0.31806 - 2$$

Treating this as an ordinary linear equation, we obtain

$$0.77815x = 0.31806 - 2.00000$$

$$0.77815x = -1.68194$$

$$x = \frac{-1.68194}{0.77815}$$

$$x = -2.1615$$

EXERCISE 18

Solve for x in the following exponential equations:

1. $2^x = 75$
2. $(1.07)^x = 3$
3. $125^x = 48(5)^x$
4. $5^x = 1{,}000$
5. $(1.05)^{-x} = 0.36$
6. $3^{x+1} = 5^{x-1}$
7. $4^{x+2} = 8^{2x-1}$
8. $6^{-x} = 0.02$
9. $(1.04)^{-x} = 0.75$
10. $\dfrac{(1.06)^x - 1}{0.06} = 12$
11. $8^x = \dfrac{8}{2^{x-3}}$
12. $5^x = 20^{1/x}$

10·31 Aids to logarithmic computation

Computation involving logarithms may be expedited by observing a few details of technique, of which the following are representative:

1. Follow some orderly plan of development, such as that set forth in Example 12, Sec. 10·24.
2. Cancel or combine simple numbers where possible to reduce the number of logarithms to be handled.
3. Improve the arrangement for logarithmic computation, e.g.,
   (a) $2\pi r^2 + 2\pi rh = 2\pi r(r + h)$. Once r and h are added, there will be no further obstacle to logarithmic computation.
   (b) $\sqrt{c^2 - a^2} = \sqrt{(c + a)(c - a)}$. Here we enter a "straightaway" as soon as $c + a$ and $c - a$ are evaluated.
4. Negative mantissas or characteristics may often be avoided by multiplying by 10^n; e.g., $0.03152/0.00567 = 31.52/5.67$.
5. Another device to circumvent negative logarithms is multiplication by a^n; e.g., the equation $47.59 = (1.52)^{-3}(N)$ may be multiplied throughout by $(1.52)^3$; thus we get $(47.59)(1.52)^3 = N$.

EXERCISE 19

The following problems are drawn from various fields of technology. In each case compute the answer to the degree of accuracy you think is warranted by the data.

1. The population of a small city in 1950 was 27,000; in 1960 it was 38,500. Find the annual percentage rate of increase, assuming it to be uniform. What was the probable population in 1957?
2. A solid cast-iron sphere 4¾ in. in diameter weighs 14.6 lb. Find to the nearest 0.01 in. the diameter of a cast-iron sphere weighing 32 lb.

3. The speed of a chemical reaction doubles for each 18°F rise in temperature. What temperature rise will be needed to produce a 20-fold increase in the velocity of the reaction? (HINT: If \$1.00, at compound interest, grows to \$2.00 in 18 yr, what will it amount to after the first year?)
4. By the use of logarithms find the radius r of a circle inscribed in a triangle whose sides are a, b, and c if

$$r = \sqrt{\frac{(s-a)(s-b)(s-c)}{s}}$$

where s is half of the perimeter and the sides are 53.60, 41.90, and 38.40.
5. Find the diameter of a circle inscribed in a triangle whose sides are 287.6, 303.1, and 365.9.
6. In the formula $P = 29.92e^{-h/5}$, P is the barometer reading in inches of mercury, h is the altitude in miles, and $e = 2.718$ (base of natural logarithms).
   (a) What will the pressure be at 28,000 ft?
   (b) What altitude in feet corresponds to a pressure of 19.50 in.?
   (c) What is the sea-level pressure?

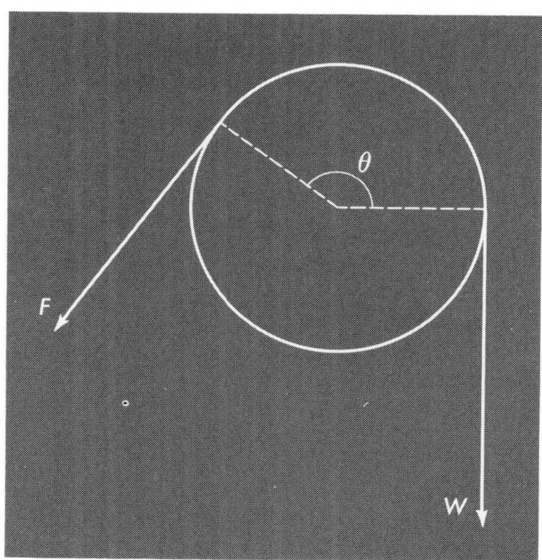

fig. 10·3

7. In Fig. 10·3 a weight W is suspended by a rope over a round beam. The rope is prevented from slipping by a force F at the other end.
   (a) Using the formula $F = We^{-a\theta}$, where $e = 2.718$, a is a constant, and θ is the angle of contact of the rope on the beam (expressed in turns), find a to 0.01 if 170 lb supports 200 lb when $\theta = 150°$.
   (b) What force is needed to support 200 lb, using two complete turns of rope?
   (c) How many turns would be required for 50 lb to support 200 lb?

8. The electrical resistance of a wire doubles (approximately) as the B & S gauge number increases 3 units. If the resistance of No. 10 copper wire is 1 ohm per 1,000 ft, find the resistances of No. 13 and No. 4 wire.
9. Find the resistance of No. 5 copper wire.
10. What is the resistance ratio between two successive B & S wire sizes?
11. The diameters of successive wire gauges are in geometric progression. If the diameter of No. 10 wire is 0.102 in. and that of No. 4 is 0.204 in., find the diameter of No. 6 wire.
12. What is the diameter ratio between two successive B & S wire sizes?
13. What is the resistance ratio between two wires five sizes apart?
14. What is the diameter ratio between two wires five sizes apart?
15. Find the diameter of a hemispherical cup holding exactly one-half pint.
16. In public-address systems the decibel gain $D = 10 \log P_A/P_B$, where P_A and P_B are the power levels of the two sounds A and B, and D is the difference in loudness (in decibels) between the sounds A and B. Find the decibel gain in an electric circuit if the input is 2 watts and the output is 5 watts.
17. What is the decibel loss in a circuit if the output is 0.07 watt and the input is 0.10 watt?
18. If the power ratio between input and output of an amplifier is ⅓, what is the decibel gain?
19. A loudspeaker requires 1.2 watts to produce the proper volume of sound. If we assign to this sound level an arbitrary value of 1, calculate the volume range within which the speaker operates if the power varies between 1.0 and 1.5 watts.
20. If the sound output of an amplifier varies from 4 db above to 3 db below the normal value, between what power levels does the amplifier operate?
21. The ratio of sound volume in speech may range as high as 250 to 1. What is the range in decibels?
22. The normal power rating of an amplifier is 1.6 watts. To what should this be increased to produce a perceptible (i.e., 1-db) increase in sound level?

For radio and public-address work, etc., 0.006 watt is a common reference level from which to figure sound-energy levels. If the output of an amplifier is 0.24 watt, the decibel difference between this level and 0.006 watt is

$$L_{db} = 10 \log \frac{0.24}{0.006} = 10 \log 40 = 10 \times 1.60206 = 16 \text{ db}$$

where L_{db} is the so-called power level at the amplifier. For convenience, the power level of this amplifier is said to be 16 db. We understand, however, that we really should say that the power level of the amplifier output is 16 db above 0.006 watt.

23. What is the decibel level equivalent to 0.0005 watt?
24. What is the decibel level equivalent to 0.46 watt?
25. What is the decibel gain in amplifier with 0.005 watt input and 0.46 watt output?
26. What is the difference between the decibel levels in Probs. 23 and 24?
27. What power level is equivalent to 59 watts?

Problems having to do with air conditioning, refrigeration, internal-combustion engines, air compressors, etc., often use formulas based on the following fundamental types of equations:

$$V = \frac{KT}{P} \tag{12}$$

(By Charles' and Boyle's laws, the volume V of a given weight of gas varies directly as the absolute temperature T and inversely as the absolute pressure P.)

$$\frac{PV}{T} = K \tag{13}$$

Under two separate sets of conditions of pressure, volume, and temperature for the *same weight* of gas we may write

$$\frac{P_1V_1}{T_1} = K \tag{14}$$

for the first set of conditions and

$$\frac{P_2V_2}{T_2} = K \tag{15}$$

for the second set of conditions. Any consistent set of units may be used as long as P and T are expressed on an absolute scale. Usually P is expressed in pounds per square inch absolute (equals pounds per square inch gauge $+14.7$, abbreviated psia), and T is expressed in Rankine or Fahrenheit absolute (equals Fahrenheit $+460$).

From Eqs. (14) and (15) we obtain

$$\frac{P_1V_1}{T_1} = \frac{P_2V_2}{T_2} \tag{16}$$

If we wish to express the pressure-volume relationship of a given weight of gas undergoing adiabatic (with no gain or loss of heat from the system) compression or expansion without being concerned about any accompanying temperature change, we could write, from thermodynamic considerations,

$$PV^n = C \tag{17}$$

where n and C are constants.

Then for two distinct sets of conditions for the same weight of gas we may write

$$P_1V_1^n = C \tag{18}$$

and

$$P_2V_2^n = C \tag{19}$$

From Eqs. (18) and (19) we obtain

$$P_1V_1^n = P_2V_2^n \tag{20}$$

In Probs. 28 and 29 we develop formulas to be used when we are not interested in pressure changes involved or when the pressure is unknown.

28. From Eqs. (16) and (20) show that

$$\frac{T_1}{T_2} = \left(\frac{V_2}{V_1}\right)^{n-1}$$

29. From Prob. 28 show that

$$\frac{V_2}{V_1} = \left(\frac{T_1}{T_2}\right)^{\frac{1}{n-1}}$$

Formulas in Probs. 30 and 31 are used when we are not concerned with changes in volume or when data are unavailable.

30. From Eq. (20) and Prob. 29 show that

$$\frac{T_1}{T_2} = \left(\frac{P_1}{P_2}\right)^{\frac{n-1}{n}}$$

31. From Prob. 30 show that

$$\frac{P_1}{P_2} = \left(\frac{T_1}{T_2}\right)^{\frac{n}{n-1}}$$

32. Find the final gauge pressure of a quantity of gas if the volume is compressed from 220 to 150 cu ft. P_1 is atmospheric pressure and $n = 1.39$.
33. Show that if $n = 0$, the pressure is constant, that if $n = 1$, the temperature is constant, and that if $n = \infty$, the volume is constant (see formulas in Probs. 28 to 31).
34. If $n = 1.64$, find the final volume of 68 cu ft of gas when, under compression, the temperature rises from 135 to 200°F.
35. A gas is compressed from 4.32 to 2.09 cu ft. Find the final temperature if the original temperature was 30°F and $n = 1.4$.
36. When 10 cu ft of a vapor expanded to 32 cu ft, the temperature fell from 191 to 0°F. Find n to 0.01.
37. The pressure on 220 cu ft of a gas is increased from 1 to 2 atm, while the volume decreases to 127 cu ft. Find n.

38. Following is a formula for the velocity of air being discharged through an orifice to the atmosphere:

$$V = 108.9\sqrt{T\left[1 - \left(\frac{14.7}{P}\right)^n\right]}$$

Find n if the air is being discharged at the rate of 323 cfm through a 1⅝-in.-diameter orifice. The pressure in the tank is 1.2 (psi gauge), and the temperature in the tank is 65°F.

V = linear air flow, fps
T = air temperature in tank, °R (Fahrenheit absolute)
P = absolute air pressure in tank, psi

39. 1,000 ml of a salt solution contains a suspended sludge. The sludge is washed by allowing it to settle; part of the clear, overlying salt solution is poured off, replaced by an equal volume of pure water, stirred, and allowed to settle. This cycle is to be repeated until the necessary amount of salt is washed out. The required equation is

$$C_n = \left(\frac{1{,}000 - w}{1{,}000}\right)^n C_0$$

where C_0 = original concentration of salt = 15.8 g per liter
C_n = final concentration of salt
w = milliliters of solution removed and replaced by water each cycle = 400 ml
n = number of washings

a. If $n = 8$, find C_n.
b. Find n to reduce C_n to less than 0.085 g per liter.

40. In the measurement of heat flow through pipe insulation the log mean diameter is computed. This is

$$D_{av} = \frac{D_2 - D_1}{2.3 \log D_2/D_1}$$

where D_1 = outer diameter of pipe
D_2 = outer diameter of insulation

Find D_{av} when the outer pipe diameter is 2⅝ in. and the insulation is 2⁵⁄₁₆ in. thick. Compare with the arithmetic mean.

41. The equation $h = 0.22C_pT^{2/3}v^{0.8}/D^{0.2}$ is used to determine the coefficient of heat transfer h for turbulent flow of gas inside a pipe.

C_p = average specific heat at constant pressure = 0.53
T = temperature of gas film = 695°R
v = lb gas per sec per sq ft of free area = 0.38
D = equivalent diameter of pipe = 5½ in.

Find h to 0.01.

42. Find to the nearest ¼ in. the pipe diameter required to deliver natural gas. Use the formula

$$D = 0.56\left(\frac{Q^2GL}{H}\right)^{0.225}$$

where D = pipe diameter, in.
Q = rate of gas flow = 280 cu ft per hr
G = specific gravity of the gas relative to air = 0.433
L = pipe length, yd = 5½ miles
H = pressure drop = 8¼ in. water

43. Find the size (in circular mils) of a bare copper wire required to transmit safely 8½ amp. Use the formula

$$I = 0.00004584(\text{cir mils})^{1.5}$$

where I = safe current-carrying capacity in amperes.

44. The equation $T_1/T_2 = (P_1/P_2)^{(n-1)/n}$ relates to the temperature changes occurring during adiabatic compression or expansion of a gas, where T_1 and T_2 are the absolute temperatures at absolute pressures P_1 and P_2, respectively. n is a constant for any particular gas; for dry air, $n = 1.40$ (see Prob. 30).

The equation $H = 60{,}470 \log (B_2/B_1)$ is used in the determination of altitudes by the use of barometer readings, where H is the difference in elevation (in feet) between two points at which the respective barometer readings are B_1 and B_2.

Derive an expression for H in terms of T_1 and T_2 only, eliminating P_1, P_2, B_1, and B_2.

45. A westerly wind, locally known as the *chinook,* or *snow eater,* descending the east slope of the Rocky Mountains is subjected to adiabatic compression and becomes relatively warm and dry. Use the formula derived in Prob. 44 to compute the final temperature at 3,000 ft altitude of an air stream originally at 0°F at 12,000 ft.

46. The average molecular weight M of a petroleum fraction may be approximately determined from its atmospheric boiling point t (degrees centigrade) by the equation

$$\log M = 2.51 \log (t + 393) - 4.7523$$

(a) Calculate M, to the nearest unit, when $t = 160$°C.
(b) Solve the above equation for t (exponential form).

47. The magnitude, or brightness, of a star is given by the equation

$$M = 2.5 \log \left(\frac{I_1}{I}\right)$$

where M = magnitude of star whose light intensity is I
I_1 = light intensity of star of first magnitude

Determine the ratio of the light intensities I/I_1 for a star of the fourth magnitude ($M = 4$). (Note that the brighter the star, the lower the magnitude; in fact, for the brighter planets M is negative.)

48. The rate of heat transfer (Btu per hr) by radiation is given by the equation

$$Q = K\left[\left(\frac{T_1}{100}\right)^4 - \left(\frac{T_2}{100}\right)^4\right]$$

where K = constant depending upon physical properties of objects involved
T_1 = absolute temperature of hot body, °F
T_2 = absolute temperature of cooler body, °F

If the rate of heat transfer is 7,500 Btu per hr when the hot and cold objects are at 1050 and 70°F, respectively, find the necessary hot-body temperature (in degrees Fahrenheit) to double the rate of radiant heat transfer, keeping the cooler body at 70°F.

49. Under certain conditions the drying of sheets of wallboard may be expressed by the equation

$$\log\left(\frac{T_0 - E}{T - E}\right) = K\theta$$

where T_0 = pounds of moisture per pound of bone-dry stock before drying
T = amount of moisture remaining (same basis) after θ hours
E = pounds of moisture per pound of bone-dry stock remaining in stock after coming to equilibrium with air used for drying; i.e., E represents limit to drying possible under given conditions
K = constant

If the moisture content drops from 1.2 to 0.8 in 3 hr, with a further drop to 0.64 in another 6 hr, find the amount of moisture remaining in the stock after a drying period of indefinitely great length.

50. The resistance of a tungsten lamp filament is given by the relationship

$$\frac{R_1}{R_2} = \left(\frac{T_1}{T_2}\right)^{1.2}$$

where R_1 = resistance at room temperature T_1
R_2 = resistance at operating temperature T_2

Temperatures are both Kelvin (centigrade absolute) or both Rankine (Fahrenheit absolute). If the resistance at 20°C is 16 ohms and the operating resistance is 232 ohms, find the operating temperature in degrees centigrade.

51. A tungsten lamp is rated at 60 watts at 115 volts. If the resistance measured at 75°F is 15.2 ohms, find the operating temperature in degrees Fahrenheit. Ohms = (volts)^2/watts (see Prob. 50).

52. The horsepower necessary to compress a gas in a single-stage compressor is given by the formula

$$\text{hp} = \frac{144nP_1V_1}{33{,}000(n-1)}\left[\left(\frac{P_2}{P_1}\right)^{\frac{n-1}{n}} - 1\right]$$

Find the horsepower necessary to compress, in 1 min, 240 cu ft of helium from atmospheric pressure (14.7 psia) to 250 psi gauge. For helium, $n = 1.66$. Other symbols have the same meanings as in Probs. 28 to 31, page 240.

53. The weight P in pounds that will crush a solid cylindrical cast-iron column is given by the formula

$$P = 6.759 \times 10^6 \frac{d^{3.55}}{l^{1.7}}$$

where d and l are the diameter and length of the cylinder in inches. What weight will crush a cast-iron column 72 in. high and 4.3 in. in diameter?

54. The weight in pounds W of a cubic foot of saturated steam depends upon the boiler pressure P (pounds per square inch absolute) according to the formula

$$W = \frac{P^{0.941}}{330.36}$$

Find W when P is 265 psi gauge. Assume atmospheric pressure is 15 psi.

10·32 Relation of logarithms to the slide rule

An arrangement of uniform scales similar to those illustrated in Fig. 10·4 could be used for mechanically adding or subtracting numbers.

This figure illustrates the addition $0.22 + 0.26 = 0.48$. It also illustrates the subtraction $0.48 - 0.26 = 0.22$.

As an example of multiplication, multiply 1.66 by 1.82. Looking up three-place logarithms, we find 0.220 and 0.260 to be the respective mantissas. We may use the scales to add 0.220 and 0.260, obtaining 0.480, as in Fig. 10·4. Looking up the antilogarithm of 0.480, we obtain 3.02.

fig. 10·4

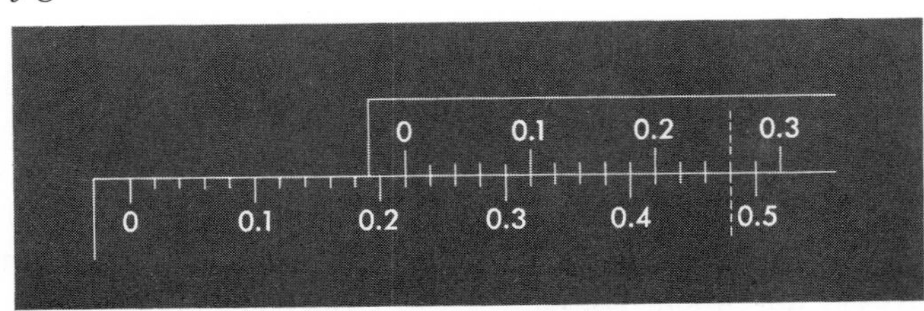

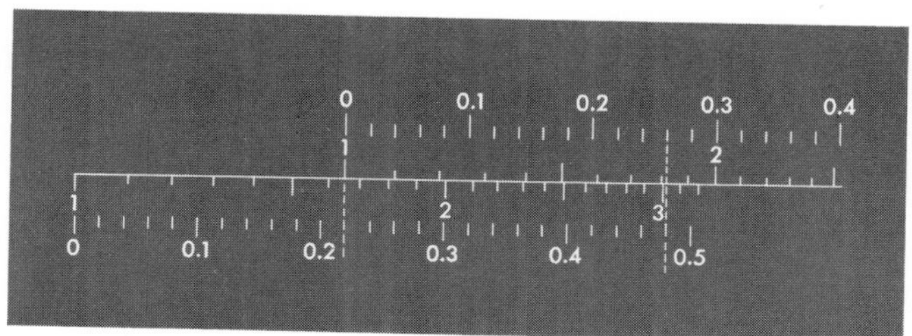

fig. 10·5

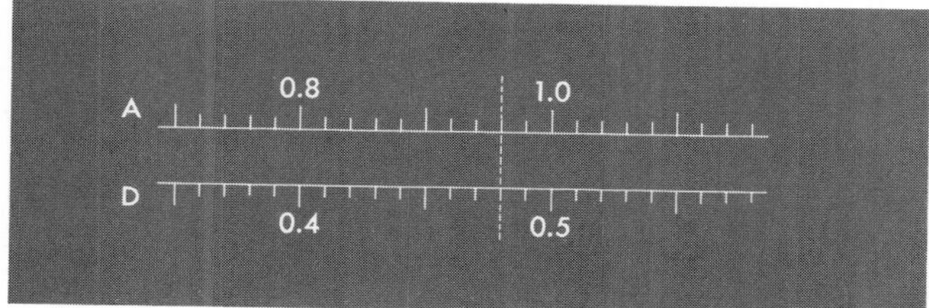

fig. 10·6

fig. 10·7

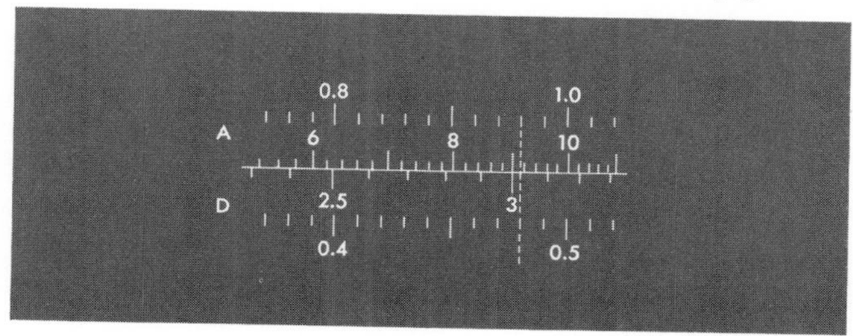

Now, such a slide rule would not be of much help to us. However, if we replace the uniform scales which we have been using to represent mantissas by scales bearing the numbers to which these mantissas correspond, we will have eliminated the necessity of looking up logarithms and antilogarithms (Fig. 10·5). Thus the scheme for mechanically adding 0.22 and 0.26 becomes a means of multiplying the antilogarithms 1.66 and 1.82 to get 3.02. Evidently, by reversal of the procedure, $0.48 - 0.26 = 0.22$ corresponds to $3.02 \div 1.82 = 1.66$.

In Fig. 10·6 it will be observed that opposite any given number n on the D scale we read $2n$ on the A scale.

If we wished to square 3.02, we could look up the (three-place) mantissa, 0.480, double by the arrangement in Fig. 10·6, and look up the antilogarithm of 0.96, obtaining 9.12. Obviously we stand to gain here also by placing the antilogarithms in the place of the corresponding mantissas. Thus the process of mechanically multiplying 0.48 by 2 to get 0.96 becomes the operation of squaring 3.02 to obtain 9.12. Likewise the operation $0.96/2 = 0.48$ is replaced by $\sqrt{9.12} = 3.02$ (Fig. 10·7).

These illustrations will serve to indicate that the slide rule is basically a device to add or subtract quantities (mantissas) mechanically. A knowledge of the laws of logarithms (Sec. 10·5) will be naturally helpful in developing facility in the use of the slide rule.

10·33 Logarithmic computations on the slide rule

It will be noticed that the uniform scale we discussed in Sec. 10·32 is engraved on the slide rule as the L scale. If we set the hairline over a given number on the D scale, we shall at the same time find under the hairline on the L scale the mantissa of the logarithm of that number. Thus in Fig. 10·8 we find illustrated log 4 = 0.602; in Fig. 10·9, log 8 = 0.903; in Fig. 10·10, the mantissa of log 16 = 0.204, or log 16 = 1.204.

Let us illustrate the use of the L scale in certain logarithmic computations.

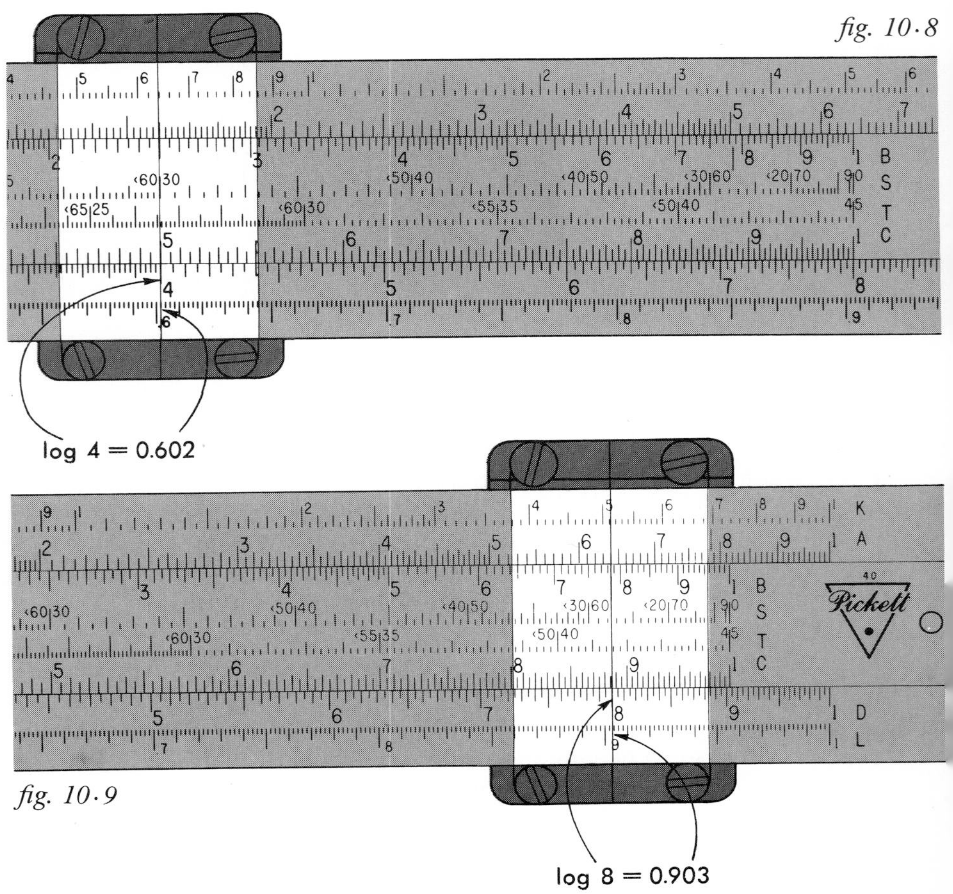

fig. 10·8

fig. 10·9

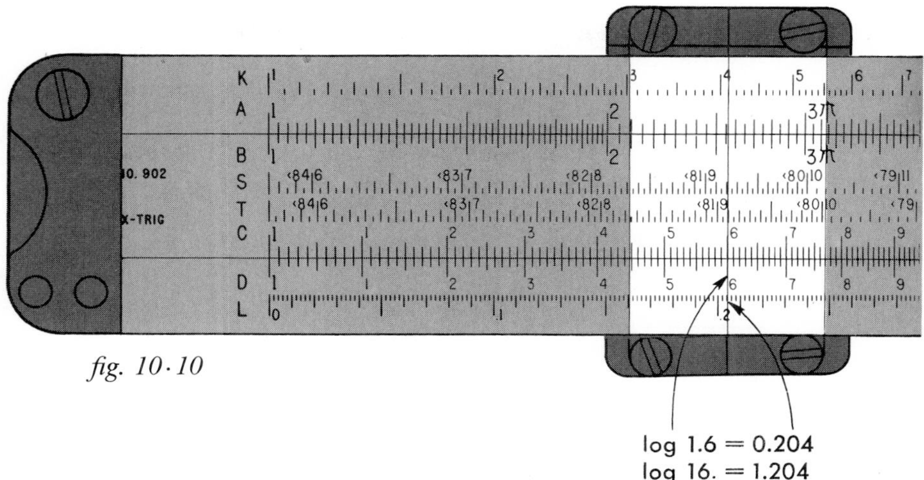

fig. 10·10

example 27 Solve the equation $4^{3/2} = x$.

Taking logarithms, we have $1.5 \log 4 = \log x$ (Sec. 10·26). In Fig. 10·8 we have shown that $\log 4 = 0.602$. Figure 10·11 shows that $1.5 \times 0.602 = 0.903$. If $\log x = 0.903$, then antilog $0.903 = x = 8$. This step is illustrated in Fig. 10·9.

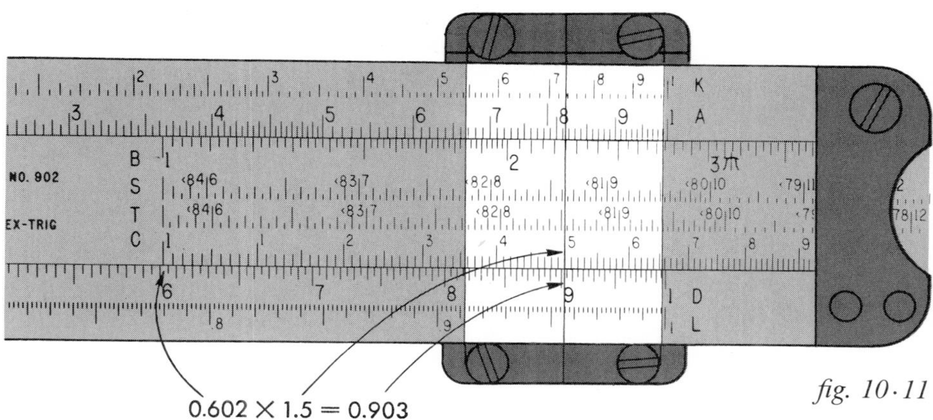

fig. 10·11

example 28 Solve the equation $16^x = 8$.

Taking logs of both sides, we have $x \log 16 = 8$. Since the settings in Figs. 10·10 and 10·9 show that $\log 16 = 1.204$ and $\log 8 = 0.903$, we may write $1.204x = 0.903$. Finally Fig. 10·12 illustrates the division $0.903 \div 1.204 = 0.75 = x$.

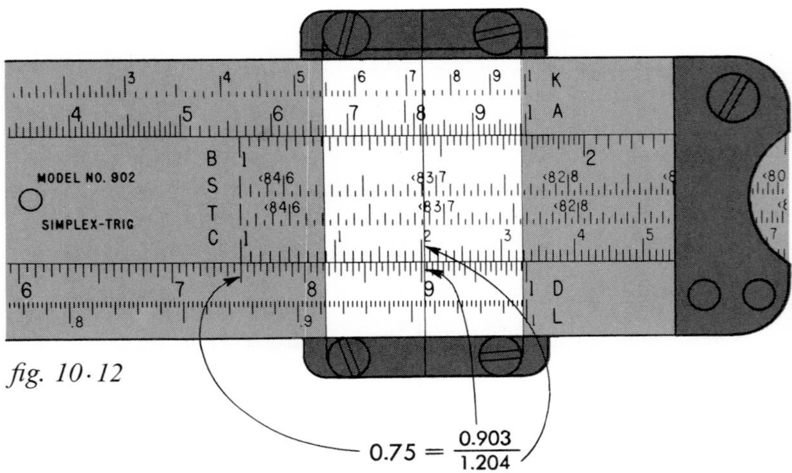

fig. 10·12

11

exponential functions—rate of growth

Many phenomena of the physical sciences are governed by laws of growth and decay which involve e, the base of natural logarithms. It develops in calculus that this is indeed a "natural" logarithm.

The natural logarithm is the logical outgrowth of the situation in which the rate of growth or depreciation of a variable at any time is proportional to the amount of the variable itself at that time. To cite some fields in which e commonly occurs, we might mention heat transfer, radioactive materials, rate of chemical reaction, thermodynamics, transient electric currents, and characteristic impedance of transmission lines.

11·1 Power function versus exponential function

An expression such as x^3 in which a variable is raised to a fixed power is called a *power function.* An expression in which the variable occurs in the exponent is called an *exponential function.* Table 11·1 contrasts these functions.

table 11·1

x	0	1	2	3	4	5	6	7
x^3	0	1	8	27	64	125	216	343
3^x	1	3	9	27	81	243	729	2,187

11·2 Compound-interest law

Many quantities in nature grow in much the same way as a sum of money at compound interest; i.e., the rate of growth is a fixed percentage of the amount on hand at the beginning of the interest period in question. However, there is one important difference. The growth of money occurs stepwise at the end of each interest-conversion period, whereas growth (and decay) in nature is usually a smooth, continuous operation; i.e., the interest is converted exceedingly often (or, in effect, continuously), and the rate of growth at any time is a fixed percentage of the magnitude of the quantity at that time.

11·3 Significance of e

Reference to any standard text on the mathematics of investment will indicate that a common formula in the field of compound interest is $S = P(1 + i/m)^{mn}$, in which P is the amount invested, i is the stated rate of interest, m is the number of times interest is compounded in a year, n is the number of years, and S is the total amount of original principal plus accrued interest.

If we consider the growth of \$1 at 100 per cent compounded m times a year for one year, P, i, and n each become equal to 1, and we obtain the equation $S = (1 + 1/m)^m$.

It is apparent that for semiannual compounding $m = 2$ and $S = 2.25$. For quarterly compounding $m = 4$ and $S = 2.441$. If it were possible to compound 100 times a year, S would equal 2.705, and when $m = 10{,}000$, $S = 2.718$. Evidently S is approaching a limit of some kind as m becomes extremely large.

To arrive at a more accurate value of this limit, we shall expand $(1 + 1/m)^m$ by the binomial theorem and allow m to increase indefinitely in the result. Thus we obtain

$$\left(1+\frac{1}{m}\right)^m = 1 + m\frac{1}{m} + \frac{m(m-1)}{2!}\frac{1}{m^2} + \frac{m(m-1)(m-2)}{3!}\frac{1}{m^3} + \frac{m(m-1)(m-2)(m-3)}{4!}\frac{1}{m^4} + \cdots$$

$$= 1 + 1 + \frac{1}{2!}\left(1-\frac{1}{m}\right) + \frac{1}{3!}\left(1-\frac{1}{m}\right)\left(1-\frac{2}{m}\right) + \frac{1}{4!}\left(1-\frac{1}{m}\right)\left(1-\frac{2}{m}\right)\left(1-\frac{3}{m}\right) + \cdots$$

As m increases indefinitely, $1/m$, $2/m$, $3/m$, etc., approach zero, and we have

$$e = \lim_{m\to\infty}\left(1+\frac{1}{m}\right)^m = 1 + 1 + \frac{1}{2!} + \frac{1}{3!} + \frac{1}{4!} + \cdots = 2.7183 \text{ approx} \qquad \textbf{(1)}$$

which is the base of natural logarithms and occurs frequently in problems concerned with natural growth or decay, e.g., speed of chemical reactions, decrease of atmospheric pressure with increasing altitude, radioactive decay, and rate of cooling of a warm object.

A compact arrangement for calculating e to six figures is shown below:

$$
\begin{array}{r}
1.000000 \\
2\,/\,\underline{1.000000} \\
3\,/\,\underline{0.500000} \\
4\,/\,\underline{0.166667} \\
5\,/\,\underline{0.041667} \\
6\,/\,\underline{0.008333} \\
7\,/\,\underline{0.001389} \\
8\,/\,\underline{0.000198} \\
9\,/\,\underline{0.000025} \\
\underline{0.000003} \\
2.718282
\end{array}
$$

Or $e = 2.71828$ to six significant figures.

A value for any power of e may be found by evaluating

$$\left[\left(1 + \frac{1}{m}\right)^m\right]^x = \left(1 + \frac{1}{m}\right)^{mx}$$

as above. Thus we obtain

$$
\begin{aligned}
\left(1 + \frac{1}{m}\right)^{mx} &= 1 + mx\frac{1}{m} + \frac{mx(mx-1)}{2!}\frac{1}{m^2} \\
&\qquad + \frac{mx(mx-1)(mx-2)}{3!}\frac{1}{m^3} + \cdots \\
&= 1 + x + \frac{x^2}{2!}\left(1 - \frac{1}{mx}\right) + \frac{x^3}{3!}\left(1 - \frac{1}{mx}\right)\left(1 - \frac{2}{mx}\right) + \cdots
\end{aligned}
$$

As m increases without limit, $1/mx$, $2/mx$, etc., approach zero, and we obtain the series for e^x:

$$e^x = \lim_{m\to\infty}\left(1 + \frac{1}{m}\right)^{mx} = 1 + x + \frac{x^2}{2!} + \frac{x^3}{3!} + \frac{x^4}{4!} + \cdots \qquad \textbf{(2)}$$

In using Eq. (1) or (2) for computation, enough terms should be used so that the first term omitted is less than half the allowable error.

11·4 Natural logarithms

Common logarithms are based upon the fact that every positive number can be expressed as a power of 10. Similarly, it is true that every such number may be expressed as a power of e. For example, $3.8 = e^{1.335}$, and we say that the logarithm of 3.8 to the base e is 1.335. This is written $\log_e 3.8 = 1.335$ or $\ln 3.8 = 1.335$.

Natural logarithms (ln), or logarithms to the base e, follow the same rules of combination that apply to common logarithms, as set forth in Sec. 10·5.

11·5 Use of the table

A few lines of a table of natural, or Napierian, logarithms are reproduced as Table 11·2 below:

table 11·2

N	*0*	*1*	*2*	*3*	*4*	*5*	*6*	*7*	*8*	*9*
7.0	1.9459	473	488	502	516	530	544	559	573	587
7.1	601	615	629	643	657	671	685	699	713	727
10.0	2.3026	036	046	056	066	076	086	096	106	115

From this table we read that

$$\ln 7.16 = 1.9685 \quad \text{or} \quad 7.16 = e^{1.9685}$$
$$\ln 10 = 2.3026 \quad \text{or} \quad 10 = e^{2.3026}$$

In order to find the natural logarithm of a number which lies outside the limits of the table, we cannot simply change the characteristic as in common logs. The common logarithm of 716 is $\log 7.16 + \log 100$, or $0.8549 + 2$; but since e^2 is not 100, the natural logarithm of 100 is not 2. However, we can make use of scientific notation to carry out much the same idea.

Hence we write

$$716 = 7.16 \times 10^2$$

and

$$\ln 716 = \ln 7.16 + 2 \ln 10 = 1.9685 + 2(2.3026) = 6.5737$$

Conversely, to find anti-ln 6.5737 (or the value of $e^{6.5737}$), we would subtract from 6.5737 as many 2.3026's as necessary to work within the scope of the table, which would be two. Therefore we would write $6.5737 - 2(2.3026) = 1.9685$ or $\ln N - 2 \ln 10 = \ln N/100$. Hence the anti-ln $1.9685 = 7.16 = N/100$, and $N = 716$.

If we wish to find $\ln 0.703$, we write $0.703 = 7.03 \times 10^{-1}$ and $\ln 0.703 = \ln 7.03 - \ln 10 = 1.9502 - 2.3026 = -0.3524$. Note that with natural logarithms we make no attempt to make the mantissa positive, since the mantissas for, say, $\ln 70.3$, $\ln 7.03$, and $\ln 0.703$ would bear no resemblance to one another.

Let it be required to find anti-ln (-4.9505). We shall add only enough 2.3026's to -4.9505 to make the total positive. We shall need three. Hence we write $-4.9505 + 3(2.3026) = 1.9573$, or $\ln N + 3 \ln 10 = \ln (1{,}000\, N) = 1.9573$. Anti-ln $1.9573 = 7.08 = 1{,}000\, N$. Hence $N = 0.00708$.

EXERCISE 1

1. Look up the natural logarithms of

(a) 6.14 (b) 9.08 (c) 1.97 (d) 33.8
(e) 417 (f) 0.216 (g) 0.0117

2. Use interpolation to obtain the natural logarithms of

(a) 49.73 (b) 0.06492 (c) 3,584 (d) 0.1856

3. Look up the antilogarithms of

(a) 3.65325 (b) 9.06878 (c) −3.00376 (d) −4.05705
(e) 11.28351

4. Use interpolation where necessary to find the antilogarithms of

(a) 4.08770 (b) 10.06228 (c) −6.72112 (d) −0.12461
(e) 7.58732

5. Using natural logarithms, calculate

(a) $e^{3.8}$ (b) $e^{2.6}$ (c) $e^{-1.4}$ (d) $e^{-0.9}$
(e) $56e^{-2.2}$ (f) $452e^{1.85}$ (g) $0.087e^{4.732}$ (h) $5300e^{-6.185}$
(i) Confirm answers to parts a to d, inclusive, using a table of e^x.

6. Solve the following for n. Note that our task of looking up natural logarithms will be facilitated by first dividing through by [in part (a)] 100, giving us $3.46 = 1.95e^{10n}$.

(a) $346 = 195e^{10n}$ (b) $14.7 = 68.3e^{-0.6n}$
(c) $0.0183 = 0.087e^{-0.02n}$ (d) $0.0964 = 0.0529e^{1.28n}$
(e) $450 = 2{,}000e^{20n}$ (f) $3{,}000 = 11.8e^{-50n}$

11·6 Relation between common and natural logarithms

The general formula for converting the logarithm of a number from one base to another is

$$\log_a N = \frac{1}{\log_b a} \log_b N \qquad \text{[Eq. (10), Sec. 10·12]}$$

Rearranging, we obtain

$$(\log_b a)(\log_a N) = \log_b N \tag{3}$$

Hence it follows that if $b = e$ and $a = 10$, substitution in Eq. (3) produces the formula for converting common logarithms to natural logarithms:

$$(\log_e 10)(\log_{10} N) = \log_e N$$

or

$$2.3026 \log N = \ln N \tag{4}$$

Hence, also,

$$\frac{1}{2.3026} \ln N = \log N$$

or

$$0.43429 \ln N = \log N \qquad (5)$$

EXERCISE 2

1. Convert the following to common logarithms:

(a) $\ln x = 3.0425$ (b) $\ln x = 0.00488$
(c) $\ln x = -2.0714$ (d) $\ln x = -1.3507$
(e) $\ln x = -1.7106$ (f) $\ln x = -3.3822$

2. Convert the following to natural logarithms:

(a) $\log x = 2.1734$ (b) $\log x = 0.01007$
(c) $\log x = 8.7466 - 10$ (d) $\log x = 0.7843 - 2$
(e) $\log x = -1.2755$ (f) $\log x = 9.0843 - 10$

3. In Prob. 1 find x, using the values of common logarithms obtained.
4. Using only a table of common logarithms, find

(a) ln 5.828 (b) ln 73.46 (c) ln 10,000
(d) ln 0.08469 (e) ln 0.005497 (f) ln $\frac{1}{15}$

11·7 Equivalent expressions

Because of an occasional lack of a table of natural logarithms or for other reasons, it is desirable to be able to express an equation in the exponential form to any required base or in terms of either system of logarithms. The following typical problem will illustrate the steps involved.

example 1 Given the equation $y = 8.3e^{1.2x}$.

(a) Convert to the form $y = kb^x$.
(b) Express as a natural logarithmic equation.
(c) Express as a common logarithmic equation.

(a) Since we may write $y = 8.3(e^{1.2})^x$, we can find from tables that $e^{1.2} = 3.3201$. Hence $y = 8.3(3.3201)^x$.

(b) Taking natural logarithms of both sides of the equation,

$$\ln y = \ln (8.3e^{1.2x}) = \ln 8.3 + \ln e^{1.2x}$$

or

$$\ln y = 2.1163 + 1.2x$$

(c) Taking common logarithms of both sides, we obtain

$$\begin{aligned} \log y &= \log (8.3e^{1.2x}) \\ &= \log 8.3 + 1.2x \log e \\ &= \log 8.3 + 1.2x(0.43429) \\ &= 0.91908 + 0.52115x \end{aligned}$$

Perhaps the most frequently used of these procedures is *c*, in which the equation is immediately expressed in terms of common logs.

EXERCISE 3

1. Prove, without using tables, that $1/\ln 10 = \log e$.
2. Express the following in exponential form (solve for y):

   (a) $\ln y = x$ (b) $\ln y + \ln a = x$ (c) $a \ln y = x$

3. Express the following in natural logarithmic form:

   (a) $z = e^w$ (b) $y = ae^{cx}$ (c) $y = \dfrac{3}{\sqrt{e}}$

4. Find the value of the following, first using only a table of natural logarithms, then using only a table of common logarithms:

   (a) $e^{2.5}$ (b) $e^{-3.5}$ (c) $0.08552e^{3.52}$

5. Convert the following to the form $y = be^{kx}$:

   (a) $y = 5(1.6)^x$ (b) $y = 3.2(0.275)^x$
   (c) $y = 3(2)^{5x}$ (d) $y = e^{(0.94+x)/2}$

6. Convert the following to the form $y = kb^x$:

   (a) $y = 0.63e^{2.7x}$ (b) $y = 1.62e^{-1.4x}$

7. Solve for x in each of the following:

   (a) $T = ae^{-kx}$ (b) $\dfrac{c^2}{x^2} = e^{-1.44t^2}$ (c) $y = \ln\left(\dfrac{1}{x^n}\right)$ (d) $2.5 = 5e^{-0.3x}$

8. (a) If $\ln \sqrt{x} = 2$, find $\ln x^3$. (b) If $\ln ex = 4$, find $\ln x$.
   (c) If $\ln x^3 = 27$, find $\ln x$.

9. Solve for x in terms of e: (a) $\ln \dfrac{e}{x} + ½ = 0$, (b) $2 \ln x = 6 - \ln 16$,
   (c) $\ln (x^2 - e^2) - \ln (x + e) = 1$.

In the following problems, given only that $e = 2.718$, $\ln 10 = 2.303$, $\ln 7 = 1.946$, $\ln 17 = 2.833$, $\log 8 = 0.903$, and $\log 9 = 0.954$, calculate without tables or slide rule the values of

10. $\log e$
11. $\ln 8$
12. $\ln 9$
13. $\ln 3$
14. $\ln 0.008$
15. $\ln 90$
16. $\ln ⅛$
17. $\ln 4$
18. $\ln 27.18$
19. $\log 0.2718$
20. $\log 170$
21. anti-ln 2.946

22. anti-ln 1.833 23. anti-ln (−1.946) 24. t if $8 = \frac{1}{e^{3t}}$

25. y if $y = 7e^{0.53}$

EXERCISE 4

1. In a d-c circuit containing a capacitor C and a resistance R in series, the instantaneous value of the current i at any time t after the circuit has been closed is given by the equation

$$\ln i = -\frac{t}{RC} + \ln E - \ln R$$

Convert this equation to the exponential form (i.e., solve for i rather than $\ln i$).

2. Use the answer obtained in Prob. 1 to find the current 0.00002 sec after the circuit has been closed, if $E = 24$ volts, $R = 9.5$ ohms, and $C = 0.000029$ farad.
3. Find i in Prob. 1 when $E = 100$, $R = 250$, $C = 25 \times 10^{-6}$, and $t = 3 \times 10^{-5}$.
4. Find i in Prob. 1 when $t = 0$.
5. In Prob. 1 what is the approximate value of i when t is very large?
6. In Prob. 1 what percentage is i of E/R when $t = RC$?
7. (a) The emission current for a heated filament is given by the equation

$$i = AT^2e^{-B/T}$$

where i is expressed in amperes, A is a constant equal to 60, B is a constant equal to 5.24×10^4 for a tungsten filament, and T is the temperature in degrees Kelvin. Find i when $T = 2400°$K.

(b) How would you proceed to solve an equation of the type in (a) in which T is the unknown?

8. In a simple steam engine the equation for the mean effective pressure is

$$P_m = P\left(\frac{1 + \ln r}{r}\right) - p$$

Determine P_m if $P = 100$ psi, $p = 14.7$, and $r = 3.54$.

9. When light passes through a transparent medium, its intensity is reduced according to the equation

$$I = I_o e^{-kd}$$

where I_o is the initial light intensity, I is the intensity after passing through a medium of thickness d, and k is a constant depending upon the nature of the light and of the medium. If the intensity of sunlight is reduced to half its original value after penetrating water to a depth of 4 ft, at what depth will the light intensity be 10 per cent of that at the surface?

10. The temperature of a body surrounded by a medium at a different temperature is given by the equation

$$T = T_o e^{-kt}$$

where T_o is the initial difference between the temperatures of body and surroundings, T is the temperature difference at any time t, and k is a heat-transfer constant dependent upon various physical conditions and the units involved. If, during a power failure, a home freezer warms up from -10 to $+2°F$ after standing for 3 hr in a room at 50°F, how much longer will it take to warm up to 32°F?

11. A radioactive material disintegrates according to the relation

$$A = A_o e^{-kt}$$

where A_o is the original amount of active material, A is the amount of active material remaining at time t, and k is a constant characteristic of the given material. It is frequently desirable to determine the period of half-life, i.e., that time at which half of the original material still remains.

(a) Show that the period of half-life is equal to $0.6932/k$.

(b) If 3 per cent of a certain radioactive material disintegrates in 1 hr, find the period of half-life.

12. A problem in electrical engineering required the solution of the following system of simultaneous equations:

$$E_m(1 - e^{-3n}) = 13$$
$$E_m(1 - e^{-n}) = 8$$

Solve for E_m and n to four significant figures. (HINT: Divide the first equation by the second.)

13. If

$$i = \frac{E}{R}(1 - e^{-Rt/L})$$

find i when $E = 10$, $L = 0.9$, $R = 12$, and $t = 0.005$.

14. Find i in Prob. 13 if $t = 0$.

15. Approximately what is the value of i in Prob. 13 when t is very large?

16. If you were given i, E, L, and t, how would you go about solving for R in Prob. 13?

17. When $t = L/R$, what percentage is i of E/R? Is this percentage independent of the actual values of the variables?

18. If $x = y$, refer to the principles relating e and natural logarithms to show that $x = e^{\ln y}$. (This problem is referred to in Chap. 23.)

19. The work done in compressing a gas at constant temperature from a pressure p_0 lb per sq ft and volume v_0 cu ft to a pressure p_1 lb per sq ft and volume v_1 cu ft is given by

$$W = p_0 v_0 \ln \frac{v_1}{v_0} \qquad \text{ft-lb}$$

Determine W if $p_0 = 20$ psi, $p_1 = 35$ psi, and $v_0 = 3$ cu ft. v_1 can be determined from the relation $p_1 v_1 = p_0 v_0$.

20. The current flowing in a series circuit (with inductance L henrys, resistance R ohms, and voltage E volts) is given by

$$I = \frac{E}{R}(1 - e^{-Rt/L}) \qquad \text{amp}$$

and the power going into the magnetic field is given by

$$P = \frac{E^2}{R}(e^{-Rt/L} - e^{-2Rt/L})$$

(a) If $R = 10$ ohms, $L = 0.0001$ henry, and $E = 15$ volts, sketch graphs of P and I as functions of the time t.
(b) Sketch graphs of RI/E and RP/E^2 as functions of Rt/L. These are dimensionless groups.

21. The following is taken from an article in *Chemical Engineering* on gasoline cracking. Sketch graphs of x and y as functions of the time t if

$$x = 100(1 - e^{-kt}) \qquad \text{and} \qquad y = 100e^{-kt}$$

where $k = 0.01076$.

11·8 General formula

In order to determine the effect of continuous compounding at any rate for any length of time, we shall again refer to the formula $S = P(1 + i/m)^{mn}$, expand by the binomial theorem, and allow m to increase without limit in the result. Thus we obtain the expansion

$$\left(1 + \frac{i}{m}\right)^{mn} = 1 + mn\frac{i}{m} + \frac{mn(mn - 1)}{2!}\frac{i^2}{m^2} + \frac{mn(mn - 1)(mn - 2)}{3!}\frac{i^3}{m^3} + \cdots$$

$$= 1 + ni + \frac{n^2 i^2}{2!}\left(1 - \frac{1}{mn}\right) + \frac{n^3 i^3}{3!}\left(1 - \frac{1}{mn}\right)\left(1 - \frac{2}{mn}\right) + \cdots$$

and

$$\lim_{m\to\infty}\left(1 + \frac{i}{m}\right)^{mn} = 1 + ni + \frac{n^2 i^2}{2!} + \frac{n^3 i^3}{3!} + \cdots$$

However it can be shown by analogy to Eq. (2) that

$$e^{ni} = \lim_{m\to\infty}\left(1 + \frac{1}{m}\right)^{mni}$$

also equals

$$1 + ni + \frac{n^2 i^2}{2!} + \frac{n^3 i^3}{3!} + \cdots$$

Hence we may write

$$\lim_{m\to\infty}\left(1 + \frac{i}{m}\right)^{mn} = e^{ni}$$

or

$$S = \lim_{m\to\infty} P\left(1 + \frac{i}{m}\right)^{mn} = Pe^{ni} \qquad \text{(growth)} \qquad \textbf{(6)}$$

Observe that in computations of continuous depreciation or decay instead of growth, i will be negative and

$$S = \lim_{m\to\infty} P\left(1 - \frac{i}{m}\right)^{mn} = Pe^{-ni} \qquad \text{(depreciation)} \tag{7}$$

The proof of Eq. (7) is left as an exercise for the student.

example 2 The number of bacteria in a colony increased at an instantaneous rate (per hour) continuously equal to 20 per cent of the number at that time. Starting from a colony of 1,000 bacteria, how many would there be in 6 hr?

Substituting, in Eq. (6), $P = 1{,}000$, $n = 6$, and $i = 0.2$, we have

$$S = 1{,}000e^{1.2}$$

From tables of e^x,

$$e^{1.2} = 3.320$$

Hence $$S = 1{,}000(3.320) = 3{,}320$$

example 3 Radium decomposes at an instantaneous rate (per century) continuously equal to 4.1 per cent of the amount remaining at that time. If 25 mg are present at the start, how much will be left after 2,000 years?

Substituting, in Eq. (7), $P = 25$, $n = 20$, and $i = 0.041$, we have

$$S = 25e^{-0.82}$$

From tables of e^{-x},

$$e^{-0.82} = 0.44043$$

Hence $$S = 25(0.44043) = 11.011$$

EXERCISE 5

1. Using the series, calculate the value of $e^{0.2}$ to five significant figures. Check your answer by the table.
2. Repeat Prob. 1 for $e^{-0.5}$.
3. The speed of a given chemical reaction depends upon the temperature t according to the formula $V = 0.8e^{0.15t}$. Find V (a) when $t = 20°$; (b) when $t = 60°$. (c) Determine the temperature at which $V = 100$. (d) Determine what temperature rise is required to double V.
4. The curve which a chain or rope assumes when hanging under its own weight is called a catenary. The equation for the catenary is $y = (a/2)(e^{x/a} + e^{-x/a})$. If $a = 1$, plot the graph from $x = 2$ to $x = -2$.
5. According to Halley's law the atmospheric pressure P in inches is related to the height above sea level by the following equation: $P = 29.92e^{-h/5}$, where h is the altitude in miles. What is the barometer reading at (a) sea level; (b) 2,640 ft; (c) 3 miles? (d) What is the elevation in feet if the barometer reads 23.62 in.?

6. The speed V of a rotating wheel after the power was cut off decreased at a rate (per minute) which at every instant was 35 per cent of V itself. If the original value of V was 1,500 rpm, find its value after (a) 5 min; (b) 10 min; (c) 15 min. (d) How long will it take for the speed to drop to one-tenth of its original value?
7. If 80 g of cane sugar is inverted by acid so that the inversion rate is constantly 13.5 per cent (per hour) of the remaining cane sugar, find the amount of cane sugar remaining after 12 hr.
8. The temperature of a warm object initially 150° warmer than the surroundings is falling at an instantaneous rate of 60 per cent (per hour) of the temperature difference at the time. Find the temperature difference remaining after (a) 40 min; (b) 2 hr.
9. If a plant is growing so that its rate of growth is constantly 40 per cent (per week) of its weight, find the actual percentage increase in weight in a week.
10. In Example 3, page 259, what is the period of half-life; i.e., when will the radium be 50 per cent disintegrated?

11·9 Some properties of e^{jx}

Equation (2) is applicable in a general way to develop the series for any power of e. In Chap. 23 it will appear that a particularly important quantity is e^{jx}. If we develop the series for e^{jx} according to Eq. (2), we obtain

$$\begin{aligned} e^{jx} &= 1 + jx + \frac{j^2x^2}{2!} + \frac{j^3x^3}{3!} + \frac{j^4x^4}{4!} + \frac{j^5x^5}{5!} + \frac{j^6x^6}{6!} + \cdots \\ &= 1 + jx - \frac{x^2}{2!} - \frac{jx^3}{3!} + \frac{x^4}{4!} + \frac{jx^5}{5!} - \frac{x^6}{6!} \cdots \\ &= \left(1 - \frac{x^2}{2!} + \frac{x^4}{4!} - \frac{x^6}{6!} \cdots\right) + j\left(x - \frac{x^3}{3!} + \frac{x^5}{5!} \cdots\right) \end{aligned} \tag{8}$$

which may be generalized to read

$$e^{jx} = A + jB \tag{9}$$

It is also interesting to observe that A and B are related by the equation $A^2 + B^2 = 1$.

From Eq. (8),

$$A = 1 - \frac{x^2}{2!} + \frac{x^4}{4!} - \frac{x^6}{6!} \cdots = 1 - \frac{x^2}{2} + \frac{x^4}{24} - \frac{x^6}{720} \cdots$$

and

$$B = x - \frac{x^3}{3!} + \frac{x^5}{5!} \cdots = x - \frac{x^3}{6} + \frac{x^5}{120} \cdots$$

In Sec. 23·3 it is shown that A is the series for cosine x and B is the series for sine x.

For the sake of clarity the operation of squaring is shown below.

$$
\begin{array}{rl}
 & 1 - \frac{x^2}{2} + \frac{x^4}{24} - \frac{x^6}{720} \cdots \\
 & 1 - \frac{x^2}{2} + \frac{x^4}{24} - \frac{x^6}{720} \cdots \\
\hline
 & 1 - \frac{x^2}{2} + \frac{x^4}{24} - \frac{x^6}{720} \cdots \\
 & \quad - \frac{x^2}{2} + \frac{x^4}{4} - \frac{x^6}{48} \cdots \\
 & \quad\quad \frac{x^4}{24} - \frac{x^6}{48} \cdots \\
 & \quad\quad\quad - \frac{x^6}{720} \cdots \\
\hline
A^2 = & 1 - x^2 + \frac{x^4}{3} - \frac{2x^6}{45} \cdots
\end{array}
$$

$$
\begin{array}{rl}
 & x - \frac{x^3}{6} + \frac{x^5}{120} \cdots \\
 & x - \frac{x^3}{6} + \frac{x^5}{120} \cdots \\
\hline
 & x^2 - \frac{x^4}{6} + \frac{x^6}{120} \cdots \\
 & \quad - \frac{x^4}{6} + \frac{x^6}{36} \cdots \\
 & \quad\quad \frac{x^6}{120} \cdots \\
\hline
B^2 = & x^2 - \frac{x^4}{3} + \frac{2x^6}{45} \cdots
\end{array}
$$

It can be shown that the error incurred in approximating the sum of these series, A^2 and B^2, by summing the first n terms is numerically less than the $(n + 1)$st term.

$$A^2 + B^2 = \left(1 - x^2 + \frac{x^4}{3} - \frac{2x^6}{45} \cdots\right) + \left(x^2 - \frac{x^4}{3} + \frac{2x^6}{45} \cdots\right) = 1 \quad (10)$$

12
quadratic equations in one unknown

Quadratic equations are so called because the highest power of the unknown is the *square;* in general, they are second-degree equations. These equations are of considerable interest in that they usually contain maximum or minimum values (maximum return, minimum cost, etc.). Secondary answers often suggest a broader scope of a problem than is indicated by the original question.

12·1 Quadratic equations

An equation which can be reduced to the form

$$ax^2 + bx + c = 0 \tag{1}$$

is called a *quadratic equation* in x and is the type form for the general quadratic. If either b or $c = 0$ (note that a cannot be zero), the equations

$$ax^2 + c = 0$$

and

$$ax^2 + bx = 0$$

are known as *incomplete quadratic equations.*

12·2 Solution of incomplete quadratics

Both types of incomplete quadratic equations are easily solved.

example 1 Solve the equation $4x^2 - 9 = 0$.

Transposing and dividing by 4,

$$x^2 = 9/4$$

Extracting the square root,

$$x = \pm 3/2$$

That is,

$$x = 3/2 \text{ or } -3/2$$

Note that both answers, or roots, are possible, since either 3/2 or −3/2, upon squaring, produces 9/4. Note also that while one might logically write $\pm x = \pm 3/2$, no additional answers are obtained.

The same example might have been solved by the factoring method as follows:

$$4x^2 - 9 = 0$$
$$(2x + 3)(2x - 3) = 0$$

whereby

$$2x + 3 = 0$$

or

$$x = -3/2$$
$$2x - 3 = 0$$

or

$$x = 3/2$$

as above.

This procedure is justified by recalling from past experience that if the product of two quantities is zero, one or both of those quantities must have been equal to zero. Therefore we set each factor equal to zero in turn.

example 2 Solve the equation $2x^2 + 6x = 0$.

Factoring,

$$2x(x + 3) = 0$$

Setting each factor equal to zero,

$$2x = 0 \quad \text{or} \quad x = 0$$
$$x + 3 = 0 \quad \text{or} \quad x = -3$$

EXERCISE 1

Solve the following incomplete quadratic equations, regarding x, y, z, and w as unknown quantities.

1. $y^2 - 9 = 0$
2. $z^2 - 16z = 0$
3. $x^2 = 49$
4. $144 - w^2 = 0$
5. $y^2 = 121$
6. $x^2 - 81 = 0$
7. $z^2 = 8$
8. $12 - w^2 = 0$
9. $x^2 - 30 = 0$
10. $z^2 = c^2$
11. $y^2 = 9a^2$
12. $x^2 - 16b^2 = 0$
13. $w^2 = aw$
14. $y^2 = a^2 + b^2$
15. $z^2 = \frac{1}{c^2}$
16. $\frac{a^2}{b^2} - y^2 = 0$
17. $16x^2 = 1$
18. $9y^2 - 25 = 0$
19. $12w^2 = 1$
20. $9z^2 = 8$
21. $w^2 + 121 = 5w^2$

22. $3y^2 - 17 = 8 - y^2$

23. $\frac{x^2}{3} = 48$

24. $\frac{z^2}{b} = 4b$

25. $\frac{4}{y^2} = 49$

26. $\frac{1}{y^2} = 36$

27. $\frac{m^2}{x^2} = 25$

28. $\frac{1}{20y^2} = 5$

29. $\frac{1}{z^2} = \frac{1}{16}$

30. $\frac{a^2}{c^2} = \frac{1}{w^2}$

31. $\frac{4}{x} = \frac{x}{9}$

32. $\frac{1}{2x} = \frac{8x}{9}$

33. $\frac{3w}{4} - \frac{9}{2w} = \frac{5w}{8}$

34. $\frac{x^2 - 1}{6} - \frac{x^2 + 2}{9} = 1$

12·3 Solution of the quadratic $ax^2 + bx + c = 0$

The solution of the equation $ax^2 + bx + c = 0$ may be accomplished by the following means:

1. Plotting (approximate values—limited by accuracy of reading)
2. Factoring
3. Completing the square
4. Quadratic formula
5. Short graphical method (approximate values—limited by accuracy of reading)

12·4 Solution by plotting

While exact answers can be obtained by plotting if they are integers, fractional values are apt to be approximated, and irrational answers will always be approximations. Imaginary roots cannot normally be found by plotting. However by a suitable shift in the relative positions of the curve and the X axis, such roots may be approximated.

example 3 Solve the equation $x^2 - 2x - 11 = 0$ by plotting.

Set $x^2 - 2x - 11 = y$. Substitute various values of x, and determine the corresponding values of y. For instance, if $x = 7$, then

$$y = (7)^2 - 2(7) - 11 = 49 - 14 - 11 = 24$$

In like manner make out a table, continuing to substitute various values of x until it becomes evident that y is receding from zero at an increasing rate.

x	6	5	4	3	2	1	0	−1	−2	−3	−4	−5
y	13	4	−3	−8	−11	−12	−11	−8	−3	4	13	24

Plot these values on coordinate paper. Answers correspond to the intersection of the curve and the X axis. This is reasonable because, in effect, we are solving for the simultaneous equations $y = x^2 - 2x - 11$ and $y = 0$.

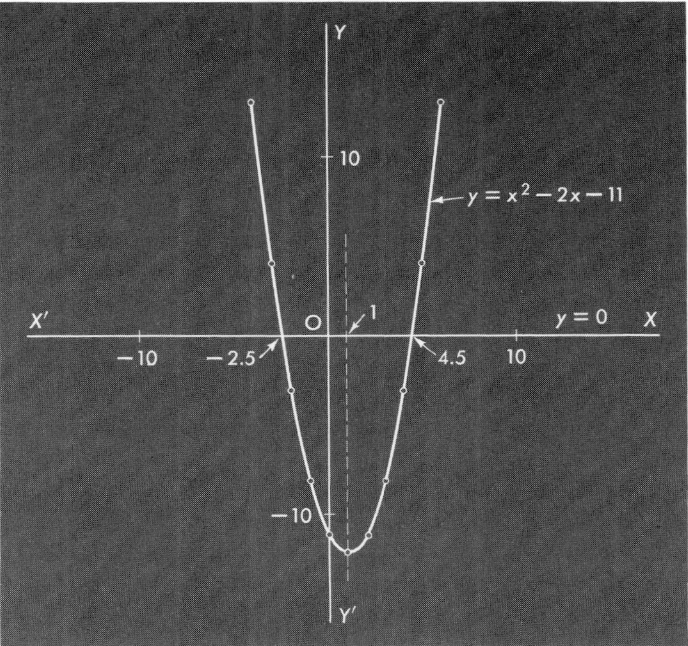

fig. 12·1

Figure 12·1 shows the result obtained by plotting these data. The indicated answers are roughly $x = 4.5$ and $x = -2.5$.

Tabulation may be facilitated if we take uniformly spaced values of x and list increments in y (represented by Δy) and also increments in Δy [that is, $\Delta(\Delta y)$], which we abbreviate to $\Delta^2 y$.

Δx		-1		-1		-1		-1		-1		-1		-1		-1		-1		-1	
x	6		5		4		3		2		1		0		-1		-2		-3		-4
y	13		4		-3		-8		-11		-12		-11		-8		-3		4		13
Δy		-9		-7		-5		-3		-1		1		3		5		7		9	
$\Delta^2 y$			2		2		2		2		2		2		2		2		2		

The table may be extended quite rapidly by taking advantage of the fact that $\Delta^2 y$ constantly equals 2.

Note also that the curve is symmetrical about the line $x = 1$. If a series of points has been plotted on one side of the axis of symmetry, corresponding points may be located on the opposite side, as in a mirror image. The edge of the mirror rests on the axis of symmetry.

To use a more analytical approach, we rewrite the equation $x^2 - 2x - 11 = y$ to read $x^2 - 2x + 1 - 12 = y$ or $(x - 1)^2 - 12 = y$.

It is apparent that the smallest possible value of $(x - 1)^2$ is zero. This occurs at $x = 1$. Thus y has a minimum value of -12 at $x = 1$. Note that for $x = 2$ or 0, $(x - 1)^2 = 1$ and $y = -11$. For $x = 3$ or -1, $(x - 1)^2 = 4$ and $y = -8$, etc., thus indicating a symmetry about the line $x = 1$.

Sketching the curve (Sec. 13·4) yields practically the same results and does so in an even more informative way.

EXERCISE 2

Solve the following quadratic equations by plotting.

1. $x^2 - 2x - 3 = 0$
2. $x^2 + x - 6 = 0$
3. $x^2 + x = 56$
4. $x^2 - 21 = 4x$
5. $x(x + 5) = 24$
6. $2x^2 - 3x + 1 = 0$
7. $3x^2 - x - 2 = 0$
8. $5x^2 - 11x - 2 = 0$
9. $(x - 2)(x - 5) = x - 5$
10. $(x - 5)(x + 8) = x - 16$

12·5 Solution by factoring

This method is useful when factors of an expression are fairly obvious. However, the student should not spend too much time looking for factors that may not exist.

example 4 Solve the equation $x(2x - 1) = 15$ by factoring.

Carrying out the indicated multiplication,

$$2x^2 - x = 15$$

Transposing,

$$2x^2 - x - 15 = 0$$

Inspection will show that the factored form is

$$(2x + 5)(x - 3) = 0$$

Therefore,

$$2x + 5 = 0 \quad \text{and} \quad x = -5/2$$
$$x - 3 = 0 \quad \text{and} \quad x = 3$$

Note that, if the equation had been written $12x^2 - 6x - 90 = 0$, our first step would be the division by a common monomial factor—in this case, by 6.

EXERCISE 3

Solve the following quadratic equations by the method of factoring:

1. $x^2 - 4x + 4 = 0$
2. $x^2 - x - 30 = 0$
3. $x^2 + x = 72$
4. $x^2 - 2x = 15$
5. $x^2 + 7x = -12$
6. $x^2 - 33 = 8x$
7. $x^2 - 48 = 2x$
8. $x(x - 5) = 36$

9. $x(x + 3) = 40$
10. $x^2 + 3(x - 18) = 0$
11. $2x^2 + 3x + 1 = 0$
12. $5x^2 - 2x - 3 = 0$
13. $8x^2 + 10x - 12 = 0$
14. $21x^2 - 12x - 9 = 0$
15. $(x - 4)(x - 7) = x - 4$
16. $(x + 6)(x - 6) = 5x$
17. $\dfrac{1}{y + 4} = \dfrac{3}{y^2 + 12}$
18. $\dfrac{2}{w - 3} = \dfrac{w + 3}{8}$

12·6 Solution by completing the square

Under certain special conditions this method offers a ready solution. It will be used in Sec. 12·7 to derive the quadratic formula.

example 5 Solve the equation $x^2 + 8x + 52 = 0$ by completing the square.

Rearranging so that all terms containing the unknown are on one side of the equation and all constant terms are on the other, we have

$$x^2 + 8x = -52$$

Making the left side a perfect square by adding 16 to both sides,

$$x^2 + 8x + 16 = -36$$

Extracting the square root,

$$x + 4 = \pm 6\sqrt{-1} = \pm j6$$
$$x = -4 + j6 \qquad \text{or} \qquad x = -4 - j6$$

The selection of the quantity to be added to both sides before taking the square root is governed by considering the identity

$$(x + k)^2 = x^2 + 2kx + k^2$$

Here it is evident that if we have the expression $x^2 + 2kx$, the missing quantity which will complete the square is found by evaluating $(2k/2)^2$ or k^2.

Thus in our example we square half the coefficient of x, or $(8/2)^2 = 16$.

example 6 Solve, by completing the square, the equation $3x(x - 3) = 2(1 - 2x)$.

Carrying out indicated multiplications,

$$3x^2 - 9x = 2 - 4x \tag{2}$$

Transposing, leaving the constant term on the right,

$$3x^2 - 5x = 2 \tag{3}$$

Dividing by the coefficient of x^2,

$$x^2 - \frac{5x}{3} = \frac{2}{3} \tag{4}$$

The term to be added to both sides will be the square of half the coefficient of the x term

$$\left(\frac{-5/3}{2}\right)^2 = \frac{25}{36}$$

Adding $25/36$ to both sides of Eq. (4),

$$x^2 - \frac{5x}{3} + \frac{25}{36} = \frac{2}{3} + \frac{25}{36} = \frac{49}{36} \tag{5}$$

Extracting the square root,

$$x - 5/6 = \pm 7/6 \tag{6}$$

$$x = 5/6 + 7/6 \quad \text{or} \quad x = 2$$

$$x = 5/6 - 7/6 \quad \text{or} \quad x = -1/3$$

example 7 Solve, by the method of completing the square, the equation

$$x^2 - 6cx = 4a^2 - 12ac \tag{7}$$

In this example the terms not containing x have already been separated from those containing x. The missing quantity which will make the left side a perfect square is $(-6c/2)^2 = 9c^2$. Adding $9c^2$ to both sides of Eq. (7), we obtain

$$x^2 - 6cx + 9c^2 = 4a^2 - 12ac + 9c^2 \tag{8}$$

Extracting the square root of both sides,

$$x - 3c = \pm(2a - 3c) \tag{9}$$

Hence $\quad x = 3c + (2a - 3c) = 2a$

Also $\quad x = 3c - (2a - 3c) = 6c - 2a$

Each of these answers will be found to check the original equation.

It is evident that the method of completing the square can be used to the greatest advantage when the coefficient of the second-degree term is unity and that of the first-degree term contains 2 as a factor.

To summarize, the solution of a quadratic by the method of completing the square consists in the following steps:

1. *Transpose, if necessary, so that the constant term is on one side of the equation, and terms containing the unknown are on the other side.*
2. *Make the coefficient of* x^2 *equal to unity by dividing by the coefficient of* x^2 *unless it is already equal to* 1. *The equation now has the form* $x^2 + px = q$.
3. *Add to both sides of the equation the square of half the coefficient of* x. *This transforms the left side of the equation to* $x^2 + px + p^2/4$, *a perfect square.*
4. *Extract the square roots of both sides, remembering to place a* $\pm$ *sign before the square root of the right-hand number.*

5. *Solve the two equations so formed for the unknown.*
6. *Check the results in the original equation.*

EXERCISE 4

Solve the following equations by means of completing the square, leaving any irrational answers in radical form.

1. $x^2 + 2x - 3 = 0$
2. $x^2 - 4x - 21 = 0$
3. $x^2 + 6x - 7 = 0$
4. $x^2 - 8x - 20 = 0$
5. $x^2 + 10x - 24 = 0$
6. $y^2 - 12y + 27 = 0$
7. $x(x - 10) = 39$
8. $z(z + 8) = 48$
9. $x^2 + 2bx = a^2 - b^2$
10. $x^2 - 2dx = c^2 + 2cd$
11. $x^2 + 2ax = -6ab + 9b^2$
12. $x^2 - 4cx = 9b^2 + 12bc$
13. $x^2 + \frac{2x}{3} = \frac{15}{9}$
14. $y^2 - \frac{4y}{5} = \frac{9}{5}$
15. $y^2 - 20y + 105 = 0$
16. $x^2 - \frac{6x}{5} = \frac{8}{5}$
17. $w^2 - 4w = 8$
18. $x^2 + 10x = 55$
19. $y^2 - 14y = 11$
20. $x^2 - 8x + 27 = 0$
21. $x^2 + 8x = 32$
22. $w^2 - 12w = -16$
23. $x^2 - 14x = -59$
24. $z^2 - 12z = -43$

12·7 Solution by the formula

The most generally applicable method of solving a quadratic equation is that employing the *quadratic formula*. The derivation of this formula begins with the general quadratic

$$ax^2 + bx + c = 0$$

Transposing,

$$ax^2 + bx = -c \tag{10}$$

Dividing by the coefficient of x^2,

$$x^2 + \frac{bx}{a} = -\frac{c}{a} \tag{11}$$

Adding the square of half the coefficient of x to both sides,

$$x^2 + \frac{bx}{a} + \frac{b^2}{4a^2} = \frac{b^2}{4a^2} - \frac{c}{a} \tag{12}$$

Combining fractions on the right,

$$x^2 + \frac{bx}{a} + \frac{b^2}{4a^2} = \frac{b^2 - 4ac}{4a^2} \tag{13}$$

Taking square roots of both sides,

$$x + \frac{b}{2a} = \pm \frac{\sqrt{b^2 - 4ac}}{2a} \tag{14}$$

Transposing,

$$x = -\frac{b}{2a} \pm \frac{\sqrt{b^2 - 4ac}}{2a} \tag{15}$$

Combining fractions,

$$x = \frac{-b \pm \sqrt{b^2 - 4ac}}{2a} \tag{16}$$

This formula has the advantage of being applicable to any quadratic equation. Under special conditions, the methods of factoring or completing the square may be more convenient. With practice, there should be no difficulty in selecting the shortest method for the equation at hand.

It should be remembered that a is the coefficient of the second-degree term, b is the coefficient of the first-degree term, and c includes all terms not containing the unknown.

example 8 Use the quadratic formula to solve the quadratic equation

$$2x(4x - 1) = 15$$

Performing the indicated multiplication,

$$8x^2 - 2x = 15$$

Transposing, leaving zero on the right,

$$8x^2 - 2x - 15 = 0$$

According to the formula, $a = 8$, $b = -2$, and $c = -15$. Then

$$x = \frac{-(-2) \pm \sqrt{(-2)^2 - 4(8)(-15)}}{(2)(8)}$$

$$x = \frac{2 \pm \sqrt{4 + 480}}{16} = \frac{2 \pm 22}{16}$$

$$x = \frac{2 + 22}{16} = \frac{3}{2}$$

$$x = \frac{2 - 22}{16} = -\frac{5}{4}$$

EXERCISE 5

Solve the following equations by the formula, leaving any irrational answers in the radical form:

1. $x^2 - 17x + 60 = 0$
2. $x^2 + x - 156 = 0$
3. $x^2 - 4x = 165$
4. $3x^2 + 7x = 6$
5. $5y - 6y^2 + 1 = 0$
6. $12z^2 + 24z = -9$

7. $x^2 + x + 1 = 0$

8. $\frac{x-1}{1} = \frac{1}{x}$

9. $3w^2 - 6w + 5 = 0$

10. $5x^2 - 55x - 5 = 0$

11. $3x^2 - 1 = \frac{11x}{12}$

12. $30y^2 + 76y + 48 = 0$

13. $w^2 + 5w + 7 = 0$

14. $7y^2 + 12y + 4 = 0$

15. $5p^2 - 3p + 1 = 0$

16. $\frac{1}{y-1} + \frac{2}{y+2} = \frac{1}{y+1}$

12·8 Short graphical method

This method is designed for rapid, routine approximation. It depends upon separating the second-degree term from the rest of the expression and dividing by the coefficient of the second-degree term so that the equation is of the type $x^2 = mx + k$. From this equation we form the two equations $y = x^2$ and $y = mx + k$. If we were to plot the graphs of these simultaneous equations on a common coordinate system, the roots would be indicated by the abscissas of the intersections (see Fig. 12·2 and Example 9 below).

It will be observed that the plot of $y = x^2$ is a parabola, while that of $y = mx + k$ is a straight line. The advantage of this method lies in the fact that the graph of $y = x^2$ may be drawn once and for all. A straight line scratched on the underside of a transparent strip will, upon proper positioning, represent the graph of $y = mx + k$. The abscissas of the intersections will represent the roots of the equation $x^2 = mx + k$.

fig. 12·2

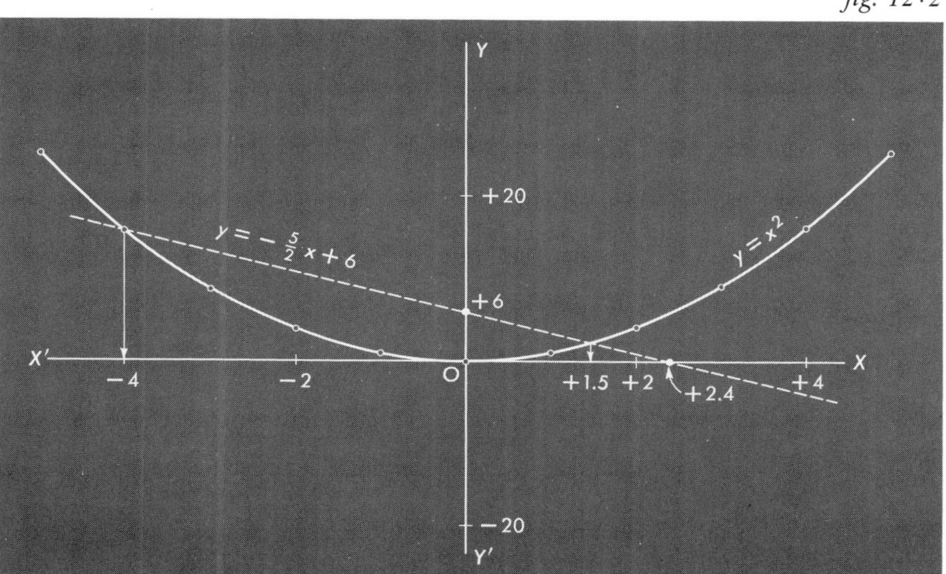

example 9 Solve the equation

$$2x^2 + 5x - 12 = 0$$

Transposing,

$$2x^2 = -5x + 12$$

Dividing by the coefficient of x^2,

$$x^2 = \frac{-5x}{2} + 6$$

It is assumed that the graph of $y = x^2$, having been used in other problems, has already been drawn. The plastic strip is then laid on the graph paper so that the straight-line scratch passes through the points (0,6) and (2.4,0) (the y and x intercepts of the graph of $y = -5x/2 + 6$). The intersections of the two curves have abscissas of $3/2$ and -4, which are the roots.

Note that, for convenience in reading, the horizontal scale is 10 times as open as the vertical scale.

12·9 Literal quadratic equations

In a *literal* quadratic equation some or all of the constants are letters. These constants are usually represented by the first several letters of the alphabet or may involve π. In some cases it is preferable not to substitute the numerical value of π until a later stage of the solution.

The formula usually offers the easiest means of solution in the long run.

example 10 Solve the equation $2(x^2 + c^2) + d(x + c - d) = 5cx$.

Carrying out the indicated multiplication,

$$2x^2 + 2c^2 + dx + dc - d^2 = 5cx$$

Transposing and arranging in descending powers of x,

$$2x^2 + dx - 5cx + 2c^2 + cd - d^2 = 0$$

Grouping and factoring x^2 and x terms,

$$2x^2 + (d - 5c)x + 2c^2 + cd - d^2 = 0$$

Tabulate the values **a**, **b**, and **c** of the quadratic formula, remembering that all terms not containing the unknown, no matter how many there may be, are grouped under **c**. Thus $\mathbf{a} = 2$, $\mathbf{b} = d - 5c$, $\mathbf{c} = 2c^2 + cd - d^2$. Then

$$x = \frac{-(d - 5c) \pm \sqrt{(d - 5c)^2 - 4(2)(2c^2 + cd - d^2)}}{2(2)}$$

$$= \frac{-d + 5c \pm \sqrt{d^2 - 10cd + 25c^2 - 16c^2 - 8cd + 8d^2}}{4}$$

$$= \frac{-d + 5c \pm \sqrt{9d^2 - 18cd + 9c^2}}{4}$$

$$= \frac{-d + 5c \pm (3d - 3c)}{4}$$

$$x = \frac{-d + 5c + (3d - 3c)}{4} = \frac{2d + 2c}{4} = \frac{d + c}{2}$$

$$x = \frac{-d + 5c - (3d - 3c)}{4} = \frac{-4d + 8c}{4} = 2c - d$$

In cases in which the equation or the roots are more involved, checking by direct substitution may entail as much time and effort as the original solution. The process may be facilitated by assigning numerical values to the literal constants. Avoid assigning numerical values which will make a denominator equal to zero.

example 11 Check the equation $(n - k)x^2 + (k - m)x + m - n = 0$ whose roots are $x = (m - n)/(n - k)$ and $x = 1$. Assigning arbitrary simple numerical values (other than 0 and 1) to m, n, and k such that x will also be a simple integer, we might select $m = 10$, $n = 4$, and $k = 2$; therefore

$$x = \frac{10 - 4}{4 - 2} = 3$$

Substituting in the original equation,

$$(4 - 2)(3)^2 + (2 - 10)(3) + 10 - 4 = 0$$

or

$$(2)(9) + (-8)(3) + 6 = 0$$

or

$$18 - 24 + 6 = 0$$
$$0 = 0$$

EXERCISE 6

Solve the following literal quadratic equations for w, x, y, or z as the case may be:

1. $15x^2 - mx - 2m^2 = 0$
2. $4x^2 + (x + 3a)^2 = 17a^2$
3. $w^2 + aw + bw - cw = c(a + b)$
4. $abcx^2 + b^2cx + ac^2x + bc^2 = 0$
5. $(b - c)y^2 + (c - a)y + a - b = 0$
6. $w^2 - \left(\frac{a}{b} + \frac{b}{a}\right)w + 1 = 0$
7. $3z^2 - hz - 5 = 0$
8. $\frac{c^2}{x^2} = \frac{c + 1}{x + 1}$
9. $(x - k)^2 + (x - h)^2 = k^2 + h^2$
10. $a = \pi x(x + 2h)$

12·10 Precautions regarding roots

At this point it is important to guard against two common errors resulting from apparently legitimate operations. These pitfalls are vanishing roots and extraneous roots. *Extraneous roots* are values which are created in the process of solving of an equation but which do not check the original equation.

12·11 Vanishing roots

It is not advisable to divide an equation through by an expression containing the unknown. By such division a root may be lost.

example 12 Solve the equation $x^2 - 5x = 0$.

Dividing through by x,

$$x - 5 = 0$$

or

$$x = 5$$

It is evident that another root, $x = 0$, has been lost in this process. Clearly we should have factored and set each factor equal to zero. Thus we obtain the equation $x(x - 5) = 0$ and the roots $x = 0$ and $x = 5$.

example 13 Solve the equation $2x^2 + 3x - 2 = x^2 - 4$.

Dividing through by $x + 2$,

$$2x - 1 = x - 2$$

Transposing,

$$x = -1$$

In this case, by dividing by $x + 2$, we have lost the root $x = -2$.

12·12 Extraneous roots

These fictitious values usually arise from multiplying by an expression containing the unknown.

example 14 Solve the equation

$$3 + \frac{4}{x + 2} = \frac{x^2}{x + 2} - 1$$

Multiplying by $x + 2$,

$$3(x + 2) + 4 = x^2 - (x + 2)$$

Clearing of parentheses,

$$3x + 6 + 4 = x^2 - x - 2$$

Transposing and collecting terms,

$$0 = x^2 - 4x - 12$$

Factoring,

$$0 = (x - 6)(x + 2)$$
$$x - 6 = 0 \qquad \text{or} \qquad x = 6$$
$$x + 2 = 0 \qquad \text{or} \qquad x = -2$$

The root $x = 6$ satisfies the equation, but the root $x = -2$ does not.
Note that this situation could have been avoided by transposing and combining fractions. Thus

$$3 + 1 = \frac{x^2}{x + 2} - \frac{4}{x + 2}$$

Combining fractions and reducing,

$$4 = \frac{x^2 - 4}{x + 2} = x - 2$$

or

$$x = 6$$

12·13 Checking

Checking is usually accomplished by direct substitution of the answers, or roots, in the original equation. However, if the original equation is in the type form for the general quadratic, a shorter method is available, especially if one or both roots are fractions. It depends upon the fact that if $(x - m)(x - n) = 0$, the roots are $x = m$ and $x = n$. Conversely, if the roots are m and n, we may write $(x - m)(x - n) = 0$. [The *factor theorem* states that if r is a root of the equation $f(x) = 0$, then $x - r$ is a factor of the polynomial $f(x)$. See also Appendix D.] Referring back to Example 6 and the equation $3x^2 - 5x = 2$ whose roots are 2 and $-\frac{1}{3}$, we may check by writing

$$(x - 2)[x - (-\tfrac{1}{3})] = 0$$

Multiplying by 3,

$$(x - 2)(3x + 1) = 0$$
$$3x^2 - 5x - 2 = 0$$

which checks all but the preliminary multiplication and transposition.

NOTE: *The alert student will appreciate that we have here an aid to factoring expressions of the type* $acx^2 + (ad + bc)x + bd$ *(expansion 6, Sec. 4·17). If necessary, first factor the expression to free it of monomial factors. Set the resulting expression, such as* $3x^2 - 5x - 2$*, equal to zero, determine the roots by Eq. (16), the quadratic formula, and derive the factored form of the expression* $(x - 2)(3x + 1)$ *as above.*

12·14 Summary of procedure for solving quadratic equations

1. *Simplify any reducible fractions and combine any fractions having a common denominator.*
2. *Clear of fractions.*
3. *If there is a factor (not containing the unknown) common to all terms, divide through by that factor.*
4. *The choice of the method of solution might well be based upon consideration of the following suggestions in the order given:*
   (a) *Use the factoring method if the factors are readily discernible.*
   (b) *Use the method of completing the square if the coefficient of the second-degree term is unity and that of the first-degree term is divisible by 2.*
   (c) *If neither (a) nor (b) is applicable, use the quadratic formula. This is somewhat longer but has general application to all cases.*
5. *Check all answers, discarding any extraneous roots.*

EXERCISE 7

Solve the following equations by the most convenient method, rejecting any extraneous roots and leaving any irrational answers in the radical form.

1. $\frac{y}{y+1} = \frac{y+2}{3y}$
2. $(w+2)^3 - w^3 = 56$
3. $\frac{1}{z-3} + \frac{1}{z+4} = \frac{1}{12}$
4. $x + \frac{1}{5} = 5 + \frac{1}{x}$
5. $y + \frac{mn}{y} = m + n$
6. $\frac{1}{r} + r = 3 + \frac{3}{r}$
7. $11d^2 + 7d + 1 = 0$
8. $\frac{10}{x} - \frac{9}{x+1} - \frac{8}{x+2} = 0$
9. $\frac{h}{5} - \frac{5}{6} = \frac{6}{5} - \frac{5}{h}$
10. $\frac{1}{x} - \frac{1}{d} = \frac{1}{x+d}$
11. $\frac{1}{c} + \frac{1}{8-c} = \frac{1}{8}$
12. $x(2x-c) + x(x-c) = bx$
13. $2y(7y-a) = (a+y)(a-y)$
14. $\frac{1}{x+3} + \frac{1}{x+2} - \frac{1}{x+1} = 0$
15. $\pi x^2 + 2\pi nx - A = 0$
16. $8w = -3(1+4w^2)$
17. $\frac{2}{m+5} - \frac{m+3}{(m+4)(m+5)} = \frac{1}{4(m-8)}$
18. $\frac{a}{x-b} + \frac{b}{x-a} = 2$
19. $c(x^2-1) = (ax+b)(x-1)$
20. $\frac{1}{w-2} + 1 = \frac{6-w}{w^2-4} + \frac{1}{w+2}$
21. $\frac{a}{x} + \frac{x}{a} = \frac{33a^2 - x^2}{ax}$
22. $\frac{1}{c+d+x} = \frac{1}{c} + \frac{1}{d} + \frac{1}{x}$
23. $9x^2 - hx + h^2 = 0$

12·15 Discriminant

In the quadratic formula

$$x = \frac{-b \pm \sqrt{b^2 - 4ac}}{2a}$$

the expression $b^2 - 4ac$ is called the *discriminant*. The value of the discriminant may usually be determined by inspection and indicates the nature of the roots of the equation $ax^2 + bx + c = 0$. The relationships are summarized in Table 12·1.

table 12·1

Discriminant	Positive and a perfect square	Positive but not a perfect square	Zero	Negative
Character of the roots	Real, rational, and unequal	Real, irrational, and unequal	Real, rational, and equal	Imaginary and unequal
Graph of $ax^2 + bx + c = y$	Cuts X axis in two points		Tangent to X axis	Does not intersect X axis

example 15 Determine the nature of the roots of the equation $2x^2 - 7x - 5 = 0$.

Here $b^2 - 4ac = (-7)^2 - 4(2)(-5) = 49 + 40 = 89$. Since 89 is positive but not a perfect square, the roots are real, irrational, and unequal.

example 16 Determine the nature of the roots of the equation $25x^2 - 30x + 9 = 0$.

In this example, $b^2 - 4ac = (-30)^2 - 4(25)(9) = 0$. Hence the roots are real, rational, and equal.

EXERCISE 8

Calculate the discriminant and describe the character of the roots without solving:

1. $x^2 + 4x - 12 = 0$
2. $x^2 - x - 20 = 0$
3. $x^2 - 6x + 9 = 0$
4. $x^2 - 3x - 5 = 0$
5. $2x^2 + 5x - 3 = 0$
6. $4x^2 + 20x + 25 = 0$
7. $6x^2 - x - 2 = 0$
8. $x^2 + 7x + 18 = 0$
9. $3x^2 - 18x + 27 = 0$
10. $2x^2 + 7x + 9 = 0$
11. $5x^2 - x - 10 = 0$
12. $28x^2 + 84x + 63 = 0$
13. $20x^2 - 7x - 3 = 0$
14. $14x^2 + 13x - 12 = 0$

12·16 Axis of symmetry—extreme value

It will be recalled from Sec. 12·4 that the equation $ax^2 + bx + c = y$ has a vertical axis of symmetry and that the extreme value of y, or the turning point of the curve, lies on this axis.

We take advantage of the properties of symmetry to note that the abscissa of the axis of symmetry, and therefore of the extreme point, must be the average of the x intercepts or roots $(-b + \sqrt{b^2 - 4ac})/2a$ and $(-b - \sqrt{b^2 - 4ac})/2a$ (Fig. 12·3). The average of these values is clearly $x = -b/2a$. Substitution of $-b/2a$ for x in the equation $ax^2 + bx + c = y$ gives us $y = c - b^2/4a$, which may be confirmed readily.

Hence the extreme value or turning point of the curve will correspond to the point

$$x = -\frac{b}{2a} \qquad y = c - \frac{b^2}{4a} \tag{17}$$

A brief check will show that if a is positive, the curve opens upward, $\smile$, and the extreme is a minimum. On the other hand, if a is negative, the curve opens downward, $\frown$, and the extreme is a maximum.

fig. 12·3

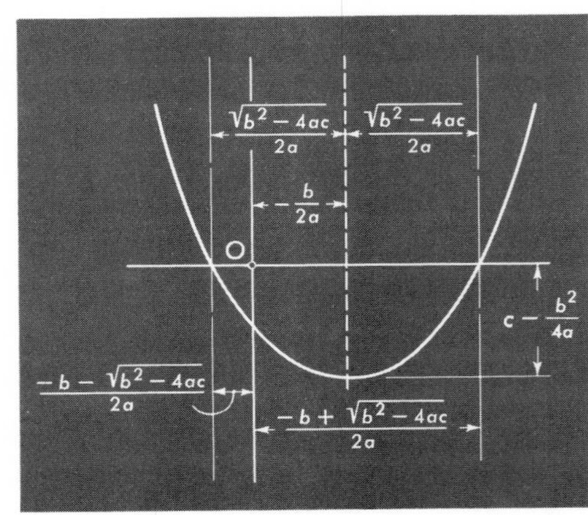

EXERCISE 9

Determine the nature and coordinates of the extreme point of the graphs of the following equations.

1. $x^2 - 2x - 15 = y$
2. $x^2 + 4x - 12 = y$
3. $x^2 + 7x + 6 = y$
4. $2x^2 + 5x - 3 = y$
5. $-x^2 + 6x - 8 = y$
6. $5x^2 - 6x - 8 = y$
7. $-6x^2 + 7x - 2 = y$
8. $3x^2 - x - 10 = y$
9. $-4x^2 - 4x + 15 = y$
10. $-2x^2 + x + 28 = y$

12·17 Equations of the quadratic type

Equations of the quadratic type may be represented by the general equation $ax^{2n} + bx^n + c = 0$. Such equations may be solved by methods comparable to those used in the solution of ordinary quadratics.

example 17 Solve the equation $x^4 - 29x^2 + 100 = 0$.

Factoring,

$$(x^2 - 25)(x^2 - 4) = 0$$
$$(x + 5)(x - 5)(x + 2)(x - 2) = 0$$
$$x = \pm 5, \pm 2$$

example 18 Solve the equation $6x - 7x^{1/2} - 20 = 0$.

Let $y = +\sqrt{x}$. Then $y^2 = x$ and $6y^2 - 7y - 20 = 0$. By the quadratic formula,

$$y = \frac{7 \pm \sqrt{49 - 4(6)(-20)}}{(2)(6)} = \frac{7 \pm 23}{12}$$

so that $y = 5/2, -4/3$ and $y^2 = x = 25/4, 16/9$.

But the root $16/9$ does not check, since we agreed to let y represent the *positive* square root of x. To confirm our conclusion, let $y = -\sqrt{x}$. Then $y^2 = x$, and the equation $6x + (7)(-x^{1/2}) - 20 = 0$ becomes $6y^2 + 7y - 20 = 0$. Solution by the formula leads to the roots $y = 4/3$, $-5/2$ and $y^2 = x = 16/9, 25/4$. But again the root $16/9$ is unacceptable, since y represented the *negative* square root of x.

example 19 Solve the equation $x^6 + 7x^3 - 8 = 0$.

Factoring,

$$(x^3 - 1)(x^3 + 8) = 0$$

or

$$(x - 1)(x^2 + x + 1)(x + 2)(x^2 - 2x + 4) = 0$$

Hence the roots are

$$x = 1, \frac{-1 \pm \sqrt{-3}}{2}, -2, 1 \pm \sqrt{-3}$$

EXERCISE 10

Solve the following equations of the quadratic type:

1. $x^4 - 10x^2 + 9 = 0$
2. $z^4 - 13z^2 + 36 = 0$
3. $x^6 - 28x^3 + 27 = 0$
4. $y + 2y^{1/2} - 15 = 0$
5. $x^{2/3} - 2x^{1/3} - 3 = 0$
6. $2w^{1/2} - 5w^{1/4} + 2 = 0$
7. $x^{-2} + x^{-1} - 6 = 0$
8. $z^{-1} + z^{-1/2} - 6 = 0$

12·18 Applications leading to quadratic equations containing one unknown

In the following problems it is necessary to decide whether one answer or both are consistent with the physical conditions of the problem. It is frequently interesting and instructive to determine the significance of the secondary answer.

Remember that a "check," unless made on the original stated problem, is no check at all.

EXERCISE 11

1. Find two numbers whose sum is 23 and whose product is 126.
2. Separate 19 into two parts whose product is 84.
3. The difference between two positive numbers is 7 and their product is 78. Find the numbers.
4. Separate 132 into two positive parts such that one part is the square of the other.
5. The sum of a positive number and its square is 72. Find the number.
6. Find two consecutive positive integers whose product is 156.
7. Find two consecutive positive even integers whose product is 224.
8. Find two consecutive positive odd integers whose product is 195.
9. Find a positive number whose square exceeds 36 by as much as 36 exceeds the number.
10. What number added to its reciprocal equals 2.9?
11. A ball is thrown upward from a building 380 ft high with a speed of 112 fps. Under these conditions the height h of the ball in feet at any time t seconds after throwing the ball is given by the equation $h = -16t^2 + 112t + 380$. When will the ball be 476 ft above the ground?
12. Repeat Prob. 11 for the time at which the ball is 252 ft above the ground. Can you explain the secondary (negative) answer?
13. A strip of metal 8 in. wide is to be bent into a trough of rectangular cross section (open top) whose cross-sectional area is to be 7½ sq in. Find the depth and width of the trough. How many answers?
14. The hypotenuse of a right triangle is 10 ft longer than the shorter side and 5 ft longer than the longer side. Find the sides of the triangle.
15. How high is a tree if it takes 3 sec for a stone thrown over it to return to the ground? Use the formula $s = 16t^2$, where s is the distance in feet covered by a freely falling body in t sec (starting from rest).
16. A bomber traveling at 375 mph releases a bomb at 8,200 ft. How long after its release will the bomb land? How far ahead of the target is the bomb released? Neglect air resistance.
17. If the cross-sectional area of the angle beam in Fig. 12·4 is 6¼ sq in., find the thickness x.
18. A group of boys bought a canoe for \$70, planning to divide the expense equally. However, two boys dropped out, increasing the share of each boy by \$1.75. How many boys were there in the original group?

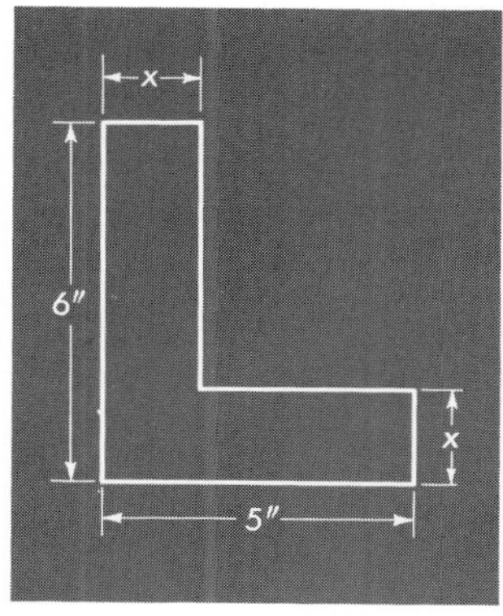

fig. 12·4

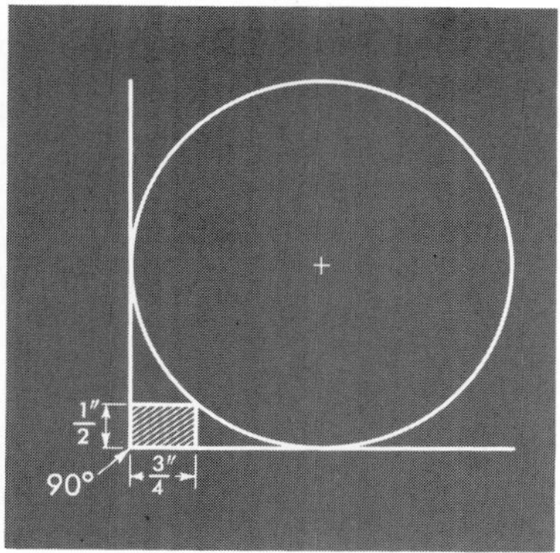

fig. 12·5

19. Find the diameter of the circle in Fig. 12·5.
20. Two resistances in parallel have a joint resistance of 4.2 ohms. The same two resistances in series have a resistance of 20 ohms. Find the value of each resistance.
21. A park is 480 yd long by 320 yd wide. It is decided to double its area, retaining the rectangular shape, by adding strips of equal width to one end and one side. Find the width of the strips.
22. A man bought two farms for \$3,600 each. The larger, which contained 15 acres more than the smaller, cost \$8 an acre less than the smaller. How many acres did each contain?
23. Figure 12·6 shows a beam that supports its own weight of 300 lb per ft and a concentrated load of 1,000 lb at a point 4 ft from the left end. There is a point x ft from the left end where there is no compression or tension (push or pull) in the beam. x must be larger than 4 and less than 16 and is a root of the equation

$$3{,}000x - 1{,}000(x - 4) - 150x^2 = 0$$

Find x.
24. The perimeter of a rectangular field is 274 yd and the diagonal is 97 yd. Find its dimensions.

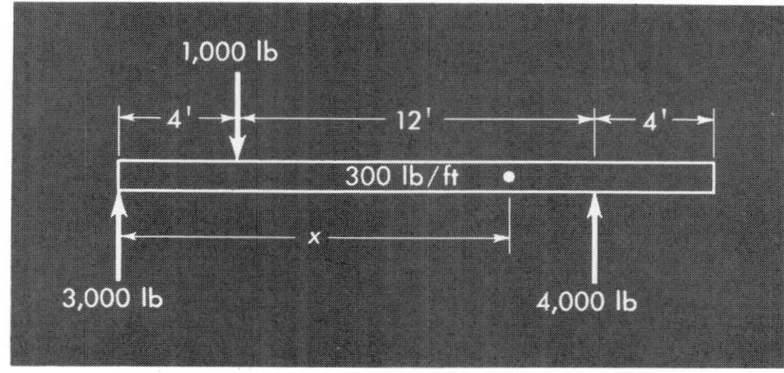

fig. 12·6

25. The sum of the areas of the two inner circles in Fig. 12·7 is ¾ the area of the outer circle. Find the diameter of the smallest circle.
26. The outer portion of a garden 22 by 30 ft is to be occupied by a walk of uniform width. If the garden is to be reduced to three-quarters of its original area, find the width of the walk.
27. How large a cube can be covered with 387 cu in. of insulation if the insulation is 1½ in. thick? Edges and corners are not to be rounded.
28. When a flexible rope or wire t ft long is strung between two poles l ft apart (points of attachment at same elevation), the formula $t = \sqrt{l^2 + 5.3s^2}$ applies, where s is the sag in feet. A copper telegraph wire is being installed at 60°F, the poles being 140 ft apart. Find the necessary sag (in inches) in order to provide against a temperature of −20°F. The linear coefficient of expansion of copper is 0.00001 per Fahrenheit degree.
29. An express train makes the run between two cities 250 miles apart in 1¼ hr less time than a local whose speed is 10 mph less. Find the average speed of the express.
30. A motorboat takes 2 hr 8 min longer to make a trip of 48 miles up a stream than it takes on the return trip downstream. If the average rate of the current is 4 mph, find the rate of the boat in still water.
31. A bomb was released from a plane in a glide at an altitude of 20,000 ft. If the vertical component of the speed of the plane was 150 mph, find the time required for the bomb to strike the target. $s = vt + \frac{1}{2}gt^2$, where s is the vertical distance in feet, v is the initial vertical component of the speed in feet per second, t is the time in seconds, and g is the gravitational constant (32 ft per sec²). Air resistance is neglected.
32. Find the diameter of the circle in Fig. 12·8.
33. Find the radius R of the arc in Fig. 12·9.
34. Find the radius R of the cylindrical gauge in Fig. 12·10.

fig. 12·7

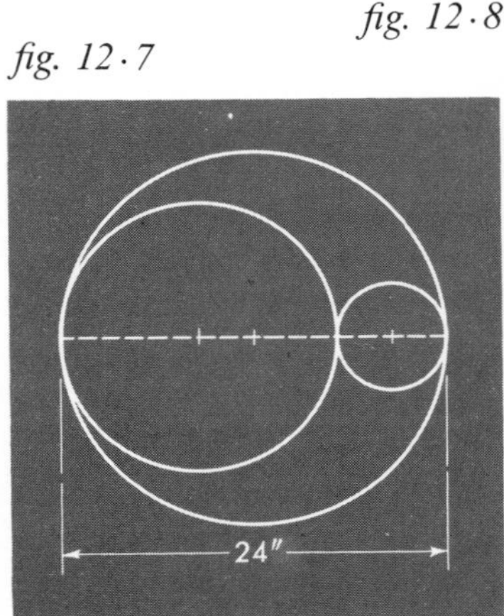

fig. 12·8

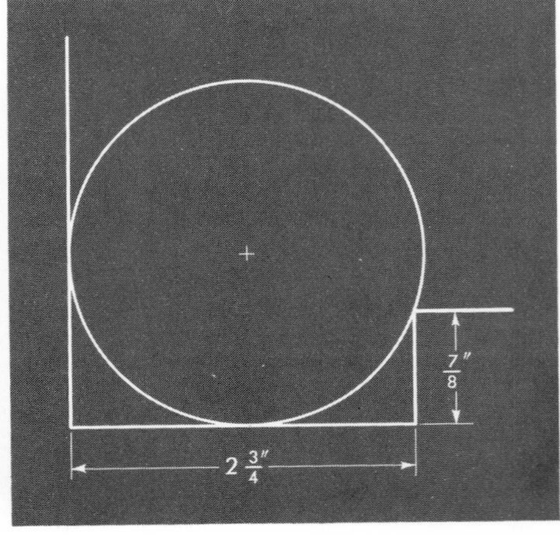

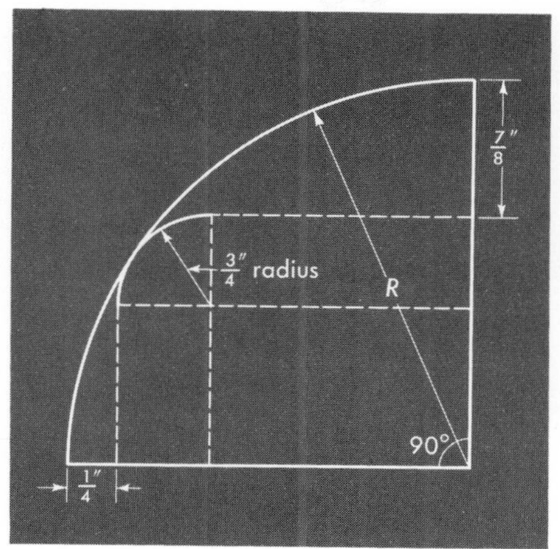

fig. 12·9

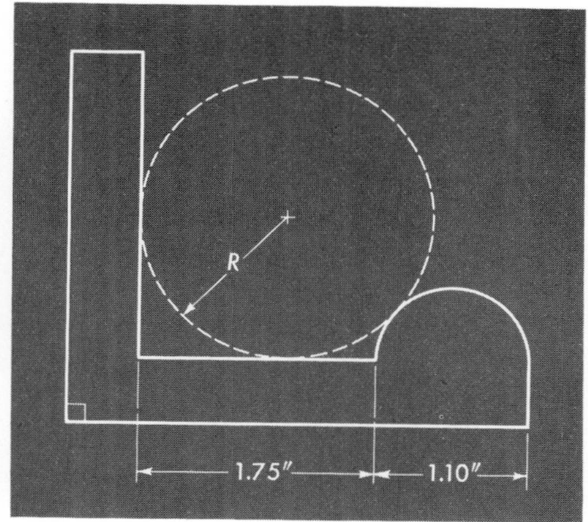

fig. 12·10

35. A 2-ft walk surrounds a circular flower bed. If the area of the walk is one-tenth the area of the flower bed, find the diameter of the bed.
36. Ice on a power-transmission line may be melted off by increasing the voltage. If $E^2/a(1 + bt) = K(t - t_0)$, find the temperature t(°F) of the wire if the voltage E is 580; a is the resistance of the line at 0°F and is equal to 52 ohms; b is the temperature coefficient of resistance of the wire, or 0.003; K is the coefficient of heat transfer by convection and conduction, or 350; t_0 is the air temperature, or 24°F.
37. A triangle has a 12-in. altitude and a 20-in. base. How wide a strip should be cut off by a line parallel to the base to leave 55 sq in. at the top?
38. A 50-cp lamp and a 120-cp lamp are 30 ft apart. Find the point on a line between them which is equally illuminated by both lights. When an object is equally illuminated by two light sources, the light intensities vary directly as the squares of their respective distances from the object. What significance attaches to the secondary solution of this problem? What can you say about the locus of all such equally illuminated points (a) in the same plane, (b) in three-dimensional space? (The relationship in this problem might have been restated to read that "the intensity of illumination varies inversely as the square of the distance from the light source." A similar relationship holds for other forms of energy or force, e.g., heat, electricity, magnetism, and gravity.)
39. An object is weighed on a platform balance and is found to balance 236.0 g. When the positions of object and weights are reversed, the indicated weight is 249.0 g because of unequal balance arms. Find the true weight correct to 0.1 g.

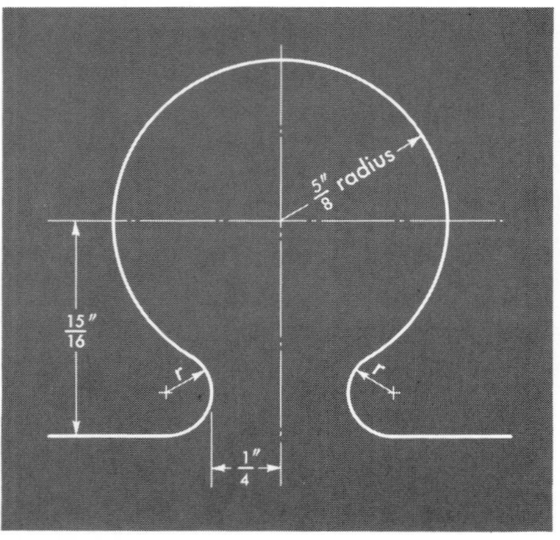

fig. 12·11

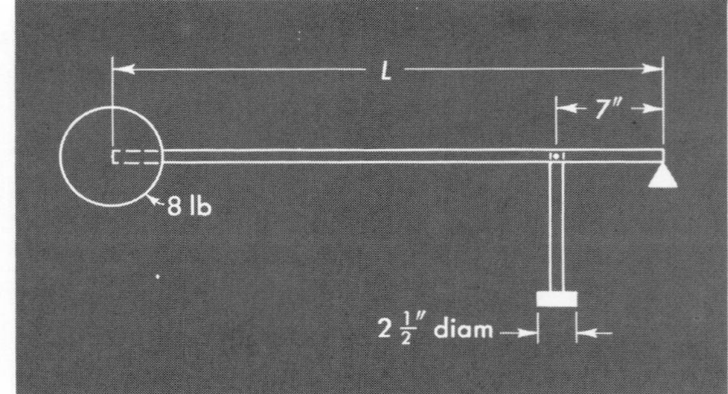

fig. 12·12

40. Find the radius of curvature in Fig. 12·11.
41. Confirm by an algebraic solution the answer to Prob. 4, Exercise 13, Chap. 6. (How long will the object take to fall 800 ft?)
42. Two steamers ply between two ports 450 miles apart. One steamer runs 2½ mph faster and takes 2½ hr less for the trip than the other. Find their rates in miles per hour.
43. A man travels 30 miles by bus and returns by a train which runs 15 mph faster. If the total running time is 1 hr 57 min, find the rates of the bus and the train.
44. Find the length of the bar in Fig. 12·12 to balance a steam pressure of 18 psi. An 8-lb weight is attached at the free end of the bar. The bar weighs 1.2 lb per lin ft.
45. A right triangle containing 210 sq ft is roped off by a line 70 ft long. Find the three sides of the triangle.
46. Six seconds after a stone is dropped into a mine shaft the sound of the impact at the bottom reaches the top. If the velocity of sound is 1,120 fps and the usual formula for a freely falling body applies to the falling stone, find the depth of the shaft.
47. A flat disk 1⅜ in. in diameter is to be pressed into an open-top cylinder ⅝ in. deep. If the total surface of the metal is unchanged during the operation, find the diameter of the cylinder.
48. A rail-diesel coach has an acceleration of 0.8 ft per sec^2 and a braking deceleration of 1.2 ft per sec^2. If two stations are 1¼ miles apart, what is the maximum speed reached when the power is shut off and the brakes applied? What time is required between the two stops?
49. The specific heat of a gas at any centigrade temperature t is $s = 0.8 + 0.0005t$. To what temperature will 1,000 cal heat 4 g of gas originally at 20° C? (First find an expression for the average specific heat of the gas over the temperature range involved.)
50. Find the diameter of the circle in Fig. 12·13.

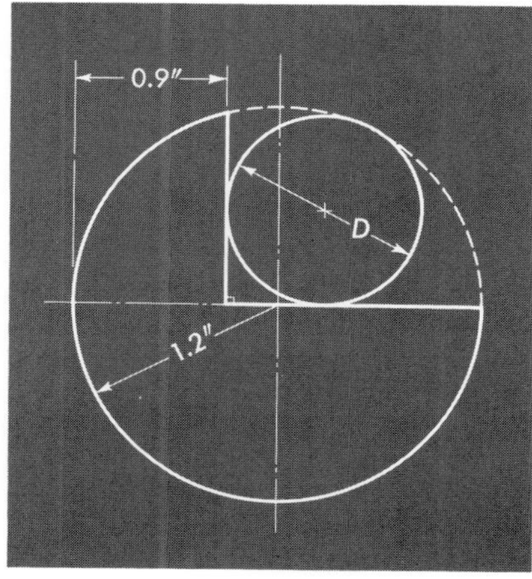

fig. 12·13

51. Two boats leave simultaneously from the opposite shores of a bay which is 2¼ miles wide and pass each other in 6 min. The faster boat completes the trip 4½ min before the other boat docks. Find the rates of the boats in miles per hour.
52. The specific heat of iron is given as $0.0001135t + 0.1055$, where t is the temperature in centigrade degrees. A block of iron weighing 60 g is transferred from a heat-treating furnace to 500 g of water. The water temperature rises from 18.0 to 26.4°C. Find the temperature of the furnace. (See Prob. 49.)
53. An open-top box is to be made from a 15-in.-square sheet of brass by cutting out squares of a certain size from each corner and turning up the resulting tabs. It was found that the capacity of the box would remain unchanged whether the squares to be cut out were of a given size or ½ in. larger. What was the smaller size of square cut out? What was the capacity of the box?
54. In the trapezoid shown in Fig. 12·14 find x such that a line drawn parallel to the base shall divide the area in half.

fig. 12·14

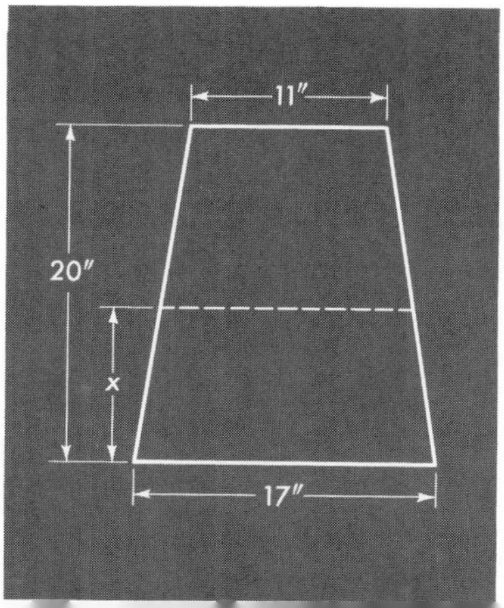

55. The length L of a parabolic bridge cable of span a and sag h is given approximately by the formula $L = a[1 + \frac{8}{3}(h/a)^2 - \frac{32}{5}(h/a)^4]$. Determine the sag if a 200-ft cable is suspended from two points 198 ft apart and in the same horizontal plane ($a = 198$). Solve first for h/a, then for h, (a), using the entire formula, (b) by neglecting the term containing $(h/a)^4$.

56. If the radius of the earth is 3,960 miles, h is the elevation of the observer (feet above sea level), and d is the distance in miles of the horizon at sea, derive an equation for d in terms of h (see Fig. 12·15). In this approximation a term is dropped, since its importance is considered to be less than that of light refraction. Show that this assumption is probably justified for such values of h as 100 ft, 1,000 ft, and even 5 miles.

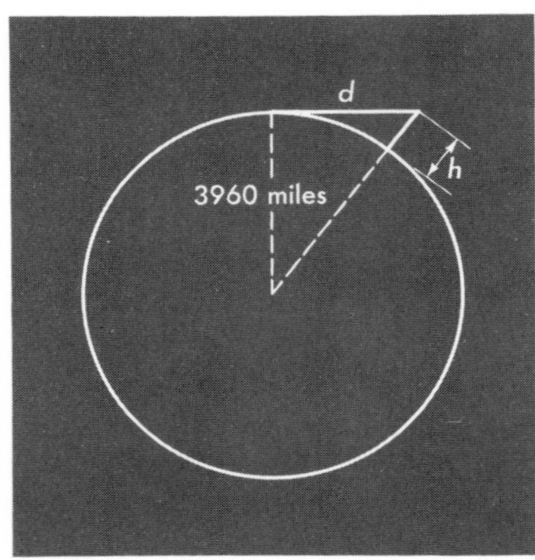

fig. 12·15

57. The following is an approximate rule for obtaining the variation in the size of a tube corresponding to a given amount of side play in the calipers (see Prob. 86, page 38). The rule has the merit of extreme simplicity and can be applied equally well to all diameters, except the very smallest. In most cases, the calculation is so simple that it can be done without recourse to pencil and paper. If

A = side play of calipers or end-measuring rod, in sixteenths of an inch
B = dimensions to which calipers are set, or length of measuring rod, in inches
C = difference between diameter of tube and length of B, in thousandths of an inch

then

$$C = A^2/2B$$

within a very small limit.

Show that the above approximation is valid when A is relatively small, say not over one-eighth the caliper setting.

Specifically, find the error in the tube diameter, as calculated by this approximation, when $A = 3/8$ in. and $B = 3.5000$ in.

58. A study of the flow of a gas through a nozzle requires the solution of the equation

$$\frac{2}{k}[r^{(2/k)-1}] - \left(\frac{k+1}{k}\right)(r^{1/k}) = 0$$

for r in terms of k. p_1 is the pressure at the nozzle entrance, and p_c is the critical pressure or the pressure at the throat of the nozzle where there is a maximum flow of gas. Then $r = p_c/p_1$, and the solution for r determines the critical pressure p_c, when p_1 is given.

12·19 Equations involving radicals

In the simplest cases the equation may be solved by squaring both sides to remove the radical sign. In some other cases the solution can be effected by making substitutions according to the method of Example 18, Sec. 12·17. Regardless of the method chosen, each root should be tested by substituting in the original equation. Any root not satisfying the original equation is extraneous and should be rejected.

example 20 Solve the equation $2\sqrt{x+4} = x + 1$.

Squaring both sides,

$$4(x+4) = (x+1)^2$$

or

$$x^2 - 2x - 15 = 0$$

whence

$$x = 5 \qquad \text{and} \qquad x = -3$$

Only the root $x = 5$ satisfies the original equation, since $2\sqrt{9} = 5 + 1$, but $2\sqrt{1} \neq -3 + 1$.

If we solve the foregoing example by the substitution method, we let $u = \sqrt{x+4}$ and $u^2 = x + 4$. Then the equation

$$2\sqrt{x+4} = x + 1$$

becomes

$$2u = u^2 - 3$$

or

$$u = 3 \text{ or } -1$$

whence $x + 4 = 9$ or 1 and $x = 5$ or -3 as before.

If the expression contains more than one radical, transpose so that the most complicated radical expression is alone on one side. Square both sides of the equation, combine terms, and repeat the foregoing process until the resulting equation contains no radicals involving the unknown. Solve and check as before.

example 21 Solve the equation $3\sqrt{x} - \sqrt{5x-4} = 2$.

Transposing, we get

$$3\sqrt{x} - 2 = \sqrt{5x-4}$$

Squaring both sides,

$$9x - 12\sqrt{x} + 4 = 5x - 4$$

Transposing, we have

$$4x + 8 = 12\sqrt{x}$$

Dividing by 4,

$$x + 2 = 3\sqrt{x}$$

Squaring both sides,

$$x^2 + 4x + 4 = 9x$$

or $$x^2 - 5x + 4 = 0$$

whence $$x = 4 \qquad \text{and} \qquad x = 1$$

Both roots satisfy the original equation.

EXERCISE 12

In Probs. 1 to 14 find the real roots.

1. $\sqrt{3x+7} = x + 1$
2. $\sqrt{x^2 - 28} - 6 = 0$
3. $\sqrt{x+7} + 2 = \sqrt{3x-5}$
4. $\sqrt{5x-6} = \sqrt{3x+7} + 1$
5. $\sqrt{3x+4} + \sqrt{4x+1} = 1$
6. $\sqrt{x^2+24} - \sqrt{x^2-21} = 5$
7. $\sqrt{x+10} - \sqrt{x+1} - \sqrt{x-14} = 0$
8. $\sqrt{2x+5} - \sqrt{4x+3} = 1$

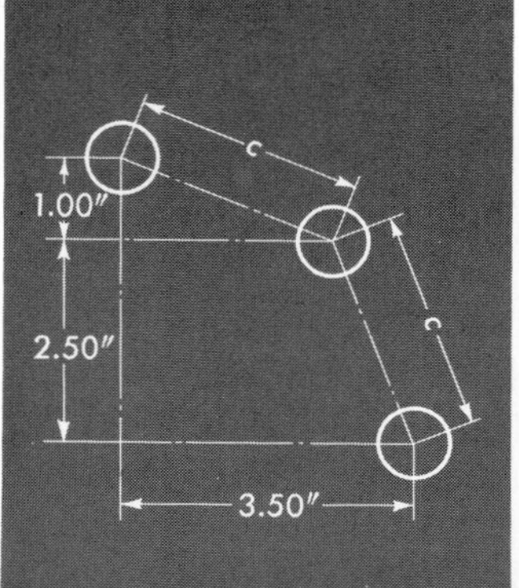

fig. 12·16

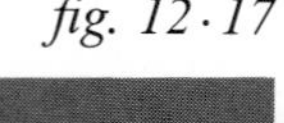
fig. 12·17

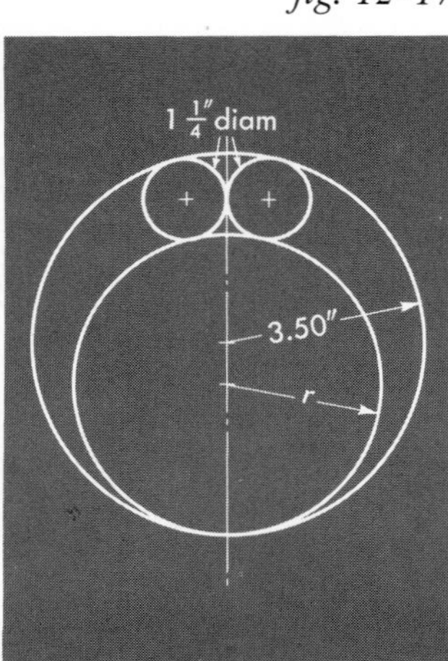

fig. 12·1

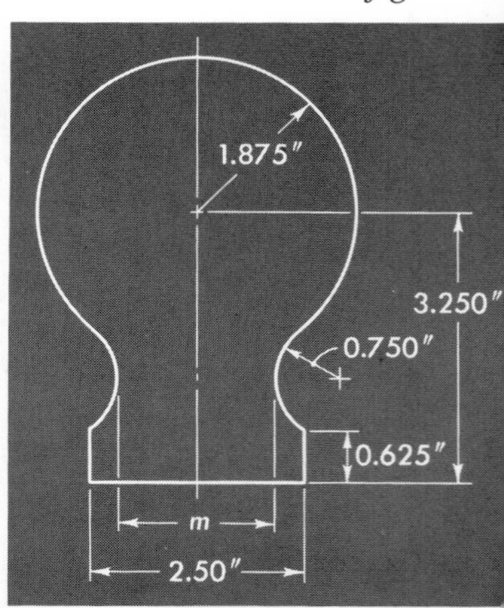

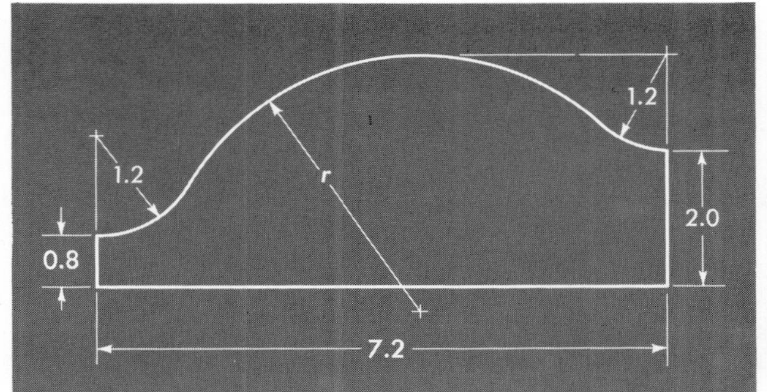

fig. 12·19

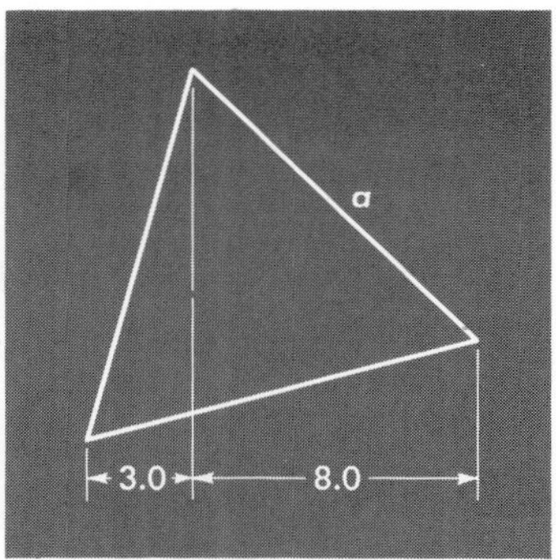

fig. 12·20

9. $\sqrt{x - 3} = \sqrt{x + 42} - \sqrt{3x + 4}$
10. $\sqrt{x + 2} + \sqrt{x} = \dfrac{3}{\sqrt{x + 2}}$
11. $\sqrt{2x - 2} + \sqrt{3x - 2} = \dfrac{4x + 9}{\sqrt{3x - 2}}$
12. $(x^2 + 4x - 7) - 4\sqrt{x^2 + 4x - 7} = 5$
13. $3x^2 + 5x - 4\sqrt{3x^2 + 5x + 3} = 2$
14. $2x^2 - 6x - 7\sqrt{x^2 - 3x - 2} = 8$

Solve the following problems, rejecting roots incompatible with the dimensions given:

15. Determine the distance c in Fig. 12·16.
16. Determine the radius r in Fig. 12·17.
17. Determine the distance m in Fig. 12·18.
18. Determine the radius r in Fig. 12·19.
19. Determine a side a in the equilateral triangle in Fig. 12·20.
20. Find the diameter of the small circle in Fig. 12·21.

fig. 12·21

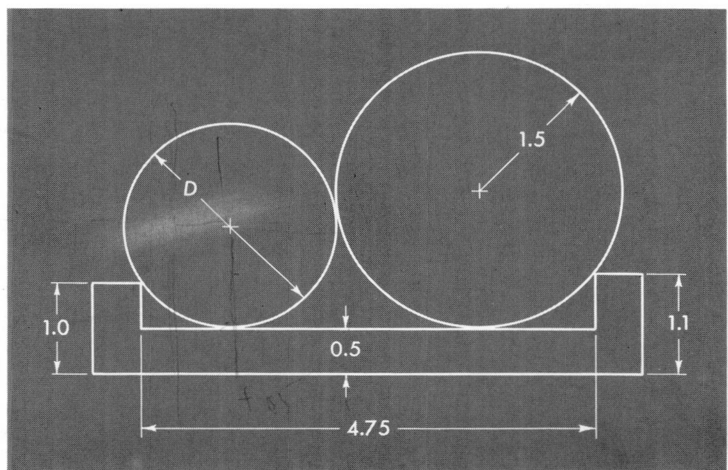

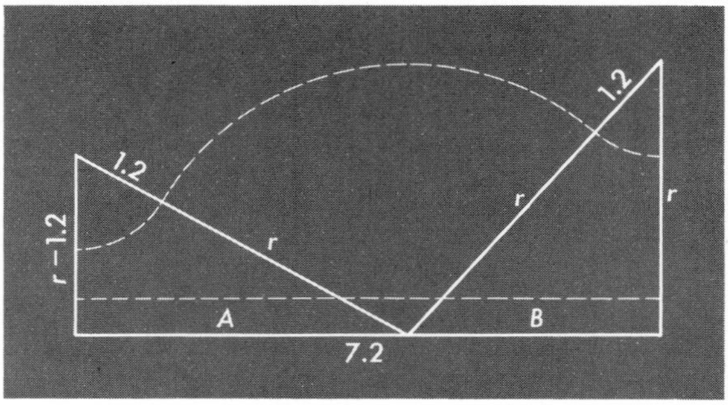

fig. 12·22

21. A ship canal lock has vertical sides and a rectangular horizontal cross section of area M. The water discharges through an outlet of area A. The time (t sec) required for the water level to fall from a height h_2 to a height h_1 is approximately

$$t = \frac{M}{2A}(\sqrt{h_2} - \sqrt{h_1})$$

(a) If $h_2 = h_1 + y$, derive a formula for y.
(b) If $A = 4\pi$ sq ft and $M = 30{,}000$ sq ft, determine the fall in 20 min ($t = 1{,}200$ sec). Give the result in terms of h_1.

NOTE: The method of "false position" is occasionally useful. Taking Prob. 18 as an example, we would assume a reasonable value of r and test the value of $A + B$ against the required value of 7.2. The value of $A + B$ will indicate whether to take a larger or smaller value of r for a closer approximation. The process is repeated until an answer of the required accuracy is obtained (see Fig. 12·22). The bottom row is determined by interpolation.

r	$r + 1.2$	$r - 1.2$	$\sqrt{(r + 1.2)^2 - (r - 1.2)^2} = \sqrt{4.8r} = A$	$\sqrt{(r + 1.2)^2 - r^2} = \sqrt{2.4r + 1.44} = B$	$A + B$
3	4.2	1.8	3.7947	2.9394	6.7341
4	5.2	2.8	4.3818	3.3236	7.7044
3.5	4.7	2.3	4.0988	3.1369	7.2357
3.463	4.663	2.263	4.0771	3.1227	7.1998

12·20 Applied problems in maxima and minima

A variety of interesting applications involving maxima and minima can be solved by making use of the principles set forth in Sec. 12·16.

example 22 The average attendance at a moving-picture theater at which the admission fee is 60 cents is 400. The manager has good reason to believe that with each reduction of 5 cents in the admission fee the attendance would increase by 50. What admission fee and corresponding attendance would produce the maximum return? What is the maximum return for a performance?

Let n equal the number of admissions and t equal the cost of one admission (in cents). Then the total receipts $R = nt$. But

$$n = 400 + 50\frac{(60 - t)}{5} = 400 + 10(60 - t)$$

Therefore,

$$R = t[400 + 10(60 - t)] = -10t^2 + 1{,}000t$$

Referring back to Eq. (17), Sec. 12·16, we read that if

$$y = ax^2 + bx + c$$

$$y_{(\text{max or min})} = c - \frac{b^2}{4a}$$

when $x = -b/2a$.

In our illustration, $y = R$, $x = t$, $a = -10$, $b = 1{,}000$, and $c = 0$. Therefore

$$R_{(\text{max or min})} = 0 - \frac{(1{,}000)^2}{4(-10)} = 25{,}000 \text{ cents} = \$250$$

$$t = \frac{-1{,}000}{2(-10)} = 50 \text{ cents optimum admission charge}$$

The attendance is evidently 250/0.50, or 500 people.

Note that this problem is not concerned at all with incidental factors such as increased operating costs or ability to take care of increased patronage.

EXERCISE 13

1. Divide 17 into two parts such that their product will be a maximum.
2. Find the dimensions of the largest possible rectangular area that may be enclosed by 140 ft of fencing.
3. The work done by exploding a mixture of 1 cu ft of water gas and v cu ft of air is $w = 84v - 3.15v^2$. What value of v will lead to the maximum value of w? What is the maximum value of w?
4. Show that if P is the perimeter of a rectangle, the maximum possible area is represented by a square whose side equals $P/4$ and whose area equals $P^2/16$.
5. A ball is thrown upward with a speed of 112 fps from a building 340 ft high. If the height of the ball in feet h at any time t sec after throwing is given by the equation $h = 340 + 112t - 16t^2$, find the maximum height reached.

6. The power delivered to an external circuit by a 32-volt generator whose internal resistance is 2 ohms is $32a - 2a^2$ watts, where a is the current in amperes. At what current will this generator deliver the maximum power?
7. What would be the diameter of the inner circles in Prob. 25 in Exercise 11 to make their combined area a minimum?
8. A long sheet of copper 22 in. wide is to be made into a gutter by turning strips up vertically along the two sides. How many inches should be turned up at each side to obtain the greatest carrying capacity?
9. The manager of a theater found that with an admission charge of 60 cents per person the average daily attendance was 2,000, while with every decrease of 5 cents the attendance increased by 250. What admission price will provide the maximum daily receipts? What will be the maximum daily receipts?
10. A telephone company can get 1,200 subscribers at a monthly rate of \$5 each. It can get 60 more subscribers for each decrease of \$0.10 in the rate. What rate will yield the maximum gross income? What will the income be?
11. An impulse turbine with a peripheral speed of t fps is driven by a jet of water flowing at the rate of w fps. Under these conditions the power P generated is equal to $\frac{1}{800}t(w - t)$. If 12 kw are generated where $t = 120$ fps and $w = 300$ fps, find the turbine speed required to generate the maximum power. What is the maximum power? (w remains constant at 300 fps.)
12. An automobile manufacturer estimates that he can sell 5,000 cars a month at \$2,800 each and that he can sell 400 more cars a month for each \$100 decrease in price. If each car costs the manufacturer \$1,300 to make, at what price should he sell to obtain the maximum profit?
13. A printer contracts to print 3,000 circulars or less at the rate of \$1 per hundred. If the number of circulars exceeds 3,000, he will deduct 1 cent per hundred on the whole contract for each hundred printed in excess of 3,000. For what number of circulars would the printer realize maximum gross receipts, and what would the receipts be?
14. A Norman window has vertical sides and a horizontal base, but the top is a semicircle. If the perimeter is 14 ft, what dimensions will lead to the largest possible area?
15. Road tests show that the gas mileage of a certain automobile may be expressed by the formula $M = 20/(1 + 0.0043A)$, where M is in miles per gal and A is the percentage by volume of alcohol in an alcohol-gasoline blend. The cost (c cents) of a gallon of such a blend may be expressed by the formula $c = 0.24(100 - A) + 0.14A$. Derive, in terms of A, a formula for the fuel cost F in cents per mile.
16. (a) In Prob. 15 find the percentage by volume of alcohol resulting in the least economical performance in cents of fuel cost per mile. (b) What percentage of alcohol must be contained in the alcohol-

gasoline blend before any saving in fuel costs over that of straight gasoline is realized?

17. A 20-in. length of wire is to be cut into two parts, one of which is formed into a circle, the other into a square. Find the diameter of the circle and the side of the square if their combined area is to be a minimum.

unit four curve sketching, non-linear empirical equations

analyzing a curve by taking it apart and putting it together again—treatment of nonlinear experimental data

13
simultaneous quadratic equations and curve sketching

There is no simple general algebraic solution for two simultaneous quadratic equations of the type

$$Ax^2 + Bxy + Cy^2 + Dx + Ey = F$$

An approximate graphical solution may be obtained by plotting. This is also useful at any time as a rough check on the algebraic solution. The algebraic solutions will be limited to the simpler cases.

In most cases point-by-point curve plotting will be accomplished more efficiently if it is preceded by curve sketching. In fact, curve sketching is a very effective way of analyzing the properties of a function, whether or not we intend to do any plotting. Curve sketching will be outlined in Secs. 13·2 to 13·13.

13·1 Characteristic types of quadratic curves

In more advanced mathematics it is stated that the graph of any quadratic equation in two variables is always a parabola, ellipse, circle, hyperbola, two straight lines, or occasionally a single point or no graph at all.

The following statements are confirmed in analytic geometry:

Parabola

An equation in x and y that is linear in one variable and quadratic in the other and contains no xy term represents a parabola whose axis of symmetry is parallel to either the X axis or the Y axis (Fig. 13·1). Plotting of the parabola is discussed in Sec. 12·4.

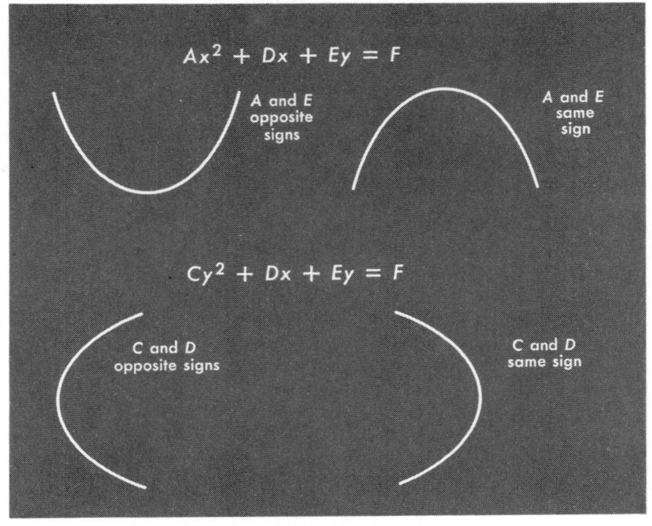

fig. 13·1

Ellipse

An equation of the type

$$Ax^2 + Cy^2 = F$$

where A, C, and F all have the same sign and $A \neq C$, represents an ellipse symmetrical about both axes.

example 1 Outline the graph of the equation

$$4x^2 + 9y^2 = 100$$

In order to outline the curve roughly (Fig. 13·2*a*), find the intercepts as follows: Substitute $y = 0$, obtaining

$$4x^2 = 100$$

whereby

$$x = \pm 5$$

Substituting $x = 0$ in the original equation, we have

$$9y^2 = 100 \qquad \text{or} \qquad y = \pm 10/3$$

If a more accurate curve is required, other substitutions may be made. For example, if we let $x = \pm 3$, then $y = \pm 8/3$, giving us the four points A, B, C, and D.

Similarly when $A > C$, such as in the equation $9x^2 + 4y^2 = 100$, we obtain x intercepts of $\pm 10/3$ and y intercepts of ± 5 (Fig. 13·2*b*).

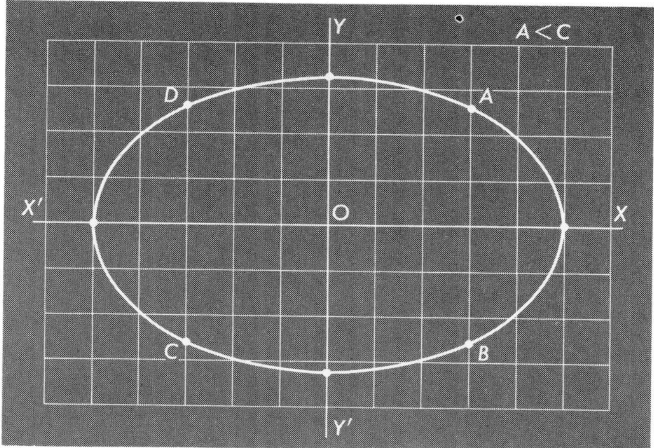

fig. 13·2a

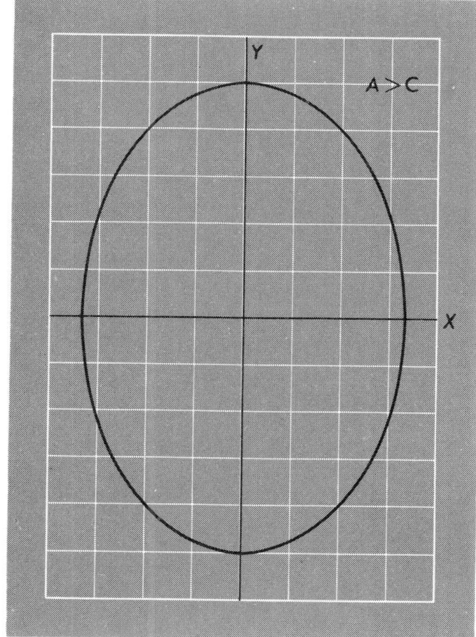

fig. 13·2b

Circle

An equation of the type

$$Ax^2 + Cy^2 = F$$

where A, C, and F all have the same sign and $A = C$, represents a circle of radius $\sqrt{F/A}$ with its center at the origin. (NOTE: the circle is a special case of the ellipse.)

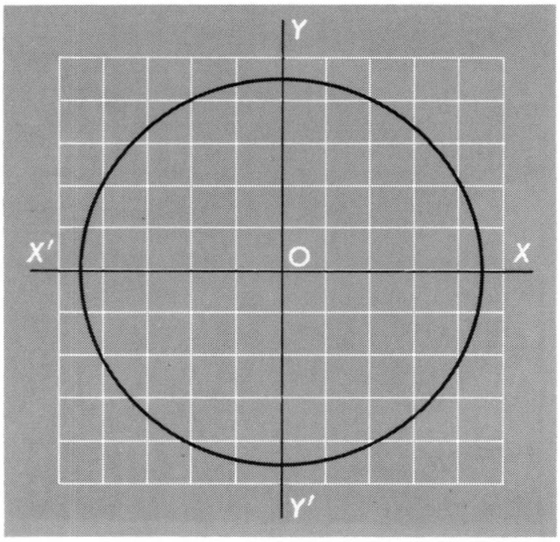

fig. 13·3

example 2 Outline the graph of the equation (Fig. 13·3)

$$4x^2 + 4y^2 = 81$$

Dividing through by 4, we obtain

$$x^2 + y^2 = {}^{81}\!/\!_4$$

or

$$\sqrt{x^2 + y^2} = {}^9\!/\!_2$$

Since the distance from the origin to any point (x, y) is $\sqrt{x^2 + y^2}$ (Sec. 6·13), the graph is the locus of all points whose distances from the origin are $^9\!/\!_2$. Hence we have a circle of radius $^9\!/\!_2$ with its center at the origin. Obviously this curve is best drawn with a compass.

Two intersecting straight lines

An equation of the type

$$Ax^2 + Cy^2 = 0$$

where A and C have opposite signs, represents a pair of straight lines intersecting at the origin.

example 3 Plot the locus of

$$9x^2 - 25y^2 = 0 \tag{1}$$

Factoring Eq. (1), we obtain

$$(3x + 5y)(3x - 5y) = 0 \tag{2}$$

This equation may be transformed into two equations (Example 1, Sec. 12·2).

$$3x + 5y = 0$$
$$3x - 5y = 0$$

These straight lines constitute the locus of Eq. (1). They are drawn as dashed lines in Fig. 13·4.

Hyperbola

An equation of the type

$$Ax^2 + Cy^2 = F$$

where A and C have opposite signs and $F \neq 0$, represents a hyperbola symmetric about the coordinate axes.

example 4 Sketch the graph (Fig. 13·4) of

$$9x^2 - 25y^2 = 144 \tag{3}$$

Substituting $y = 0$, we find $x = \pm 4$.

If we attempt to find the y intercepts by substituting $x = 0$ in Eq. (3), we find $y = \pm\frac{12}{5}\sqrt{-1}$, which, being an imaginary quantity, cannot be plotted.

If we solve Eq. (3) for y, we obtain

$$y = \pm\tfrac{3}{5}\sqrt{x^2 - 16}$$

It is apparent that the curve does not occur in the band between the lines $x = 4$ and $x = -4$ and that there is no y intercept.

Replacing the value of the constant F in Eq. (3) by 0, we obtain Eq. (1), discussed above and plotted as dashed lines in Fig. 13·4.

These lines are the *asymptotes* of the graph of Eq. (3). (An *asymptote* of a curve is a line which the curve approaches but never reaches as the absolute numerical value of one of the variables increases without limit.) This property will be treated at greater length in Sec. 13·7.

fig. 13·4

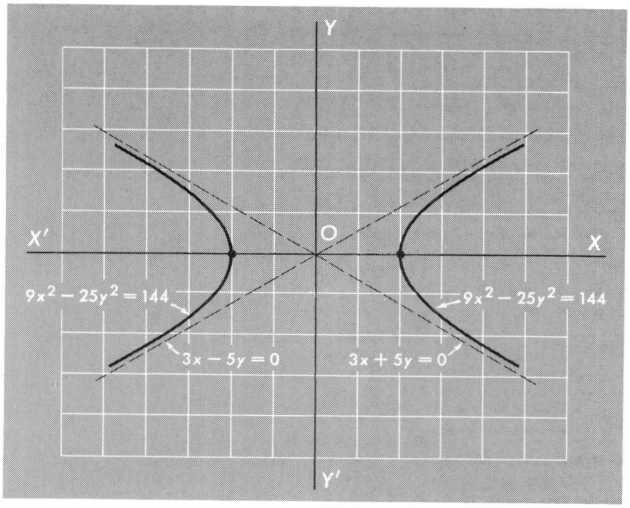

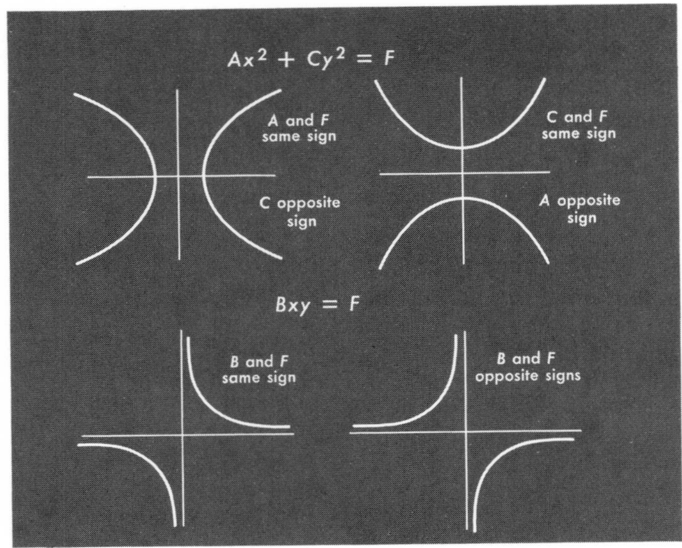

fig. 13·5

A hyperbola may be sketched roughly by locating x or y intercepts and using the asymptotes as guiding lines. As in our previous discussion, additional points may be obtained by substitution. For this purpose it is suggested that an equation such as Eq. (3) be converted to the form

$$x = \pm \tfrac{1}{3}\sqrt{25y^2 + 144}$$

The advantage of this transformation lies in the fact that all values of y will correspond to real points on the curve.

Simple forms of hyperbola are illustrated in Fig. 13·5.

13·2 Advantages of sketching

We learned in Chap. 6 how to draw curves by plotting a number of points. This is adequate for the straight lines and simple curves encountered there. In this chapter we shall be interested in nonlinear functions and their graphs.

Plotting has several weaknesses when applied to more complicated curves:

1. Too much time is wasted on less significant parts of the curve.
2. The important properties of the curve are not emphasized.
3. It gives no indication of a proper choice of units on the two axes.
4. One cannot be sure when enough points have been plotted to reveal all characteristic properties of the graph.

The most commonly sought properties of a graph include: intercepts, symmetry, extent, discontinuities, asymptotes, and excluded regions. Additional properties such as max and min points, singular points, extreme slopes, etc., usually require methods of calculus (see Chap. 25).

13·3 Intercepts

The intercepts of a graph have been discussed in Secs. 6·8 and 12·4. By way of review, the following examples and exercise are included.

example 5 Find the intercepts of the curve $y = x^2 - 9$.

When $x = 0$, $y = -9$. When $y = 0$, $x = \pm 3$. Hence the intercepts of the graph of this equation are $(0,-9)$, $(3,0)$, and $(-3,0)$.

example 6 Determine the intercepts of the curve $x^2 - 4y^2 - x - 6y + 10 = 0$.

When $x = 0$, $y = 1$ or $-5/2$. When $y = 0$, the roots are imaginary. Therefore the graph does not meet the X axis.

EXERCISE 1

Find the intercepts (if any) of the following curves.

1. $y = (x + 10)/(x + 2)$
*2. $x^2 - y^2 - 4 = 0$
*3. $x^2 + 4y^2 = 36$
*4. $y = x^2 + 2x$
*5. $y = 8/x$
*6. $y = -2x$
7. $y = 9/x^2$
*8. $x = y^2 - y - 30$
9. $(x - 2)^2 + (y + 5)^2 = 49$

*Give the name of the curve.

13·4 Symmetry

The graph of an equation may be symmetric with respect to one or more lines, or to a point.

Symmetry to X *axis*

The graph of an equation is symmetric with respect to the X axis if and only if the equation obtained by replacing y with $-y$ is equivalent to the original equation. (That is, the equation contains only even powers of y.)

example 7 The graph of $y^2 = 4x + 1$ is symmetric with respect to the X axis since $(-y)^2 = 4x + 1$ is equivalent to $y^2 = 4x + 1$ (Fig. 13·6).

Symmetry to Y *axis*

The graph is symmetric with respect to the Y axis if and only if the equation obtained by replacing x with $-x$ is equivalent to the original equation. (That is, the equation contains only even powers of x.)

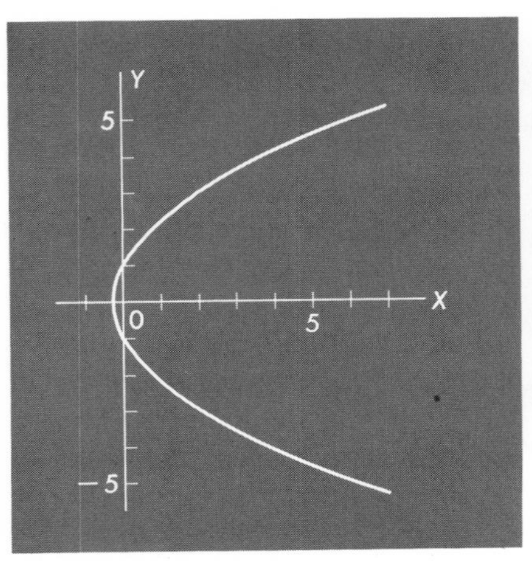

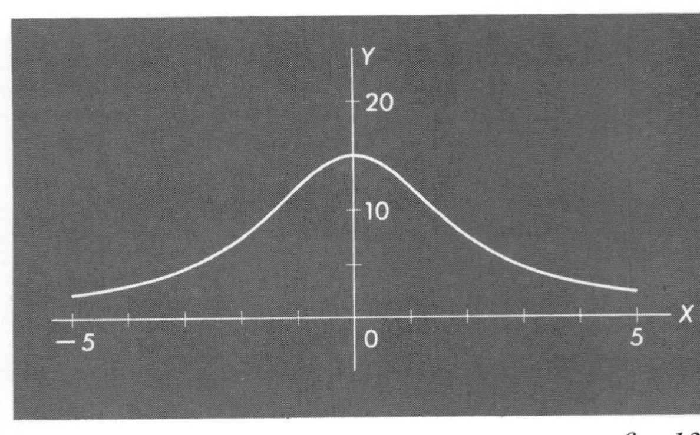

fig. 13·6

fig. 13·7

example 8 The graph of $y = 60/(x^2 + 4)$ is symmetric with respect to the Y axis (Fig. 13·7).

Symmetry about the line y = x

The graph is symmetric with respect to the line $y = x$ if y may be replaced by x while simultaneously x is replaced by y.

example 9 In Fig. 13·8 the parabola $x^2 - 2xy + y^2 - 6ax - 6ay + 9a^2 = 0$ meets the test of interchangeability of x and y.

Symmetry about the line y = −x

Symmetry about the line $y = -x$ is indicated if y may be replaced by $-x$ while simultaneously x is replaced by $-y$.

example 10 The circle $x^2 + 8x + y^2 - 8y = 0$ is symmetric about the line $y = -x$ (Fig. 13·9).

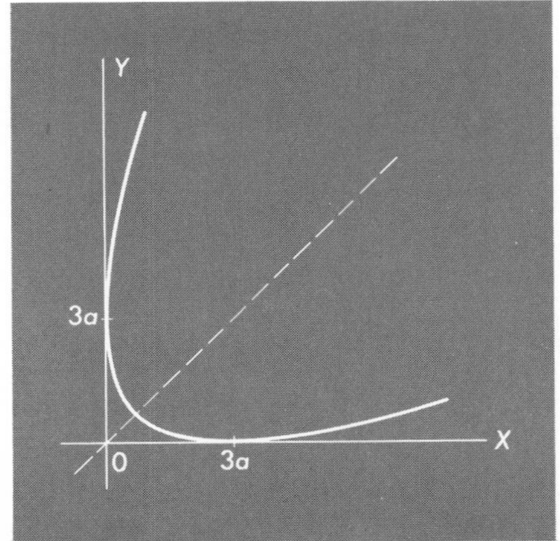

fig. 13·8

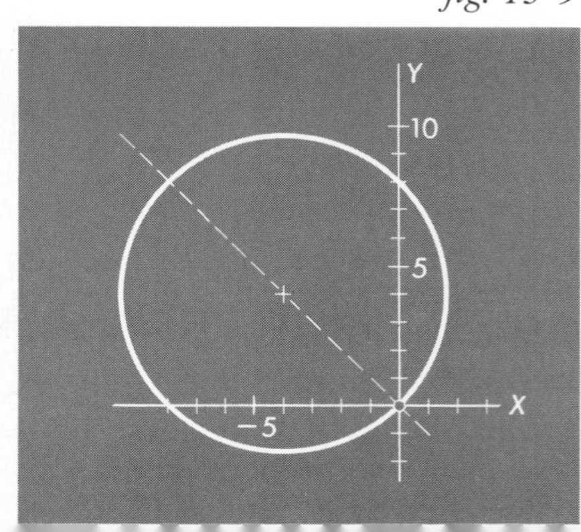

fig. 13·9

Symmetry about any line

In general, two distinct points P and P' are symmetric with respect to a line L if L is the perpendicular bisector of the line segment PP'. P and P' are said to be symmetric partners with respect to the line L.

example 11 The parabola $y = x^2 - 4x - 21$ shows symmetry about the vertical line $x = 2$ (Fig. 13·10). The horizontal line $y = -9$ intersects the curve, making $PP_m = P_mP' = 4$.

NOTE: Our equation may be rewritten $y = (x - 2)^2 - 25$. This procedure was suggested in Sec. 12·4.

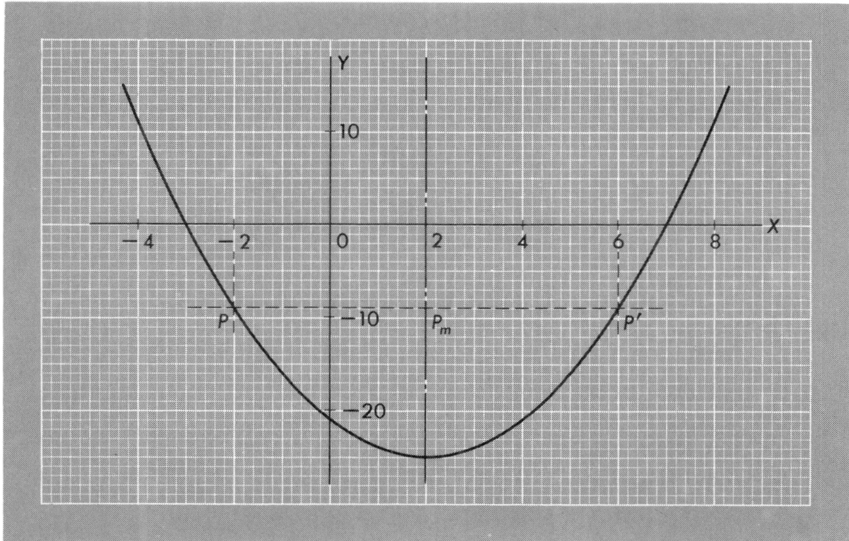

fig. 13·10

Symmetry about the origin

The graph is symmetric with respect to the origin if the equation obtained by replacing x by $-x$ and y by $-y$ is identical with the original equation. Graphically it will be noted that a straight line passing through the origin O intersects the curve at P and P' such that line segments PO and OP' are equal.

example 12 The graph of $y = x^3$ is symmetric with respect to the origin since the curve $-y = (-x)^3$ is identical with the curve $y = x^3$. In Fig. 13·11 the line $y = 4x$ intersects the curve $y = x^3$ at (2,8), (0,0), and (−2,−8). Thus $PO = P'O = \sqrt{68}$.

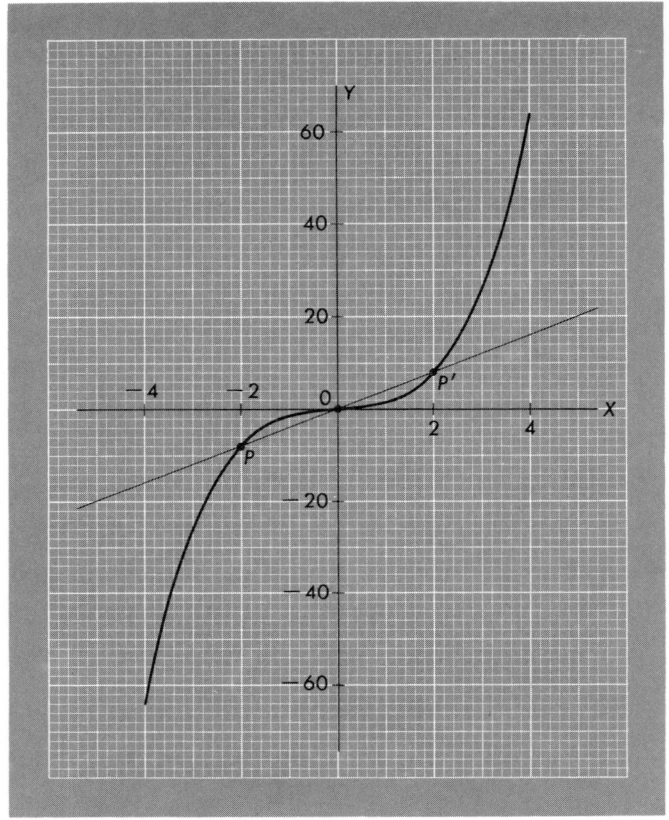

fig. 13·11

Symmetry about any point

By analogy to symmetry about the origin above, a straight line passing through a point of symmetry P_m intersects the curve at P and P' such that PP_m equals P_mP'. P and P' are called symmetric partners with respect to P_m.

example 13 Figure 13·12 shows the circle $(x - 9)^2 + (y - 8)^2 = 20$ and the straight line $y = 2x - 10$ passing through its center. The circle has a radius equal to $\sqrt{20}$ with center at (9,8). The intersection points are (11,12) and (7,4) with PP_m and P_mP' each equal to $\sqrt{20}$.

EXERCISE 2

Discuss the symmetry of the following curves.

1. $x^2 + y^2 = 4$
2. $x^2 - y^2 = 4$
3. $x^2 - 4y = 0$
4. $y = (x - 4)^2$
5. $y = 8/x$
6. $x^2/36 + y^2/9 = 1$
7. $y = x^2 - 8x + 16$
8. $y^2 = x^3$
9. $x^2 + y^2 + 6y = 16$
10. $y = x^3 - x$
11. $x^2y + y - 4x = 0$

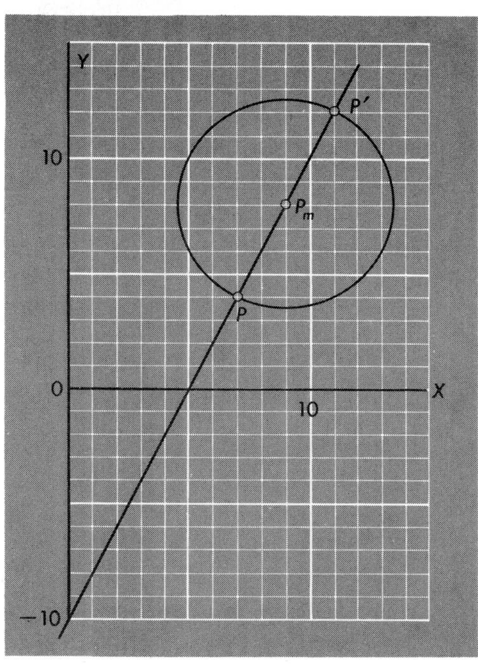

fig. 13·12

13·5 Extent

The extent of the graph includes the *domain* (the "spread" of real values of x), and the *range* (the "spread" of real values of y).

example 14 Determine the extent of the graph of $(y + 15)^2 = 25 - (x - 20)^2$.

From Fig. 13·13 it can be seen that the domain is $15 \leq x \leq 25$ (read "x is equal to or greater than 15 and equal to or less than 25"), and the range is $-20 \leq y \leq -10$ (read "y is equal to or greater than -20 and equal to or less than -10").

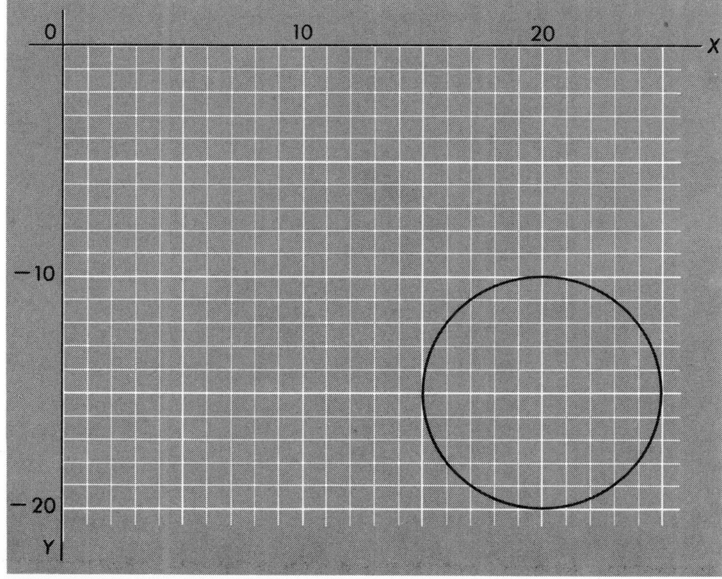

fig. 13·13

13·6 Discontinuities

Occasionally one encounters an equation whose graph may consist of two or more separated sections. In contrast, we think of a function as being *continuous* over a given range if anywhere within that region as we take values of the independent variable closer and closer together the corresponding values of the dependent variable also become closer and closer together so that their difference approaches zero.

The matter of continuity, if treated rigorously, is enormously complex. Fortunately, however, the engineering technician is unlikely to encounter situations in which the more subtle aspects of continuity are critical. He usually deals with functions that are continuous over the region of interest or in which discontinuities, if they exist, are easily detected.

Therefore, the intuitive notion of continuity outlined in the first paragraph of this section is usually sufficient. It is admittedly inadequate in certain situations.

As a practical matter, if we plot a function over a given interval, using enough points, and find that the graph appears to be a smooth, unbroken line with no abrupt changes, the function it represents is *probably* continuous in this interval.

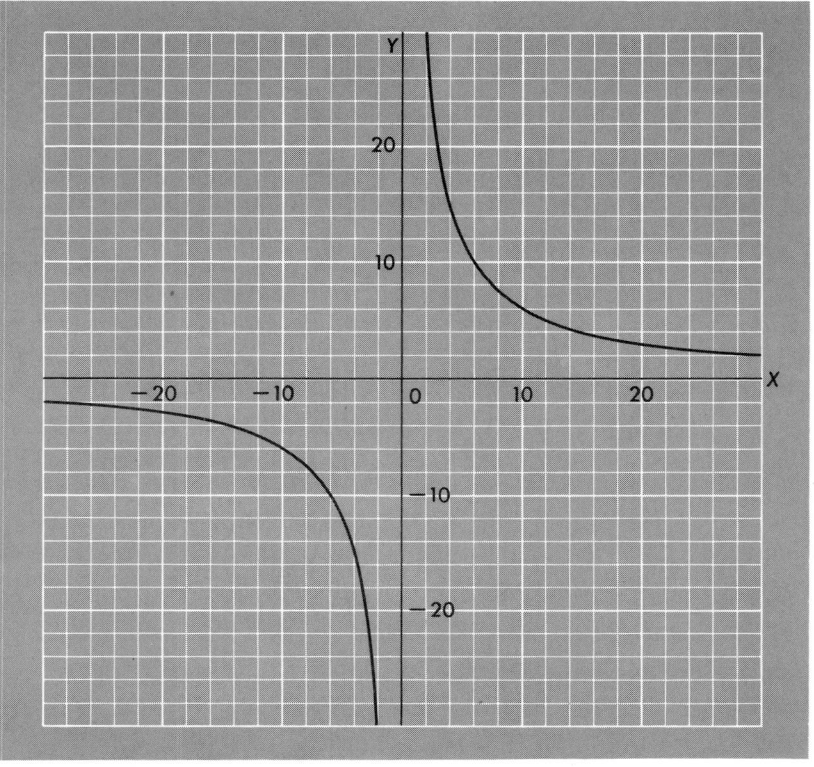

fig. 13·14

Since division by zero is impossible, a discontinuity will occur for a value of the independent variable which leads to an indicated division by zero. This is illustrated in Example 15 below.

example 15 Graph the function $f(x) = y = 60/x$ (Fig. 13·14).

Observe that the domain of this function is $-\infty < x < 0$ and $0 < x < +\infty$. The range is $\infty > y > 0$ and $0 > y > -\infty$. Also note that since division by zero is undefined, there is a discontinuity at $x = 0$.

Another cause of a discontinuity is the presence of complex quantities, since in the coordinate system with which we are working there is no provision for other than real numbers.

example 16 Sketch the graph of the equation $y = \sqrt{x^2 - 2x - 15}$ (Fig. 13·15).

If we rearrange this as $y = \sqrt{(x + 3)(x - 5)}$, it is clear that if $x > 5$ (x is greater than 5), both factors in the radicand are positive and the radicand is positive. If $x < -3$ (x is less than -3), both factors in the radicand are negative and again the radicand is positive. But if $-3 < x < +5$ (x is greater than -3 and less than $+5$), the factor $x + 3$ is positive and the factor $x - 5$ is negative; accordingly the radicand is negative, and we obtain imaginary values of y. Therefore such values of x must be excluded from the coordinate system. It follows that the domain is $-\infty < x \leq -3$ and $5 \leq x < +\infty$. (The points $-3,0$ and $5,0$ are called *end minima*.)

Negative values of y cannot exist, since, by definition, y is the positive square root of $x^2 - 2x - 15$. In other words, the range of y is zero and the set of all positive real numbers.

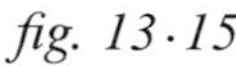
fig. 13·15

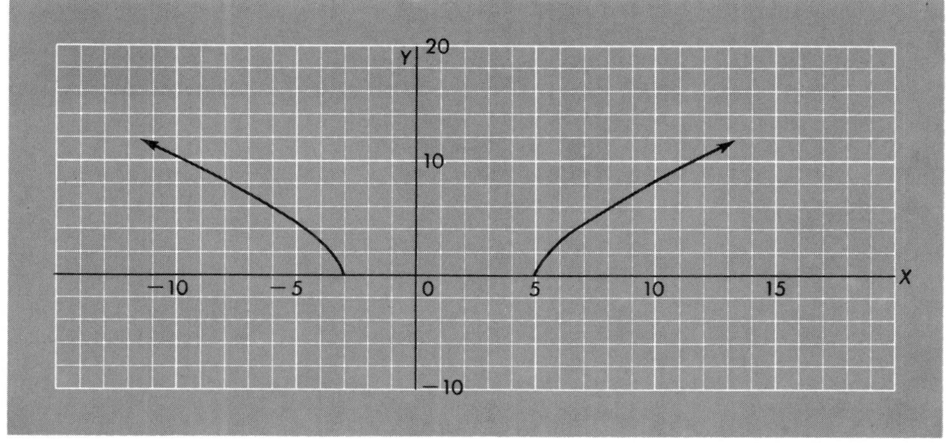

13·7 Asymptotes

We have noted that discontinuities may result from division by zero. This leads us to the consideration of asymptotes. Returning to Fig. 13·14, we can see that as we scan the graph upward from the origin, the graph continually approaches the Y axis. The same is true as we scan the graph downward from the origin. In fact, as we attempt to reduce $|x|$ further, the graph recedes even more rapidly from the origin and, for $x = 0$, we can assign no finite value for y. We say that y is undefined. The Y axis is said to be an asymptote of the graph.

If we rewrite the equation as $x = 60/y$, inspection indicates that the X axis is also an asymptote.

Although a technically precise definition of an asymptote is not appropriate at this time, we can describe the idea well enough for practical use. A line is an asymptote of a graph if the distance between the line and the graph becomes less and less as the distance moved along the line from some fixed point on it increases without limit. This line is usually vertical or horizontal, but may be inclined, and occasionally even curved (see Fig. 13·18).

example 17 Consider the graph of the equation $2y = \pm\sqrt{x^2 - 9}$ (Fig. 13·16).

Rearranging, we have $\quad y = \pm\frac{x}{2}\sqrt{1 - \frac{9}{x^2}}$

It will be observed that as $|x|$ increases indefinitely, y approximates more and more closely the value $\pm x/2$ in both the equation and the graph. Therefore the lines $y = x/2$ and $y = -x/2$ are asymptotes of the curve $2y = \pm\sqrt{x^2 - 9}$.

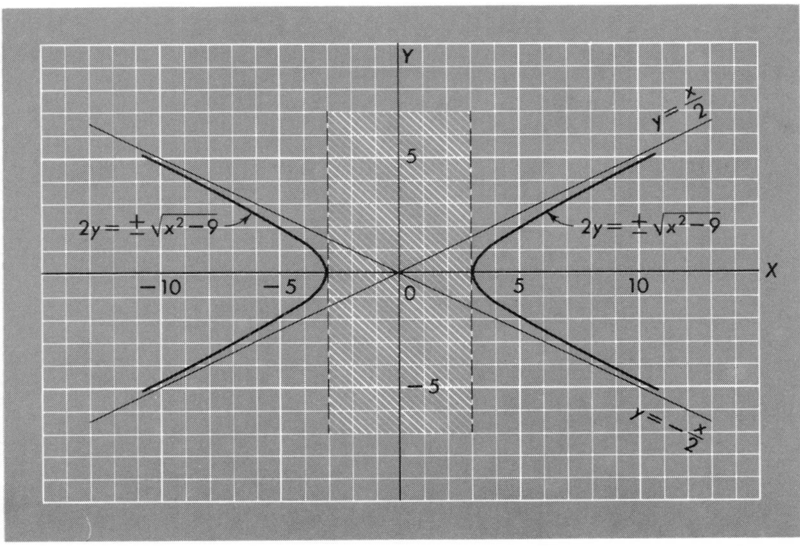

fig. 13·16

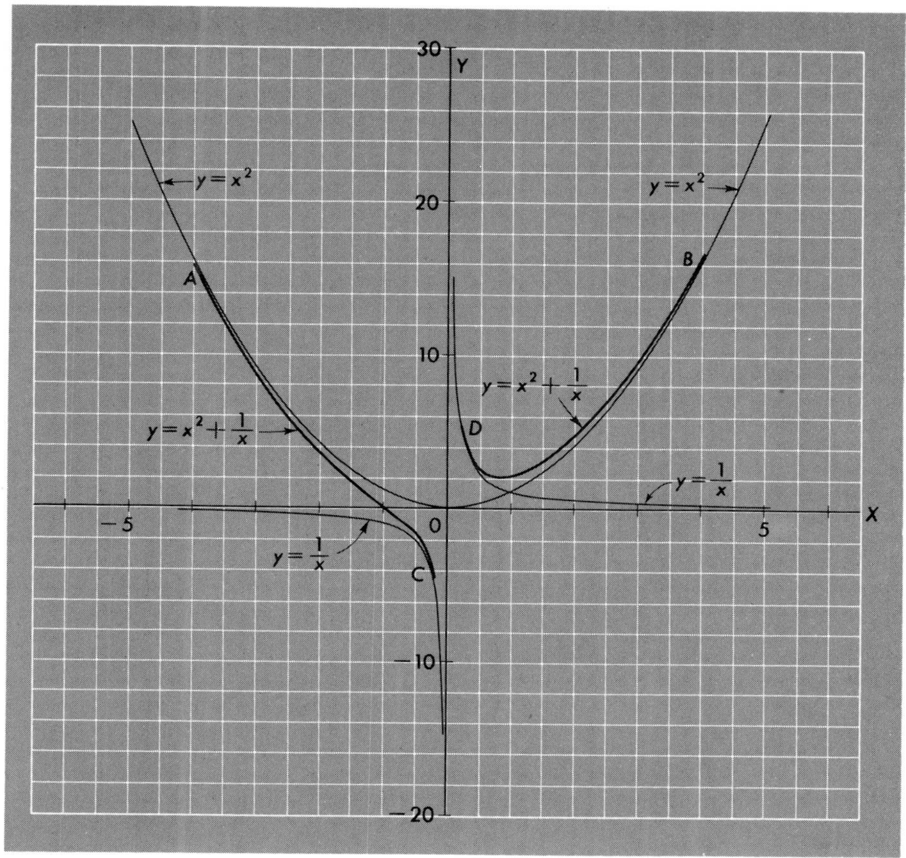

Fig. 13·17

example 18 Determine the asymptotes of the graph of the equation $y = x^2 + \frac{1}{x}$ (Fig. 13·17).

As we allow x to increase indefinitely, it can be seen that the equation $y = x^2 + \frac{1}{x}$ approximates more and more closely the equation $y = x^2$. Hence the graph of $y = x^2 + \frac{1}{x}$ continually gets closer to the asymptotic line $y = x^2$ as $|x|$ increases without limit (see points A and B). As $|x|$ continually gets closer to zero, the expression $x^2 + \frac{1}{x}$ approximates $\frac{1}{x}$ ever more closely. Therefore the equation $y = 1/x$ is also an asymptote, as suggested by points C and D.

13·8 Excluded regions

The terms "excluded region" and "extent" are mutually exclusive. Referring to Example 17 and Fig. 13·16 above, it is evident that for the region $-3 < x < 3$ the radicand is negative and y is imaginary. Hence we say that $-3 < x < 3$ is an excluded region (represented by the shaded area), whereas the domain is $-\infty < x \leq -3$ and $3 \leq x < +\infty$. At this point it will be agreed that we shall delineate excluded regions by vertical or horizontal lines.

If we solve the equation for x, obtaining $x = \pm\sqrt{4y^2 + 9}$, it follows that for all real values of y the radicand is positive and there is an unlimited range of y. Note also that the smallest possible value of $|x|$ is 3, occurring when $y = 0$, confirming the conclusion reached as to domain.

We must be careful not to confuse extent and asymptote. The values $x = 3$ and $x = -3$ are not asymptotes. The curve does not continually approach the lines $x = 3$ and $x = -3$ as y becomes smaller. On the contrary, the curve approaches these lines, touches them, and then recedes.

EXERCISE 3

Determine the asymptotes, if any, and also any excluded regions, of each of the following.

1. $x^2 + y^2 = 16$
2. $x^2 + 4y^2 = 25$
3. $x^2 - y^2 = -9$
4. $x^2/9 - y^2/4 = 1$
5. $x = 4y$
6. $xy = -8$
7. $y = \dfrac{60}{x^2 + 4}$
8. $y = x^2 - 4x - 21$
9. $y = \dfrac{4x + 1}{x - 1}$
10. $y = -x^2 + 9$

13·9 Composition of ordinates

Plotting of a curve can often be simplified by the composition of ordinates. This consists of expressing an equation as the combination of two or more simpler equations. Thus, by separately sketching the ordinates

fig. 13·18

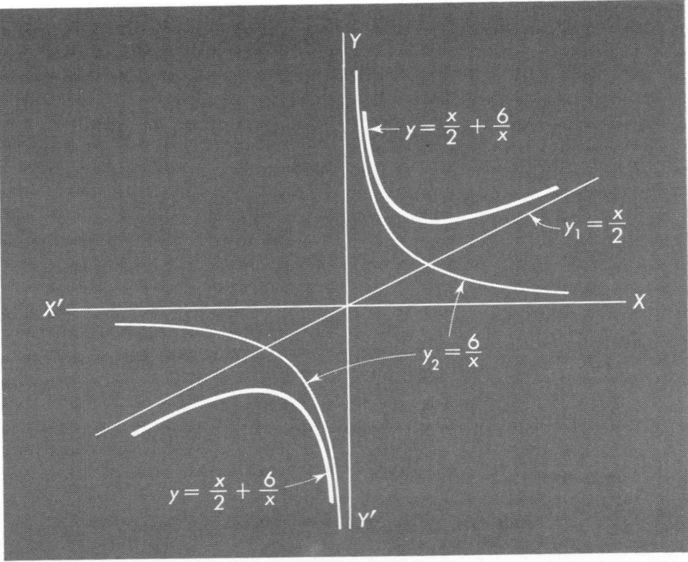

of the component equations on a common area and then adding, multiplying, or dividing the ordinates graphically, there will often result an easier method for sketching the curve of an equation than by graphing it as a unit (Examples 19 to 21).

The sketching of reciprocals, squares, or square roots of ordinates of certain equations can also be used to advantage (Examples 22 to 24).

Addition of ordinates

example 19 Sketch the curve

$$y = \frac{x}{2} + \frac{6}{x}$$

Here we separately sketch (Fig. 13·18)

$$y_1 = \frac{x}{2}$$

$$y_2 = \frac{6}{x}$$

Algebraic addition of ordinates gives us the equation

$$y_1 + y_2 = y = \frac{x}{2} + \frac{6}{x}$$

while by graphical addition we obtain the graph of $y = \frac{x}{2} + \frac{6}{x}$ shown as a heavy line.

It will be seen that large absolute values of x make $x/2$ the dominant term, while small absolute values of x make the term $6/x$ dominant.

The graph emphasizes this relationship in a slightly different way. The curves $y = x/2$ and $y = 6/x$ appear as the asymptotes.

The choice of scales will be dictated by the range of the variables to be covered. They may not be equal. In any event one scale division should equal 1, 2, or 5 times some integral power of 10.

Multiplication of ordinates

example 20 Sketch the curve $y = x^3 - 16x$ (Fig. 13·19).

Let $y_1 = x$ and $y_2 = x^2 - 16$. Then $y_1y_2 = y = x^3 - 16x$.

Division of ordinates

example 21 Sketch the curve $y = (x + 6)/(x - 2)$ (Fig. 13·20).

Let $y_1 = x + 6$ and $y_2 = x - 2$. Then $y_1/y_2 = y = (x + 6)/(x - 2)$.

Y

$y = x^3 - 16x$

50

$y_2 = x^2 - 16$

25

$y_1 = x$

X

−10 −5 0 5 10

−25

$y_1 = x$

$y_2 = x^2 - 16$

$y = y_1 y_2 = x^3 - 16x$

−50

fig. 13·19

fig. 13·20

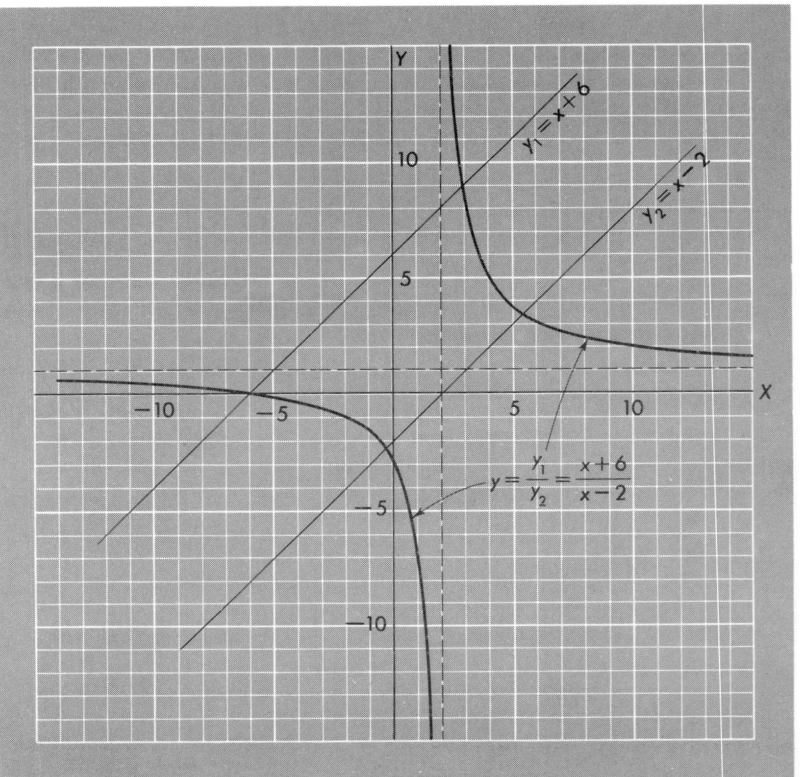

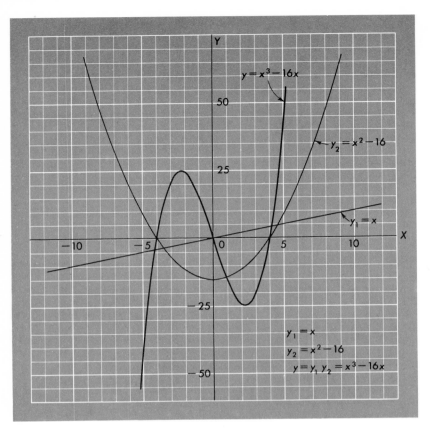

NOTE 1: As an algebraic confirmation of the graph, write

$$y = \frac{1 + \dfrac{6}{x}}{1 - \dfrac{2}{x}}$$

from which it follows that as $|x|$ increases without limit, y approaches 1. Also, as x approaches 2, the denominator approaches zero, and $|y|$ increases without limit.

NOTE 2: If we carry out the indicated division and write $y = 1 + \dfrac{8}{x - 2}$, the same conclusion is indicated by inspection.

Reciprocals of ordinates

example 22 Sketch the curve $y = \dfrac{1}{2x - 6}$ (Fig. 13·21).

Let $y_1 = 2x - 6$. Then $1/y_1 = y = \dfrac{1}{2x - 6}$.

fig. 13·21

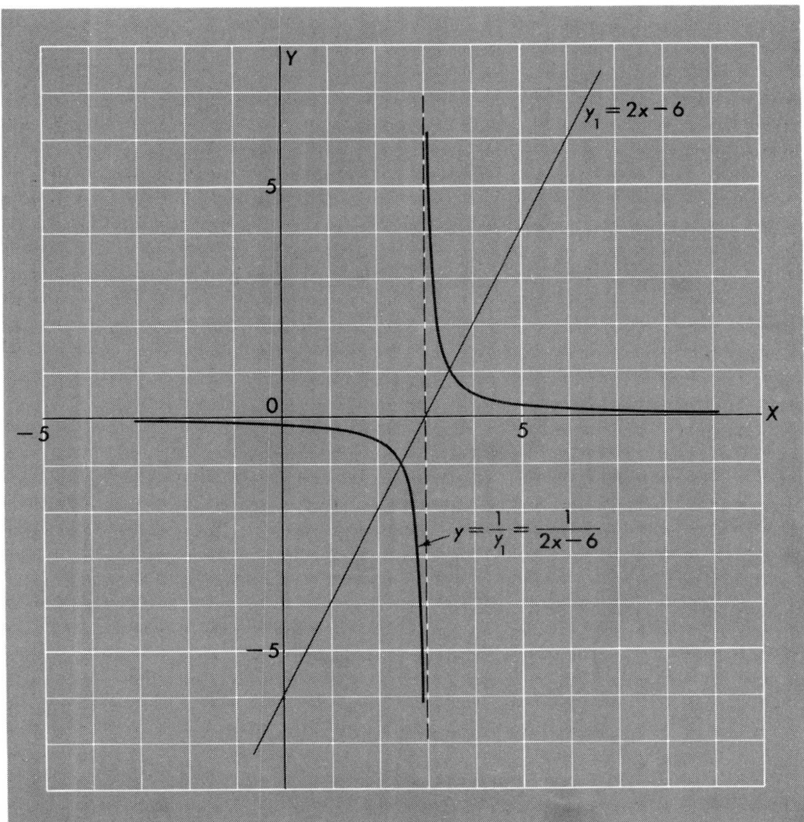

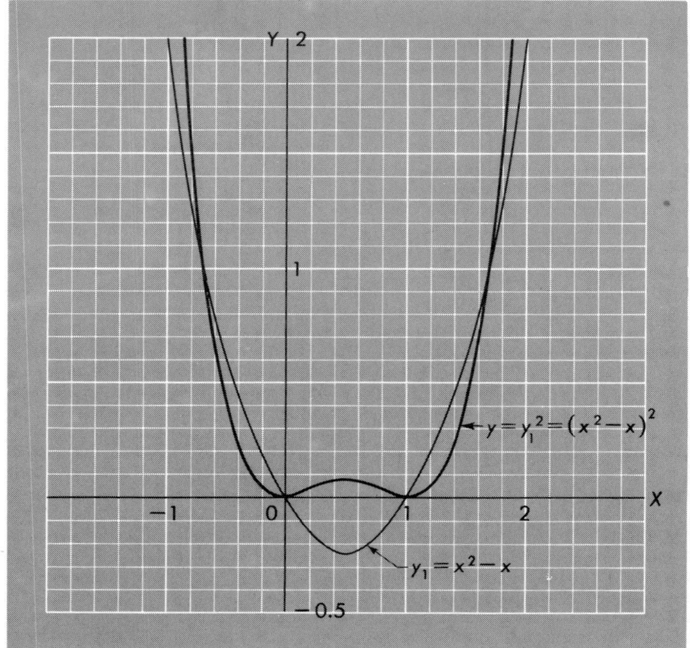

fig. 13·22

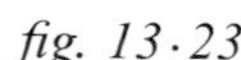
fig. 13·23

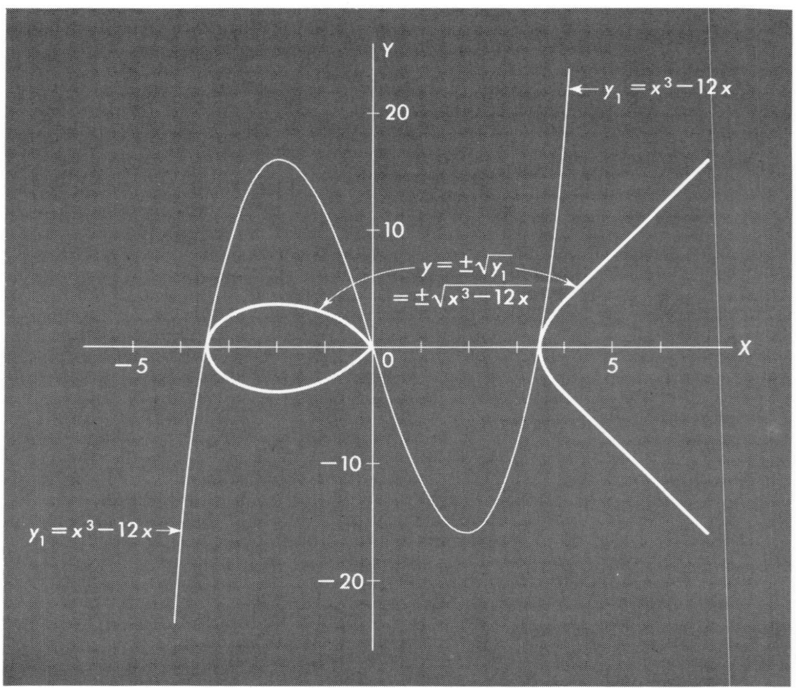

Squares of ordinates

example 23 Sketch the curve $y = (x^2 - x)^2$ (Fig. 13·22).

Let $y_1 = x^2 - x$. Then $(y_1)^2 = y = (x^2 - x)^2$.

Square roots of ordinates

example 24 Sketch the curve $y^2 = x^3 - 12x$ (Fig. 13·23).

First we take the square root of both sides, obtaining $y = \pm\sqrt{x^3 - 12x}$. Let $y_1 = x^3 - 12x$. Then $\sqrt{y_1} = y = \pm\sqrt{x^3 - 12x}$.

example 25 Figure 13·15 is repeated in Fig. 13·24 as the solid curve. It was derived by first sketching the dashed curve, $y_1 = x^2 - 2x - 15$, and then taking the square root of all positive ordinates.

EXERCISE 4

Sketch the following curves, using the composition-of-ordinates techniques.

1. $y = (x + 4)^2$
2. $y = x^2 - 6x - 16$
3. $y = (x + 4)^2 - 4$
4. $y = x^3 + 6x$
5. $y = \sqrt{x^2 - 9}$
6. $y = \sqrt{9 - x^2}$

fig. 13·24

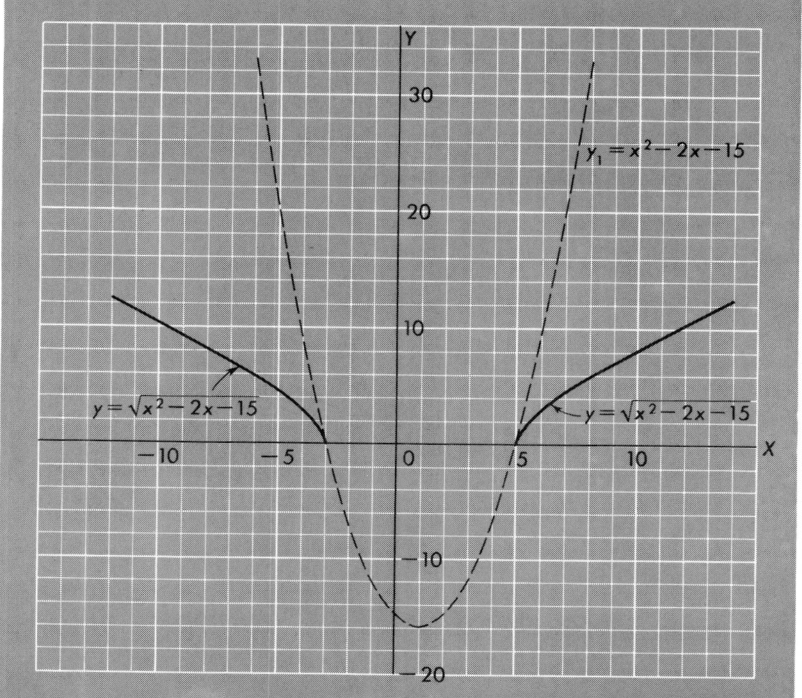

7. $y = \dfrac{60}{x^2 + 4}$ 8. $y = x^2 - 8/x$ 9. $y = \dfrac{20x}{x^2 + 4}$

10. $y = \dfrac{20x}{x^2 - 4}$

11. The fuel tank of a rocket is 40 ft long and has a uniform cross section of 5 sq ft. It weighs 500 lb when empty. It is to be filled with liquid fuel weighing 50 lb per cu ft. As the fuel is consumed, the overall center of gravity (cg) of the vertical tank and the remaining fuel will reach a low point. At what depth of fuel will this occur?

If h = the depth of liquid (ft), show that the expression for cg $= \dfrac{h}{2} - 1 + \dfrac{42}{h + 2}$. Sketch two curves, $y_1 = \dfrac{h}{2} - 1$ and $y_2 = \dfrac{42}{h + 2}$, and, by addition of ordinates, sketch the curve $y_1 + y_2 =$ cg.

Estimate the value of h corresponding to a minimum in cg.

13·10 Logarithmic Functions

An equation of the form $y = \log_b x$ is called a logarithmic function. Here b may be any positive real number other than unity. For the sake of simplicity we shall make $b > 1$. (Note that if $b = e$, the equation involves natural logarithms.) Since b has been restricted, we have guaranteed that $x > 0$. This last statement should then suggest that the graph of $y = \log_b x$ will lie to the right of the Y axis. This can be verified by considering values of x between 0 and 1. We note that y is negative in this range. It is also apparent that as $x \to 0$, $y \to -\infty$. (Read "as x approaches zero, y becomes infinitely more negative.") Hence the line $x = 0$ is an asymptote of the curve $y = \log_b x$. At the same time, as x increases, y is also increasing. When x takes on the value of 1, $y = 0$, and hence the x intercept is located. Since this is an increasing function, the shape of the curve is now apparent. It is also obvious that there is no symmetry, as may be confirmed by the usual test (see Fig. 13·25).

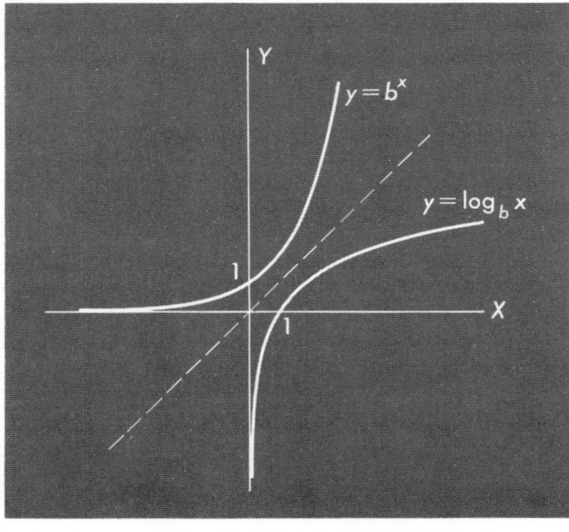

fig. 13·25

13·11 Exponential function

Any function of the form $y = b^x$ where x represents the set of all real numbers, and $b \neq 0$, is considered to be an exponential function. It is apparent that if $b = e$ (the base of natural logarithms), we have the familiar exponential function used so frequently in mathematics. In this discussion, we will confine ourselves to the case where $b > 1$.

It would be well worth while to try to capitalize on an intuitional approach to sketching the graph of $y = b^x$ (see Fig. 13·25). We have no restrictions on x except that it be real. At the same time, we have agreed to consider only cases where $b > 1$. This, in fact, says that as x increases without limit ($x \to +\infty$), y also increases very rapidly and does indeed become infinite (hence, as $x \to +\infty$, $y \to +\infty$). On the other hand, when $x \to -\infty$ (meaning x increases negatively without limit), it can be seen that $y \to 0$ (y approaches zero), since in the equation $y = b^x$ (where $x \to -\infty$) the term $b^x \to 0$ and hence the above statement holds. The curve does cross the Y axis as can readily be seen by letting $x = 0$. This condition will produce a value of 1 for y. Hence, the y intercept is at (0,1). As previously mentioned, condition $x \to -\infty$ shows that the function is approaching zero. However, it actually never does touch the X axis for any finite value of x. Hence, this condition implies that the line $y = 0$ (or the X axis) is the asymptote of the curve. There is no symmetry in the usual sense. Note however, in referring to Fig. 13·25, that a symmetry does exist between the related curves $y = \log_b x$ and $y = b^x$. If we apply the principles of symmetry about the line $x = y$ (Sec. 13·4) and interchange the variables in the equation $y = \log_b x$, we obtain the equation $x = \log_b y$, which is equivalent to writing $y = b^x$.

13·12 Determination of characteristic properties

We are now in a position to sketch many of the more common curves, with the exception of cases involving translation of axes, which will be discussed in Sec. 13·13.

example 26 Sketch the function
$$y = \frac{60}{x^2 - 4}$$

We first sketch the curve $y_1 = x^2 - 4$ (dashed line in Fig. 13·26), and from this sketch the reciprocal curve $y = \dfrac{1}{x^2 - 4}$, using the principle set forth in Sec. 13·9 (solid lines). We are not concerned about the numerator, whether 1 or 60 or any positive number. The numerator simply affects the vertical scale, and this can be handled by writing in the appropriate numbers after sketching. The sketch reveals most of the properties which are then confirmed by the analysis described in earlier sections.

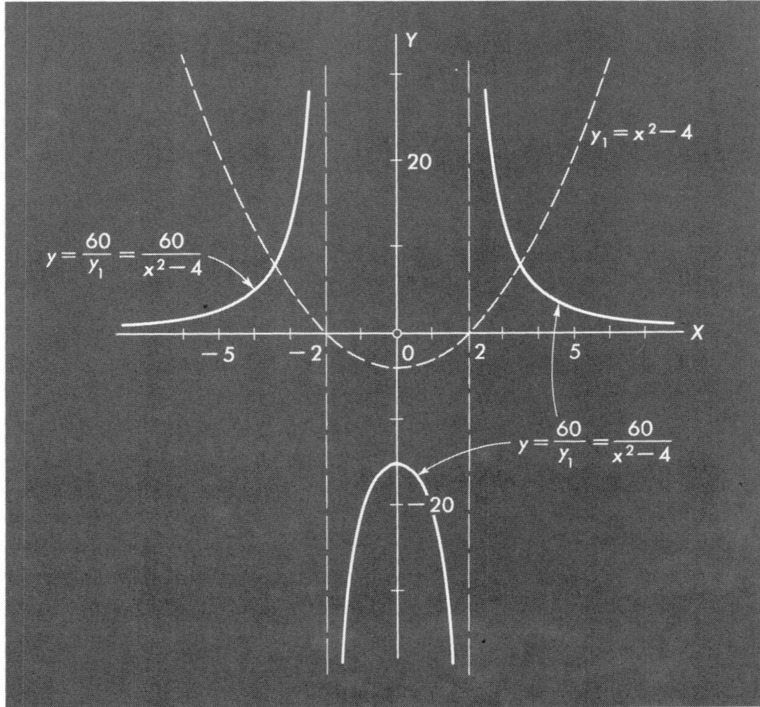

fig. 13·26

Intercepts

Since the fraction can never take on the value zero except at infinite values of $|x|$, there are no x intercepts. When $x = 0, y = -15$, which is the only intercept and is written in after the curve is sketched, thus justifying our earlier temporary disregard of the numerator.

Symmetry

Since the equation contains only even powers of x, the graph is symmetric about the Y axis.

Discontinuities

It is quite evident that there must be two discontinuities in the graph, one at $x = 2$, the other at $x = -2$, since each of these values leads to an indicated division by zero.

Extent and excluded regions

Since for all real values of x (excepting $+2$ and -2 noted above) there are corresponding real values of y, the domain of x is unlimited.

Further, since the denominator cannot be algebraically less than -4, there can be no values of y between 0 and -15. Therefore the range is $\infty > y > 0$ and $-15 \geq y > -\infty$.

Asymptotes

It can be seen that as $|x|$ approaches 2 from the high side, the denominator, while remaining positive, is approaching zero, and y is increasing without limit. As $|x|$ approaches 2 from the low side, the denominator, while remaining negative, is approaching zero, and y becomes increasingly negative without limit. When $x = 2$, the denominator equals zero, and y is undefined.

EXERCISE 5

Sketch the following equations, indicating any intercepts, symmetry, extent, discontinuities, asymptotes, and excluded regions.

1. $y = \dfrac{4}{x^2 - 16}$
2. $y = \dfrac{20x}{x^2 + 4}$
3. $y = x^2 - 2x - 15$
4. $y = x^2 - 8/x$
5. $y = \sqrt{25 - x^2}$
6. $y^2 = \dfrac{x - 9}{x - 1}$
7. $y^2 = \dfrac{9x}{x + 9}$
8. $y = \ln x$
9. $x = e^y$
10. $y = \log \dfrac{1}{x}$
11. $y = 1 - e^{-x}$
12. $y = e^{-2x}$
13. $y = e^{-x^2}$

13·13 Translation of axes

In most of our graphing so far, the curves have been symmetric with respect to the origin or to an axis. In this section we shall develop methods for relating the equation of an "off-center" curve to the equation of the same curve after being moved to a position of symmetry.

We shall refer such curves to two different coordinate systems (Fig. 13·27). Referred to the X and Y axes, the coordinates of origin O' are (h,k). Now let $P(x',y')$ be any point referred to the X' and Y' axes. Its coordinates with respect to the X and Y axes are $x' + h$ and $y' + k$.

That is,

$$x = x' + h \tag{4}$$

or

$$x' = x - h \tag{5}$$

and

$$y = y' + k \tag{6}$$

or

$$y' = y - k \tag{7}$$

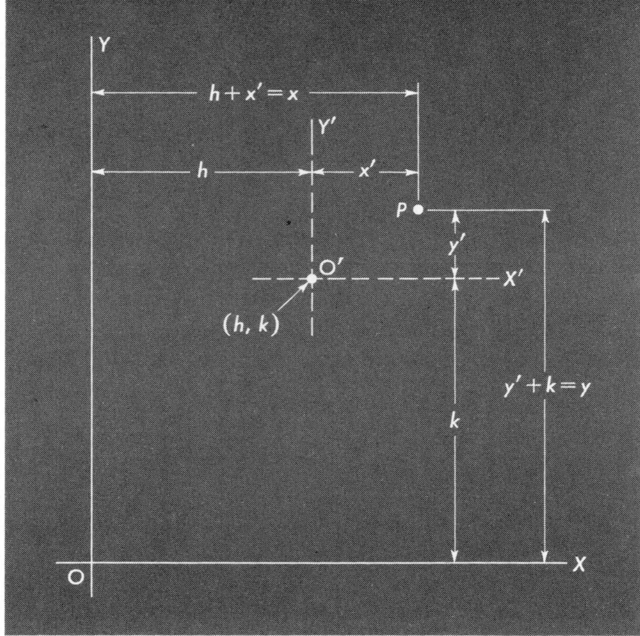

fig. 13·27

example 27 Sketch the graph of the equation

$$(x + 20)^2 + (y - 15)^2 = 25 \tag{8a}$$

Applying Eqs. (4) through (7), we may write

$$(x - h)^2 + (y - k)^2 = 25 \tag{8b}$$

and

$$x'^2 + y'^2 = 25 \tag{9}$$

We note that Eq. (9) (which is our "basic equation") is a decided simplification of Eq. (8*a*).

On comparing Eqs. (8*a*) and (8*b*), we find that $h = -20$ and $k = 15$. Therefore Eq. (8*a*) represents a circle of radius 5 with center located at $(-20, +15)$ (Fig. 13·28*a*).

Figure 13·28 relates the position of the center of the circle to the constants h and k contained in its equation. It will be noted that negative values of h move the curve h units to the right and vice versa. Negative values of k move the curve k units upward and vice versa.

Usually the equation will appear in the expanded form rather than in the factored form of Eq. (8*a*). The following illustrates how such a curve is moved to new axes.

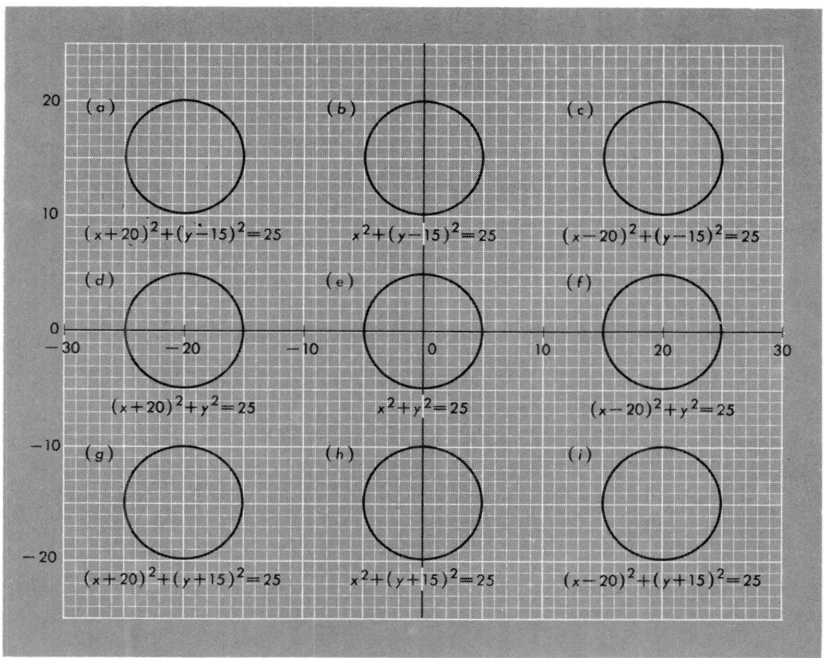

fig. 13·28

example 28 Convert the equation $x^2 + 40x + y^2 - 30y = -600$ to the factored form.

$$\begin{array}{rl} x^2 + 40x \qquad + y^2 - 30y \qquad & = -600 \\ + 400 \qquad\qquad + 225 & = \quad 625 \\ \hline x^2 + 40x + 400 + y^2 - 30y + 225 & = \quad 25 \end{array} \qquad \text{(completing squares)}$$

or

$$(x + 20)^2 + (y - 15)^2 = 25$$

which we recognize as Eq. (8*a*).

It then follows that replacing x by $x' - 20$ and y by $y' + 15$, we obtain Eq. (9).

Graphically then we would draw the circle, radius = 5, with center at the origin and then draw a like circle with center moved 20 units to the left and 15 units up. As a practical expedient, it is equivalent and much easier for most curves to locate new axes about a new origin 20 units to the right and 15 units down from the origin of Eq. (8*a*). The X' and Y' axes for Eq. (9) would be drawn lightly or dashed and the X and Y axes for Eq. (8*a*) in heavy solid lines. Let us illustrate the method of shifting axes by the following example.

example 29 Sketch the curve

$$y^2 - 6y - 4x + 5 = 0 \tag{10}$$

Rearranging and completing the square,

$$\begin{array}{rcl} y^2 - 6y \quad\;\; &=& 4x - 5 \\ 9 &=& \quad\;\; 9 \\ \hline y^2 - 6y + 9 &=& 4x + 4 \end{array}$$

or

$$(y-3)^2 = 4(x+1) \tag{11}$$

This indicates that the "basic equation" is $y'^2 = 4x'$, which is drawn in Fig. 13·29*a*.

According to Example 28, we shall draw on the same area a new set of (heavy solid) axes 1 unit to the right and 3 units down (Fig. 13·29*b*). Thus the curve when related to the X' and Y' axes will have the equation $y'^2 = 4x'$. The same curve when related to the solid X and Y axes will be represented by Eq. (10). The dashed X' and Y' axes may now be erased if desired.

Whenever possible, we should check by computing intercepts. For this purpose Eq. (11) is much more convenient than Eq. (10). It can readily be seen that when $x = 0$, $y - 3 = \pm 2$, and the y intercepts are 1 and 5. When $y = 0$, $9 = 4(x + 1)$ or $x = 5/4$, which checks the sketch.

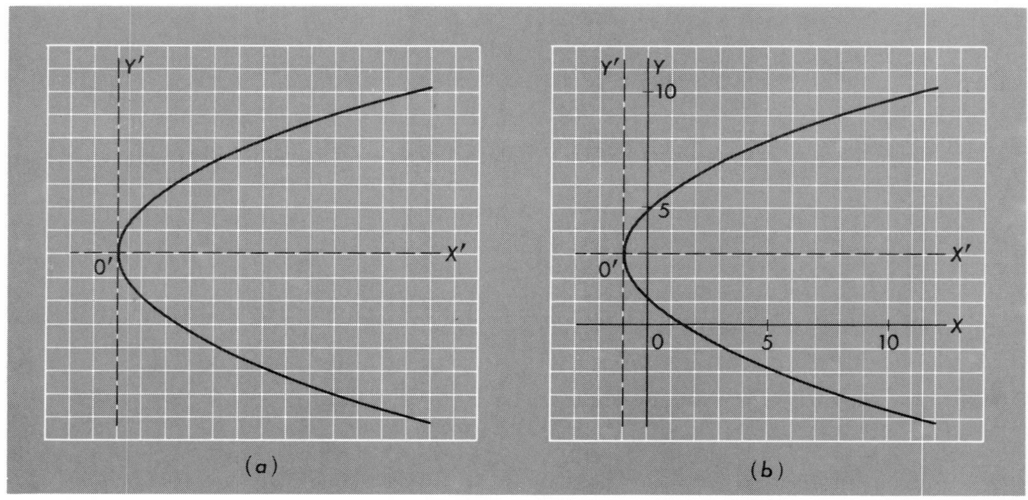

fig. 13·29

example 30 Sketch the curve

$$2x^2 + 3y^2 - 8x + 6y = 7 \tag{12}$$

Completing squares,

$$\begin{array}{rcl} 2x^2 - 8x \quad\;\; + 3y^2 + 6y \quad\;\; &=& 7 \\ 8 \qquad\qquad\quad\; + 3 &=& 11 \\ \hline 2x^2 - 8x + 8 + 3y^2 + 6y + 3 &=& 18 \end{array}$$

or

$$2(x-2)^2 + 3(y+1)^2 = 18 \tag{13}$$

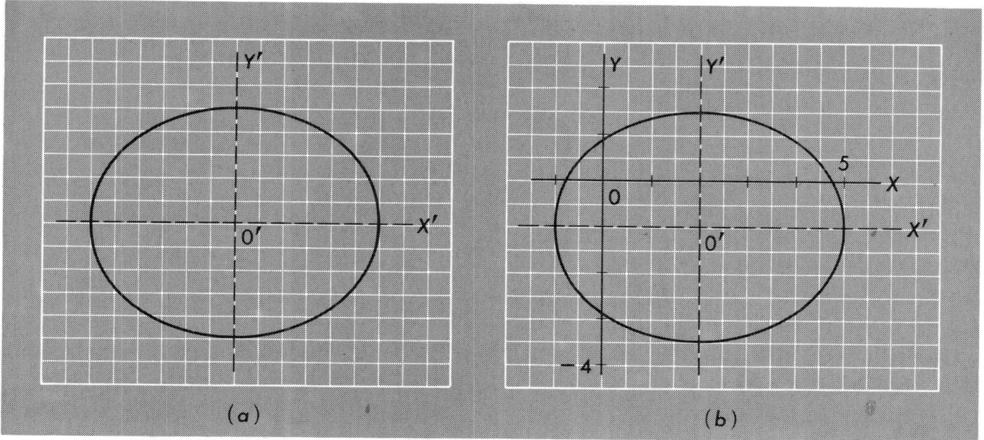

fig. 13·30

This indicates that our basic equation is $2x'^2 + 3y'^2 = 18$ (an ellipse), which we sketch in relation to the dashed X' and Y' axes (Fig. 13·30*a*). We then draw our solid X and Y axes 2 units to the left and 1 unit up, respectively (Fig. 13·30*b*), and check the intercepts for Eq. (13).

The calculation of the x intercepts is shown in detail to emphasize the advantage of using the equation in the form of (13) rather than (12). Substituting $y = 0$,

$$2(x - 2)^2 + 3(1)^2 = 18$$
$$(x - 2)^2 = (18 - 3)/2 = 7.5$$
$$x - 2 = \pm\sqrt{7.5} = \pm 2.74$$

Therefore the x intercepts are 4.74 and −0.74.

In similar fashion the y intercepts are found to be 0.82 and −2.82.

Summary

1. Derive the "basic equation."
2. Sketch the basic equation referred to the dashed axes X' and Y' by the procedure outlined above. The straight line and the parabola will pass through the origin O'. The circle, ellipse, and hyperbola will be symmetric about the origin O'.
3. Draw the solid Y axis h units to the right of the Y' axis if h is positive; to the left if h is negative.
   Draw the solid X axis k units above the X' axis if k is positive; below if k is negative.
4. If possible, check the curve by the method of intercepts.

EXERCISE 6

In Probs. 1 to 12, inclusive, sketch the curves, using the method of translation of axes. Write the basic equation in each case.

1. $y = 1 + 2/x$
2. $(x - 2)^2 + (y + 5)^2 = 49$
3. $y = x^2 - 2x - 15$
4. $y = x^2 - 4x - 21$
5. $(y - 1)(x - 2) = 8$
6. $y = 2(x - 1)^3 + 4$
7. $y^2 - 4y - 9x - 23 = 0$
8. $3x^2 - 4y^2 + 12x + 8y - 28 = 0$
9. $x^2 + y^2 + 2x - 4y - 31 = 0$
10. $x^2 + 5y^2 - 2x - 20y - 28 = 0$
11. $3x^2 + 3y^2 - 12x + 12y - 1 = 0$
12. $xy - x + 2y = 10$
13. A cable supporting a suspension bridge hangs in the form of a parabola. The tops of the supporting towers are 35 ft above the floor of the bridge, and the lowest point of the cable is 5 ft above the bridge. The distance between the supporting towers is 60 ft. Determine the length of a suspending cable (a vertical cable from the bridge to the parabolic cable) 10 ft from one of the supporting towers.
14. An arch has a cross section, as shown in Fig. 13·31, with the curve a semiellipse.
    (a) Determine the lengths of the ordinates to the arch measured from the ground at 2, 4, and 6 ft from the point A.
    (b) If the arch is 10 ft thick, determine the number of cubic yards of concrete necessary in its construction.
15. Sketch a graph of X as a function of the positive values of f if $X = 2\pi fL - 1/(2\pi fC)$ for the following sets of values for L and C. Determine algebraically and from your graph the value of f that makes X zero.
    (a) $L = 0.00025$ henry, $C = 10^{-10}$ farad (data for a radio circuit).
    (b) $L = 1$ henry, $C = 7(10^{-6})$ farad (data for a power circuit).

    NOTE: This equation gives the net "reactance" X in an a-c circuit containing inductance L and capacitance C (as well as resistance R) in series with a sinusoidal voltage of frequency f.

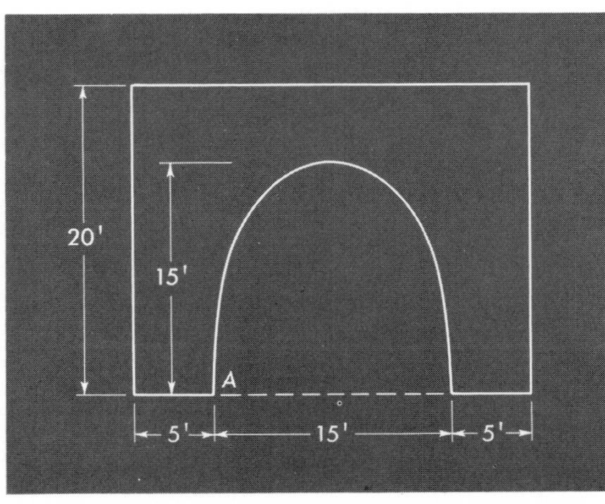

fig. 13·31

16. The following is given as a graphical method of determining the roots of the equation $x^2 + px + q = 0$. On a coordinate area locate the points $A(0,1)$ and $B(p,q)$. (Be sure to take account of the signs of p and q.) Draw the circle whose diameter is AB. If the equation has real roots, the circle will intersect the X axis at points k_1 and k_2. Show that the factors of $x^2 + px + q$ are $x + k_1$ and $x + k_2$ and that the roots are therefore $-k_1$ and $-k_2$.

13·14 Graphical solution

An approximate graphical solution of a system of two quadratic equations (or one quadratic and one linear equation) may be obtained by sketching their loci. Estimate the coordinates of the points of intersection or tangency of the two curves. The coordinates of each such point satisfying both equations constitute a solution.

It is evident that two quadratic curves intersect in at most four points, while a system consisting of one linear and one quadratic curve has at most two real solutions.

Figure 13·32

a. Four real distinct roots

b. Four real roots—two identical

c. Two real roots—two imaginary

d. Four imaginary roots

Figure 13·33

a. Two imaginary roots

b. Two real identical roots

c. Two real distinct roots

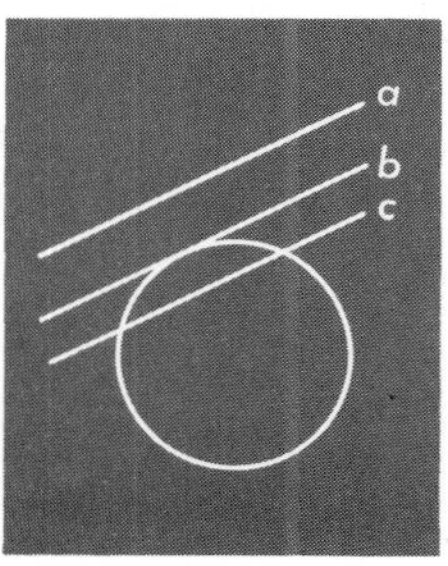

fig. 13·33

fig. 13·32

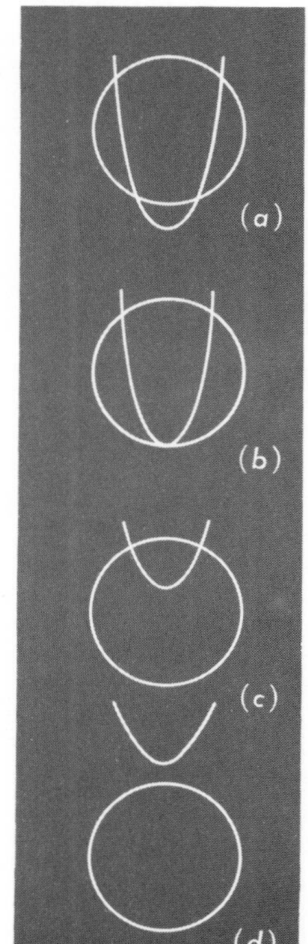

More accurate information may be obtained by plotting more points in the vicinity of the intersection, and often it will be advisable to plot the critical portion to a larger scale.

example 31 Solve graphically the system

$$x^2 - 4x + y^2 - 4y = 9 \tag{14}$$
$$y = x^2 - 3 \tag{15}$$

Using the methods of Sec. 13·13, we can write Eq. (14) as

$$(x - 2)^2 + (y - 2)^2 = 17 \tag{16}$$

This is sketched in Fig. 13·34*a*, where it appears as a circle of radius $\sqrt{17}$ and center at (2,2). In the same figure is shown the graph of Eq. (15), a parabola shifted 3 units downward. From the sketch it is apparent that we can confine our point-by-point plotting to areas in the vicinity of points *A*, *B*, and *C*.

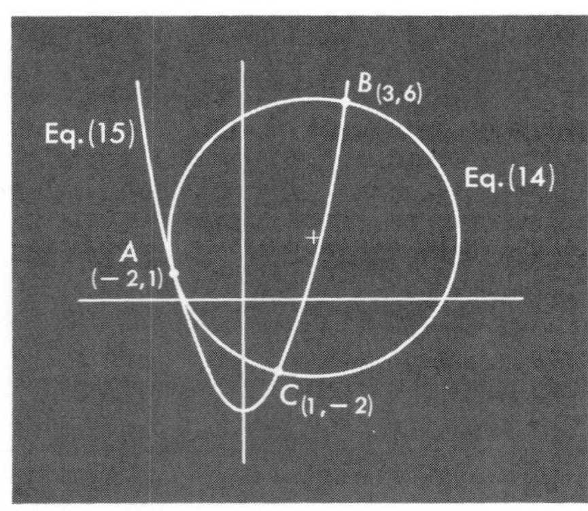

fig. 13·34a

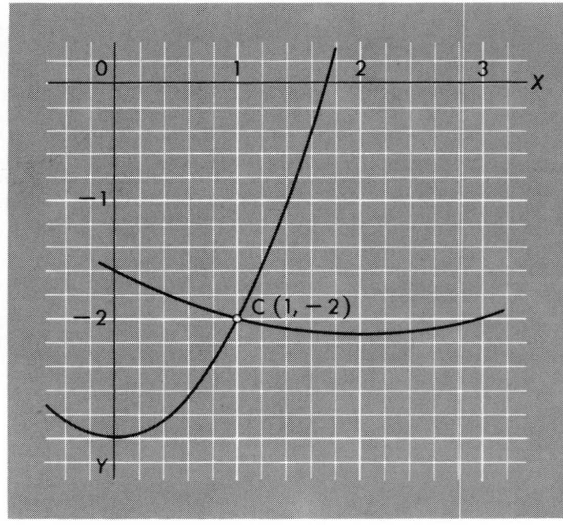

fig. 13·34b

The detailed plotting is shown in Fig. 13·34*b* for point *C*, with Eq. (16) used to obtain points on the circle, as described in Sec. 13·13. Of course, in the case of the circle, it would be preferable to use a compass. The point of tangency *A* corresponds to two real identical roots. Hence the solution is

$$\begin{aligned} A:&\quad x = -2, y = 1 \\ &\quad x = -2, y = 1 \\ B:&\quad x = 3, y = 6 \\ C:&\quad x = 1, y = -2 \end{aligned}$$

EXERCISE 7

Solve the following systems graphically. Sketch the curves, and then plot critical areas in detail estimating any nonintegral answers to two significant figures.

1. $xy = 6$
   $3x - y = 7$
2. $x^2 + y^2 = 20$
   $x - y = 6$
3. $y = x^2 - 4x - 1$
   $2x + y = -2$
4. $x^2 + 4y^2 = 36$
   $2x - 3y = 18$
5. $x^2 - y^2 = 9$
   $5x + 4y = -9$
6. $3x^2 + 3y^2 = 40$
   $3x + 2y = -18$
7. $x^2 + y^2 + 6x - 8y = 0$
   $16x^2 + 9y^2 = 144$
8. $xy = -12$
   $x^2 + y^2 = 25$
9. $y = x^2 - 6$
   $x = y^2 - 6$
10. $4x^2 + 9y^2 = 36$
    $9y - x^2 = 0$
11. $4y^2 - x^2 = 25$
    $x^2 + y^2 = 4$
12. $9x^2 + 25y^2 = 144$
    $xy = 6$

13·15 Algebraic solutions of quadratic systems

Since the graphical solution of a quadratic system leads to only approximate real solutions and yields no imaginary solutions at all, we shall require algebraic solutions for more accurate results. Our study of algebraic solutions will be confined to the simple types of systems.

13·16 Solution of systems consisting of one linear and one quadratic equation

In order to solve a system consisting of one linear and one quadratic equation, solve the linear equation for one unknown in terms of the other and substitute the expression in the quadratic equation. Solve the resulting quadratic equation in one unknown and substitute each value in turn in the linear equation to find values of the unknown.

example 32 Solve the system

$$x^2 - 3xy - 2y^2 = 4 \qquad (17)$$
$$4x + y = 5 \qquad (18)$$

Solve Eq. (18) for y:

$$y = 5 - 4x \qquad (19)$$

(Note that we chose y in preference to x because of the simpler resulting expression.) Substituting Eq. (19) in Eq. (17), we obtain

$$x^2 - 3x(5 - 4x) - 2(5 - 4x)^2 = 4$$

Simplifying,

$$19x^2 - 65x + 54 = 0 \tag{20}$$

Solving Eq. (20), we find

$$x = 2 \qquad \text{and} \qquad x = {}^{27}\!/_{19}$$

Substituting these values successively in Eq. (19), we obtain

$$y = -3 \qquad \text{and} \qquad y = -{}^{13}\!/_{19}$$

The solutions are therefore

$$x = 2,\ y = -3 \qquad \text{and} \qquad x = {}^{27}\!/_{19},\ y = -{}^{13}\!/_{19}$$

EXERCISE 8

In each of Probs. 1 to 10 solve for x and y algebraically.

1. $xy = 48$
   $3x - y = 0$
2. $xy = -36$
   $4y + x = 0$
3. $xy = 80$
   $4x - 5y = 0$
4. $xy = -96$
   $3x + 2y = 0$
5. $x^2 + y^2 = 25$
   $x + y = -1$
6. $x^2 + y^2 = 100$
   $x - y = 2$
7. $x^2 - y^2 = 40$
   $x + 2y = 13$
8. $x^2 - 2y^2 = -34$
   $5x - y = 15$
9. $x^2 + xy + y^2 = 12$
   $5x + 2y = 2$
10. $5x^2 - xy = 15$
    $3x + 2y = 26$

13·17 Equations of the form $ax^2 + by^2 = c$

When both equations have the form $ax^2 + by^2 = c$, the system is linear in x^2 and y^2 and can be solved for them by the usual procedure applicable to systems of linear equations. From the values of x^2 and y^2, usually four solutions will be obtained which, if real, will correspond to four points symmetrically grouped about the origin.

example 33 Solve the system (Fig. 13·35)

$$5x^2 + 7y^2 = 47 \tag{21}$$
$$6x^2 - 10y^2 = 15 \tag{22}$$

Multiply Eq. (21) by 6:

$$30x^2 + 42y^2 = 282 \tag{23}$$

Multiply Eq. (22) by 5:

$$30x^2 - 50y^2 = 75 \tag{24}$$

Subtract Eq. (24) from Eq. (23):

$$92y^2 = 207$$

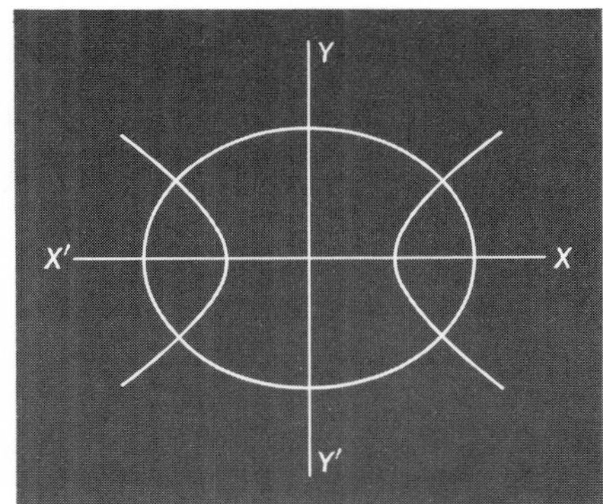

fig. 13·35

Solving for y,

$$y = \pm 3/2$$

Substitute $y^2 = 9/4$ in Eq. (22):

$$6x^2 - 10(9/4) = 15$$
$$x = \pm 5/2$$

There are four solutions:

$$x = 5/2,\ y = 3/2 \qquad x = 5/2,\ y = -3/2$$
$$x = -5/2,\ y = 3/2 \qquad x = -5/2,\ y = -3/2$$

EXERCISE 9

Solve algebraically for all values of x and y.

1. $3x^2 + y^2 = 12$, $x^2 + 2y^2 = 19$
2. $2x^2 - 3y^2 = 5$, $4x^2 + y^2 = 17$
3. $5x^2 - 2y^2 = 20$, $x^2 + 3y^2 = 4$
4. $2y^2 - 3x^2 = 18$, $x^2 + y^2 = 9$
5. $4x^2 + 4y^2 = 15$, $6x^2 - 5y^2 = 20$
6. $6x^2 + 6y^2 = 25$, $9y^2 - 5x^2 = 30$
7. $4x^2 - y^2 = 20$, $2y^2 - x^2 = 8$
8. $3x^2 + 8y^2 = 20$, $5x^2 + 5y^2 = 28$

13·18 Elimination of constants

A quadratic system in two unknowns in which all terms containing the variables are of the second degree may often be solved by first eliminating the constant terms from the original system. The method is as follows:

1. *Using the method of addition or subtraction, combine the two equations, eliminating the constant terms and obtaining a single equation of the type*

$$Ax^2 + Bxy + Cy^2 = 0$$

2. *Factor this quadratic equation and express one of the unknowns as a multiple of the other.*
3. *Substitute the relations in step 2 successively in one of the original equations, and solve the resulting equations in one unknown.*
4. *Substitute in step 2 the values obtained in step 3 to determine the other unknown.*

example 34 Solve the system

$$2x^2 - 3xy + 2y^2 = 28 \tag{25}$$
$$4x^2 + 3xy - y^2 = 21 \tag{26}$$

Multiplying Eq. (26) by 4 and Eq. (25) by 3, we obtain

$$16x^2 + 12xy - 4y^2 = 84 \tag{27}$$
$$6x^2 - 9xy + 6y^2 = 84 \tag{28}$$

Subtracting,

$$10x^2 + 21xy - 10y^2 = 0 \tag{29}$$

Factoring Eq. (29), we obtain

$$(5x - 2y)(2x + 5y) = 0 \tag{30}$$

From Eq. (30) we get two solutions:

$$x = \tfrac{2}{5}y \tag{31}$$
$$x = -\tfrac{5}{2}y \tag{32}$$

Substituting Eq. (31) in Eq. (25), we obtain

$$2(\tfrac{2}{5}y)^2 - 3y(\tfrac{2}{5}y) + 2y^2 = 28$$
$$8y^2 - 30y^2 + 50y^2 = 700$$

from which

$$y^2 = 25$$
$$y = \pm 5$$

Since $x = \frac{2}{5}y$, the corresponding values of x are ± 2. Substituting Eq. (32) in Eq. (25), we have

$$2(-\tfrac{5}{2}y)^2 - 3y(-\tfrac{5}{2}y) + 2y^2 = 28$$
$$25y^2 + 15y^2 + 4y^2 = 56$$

from which

$$y^2 = \tfrac{14}{11}$$
$$y = \pm \tfrac{1}{11}\sqrt{154}$$

Since $x = -\frac{5}{2}y$, the corresponding values of x are $\mp \frac{5}{22}\sqrt{154}$. Pairing the values of x and y, we obtain

	FROM $x = \frac{2}{5}y$		FROM $x = -\frac{5}{2}y$	
x	2	-2	$\frac{5}{22}\sqrt{154}$	$-\frac{5}{22}\sqrt{154}$
y	5	-5	$-\frac{1}{11}\sqrt{154}$	$\frac{1}{11}\sqrt{154}$

EXERCISE 10

Solve Probs. 1 to 8, inclusive, by eliminating the constant terms.

1. $x^2 + xy = 3$
   $xy + y^2 = 10$

2. $4x^2 + 3xy + y^2 = 22$
   $x^2 + xy = 4$

3. $x^2 - 8xy + 17y^2 = 5$
   $x^2 - 5xy + 9y^2 = 15$

4. $2x^2 + 3xy + 2y^2 = 64$
   $x^2 - 6xy + 6y^2 = -8$

5. $(2x - 9y)(x - 2y) = -12$
   $(2x + y)(x - 3y) = 16$

6. $x + y = \dfrac{20}{x}$
   $x - y = \dfrac{3}{y}$

7. $3x^2 + 3xy + y^2 = 7$
   $x^2 + 11xy + 5y^2 = 19$

8. $4x + 5y = \dfrac{84}{x}$
   $3x + 16y = \dfrac{28}{y}$

9. In electrical engineering occur the two simultaneous equations

$$\frac{SK}{K^2 - 1} = R \qquad S\left(\frac{K^2 + 1}{K^2 - 1}\right) = D \qquad (K \text{ cannot be } \pm 1)$$

Eliminate S and solve for K in terms of D and R. Also show that the two answers for K are reciprocals.

14
nonlinear empirical equations

In Chap. 6 we discussed empirical linear equations. We shall now describe how to derive empirical equations to fit curved lines. In order to avail ourselves of the convenient relationships of the straight line, we shall learn how to convert a nonlinear relationship to a linear relationship whenever possible.

14·1 Rectification of data

If a set of data can be expressed by an equation whose graph is a straight line on some type of coordinate paper, plotting and interpolation will be simplified. The process of conversion to an equation of linear characteristics is called *rectification.*

Extrapolation of a graph beyond the range of the given data is made possible by rectification but is a risky procedure and should be attempted only as a last resort. In fact, it may prove necessary to represent various portions of the curve by different equations.

Short intervals of a given curve may often be expressed by a variety of equations. These equations may or may not be a rational expression of the law involved. In any event, we should expect our equation to be dimensionally sound with respect to the variables involved; otherwise its utility is likely to be sharply limited.

14·2 Procedure for rectification of data

In general, our first step in rectification of data is to plot them on ordinary cross-section paper. This plot will often indicate the relationship involved.

If the graph exhibits only a slight curvature, the *polynomial* relationship $y = a + bx + cx^2 + dx^3 + \cdots$ should be tested first. If a sharp curvature is displayed, the power and exponential types should also be investigated. It is obvious that we must have sufficient data to set up as many equations as there are constants to be determined. If there are more points available than constants to be determined, we shall use the method of averages. However, it should be stressed that the method of averages can be applied only to data which can be represented by a straight line. Occasionally, when but few points are known, they can be shown to fit more than one type of equation.

14·3 Parabolic relationship

It can be stated that, in general, through any three points not in the same straight line, one, and only one, parabola of the general equation $y = ax^2 + bx + c$ may be passed. The constants a, b, and c are determined by substituting the coordinates of the given points in the general equation and solving simultaneously the three resulting equations.

example 1 Determine the constants of the equation $y = ax^2 + bx + c$ which passes through the points (5,6); (8,3); (10,−1).

Substituting the pairs of coordinates successively in the general equation, we have

$$\begin{aligned} 6 &= a(5)^2 + b(5) + c & \text{or} \quad 6 &= 25a + 5b + c \\ 3 &= a(8)^2 + b(8) + c & \text{or} \quad 3 &= 64a + 8b + c \\ -1 &= a(10)^2 + b(10) + c & \text{or} \quad -1 &= 100a + 10b + c \end{aligned}$$

Solution of this system of equations yields $a = -0.2$, $b = 1.6$, $c = 3$.

Hence the required equation is $y = -0.2x^2 + 1.6x + 3$, which passes through the three given points.

EXERCISE 1

Determine the constants of the equation $y = ax^2 + bx + c$ which passes through the three given points in each case.

1. (3,−5); (5,7); (9,55)
2. (1,−3); (4,30); (7,99)
3. (2,30); (5,18); (7,0)
4. (2,5); (4,17); (6,21)
5. (5,1); (17,10); (26,20)
6. (a) Show that a parabola $x = py^2 + qy + r$ may be passed through the points given in Prob. 4. (b) Sketch both curves between $x = -2$ and $x = +10$ for comparison.

We make no attempt in this text to rectify the polynomial relationship. For this reason we cannot take averages but instead resort to the method of selected points. In passing, it is possible, when dealing with a quadratic function $y = ax^2 + bx + c$, to plot Δy against x when the values of Δx are uniform. In the ideal case the relation is exactly linear

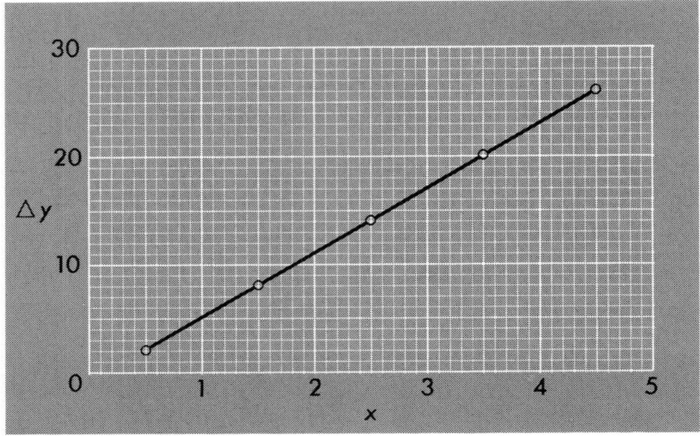

fig. 14·1

(see Fig. 14·1 and the accompanying table). Less precise experimental data may be smoothed as in Sec. 6·17. In effect, by smoothing, we approximate the best values of the constants a and b, but the best value of c remains to be found (by trial and error). However, for this and more refined methods of deriving the empirical equation for a polynomial function, more advanced textbooks dealing with experimental data must be consulted.

x	y	Δy
0	−2	
		2
1	0	
		8
2	8	
		14
3	22	
		20
4	42	
		26
5	68	

(Equation:
$y = 3x^2 - x - 2$)

14·4 General polynomial relationship

If, for evenly spaced values of x, the second, third, or nth differences of y are reasonably constant, a second, third, or, in general, nth degree function of x is indicated. If the x values contained in the data are not evenly spaced, the data should be plotted and the ordinates corresponding to evenly spaced abscissas should be read off from the graph.

example 2 The following data are thought to represent y as a polynomial function of x. Determine the equation best fitting the data.

x	10	20	30	40	50	60	70	80
y	11.55	14.79	18.31	22.55	27.80	34.46	42.88	53.42

Rearranging the data so that successive differences in y may be better shown, we have

x	y	Δy	$\Delta^2 y$	$\Delta^3 y$	$\Delta^4 y$
10	11.55				
		3.24			
20	14.79		0.28		
		3.52		0.44	
30	18.31		0.72		−0.15
		4.24		0.29	
40	22.55		1.01		0.11
		5.25		0.40	
50	27.80		1.41		−0.05
		6.66		0.35	
60	34.46		1.76		0.01
		8.42		0.36	
70	42.88		2.12		
		10.54			
80	53.42				

Since the column of third differences ($\Delta^3 y$) shows the least variation, we shall be dealing with a cubic equation of the form $y = a + bx + cx^2 + dx^3$. We shall need four independent equations in order to determine the four constants a, b, c, and d. In order to cover the range of the data we shall select the points $x = 20, 40, 60, 80$. If the data indicate sharp curvature over any range, this range should be well represented; correspondingly selected points can be more widely spaced over a flat portion of the curve.

The equations in this example will therefore be:

$$\begin{aligned} 14.79 &= a + 20b + (20)^2c + (20)^3d \\ 22.55 &= a + 40b + (40)^2c + (40)^3d \\ 34.46 &= a + 60b + (60)^2c + (60)^3d \\ 53.42 &= a + 80b + (80)^2c + (80)^3d \end{aligned}$$

The solution of this system of equations is

$$a = 8.28 \qquad b = 0.343 \qquad c = -2.06 \times 10^{-3} \qquad d = 6.04 \times 10^{-5}$$

Accordingly, the desired equation is

$$y = 8.28 + 0.343x - 2.06(10)^{-3}x^2 + 6.04(10)^{-5}x^3$$

14·5 Power functions

Typical of a *power function* is the equation $y = bx^a$, where a and b are constants. In the simplest case where only two points are given and the relation is known to be a power function, we may solve the equations $y_1 = bx_1{}^a$ and $y_2 = bx_2{}^a$ simultaneously.

example 3 Derive the constants of the equation $y = bx^a$ satisfied by the points (2,6) and (10,2).

Substituting data in the general equation,

$$6 = b(2)^a \quad (1)$$
$$2 = b(10)^a \quad (2)$$

Dividing (1) by (2), we obtain $3 = (0.2)^a$.

Taking logs,

$$\log 3 = a \log 0.2$$
$$0.47712 = a(0.30103 - 1) = -0.69897a$$
$$a = -0.6826$$

Substituting in (2),

$$2 = b(10)^{-0.6826} = b(0.2077)$$
$$b = 9.629$$

Therefore our equation is

$$y = 9.63x^{-0.683}$$

In order to rectify experimental data represented by a power function, we take logarithms of both sides of the equation $y = bx^a$.

We obtain

$$\log y = \log b + a \log x \quad (3)$$

Substituting Y for $\log y$, B for $\log b$, and X for $\log x$, we obtain

$$Y = B + aX$$

where B is also a constant.

The similarity between this equation and the straight-line equation $y = ax + b$ will at once be apparent.

Let us illustrate this relationship with the pressure-volume relationship for ethane gas $PV^{1.22} = K$. In this instance we shall deal with 40 cu ft of ethane at one atmosphere pressure, from which we obtain

$$1(40)^{1.22} = K = 90$$

In order to do this we shall first rearrange our equation to read $P = 90V^{-1.22}$ and then tabulate values of V, P, and their logarithms.

V	P	$\log V = X$	$\log P = Y$
1	90	0	1.954
2	38.7	0.301	1.587
5	12.6	0.699	1.101
10	5.42	1.000	0.734
20	2.33	1.301	0.367
40	1.00	1.602	0.000

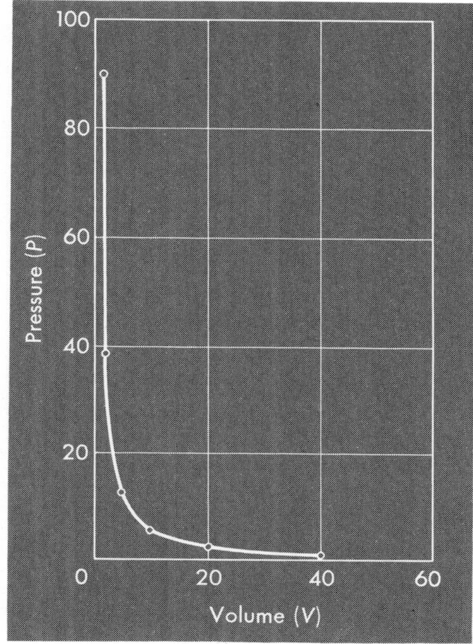

fig. 14·2

The plot of V against P on ordinary cross-section paper is shown in Fig. 14·2, while the plot of X against Y is illustrated in Fig. 14·3.

Now, if we use logarithmic scales for both variables (log-log paper), we shall retain the linear feature of Fig. 14·3 and yet be able to plot values of V and P directly without looking up logarithms (Fig.

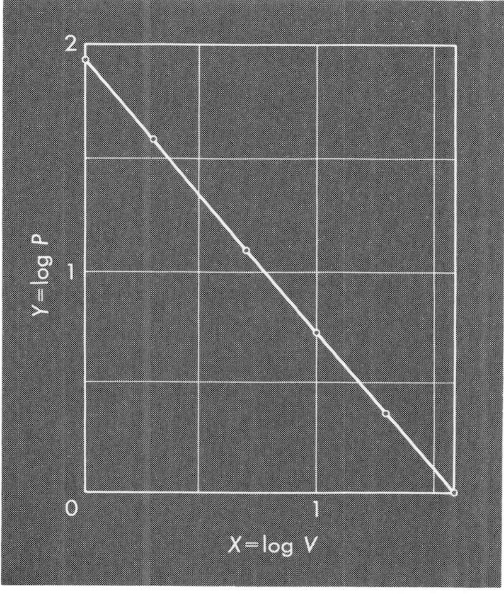

fig. 14·3

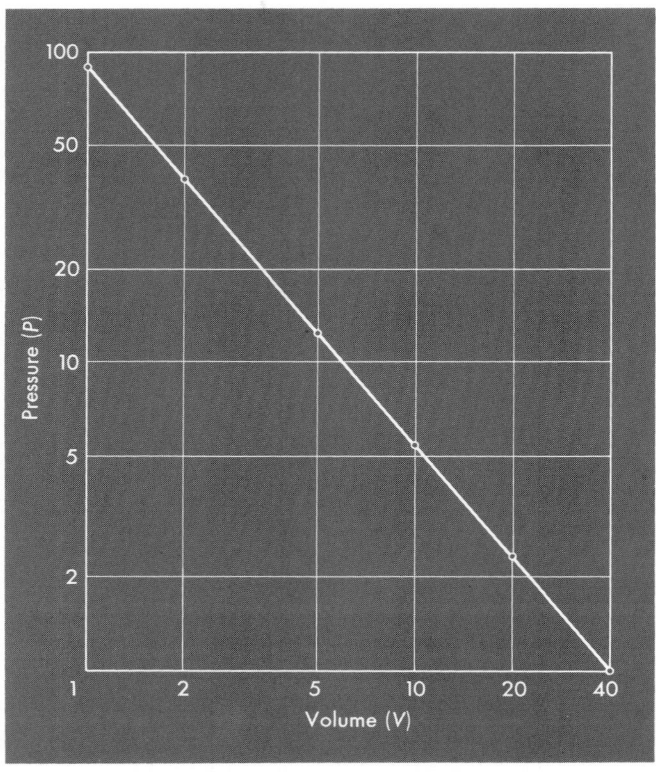

fig. 14·4

14·4). We note that the y intercept indicates a multiplying factor (that is, $y = b$ when $x = 1$) while the slope a of the line represents the power of the independent variable. Note that the slope is determined by measuring vertical and horizontal distances in actual inches, not in scale units.

example 4 Determine the empirical formula corresponding to the following data:

x	1.5	2.2	3.1	4.4	7.4	12.5
y	9.8	8.0	6.8	5.7	4.4	3.4

The plot of these data on ordinary cross-section paper has a definite curvature whereas the plot on log-log paper is reasonably straight, indicating a relationship of the type $y = bx^a$. Inspection on this straight line indicates a y intercept of about 12 ($=b$) and an approximate slope of $-\frac{1}{2}$ ($= a$). Hence we may venture to predict that our equation will be approximately $y = 12/\sqrt{x}$.

A more accurate result may be obtained by employing the method of averages analogous to that illustrated in Sec. 6·17. In this type of problem, however, we shall take averages of the logarithms as indicated in the following procedure:

x	y	*Average* log x	log x	log y	*Average* log y
1.5	9.8		0.176	0.991	
2.2	8.0	0.336	0.342	0.903	0.909
3.1	6.8		0.491	0.833	
4.4	5.7		0.643	0.756	
7.4	4.4	0.870	0.869	0.643	0.644
12.5	3.4		1.097	0.532	

Three-place logarithms will be accurate enough for the data.

Substituting the average logarithms in Eq. (3), we obtain

$$0.909 = \log b + 0.336a \tag{4}$$
$$0.644 = \log b + 0.870a \tag{5}$$

Subtracting (5) from (4),

$$0.265 = -0.534a$$

and solving for a,

$$a = -0.497$$

Substituting $a = -0.497$ in Eq. (5), we have

$$0.644 = \log b + (0.870)(-0.497)$$
$$1.076 = \log b$$
$$b = 11.9$$

Hence the required equation is $y = 11.9x^{-0.497}$, which was closely predicted by inspection of the graph.

EXERCISE 2

1. Plot on a common area of log-log paper the equations (a) $y = x$, (b) $y = x^2$, (c) $y = 1/x$, (d) $y = \sqrt{x}$, (e) $y = 1/\sqrt{x}$. Label each line with its equation.
2. Same as Prob. 1 for the equations (a) $y = 5x^2$, (b) $y = \pi x^2$, (c) $y = 1.5x^2$, (d) $y = x^2/2$.
3. Same as Prob. 1 for the equations (a) $y = x^3/4$, (b) $y = 4/x^2$, (c) $y = x^{3/2}$, (d) $y = 2\sqrt{x}$, (e) $y = x^{-1/3}$, (f) $y = 5\sqrt[3]{x}$.

14·6 Exponential functions

An exponential function is characterized by a constant to a variable power. It may be represented by the type equation $y = ba^x$, where a and b are constants. In the simplest case, where only two points are given and the relation is known to be exponential, we may solve the equations $y_1 = ba^{x_1}$ and $y_2 = ba^{x_2}$ simultaneously.

example 5 Derive the constants of the equation $y = ba^x$ satisfied by the points (4,1.5) and (14,6).

Substituting data in the general equation,

$$1.5 = ba^4 \tag{6a}$$
$$6 = ba^{14} \tag{6b}$$

Dividing (6*b*) by (6*a*), we obtain

$$4 = a^{10}$$

It follows that

$$a = \sqrt[10]{4} = 1.1487$$

Substituting the value of *a* just found in (6*a*),

$$1.5 = b(1.1487)^4$$
$$b = 0.8615$$

Therefore our equation is

$$y = 0.862(1.149)^x$$

In order to rectify exponential experimental data we take logs of both sides of the equation $y = ba^x$, obtaining

$$\log y = \log b + x \log a \tag{7}$$

Since log b and log a are constants, it follows that a straight line should result if y values are located on a logarithmic scale and x values on a uniform scale.

To confirm this statement, consider the equation $S = 10(1.03)^n$ which represents the amount of \$10 at continuously compounded interest for n years. The rate is equivalent to 3 per cent compounded annually. It has been plotted on ordinary graph paper in Fig. 14·5 and on semi-logarithmic paper in Fig. 14·6.

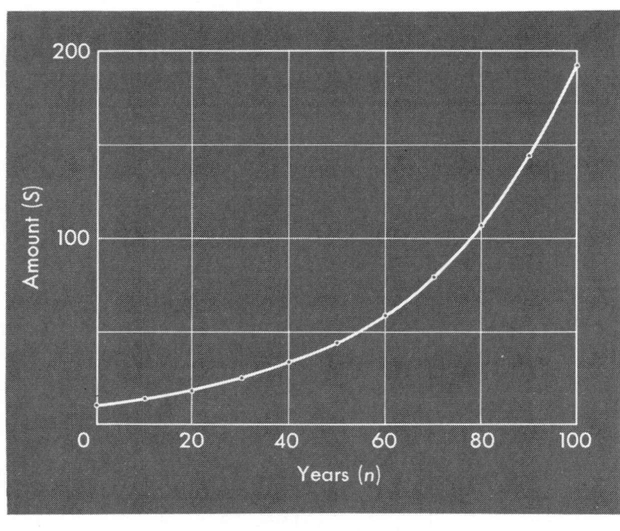

fig. 14·5

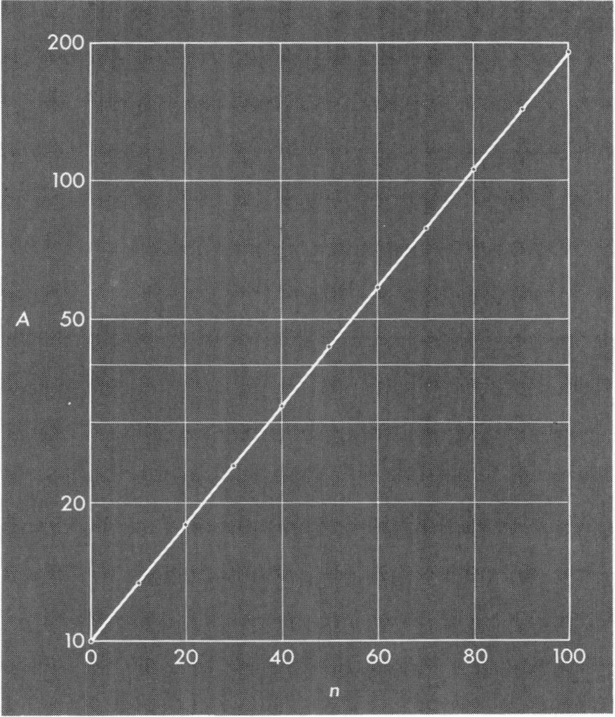

fig. 14·6

Returning to our type equation $y = ba^x$, it will be seen that the constant b corresponds to the y intercept just as it does in the power relationship. Also, while we instinctively realize that the slope of the graph on semilog paper is somehow related to the value of the constant a, it is not immediately apparent how a can be determined by measuring the slope of the line.

Referring to Fig. 14·7, let $P(x, y_0)$, $Q(x + 1, y_1)$, and $R(x + n, y_n)$ represent points on the graph $y = ba^x$.

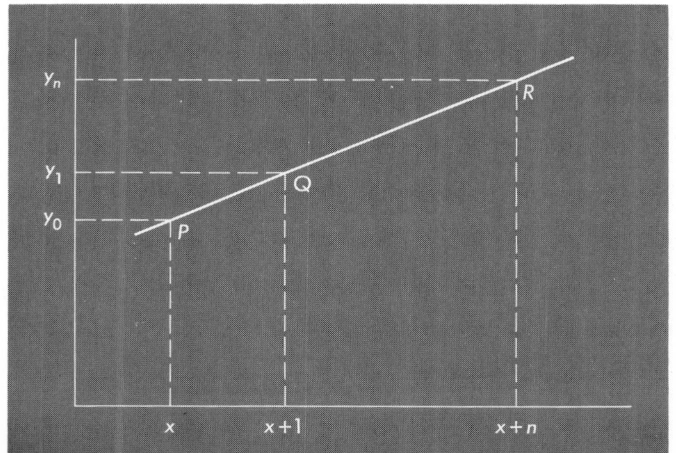

fig 14·7

If we substitute the coordinates of Q in the type equation, we obtain

$$y_1 = ba^{x+1} \tag{8}$$

Repeating for point P, we have

$$y_0 = ba^x \tag{9}$$

Dividing (8) by (9),

$$\frac{y_1}{y_0} = \frac{ba^{x+1}}{ba^x} = a \tag{10}$$

Hence if $P(x,y_0)$ and $Q(x + 1, y_1)$ represent any two points on the graph whose abscissas differ by 1, the ratio of the ordinates y_1/y_0 (in scale units) will be a measure of a.

If the slope of the line is nearly horizontal, greater accuracy may be obtained by taking the more widely spaced points $P(x,y_0)$ and $R(x + n, y_n)$.

Substituting the coordinates of R in the type equation, we have

$$y_n = ba^{x+n} \tag{11}$$

Dividing (11) by (9),

$$\frac{y_n}{y_0} = \frac{ba^{x+n}}{ba^x} = a^n$$

or

$$a = \sqrt[n]{\frac{y_n}{y_0}} \tag{12}$$

From this we conclude that *if* $P(x, y_0)$ *and* $R(x + n, y_n)$ *represent any two points on the graph whose abscissas differ by* n, *the* n*th root of the ratio of the ordinates* y_n/y_0 *will equal the value of* a.

example 6 Determine the equation of the type $y = ba^x$, which best fits the following data:

x	0.8	2.0	2.75	3.7	5.0	6.45
y	3.5	5.85	8.0	12.0	21.0	39.0

Plotting the ordinate of these points on a logarithmic scale and the abscissas on a uniform scale, we find we have a well-defined linear relationship. Extension of the line indicates a y intercept of about 2.5, the approximate value of b.

Reading the ordinates corresponding to two consecutive values of x, say, 1 and 2, we find 3.8 and 5.85, respectively. The ratio $5.85/3.8 = 1.54$, the approximate value of a. Hence we may predict that our relationship may be roughly represented by the equation

$$y = 2.5(1.54)^x \tag{13}$$

It is often desirable to express an exponential function as $y = be^{kx}$. In this example the equation

$$y = 2.5(1.54)^x \qquad \text{becomes} \qquad y = 2.5e^{0.432x} \tag{14}$$

Note that Eq. (13) indicates a constant rate of growth of y of 54 per cent per unit increase in x, whereas Eq. (14) indicates that the equivalent instantaneous rate is 43.2 per cent (Sec. 11·8).

In using the method of averages, a glance at Eq. (7) will show that we should average the logarithms of y and should average x directly.

Average x	x	y	$\log y$	*Average* $\log y$
	0.8	3.5	0.544	
1.85	2.0	5.85	0.767	0.738
	2.75	8.0	0.903	
	3.7	12.0	1.079	
5.05	5.0	21.0	1.322	1.331
	6.45	39.0	1.591	

Substituting our average values in Eq. (7), we obtain

$$1.331 = \log b + 5.05 \log a \tag{15}$$

$$0.738 = \log b + 1.85 \log a \tag{16}$$

Subtracting (16) from (15),

$$\begin{aligned} 0.593 &= 3.20 \log a \\ 0.1853 &= \log a \\ a &= 1.53 \end{aligned}$$

Substituting $\log a = 0.1853$ in Eq. (16), we have

$$\begin{aligned} 0.738 &= \log b + 1.85(0.1853) \\ 0.395 &= \log b \\ b &= 2.48 \end{aligned}$$

Therefore the equation is $y = 2.48(1.53)^x$, which agrees well with the result anticipated by inspection.

EXERCISE 3

1. Plot on a common area of semilog paper the equations (a) $y = 2^x$, (b) $y = 5^x$, (c) $y = 1.5^x$, (d) $y = 0.5^x$, (e) $y = 2^{-x}$, (f) $y = e^x$. Label each line with its equation.
2. Same as Prob. 1 for the equations (a) $y = 5(1.5)^x$, (b) $y = 2(1.5)^x$, (c) $y = 0.7(1.5)^x$.
3. Same as Prob. 1 for the equations (a) $y = 3(2)^x$, (b) $y = 0.2(5)^x$, (c) $y = 5(2)^{-x}$, (d) $y = 4e^{-x}$, (e) $y = 0.5e^x$, (f) $y = e^{-0.47x}$. (This is a constant percentage depreciation curve. Instantaneous rate is 47 per cent, annual rate is 37½ per cent, initial value = 1.)

EXERCISE 4

Referring to Figs. 14·8 and 14·9, write, by inspection, the equation for each line a through n, inclusive.

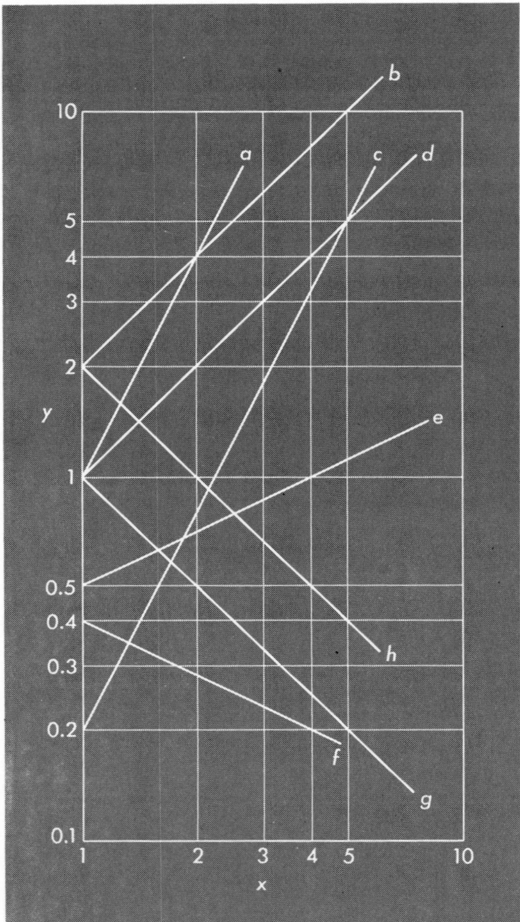

fig. 14·8

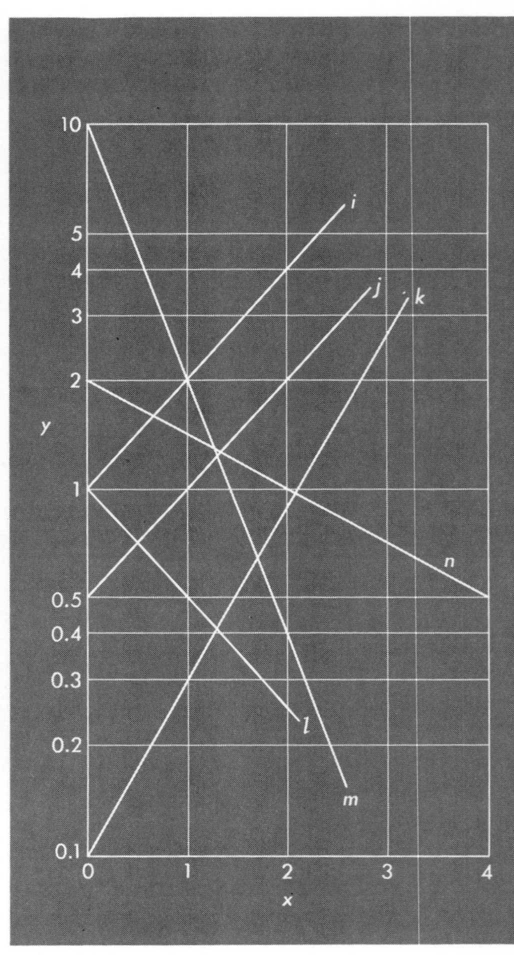

fig. 14·9

14·7 Summary of suggestions for determining the nature of the relationship between the variables

1. Plot the data on ordinary cross-section paper. A straight line indicates the relationship $y = mx + b$.
2. If the graph is almost linear, try the polynomial equation $y = a + bx + cx^2 + \cdots$. If this fails, try $x = a + by + cy^2 + \cdots$.
3. If the graph shows considerable curvature, plot the data on log-log paper. A straight line indicates a power relationship $y = bx^a$.

4. Plot the data on semilog paper with y plotted on the log scale. A straight line indicates an equation of the type $y = ba^x$. However, it may happen that the curvature is not reduced; it may even be accentuated. In this event reverse the positions of x and y and plot x on the log scale, in which case a straight line indicates the type equation $x = ba^y$.

This procedure is designed to cover only the simpler cases illustrated. More involved relationships are beyond the scope of this text. They are covered in detail in more specialized works on empirical equations and curve fitting, such as the following:

Davis, D. S.: "Empirical Equations and Nomography," McGraw-Hill Book Company, New York, 1943.

Lipka, J.: "Graphical and Mechanical Computation," John Wiley & Sons, Inc., New York, 1918.

Worthing, Archie G., and J. Geffner: "Treatment of Experimental Data," John Wiley & Sons, Inc., New York, 1943.

EXERCISE 5

In Probs. 1 to 13 the type of equation fitting the data has been indicated. Determine the best values of the constants of the equations.

1. (a) Evaluate the constants a and b in the equation $y = ba^x$ if $y = 2$ when $x = 2$ and $y = 50$ when $x = 12$.
   (b) Transform your answer in (a) to the form $y = be^{kx}$.
2. Repeat Prob. 1 if $y = 10$ when $x = 0.2$ and $y = 0.2$ when $x = 1.1$.
3. Evaluate the constants a and b in the equation $y = bx^a$ if $y = 370$ when $x = 4.4$ and $y = 830$ when $x = 20$.
4. Repeat Prob. 3 if $y = 7$ when $x = 16.5$ and $y = 1.6$ when $x = 38$.
5. The following data give the discharge Q (cu ft per sec) over a rectangular weir for a given head H (ft).

H	0.166	0.509	0.989	1.152	1.792	3.970
Q	0.93	5.58	13.85	17.52	34.05	107.0

The formula for Q is known to be $Q = CLH^n$, where C and n are constants. C is called the mean value of the coefficient of discharge. L is the length of the weir in feet and is 4.26 for these data. Plot on log-log paper to confirm nature of equation. Determine the best values of C and n.

6. A 120-volt tungsten lamp was found to have the following voltage-amperage characteristics:

E (volts)	2	8	25	50	100	150
i (amp)	0.0368	0.0855	0.1688	0.2572	0.3908	0.4942

Derive an equation of the type $i = bE^a$. (First confirm nature of relationship.)

7. (a) The rpm (N) of a flywheel was noted at various times (t min) after power was shut off.

t	0	0.5	1.0	1.5	2.0	2.5	3.0
N	20	9.94	4.94	2.44	1.22	0.60	0.28

Determine an equation of the type $N = ba^t$. (First plot on semilog paper to confirm nature of equation.)

(b) Convert your answer in (a) to the form $N = be^{kt}$.

8. (a) The temperature of an object when placed in cooler surroundings drops according to the equation $T = ba^{\theta}$ (Newton's law of cooling), where T is the temperature differential between the object and the room at any time θ since the beginning of observations. Confirm the type of equation and determine the values of a and b.

θ	0	6.9	21.7	38.6	57.6	80.2	107.5	141.9
T	39.9	37.8	33.5	29.8	25.9	22.0	17.6	13.8

(b) Convert your answer in (a) to the form $T = be^{k\theta}$.

9. A Chromel-Alumel thermocouple generates a certain number of millivolts (E) at various centigrade temperatures (t) according to the following table (cold junction at 0°C):

t	0	100	200	300	400	500	600	700	800	900	1,000	1,100
E	0	4.08	8.19	12.31	16.48	20.74	25.00	29.21	33.28	37.25	41.13	44.85

Confirm a cubic relationship and express in the form of the equation

$$E = a + bt + ct^2 + dt^3$$

10. Compute as in Prob. 9 for a copper-constantan thermocouple, data for which appear in the following table:

t	−200	−150	−100	−50	0	50	100	150	200	250	300	350
E	−5.54	−4.60	−3.35	−1.81	0	2.03	4.28	6.70	9.29	12.01	14.86	17.82

11. According to Kick's law the equation $E = b \log (L_1/L_2)$ represents the energy E required to reduce a mass of ore from particle size L_1 to particle L_2 (b is a constant). From the following table calculate the best value of b if L_1 is 1½.

L_2 (in.)	1	½	3/16	1/16	1/32
E (hp-hr)	1	2.6	5	7.6	9.3

12. Adsorption of moisture by silica gel may be considered to proceed according to the equation

$$x = ap^{1/n}$$

where x = quantity of moisture adsorbed per unit weight of silica gel
P = partial pressure of water vapor in equilibrium with gel
a and n = constants

Confirm nature of equation and compute a and n from the following data:

p	57	225	600	1,300
x	10	15	20	25

13. Barometer reading (p in. mercury) is related to the height above sea level (h ft) as follows:

h	0	500	1,000	1,500	2,000	2,500	3,000	3,500	4,000	4,500	5,000	5,500	6,000
p	29.92	29.36	28.80	28.26	27.72	27.20	26.68	26.18	25.68	25.20	24.72	24.26	23.79

Confirm and derive an equation of the type

$$p = ba^{h/10,000}$$

In Probs. 14 to 26 determine the type of equation fitting the data and compute its constants. (Consider the second variable to be the dependent variable in all cases.)

14.

x	2	7	9	11
y	0.8	3.0	5.0	8.5

15.

x	0.12	0.31	0.59	1.20	1.85	3.1	5.7	9.1
y	80	57	45	35	30	25	20	17

Find y when $x = 1$.
Find x when $y = 68$.

16.

x	1	3.5	5.5	9
y	4	7	11	24

17.

x	2	10	40	80
y	19	10	5.8	4.2

18. A quantity of saturated steam showed the following pressure-volume relationship:

p	7.35	8.765	10.40	12.27	14.42	16.86	19.62	22.74
V	13.22	11.20	9.54	8.16	7.02	6.06	5.265	4.574

19. The volume in milliliters of 1 g of ethyl alcohol at various centigrade temperatures is given in the following table:

t	0	5	10	15	20
V	1.24031	1.24677	1.25332	1.25997	1.26670
t	25	30	35	40	45
V	1.27353	1.28038	1.28735	1.29443	1.30160

20. An experimental run with a gas engine yielded the following data:

p (psi)	29.8	35.9	49.0	57.2	75.5	90.5
V (cu in.)	14.06	11.3	7.80	6.47	4.70	3.80

21. Force (F lb) required to restrain a weight W suspended by a rope θ turns of which are wound around a cylinder:

θ	0.5	1.0	1.4	2.0	2.4	3.0
F	900	420	230	92	48	20

22. Metering of illuminating gas (V cu ft per hr) in a laboratory flow meter when the pressure drop is h in. of water:

h	2.59	2.29	2.25	2.16	2.13	2.09	1.80	1.75	1.20	0.68
V	0.900	0.843	0.838	0.823	0.819	0.794	0.743	0.722	0.587	0.437

23. Road construction; $V =$ safe speed, mph; $a =$ "degree of curve":

a	5	7.5	10	15	20	25	30
V	64	52	45.6	37.4	32	28.6	26.4

24. Rope over a round beam; $\theta =$ angle of contact, turns; $F =$ lb force to restrain a dead weight at the free end of the rope:

θ	½	1	1¼	1¾
F	325	148	100	44.5

What is the significance of the multiplying constant?

25. Pressure (psia) required to compress 250 cu ft of helium originally at atmospheric pressure (15 psia) to various volumes V:

V	26.5	37.5	51	60	80	97	135	250
P	620	350	210	160	100	72	42	15

26. The following data were taken in an ingenious method for estimating the solar energy which the earth's surface would receive if not weakened by atmospheric absorption (see Fig. 14·10):

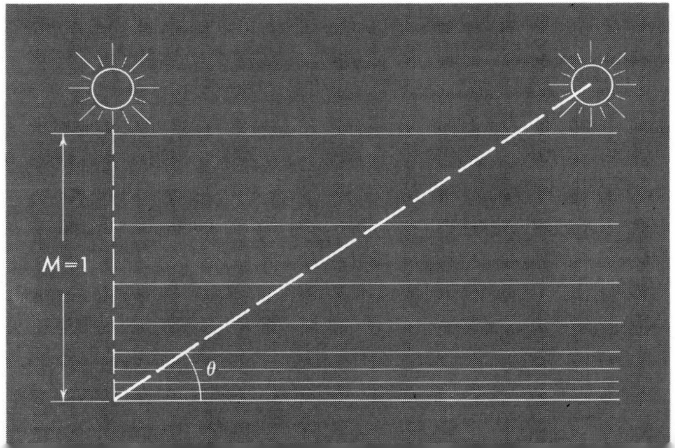

fig. 14·10

θ	*M*, *air mass*	*E*, *solar energy received, g cal per sq cm per sec*
	0	
90°	1	1.66
30°	2	1.42
19°28′	3	1.22
14°29′	4	1.05
11°32′	5	0.90

Taking the air layer as unit thickness (air mass $= 1$ when $\theta = 90°$), then cosec θ will indicate the relative thickness of air layers traversed at various angles of elevation of the sun.

By plotting these data (E versus M) on the proper kind of paper and extrapolating, we can estimate the solar energy entering the upper atmosphere. In other words, we can climb above our surrounding blanket of air mathematically if not physically.

Estimate the value of E to the nearest 0.01 when $M = 0$.

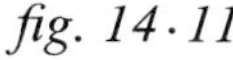

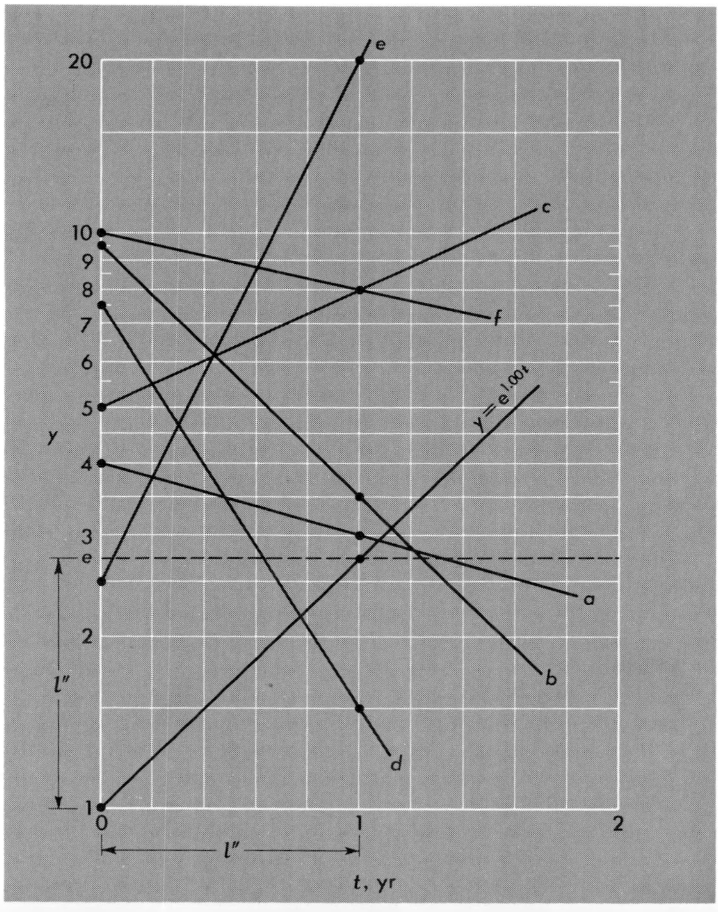

27. In the semilog chart in Fig. 14·11 we have made the two scale moduli (t and $\ln y$) equal as shown. Under these conditions the line $y = e^{1.00t}$, which represents a constant growth rate of 100 per cent, actually appears as a 45 deg line, or a slope of 1.00.

What is the value of y at $t = 0$, at $t = 1$? Therefore what is the annual per cent rate of growth?

By inspection we see that line a represents a 25 per cent depreciation in one year. By actual measurement in inches, we find that the slope is -0.288. The equation for a may then be written $y = 4(0.75)^t$ indicating a 25 per cent annual depreciation rate or $y = 4e^{-0.288t}$ indicating a 28.8 per cent instantaneous depreciation rate.

By inspection determine the approximate instantaneous and annual growth (or depreciation) rates for each of the lines b through f.

15
ratio, proportion, variation, progressions

The comparison of quantities, often indicated by their ratio, is a very common occurrence. In business it often takes the form of percentage (e.g., profit, loss, discount, interest rate). In engineering, physics, and other sciences, we find it in such characteristics as specific gravity, specific heat, and atomic weight.

15·1 Quantities of the same kind

Quantities of the same kind may be compared (1) by stating the difference in magnitude of the two quantities or (2) by finding the quotient of the two quantities when expressed in the same units.

Thus in a group consisting of 100 men and 20 women we may say (1) that there are 80 more men than women or (2) that there are five times as many men as women.

The second type of comparison is called the *ratio* of the quantities. It is expressed as a fraction, in this illustration $^{100}/_{20}$, which is then reduced to lowest terms, $^{5}/_{1}$. We may say that the number of men is to the number of women as 5 is to 1.

If the numbers are prime to each other, the division indicated by the fraction is often carried out; e.g., the rate of 56 to 39 is 1.436 to 1 (to four significant figures).

Note that the comparison must be made between like dimensions, e.g., between a length and a length—not between, say, a length and a weight. The dimensions must be expressed in the same units; e.g., the ratio between 2 lb and 12 oz is $^{32}/_{12}$ or $^{8}/_{3}$.

It will be seen that percentage simply expresses the ratio between a given number of units and 100 units of the same kind.

It should be noted also that the ratio of two like quantities has no units of its own—it is said to be dimensionless. A good illustration of this is π, the ratio between the circumference and diameter of any circle.

EXERCISE 1

Express each of the following ratios in the simplest form:

1. 4 hr to 40 min
2. 5 lb to 10 oz
3. 8 in. to 2 yd
4. 330 ft to 1 mile
5. 480 sq in. to 1 sq ft
6. 6 cu ft to 1 cu yd
7. 13,200 sq ft to 1 acre
8. 1°7′30″ to 360° (angular measurement)
9. Circumference of a 9-in. circle to circumference of a 2-ft circle
10. Area of an 8-in. square to area of a 12-in. square
11. $6ax^2$ to $8a^2x$
12. $6xy - 4y^2$ to $9x^2 - 6xy$
13. ⅝ to $^{15}/_{32}$
14. 3⅓ to 6¼

15·2 Proportions

A statement of equality between two ratios is called a *proportion.* Thus $3/$2 = 84 miles/56 miles is a proportion and is read "$3 is to $2 as 84 miles is to 56 miles." The four quantities are called the *terms* of the proportion. The first and fourth terms are called the *extremes,* and the second and third terms are called the *means,* of a proportion.

Among the properties of proportions, perhaps the most important may be listed in terms of the proportion

$$\frac{a}{b} = \frac{c}{d}$$

1. *The product of the extremes is equal to the product of the means. Thus* ad = bc.
2. *The terms are in proportion by inversion. Thus* b/a = d/c.
3. *The terms are in proportion by alternation. Thus* a/c = b/d.

Each of these statements may be confirmed by the ordinary operations of equations.

If the means of a proportion are equal, as in the proportion $m/x = x/n$, it is called a mean proportion, and x is said to be the *mean proportional* between m and n. Strictly speaking, $x = \pm\sqrt{mn}$. However we shall usually confine ourselves to the positive root.

A *continued proportion* between six or more quantities is illustrated by the expression $a:b:c = x:y:z$. This is a compact notation for expressing the simultaneous proportions

$$\frac{a}{b} = \frac{x}{y} \qquad \frac{a}{c} = \frac{x}{z} \qquad \frac{b}{c} = \frac{y}{z} \qquad \text{or} \qquad \frac{a}{x} = \frac{b}{y} = \frac{c}{z}$$

example 1 The sum of $4,628.20, representing the profits of a venture, is to be divided among three partners in the ratio of 2:3:7. How much does each receive?

We may represent the amounts by $2x$, $3x$, and $7x$, since

$$2x:3x:7x = 2:3:7$$

Therefore,

$$\begin{aligned} 2x + 3x + 7x &= \$4{,}628.20 \\ 12x &= 4{,}628.20 \\ x &= 385.683 \\ 2x &= 771.37 \\ 3x &= 1{,}157.05 \\ 7x &= 2{,}699.78 \end{aligned}$$

EXERCISE 2

In Probs. 1 to 10 solve the proportions for x.

1. $\frac{3}{4} = \frac{x}{14 - x}$
2. $\frac{5}{3} = \frac{20 - x}{x}$
3. $\frac{x + 3}{x - 3} = \frac{4}{3}$
4. $\frac{x - 5}{x + 5} = \frac{2}{7}$
5. $\frac{a}{b} = \frac{x}{c}$
6. $\frac{m}{n} = \frac{k}{x}$
7. $\frac{a}{b} = \frac{c - x}{x}$
8. $\frac{h}{k} = \frac{x}{k - x}$
9. $\frac{x + a}{x + b} = \frac{x - c}{x - d}$
10. $\frac{x - a}{x + b} = \frac{x + a}{x - k}$

In Probs. 11 to 20 find the mean proportional between the given quantities.

11. 6 and 24
12. 8 and 50
13. 2½ and ⅝
14. 8⅓ and 12
15. $2a^2x$ and $8b^2x$
16. $\frac{x}{y}$ and $\frac{y}{x}$
17. $x^2 - y^2$ and $\frac{4(x + y)}{x - y}$
18. $x^2 - 2xy + y^2$ and $x^2 + 2xy + y^2$
19. $\frac{18ab^3}{c}$ and $\frac{2ac}{b}$
20. $x + a$ and $x - a$ (Find the approximate value if a is very small relative to x.)

15·3 Variation

If two variables are so related that their ratio is constant, such as the relation $y/x = k$, we say that y *varies directly* as x, or simply y *varies* as x, or y is *proportional* to x. The constant k is called the *constant of proportionality* or the constant of variation.

An equivalent notation is $y \propto x$, in which the symbol $\propto$ is read "varies as" or "is proportional to." This is *not* an equation but can be converted to the notation of an equation $y = kx$ by introducing the proportionality constant k.

For example, we say that the circumference of a circle varies as the diameter, or $C \propto D$, or $C = kD$. In this instance the proportionality constant k is π.

We note that the relation between y and x is a mutual one. That is, if y varies as x, then $y = kx$; but x is also proportional to y, or $x = (1/k)y$. Therefore, if y varies as x with the constant of proportionality equal to k, then x varies as y with the constant of proportionality equal to $1/k$.

Inverse variation

If one variable varies directly as the reciprocal of a second, then the first is said to *vary inversely* as the second, or the first is said to be *inversely proportional* to the second. Thus $y = k \cdot 1/x$ or $y = k/x$. Since it is evident that $xy = k$, it follows that if the product of two variables is constant, either variable varies inversely as the other.

A common example of inverse variation is found in the inverse relationship between rate and time when a fixed distance is being covered. Here $rt = d$ or $t = d/r$. The constant of proportionality here is d.

Joint variation

If a variable x varies directly as the product of y and z, i.e., if $x = kyz$, we say that x varies jointly as y and z.

If $x = ky \cdot 1/z = ky/z$, it may be said that x varies directly as y and inversely as z.

Types of variation can be combined. For example, the electrical resistance of a wire varies directly as the length and inversely as the square of the diameter. Translated into algebraic notation, this may be written $R = kl/d^2$.

Solution of variation problems

Usually we know the type of variation involved and a set of corresponding values of the variables. From these data we can determine the proportionality constant k and any one missing value in a second set of values of the variables.

example 2 We are given the relation that x is directly proportional to the square root of y and inversely proportional to z. Further, it is known that $x = 4$ when $y = 9$ and $z = 15$. Find the formula for x and find x when $y = 25$ and $z = 40$.

Expressing the relationship in algebraic notation, we have the equation of variation:

$$x = \frac{k\sqrt{y}}{z} \tag{1}$$

Substituting in Eq. (1) $x = 4$, $y = 9$, and $z = 15$, we have

$$4 = \frac{k\sqrt{9}}{15} = \frac{3k}{15}$$

or
$$k = 20 \tag{2}$$

From Eqs. (1) and (2) we write the formula

$$x = \frac{20\sqrt{y}}{z} \tag{3}$$

To solve the last part of our problem, we substitute $y = 25$ and $z = 40$ in Eq. (3), obtaining

$$x = \frac{20\sqrt{25}}{40} = \frac{(20)(5)}{40} = 2.5 \tag{4}$$

The illustration points up the following rules:

1. *Translate the statement of variation into an equation involving an unknown constant of proportionality.*
2. *Solve for the proportionality constant by substituting given data.*
3. *Substitute the value of the constant of proportionality in the equation of variation.*
4. *Use the formula or equation in step 3 to obtain the missing value of a variable when a second set of values of the other variables is given.*

There will be occasions when there are insufficient data to evaluate k or when we are not interested in determining k. To continue with the illustration just given, we represent the first set of values by x_1, y_1, and z_1, and the second set by x_2, y_2, and z_2. Hence we obtain

$$x_1 = \frac{k\sqrt{y_1}}{z_1} \tag{5}$$

and
$$x_2 = \frac{k\sqrt{y_2}}{z_2} \tag{6}$$

Dividing Eq. (5) by Eq. (6),

$$\frac{x_1}{x_2} = \frac{z_2\sqrt{y_1}}{z_1\sqrt{y_2}} \tag{7}$$

Substituting values in Eq. (7),

$$\frac{4}{x_2} = \frac{40\sqrt{9}}{15\sqrt{25}}$$

$$\frac{4}{x_2} = \frac{120}{75}$$

$$x_2 = 2.5$$

It should be noted that the computation in Eq. (7) will often be facilitated if we write it in the form

$$\frac{x_1}{x_2} = \frac{z_2}{z_1}\sqrt{\frac{y_1}{y_2}}$$

If, for example, $y_1 = 63$ and $y_2 = 28$, the preference is obvious when we write

$$\frac{\sqrt{63}}{\sqrt{28}} = \sqrt{\frac{63}{28}} = \sqrt{\frac{9}{4}} = \frac{3}{2}$$

Similarly, if the equation includes the expression $w_1{}^2/w_2{}^2$, the alternative form $(w_1/w_2)^2$ is often preferable. For example, suppose $w_1 = {}^{15}\!/_{32}$ and $w_2 = {}^{9}\!/_{16}$. Then

$$\frac{(15/32)^2}{(9/16)^2} = \left(\frac{15/32}{9/16}\right)^2 = (15/32 \times 16/9)^2 = (5/6)^2 = 25/36$$

The process of eliminating the proportionality constant may be used to demonstrate that variation and proportion are equivalent ideas. In general, for repeated application of the same operation, it is convenient to evaluate k. However, for occasional application, the actual value of k is seldom required, and a simpler solution results from its elimination.

Given $$y_1 = kx_1 \tag{8}$$
and $$y_2 = kx_2 \tag{9}$$

(y varies directly as x.) Dividing Eq. (8) by Eq. (9),

$$\frac{y_1}{y_2} = \frac{x_1}{x_2} \tag{10}$$

(y is directly proportional to x.)

Given $$y_1 = \frac{k}{x_1} \tag{11}$$

and $$y_2 = \frac{k}{x_2} \tag{12}$$

(y varies inversely as x.) Dividing Eq. (11) by Eq. (12),

$$\frac{y_1}{y_2} = \frac{x_2}{x_1} \quad \text{or} \quad x_1y_1 = x_2y_2 \tag{13}$$

(y is inversely proportional to x.)

15·4 Dimensionality of the proportionality constant

It is frequently instructive to determine the dimensionality of k or the units in which k is expressed (see Sec. 5·6).

example 3 It is known that the weight of a rectangular block of wood varies jointly with the thickness, width, and length. If the weight is expressed in pounds and the dimensions in inches, determine in what units k is expressed.

The equation of variation is

$$W = ktwl$$

Solving for k,

$$\frac{W}{twl} = k$$

Substituting units,

$$\frac{\text{lb}}{(\text{in.})(\text{in.})(\text{in.})} = \frac{\text{lb}}{(\text{in.})^3}$$

Hence k is expressed in pounds per cubic inch—a density figure.

example 4 The volume of a given quantity of a gas varies inversely as the pressure (temperature remaining constant). Determine the units of k if volume is expressed in cubic inches and pressure in pounds per square inch.

The equation of variation is

$$V = \frac{k}{P} \qquad \text{or} \qquad PV = k$$

Substituting units,

$$\frac{\text{lb}}{(\text{in.})^2}(\text{in.})^3 = (\text{in.})(\text{lb})$$

Hence k is expressed in inch-pounds—a work unit.

EXERCISE 3

Express each of the relations in Probs. 1 to 5 as an equation containing an unknown constant of proportionality.

1. W varies jointly as x and y.
2. Q varies directly as x and inversely as y.
3. V varies directly as the cube of x and inversely as d.
4. M varies directly as b and inversely as the square root of c.
5. R varies directly as w and the square root of x and inversely as the cube of h.

In Probs. 6 to 10 write the formula for the first variable in terms of the other variables and the computed value of k.

6. H varies directly as x. $H = 8$ when $x = 20$.
7. N varies inversely as y. $N = 20$ when $y = 0.35$.
8. Q varies jointly as a, b, and c. $Q = 300$ when $a = 3$, $b = 7.5$, and $c = 8$.
9. V varies directly as m and inversely as the square of t. $V = 2$ when $m = 15$ and $t = 6$.
10. R varies directly as the fourth power of T and inversely as the square root of x. $R = \frac{1}{3}$ when $T = 2$ and $x = 36$.

EXERCISE 4

In Probs. 1 to 7 determine the numerical value and the units of k that refer to the units in which the first set of values of the variables is expressed. Solve for the unknown value of the variable in the second set of values.

1. P varies inversely as V. If $V = 30$ cu in. when $P = 84$ psi, find V when $P = 63$ psi.
2. R varies directly as l. If $R = 6.8$ ohms when $l = 23.5$ ft, find R when $l = 31.8$ ft.
3. v varies directly as t. If $v = 45$ fps when $t = 25$ sec, find v when $t = 1$ min.
4. W varies directly as d^2. If $W = 12$ oz when $d = 8$ in., find W when $d = 1$ ft.
5. N varies inversely as d^2. If $N = 10{,}890$ plants per acre when set $d(= 2$ ft) apart, find N when $d = 5\frac{1}{2}$ ft.
6. m varies inversely as d. If $m = 12$ men when $d = 10$ days, find m when $d = 8$ days.
7. v varies jointly as the square root of g and the square root of h. If $v = 3.8$ fps when $g = 32$ ft per sec^2 and $h = 0.17$ ft, find v when $g = 30$ ft per sec^2 and $h = 8$ in.

In Probs. 8 to 12 determine the unknown quantity without solving for k.

8. C varies directly as d^2. If $C = 80$ when $d = 12$, find C when $d = 15$.
9. v varies directly as $\sqrt{h}$. If $v = 28$ when $h = 3$, find v when $h = 12$.
10. R varies directly as l and inversely as d^2. If $R = 35$ when $l = 110$ and $d = 0.006$, find R when $l = 75$ and $d = 0.004$.
11. V varies directly as r^4 and p and inversely as l. If $V = 120$ when $r = 0.012, p = 20$, and $l = 30$, find V when $r = 0.016, p = 36$, and $l = 25$.
12. a varies directly as v^2 and inversely as r. If $a = 540$ when $v = 84$ and $r = 5$, find a when $v = 119$ and $r = 4$.

15·5 Applications

A few of the more common principles of mathematics and the physical sciences that may be expressed as variations are as follows:

Areas of similar figures vary as the squares of corresponding dimensions.

Volumes of similar solids vary as the cubes of corresponding dimensions. (Note that a 1-in. square and a 2-in. square, each cut from a ¼-in. sheet of steel, are not similar solids, since not all three dimensions are doubled. Weights are as $1^2:2^2$, not $1^3:2^3$.)

Volumes of gases vary inversely as the absolute pressure and directly as the absolute temperature.

In any given chemical reaction between substances A and B, the reacting amount of A varies directly as the reacting amount of B.

The time required to finish a given job varies inversely as the number of men working on the job.

The rate of energy reception (heat, light, magnetism, etc.) varies inversely as the square of the distance from the source of energy.

The revolutions per minute of two pulleys belted together vary inversely as their diameters.

The revolutions per minute of two gears in mesh vary inversely as the number of teeth.

Rate of heat conduction through a flat plate varies jointly as the area of one face of the plate and the difference between the temperatures of the opposite faces and inversely as the thickness of the plate.

Electrical resistance of a conductor varies directly as the length and inversely as the cross-section area.

EXERCISE 5

1. Hydrogen used for inflation of balloons may be made by passing steam over red-hot scrap iron. If 8.5 lb of iron will make 78 cu ft of hydrogen, how much iron would be needed to make 500 cu ft of hydrogen?
2. Seven men take eighteen 8-hr days to finish a job. How many men will be needed to finish a like job in twelve 7½-hr days?
3. A train usually makes its run in 2 hr 25 min at an average speed of 42 mph. How long would it take if the speed were reduced to 34 mph?
4. The weight of 195 machine screws is 8½ oz. Find the number in 2 lb 7 oz.
5. The resistance of a spool of enameled magnet wire was 955 ohms. A piece 1 ft 9½ in. long was cut off and found to have a resistance of 5.37 ohms. Find the length of wire originally on the spool.
6. The air-line distance between two points is 235 miles. They are 5⅛ in. apart on the map. What is the air-line distance between two points 3 13/16 in. apart on the same map?
7. A 250-ml Erlenmeyer flask has a height of 5.00 in. How high must a 500-ml Erlenmeyer flask be if it has the same shape as the smaller one?
8. A 16-in. disk cut from a piece of sheet steel weighs 5.65 lb. What will be the diameter of a disk weighing 2.08 lb cut from the same piece of stock?
9. A 2½-in. cast-iron sphere weighs 1.87 lb. How much will a 3½-in. cast-iron sphere weigh?
10. A line L units long is said to be divided harmonically if the longer segment is a mean proportional between the shorter segment and the entire line. Derive an expression for the shorter segment x in terms of L. This relation is applied in some geometrical constructions and serves as a guide in maintaining proper proportion in art (where the term "golden mean" is used).

11. The profits of a partnership amount to \$1,283.67. This is to be divided among four partners in proportion to their investments. Johnson, Miller, Spencer, and Weston invested \$842, \$1,363, \$1,759, and \$1,876, respectively. Find each man's share of the profits to the nearest cent.
12. A pilot flew a glider plane a distance of 87 miles in 50 min. During this time he descended from 12,800 to 8,000 ft. How much longer could he have remained aloft, and how far would he have glided?
13. The analysis of a paint shows 46 per cent vehicle and 54 per cent pigment. The analysis of the pigment shows 15 per cent zinc oxide, 60 per cent titanium dioxide, and 25 per cent lithopone. What is the percentage of each pigment in the ready-mixed paint?
14. The gravitational acceleration at the earth's surface may be taken as 32.2 ft per sec². What will be the value of the gravitational constant for a guided missile 150 miles above the earth's surface? Gravitational force is inversely proportional to the square of the distance from the center of the earth. Assume the earth's radius is 3,960 miles.
15. Given the formula $x = m\sqrt{f}/[W(a + b^2/k)]$. Indicate, quantitatively where possible, the effect on x of doubling each of the other letters one at a time.
16. If 4,250 ft of 5⁄32-in. wire has a resistance of 13.6 ohms, what length of wire 3⁄16 in. in diameter will have a resistance of 4.2 ohms? In what units would the proportionality constant be expressed? The resistance of a wire of a given material varies directly as the length and inversely as the square of the diameter.
17. From a 1:2:3 mixture of cement, sand, and gravel, 84 cu yd of concrete are to be made. How many cubic yards of each will be needed, allowing for a 20 per cent shrinkage on mixing?
18. Given $D = kWL^3/th^3$, where D is the deflection (in inches) of a beam loaded at the center and supported at the ends. k is a constant, L is the distance between the supports in feet, t is the width of the beam in inches, h is the depth in inches, and W is the load in pounds. If D is 4 when W is 250, L is 12, h is 3, and t is 2½, find D when W is 400, L is 10, h is 4, and t is 2.
19. An inverted cone is 32 in. high and 18 in. in diameter at the top. If water flowing into the cone at a uniform rate reaches a depth of 12 in. in 5 min, how much longer would it take to reach a depth of 15 in.?
20. The outline of an estate is cut out from a map and found to weigh 42.78 g. A rectangular section 5 by 8 in. was cut from the same sheet and found to weigh 5.31 g. If the scale of the map is 1 in. to 150 ft, find the number of acres in the estate.
21. The gravity rate of flow of water from the bottom of a tank varies directly as the square root of the depth h of the water in the tank. The rate of flow v was 20 gpm when the water was 9 ft deep.
    a. Derive a formula for v in terms of h.
    b. Find v when $h = 15$ ft.
    c. Find h when $v = 12$ gpm.

22. A man 5 ft 4 in. tall weighs 140 lb. Another man, of about the same build, is just 6 ft tall. How much would you expect the taller man to weigh?
23. The distance of the horizon at sea varies directly as the square root of the elevation of the observer above sea level. If the horizon is 4½ miles distant at 13½ ft elevation, find the distance at 380 ft elevation.
24. In Prob. 23 how high above sea level must a lighthouse be to be visible 15 miles out to sea?
25. A city of 50,000 people is supplied by a 25-in. water main. If a future population of 120,000 is anticipated within 30 years, what size main (to the nearest inch) will provide for this population?
26. The intensity of illumination at a given point is directly proportional to the intensity of the light source and inversely proportional to the square of the distance from the light source. If a reader obtains adequate illumination with a 60-watt bulb 3 ft from the page, what size bulb will be needed to provide proper lighting at a distance of 4½ ft?
27. The horsepower required to drive a motorboat varies as the cube of the speed through the water. If 5 hp drives a boat at 10 mph, what size motor is needed to maintain a speed of 14 mph?
28. The air pressure in an automobile tire was tested after a summer day's drive and found to be 30 psi gauge. If its temperature was 120°F, what would the pressure be the next morning when the temperature is 60°F? (Absolute pressure varies directly as the absolute temperature, volume remaining constant. Absolute pressure equals gauge pressure plus 14.7 psi; absolute temperature equals Fahrenheit temperature plus 460°.)

In working Probs. 29 and 30, assume that gears with the following numbers of teeth are available from stock: 96, 84, 72, 66, 60, 54, 48, 42, 36, 30, 27, 24, 21, and 18.

29. In parts (a) to (h) compute the missing quantities, where gear A drives gear B. Select appropriate gears from stock where an asterisk replaces the number of teeth.

	No. teeth in gear A	*No. teeth in gear B*	*rpm gear A*	*rpm gear B*
(a)	42	96	56	
(b)	60	. . .	150	125
(c)	48	84	. . .	112
(d)	. . .	36	45	105
(e)	*	*	360	1200
(f)	*	*	350	550
(g)	*	*	200	640
(h)	*	*	180	840

30. Referring to Fig. 15·1, compute the missing quantities. In parts (d) to (g) select gears from stock to accomplish the speed ratio in two equal stages (or as nearly equal as possible).

	No. teeth	*No. teeth*	*No. teeth*	*No. teeth*	*rpm*	*rpm*
	A	*B*	*C*	*D*	*A*	*D*
(a)	96	60	84	48	150	
(b)	. . .	54	60	42	210	400
(c)	66	36	54	. . .	70	330
(d)	. . .	. . .	. . .	. . .	120	800
(e)	. . .	. . .	. . .	. . .	180	320
(f)	. . .	. . .	. . .	. . .	175	300
(g)	. . .	. . .	. . .	. . .	200	480

31. Eighteen seconds are required to make a photographic enlargement with the light source 33 in. from the paper. How long would it take to make a larger print with the light source placed 41 in. from the paper? Length of exposure is inversely proportional to the intensity of illumination, which, in turn, is inversely proportional to the square of the distance from the light source.

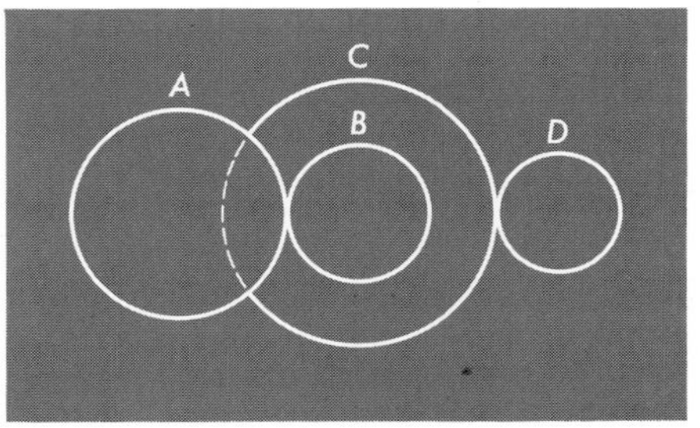

fig. 15·1

fig. 15·2

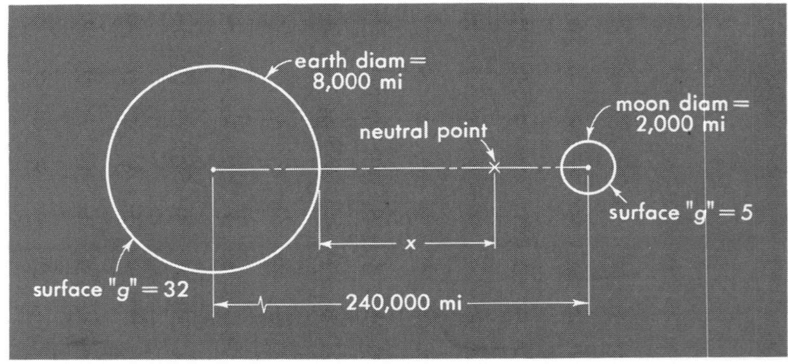

32. Two sections of a regular hexagonal pyramid are made by parallel planes 8 in. apart. The areas of the sections are 175 and 63 sq in., respectively. How far from the vertex is the smaller section?
33. A cone of slant height 12 in. holds 3 qt of water. How far from the vertex should marks be placed on the slant height to indicate 1 qt? 2 qt?
34. An artificial earth satellite at a height of 500 miles above the earth's surface orbits once every 102 min. What should be the height for a period of 24 hr? According to one of Kepler's laws, the period is proportional to the $\frac{3}{2}$ power of the distance from the earth's center. Radius of the earth is 3,960 miles. (Your answer will be the required altitude for a so-called "stationary satellite" or "synchronous orbit.")
35. A lot of soda ash containing 52 per cent by weight water of crystallization is bought at 17½ cents per pound. When the material is sold at retail, the moisture content is found to have dropped in storage to 37 per cent. What should be the retail price per pound to realize a 40 per cent profit?
36. A formula calls for 22½ lb of soda ash as originally bought in Prob. 35. Find the proper amount of the material to use after partial drying in storage.
37. The law of gravitational attraction states that the gravitational force between two objects varies inversely as the square of the distance between them. At what distance x from the surface of the earth will the gravitational attraction of the earth and moon just balance? (See Fig. 15·2.)
38. The United States makes 77 per cent of the world's automobiles, yet contains only 7 per cent of the world's population. How many times as likely is a man to be employed in the motor industry in the United States as elsewhere in the world?
39. The velocity of sound in air is independent of the density and pressure of the air and varies directly as the square root of the absolute temperature. An experimental unit carried on a rocket indicated a sound velocity of 977 fps at an altitude of 20 miles. What was the Fahrenheit temperature at that altitude if at 70°F the speed of sound in the air is 1,130 fps?
40. A car was stopped 60 ft from the point at which the driver first sighted an obstruction. If the driver's mental-reaction time was 0.4 sec, find the initial speed of the car. The braking distance is directly proportional to the square of the speed of the car and is 22 ft at 20 mph.
41. Beginning with the statement that the volume of the frustum of a cone is equal to the difference between the volumes of two cones, i.e., $V = \frac{1}{3}\pi h_2 r_2^2 - \frac{1}{3}\pi h_1 r_1^2$, where $r \propto h$ (Fig. 15·3), demonstrate that:

(a) $V = \frac{1}{3}\pi H(r_1^2 + r_1 r_2 + r_2^2)$
(b) $V = \frac{1}{3}H(A_1 + \sqrt{A_1 A_2} + A_2)$
(c) $V = \frac{1}{6}H(A_1 + 4M + A_2)$

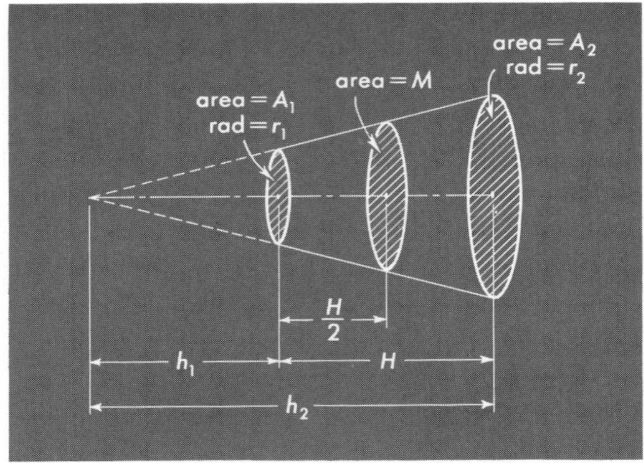

fig. 15·3

fig. 15·4

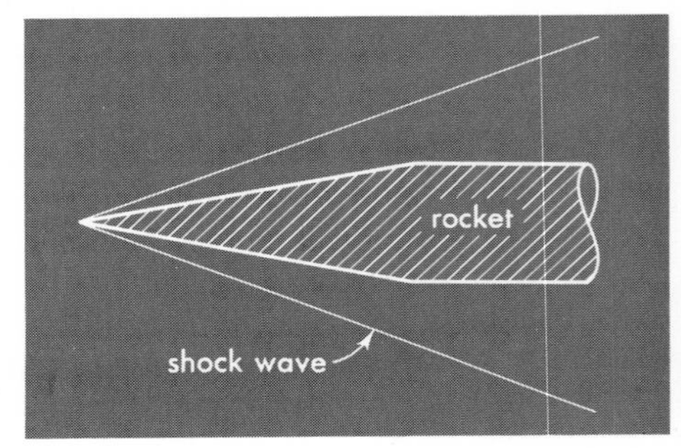

42. Figure 15·4 is taken from the cover of *Science News Letter,* December 2, 1961. Scale any measurements you think necessary to estimate the speed of the rocket.
43. A brass sphere has a diameter of 5.500 in. and weighs 26.20 lb. How thick a layer must be turned off to reduce the weight to 25.80 lb?

    Note that a slide-rule solution based on the proportion $25.80/26.20 = r^3/(2.75)^3$ would be grossly inaccurate. Set up an approximate proportion between the volume and weight of the spherical shell turned off and those of the original sphere.

    This anticipates the concept of approximate increments in calculus.

15·6 Arithmetic progression

An *arithmetic progression* (abbreviated AP) is a succession of terms so arranged that each term differs from the term immediately preceding it by a fixed amount called the *common difference.* The following are arithmetic progressions:

$$7, 10, 13, 16, 19$$
$$11, 7, 3, -1, -5$$
$$-4, -2\tfrac{5}{6}, -1\tfrac{2}{3}, -\tfrac{1}{2}, \tfrac{2}{3}, 1\tfrac{5}{6}$$
$$x - y, x, x + y, x + 2y$$

The common difference is obtained by subtracting any term from the term immediately following it. Thus the common differences in the examples just given are 3, -4, $1\frac{1}{6}$, and y, respectively.

The five *elements* of an AP and the letters usually denoting them are:

1. The first term a
2. The common difference d
3. The number of terms n
4. The last (or nth) term l
5. The sum of n terms S

Any three of the above elements are usually sufficient to determine the other two.

15·7 The nth term of an AP

If a is the first term and d is the common difference, the second term is $a + d$. The third is $a + 2d$, and in general the nth is $a + (n - 1)d$. Hence, if l is the last or nth term, we have

$$l = a + (n - 1)d \tag{14}$$

example 5 Find the 43d term of the AP 11, $12\frac{1}{2}$, 14, ...

Substituting 11 for a, 43 for n, and $1\frac{1}{2}$ for d, we obtain, by Eq. (14),

$$l = 11 + (43 - 1)(1\tfrac{1}{2}) = 74$$

example 6 Find the 39th term of the AP 193, 187, 181, ...

Substituting 193 for a, 39 for n, and -6 for d, we have

$$l = 193 + (39 - 1)(-6) = -35$$

15·8 The sum of the first n terms of an AP

Let us consider an arithmetic progression of n terms whose first term is a, last term is l, and common difference is d. If we write the sum S first in the usual order, then in reverse order, we have

$$S = a + (a + d) + (a + 2d) + \cdots + (l - 2d) + (l - d) + l \tag{15}$$
$$S = l + (l - d) + (l - 2d) + \cdots + (a + 2d) + (a + d) + a \tag{16}$$

If we add Eqs. (15) and (16), all terms containing d cancel and we obtain

$$2S = (a + l) + (a + l) + (a + l) + \cdots + (a + l) + (a + l) + (a + l) = n(a + l)$$

Hence
$$S = \frac{n}{2}(a + l) \tag{17}$$

example 7 Find the sum of an AP of 15 terms which begins with 19 and ends with 61.

Substituting, in Eq. (17), $n = 15$, $a = 19$, and $l = 61$, we have

$$S = {}^{15}\!/_2(19 + 61) = 600$$

If we substitute in Eq. (17) the expression for l in Eq. (14), we obtain

$$S = \frac{n}{2}[2a + (n - 1)d] \tag{18}$$

example 8 Find the number of terms in an AP whose sum is 126, common difference is 11, and first term is -30.

Substituting, in Eq. (18), $S = 126$, $a = -30$, and $d = 11$, we have

$$126 = \frac{n}{2}[-60 + (n - 1)11]$$

$$252 = n(11n - 71)$$

$$0 = 11n^2 - 71n - 252$$

The solution of this quadratic is $n = 9$, $n = -{}^{28}\!/_{11}$. Since in this example we must have a whole number of terms, $-{}^{28}\!/_{11}$ is inadmissible, and there are 9 terms.

example 9 Find the common difference in an AP of 17 terms whose first term is 22 and sum is 272.

Substituting, in Eq. (18), 17 for n, 22 for a, and 272 for S, we have

$$272 = {}^{17}\!/_2[2(22) + 16d]$$

or

$$d = -{}^3\!/_4$$

15·9 Arithmetic means

The first term a and the last term l of an AP are called the *extremes*. The intervening terms are called *arithmetic means* between a and l. To insert k arithmetic means between a and l is to determine an AP of $k + 2$ terms having a as the first term and l as the last term. If we substitute $k + 2$ for n in Eq. (14), we have

$$l = a + (k + 1)d$$

or

$$d = \frac{l - a}{k + 1} \tag{19}$$

example 10 Insert 5 arithmetic means between -19 and 23.

Substituting, in Eq. (19), 23 for l, -19 for a, and 5 for k, we have

$$d = \frac{23 - (-19)}{5 + 1}$$

or $$d = 7$$

and the AP is $-19, -12, -5, 2, 9, 16, 23$.

If a single arithmetic mean is to be inserted between a and l, it is called *the* arithmetic mean of a and l, or the average of a and l, and is equal to $(a + l)/2$.

If we divide both sides of Eq. (17) by n, we obtain

$$\frac{S}{n} = \frac{a + l}{2} \qquad \textbf{(20)}$$

or the average of all the terms of an AP, however many, is the average of the first and last terms. If m denotes the middle term of an AP, then $m - a = l - m$, or $m = (a + l)/2$. When m is substituted for $(a + l)/2$ in Eq. (17), we have

$$S = nm \qquad \textbf{(21)}$$

That is, the sum of an AP is equal to the number of terms multiplied by the middle term or by the midpoint, as the case may be.

example 11 The sum of 81, 89, 97, 105, 113 is $(5)(97) = 485$.

example 12 Find the sum of 73, 67, 61, 55, 49, 43, 37, 31. The midpoint or average of 55 and 49 is 52. Hence $S = (8)(52) = 416$.

EXERCISE 6

In Probs. 1 to 7 find the required terms.

1. 9th term of 2, 5, 8, . . .
2. 12th term of 3, 7, 11, . . .
3. 10th term of $-9, -7, -5, \ldots$
4. 16th term of 93, 86, 79, . . .
5. 12th term of $-\frac{3}{2}, -\frac{2}{3}, \frac{1}{6}, \ldots$
6. 8th term of $a - 3b, a - b, a + b, \ldots$
7. 7th term of $3x - y, x, y - x, \ldots$

In Probs. 8 to 13 find the sum of the indicated AP's.

8. 5, 8, 11, . . . to 13 terms
9. 23, 19, 15, . . . to 16 terms
10. $-11, -6, -1, \ldots$ to 21 terms
11. $a + b, a, a - b, \ldots$ to 11 terms
12. $\frac{1}{6}, \frac{4}{3}, \frac{5}{2}, \ldots$ to 14 terms
13. $5a - 3b, 4a - 2b, 3a - b, \ldots$ to 10 terms

In Probs. 14 to 23 determine the missing quantities.

	S	n	a	l	d
14.			9	25	2
15.		12		64	6
16.		15	71		-4

	S	n	a	l	d
17.		10	61	16	
18.	231			11	-2
19.	-132		11		-4
20.	84		5	19	
21.	80	8			4
22.	77	7		20	
23.	63	7	3		

In Probs. 24 to 33 find the arithmetic mean between the given quantities.

24. 3 and 13
25. 5 and 31
26. -2 and 15
27. -8 and 3
28. -17 and -9
29. $\frac{5}{6}$ and $\frac{3}{10}$
30. $-\frac{3}{8}$ and $\frac{1}{2}$
31. $2x$ and $2y$
32. $m + n$ and $m - n$
33. y and $1/y$

In Probs. 34 to 38 insert the required arithmetic means.

34. Three arithmetic means between 5 and 29
35. Four arithmetic means between 17 and 32
36. Six arithmetic means between -9 and 26
37. Five arithmetic means between -10 and 17
38. Four arithmetic means between 13 and -5

15·10 Applications of arithmetic progressions

In a problem involving an arithmetic progression, set down the first few terms of the progression. Evaluate as many as possible of the elements of the AP in terms of the data given. At times it may be advisable to divide the computation into two portions, one including the progression, the other representing a value easily found without using our AP formulas. Occasionally it will not be possible to meet the stated requirements exactly, in which case we shall have to seek the best possible compromise.

example 13 A home freezer costing \$560 is bought under an agreement to pay \$40 per month plus interest on the unpaid balance at the rate of 18 per cent. If the first payment is to be made one month after purchase of the unit, find: (a) the first payment, (b) the last payment, and (c) the total amount paid.

Since $\frac{560}{40} = 14$, there will be 14 payments made. For the time being we shall set aside the \$40 payments made on the principal and turn our attention to interest payments. At the end of the first month the interest payment will be

$$(0.18)(\tfrac{1}{12})(560) = (0.015)(560) = \$8.40$$

(a) Therefore the first payment will be \$40 + \$8.40, or \$48.40.

The unpaid balance during the second month will be \$520, and the interest payment at the end of the second month will be

$$(0.18)(1/12)(520) = (0.015)(520) = \$7.80$$

Similarly, the interest payment at the end of the third month will be (0.015)(480); at the end of the fourth month, (0.015)(440); and so on.

(b) It is evident that the last payment will be \$40 on the principal and (0.015)(40) = \$0.60 interest, or a total of \$40.60.

(c) Clearly the interest payments will form the AP

$$(0.015)(560), (0.015)(520), (0.015)(480), \ldots, (0.015)(40) \qquad \text{(14 terms)}$$

From Eq. (17), Sec. 15·8,

$$S = \frac{n}{2}(a + l) = 14/2[(0.015)(560) + (0.015)(40)] = \$63$$

Therefore the total amount paid will be \$560 + \$63, or \$623.

example 14 Raffle tickets are to be sold at all prices ranging from 1 cent to not more than 99 cents. It is desired to realize \$300 from the sale of tickets. How can this be done if the same number of tickets is sold at each price?

Let us first determine how much the sale of one ticket at each price from 1 cent to 99 cents would realize. According to Eq. (17), $S = (n/2)(a + l)$; in this example, $n = 99$, $a = 1$, and $l = 99$. Making these substitutions, we find $S = 4{,}950$, or \$49.50.

Since $300/49.5 = 6.1$, we shall need to sell 7 tickets at each price from 1 cent to some figure under \$1. Therefore we shall have 7 identical AP's whose combined sum is 30,000 (\$300). To evaluate one of the AP's, we shall use Eq. (18) and substitute $S = 30{,}000/7$, $a = 1$, and $d = 1$. Thus we obtain

$$\frac{30{,}000}{7} = \frac{n}{2}[2(1) + (n - 1)(1)]$$

or

$$n^2 + n = 8{,}571$$

Solving, we find $n =$ approximately 92.1, or -93.1.

Only the positive root 92.1 has any application to this problem, and the next higher integer, 93, indicates that each identical AP will contain 93 terms, with 93 cents as the highest-priced ticket. Using Eq. (8), we see that the combined sum of the 7 identical series will be

$$S = (7)(93/2)(1 + 93) = 30{,}597, \text{ or } \$305.97$$

EXERCISE 7

1. A machine having an initial value of \$1,450 depreciates in value each year \$50 less than during the preceding year. At the end of the sixth year it has a scrap value of \$190. What is its value at the end of the first year?

2. A ball rolling up an incline covers 24 ft during the first second, 21 ft during the next second, 18 ft during the next, etc. When will it be 99 ft (measured up the incline) from the starting point? (Two answers—explain.)
3. Find the sum of all the multiples of 6, beginning with zero and ending with 240.
4. If 250 raffle tickets are sold at all prices from 1 cent to $2.50, what are the total receipts?
5. Find the sum of all the integers between 1 and 500 which end in 3.
6. A freely falling object drops 116 ft during the first second, 148 ft during the second second, 180 ft during the third second, etc. How long will it take to fall 800 ft? (See Prob. 4, Exercise 13, Chap. 6.)
7. A man repays a $1,200 debt by paying $150 at the end of each year, plus 6 per cent interest on the balance remaining unpaid during that year. Find the total of his payments.
8. In a highway construction project a 1,000-ft work road leads from a gravel pit to the highway. Trucks load at the pit and lay gravel starting at the entrance to the highway. What total distance will a truck cover in laying the first mile of highway if each load lays 20 ft of highway?
9. A man accepts a position with an initial salary of $5,200 per year. It is understood that he will receive an automatic increase of $320 at the end of the first year and each year thereafter.
   (a) Find his salary for the tenth year.
   (b) What are his total earnings during the first eleven years?
10. A television set costing $450 is bought under an agreement to repay the principal at the rate of $30 at the end of each month plus 6 per cent interest on the balance remaining unpaid during that month.
    (a) Find the first payment (made a month after purchase of the set).
    (b) Find the last payment.
    (c) Find the total amount paid.
11. The product of three numbers in arithmetic progression is 224, and the largest number is 7 times the smallest. Find the numbers.
12. Show that the sum of the first n odd numbers is equal to n^2.
13. Find the sum, last term, and number of terms in the arithmetic progression 33, 40, 47, . . . , whose sum best approximates 4,000.
14. A vacation club can be used to build up a fund of $200 in 40 weekly installments which form a decreasing arithmetical progression. With the payment of the twentieth installment, three-fifths of the fund will have been accumulated. What will be the first and second installments?

15 · 11 Geometric progression

A *geometric progression* (abbreviated GP) is a succession of terms, each of which may be obtained by multiplying the preceding term by a fixed quantity called the *common ratio*. Some examples of geometric progressions are

4, 12, 36, 108, . . .	common ratio = 3
$-24, 12, -6, 3, -3/2, \ldots$	common ratio = $-1/2$
$5x^3, 10x^2, 20x, 40, \ldots$	common ratio = $2/x$

The five elements of a GP and their customary symbols are

1. The first term a
2. The common ratio r
3. The number of terms n
4. The last (or nth) term l
5. The sum of n terms S

15·12 The nth term of a GP

If a is the first term and r is the common ratio, the second term is ar, the third is ar^2, and in general the nth term is ar^{n-1}. Therefore l, the last or nth term, is

$$l = ar^{n-1} \tag{22}$$

example 15 Find the eighth term in the GP 27, -18, 12, -8, ...

In this progression, $r = -2/3$. Hence, substituting, in Eq. (22), $a = 27$, $r = -2/3$, and $n = 8$, we obtain

$$l = 27\left(-\frac{2}{3}\right)^7 = 27\left(-\frac{128}{2{,}187}\right) = -\frac{128}{81}$$

example 16 Find the tenth term in the GP $k^{11}m^2, k^9m^3, k^7m^4, \ldots$.

In this progression $r = m/k^2$. Hence, substituting, in Eq. (22), $a = k^{11}m^2$, $r = m/k^2$, and $n = 10$, we have

$$l = k^{11}m^2\left(\frac{m}{k^2}\right)^9 = k^{11}m^2\frac{m^9}{k^{18}} = \frac{m^{11}}{k^7}$$

15·13 The sum of the first n terms of a GP

If we write the sum S of the first n terms of a GP whose first term is a and common ratio is r and then multiply both sides of this equation by r, we have

$$S = a + ar + ar^2 + ar^3 + \cdots + ar^{n-2} + ar^{n-1} \tag{23}$$

$$rS = ar + ar^2 + ar^3 + ar^4 + \cdots + ar^{n-1} + ar^n \tag{24}$$

On subtraction of Eq. (24) from Eq. (23), all the intermediate terms cancel out, and we obtain

$$S - rS = a - ar^n \tag{25}$$

Solving Eq. (25) for S, we obtain

$$S = \frac{a - ar^n}{1 - r} \tag{26}$$

or

$$S = \frac{a(1 - r^n)}{1 - r} = \frac{a(r^n - 1)}{r - 1} \tag{27}$$

Since, from Eq. (22), $l = ar^{n-1}$,

$$rl = ar^n \tag{28}$$

Substituting Eq. (28) in Eq. (27), we have

$$S = \frac{a - rl}{1 - r} = \frac{rl - a}{r - 1} \tag{29}$$

example 17 Find the sum of the first seven terms of the GP 5, 15, 45, ...

Substituting, in Eq. (27), $a = 5$, $r = 3$, and $n = 7$, we have

$$S = \frac{5(3^7 - 1)}{3 - 1} = \frac{5(2{,}187 - 1)}{2} = 5{,}465$$

example 18 Find the sum of the GP 45, -30, 20, . . . , $-640/243$.

Substituting, in Eq. (29), $a = 45$, $r = -2/3$, and $l = -640/243$, we write

$$S = \frac{45 - (-2/3)(-640/243)}{1 - (-2/3)} = \frac{45 - 1{,}280/729}{5/3} = \frac{6{,}305}{243}$$

example 19 If $S = 468$, $r = 5$, and $a = 3$, find n and l.

Substituting in Eq. (29), we have

$$468 = \frac{5l - 3}{5 - 1}$$

or

$$l = 375$$

Substitution in Eq. (22) gives

$$375 = 3(5)^{n-1}$$

or

$$5^{n-1} = 375/3 = 125 = 5^3$$

Hence

$$5^{n-1} = 5^3$$

or

$$n = 4$$

15 · 14 Geometric means

In a GP the first term a and the last term l are called the *extremes* of the progression. The intermediate terms are called *geometric means* between a and l. To insert k geometric means between two given quantities a and l, we must find k numbers which, inserted between

a and l, form a GP of $k+2$ terms, with a the first term and l the last. Substituting $k+2$ for n in Eq. (22), we have

$$l = ar^{k+1}$$

or

$$r = \sqrt[k+1]{\frac{l}{a}} \tag{30}$$

If $k+1$ is even and l/a is positive, r may be either positive or negative, and two sets of means can be determined. It is understood that only real values of r will be considered.

example 20 Insert three geometric means between 80 and 0.648.

Substituting $k = 3$, $a = 80$, and $l = 0.648$ in Eq. (30), we find

$$r = \sqrt[4]{\frac{0.648}{80}} = \sqrt[4]{0.0081} = 0.3 \text{ or } -0.3$$

Hence the required GP is either

$$80, 24, 7.2, 2.16, 0.648$$

or

$$80, -24, 7.2, -2.16, 0.648$$

If a and l have the same sign and we insert between them one geometric mean m of the same sign as a and l, m is called the principal *geometric mean* of a and l. Since $l/m = m/a$, it follows that $m = \pm\sqrt{al}$. Hence

$$m = \pm\sqrt{al} \tag{31}$$

where the sign agrees with that of a and l.

example 21 Find the geometric mean of $^{25}/_6$ and $^3/_8$.

The geometric mean is $m = \sqrt{^{25}/_6 \cdot {^3/_8}} = {^5/_4}$.

The geometric mean or geometric average of n quantities is the nth root of their product.

example 22 Find the geometric average of 9, 15, and 200.

$$\sqrt[3]{(9)(15)(200)} = \sqrt[3]{27{,}000} = 30$$

EXERCISE 8

1. Find the seventh term of 3, 6, 12, ...
2. Find the eighth term of $-2, -6, -18, \ldots$.
3. Find the tenth term of 8, 4, 2, ...
4. Find the eleventh term of $^1/_8, -{^1/_4}, {^1/_2}, \ldots$.
5. Find the ninth term of $^1/_{16}, {^3/_8}, {^9/_4}, \ldots$.
6. Find the eighth term of $ax^3, ax^2, ax, \ldots$.
7. Find the fifth term of $\sqrt{2}, 2\sqrt{3}, 6\sqrt{2}, \ldots$.
8. Find the seventh term of $-\sqrt[3]{2}, \sqrt[3]{4}, -2, \ldots$.

In Probs. 9 to 14 determine the numerical value of the letter if a GP is to be formed. Determine the common ratio.

9. 8, 12, x
10. 45, x, 20
11. y, 24, -30
12. 32, k, $12\frac{1}{2}$
13. $2k - 2, 2k + 2, 2k + 8$
14. $4k + 4, 6k - 2, 9k - 13$

Determine the common ratio in Probs. 15 to 17.

15. $a, a - 2b, b$
16. $9, c - 3d, d^2$
17. $a + 3b, 4\sqrt{ab}, a + 5b$

In Probs. 18 to 24 determine the sum of the GP.

18. 3, 15, 75, . . . , to 6 terms
19. 24, 12, 6, . . . , to 7 terms
20. 5, -10, 20, . . . , to 7 terms
21. $\frac{27}{32}, \frac{9}{16}, \frac{3}{8}$, . . . , to 6 terms
22. $\frac{32}{45}, -\frac{16}{15}, \frac{8}{5}$, . . . , to 5 terms
23. 1,536, 768, 384, . . . , to 9 terms
24. 1,215, -405, 135, . . . , to 7 terms

In Probs. 25 to 32 determine the missing quantities.

	S	n	a	l	r
25.			6	750	5
26.		8		384	2
27.		5	2		-3
28.		6	192	6	
29.	20			$\frac{1}{2}$	$\frac{1}{3}$
30.	508		4		2
31.	$59\frac{1}{9}$		108	$-14\frac{2}{9}$	
32.	$277\frac{1}{12}$	6			$\frac{3}{2}$

Find the geometric mean of each pair of quantities in Probs. 33 to 41.

33. 2 and 18
34. -3 and -27
35. 50 and 8
36. 6 and 54
37. $-\frac{1}{3}$ and -48
38. $\frac{2}{3}$ and $\frac{1}{6}$
39. $\frac{27}{8}$ and $\frac{2}{3}$
40. a^3b and abc^2
41. x^{n-1} and x^{n+1}

In Probs. 42 to 47 insert geometric means as directed.

42. Two means between 5 and 40
43. Two means between 4 and -108
44. Three means between 48 and 3
45. Three means between -405 and -5
46. Four means between $3h^8$ and $96h^3$
47. Five means between $5x^4$ and $320x^{16}$

15·15 Infinite geometric progressions

If we add the first n terms of the GP $a, ar, ar^2, \ldots, ar^{n-1}$, the sum S_n by Eq. (18) is

$$S_n = \frac{a(1 - r^n)}{1 - r}$$

As an illustration of this formula consider the unending GP

$$1, \tfrac{1}{2}, \tfrac{1}{4}, \ldots, \frac{1}{2^{n-1}} \qquad (n \text{ terms}) \tag{32}$$

In progression (23), $a = 1$ and $r = \frac{1}{2}$, which, substituted in Eq. (27), gives us

$$S_n = \frac{1[1 - (\frac{1}{2})^n]}{1 - \frac{1}{2}} = 2[1 - (\tfrac{1}{2})^n] \tag{33}$$

As n increases and we continue to write more terms in Eq. (32), the value of the expression $(\frac{1}{2})^n$ in Eq. (33) becomes continually smaller. By taking n large enough, we can make $(\frac{1}{2})^n$ as near zero as we please. Thus, if we find the sum of the first 24 terms, $(\frac{1}{2})^n = 1/16{,}777{,}216$, so that $2[1 - (\frac{1}{2})^{24}]$ is very nearly equal to 2. If we find the sum of the first 48 terms, the value of $(\frac{1}{2})^{48} = 1/281{,}474{,}976{,}710{,}656$, which is practically zero, and the value of $2[1 - (\frac{1}{2})^{48}]$ is practically 2. To summarize, we say that as n becomes infinitely large, S_n approaches the limit 2, and 2 then represents the sum of the progression 1, ½, ¼, ⅛, . . . to infinitely many terms. This relation may be compactly expressed as

$$\lim_{n \to \infty} S_n = 2$$

It will be apparent that if r is any quantity between -1 and 1, the value of r^n may be made as close to zero as we please by making n sufficiently large. Hence from Eq. (27) we see that as n increases without limit, the value of S_n approaches $a(1 - 0)/(1 - r)$, or $a/(1 - r)$. That is,

$$\lim_{n \to \infty} S_n = \frac{a}{1 - r} \tag{34}$$

The limit of the sum of n terms, as n becomes infinitely large, is called the sum of the GP with infinitely many terms. If we represent the sum by S, then

$$S = \frac{a}{1 - r} \qquad -1 < r < 1 \tag{35}$$

The indicated sum of a succession of numbers is usually called a *series*. If infinitely many terms are taken, it is known as an *infinite series*. Accordingly, the expression $a + ar + ar^2 + \cdots$ is called an *infinite geometric series*. If the terms continually decrease and S approaches a limiting value as n becomes infinitely large, it is said to be a *convergent infinite series*.

Note that if $r < -1$ or $r > 1$, as in the GP 1, 2, 4, 8, . . . , where $r = 2$, S increases without limit as $n \to \infty$.

example 23 Find a rational number equivalent to the endless repeating decimal 0.53333 . . . .

We may express 0.53333 . . . as 0.5 plus the series 0.03 + 0.003 + 0.0003 + . . . to infinitely many terms. Here we evidently have an infinite geometric series in which $a = 0.03$ and $r = 0.1$. According to Eq. (35), the sum of the series is

$$\frac{0.03}{1 - 0.1} = \frac{0.03}{0.9} = \frac{1}{30}$$

Hence 0.53333 . . . $= 0.5 + \frac{1}{30} = \frac{1}{2} + \frac{1}{30} = \frac{8}{15}$.

It should be noted that any endlessly repeating decimal is a rational number, whereas an irrational number like $\sqrt{3}$ is equivalent to 1.732051 . . . , a nonrepeating decimal.

example 24 Find the fractional equivalent of the repeating decimal 0.61363636 . . . .

Rearranging, we have

$$0.61 + 0.0036 + 0.000036 + 0.00000036 + \cdots$$

After the first term, we have an infinite geometric series in which $a = 0.0036$ and $r = 0.01$. The sum of this portion of the series is

$$\frac{0.0036}{1 - 0.01} = \frac{0.0036}{0.99} = \frac{1}{275}$$

Hence

$$0.61363636 \cdots = \frac{61}{100} + \frac{1}{275} = \frac{671}{1100} + \frac{4}{1100} = \frac{675}{1100} = \frac{27}{44}$$

EXERCISE 9

In Probs. 1 to 8 find the sum of an infinitely large number of terms of the series.

1. 12, 6, 3, . . .
2. 15, 5, $\frac{5}{3}$, . . .
3. 75, -15, 3, . . .
4. 54, 36, 24, . . .
5. $\frac{3}{4}$, $-\frac{1}{2}$, $\frac{1}{3}$, . . .
6. 5, $-\frac{1}{2}$, $\frac{1}{20}$, . . .
7. $1 + x + x^2 + x^3 + \cdots$; $|x| < 1$
8. $1 - \frac{1}{x} + \frac{1}{x^2} - \frac{1}{x^3} \cdots$; $|x| > 1$

In Probs. 9 to 16 find the fractional equivalent, in lowest terms, of each of the following repeating decimals.

9. 0.666 . . .
10. 0.8888 . . .
11. 0.272727 . . .
12. 0.8333 . . .
13. 0.135135 . . .
14. 0.185185 . . .
15. 0.4090909 . . .
16. 0.41666 . . .

15·16 Applications of geometric progressions

The comments made regarding AP's in Sec. 15·10 apply in general to GP's. To these remarks it might be added that many problems involving the exponential type of equation $y = ba^x$ (see Sec. 10·30) may be solved by application of a GP. Typical of this type is a problem in which a pump removes one-tenth of the air from a tank at each stroke. After the nth stroke the remaining fraction of the original air will evidently be $(0.9)^n$.

example 25 If 50 ml of a 15 per cent aqueous solution of a uranium salt is shaken with 10 ml of ether, which is then drawn off, the concentration of uranium salt in the aqueous layer is reduced to 9 per cent; after the second extraction with 10 ml of ether, the concentration is reduced to 5.4 per cent; and so on. Find the concentration of uranium salt in the aqueous layer after 12 extractions.

We shall need to find the 13th term of the GP 0.15, 0.09, 0.054, ... Referring to Eq. (22), we shall substitute $a = 0.15$, $r = 0.6$, and $n = 13$ and obtain

$$l = (0.15)(0.6)^{12} = 0.00033, \text{ or } 0.033 \text{ per cent}$$

example 26 A block of metal at 200°C is placed in a room at 20°C. After 10 min it has cooled to 140°C; in another 10 min the temperature is 100°C. What will be its temperature after 2 hr?

We note that the original temperature differential is $200 - 20 = 180$. After 10 min it is $140 - 20 = 120$, and after 20 min it is reduced to $100 - 20 = 80$. It is evident that in any 10-min interval the temperature differential is reduced to two-thirds of its value at the beginning of that interval. Thus we see that the geometric progression is a property of Newton's law of cooling. This law also states that the rate of cooling at any instant is proportional to the temperature differential (between object and surrounding medium) at that instant (see Prob. 8, page 260).

In our problem we are dealing with twelve 10-min intervals. Hence we wish to find the 13th term of the GP 180, 120, 80, ...

Applying Eq. (22) and substituting $a = 180$, $r = \frac{2}{3}$, and $n = 13$, we obtain

$$l = (180)(\tfrac{2}{3})^{12} = 1.39$$

or

$$20 + 1.4 = 21.4°\text{C after 2 hr}$$

EXERCISE 10

1. Find two numbers whose difference is 14 and whose geometric mean is 24.
2. What number must be subtracted from each of the numbers 15, 5, and 20 so that the resulting numbers, taken in the same order, will form a geometric progression?

3. At the end of each year the value of a certain machine has depreciated by 20 per cent of its value at the beginning of that year. If its initial value was \$1,250, find its value at the end of 5 years.
4. If \$1,000 is deposited in a bank at 3 per cent interest compounded annually, find the amount in the account at the end of 4 years.
5. A tank full of a 12 per cent salt solution is emptied of one-third of its contents, after which it is filled up with fresh water and the contents well mixed. If this is done six times, what is the final concentration of the salt solution?
6. The air in a tank is at atmospheric pressure (29.92 in. of mercury). If the volume of the tank is 800 cu in. and the pump removes 50 cu in. of air at each stroke, find the air pressure in the tank after 200 strokes.
7. A flask of salt solution, originally at 95°C, cooled to 71°C after standing for 10 min in a laboratory at 23°C. Find its temperature after another hour.
8. How many ancestors have you had in the 10 preceding generations if no ancestor appears in more than one line of descent?
9. Find the sum of the first 19 positive integral powers of 1.02.
10. The radiator system of a car contains 4 gal of water. At the approach of the winter season the driver draws off a gallon and replaces it with alcohol. Subsequently a gallon of the mixture is drawn off and replaced with alcohol. By midwinter this process has been performed 5 times. Assuming no leakage or evaporation, what is the final percentage of alcohol in the cooling system?
11. Repeat Prob. 10, using 90 per cent alcohol as the replacement solution.
12. A ball is dropped from a height of 96 ft. If it always rebounds to half the height from which it falls, how far will it have traveled when it reaches the top of the fourth bounce? What distance will it have covered before coming to rest?
13. A saturated (4 per cent) aqueous solution of bromine is extracted with 20 ml of chloroform, whereupon the concentration of bromine in the aqueous layer is reduced to 1.2 per cent. Find the concentration of bromine in the aqueous layer after the sixth extraction with 20 ml of chloroform.
14. In the 60° right triangle in Fig. 15·5 find the sum of all the perpendiculars to the base $a, a_1, a_2, \ldots$ if the series is continued indefinitely.
15. The intensity of sunlight upon penetrating a layer of water 1 ft thick is diminished by 2 per cent of its value at the top of that layer. What percentage of the original light intensity remains at a depth of 50 ft?
16. When the air pressure at sea level is 750 mm of mercury, it is 600 mm at 850 m elevation. If a like percentage reduction in pressure occurs with each increase of 850 m in altitude, find the air pressure at 8,500 m.
17. The period of half-life for radium F (polonium) is 136 days. That is, in 136 days the disintegration of radium F will be one-half accomplished, in another 136 days the disintegration will be three-quarters

fig. 15·5

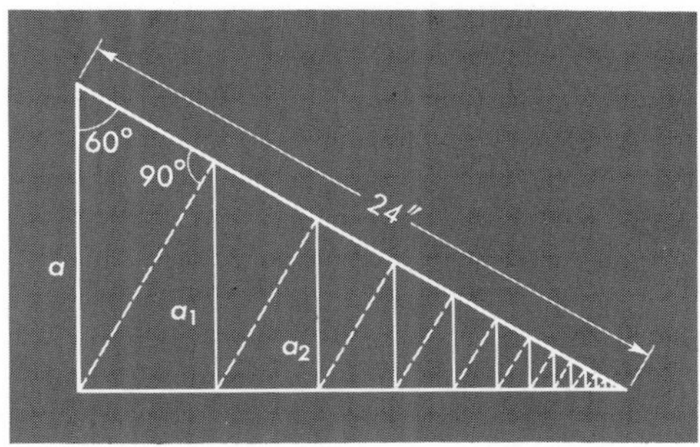

fig. 15·6

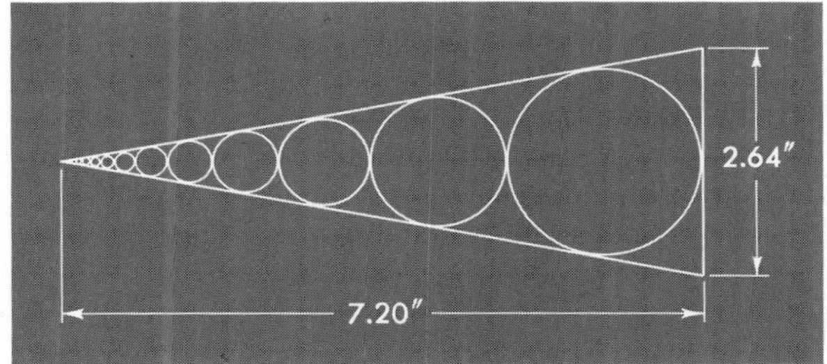

complete, in another 136 days seven-eighths, etc. What percentage will have disintegrated in 68 days?

18. In Fig. 15·6 an isosceles triangle is completely filled with tangent circles as shown. Find the total area of all the circles.
19. What is the smallest number of resistors which, when inserted in series, will provide any resistance, in steps of 1 ohm, from 1 to 15 ohms, inclusive?
20. A damped free vibration is shown in Fig. 15·7 (where displacement is plotted as a function of time). Such a vibration could be a weight

fig. 15·7

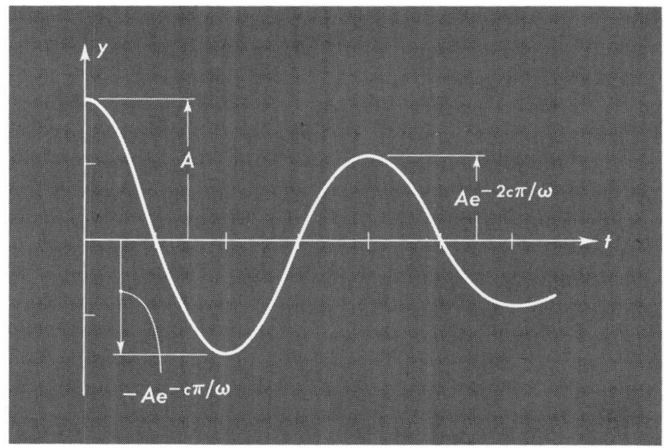

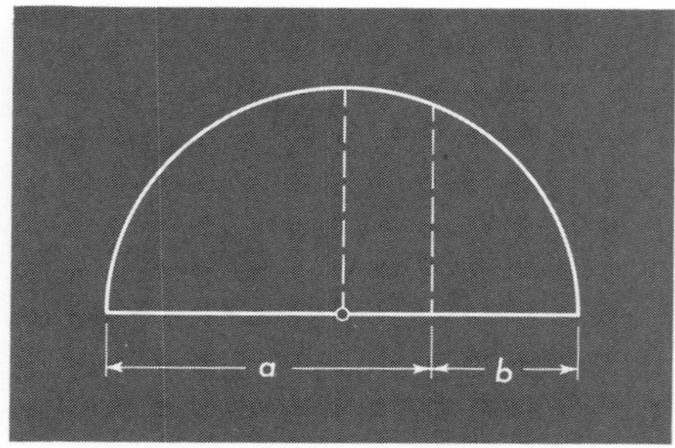

fig. 15·8

vibrating on the end of a spring. The numerical values of the extreme displacements are A, $-Ae^{-c\pi/\omega}$, $Ae^{-2c\pi/\omega}$, ...

(a) Show that these values form a geometric progression.

(b) Show that the logarithms to the base e of the absolute values of these numbers form an arithmetic progression.

The numerical value of the common difference is called the "logarithmic decrement." This term appears quite frequently in connection with vibration problems. What is its value in this problem?

21. Refer to the semicircle in Fig. 15·8 to show that the geometric mean of a and b is always less than the arithmetic mean of a and b ($a \neq b$).

unit five numerical trigonometry of the right triangle

classes which have had only a
very little algebra can study
this unit at any time

16
the right triangle

This section of the work will be concerned almost entirely with numerical trigonometry. This branch of trigonometry deals with methods by which certain sides and angles of a triangle may be computed when certain other sides and angles are known. Emphasis in this chapter will be on computation rather than analysis.

16·1 Angles

For the present purpose an angle will be described in terms of Fig. 16·1. The side r was originally coincident with the side OX. The side OX is called the initial position of r, or the *initial side* of the angle. However, r as shown in the diagram has been revolved about O in a counterclockwise direction and has become the *terminal side* of the angle.

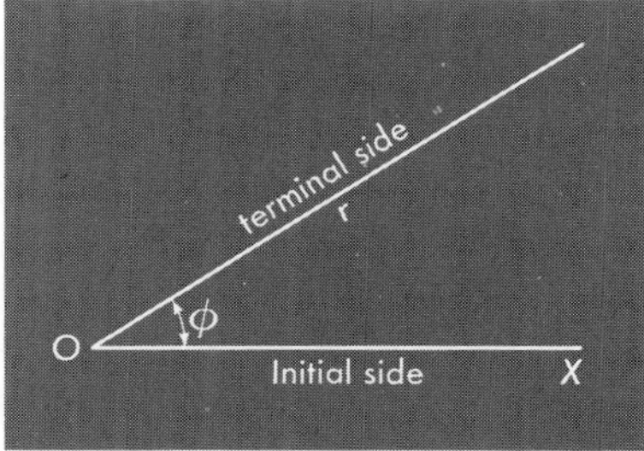

fig. 16·1

There are two systems of units ordinarily used to measure the magnitude of an angle: the *degree system* and the *radian system.* The radian system will be discussed in Chap. 18. The degree system is the only one of importance in numerical trigonometry.

If the line r had revolved about O for one complete revolution from the initial position, an angle of 360 degrees would have been generated. By definition, 1 degree is equivalent to 1/360 revolution. An angle of 90 degrees (written 90°) is equivalent to 90/360 or 1/4 revolution. An angle of 180° would be equivalent to 180/360 or 1/2 revolution.

Occasionally angles are measured in degrees and a decimal fraction of a degree, as for example 37.594°. More often they are measured in degrees and subunits of a degree, called minutes and seconds. There are, by definition, 60 minutes in 1 degree and 60 seconds in 1 minute. The angular magnitude 37 degrees 42 minutes and 36 seconds would be written 37°42′36″. Since there are 60 seconds in a minute, it follows that 6″ is equivalent to 1/10 minute. The angle 37°42′36″ could also have been written 37°42.6′, and indeed angles are frequently measured in degrees, minutes, and tenths of minutes.

16·2 Unique determination of triangles

A triangle is *determined* when enough information is at hand so that it can be drawn to scale. (If it can be drawn to scale, it can be solved numerically.) A triangle can be drawn to scale

1. If three sides are known.
2. If one side and two angles are known.
3. If two sides and one angle are known.

If the given angle is less than 90° and one of the two given sides is opposite this angle, there may possibly be two solutions. More will be said of this later in the work.

If a triangle is known to be a right triangle then, obviously, one angle is known. Thus a right triangle is determined if in addition we know two sides or one side and an acute angle.

16·3 Solution of triangles

A triangle is *solved* when the unknown sides and angles have been found. Triangles may be solved either by drawing them to scale and measuring the unknown sides and angles or by using suitable formulas to calculate the unknown dimensions.

Graphical solutions are common in surveying and mapping. They are also common in certain solutions to bridge- and roof-truss problems.

While computational methods will be the main concern of this chapter, the student should invariably make a scale drawing of the triangle he is solving. In this way he gets a far more vivid idea of the problem and the successive steps in the solution. Even more important, reference to the scale drawing will call his attention to gross errors in calculation.

Figure 16·2 illustrates a standard method of lettering a triangle. Note that capital letters are used to denote the angles and that small letters are used to denote the sides. Furthermore, side a is opposite angle A, side b is opposite angle B, and side c is opposite angle C.

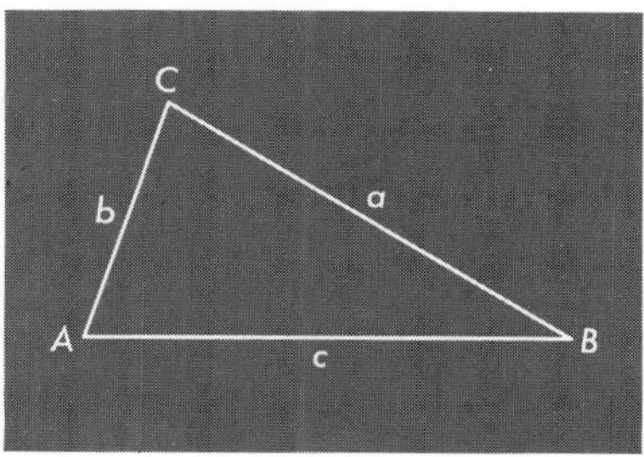

fig. 16·2

EXERCISE 1

(Even though the principal concern of this chapter is with right triangles, we have, in preparation for Chap. 18, included some oblique triangles in this exercise.)

In the following problems, the data are supposed to determine certain triangles. In some cases, these data are incomplete, inconsistent, or ambiguous. In other problems, data are correctly given. Draw these triangles full scale if correct data are given, and measure the unknown sides and angles. If the data are improperly given, tell in what respect they are improper.

1. $a = 3$ in.; $b = 4$ in.; $C = 90°$
2. $a = 4$ in.; $b = 3$ in.; $c = 5$ in.; $C = 90°$
3. $a = 10$ in.; $b = 3$ in.; $c = 5$ in.
4. $A = 30°$; $C = 90°$; $c = 5$ in.
5. $A = 30°$; $c = 3$ in.; $a = 1$ in.
6. $A = 30°$; $c = 3$ in.; $a = 1.5$ in.
7. $A = 30°$; $c = 3$ in.; $a = 2$ in.
8. $A = 130°$; $B = 120°$; $c = 5$ in.
9. $a = 4$ in.; $c = 6$ in.; $B = 30°$
10. $A = 30°$; $B = 120°$; $C = 30°$
11. $a = 4$ in.; $b = 3$ in.; $c = 3\frac{3}{4}$ in.; $C = 90°$
12. $A = 30°$; $B = 45°$; $c = 5$ in.

16·4 The trigonometric functions

The student has undoubtedly solved 30°, 60° right triangles entirely from principles learned in plane geometry. In that subject he learned that if we know the ratios among the linear dimensions of a right triangle, then we can solve the right triangle, provided we also know one linear dimension. In the special case above we found by plane geometry the six ratios which can be written among the linear dimensions of the triangle.

Referred to Fig. 16·4, these six ratios are repeated below.

$$\frac{a}{c} = \frac{1}{2} \qquad \frac{b}{c} = \frac{\sqrt{3}}{2} \qquad \frac{a}{b} = \frac{1}{\sqrt{3}}$$

$$\frac{b}{a} = \frac{\sqrt{3}}{1} \qquad \frac{c}{b} = \frac{2}{\sqrt{3}} \qquad \frac{c}{a} = \frac{2}{1}$$

The proof of these ratios is left to the student. Suggestion: Show that in Fig. 16·25, page 408, $ac = ab$ and that angle $acb = 60°$. Also show that the median drawn from c to ab bisects the angle acb.

If the acute angles of the right triangle were different from 30° and 60°, then the ratios would have been correspondingly different. In other words there is a unique correspondence between the six ratios and the acute angles.

16·5 Trigonometric tables

All six ratios associated with any angle have been calculated. The theory by which these calculations were made is beyond the scope of the present treatment, and the arithmetical work involved is too cumbersome for everyday use. (Such methods are, however, discussed in Chap. 23.) Instead, the ratios have been published in tabular form for use as needed. These ratios are said to be functions of the angle.

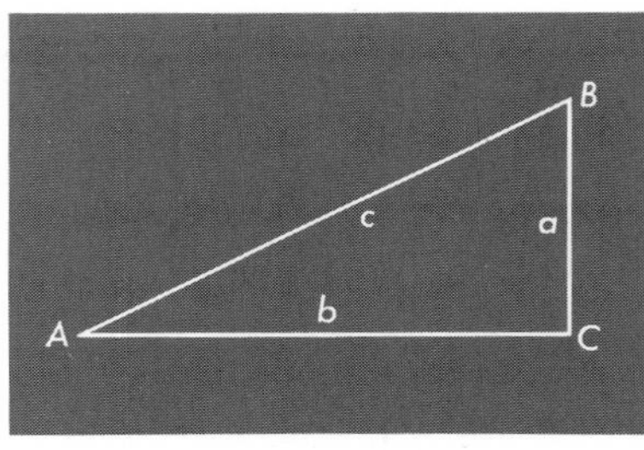

fig. 16·3

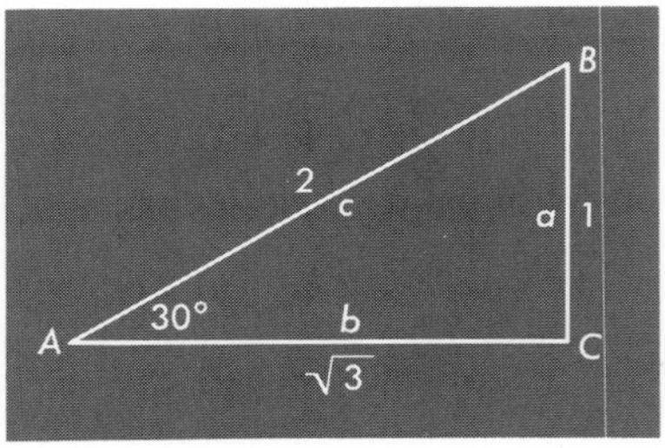

fig. 16·4

Each function is named and defined in terms of Fig. 16·3 by Eqs. (1) through (6). A more general definition of the trigonometric functions will be given in Sec. 17·7, and a still more general one will be given in Sec. 23·3.

$$\text{sine } A = a/c \qquad \text{abbreviated } \sin A \tag{1}$$
$$\text{cosine } A = b/c \qquad \text{abbreviated } \cos A \tag{2}$$
$$\text{tangent } A = a/b \qquad \text{abbreviated } \tan A \tag{3}$$
$$\text{cotangent } A = b/a \qquad \text{abbreviated } \cot A \tag{4}$$
$$\text{secant } A = c/b \qquad \text{abbreviated } \sec A \tag{5}$$
$$\text{cosecant } A = c/a \qquad \text{abbreviated cosec } A \tag{6}$$

A brief table of the functions is given in Table 16·1.

To find functions of angles between 0 and 45°, look for the angle in the *left-hand* column and look for the name of the desired function at the *top* of the table. The desired function will then be at the intersection of the row containing the angle and the column containing the name of the function.

To find functions of angles between 45 and 90°, look for the angle in the *right-hand* column and the name of the desired function at the *bottom* of the table. The desired function will then be at the intersection of the row containing the angle and the column containing the name of the function.

table 16·1

Angle *A*	*a/c* sin	*b/c* cos	*a/b* tan	*b/a* cot	*c/b* sec	*c/a* cosec	
0	0.000	1.000	0.000	...	1.000	...	90
5	0.087	0.996	0.087	11.430	1.004	11.474	85
10	0.174	0.985	0.176	5.671	1.015	5.759	80
15	0.259	0.966	0.268	3.732	1.035	3.864	75
20	0.342	0.940	0.364	2.747	1.064	2.924	70
25	0.423	0.906	0.466	2.145	1.103	2.366	65
30	0.500	0.866	0.577	1.732	1.155	2.000	60
35	0.574	0.819	0.700	1.428	1.221	1.743	55
40	0.643	0.766	0.839	1.192	1.305	1.556	50
45	0.707	0.707	1.000	1.000	1.414	1.414	45
	cos *b/c*	sin *a/c*	cot *b/a*	tan *a/b*	cosec *c/a*	sec *c/b*	Angle *A*

EXERCISE 2

Verify the following:

1. sin 20° = 0.342
2. cos 25° = 0.906
3. tan 10° = 0.176
4. cot 15° = 3.732
5. sec 40° = 1.305
6. cosec 5° = 11.474

EXERCISE 3

Verify the following:

1. cosec 45° = 1.414
2. cos 60° = 0.500
3. sin 60° = 0.866
4. cot 70° = 0.364
5. tan 75° = 3.732
6. sec 80° = 5.759

16·6 The use of Table 16·1

Instead of limiting the notion of a function to a ratio, it is often convenient to consider the functions as proportionality constants.

If $\sin A = a/c$, then $a = (\sin A) \times c$. This means that for a given angle the opposite side is directly proportional to the hypotenuse, and that $\sin A$ is the proportionality constant. If c is 1 unit in length, then,

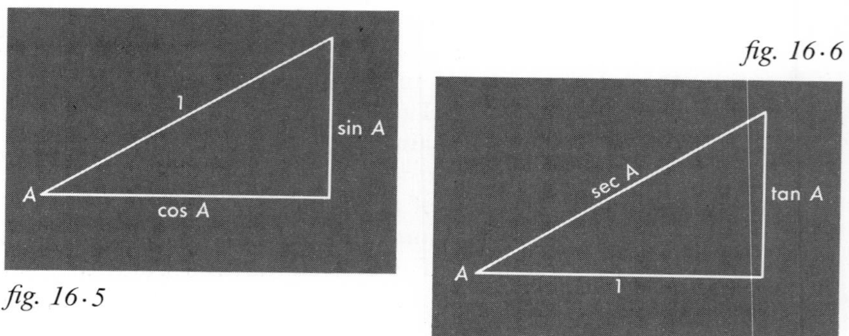

fig. 16·5

fig. 16·6

numerically,

$$a = \sin A$$

Formulas equivalent to Eqs. (1) to (6) may be written as

$$a = (\sin A) \times c \tag{7}$$
$$b = (\cos A) \times c \tag{8}$$
$$a = (\tan A) \times b \tag{9}$$
$$b = (\cot A) \times a \tag{10}$$
$$c = (\sec A) \times b \tag{11}$$
$$c = (\operatorname{cosec} A) \times a \tag{12}$$

Figures 16·5 to 16·7 illustrate the situation in which certain sides are of unit length.

example 1 Solve the right triangle shown in Fig. 16·8.

This triangle may be solved by either of two equivalent lines of reasoning. One line of reasoning starts with the functions as proportionality constants, and the other starts with the functions as ratios. Both methods are shown below.

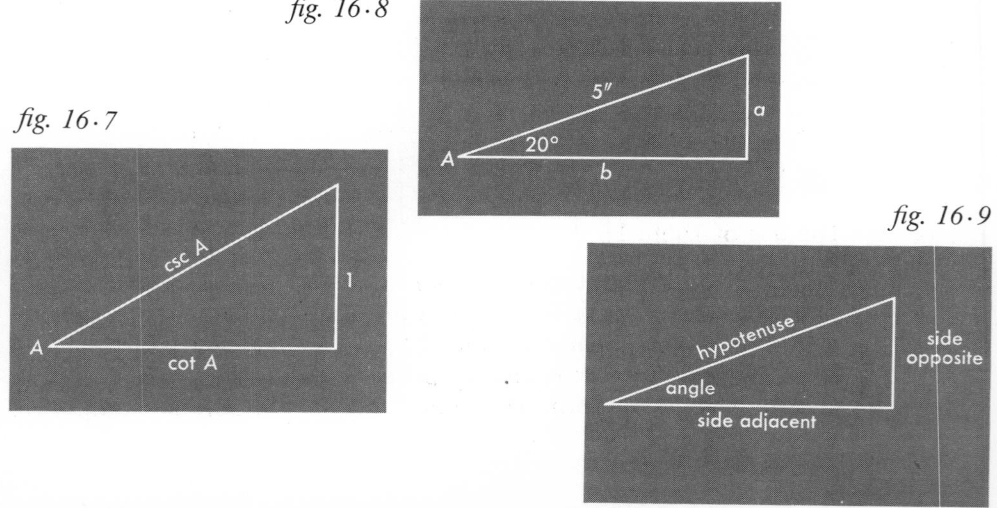

fig. 16·8

fig. 16·7

fig. 16·9

Functions as proportionality constants

If the hypotenuse had been 1 in. long, then

$$a = \sin 20° = 0.342 \text{ in.}$$
$$b = \cos 20° = 0.940 \text{ in.}$$

However, c is 5 times 1 in.; therefore,

$$a \text{ is 5 times } 0.342 \text{ in.} = 1.71 \text{ in.}$$

and

$$b \text{ is 5 times } 0.940 \text{ in.} = 4.70 \text{ in.}$$

Functions as ratios

Refer to Eqs. (1) to (6).

$$a/c = \sin A$$
$$a/5 \text{ in.} = \sin 20°$$
$$a = 5 \text{ in. } \sin 20° = 5 \text{ in.} \times 0.342$$
$$= 1.71 \text{ in.}$$
$$b/c = \cos A$$
$$b/5 \text{ in.} = 0.940$$
$$b = 5 \text{ in.} \times .940 = 4.70 \text{ in.}$$

EXERCISE 4

Verify the answers to the following problems, using Table 16·1.

1. $c = 7$ in., $A = 25°$. ANS.: $a = 2.961$ in., $b = 6.342$ in., $B = 65°$.
2. $c = 4$ in., $A = 40°$. ANS.: $a = 2.572$ in., $b = 3.064$ in., $B = 50°$.
3. $a = 10$ in., $A = 35°$. ANS.: $c = 17.43$ in., $b = 14.28$ in., $B = 55°$.
4. $b = 3$ in., $A = 15°$. ANS.: $a = 0.804$ in., $c = 3.105$ in., $B = 75°$.
5. $a = 2$ in., $A = 55°$. ANS.: $b = 1.400$ in., $c = 2.442$ in., $B = 35°$.
6. $b = 6$ in., $A = 80°$. ANS.: $c = 34.554$ in., $a = 34.026$ in., $B = 10°$.

16·7 Trigonometric functions defined

The definitions of the functions given in Eqs. (1) to (6) can be extended so as to be independent of any particular lettering system. The more general definitions are given below and refer to the right triangle in Fig. 16·9.

$$\text{Sine of an angle} = \frac{\text{side opposite}}{\text{hypotenuse}} \quad \textbf{(13)}$$

$$\text{Cosine of an angle} = \frac{\text{side adjacent}}{\text{hypotenuse}} \quad \textbf{(14)}$$

$$\text{Tangent of an angle} = \frac{\text{side opposite}}{\text{side adjacent}} \quad \textbf{(15)}$$

$$\text{Cotangent of an angle} = \frac{\text{side adjacent}}{\text{side opposite}} \quad \textbf{(16)}$$

$$\text{Secant of an angle} = \frac{\text{hypotenuse}}{\text{side adjacent}} \quad \textbf{(17)}$$

$$\text{Cosecant of an angle} = \frac{\text{hypotenuse}}{\text{side opposite}} \quad \textbf{(18)}$$

16·8 The cofunctions

In Fig. 16·3,

$$\sin A = \frac{\text{side opposite}}{\text{hypotenuse}} = \frac{a}{c}$$

But

$$\cos B = \frac{\text{side adjacent}}{\text{hypotenuse}} = \frac{a}{c}$$

Therefore,

$$\sin A = \cos B$$

The student should verify the following relationships:

$\sin A = \cos B$	**(19)**	$\cot A = \tan B$	**(22)**
$\cos A = \sin B$	**(20)**	$\sec A = \operatorname{cosec} B$	**(23)**
$\tan A = \cot B$	**(21)**	$\operatorname{cosec} A = \sec B$	**(24)**

The word *cosine* means the sine of the complementary angle. In general, a cofunction is the function of the complementary angle. One angle is said to be the complement of another if their sum is 90°. In a right triangle the two acute angles are always complementary.

EXERCISE 5

Express as functions of the complementary angle the following:

1. sin 20°
2. cos 45°
3. cos 60°
4. tan 25°
5. cot 17°
6. sec 84°
7. cos 38.5°
8. cosec 80°
9. sec 25°

16·9 Reciprocal functions

Again referring to Fig. 16·3, note that

$$\sin A = \frac{a}{c} \qquad \text{and} \qquad \operatorname{cosec} A = \frac{c}{a}$$

Therefore,

$$\sin A \times \operatorname{cosec} A = \frac{a}{c} \times \frac{c}{a} = 1$$

or

$$\sin A = \frac{1}{\operatorname{cosec} A} \qquad \text{and} \qquad \operatorname{cosec} A = \frac{1}{\sin A} \tag{25}$$

Also,

$$\tan A = \frac{a}{b} \qquad \text{and} \qquad \cot A = \frac{b}{a}$$

Therefore,

$$\tan A \times \cot A = \frac{a}{b} \times \frac{b}{a} = 1$$

or

$$\tan A = \frac{1}{\cot A} \qquad \text{and} \qquad \cot A = \frac{1}{\tan A} \tag{26}$$

Also,

$$\cos A = \frac{b}{c} \qquad \text{and} \qquad \sec A = \frac{c}{b}$$

Therefore,

$$\cos A \times \sec A = \frac{b}{c} \times \frac{c}{b} = 1$$

or

$$\cos A = \frac{1}{\sec A} \qquad \text{and} \qquad \sec A = \frac{1}{\cos A} \tag{27}$$

It is apparent, then, that

1. *The sine of an angle is the reciprocal of the cosecant of the same angle.*
2. *The cosine of an angle is the reciprocal of the secant of the same angle.*
3. *The tangent of an angle is the reciprocal of the cotangent of the same angle.*

16 · 10 Use of the five-place trigonometric tables

As a practical compromise between the accuracy of larger tables and the convenience of smaller tables, the five-place table is very commonly used. The values given in it for the various functions are good to about as many places as the data usually encountered in civil, mechanical, and electrical engineering. Yet there are times when a seven-place table is required. Some engineering organizations use them exclusively. On the other hand, slide-rule accuracy is sufficient in many cases. For the present we shall use the five-place table.

In the five-place table, one page is usually devoted to the functions of each degree. When we are concerned with angles less than 45°, we use the column headings at the top of the page and the minutes column on the left-hand margin of the page. When we are concerned with angles between 45 and 90°, we use the column headings at the bottom of the page and the minutes column on the right-hand margin of the page. Tabular entries are made for each minute.

EXERCISE 6

Find the values of the six functions of the following angles, using the five-place tables:

1. 20°30′	2. 40°27′	3. 44°59′	4. 45°01′
5. 25°45′	6. 60°42′	7. 80°28′	8. 42°38′
9. 00°10′	10. 89°30′	11. 13°25′	12. 48°05′
13. 55°55′	14. 81°36′	15. 01°45′	

Find the angle when the following functions are given:

16. $\sin A = 0.00582$	17. $\sin A = 0.18052$
18. $\sin A = 0.68179$	19. $\sin A = 0.75414$
20. $\sin A = 0.99986$	21. $\cos A = 0.71873$
22. $\cos A = 0.54708$	23. $\cos A = 0.93190$
24. $\cos A = 0.16906$	25. $\cos A = 0.99854$
26. $\tan A = 0.06993$	27. $\tan A = 1.2124$
28. $\tan A = 0.46312$	29. $\tan A = 1.4596$
30. $\tan A = 0.90251$	31. $\cot A = 0.89883$
32. $\cot A = 1.7917$	33. $\cot A = 2.1364$
34. $\cot A = 0.62487$	35. $\cot A = 5.0658$
36. $\sec A = 1.0193$	37. $\sec A = 2.6040$

38. $\sec A = 1.2265$
39. $\sec A = 1.5601$
40. $\sec A = 1.4755$
41. $\operatorname{cosec} A = 1.5212$
42. $\operatorname{cosec} A = 1.2215$
43. $\operatorname{cosec} A = 2.0466$
44. $\operatorname{cosec} A = 6.1880$
45. $\operatorname{cosec} A = 11.105$

16·11 Suggestions for solving right triangles

In the examples given below the student should understand that all given linear dimensions are known to five significant digits and that all given angles are known to the nearest second.

The labor of solving triangles can be reduced considerably by intelligently choosing a method of attack. The student will be well advised to consider the suggestions given.

As a rule, it is better to use the formula in which the unknown side appears in the numerator. For example, suppose we are to solve the triangle in which $c = 15$ and $A = 42°$. First let us find side a. We write the fraction a/c and then check Eqs. (1) to (6), looking for the fraction a/c. We find that $a/c = \sin A$, and we shall use this formula. There is another formula which would, theoretically, be just as good: $c/a = \operatorname{cosec} A$. However, in solving for a the first equation leads to a multiplication, while the second leads to a division. Obviously the one involving a multiplication is easier to use than the one involving a division.

When we have two sides given and wish to find a trigonometric function by division, it is best to choose the formula which places the number with the fewest significant digits in the denominator. This, of course, leads to an easier division.

It is always well to examine the data to see if a given decimal fraction can profitably be converted to a common fraction.

Suppose that in Fig. 16·10 the data are given as shown and the angle ϕ is to be calculated. There are two choices: either the tangent or the cotangent of ϕ may be calculated. If the tangent of ϕ is calculated, the operation involves the division of a three-figure number (0.625) by a five-figure number (1.3795); if the cotangent is calculated, the operation involves the division of a five-figure number by a three-figure

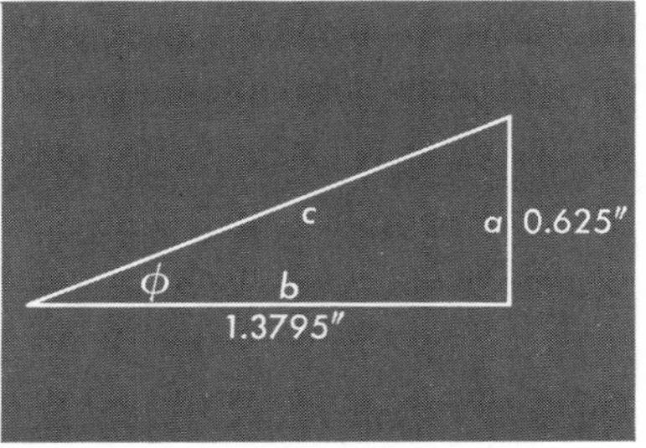

fig. 16·10

number. Obviously the arithmetic will be easier in calculating the cotangent. In this particular problem there is a still easier method if the student recognizes that 0.625 is the decimal equivalent of ⅝. The arithmetic can now be reduced to a multiplication by 8 and a division by 5, as shown below:

$$\cot \phi = \frac{1.3795}{5/8} = \frac{1.3795 \times 8}{5} = \frac{11.036}{5} = 2.2072$$

example 2 Referring to Fig. 16·3, if $c = 22.000''$ and $A = 28°32'$, find B, a, and b.

$$B = 90° - 28°32' = 61°28'$$

According to Eq. (7),

$$\begin{aligned} a &= c \sin A = 22 \sin 28°32' \\ &= 22 \times 0.47767 = 10.509'' \end{aligned}$$

Following Eq. (8),

$$\begin{aligned} b &= c \cos A = 22 \cos 28°32' \\ &= 22 \times 0.87854 = 19.328'' \end{aligned}$$

example 3 Referring to Fig. 16·3, if $a = 19.000''$ and $A = 62°27'$, find B, b, and c.

$$B = 90° - 62°27' = 27°33'$$

Following Eq. (12),

$$\begin{aligned} c &= a \operatorname{cosec} A = 19 \operatorname{cosec} 62°27' \\ &= 19 \times 1.1279 = 21.430'' \end{aligned}$$

Following Eq. (10),

$$\begin{aligned} b &= a \cot A = 19 \cot 62°27' \\ &= 19 \times 0.52168 = 9.9119'' \end{aligned}$$

example 4 Referring to Fig. 16·3, if $b = 26.000''$ and $A = 15°48'$, find B, a, and c.

$$B = 90° - 15°48' = 74°12'$$

Following Eq. (9),

$$\begin{aligned} a &= b \tan A = 26 \tan 15°48' \\ &= 26 \times 0.28297 = 7.3572'' \end{aligned}$$

Following Eq. (11),

$$\begin{aligned} c &= b \sec A = 26 \sec 15°48' \\ &= 26 \times 1.0393 = 27.022'' \end{aligned}$$

example 5 Referring to Fig. 16·3, if $a = 45.000''$ and $B = 24°00'$, find A, b, and c.

$$A = 90° - 24° = 66°$$

Following Eqs. (10) and (22) or Eq. (15),

$$\begin{aligned} b &= a \tan B = 45 \tan 24^\circ \\ &= 45 \times 0.44523 = 20.035'' \end{aligned}$$

Following Eqs. (12) and (24) or Eq. (17),

$$\begin{aligned} c &= a \sec B = 45 \sec 24^\circ \\ &= 45 \times 1.0946 = 49.257'' \end{aligned}$$

example 6 Referring to Fig. 16·3, if $b = 75.000''$ and $B = 85°00'$, find A, a, and c.

$$A = 90^\circ - 85^\circ = 5^\circ$$

Following Eqs. (9) and (21) or Eq. (16),

$$\begin{aligned} a &= b \cot B = 75 \cot 85^\circ \\ &= 75 \times 0.08749 = 6.5618'' \end{aligned}$$

Following Eqs. (11) and (23) or Eq. (18),

$$\begin{aligned} c &= b \operatorname{cosec} B = 75 \operatorname{cosec} 85^\circ \\ &= 75 \times 1.0038 = 75.285'' \end{aligned}$$

example 7 Referring to Fig. 16·3, if $c = 65.000''$ and $B = 8°00'$, find A, a, and b.

$$A = 90^\circ - 8^\circ = 82^\circ$$

Following Eqs. (7) and (19) or Eq. (14),

$$\begin{aligned} a &= c \cos B = 65 \cos 8^\circ \\ &= 65 \times 0.99027 = 64.368'' \end{aligned}$$

Following Eqs. (7) and (19) or Eq. (13),

$$\begin{aligned} b &= c \sin B = 65 \sin 8^\circ \\ &= 65 \times 0.13917 = 9.0460'' \end{aligned}$$

example 8 Referring to Fig. 16·3, if $b = 578.00''$ and $a = 483.00''$, find A, B, and c.

Following Eq. (3),

$$\tan A = \frac{a}{b} = \frac{483}{578} = 0.83564 \text{ (to five figures)}$$

and

$$A = 39^\circ 53'$$

Following Eq. (4),

$$\cot A = \frac{b}{a} = \frac{578}{483} = 1.1967 \text{ (to five figures)}$$

and

$$\begin{aligned} A &= 39^\circ 53' \\ B &= 90^\circ - 39^\circ 53' = 50^\circ 07' \end{aligned}$$

Following Eq. (11),

$$c = b \sec A = 578 \sec 39°53' = 578 \times 1.3032 = 753.25''$$

or following Eq. (12),

$$c = a \operatorname{cosec} A = 483 \operatorname{cosec} 39°53' = 483 \times 1.5595 = 753.24''$$

or following Eq. (1),

$$c = \frac{a}{\sin A} = \frac{483}{\sin 39°53'} = \frac{483}{0.64123} = 753.24$$

or following Eq. (2),

$$c = \frac{b}{\cos A} = \frac{578}{\cos 39°53'} = \frac{578}{0.76735} = 753.24$$

or using the Pythagorean theorem,

$$c = \sqrt{578^2 + 483^2} = \sqrt{567373} = 753.24''$$

example 9 Referring to Fig. 16·3, if $c = 1{,}237.0''$ and $a = 333.00''$, find A, B, and b.

Following Eq. (1),

$$\sin A = \frac{a}{c} = \frac{333}{1{,}237} = 0.26920 \text{ (to five figures)}$$

and

$$A = 15°37'$$

or following Eq. (6),

$$\operatorname{cosec} A = \frac{c}{a} = \frac{1{,}237}{333} = 3.7147 \text{ (to five figures)}$$

and

$$A = 15°37'$$
$$B = 90° - 15°37' = 74°23'$$
$$b = c \cos A = 1{,}237 \times \cos 15°37'$$
$$= 1{,}237 \times 0.96308 = 1{,}191.3''$$

or

$$b = \sqrt{c^2 - a^2} = \sqrt{1{,}237^2 - 333^2} = \sqrt{1419280} = 1{,}191.3''$$

example 10 The following example referring to Fig. 16·3 (when $c = 20.000''$ and $A = 6°00'$) is given without further comment to illustrate the inherent accuracy of various methods.

Using the sine,

$$a = 20 \sin 6° = 20 \times 0.10453 = 2.0906''$$

Using the cosecant,

$$a = \frac{20}{\operatorname{cosec} 6°} = \frac{20}{9.5668} = 2.0906'' \text{ (to five figures)}$$

Using the cosine,

$$b = 20 \cos 6° = 20 \times 0.99452 = 19.890'' \text{ (to five figures)}$$

Using the secant,

$$b = \frac{20}{\sec 6^\circ} = \frac{20}{1.0055} = 19.891'' \text{ (to five figures)}$$

Using seven-place tables of sines and cosines,

$$a = 20 \times \sin 6^\circ = 20 \times 0.1045285 = 2.090570''$$
$$b = 20 \times \cos 6^\circ = 20 \times 0.9945219 = 19.89044''$$

Using a and b as calculated from the five-place tables of sines and cosines,

$$\tan A = \frac{2.0906}{19.890} = 0.105108 \text{ or } 0.10511$$

By interpolation (see Sec. 16·12),

$$A = 6^\circ 00' 2''$$

Checking side c from the dimensions a and b calculated from five-place tables of sine and cosine,

$$c = \sqrt{2.0906^2 + 19.890^2} = \sqrt{4.3706 + 395.61}$$
$$= \sqrt{399.98} = 19.9997 \text{ (approx.)}$$

Actually, $$19.9997^2 = 399.988$$

Checking the side c from the dimensions of a and b calculated from the seven-place tables of sine and cosine,

$$c = \sqrt{2.090570^2 + 19.89044^2} = \sqrt{4.370482 + 395.6296}$$
$$= \sqrt{400.0001}$$

Actually, $$20.000003^2 = 400.0001$$

EXERCISE 7

In the following right triangles find the unknown dimensions, using a five-place table. Calculate linear dimensions accurate to five figures and angles accurate to the nearest minute. The class may of course be instructed to round off both the data and the corresponding answers to whatever number of significant figures seems appropriate. In these problems all given linear dimensions are known to five significant digits and all given angles are known to the nearest second.

1. $A = 36^\circ 14'$ $c = 94.309$ ft
2. $A = 38^\circ 19'$ $c = 8.125$ in.
3. $B = 62^\circ 52'$ $c = 132.00$ ft
4. $B = 11^\circ 10'$ $c = 89.048$ in.
5. $A = 8^\circ 8'$ $c = 2.1919$ in.
6. $B = 49^\circ 44'$ $c = 355.06$ in.
7. $A = 68^\circ 22'$ $c = 250.00$ in.
8. $A = 8^\circ 25'$ $c = 12.500$ ft
9. $B = 37^\circ 47'$ $c = 64.290$ ft
10. $B = 39^\circ 30'$ $c = 9.6354$ in.
11. $A = 82^\circ 16'$ $a = 40{,}625$ ft
12. $A = 16^\circ 4'$ $a = 0.93750$ ft
13. $A = 19^\circ 21'$ $a = 47.395$ ft
14. $A = 19^\circ 31'$ $a = 31.250$ in.
15. $A = 16^\circ 18'$ $a = 14.0625$ ft
16. $B = 74^\circ 24'$ $b = 93.750$ in.

17. $B = 47°35'$	$a = 312.50$ in.	18. $B = 50°26'$	$b = 15.625$ in.
19. $A = 48°40'$	$b = 8{,}125.0$ in.	20. $A = 72°48'$	$b = 718.75$ ft
21. $a = 347$ ft	$b = 167$ ft	22. $a = 199$ ft	$b = 160$ ft
23. $a = 67{,}130$ in.	$b = 25{,}210$ in.	24. $a = 46.370$ ft	$b = 94.720$ ft
25. $a = 141$ in.	$b = 203$ in.	26. $c = 3{,}477$ ft	$a = 2{,}638$ ft
27. $c = 2{,}691$ ft	$a = 839.0$ ft	28. $c = 505.0$ ft	$a = 457.0$ ft
29. $c = 43{,}649$ ft	$a = 17{,}962$ ft	30. $c = 248.09$ ft	$a = 218.54$ ft
31. $c = 11{,}223$ ft	$b = 10{,}454$ ft	32. $c = 87.02$ ft	$b = 55.43$ ft
33. $c = 2{,}338$ ft	$b = 1{,}877$ ft	34. $c = 455$ in.	$b = 241$ in.
35. $c = 1{,}029$ ft	$b = 985.0$ ft		

16·12 Interpolation in the five-place tables

It is often necessary to find a function of an angle intermediate between values given in a table of natural trigonometric functions. In such cases we resort to interpolation. In Sec. 2·2 we discussed some of the basic principles of interpolation, and in Sec. 10·20 we applied these principles to the use of tables of logarithms. In this section we shall therefore be somewhat brief in our discussion of interpolation applied to tables of natural trigonometric functions.

example 11 Find the sine of $26°45'12''$.

From the tables we find that $\sin 26°45' = 0.45010$ and $\sin 26°46' = 0.45036$. In the process of becoming familiar with this interpolation technique, it may be convenient to use the following pattern. See Sec. 10·20.

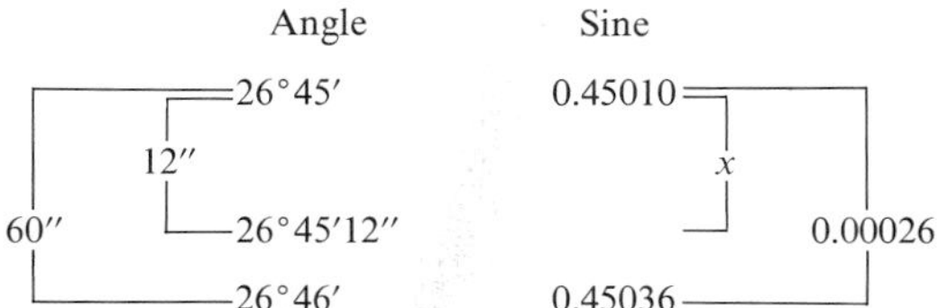

By proportion

$$\frac{x}{0.00026} = \frac{12}{60}$$

or
$$x = \tfrac{12}{60} \times 0.00026 = 0.00005$$
$$\sin 26°45'12'' = 0.45010 + 0.00005 = 0.45015$$

In the following examples we shall dispense with the above diagram.

example 12 Find the sine of $26°15.6'$.

$$\sin 26°16' = 0.44255$$
$$\sin 26°15' = \underline{0.44229}$$
$$0.00026 \qquad \tfrac{6}{10} \times 0.00026 = 0.000156 \text{ or } 0.00016$$
$$\sin 26°15.6' = 0.44229 + 0.00016 = 0.44245$$

example 13 Find the cosine of $61°13'52''$.

$$\begin{aligned} \cos 61°13' &= 0.48150 \\ \cos 61°14' &= \underline{0.48124} \\ & \quad 0.00026 \qquad \tfrac{52}{60} \times 0.00026 = 0.00023 \end{aligned}$$

$$\cos 61°13'52'' = 0.48150 - 0.00023 = 0.48127$$

Observe in the above examples that, as the angle increases, its cosine decreases.

The student should confirm from the tables that in the first quadrant, as the angle *increases,* its sine, tangent, and secant all *increase,* while its cosine, cotangent, and cosecant all *decrease.*

example 14 Find the tangent of $53°27'19''$.

$$\begin{aligned} \tan 53°28' &= 1.3498 \\ \tan 53°27' &= \underline{1.3490} \\ & \quad 0.0008 \qquad \tfrac{19}{60} \times 0.0008 = 0.0003 \end{aligned}$$

$$\tan 53°27'19'' = 1.3490 + 0.0003 = 1.3493$$

example 15 Find the cotangent of $38°41'25''$.

$$\begin{aligned} \cot 38°41' &= 1.2489 \\ \cot 38°42' &= \underline{1.2482} \\ & \quad 0.0007 \qquad \tfrac{25}{60} \times 0.0007 = 0.0003 \end{aligned}$$

$$\cot 38°41'25'' = 1.2489 - 0.0003 = 1.2486$$

example 16 Find ϕ if $\sin \phi = 0.56295$.

$$\begin{aligned} \sin 34°16' &= 0.56305 & \sin \phi &= 0.56295 \\ \sin 34°15' &= \underline{0.56280} & \sin 34°15' &= \underline{0.56280} \\ & \quad 0.00025 & & \quad 0.00015 \end{aligned}$$

$$\phi = 34°15' + \tfrac{15}{25} \times 60'' = 34°15'36''$$

example 17 Find ϕ if $\cos \phi = 0.81555$.

$$\begin{aligned} \cos 35°21' &= 0.81563 & \cos 35°21' &= 0.81563 \\ \cos 35°22' &= \underline{0.81546} & \cos \phi &= \underline{0.81555} \\ & \quad 0.00017 & & \quad 0.00008 \end{aligned}$$

$$\phi = 35°21' + \tfrac{8}{17} \times 60'' = 35°21'28''$$

If we are dealing in angular measure to the nearest second, we are in effect recognizing 60 angles between adjacent tabular entries in the angle column. However, there may be less or more than 60 five-digit numbers between corresponding tabular entries in the function column.

Therefore, if the tabular difference in the function column is small, there may be several closely grouped angles measured to the nearest second which will have the same function to five digits. If the tabular difference in the function column is large, a single angle measured to the nearest second may correspond to a range of five-figure numbers in the function column.

Refer to Example 14 above. Here, the difference between tabular entries in the tangent column is 8 in the last decimal place used. The difference in the angle is 60″. Therefore in this range of this table a difference of one unit in the last place in the tangent column corresponds to a difference of $\frac{60}{8} = 7.5''$ in the angle column. Consequently, in this portion of the five-place tables, the tangent may not be sensitive to angular changes of less than 7.5″.

If we were looking up the angle whose tangent is 1.3493, we probably should write the angle as $53°27'22'' \pm 4''$.

While we ordinarily do not go to this extreme in indicating the precision of interpolated angles, the student should certainly be aware of the limitations of the tables he uses.

In Example 14 above we calculated $\frac{19}{60}$ of 0.0008 and rounded off before adding on to 1.3490. We could, with equal reason, have found $\frac{19}{60}$ of 0.0008 to five decimal places and rounded off the tangent after addition. Usually it makes no difference. In the problems to follow it has been the policy to round off after addition.

In the absence of good reason to the contrary, all data in the following problems are assumed to have an accuracy consistent with the use of five-place tables with interpolation.

EXERCISE 8

Find the sine, cosine, tangent, cotangent, secant, and cosecant to five significant figures.

1. 2°28′15″ 2. 6°42′29″ 3. 14°17′13″ 4. 23°19′52″
5. 40°12′48″ 6. 49°36′27″ 7. 52°47′35″ 8. 71°28′18″
9. 80°59′40″ 10. 85°43.4′ 11. 27°15.3′ 12. 42°27.6′
13. 72°19.8′ 14. 85°26.2′ 15. 17°15.7′

EXERCISE 9

Find the angle to degrees, minutes, and seconds when the following functions are given:

1. $\sin\phi = 0.10572$ 2. $\sin\phi = 0.32650$ 3. $\sin\phi = 0.57461$
4. $\sin\phi = 0.81385$ 5. $\sin\phi = 0.72645$ 6. $\cos\phi = 0.49695$
7. $\cos\phi = 0.97808$ 8. $\cos\phi = 0.99981$ 9. $\cos\phi = 0.02391$
10. $\cos\phi = 0.54980$ 11. $\tan\phi = 0.86901$ 12. $\tan\phi = 1.1109$
13. $\tan\phi = 0.46430$ 14. $\tan\phi = 12.271$ 15. $\tan\phi = 1.0455$
16. $\cot\phi = 249.88$ 17. $\cot\phi = 0.06315$ 18. $\cot\phi = 2.7592$
19. $\cot\phi = 1.5476$ 20. $\cot\phi = 1.3825$ 21. $\sec\phi = 23.042$
22. $\sec\phi = 1.0670$ 23. $\sec\phi = 1.6032$ 24. $\sec\phi = 1.2130$
25. $\sec\phi = 2.3440$ 26. $\operatorname{cosec}\phi = 2.7290$ 27. $\operatorname{cosec}\phi = 9.3381$
28. $\operatorname{cosec}\phi = 1.2880$ 29. $\operatorname{cosec}\phi = 1.3834$ 30. $\operatorname{cosec}\phi = 1.3119$

EXERCISE 10

Solve the following right triangles, using five-place functions.

The class may, of course, be instructed to round off both the data and the corresponding answers to whatever number of significant figures seems appropriate.

1. $A = 38°50'45''$ $c = 0.87500$ in.
2. $A = 27°12'32''$ $c = 7.9143$ in.
3. $A = 53°35.5'$ $c = 15.453$ in.
4. $A = 37°50'10''$ $c = 98.268$ ft
5. $B = 22°32.1'$ $c = 2726.0$ ft
6. $A = 10°42'47''$ $c = 5.3805$ in.
7. $B = 53°24'34''$ $c = 10.625$ in.
8. $A = 38°14.9'$ $c = 8.1250$ ft
9. $B = 60°34'43''$ $c = 14.000$ ft
10. $A = 32°50'47''$ $c = 15.000$ ft
11. $A = 5°50'31''$ $a = 1250.0$ ft
12. $A = 11°16'44''$ $a = 457.31$ ft
13. $A = 45°15.8'$ $a = 986.91$ ft
14. $B = 36°44'2''$ $a = 12.500$ in.
15. $A = 17°48.3'$ $a = 713.85$ ft
16. $B = 38°56'46''$ $b = 63.275$ ft
17. $B = 86°11.4'$ $b = 756.23$ ft
18. $B = 89°30.6'$ $b = 1.8750$ in.
19. $A = 21°42'58''$ $b = 51.387$ ft
20. $A = 10°38'13''$ $b = 46.500$ ft
21. $a = 20.000$ in. $b = 37.998$ in.
22. $a = 12.000$ in. $b = 23.828$ in.
23. $a = 4.6397$ ft $b = 17.927$ ft
24. $a = 389.72$ in. $b = 1303.1$ in.
25. $a = 83.695$ ft $b = 177.70$ ft
26. $a = 1.1250$ in. $b = 1.4462$ in.
27. $a = 437.92$ ft $b = 1284.9$ ft
28. $a = 76.392$ ft $b = 191.67$ ft
29. $a = 31.250$ in. $b = 44.679$ in.
30. $a = 2.1875$ ft $b = 3.3878$ ft
31. $a = 147.00$ in. $c = 418.58$ in.
32. $a = 23.458$ in. $c = 236.64$ in.
33. $a = 39.738$ ft $c = 42.973$ ft
34. $a = 358.03$ ft $c = 369.16$ ft
35. $a = 939.52$ in. $c = 1,136.6$ in.
36. $b = 0.34297$ ft $c = 0.40083$ ft
37. $b = 125.00$ in. $c = 299.80$ in.
38. $b = 1.6250$ in. $c = 2.5898$ in.
39. $b = 13.794$ ft $c = 18.667$ ft
40. $b = 53.187$ in. $c = 65.142$ in.

The following problems are simplifications of various machine and tool design problems. Find the value of x to five significant figures or to the nearest second.

41. Solve for x in Fig. 16·11.
42. Solve for x in Fig. 16·12.
43. Solve for x in Fig. 16·13.
44. Solve for x in Fig. 16·14.
45. Solve for x in Fig. 16·15.
46. Solve for x in Fig. 16·16.
47. Solve for x in Fig. 16·17.
48. Solve for x in Fig. 16·18.

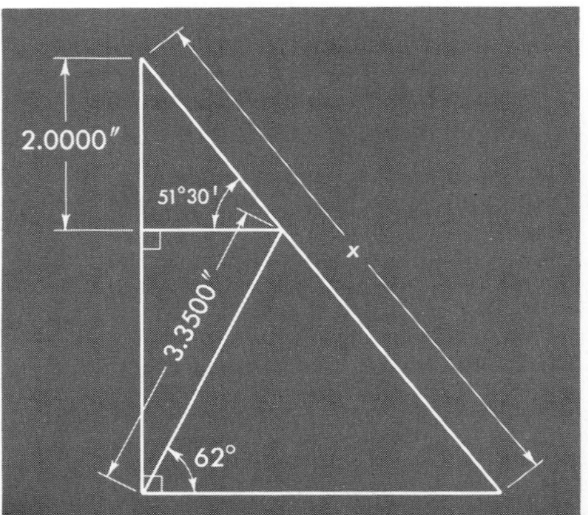

fig. 16·11

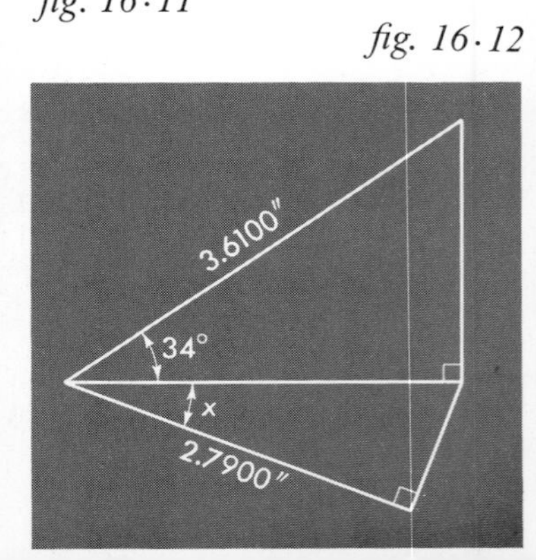

fig. 16·12

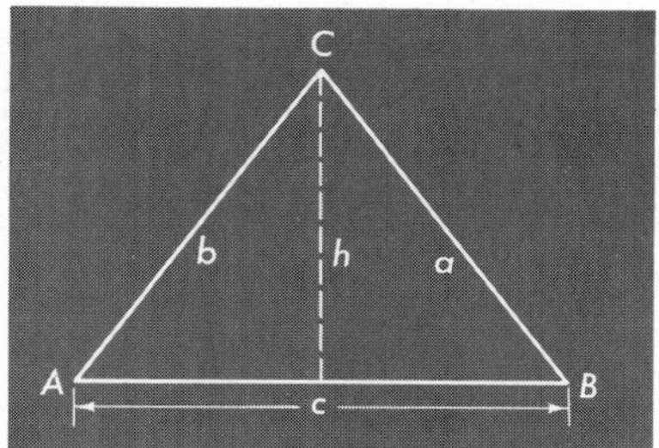

fig. 16·21

If angle C and either a or b are known, then

$$c = 2b \sin \tfrac{1}{2}C \tag{32}$$

or

$$c = 2a \sin \tfrac{1}{2}C \tag{33}$$

EXERCISE 11

1. The equal sides of an isosceles triangle are each 5.86 in. long, and each base angle is 23°51′. Find the length of the base and the altitude of the triangle.
2. A sheet of metal 15 in. wide is bent along its center line to form a V-shaped gutter. Will the gutter have a greater capacity when it is 6 in. wide at the top, or when 6 in. deep? What angle of the V will result in maximum capacity?
3. Find the angle of bend for each case in Prob. 2.
4. A right prism has for its base an equilateral triangle 7.3 in. on each side. It is cut by a plane which makes an angle of 25° with the base; one side of the section includes one side of the base. Find the sides, angles, and area of the section.
5. A sphere 5½ in. in diameter is dropped into a tin cone 8½ in. in diameter and 7½ in. deep. Is the top of the sphere above or below the rim of the cone, and how far?
6. The legs of a tripod are each 4 ft 2¾ in. long, and their feet form an equilateral triangle 2 ft 1½ in. on a side. Find the angle between one leg and a plum bob hung from its top.
7. Find the area of a segment cut off from a circle 16.82 in. in diameter by a line 2.73 in. from the center.
8. Each leaf of a swinging double door 3 ft 6 in. wide has been opened through an angle of 64°. How far apart are their edges? How far is each edge from the line of closure? Each section of the door is opened inward.

16·14 The functions of 30°, 45°, and 60°

The functions of these special angles appear frequently in the analysis of engineering problems. Consequently the student will be well advised to remember them or at least to be able to derive them at a moment's notice.

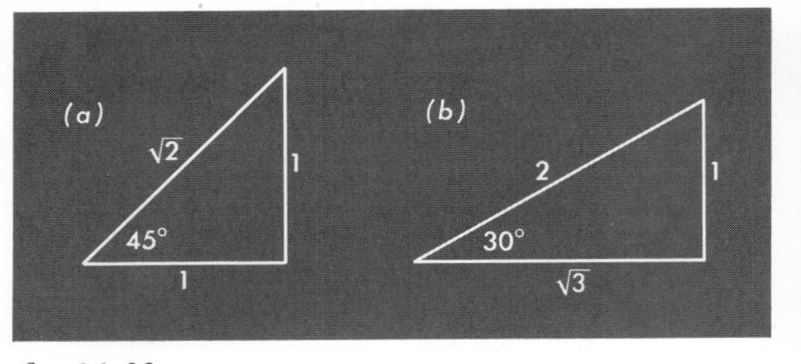

fig. 16·22

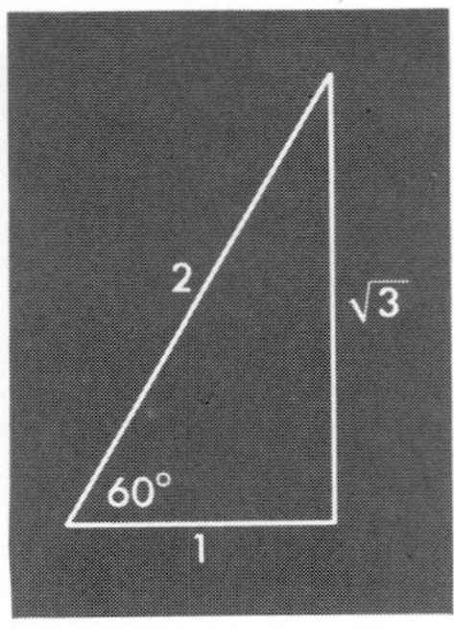

fig. 16·23

From Fig. 16·22*a* and consistent with Eqs. (13) to (18), it appears that

$$\sin 45^\circ = \frac{1}{\sqrt{2}} = \frac{\sqrt{2}}{2} = 0.707 \tag{34}$$

$$\cos 45^\circ = \frac{1}{\sqrt{2}} = \frac{\sqrt{2}}{2} = 0.707 \tag{35}$$

$$\tan 45^\circ = \frac{1}{1} = 1 \tag{36}$$

$$\cot 45^\circ = \frac{1}{1} = 1 \tag{37}$$

$$\sec 45^\circ = \frac{\sqrt{2}}{1} = \sqrt{2} = 1.414 \tag{38}$$

$$\operatorname{cosec} 45^\circ = \frac{\sqrt{2}}{1} = \sqrt{2} = 1.414 \tag{39}$$

Referring to Fig. 16·22*b* and the same basic equations,

$$\sin 30^\circ = \frac{1}{2} = 0.500 \tag{40}$$

$$\cos 30^\circ = \frac{\sqrt{3}}{2} = 0.866 \tag{41}$$

$$\tan 30^\circ = \frac{1}{\sqrt{3}} = \frac{\sqrt{3}}{3} = 0.577 \tag{42}$$

$$\cot 30^\circ = \frac{\sqrt{3}}{1} = \sqrt{3} = 1.732 \tag{43}$$

$$\sec 30^\circ = \frac{2}{\sqrt{3}} = \frac{2\sqrt{3}}{3} = 1.155 \tag{44}$$

$$\operatorname{cosec} 30^\circ = \frac{2}{1} = 2 \tag{45}$$

Referring to Fig. 16·23 and again using the same basic equations,

$$\sin 60^\circ = \frac{\sqrt{3}}{2} = 0.866 \tag{46}$$

$$\cos 60^\circ = \frac{1}{2} = 0.500 \tag{47}$$

$$\tan 60^\circ = \frac{\sqrt{3}}{1} = \sqrt{3} = 1.732 \tag{48}$$

$$\cot 60^\circ = \frac{1}{\sqrt{3}} = \frac{\sqrt{3}}{3} = 0.577 \tag{49}$$

$$\sec 60^\circ = \frac{2}{1} = 2 \tag{50}$$

$$\operatorname{cosec} 60^\circ = \frac{2}{\sqrt{3}} = \frac{2\sqrt{3}}{3} = 1.155 \tag{51}$$

EXERCISE 12

It is intended that the following problems will be done on a slide rule without the use of trigonometric tables.

1. Find x in Fig. 16·24*a*.
2. Find x in Fig. 16·24*b*.
3. Find x in Fig. 16·24*c*.
4. Find x in Fig. 16·24*d*.
5. Find x in Fig. 16·24*e*.
6. Find x in Fig. 16·24*f*.
7. Find x in Fig. 16·24*g*.

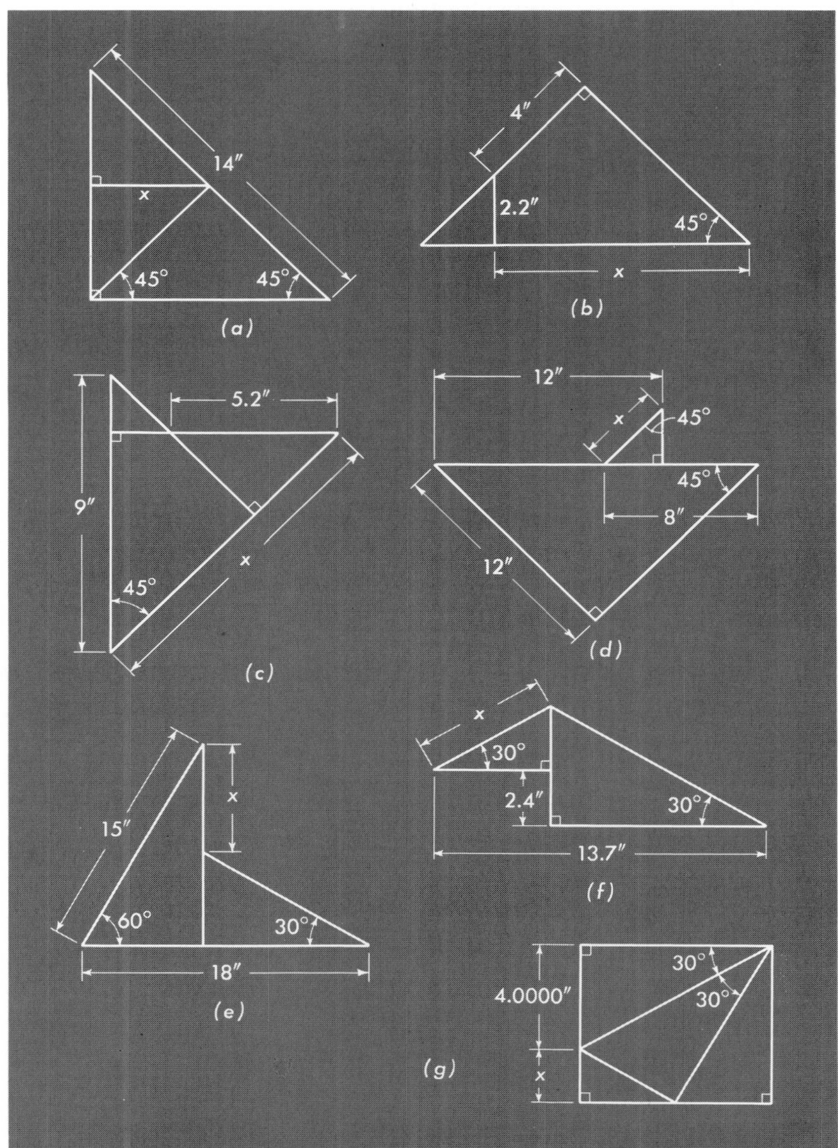

fig. 16·24

16·15 Regular polygons

A regular polygon (see Fig. 16·25) is inscribed in a circle of radius R and circumscribed about a circle of radius r. Let

s = length of one side = $\overline{ab}$
n = the number of sides
R = the radius of the circumscribed circle
r = the radius of the inscribed circle, sometimes called the *apothem*
p = the perimeter of the polygon = ns
A_t = area of a single triangle, as for example the triangle *abc*
A_p = area of the entire polygon

It can be proved that

$$A_t = \frac{s^2}{4} \cot \frac{180°}{n} \tag{52}$$

$$A_t = \frac{R^2}{2} \sin \frac{360°}{n} \tag{53}$$

$$A_t = r^2 \tan \frac{180°}{n} \tag{54}$$

$$r = \frac{s}{2} \cot \frac{180°}{n} \tag{55}$$

$$R = \frac{s}{2} \operatorname{cosec} \frac{180°}{n} \tag{56}$$

$$p = 2nR \sin \frac{180°}{n} \tag{57}$$

$$p = 2nr \tan \frac{180°}{n} \tag{58}$$

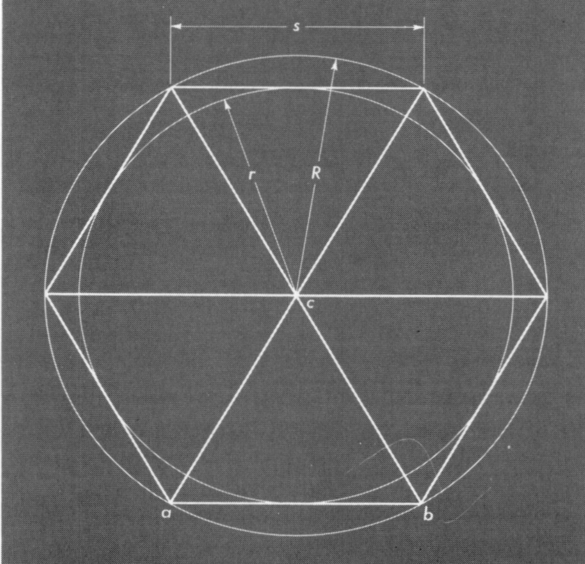

fig. 16·25

The derivations of Eqs. (52) through (58) are quite simple and should be performed by the student (see Prob. 1, Exercise 13).

Observe that in the special cases in which the central angle of the regular polygon is a multiple of 30°, 45°, or 60°, the quantities A_t, R, r, etc., can be calculated without the use of trigonometric tables from Eqs. (34) through (51).

EXERCISE 13

1. Verify Eqs. (52) through (58).
2. Complete Table 16·2.

table 16·2

Polygon	*Number of sides*	*Area*	*Radius of inscribed circle*	*Radius of circumscribed circle*
EQUILATERAL TRIANGLE	3	0.433 s^2	0.289 s	0.577 s
SQUARE	4			
HEXAGON	6			
OCTAGON	8			

3. Prove that in a regular polygon,

(a) $A_p = \frac{1}{4} ns^2 \cot \frac{180°}{n} = \frac{1}{2} nR^2 \sin \frac{360°}{n} = nr^2 \tan \frac{180°}{n}$.

(b) $r = \frac{s}{2} \cot \frac{180°}{n}$.

(c) $R = \frac{1}{2} s \operatorname{cosec} \frac{180°}{n}$.

(d) $p = 2nR \sin \frac{180°}{n} = 2nr \tan \frac{180°}{n}$.

4. One side of a regular decagon inscribed in a circle is 3.27 in. Find the radius of the circle.
5. Find the area of the decagon of Prob. 4.
6. A ring 15 in. in diameter is suspended from a point by 10 cords, each 9 in. long and equally spaced. Find the angle between two adjacent cords.
7. The length of one side of a regular polygon of 6 sides is 1 in. Find the area of a regular polygon of 12 sides inscribed in the same circle.
8. Find the difference in area between a regular polygon of eight sides and a regular polygon of nine sides if the perimeter of each is 72 in.
9. The length of a side in a regular polygon of five sides is 2 in. Find the area of the ring bounded by the circumferences of the inscribed and circumscribed circles.

10. Find the length of side of the largest regular hexagon which can be cut from a square sheet of paper 10 in. on a side. HINT: The side of the square does not necessarily contain a side of the hexagon.

16 · 16 Logarithmic solution of right triangles

The multiplication and division necessary in solving right triangles can, of course, be done by logarithms. For this purpose, tables have been published in which the logarithms of the functions are given directly. These tables are organized in exactly the same way as the corresponding tables of natural functions.

The sine or cosine of an angle can never exceed 1.00000. Therefore, the logarithm of a sine or cosine always has a negative characteristic. The logarithm of the sine of 17° (log sin 17°) is listed in the table of log functions as 9.46594. It is understood that this logarithm is followed by −10, and the complete logarithm would be written

$$\log \sin 17^\circ = 9.46594 - 10$$

or

$$\log \sin 17^\circ = \bar{1}.46594$$

or

$$\log \sin 17^\circ = 0.46594 - 1$$

The log tan 11° is listed as 9.28865. In this case it is understood that the logarithm is followed by −10, and the complete logarithm would be written

$$\log \tan 11^\circ = 9.28865 - 10$$

or

$$\log \tan 11^\circ = \bar{1}.28865$$

or

$$\log \tan 11^\circ = 0.28865 - 1$$

Remembering that the tangent of an angle greater than 45° is itself greater than 1, it should be obvious that the log tangent of an angle greater than 45° has a positive or zero characteristic. The log tangent of 76°10′ is listed as 0.60864 and is, of course, not followed by a −10.

$$\log \tan 76^\circ 10' = 0.60864$$

example 18 Find log sin 15°26′15″.

$$\begin{aligned} \log \sin 15^\circ 27' &= 9.42553 - 10 = 0.42553 - 1 \\ \log \sin 15^\circ 26' &= \underline{9.42507 - 10 = 0.42507} - 1 \\ &\ 0.00046 \qquad\qquad 0.00046 \end{aligned}$$

$$\tfrac{15}{60} \times 0.00046 = 0.000115$$

$$\begin{aligned} \log \sin 15^\circ 26' 15'' &= 9.42507 - 10 + 0.000115 \\ &= 9.425185 - 10, \text{ or } 0.425185 - 1 \end{aligned}$$

In rounding off to five places, since the number ends in exactly 5, the last digit in the rounded-off number is left the nearest even digit, or

$$\log \sin 15^\circ 26' 15'' = 9.42518 - 10 = 0.42518 - 1$$

Notice that the difference between adjacent tabular entries is published in the table under the *d* column. This avoids the need for an actual subtraction such as was done in the above example.

example 19 Find ϕ if $\log \tan \phi = 0.42765$.

This number appears directly in the table and is the log tangent of $69°31'$. Notice that $\log \tan 14°59' = 9.42755 - 10$, and the $\log \tan 1°32' = 8.42762 - 10$.

Therefore, the student should be particularly careful to make sure that he is using the correct characteristic as well as the correct mantissa.

In the solution of right triangles, there is some question as to whether it is more efficient to use natural functions or log functions. With oblique triangles it is usually better to use log functions.

example 20 In a certain right triangle, $a = 1.7320$ and $A = 26°30'$. Find b and c, using five-place log functions.

$$c = \frac{1.7320}{\sin 26°30'}$$

$$\begin{aligned}
\log c &= \log 1.7320 - \log \sin 26°30' \\
\log 1.7320 &= 1.23855 - 1 \\
\log \sin 26°30' &= \underline{0.64953 - 1} \\
\log c &= 0.58902 + 0 \\
c &= 3.8817 \\
b &= 1.7320 \cot 26°30' \\
\log b &= \log 1.7320 + \log \cot 26°30' \\
\log 1.7320 &= 0.23855 \\
\log \cot 26°30' &= \underline{0.30226} \\
\log b &= 0.54081 \\
b &= 3.4738
\end{aligned}$$

EXERCISE 14

Solve the following right triangles, using five-place log functions:

1. $A = 37°42'16''$ $c = 146.32$ in.
2. $A = 2°26'05''$ $c = 0.43792$ in.
3. $B = 72°19'28''$ $c = 157.65$ in.
4. $B = 36°28'45''$ $c = 29.463$ in.
5. $A = 28°36'20''$ $c = 1.3752$ in.
6. $A = 04°13'30''$ $b = 136.48$ in.
7. $A = 88°25'14''$ $a = 15.358$ in.
8. $B = 47°28'10''$ $a = 0.037940$ in.
9. $A = 89°21'38''$ $b = 15279$ in.
10. $A = 45°13'05''$ $a = 28.365$ in.
11. $a = 13.625$ in. $c = 142.98$ in.
12. $a = 76.500$ ft $c = 92.800$ ft
13. $a = 5.4360$ in. $c = 10.830$ in.
14. $a = 26.9320$ in. $c = 41.8670$ in.
15. $a = 0.36520$ in. $c = 0.58470$ in.
16. $a = 10.932$ in. $b = 110.36$ in.
17. $a = 95.632$ in. $b = 8.7305$ in.
18. $a = 52.693$ in. $b = 27.956$ in.
19. $a = 3.6571$ in. $b = 7.3058$ in.
20. $a = 26.328$ in. $b = 21.497$ in.

16·17 The solution of oblique triangles without special formulas

So far we have discussed only the solution of right triangles. However, the student has at this point all the information he needs to solve oblique triangles as well.

Data determining oblique triangles can be given in any of three ways. Three sides may be given, two angles and one side may be given, or two sides and one angle may be given.

In Secs. 16·18, 16·19, and 16·20 all given dimensions are known to five significant digits or to seconds.

16·18 Solution of an oblique triangle when three sides are given

example 21 Solve the oblique triangle shown in Fig. 16·26. The sides are known to five significant digits.

Draw h perpendicular to b. It is recommended that you draw h perpendicular to the longest side as was done in this example.

Then $\qquad h^2 = 17^2 - x^2 \qquad \text{and} \qquad h^2 = 25^2 - y^2$

Therefore,

$$17^2 - x^2 = 25^2 - y^2$$

$$y^2 - x^2 = 25^2 - 17^2 = 625 - 289 = 336$$

$$(y - x)(y + x) = 336$$

but

$$y + x = b = 28$$

$$(y - x)28 = 336$$

$$y - x = \frac{336}{28} = 12''$$

$$\begin{array}{rl} y - x &= 12 \\ y + x &= 28 \\ \hline 2y &= 40 \text{ (by addition)} \\ y &= 20'' \end{array} \qquad \begin{array}{rl} y - x &= 12 \\ y + x &= 28 \\ \hline 2x &= 16 \text{ (by subtraction)} \\ x &= 8'' \end{array}$$

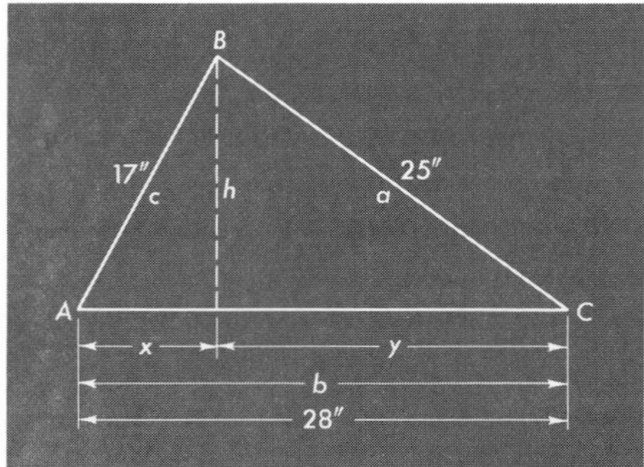

fig. 16·26

fig. 16·27

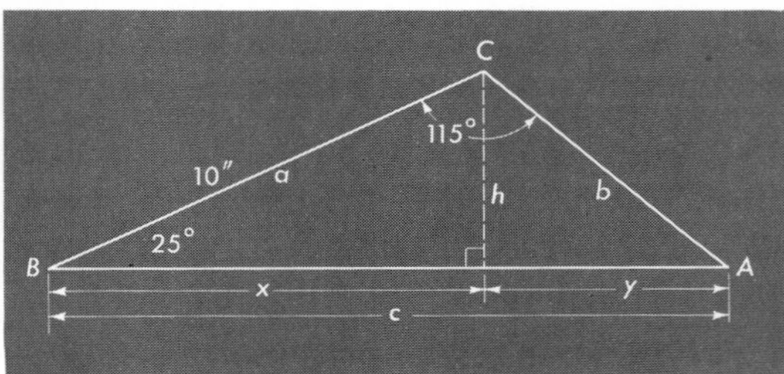

$$\cos A = \frac{x}{c} = \frac{8}{17} = 0.47059$$

$$A = 61°55'39''$$

$$\cos C = \frac{y}{a} = \frac{20}{25} = 0.80000$$

$$C = 36°52'11''$$

$$B = 180° - (61°55'39'' + 36°52'11'') = 81°12'10''$$

16·19 Solution of an oblique triangle when two angles and a side are given

example 22 Solve the oblique triangle shown in Fig. 16·27. Side a is known to five significant digits, and the angles are known to the nearest second.

Drop the perpendicular h from C to the side c.

$$h = 10 \times \sin 25° = 10 \times 0.42262 = 4.2262 \text{ in.}$$
$$x = 10 \times \cos 25° = 10 \times 0.90631 = 9.0631 \text{ in.}$$
$$A = 180° - (25° + 115°) = 40°$$
$$b = h \operatorname{cosec} 40° = 4.2262 \times 1.5557 = 6.5747 \text{ in.}$$
$$y = h \cot 40° = 4.2262 \times 1.1918 = 5.0368 \text{ in.}$$
$$c = x + y = 9.0631 \text{ in.} + 5.0368 \text{ in.} = 14.0999 \text{ in. or } 14.100 \text{ in.}$$

16·20 Solution of an oblique triangle when two sides and an angle are given

example 23 Solve the oblique triangle shown in Fig. 16·28. The sides are known to five significant digits.

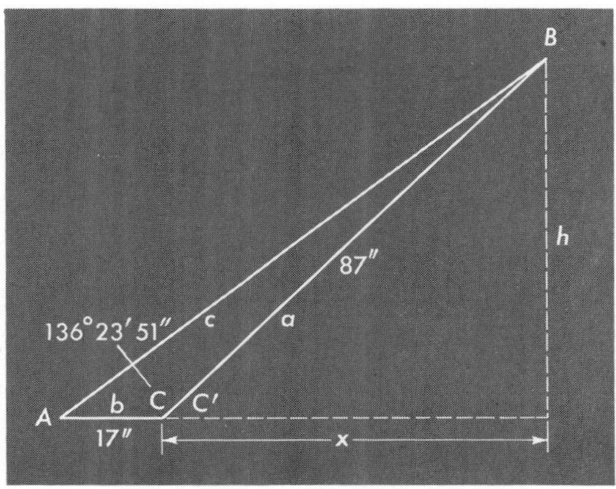

fig. 16·28

In this example, *two sides and the included angle* are given.

$$C' = 180° - 136°23'51'' = 43°36'9''$$
$$h = 87 \sin 43°36'9'' = 87 \times 0.68965 = 60''$$
$$x = 87 \cos 43°36'9'' = 87 \times 0.72414 = 63''$$
$$b + x = 17 + 63 = 80''$$
$$\cot A = \frac{b + x}{h} = \frac{80}{60} = 1.3333$$
$$A = 36°52'15''$$
$$B = 180° - (136°23'51'' + 36°52'15'') = 6°43'54''$$
$$c = \frac{h}{\sin 36°52'15''} = \frac{60}{\sin 36°52'15''}$$
$$c = \frac{60}{0.60001} = 100''$$

example 24 Solve the oblique triangle in which one side is 60.000 in. and the opposite angle is 41°06′44″. Another side is 73.000 in.

The data here are ambiguous. Observe that Figs. 16·29 and 16·30 are both consistent with the stated data, while these triangles are by no means equal.

Such ambiguity is possible only when two sides and the angle opposite one of them are given and when the given angle is less than 90°.

We shall solve the triangle in Fig. 16·29 first.

$$h = 73 \times \sin 41°06'44'' = 73 \times 0.65753 = 48 \text{ in.}$$
$$x + b = 73 \times \cos 41°06'44'' = 73 \times 0.75342 = 55 \text{ in.}$$
$$x = \sqrt{60^2 - 48^2} = 36 \text{ in.}$$
$$b = 55 - 36 = 19 \text{ in.}$$
$$\sin C' = \frac{h}{60} = \frac{48}{60} = 0.80000$$
$$C' = 53°07'49''$$
$$C = 180° - 53°07'49'' = 126°52'11''$$
$$B = 180° - (41°06'44'' + 126°52'11'') = 12°01'05''$$

fig. 16·29

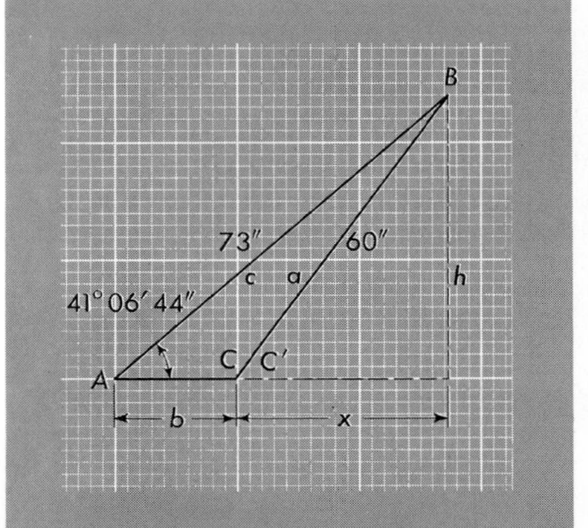

fig. 16·30

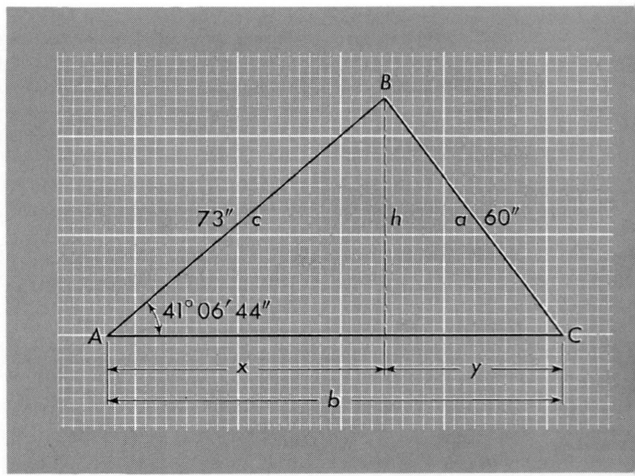

The solution for Fig. 16·30 follows.

$$h = 73 \sin 41°06'44'' = 73 \times 0.65753 = 48 \text{ in.}$$
$$x = 73 \cos 41°06'44'' = 73 \times 0.75342 = 55 \text{ in.}$$

$$\sin C = \frac{48}{60} = 0.80000$$

$$C = 53°07'49''$$
$$y = \sqrt{60^2 - 48^2} = 36 \text{ in.}$$
$$b = x + y = 55 + 36 = 91 \text{ in.}$$
$$B = 180° - (53°07'49'' + 41°06'44'') = 85°45'27''$$

EXERCISE 15

Solve the following triangles, using the methods given above. If the data are inconsistent, state why. All given linear dimensions are known to five significant digits.

1.	$a = 37$ in.	$b = 91$ in.	$c = 72$ in.
2.	$a = 52$ in.	$b = 25$ in.	$c = 63$ in.
3.	$a = 21$ in.	$b = 31$ in.	$c = 52$ in.
4.	$a = 65$ in.	$b = 89$ in.	$c = 132$ in.
5.	$A = 36°52'12''$	$b = 12$ in.	$C = 118°04'21''$
6.	$A = 73°44'23''$	$b = 75$ in.	$C = 58°20'07''$
7.	$a = 9$ in.	$b = 80$ in.	$C = 36°52'12''$
8.	$b = 53$ in.	$c = 88$ in.	$A = 58°06'34''$
9.	$A = 53°07'49''$	$a = 68$ in.	$b = 13$ in.
10.	$a = 20$ in.	$b = 5$ in.	$A = 22°37'12''$
11.	$b = 86$ in.	$c = 97$ in.	$C = 104°15'$

16·21 The slide-rule solution of right triangles

Within its inherent limit of accuracy, the slide rule may be used to solve problems in numerical trigonometry.

On the slide rule, linear dimensions can be used and computed to about one part in a thousand. Angles can be used and computed to about the nearest 0.05°. This is not strictly true over the entire scale, but it is a good working average.

On the particular rule used here for illustration, the S scale (see Fig. 16·31) is calibrated in degrees and decimal parts of a degree. The long markers are double-numbered in pairs of complementary angles, e.g., 82/8, 70/20, 60/30.

When the *right-hand* numerals are used, the hairline simultaneously indicates an angle on the S scale and the *sine* of that angle on the C scale.

When the *left-hand* numerals are used, the hairline simultaneously indicates an angle on the S scale and the cosine of that angle on the C scale.

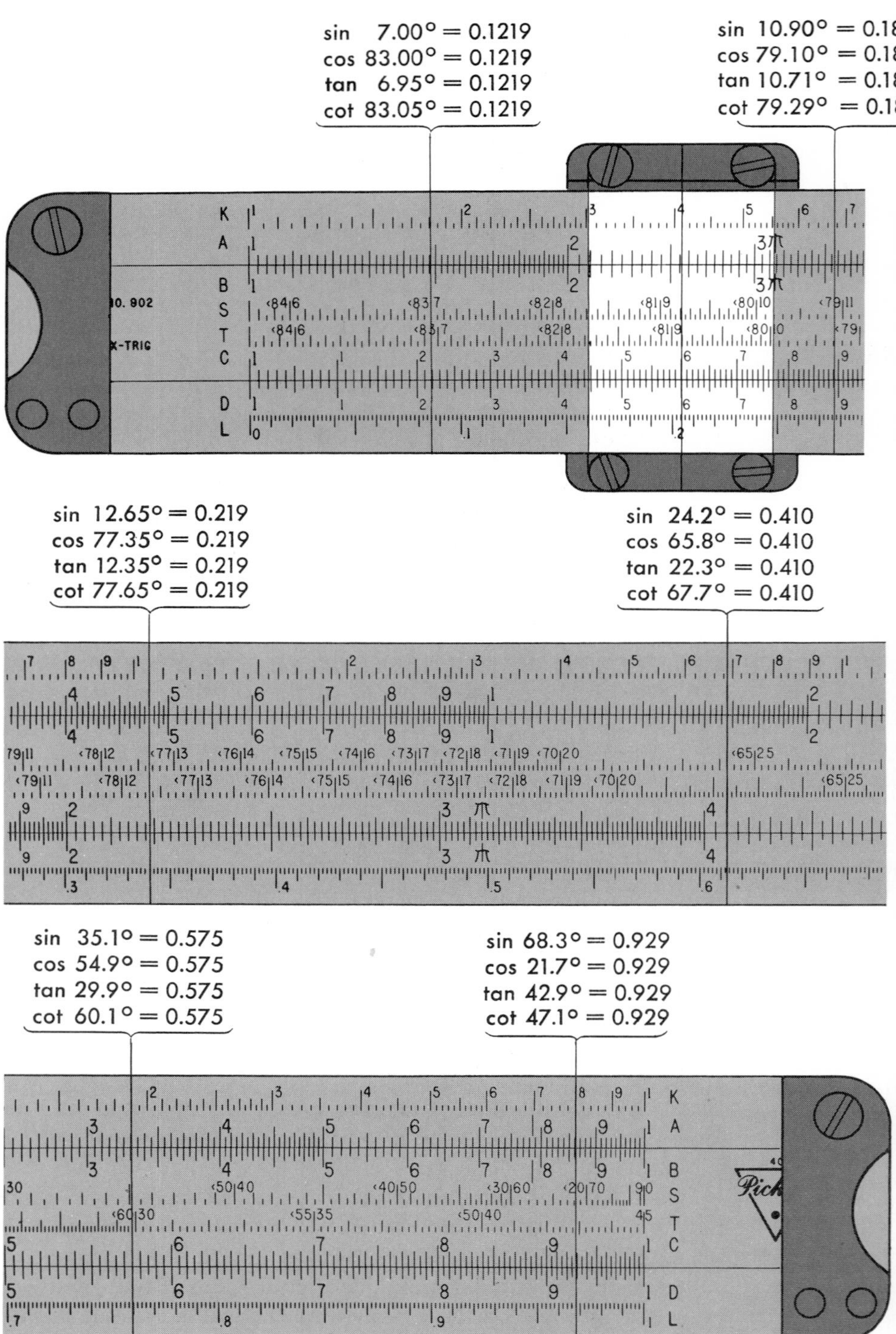
sin 7.00° = 0.1219
cos 83.00° = 0.1219
tan 6.95° = 0.1219
cot 83.05° = 0.1219
sin 10.90° = 0.18
cos 79.10° = 0.18
tan 10.71° = 0.18
cot 79.29° = 0.18
K
A
B
S
T
C
D
L
X-TRIG
sin 12.65° = 0.219
cos 77.35° = 0.219
tan 12.35° = 0.219
cot 77.65° = 0.219
sin 24.2° = 0.410
cos 65.8° = 0.410
tan 22.3° = 0.410
cot 67.7° = 0.410
sin 35.1° = 0.575
cos 54.9° = 0.575
tan 29.9° = 0.575
cot 60.1° = 0.575
sin 68.3° = 0.929
cos 21.7° = 0.929
tan 42.9° = 0.929
cot 47.1° = 0.929

fig. 16·31

The C scale is used for sines, cosines, tangents, and cotangents. The left-hand index of the C scale is used as 0.1, and the right-hand index is used as 1.0. Therefore on this particular rule we are limited to angles whose sine is between 0.1 and 1.0, angles whose cosine is between 0.1 and 1.0, and angles whose tangent or cotangent is between 0.1 and 1.0. The smallest angle we can use directly is about 5.7°. When using sines, we can process angles up to 90°, although the scale is crowded near 90°. When using cosines, we can use angles up to about 84.3°. The upper limit of the tangent scale and the lower limit of the cotangent scale are 45°. However, as will be illustrated in subsequent examples, this does not put any additional limitations on the usefulness of the slide rule.

EXERCISE 16

1. Using a slide rule, find the sine and cosine of the following angles:

(a) 28°	(b) 8°	(c) 17°	(d) 13°	(e) 20°	(f) 30°
(g) 7.2°	(h) 12.2°	(i) 26.2°	(j) 7.63°	(k) 16.75°	(l) 41.4°

The slide-rule setting illustrated in Fig. 16·32 is adequate for solving Examples 25 and 26.

example 25 The hypotenuse of a right triangle is 8 in., and one angle is 30°. Find the side opposite the 30° angle.

Here the slide rule is set to multiply 8 in. by the sine of 30°, giving 4 in. as the length of the opposite side (see Fig. 16·32).

fig. 16·32

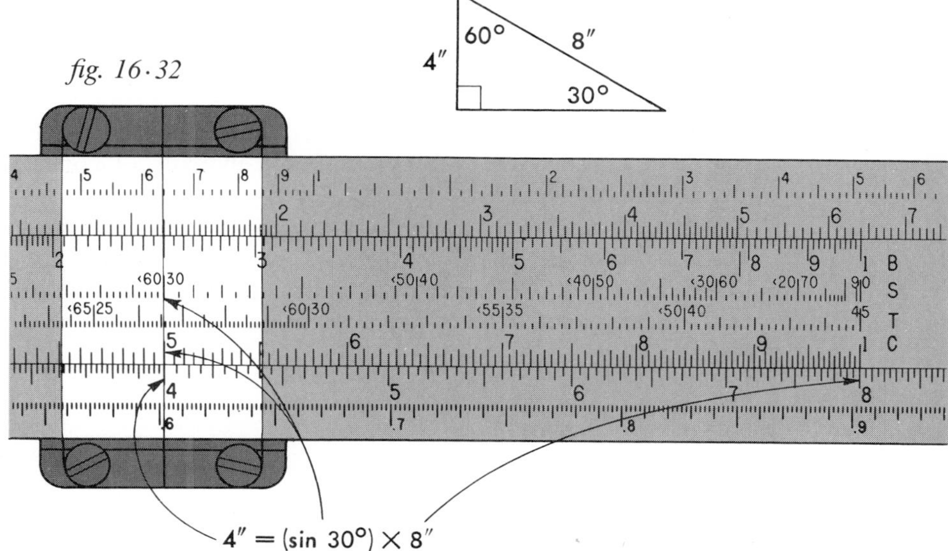

example 26 The hypotenuse of a right triangle is 8 in., and one angle is 60°. Find the side adjacent to the 60° angle.

In Fig. 16·32 the slide rule is set to multiply 8 in. by the cosine of 60°.

By reference to Examples 25 and 26 and Fig. 16·32 the student should justify for himself that when solving a right triangle where the hypotenuse appears as an unknown or a known side, (1) the 90° marker on the S scale matches the length of the hypotenuse on the D scale; (2) when using the right-hand numbers on the S scale, an acute angle on this scale matches the length of its opposite side on the D scale.

By using the above relations we can solve any right triangle (except those containing an angle less than 5.7°) if we know the hypotenuse and either acute angle or either leg. Similarly we can solve right triangles if we know either leg and either acute angle.

EXERCISE 17

1. Verify the statement that the slide-rule setting shown in Fig. 1·5 is consistent with the following relations:

(a) $\frac{2.53}{14.28} = \sin 10.21°$ (b) $\frac{2.53}{14.28} = \cos 79.79°$

(c) $14.28 \cos 79.79° = 2.53$ (d) $14.28 \sin 10.21° = 2.53$

2. Verify the statement that the slide-rule setting in Fig. 1·7 is consistent with the following relations:

(a) $\frac{8}{9.03} = \sin 62.4°$ (b) $\frac{8}{9.03} = \cos 27.6°$

(c) $9.03 \sin 62.4° = 8$ (d) $9.03 \cos 27.6° = 8$

3. Write a series of four equations similar to those given in Probs. 1 and 2 above, but consistent with Figs. 1·4, 1·11, and 1·13.
4. Using a slide rule, solve Probs. 1 to 20 and 26 to 34, Exercise 7.

The T scale is calibrated in degrees and decimal parts of a degree. The long markers are double-numbered in pairs of complementary angles in a way similar to the S scale.

When the *right-hand* numerals are used, the hairline simultaneously indicates an angle on the T scale and the *tangent* of that angle on the C scale. When the *left-hand* numerals are used, the hairline simultaneously indicates an angle on the T scale and the *cotangent* of that angle on the C scale.

EXERCISE 18

1. Using a slide rule, find

(a) tan 20° (b) tan 35.76° (c) tan 44.2°
(d) tan 7.9° (e) tan 15.82° (f) tan 29.62°
(g) cot 48.2° (h) cot 82.1° (i) cot 52.7°

The slide-rule setting illustrated in Fig. 16·33 is adequate for solving the following examples:

example 27 One side of a right triangle is 6.93 in., and the adjacent angle is 30°. Find the side opposite the 30° angle.

Use the equation

$$\text{Opposite side} = \text{adjacent side} \times \text{tangent } \phi$$

The slide-rule setting in Fig. 16·33 accomplishes this multiplication.

example 28 One side of a right triangle is 4 in., and the adjacent angle is 60°. Find the side opposite the 60° angle.

Use the equation

$$\text{Opposite side} = \frac{\text{adjacent side}}{\cot \theta}$$

The slide-rule setting shown in Fig. 16·33 accomplishes this division. Thus we avoid using tangents of angles greater than 45°.

By reference to Examples 27 and 28 and Fig. 16·33 the student should justify for himself that (1) if the 45° marker on the T scale matches the longer leg on the D scale, (2) then, when using the right-hand numbers on the T scale, an acute angle on this scale matches the length of the shorter leg on the D scale.

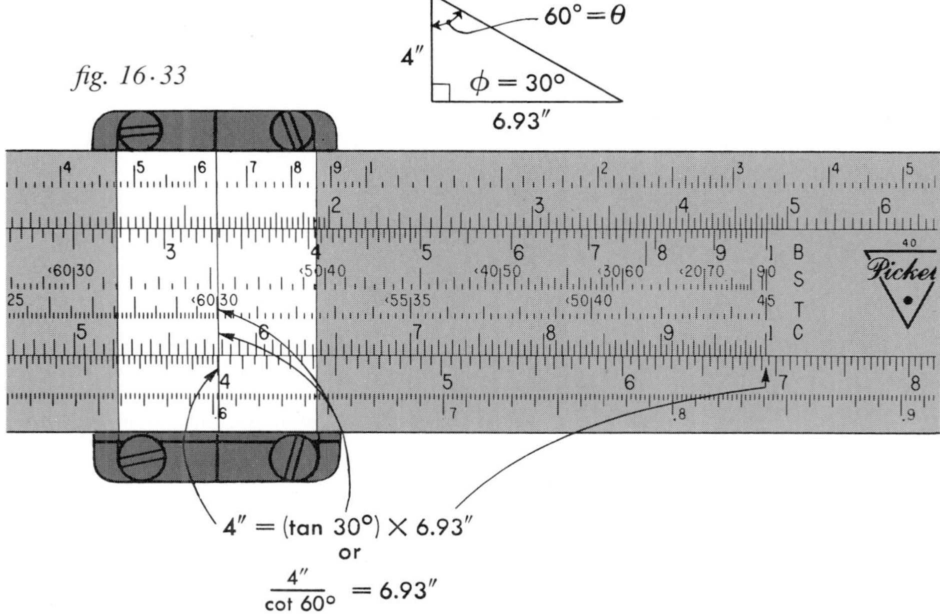

fig. 16·33

It is assumed here, of course, that neither acute angle is smaller than about 5.7°.

By the rule above, if we are given two legs or a leg and an acute angle we can solve the right triangle except for the hypotenuse. We have already discussed the situation in which the hypotenuse is involved.

EXERCISE 19

1. Verify the statement that the slide-rule setting shown in Fig. 1·5 is consistent with the following relations:

   (a) $\frac{2.53}{14.28} = \tan 10.05°$ (b) $\frac{2.53}{14.28} = \cot 79.95°$

   (c) $2.53 = 14.28 \tan 10.05°$ (d) $2.53 = 14.28 \cot 79.95°$

2. Verify the statement that the slide-rule setting shown in Fig. 1·7 is consistent with the following relations:

   (a) $\frac{8}{9.03} = \tan 41.55°$ (b) $\frac{8}{9.03} = \cot 48.45°$

   (c) $8 = 9.03 \tan 41.55°$ (d) $8 = 9.03 \cot 48.45°$

3. Write a series of four equations similar to those given in Probs. 1 and 2 above but consistent with Figs. 1·9, 1·11, and 1·13.
4. Using a slide rule, solve Probs. 21 through 25, Exercise 7.

Section 1·12 describes a method of solving Pythagorean-theorem problems on the slide rule. The method illustrated in the following example is somewhat more convenient for those with a knowledge of trigonometry.

example 29 The hypotenuse of a right triangle is 8 in., and one side is 4 in. Find the other side.

First find an acute angle, as in Fig. 16·32. Then, having found the smaller angle (in this case 30°), divide the opposite side by the tangent of the angle, as in Fig. 16·33.

example 30 The two sides of a right triangle are 4 and 6.93 in. Find the hypotenuse.

First find an acute angle, as in Fig. 16·33. Then, having found the angle, divide the sine of this angle into the opposite side to find the hypotenuse, as in Fig. 16·32.

EXERCISE 20

1. Using a slide rule, solve Probs. 21 to 30 in Exercise 10, page 402.
2. Using a slide rule, solve Probs. 31 to 40 in Exercise 10, page 402.

16·22 The slide-rule solution of oblique triangles

The slide rule can be used to solve oblique triangles, using methods similar to those just described.

example 31 Given the triangle shown in Fig. 16·34, where $b = 8$ in., $A = 30°$, and $B = 34°$, find a, c, and C.

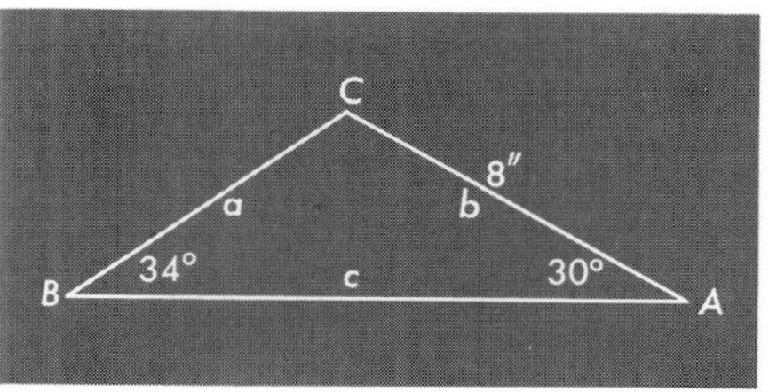

fig. 16·34

1. Set the rule to indicate h, as in Fig. 16·35.
2. Set the rule to indicate a, as in Fig. 16·36a.
3. Set the rule to indicate x, as in Fig. 16·36b.
4. Set the rule to indicate y, as in Fig. 16·37.

side $c = x + y$ angle $C = 180° - (A + B)$

fig. 16·35

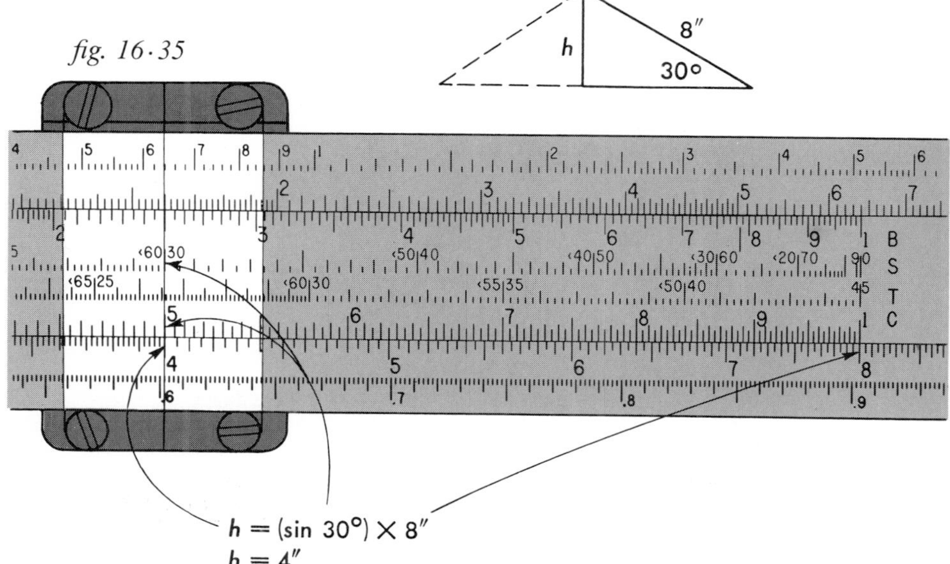

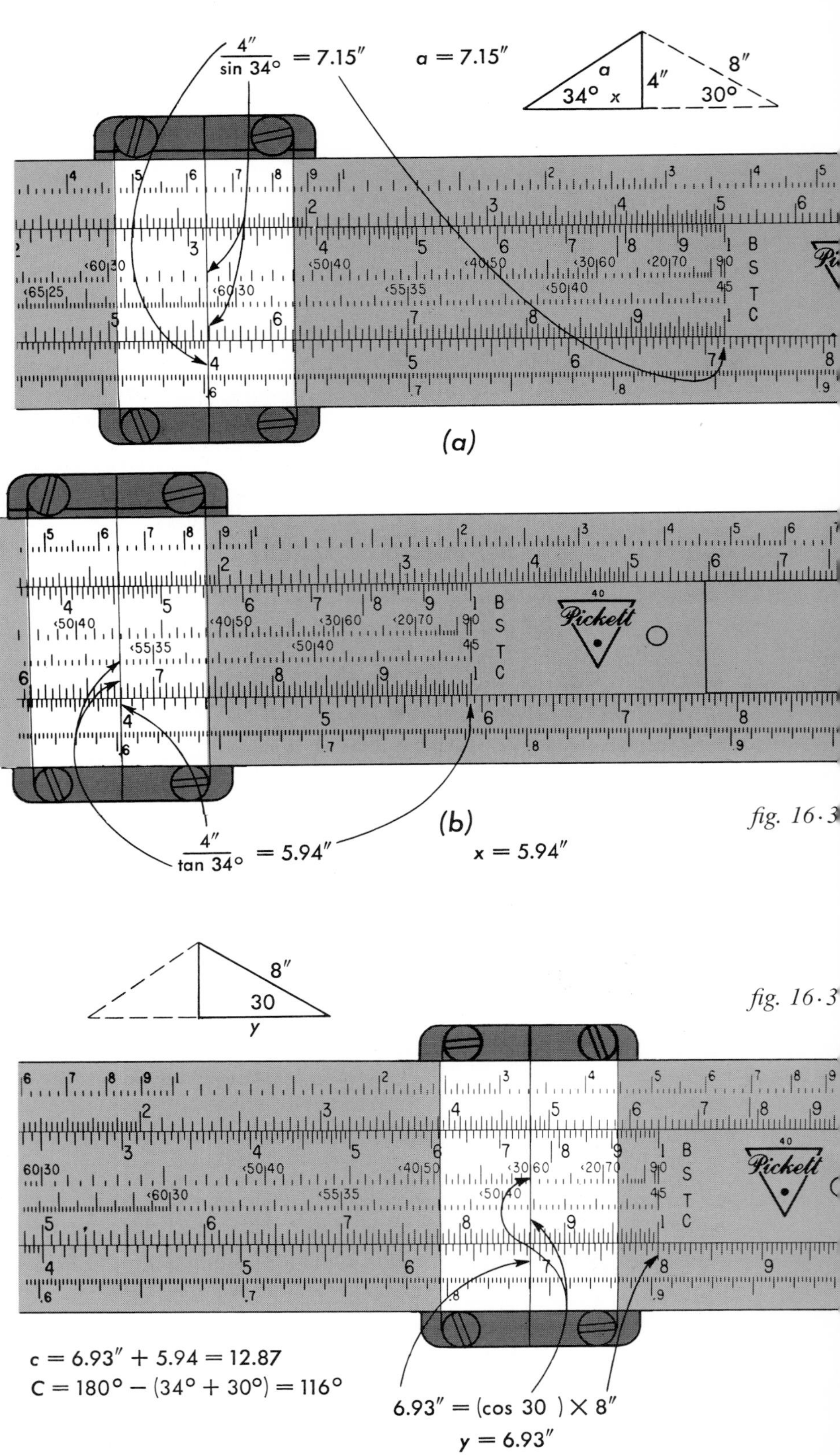

fig. 16·3

fig. 16·3

example 32 Given the triangle shown in Fig. 16·38; if $b = 8$ in., $c = 12.87$ in., and $A = 30°$, find a, B, and C.

1. Find h and y, as in Figs. 16·35 and 16·37, respectively.
2. Since $x = 12.87 - y$, the length x may be found by subtraction.
3. Knowing h and x, find B, as in Fig. 16·36*b*.
4. Knowing h and B, find a, as in Fig. 16·36*a*.

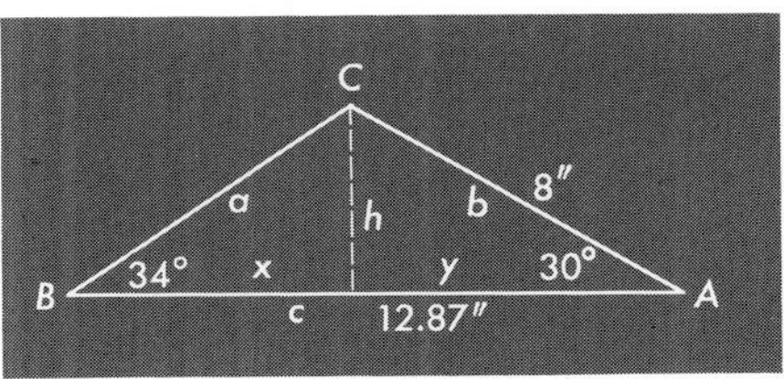

fig. 16·38

EXERCISE 21

Solve Probs. 1 to 11 in Exercise 15 on a slide rule.

16·23 The solution of right triangles involving small angles

The slide rule illustrated in this book does not indicate angles less than about 5.7°. However, the slide rule can be used to solve triangles involving smaller angles.

Some slide rules have an "SRT" scale engraved on them. This scale is often a convenience when dealing with small angles. The left-hand C index is used as 0.01 and the right-hand index is used as 0.1. The smallest angle which we can read directly on the SRT scale is about 0.57° and the largest angle is about 5.7°.

Over this range we cannot distinguish on the scale between the tangent of an angle and the sine of the same angle. Thus the SRT scale serves both when dealing with sines or tangents of these small angles.

Other aspects of the solution of right triangles involving small angles are discussed below.

example 33 Find the short side of a right triangle in which the hypotenuse is 134.4 in. and the long side is 133.6 in.

Let the hypotenuse be c, the long side be b, and the short side be a.

$$a = \sqrt{c^2 - b^2} = \sqrt{(c - b)(c + b)} \tag{59}$$

$$c - b = 134.4 - 133.6 = 0.8 \text{ in.}$$

Notice that the difference (0.8 in.) is expressed to only one significant figure, whereas the c and b are given to four significant figures.

$$c + b = 134.4 + 133.6 = 268.0 \text{ in.}$$

$$a = \sqrt{0.8 \times 268} = \sqrt{214.4} = 14.64 \text{ in.}$$

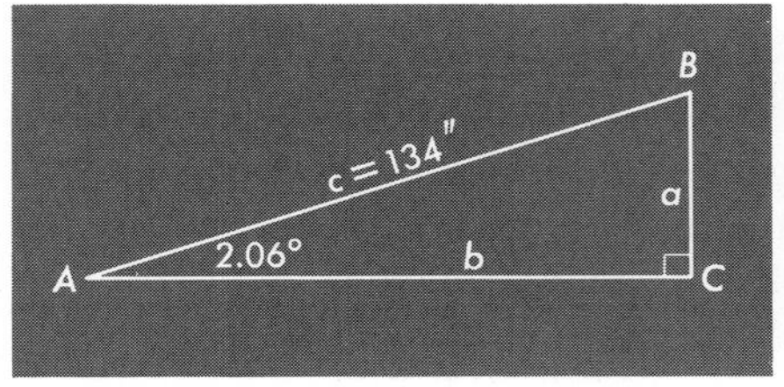

fig. 16·39

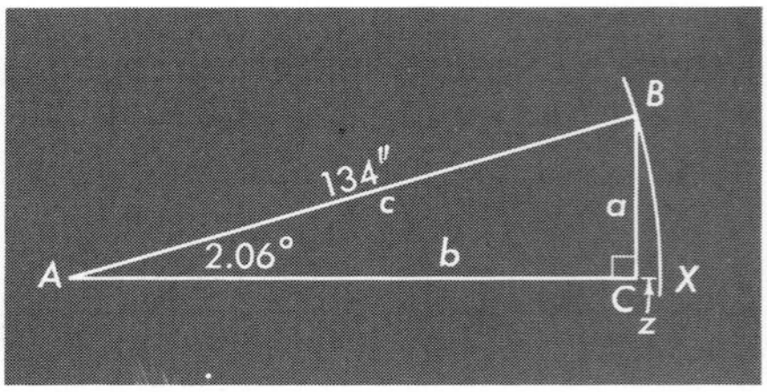

fig. 16·40

Let us investigate this approximation further. If the length of the side b is changed by 0.1 in. to make $b = 133.7$, then

$$c = \sqrt{(134.4 - 133.7)(134.4 + 133.7)} = 13.70 \text{ in.}$$

Thus a change of 0.1 in. in b makes a change of 0.94 in. in a.

example 34 Solve the right triangle shown in Fig. 16·39.

The side a in Fig. 16·39 is nearly equal to the arc length BX in Fig. 16·40. Of course this approximation will be close only when A is small. The arc length BX is a fraction of the circumference of a circle of radius 134 in. whose center is at A. This fraction is $2.06°/360°$.

In other words,

$$\frac{2.06°}{360°} \times 2\pi \times 134 = \text{arc length } BX = \frac{\pi}{180°} \times 2.06° \times 134 \tag{60}$$

Or the side a is given by the approximate formula

$$a \approx \frac{\pi}{180°} \times 2.06° \times 134 \tag{61}$$

$$a \approx 0.0359 \times 134 = 4.82 \text{ in.}$$

See Fig. 16·41 for the appropriate settings to solve Eq. (61).

The general formula for a is

$$a \approx \frac{\pi}{180} \times A \times c \tag{62}$$

To find b, we first find the length z (Fig. 16·40). In Fig. 16·40,

$$c = b + z \tag{63}$$

and

$$c - b = z \tag{64}$$

since both c and $b + z$ are radii of the same circle. But, by the Pythagorean theorem,

$$a^2 = c^2 - b^2 = (c - b)(c + b) \tag{65}$$

$$a^2 = z(c + b) \tag{66}$$

or

$$z = \frac{a^2}{c + b} \tag{67}$$

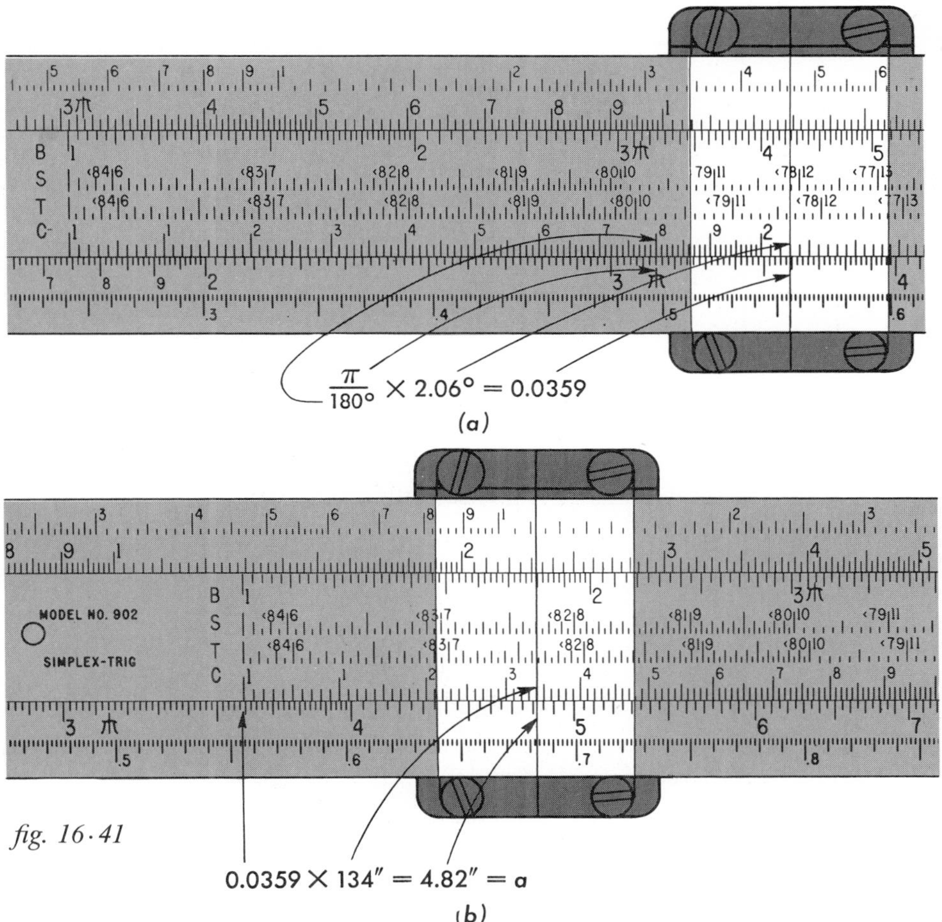

fig. 16·41

If c and b are nearly equal, we may write

$$z \approx \frac{a^2}{2c} \tag{68}$$

In the present example,

$$a = 4.82 \text{ in.}$$
$$c = 134 \text{ in.}$$

Therefore,

$$z \approx \frac{4.82^2}{2 \times 134} = 0.0867 \text{ in.} \tag{69}$$

and

$$b \approx 134.0 \text{ in.} - 0.0867 \text{ in.} \tag{70}$$

or, within slide-rule precision,

$$b \approx 134.0 \text{ in.} - 0.1 \text{ in.} = 133.9 \text{ in.}$$

(See also part III of Table B·1, page 848.)

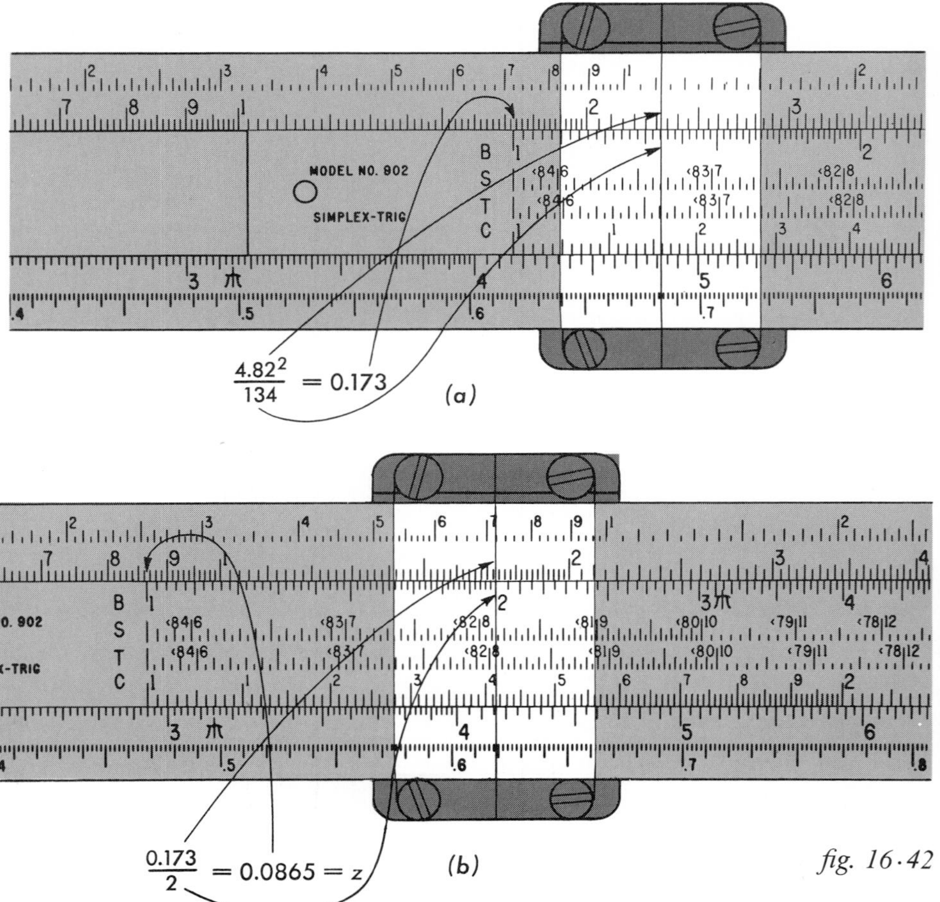

fig. 16·42

The slide-rule settings used to solve Eq. (69) are illustrated in Fig. 16·42. Note the discrepancy of about 0.2 per cent between 0.0867 obtained in Eq. (69) by using a desk calculator and 0.0865 obtained in Fig. 16·42 by slide rule.

example 35 Solve the right triangle shown in Fig. 16·43.

Following Eq. (62),

$$\frac{a}{c} \approx \frac{\pi}{180} \times A \tag{71}$$

The ratio a/c is set on the slide rule shown in Fig. 16·41*b*. To this ratio we match the ratio $\pi/180$ multiplied by the value of A (as yet unknown) (see Fig. 16·41*a*). This requires that A be 2.06°.

The side b is calculated as in Example 34.

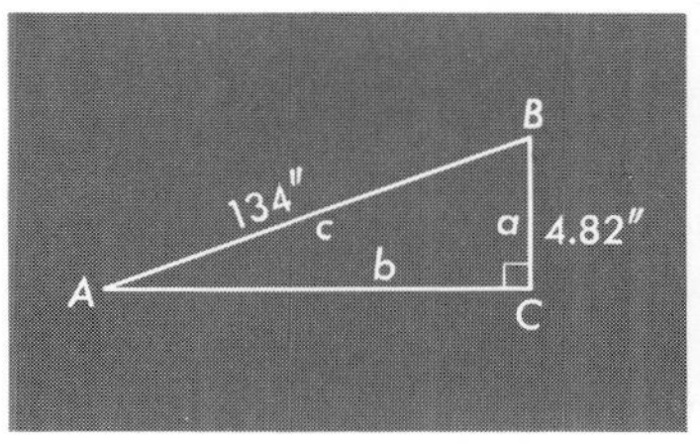

fig. 16·43

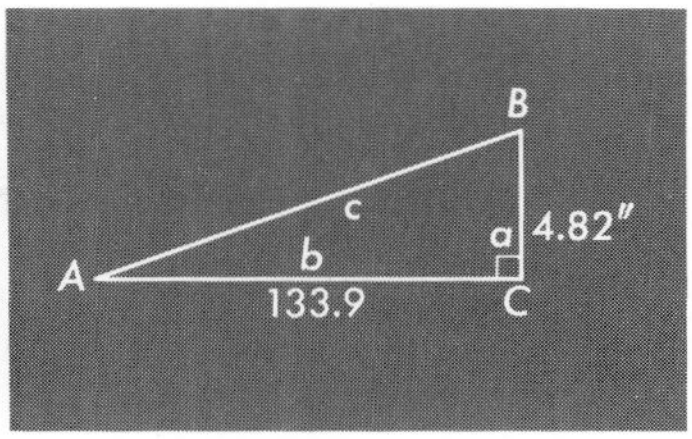

fig. 16·44

example 36 Solve the triangle shown in Fig. 16·44.

Since b and c are nearly equal, Eq. (62) may be altered to read

$$\frac{a}{b} \approx \frac{\pi}{180°} \times A \tag{72}$$

To solve for c, we alter Eq. (67) as follows:

$$z \approx \frac{a^2}{2b} \tag{73}$$

Therefore,

$$c \approx b + \frac{a^2}{2b} \tag{74}$$

(See also part III of Table B·1, page 848.)

EXERCISE 22

1. The length of c in Fig. 16·45 is 95.000 in. If the side b is 94.000 in., find the length of side a to five significant figures using a table of squares and square roots.

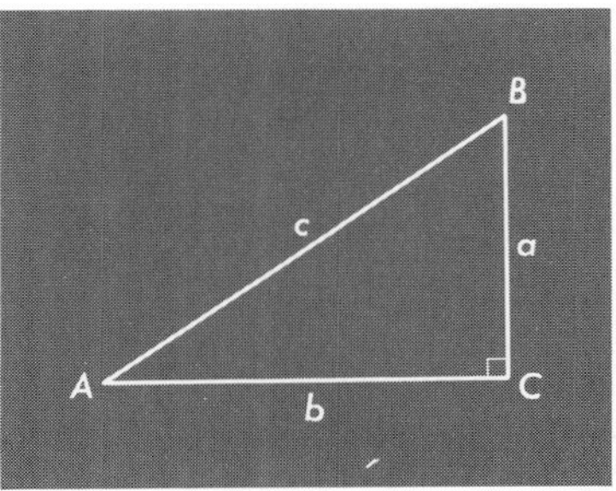

fig. 16·45

2. If the side b in Prob. 1 were decreased to 93.000 in., with c the same as before (95.000 in.), find side a to five significant figures using a table of squares and square roots.
3. As between Probs. 1 and 2, what was the percentage decrease in the length of b? What was the percentage increase in a?
4. (a) In Fig. 16·45 the side c is 125.00 in. and $A = 1.95°$. Calculate a and b on a slide rule using the approximations given above.

(b) From a seven-place table of natural functions we find that $\sin 1.95° = 0.0340274$ and $\cos 1.95° = 0.9994209$. Using these values, calculate a and b to five significant digits and compare with the answers obtained in part (a).

5. In Fig. 16·45 $a = 2.0000$ in. and $b = 60.000$ in. Calculate c to five significant digits using a number table. Also calculate c using the approximations above.
6. Using the approximations discussed above, find A and b in Fig. 16·45 to slide-rule accuracy if $c = 125$ in. and $a = 5.00$ in.

unit six

introduction to analytical trigonometry

this unit will be of
particular interest
to electrical
and mechanical students

17
vectors and trigonometry

Practical experience in engineering has demonstrated that a close association between trigonometry and rectangular coordinates leads to powerful techniques in the analysis and solution of many engineering problems.

In the course of developing this association we shall have occasion to deal with the concept of vectors. In this chapter we shall not emphasize the vector representation of any particular physical quantities. We shall reserve that treatment for Chap. 20.

For the present we shall use vectors in connection with rectangular coordinates in order to develop certain important basic and abstract mathematical techniques without regard to specific applications.

17·1 Vector representation

For our purpose we shall define a vector as follows: A vector is a line segment or simply a line whose distinctive properties are *length, direction,* and *sense*. The *length* of a vector is the linear distance between the extremities. *Direction* is measured in terms of the angular orientation of the vector with respect to some reference line. If we consider the vector to have been generated by a moving point, the *sense* of the vector is determined by the order in which the point coincides with the extremities.

The line $\overrightarrow{AB}$ in Fig. 17·1 is a vector, since it is distinguished by a *length* (7 units), a *direction* (30° referred to *xy*), and a *sense* as indicated by the arrow.

The vector would be referred to in written symbols as $\overrightarrow{AB}$. The arrow above the letters indicates that it is a vector quantity which is under consideration and not some other sort of quantity. As we mentioned above, it may be convenient to think of the vector $\overrightarrow{AB}$ as the path generated by a point which moved from position A to position B. Consequently the sense is from A toward B and is so indicated by the sequence of the letters AB.

If we happen to be interested only in the length, or magnitude, of $\overrightarrow{AB}$, we use the symbol $|AB|$.

Two vectors are said to be equal if their lengths are equal and if their direction and sense are identical (see Fig. 17·2). Here $\overrightarrow{AB} = \overrightarrow{CD}$ because of three facts: (1) their lengths are equal; (2) their directions are the same; (3) their senses are identical.

It is true that

$$|AB| = |CD| = |EF| \tag{1}$$

It is also true that the direction of all three vectors is the same, since they are parallel. However, the sense of $\overrightarrow{EF}$ is not the same as the sense of $\overrightarrow{AB}$ and $\overrightarrow{CD}$. Therefore

$$\overrightarrow{EF} \neq \overrightarrow{AB} \tag{2}$$

$$\overrightarrow{EF} \neq \overrightarrow{CD} \tag{3}$$

The sense of $\overrightarrow{EF}$ is exactly opposite to the sense of $\overrightarrow{AB}$ and $\overrightarrow{CD}$. By definition, one vector is said to be the negative of another if their senses are exactly opposite while their magnitudes and directions are equal. Therefore

$$\overrightarrow{EF} = -\overrightarrow{AB} \tag{4}$$

$$\overrightarrow{EF} = -\overrightarrow{CD} \tag{5}$$

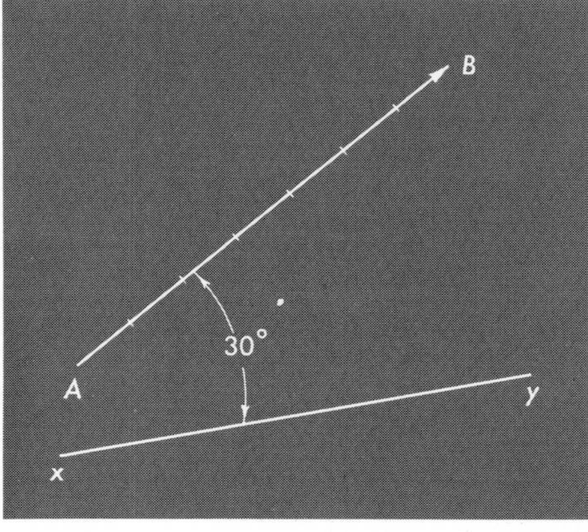

fig. 17·1

fig. 17·2

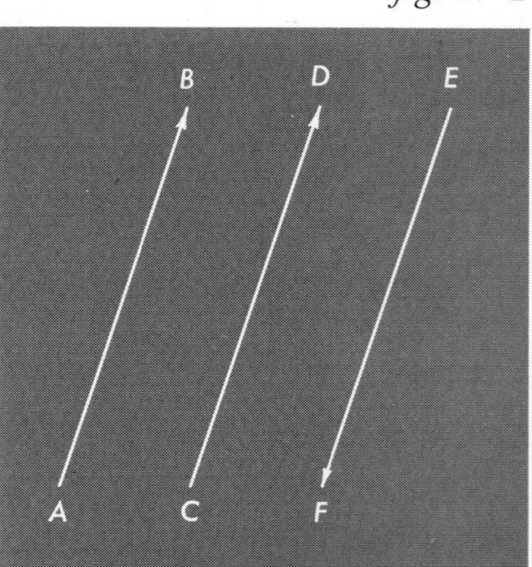

EXERCISE 1

1. Which of the vectors in Fig. 17·3 are equal?
2. Which of these vectors are the negative of $\overrightarrow{AB}$?
3. Which of these vectors have equal magnitudes?

17·2 Position vectors

The type of vector to which we shall direct our attention in the remainder of this chapter is known as a *position vector*. A position vector is a vector drawn from the origin of a coordinate system to some other point in the coordinate plane, usually for the purpose of locating this point.

For example, the position vector $\overrightarrow{OP}$ in Fig. 17·5 is drawn from the origin of the coordinate system to the point P in the coordinate plane. This vector serves to locate and emphasize the point P.

The position vector $\overrightarrow{OP}$ in Fig. 17·4 is on the positive side of the X axis. Now we shall rotate this vector about the point O in a counterclockwise direction to the position shown in Fig. 17·5. During this rotation it has generated the angle $+\phi$. The angle ϕ then defines the direction of $\overrightarrow{OP}$ with reference to the positive side of the X axis.

fig. 17·3

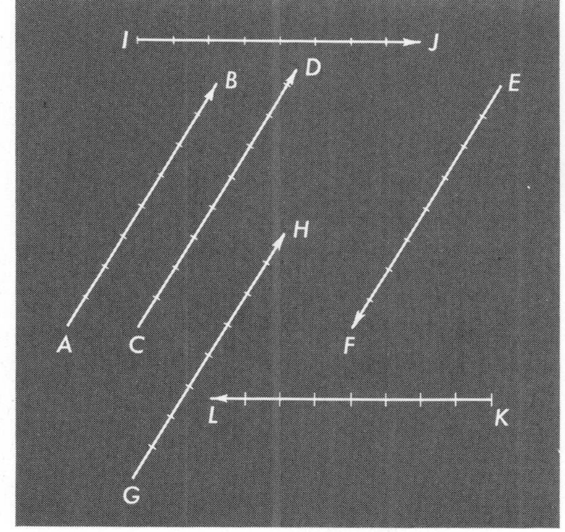

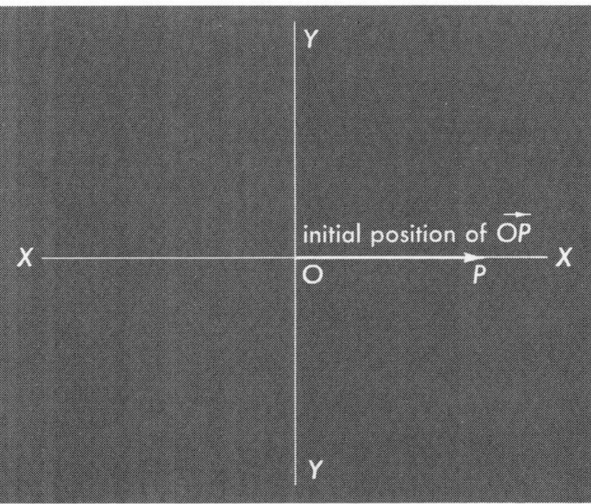

fig. 17·4

An angle is said to be drawn in standard position if, as in Fig. 17·5, it has its vertex at the origin of a system of rectangular coordinates and its initial side coincident with the positive side of the X axis. The terminal side of the angle may occupy any position in the coordinate plane, depending on the size of the angle.

17·3 Positive and negative angles

The relative direction of the terminal position of the position vector $\overrightarrow{OP}$ compared with its initial position is important, but so also is the direction of rotation which brought this particular relative position into being.

A positive angle may be defined as an angle generated by the counterclockwise rotation of a position vector.

A negative angle may be defined as an angle generated by the clockwise rotation of a position vector.

17·4 Angles of any magnitude

In the process of making one complete revolution, the rotating position vector assumes all directions in the coordinate plane. However, the vector can be made to continue its rotation through the 360° position and go around again, generating angles between 360 and 720°. During another revolution it would generate angles between 720 and 1,080°, and so on indefinitely. The vector would then repeat each direction in the coordinate plane periodically, once, and only once, for each revolution.

Figure 17·6 illustrates angles of several magnitudes. Note particularly that the angles $+30°$, $+390°$, $-330°$, and $-690°$ all define the same direction.

EXERCISE 2

Using a protractor, draw the following angles in standard position on

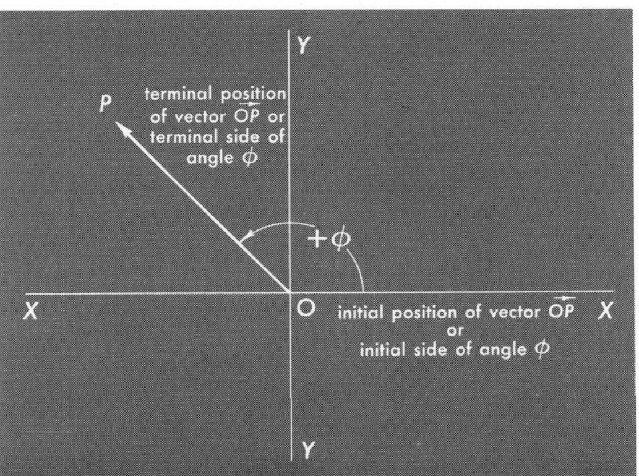

fig. 17·5

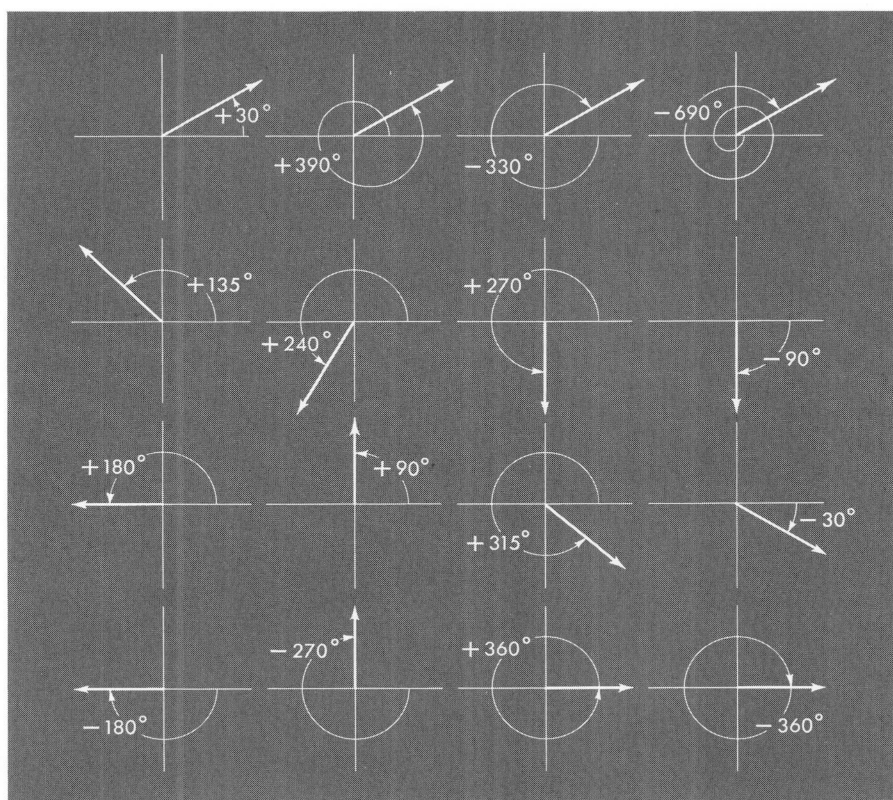

fig. 17·6

a system of rectangular coordinates. Dimension the angles with a curved arrow, as in Fig. 17·6. Let the arrow indicate the direction of rotation.

1.	35°	110°	185°	275°	472°
2.	70°	138°	200°	300°	1,596°
3.	10°	175°	260°	315°	720°
4.	28°	135°	210°	350°	975°
5.	30°	110°	225°	320°	643°
6.	−25°	−150°	−290°	−250°	−720°
7.	−82°	−120°	−250°	−300°	−1,256°

17·5 Addition and subtraction of angles

Addition of angles is illustrated in Fig. 17·7, where $\alpha = \phi + \beta$.

The positive angle ϕ is generated by the counterclockwise rotation of $\overrightarrow{OA}$ from its initial position on the positive side of the X axis to its terminal position, as shown in Fig. 17·7. The positive angle β is generated by the *counterclockwise* rotation of the vector $\overrightarrow{OB}$ from its initial position coincident with the terminal position of $\overrightarrow{OA}$ to the terminal position of $\overrightarrow{OB}$, as shown in Fig. 17·7.

Subtraction of angles is illustrated in Fig. 17·8 where $\alpha = \phi - \beta$.

The positive angle ϕ is generated as before by the counterclockwise rotation of $\overrightarrow{OA}$. The angle β is subtracted from ϕ by rotating the vector $\overrightarrow{OB}$ in a *clockwise* direction from its initial position coincident with the terminal position of $\overrightarrow{OA}$ to its terminal position, as shown in Fig. 17·8.

17·6 The quadrants

The coordinate plane is divided into four parts, as shown in Fig. 17·9.

An angle is said to be a first-, second-, third-, or fourth-quadrant angle accordingly as its terminal side lies in the first, second, third, or fourth quadrant (see Fig. 17·10).

An angle whose terminal side lies on an axis is not named in terms of any quadrant. Such angles are 0, 90, 180, 270, 360, 450°, etc. These are called boundary angles (see Secs. 17·11 to 17·14).

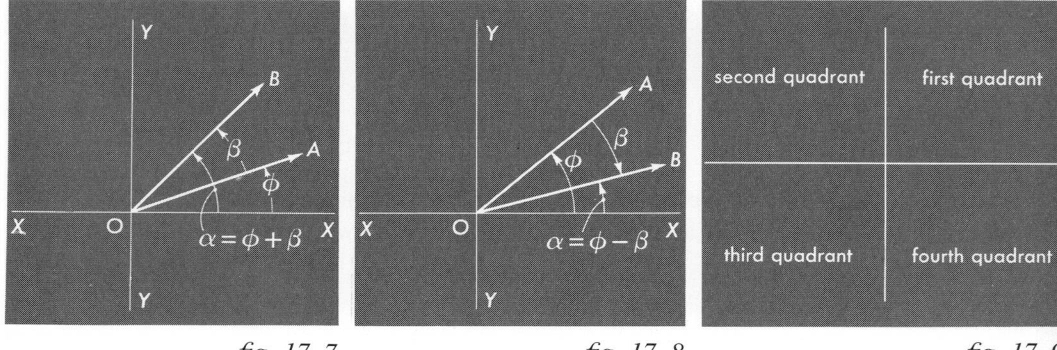

fig. 17·7 *fig. 17·8* *fig. 17·9*

17·7 The functions of angles of any magnitude

In Chap. 16 we were interested in the numerical solution of right triangles. In that chapter we introduced definitions of the trigonometric functions which, while lacking in generality, were completely adequate for that limited application. However in subsequent work using oblique triangles and in the more sophisticated areas of trigonometric analysis we shall need to define the trigonometric functions of angles in any of the four quadrants.

In Sec. 16·7 we defined the trigonometric functions of an acute angle by Eqs. (13) through (18) referred to Fig. 16·9. This figure and those equations are repeated below for reference as Eqs. (6) through (11) and Fig. 17·11.

$$\text{Sine of an angle} = \frac{\text{side opposite}}{\text{hypotenuse}} \tag{6}$$

$$\text{Cosine of an angle} = \frac{\text{side adjacent}}{\text{hypotenuse}} \tag{7}$$

$$\text{Tangent of an angle} = \frac{\text{side opposite}}{\text{side adjacent}} \tag{8}$$

$$\text{Cotangent of an angle} = \frac{\text{side adjacent}}{\text{side opposite}} \tag{9}$$

$$\text{Secant of an angle} = \frac{\text{hypotenuse}}{\text{side adjacent}} \tag{10}$$

$$\text{Cosecant of an angle} = \frac{\text{hypotenuse}}{\text{side opposite}} \tag{11}$$

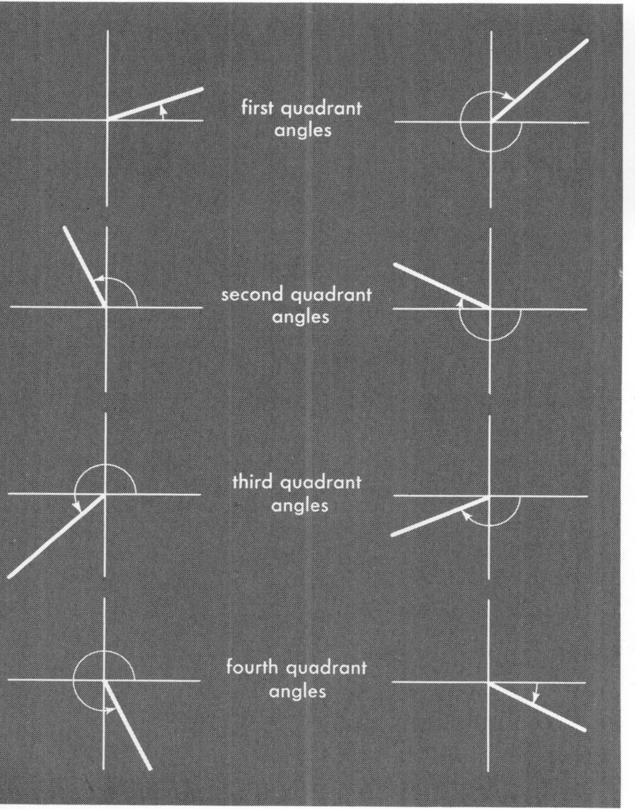

fig. 17·10

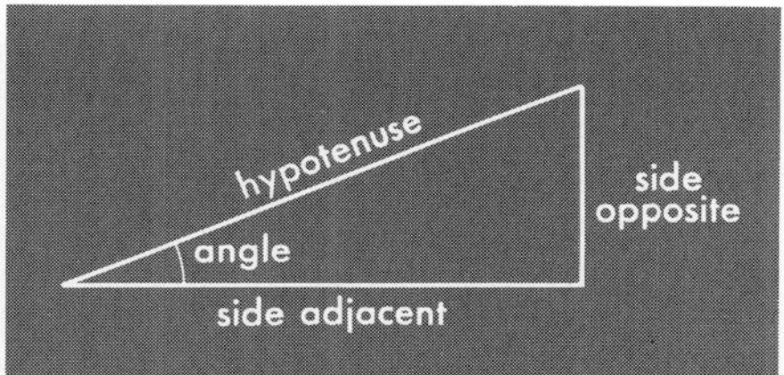

fig. 17·11

Now as our first step in the process of generalizing our definitions of the trigonometric functions, let us consider Fig. 17·12. This figure shows the position vector $\overrightarrow{OP}$ in the first quadrant together with the first-quadrant angle ϕ.

Next we shall adapt the already familiar nomenclature of Eqs. (6) through (11) to Fig. 17·12. Thus we may write (where $r = |\overrightarrow{OP}|$)

$$\sin\phi = \frac{y}{r} = \frac{Y \text{ projection of } \overrightarrow{OP}}{\text{length of } \overrightarrow{OP}} \tag{12}$$

$$\cos\phi = \frac{x}{r} = \frac{X \text{ projection of } \overrightarrow{OP}}{\text{length of } \overrightarrow{OP}} \tag{13}$$

$$\tan\phi = \frac{y}{x} = \frac{Y \text{ projection of } \overrightarrow{OP}}{X \text{ projection of } \overrightarrow{OP}} \tag{14}$$

$$\cot\phi = \frac{x}{y} = \frac{X \text{ projection of } \overrightarrow{OP}}{Y \text{ projection of } \overrightarrow{OP}} \tag{15}$$

$$\sec\phi = \frac{r}{x} = \frac{\text{length of } \overrightarrow{OP}}{X \text{ projection of } \overrightarrow{OP}} \tag{16}$$

$$\operatorname{cosec}\phi = \frac{r}{y} = \frac{\text{length of } \overrightarrow{OP}}{Y \text{ projection of } \overrightarrow{OP}} \tag{17}$$

Observe that a position vector drawn in any other quadrant also has a length, an X projection, and a Y projection. Therefore the nomenclature used in Eqs. (12) through (17) may be applied with equal validity to angles in any quadrant.

Figures 17·13 to 17·15 show the position vectors $\overrightarrow{OP_2}$, $\overrightarrow{OP_3}$, and $\overrightarrow{OP_4}$

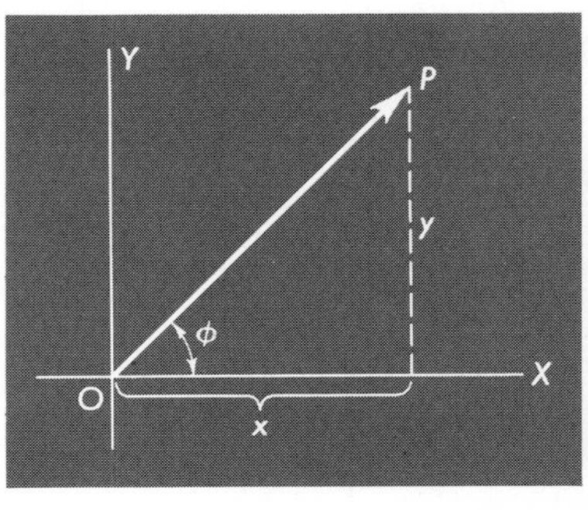

fig. 17·12

fig. 17·13

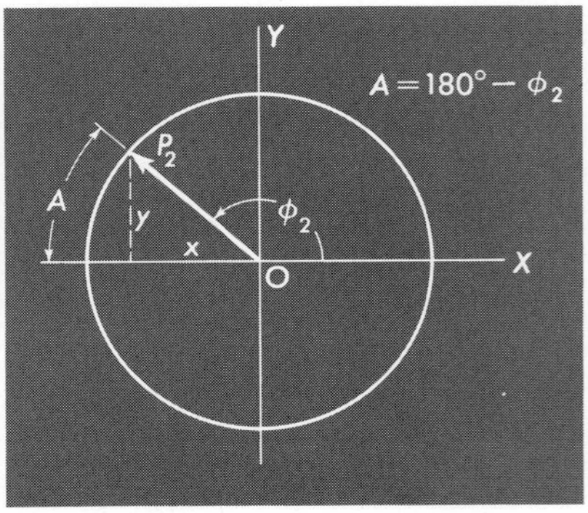

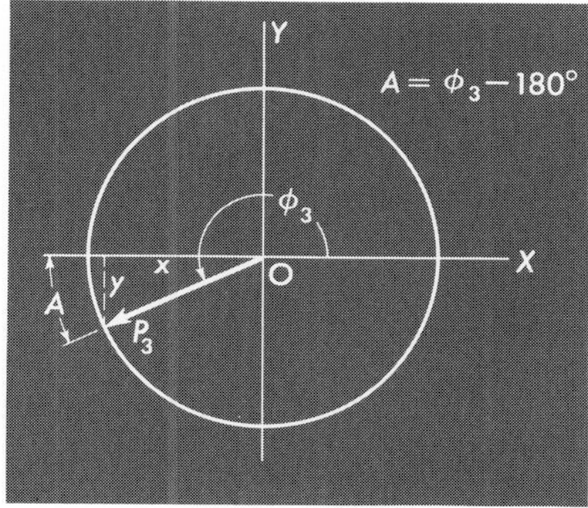

fig. 17·14

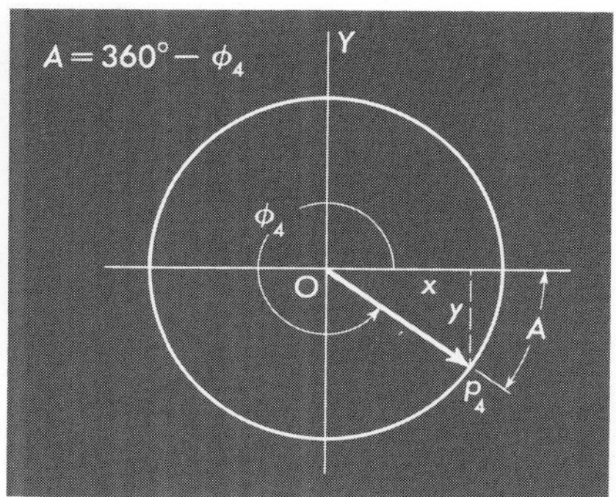

fig. 17·15

drawn in the second, third, and fourth quadrants, respectively, with their reference angles ϕ_2, ϕ_3, and ϕ_4.

Now observe the acute angle A, which we call the *working angle*. This is in each case the acute angle between the position vector and the X axis. The working angle is not a vector reference angle drawn in standard position. It is simply an acute angle of the right triangle, the absolute lengths of whose sides are the absolute lengths of x, y, and r. Absolute length means "length without regard to algebraic sign."

As we learned in Chap. 16, the six trigonometric functions of the angle A are defined in terms of appropriate ratios among the linear dimensions r, x, and y. Since these same linear dimensions also appear in Eqs. (12) through (17), which define the functions of angles in any quadrant, it is quite evident that the absolute values of the functions of the angle A are equal to the absolute values of same named functions of the angles ϕ_2, ϕ_3, and ϕ_4. Now observe that the angle A is the smallest angle between the position vector and the X axis; this is of course an acute angle. It is related to the angles ϕ_2, ϕ_3, and ϕ_4 by the equations

$$A = 180^\circ - \phi_2 \qquad \text{for second quadrant} \qquad (18)$$
$$A = \phi_3 - 180^\circ \qquad \text{for third quadrant} \qquad (19)$$
$$A = 360^\circ - \phi_4 \qquad \text{for fourth quadrant} \qquad (20)$$

example 1 Find the working angle A whose functions are equal to the absolute values of the same named functions of 160°.

The angle 160° is a second-quadrant angle. Therefore Eq. (18) is appropriate. In this case

$$A = 180^\circ - 160^\circ = 20^\circ$$

Therefore the absolute values of the functions of 160° are equal to the same named functions of 20°.

example 2 Find the working angle A whose functions are equal to the absolute values of the same named functions of 200°.

The angle 200° is a third-quadrant angle. Therefore Eq. (19) is appropriate. In this case

$$A = 200° - 180° = 20°$$

Consequently 20° is the acute angle whose functions are equal to the absolute values of the same named functions of 200°.

example 3 Find the working angle A whose functions are equal to the absolute values of the same named functions of 340°.

The angle 340° is a fourth-quadrant angle. Therefore Eq. (20) is appropriate. In this case

$$A = 360° - 340° = 20°$$

Consequently 20° is the acute angle A whose functions are equal to the absolute values of the same named functions of 340°.

We now know from Examples 1 to 3 that if we look up the functions of the acute angle 20° in a table of the trigonometric functions, we have thereby found the absolute values of the functions of the same name for 160°, 200°, and 340°.

EXERCISE 3

1. Find the absolute values of all six functions of 137°.
2. Find the absolute values of all six functions of 205°.
3. Find the absolute values of all six functions of 316°.

17·8 The signs of the functions of angles in any quadrant

Thus far we have discussed only the absolute, numerical values of the trigonometric functions of angles in any quadrant. Actually, however, according to the conventions of rectangular coordinates (see Fig. 17·16) the projections x and y are signed numbers. For purposes of calculation, r is always treated as a positive number.

Using the definitions given in Eqs. (12) through (17) applied to Fig. 17·16, we can write Table 17·1. The student should very carefully verify each item by reference to Fig. 17·16 and Eqs. (12) through (17).

table 17·1

Function	*First quadrant*	*Second quadrant*	*Third quadrant*	*Fourth quadrant*
sin ϕ	$\frac{+y}{+r} = +\frac{y}{r}$	$\frac{+y}{+r} = +\frac{y}{r}$	$\frac{-y}{+r} = -\frac{y}{r}$	$\frac{-y}{+r} = -\frac{y}{r}$
cos ϕ	$\frac{+x}{+r} = +\frac{x}{r}$	$\frac{-x}{+r} = -\frac{x}{r}$	$\frac{-x}{+r} = -\frac{x}{r}$	$\frac{+x}{+r} = +\frac{x}{r}$
tan ϕ	$\frac{+y}{+x} = +\frac{y}{x}$	$\frac{+y}{-x} = -\frac{y}{x}$	$\frac{-y}{-x} = +\frac{y}{x}$	$\frac{-y}{+x} = -\frac{y}{x}$
cot ϕ	$\frac{+x}{+y} = +\frac{x}{y}$	$\frac{-x}{+y} = -\frac{x}{y}$	$\frac{-x}{-y} = +\frac{x}{y}$	$\frac{+x}{-y} = -\frac{x}{y}$
sec ϕ	$\frac{+r}{+x} = +\frac{r}{x}$	$\frac{+r}{-x} = -\frac{r}{x}$	$\frac{+r}{-x} = -\frac{r}{x}$	$\frac{+r}{+x} = +\frac{r}{x}$
cosec ϕ	$\frac{+r}{+y} = +\frac{r}{y}$	$\frac{+r}{+y} = +\frac{r}{y}$	$\frac{+r}{-y} = -\frac{r}{y}$	$\frac{+r}{-y} = -\frac{r}{y}$

Table 17·2 below is an abbreviation of Table 17·1. In Table 17·2 we show only the signs of the functions in each quadrant.

table 17·2

Function	*First quadrant*	*Second quadrant*	*Third quadrant*	*Fourth quadrant*
sin	+	+	−	−
cos	+	−	−	+
tan	+	−	+	−
cot	+	−	+	−
sec	+	−	−	+
cosec	+	+	−	−

example 4 Find all six functions of 160°.

As in Example 1, the working angle corresponding to 160° is 20°. By consulting a table of the trigonometric functions of angles between 0 and 90°, we find that sin 20° = 0.34202, cos 20° = 0.93969, tan 20° = 0.36397, cot 20° = 2.7475, sec 20° = 1.0642, and cosec 20° = 2.9238.

Consequently the absolute values of the sine, cosine, tangent, cotangent, secant, and cosecant of 160° are, respectively, 0.34202, 0.93969, 0.36397, 2.7475, 1.0642, and 2.9238.

However, by inspection of Fig. 17·16 or by consulting Table 17·2, we can see that

$$\sin 160° = +0.34202 \qquad \cot 160° = -2.7475$$
$$\cos 160° = -0.93969 \qquad \sec 160° = -1.0642$$
$$\tan 160° = -0.36397 \qquad \text{cosec } 160° = +2.9238$$

example 5 Find all six functions of 200°.

As in Example 2, the working angle corresponding to 200° is 20°. By consulting a table of the trigonometric functions of angles between 0 and 90°, we find that sin 20° = 0.34202, cos 20° = 0.93969, tan 20° = 0.36397, cot 20° = 2.7475, sec 20° = 1.0642, and cosec 20° = 2.9238.

Consequently the absolute values of the sine, cosine, tangent, cotangent, secant, and cosecant of 200° are, respectively, 0.34202, 0.93969, 0.36397, 2.7475, 1.0642, and 2.9238.

However by inspection of Fig. 17·16 or by consulting Table 17·2, we see that

$$\sin 200° = -0.34202 \qquad \cot 200° = +2.7475$$
$$\cos 200° = -0.93969 \qquad \sec 200° = -1.0642$$
$$\tan 200° = +0.36397 \qquad \text{cosec } 200° = -2.9238$$

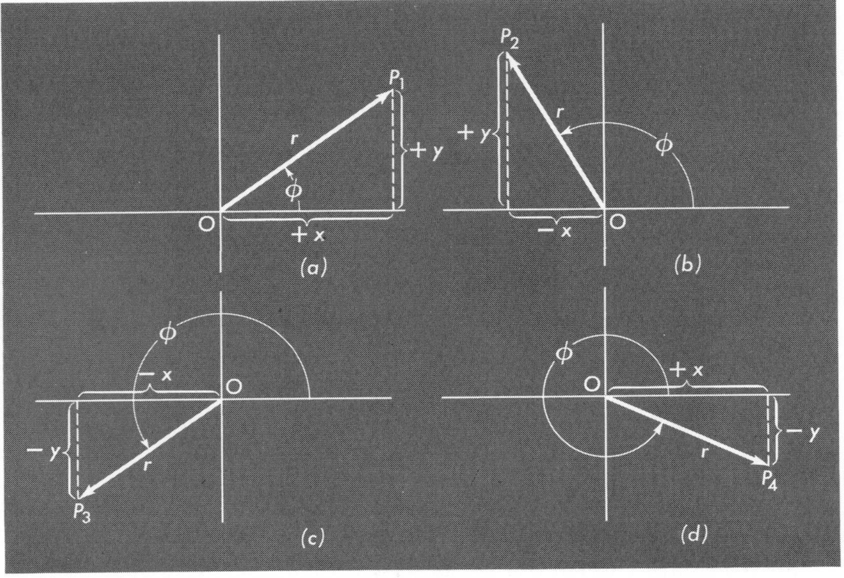

fig. 17·16

example 6 Find all six functions of 340°.

As in Example 3, the working angle corresponding to 340° is 20°. By consulting a table of the trigonometric functions of angles between 0 and 90°, we find that sin 20° = 0.34202, cos 20° = 0.93969, tan 20° = 0.36397, cot 20° = 2.7475, sec 20° = 1.0642, and cosec 20° = 2.9238.

Consequently the absolute values of the sine, cosine, tangent, cotangent, secant, and cosecant of 340° are, respectively, 0.34202, 0.93969, 0.36397, 2.7475, 1.0642, and 2.9238.

However by inspection of Fig. 17·16 or by consulting Table 17·2, we see that

$$\sin 340^\circ = -0.34202 \qquad \cot 340^\circ = -2.7475$$
$$\cos 340^\circ = +0.93969 \qquad \sec 340^\circ = +1.0642$$
$$\tan 340^\circ = -0.36397 \qquad \operatorname{cosec} 340^\circ = -2.9238$$

EXERCISE 4

Find the six functions of the following angles to five significant figures:

1. 140°
2. 170°
3. 95°30′
4. 125°46′17″
5. 113°29′50″
6. 165°27′50″
7. 175°09′55″
8. 100°10′20″
9. 179°40′30″

EXERCISE 5

Find two angles ϕ less than 360° which have each of the functions listed below.

1. $\sin\phi = 0.10572$
2. $\sin\phi = -0.32650$
3. $\sin\phi = 0.57461$
4. $\sin\phi = -0.81385$
5. $\sin\phi = 0.72645$
6. $\cos\phi = -0.49695$
7. $\cos\phi = 0.97808$
8. $\cos\phi = -0.99981$
9. $\cos\phi = 0.02391$
10. $\cos\phi = 0.54980$
11. $\tan\phi = -0.86901$
12. $\tan\phi = 1.1109$
13. $\tan\phi = -0.46430$
14. $\tan\phi = 12.271$
15. $\tan\phi = 1.0455$
16. $\cot\phi = 249.88$
17. $\cot\phi = -0.06315$
18. $\cot\phi = 2.7592$
19. $\cot\phi = -1.5476$
20. $\cot\phi = 1.3825$
21. $\sec\phi = 23.042$
22. $\sec\phi = -1.0670$
23. $\sec\phi = 1.6032$
24. $\sec\phi = -1.2130$
25. $\sec\phi = 2.3440$
26. $\operatorname{cosec}\phi = -2.7290$
27. $\operatorname{cosec}\phi = 9.3381$
28. $\operatorname{cosec}\phi = 1.2880$
29. $\operatorname{cosec}\phi = -1.3834$
30. $\operatorname{cosec}\phi = 1.3119$

17·9 The inverse trigonometric functions

The expression

$$\sin\phi = z$$

is equivalent to the statement "ϕ is the angle whose sine is z." This is often abbreviated to either

$$\phi = \arcsin z \tag{21}$$

or

$$\phi = \sin^{-1} z \tag{22}$$

where either "arcsin" or "$\sin^{-1}$" means, literally, "the angle whose sine is." Such functions are called *inverse trigonometric functions.* Observe carefully that $\sin^{-1}\phi$ *must not be interpreted as the* -1 *power of* $\sin\phi$.

Similarly, the equation

$$\phi = \arccos z$$

means "ϕ is the angle whose cosine is z." Likewise, the equations

$$\phi = \arctan z$$

and

$$\phi = \operatorname{arccot} z$$

mean respectively "ϕ is the angle whose tangent is z" and "ϕ is the angle whose cotangent is z."

We shall omit any discussion of the arc functions involving the secant and the cosecant.

From an inspection of Fig. 17·16 or Table 17·2 it is evident that there are two angles less than 360° which are consistent with the relations shown in Eq. (21) or (22). For example, we see from Examples 5 and 6 that both 200° and 340° have sines of -0.34202.

Furthermore, any angle whose terminal side coincides with the terminal side of either 200° or 340° would also have a sine of -0.34202.

In general, the angles $(200° + n360°)$ and $(340° + n360°)$ are in this category, where n is an integer.

In order to avoid the ambiguity involved when we are confronted with this multiplicity of angles, we ordinarily understand ϕ in the equation

$$\phi = \arcsin z$$

to mean the *principal value* of arcsin z.

The principal value of arcsin z is defined such that

$$z = \sin\phi$$

where

$$-90° \leq \phi \leq +90°$$

Similarly, we define the principal value of arccos z such that

$$z = \cos\phi$$

where

$$0° \leq \phi \leq 180°$$

Also we define the principal value of arctan z such that

$$z = \tan\phi$$

where

$$-90° < \phi < +90°$$

and the principal value of arccot z such that

$$z = \cot\phi$$

where

$$0° < \phi < 180°$$

Now if we are given the problem "Evaluate arcsin (−0.34202)," the implication is that we are to find the *principal value of arcsin* (−0.34202).

By definition, the principal value of arcsin (−0.34202) is that angle between −90° and +90° whose sine is −0.34202.

From Example 6 the angle which meets this condition is the angle 340°, which is the equivalent of −20°.

example 7 Evaluate arccos (−0.93969).

From a table of trigonometric functions, the working angle associated with arccos (−0.93969) is 20°.

The two reference angles less than 360° which apply are

$$180° - 20° = 160°$$

and

$$180° + 20° = 200°$$

By definition, the principal value of arccos (−0.93969) is that angle between 0° and 180° whose cosine is −0.93969. Therefore the principal value of arccos (−0.93969) is 160°.

example 8 Evaluate arctan (−0.36397).

From a table of trigonometric functions the working angle associated with arctan (−0.36397) is 20°.

The two reference angles less than 360° which apply are

$$180° - 20° = 160°$$

and

$$360° - 20° = 340°$$

By definition, the principal value of arctan (−0.36397) is that angle between −90° and +90° whose tangent is −0.36397. Therefore the principal value of arctan (−0.36397) is −20° (the equivalent of 340°).

example 9 Evaluate arccot (+0.36397).

From a table of trigonometric functions the working angle associated with arccot (+0.36397) is 70°.

The two reference angles less than 360° which apply are

$$70°$$

and

$$70° + 180° = 250°$$

By definition, the principal value of arccot (+0.36397) is that angle between 0° and 180° whose cotangent is +0.36397. Therefore the principal value of arccot (+0.36397) is 70°.

EXERCISE 6

For the problems below find the principal value of the given inverse trigonometric functions:

1. $\arctan(1/\sqrt{3})$
2. $\tan^{-1}(1)$
3. $\sin^{-1}(1/2)$
4. $\arcsin(\sqrt{2}/2)$
5. $\arccos(-1/2)$
6. $\tan^{-1}(-1)$
7. $\cot^{-1}\dfrac{a}{b}$, where $a = b$
8. $\arctan[-(\sqrt{3}/3)]$
9. $\tan^{-1}\left(\dfrac{+1}{-\sqrt{3}}\right)$
10. $\sin^{-1}[-(\sqrt{3}/2)]$

17·10 Relation among ϕ, r, and the coordinates of P

In Fig. 17·17 we show an angle ϕ in the second quadrant. The rectangular coordinates of P are, respectively, x and y. The coordinates of P are related to the length of the position vector $\overrightarrow{OP}$ by the equation

$$r = |OP| = \sqrt{x^2 + y^2} \tag{23}$$

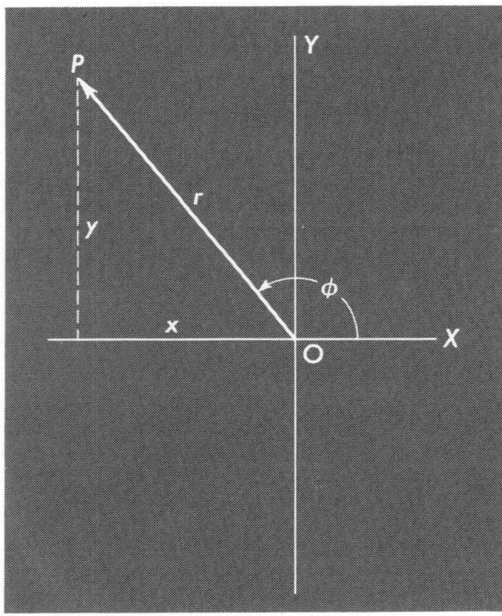

fig. 17·17

The algebraic value of r is the principal root of the radical.

In the special case in which $r = 1$, we may write

$$1 = x^2 + y^2 \tag{24}$$

Furthermore, as we see from Eq. (14),

$$\tan \phi = \frac{y}{x} \tag{25}$$

If we have both rectangular coordinates of P given, then only one angle less than 360° is consistent with the data (see Example 10 below).

If r and only one coordinate of P are given, then there are two angles less than 360° which are consistent with the data (see Example 11 below).

example 10 Calculate r and ϕ if the coordinates of P are $(-4,3)$.

From Eq. (23),

$$r = \sqrt{(-4)^2 + (3)^2} = \sqrt{16 + 9} = \sqrt{25} = 5$$

As the data are given in this example, we know that the ordinate of P is positive and the abscissa is negative. This definitely establishes the position vector in the second quadrant.

From Eq. (25),

$$\tan \phi = \frac{3}{-4} = -0.75$$

The working angle is the acute angle whose tangent is 0.75. From a table of trigonometric functions we find this angle to be 36°52′12″.

From Eq. (18), appropriate to second-quadrant angles,

$$\phi = 180° - 36°52'12'' = 143°07'48''$$

example 11 Calculate the reference angle ϕ of the position vector $\overrightarrow{OP}$ if $|OP| = 5$ and the abscissa of P is -3. From Fig. 17·18 we see that each of two angles ϕ and ϕ' is consistent with the given data.

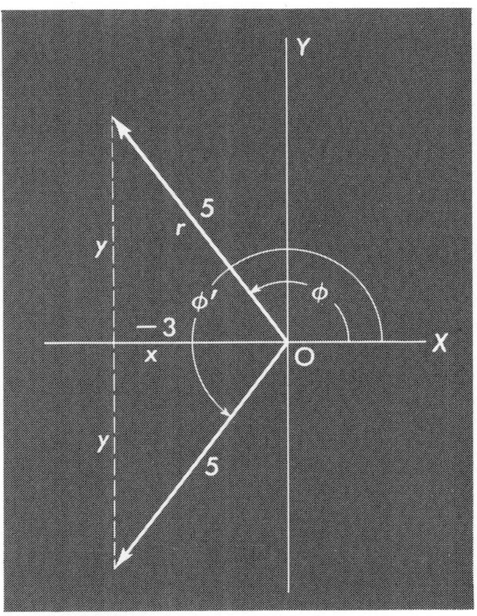

fig. 17·18

From Fig. 17·18 we see that the absolute value of the cosine of the working angle A is

$$\cos A = 3/5 = 0.60000$$

The working angle is therefore 53°07′48″.

By inspection of Fig. 17·18, ϕ is a second-quadrant angle, and Eq. (18) is appropriate. Therefore

$$\phi = 180 - 53°07'48'' = 126°52'12''$$

The angle ϕ' is a third-quadrant angle. Therefore Eq. (19) is appropriate, and

$$\phi' = 180 + 53°07'48'' = 233°07'48''$$

EXERCISE 7

Calculate r and ϕ when the rectangular coordinates of P are as given below (see Fig. 17·16). It is suggested that the student use a slide rule.

1. (7,4)	2. (4,7)	3. (−3.7,10)
4. (−7,7.2)	5. (7.8,−1.4)	6. (−8.6,−4.8)
7. (−3,5.2)	8. (−9.2,−7.8)	9. (1.4,7.9)
10. (6.2,−3)	11. (3,−8)	12. (−2,−3.5)
13. (8.5,3.1)	14. (−6.8,−8)	15. (−10,8.2)

Calculate two angles less than 360° and the corresponding unknown projections consistent with the data given in each problem below.

16. $r = 8,\quad x = +7$	17. $r = 5,\quad y = -3.2$
18. $r = 11,\ x = +8$	19. $r = 9,\quad x = -7.9$
20. $r = 12,\ x = -8$	21. $r = 11,\ y = -3.8$
22. $r = 8,\quad y = +4.5$	23. $r = 10,\ y = +3.3$

17·11 The functions of zero degrees

(See also Sec. 22·1.) When ϕ is zero, as in Fig. 17·19a, $y = 0$, and x is numerically equal to r. Accordingly,

$$\sin 0° = \frac{y}{r} = \frac{0}{r} = 0 \tag{26}$$

$$\cos 0° = \frac{+x}{r} = +1 \tag{27}$$

$$\tan 0° = \frac{y}{x} = \frac{0}{x} = 0 \tag{28}$$

$$\sec 0° = \frac{r}{+x} = +1 \tag{29}$$

The cotangent and the cosecant of zero degrees do not exist, since a calculation of them involves a division by zero. However, if ϕ is a very small positive angle, then y will be a very small linear dimension, and both the cotangent and cosecant will be large numbers. The smaller ϕ is made while still positive, the larger the cotangent and cosecant become.

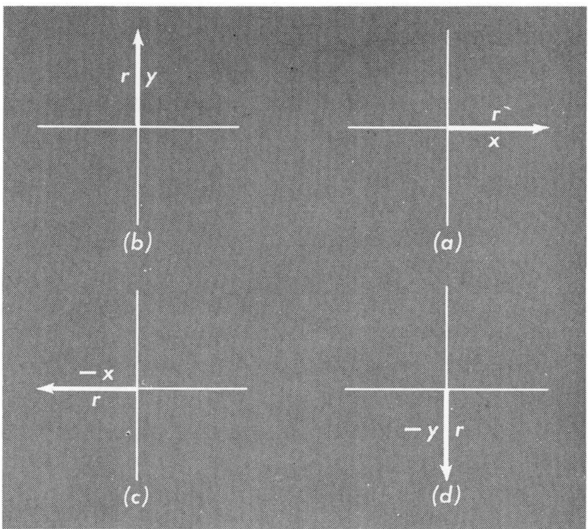

fig. 17·19

17·12 The functions of 90°

(See also Sec. 22·1.) When $\phi = 90°$, as in Fig. 17·19*b*, y is numerically equal to r, and $x = 0$. Accordingly,

$$\sin 90° = \frac{+y}{r} = +1 \tag{30}$$

$$\cos 90° = \frac{x}{r} = \frac{0}{r} = 0 \tag{31}$$

$$\cot 90° = \frac{x}{+y} = \frac{0}{+y} = 0 \tag{32}$$

$$\text{cosec } 90° = \frac{r}{+y} = +1 \tag{33}$$

Here the tangent and the secant do not exist. But if ϕ is slightly less than 90°, then the tangent and secant are enormously large numbers. The closer ϕ approaches 90° while remaining in the first quadrant, the larger the tangent and secant become.

It is important to observe that if ϕ is made ever so slightly greater than 90°, then the signs of the tangent and secant change and become negative. The tangent and secant would then be extremely large in absolute value but negative in sign, or (what amounts to the same thing) extremely small numbers.

If the angle ϕ approaches 90° from the second quadrant, the tangent decreases without limit. If the angle ϕ approaches 90° from the first quadrant, the tangent increases without limit.

17·13 The functions of 180°

(See also Sec. 22·1.) When $\phi = 180°$, as in Fig. 17·19*c*, y is zero, while x is negative and numerically equal to r. Accordingly,

$$\sin 180° = \frac{y}{r} = 0 \tag{34}$$

$$\cos 180° = \frac{-x}{r} = -1 \tag{35}$$

$$\tan 180° = \frac{y}{-x} = \frac{0}{-x} = 0 \tag{36}$$

$$\sec 180° = \frac{r}{-x} = -1 \tag{37}$$

The cotangent and cosecant of 180° do not exist.

17·14 The functions of 270° and 360°

(See also Sec. 22·1.) It is left to the student to verify the following equations by consulting Fig. 17·19*a* and *d*.

$\sin 270° = -1$	$\sin 360° = 0$	(38)
$\cos 270° = 0$	$\cos 360° = 1$	(39)
$\tan 270°$ does not exist	$\tan 360° = 0$	(40)
$\cot 270° = 0$	$\cot 360°$ does not exist	(41)
$\sec 270°$ does not exist	$\sec 360° = 1$	(42)
$\operatorname{cosec} 270° = -1$	$\operatorname{cosec} 360°$ does not exist	(43)

17·15 Variations in the functions

As the position vector $\overrightarrow{OP}$ rotates from the initial position through the first quadrant to the 90° position, the sine of the angle ϕ increases from 0 to 1. In the second quadrant the sine decreases from 1 at the 90° position to 0 at the 180° position. In the third quadrant, the sine decreases from 0 to -1, and in the fourth quadrant it increases from -1 to 0.

In a like manner the variations in the other five functions can be traced.

EXERCISE 8

1. Write all the functions of 0°, 30°, 45°, 60°, 90°, 120°, 135°, 150°, 180°, 210°, 225°, 240°, 270°, 300°, 315°, 330°, and 360° in decimals, using proper signs.
2. In which quadrants does the sine increase as the radius vector rotates counterclockwise? In which quadrant does the cosine increase? The tangent? The cotangent? The secant? The cosecant?

3. Within what numerical limits can the sine, the cosine, the tangent, the cotangent, the secant, and the cosecant exist?
4. What are the maximum and minimum values of each of the six functions?
5. Sketch a graph of each function with the value of the function plotted vertically against the angle plotted horizontally.

unit seven oblique triangles and applications of numerical trigonometry

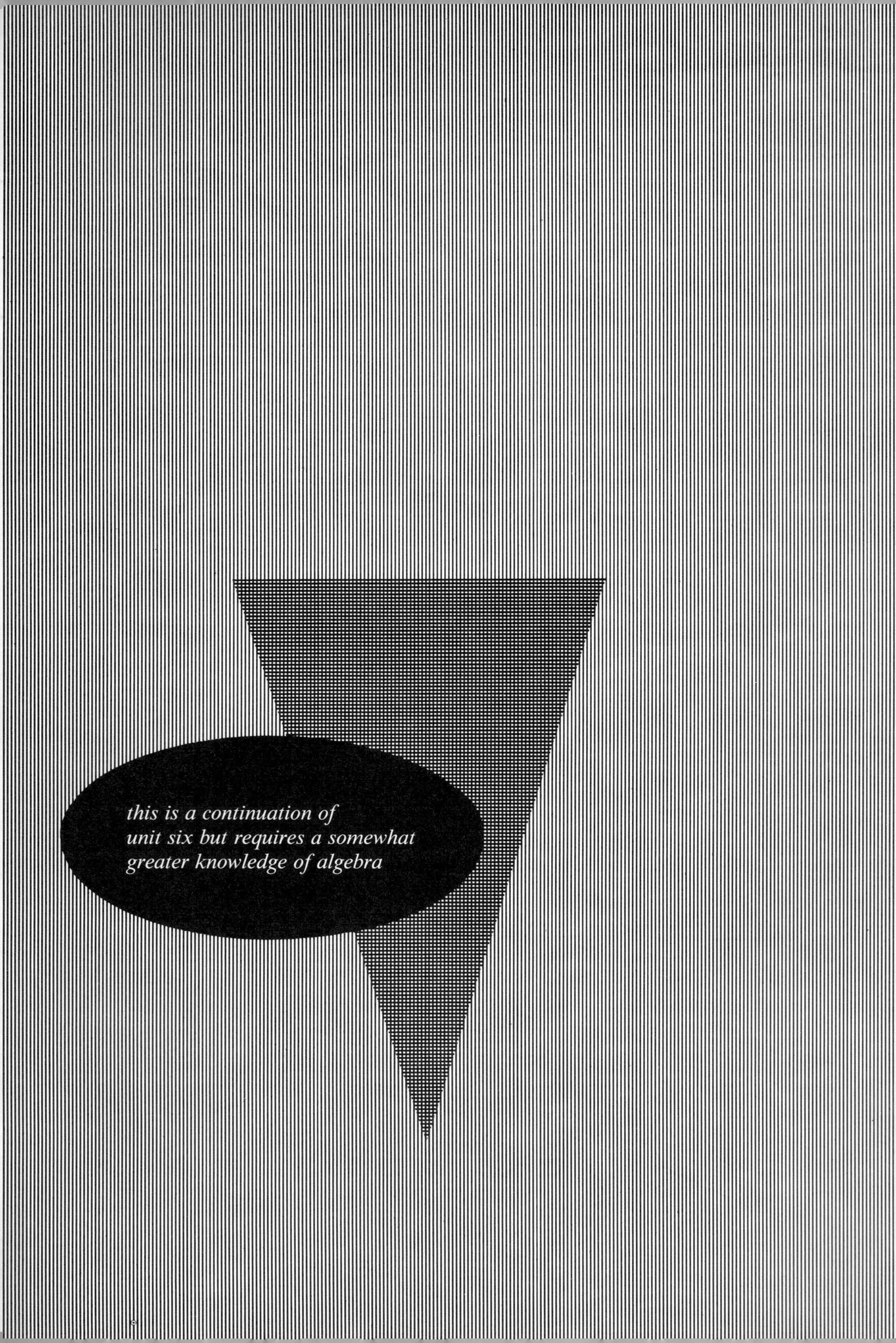
this is a continuation of
unit six but requires a somewhat
greater knowledge of algebra

18
oblique triangles

For efficiency and convenience, the solution of oblique triangles is often accomplished by the use of special formulas rather than by the methods outlined in Secs. 16·17 to 16·20. We shall emphasize four of these formulas. All four formulas refer to the general triangle shown in Fig. 18·1.

18·1 The sine law

This formula is useful when we know two angles and a side or when we know two sides and the angle opposite one of them. The formula is usually stated in the form:

$$\frac{a}{\sin A} = \frac{b}{\sin B} = \frac{c}{\sin C} \qquad \textbf{(1)}$$

Equation (1) is equivalent to Eqs. (2) to (4) below.

$$\frac{a}{\sin A} = \frac{b}{\sin B} \qquad (2)$$

$$\frac{a}{\sin A} = \frac{c}{\sin C} \qquad (3)$$

$$\frac{b}{\sin B} = \frac{c}{\sin C} \qquad (4)$$

If one of the angles in the triangle is obtuse, its sine may be found by the following rule:

To find the sine of an obtuse angle, subtract the obtuse angle from 180°, and use the sine of the acute angle so found. See Sec. 17·8.

In general, when the angle A is an obtuse angle,

$$\sin A = \sin (180° - A) \qquad (5)$$

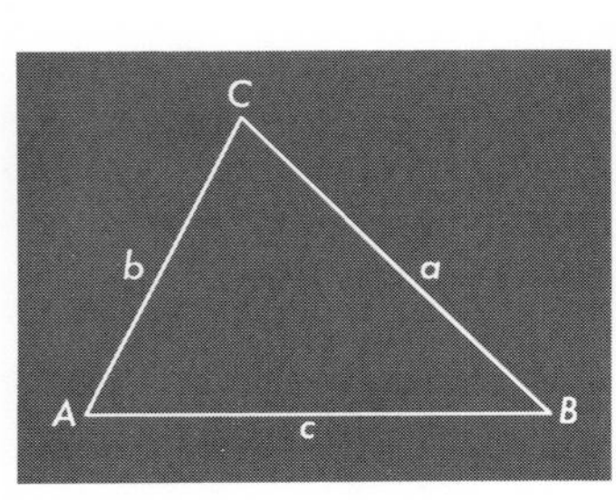

fig. 18·1

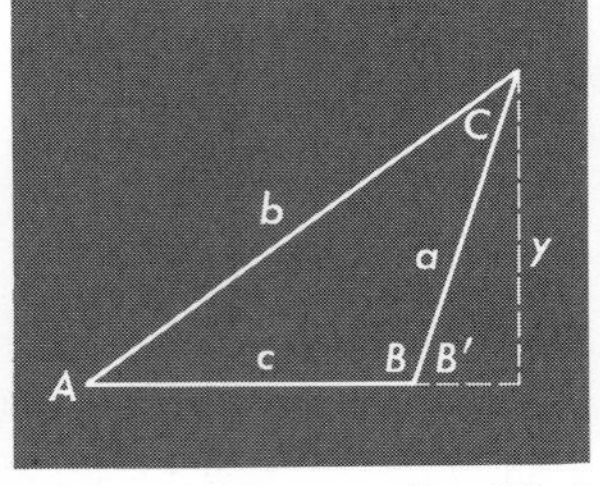

fig. 18·2

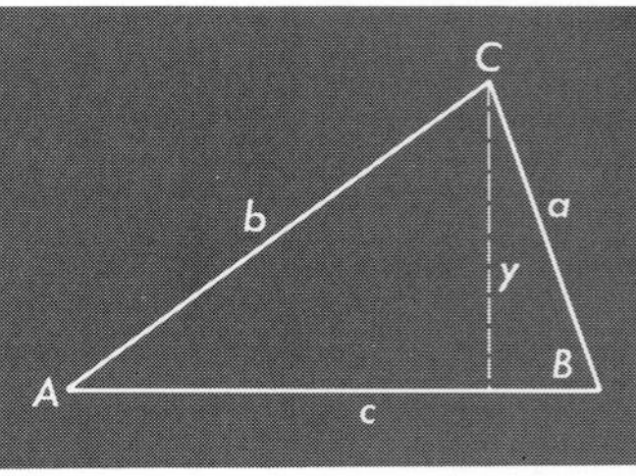

fig. 18·3

example 1 Find the sine of 126°.

$$\sin 126^\circ = \sin(180^\circ - 126^\circ) = \sin 54^\circ$$

From the five-place table,

$$\sin 54^\circ = 0.80902$$

Therefore, $\sin 126^\circ = 0.80902$

EXERCISE 1

See also Exercise 4 page 443.
Find the sine of each of the following angles:

1. 140°
2. 170°
3. 95°30′
4. 125°46′17″
5. 113°29′50″
6. 165°27′50″
7. 175°09′55″
8. 100°10′20″
9. 179°40′30″

Find each of two angles less than 180° which have their sine listed below.

10. 0.05814
11. 0.33244
12. 0.57715
13. 0.72837
14. 0.90766
15. 0.99824

18·2 Derivation of the sine law

Referring to Fig. 18·2,

$$y = b \sin A \tag{6}$$

and

$$y = a \sin B' \tag{7}$$

But from the geometry of the figure the angles B and B' are supplementary angles; therefore, from Eq. (5), their sines are equal, and Eq. (7) may be written

$$y = a \sin B \tag{8}$$

Combining Eqs. (6) and (8),

$$a \sin B = b \sin A \tag{9}$$

Similarly, in Fig. 18·3,

$$y = a \sin B \tag{10}$$

and

$$y = b \sin A \tag{11}$$

Therefore,

$$a \sin B = b \sin A \tag{12}$$

Equation (9) or (12) may be written

$$\frac{a}{\sin A} = \frac{b}{\sin B} \tag{13}$$

The same equation applies whether B is obtuse or acute. We may extend the above derivation to obtain

$$\frac{a}{\sin A} = \frac{b}{\sin B} = \frac{c}{\sin C} \tag{14}$$

Since Eq. (14) involves multiplication and division, logarithms may be used to good advantage in the solution.

example 2 Solve the triangle $A = 42°10'00''$, $B = 78°40'00''$, $c = 150.00$ in.

$$C = 180° - (42°10' + 78°40') = 59°10'$$

$$\frac{a}{\sin A} = \frac{c}{\sin C} \qquad \frac{b}{\sin B} = \frac{c}{\sin C}$$

$$\frac{a}{\sin 42°10'} = \frac{150}{\sin 59°10'} \qquad \frac{b}{\sin 78°40'} = \frac{150}{\sin 59°10'}$$

$$a = \frac{150 \sin 42°10'}{\sin 59°10'} \qquad b = \frac{150 \sin 78°40'}{\sin 59°10'}$$

log 150 in. =	2.17609	log 150 in. =	2.17609
log sin 42°10′ =	9.82691 − 10	log sin 78°40′ =	9.99145 − 10
	12.00300 − 10		12.16754 − 10
log sin 59°10′ =	9.93382 − 10	log sin 59°10′ =	9.93382 − 10
log a =	2.06918	log b =	2.23372
a =	117.27 in.	b =	171.28 in.

The labor of calculation can be reduced somewhat by the use of cologarithms (see Sec. 10·25).

log 150 in. =	2.17609	log 150 in. =	2.17609
log sin 42°10′ =	9.82691 − 10	log sin 78°40′ =	9.99145 − 10
colog sin 59°10′ =	0.06618	colog sin 59°10′ =	0.06618
log a =	12.06918 − 10	log b =	12.23372 − 10
a =	117.27 in.	b =	171.28 in.

If the basic equations are written in the form

$$\frac{\sin 42°10'}{a} = \frac{\sin 59°10'}{150}$$

and treated as a proportion, the problem may conveniently be checked on the slide rule (see Secs. 1·8, 16·21, and 16·22).

Here, if we match 59° 10′ (59.2°) on the S scale to 150 on the D scale, we shall find 78°40′ (78.7°) opposite 171.3 and 42° 10′ (42.2°) opposite 117.3.

example 3 Solve the oblique triangle $B = 40°00'00''$, $C = 25°00'00''$, and $a =$ 23.529 in.

$$A = 180° - (40° + 25°) = 180 - 65° = 115°$$

$$\frac{b}{\sin B} = \frac{a}{\sin A} \qquad \frac{c}{\sin C} = \frac{a}{\sin A}$$

$$\begin{aligned} \log \sin 115° &= \log \sin (180° - 115°) = \log \sin 65° \\ \log \sin 65° &= 9.95728 - 10 \\ \log \sin 115° &= 9.95728 - 10 \end{aligned}$$

$$\begin{aligned} \log 23.529 \text{ in.} &= 1.37160 \\ \log \sin 40° &= 9.80807 - 10 \\ \text{colog} \sin 115° &= 0.04272 \\ \hline \log b &= 11.22239 - 10 \\ b &= 16.687 \text{ in.} \end{aligned} \qquad \begin{aligned} \log 23.529 \text{ in.} &= 1.37160 \\ \log \sin 25° &= 9.62595 - 10 \\ \text{colog} \sin 115° &= 0.04272 \\ \hline \log c &= 11.04027 - 10 \\ c &= 10.972 \text{ in.} \end{aligned}$$

example 4 Solve the oblique triangle $A = 25°00'00''$, $b = 125.00$ in., and $a =$ 80.000 in.

Here, two sides and the angle opposite one of them are given. In Sec. 16·2 it was indicated that under these conditions there is a possibility of two solutions consistent with the given data.

Figures 18·4*a* and *b* are drawn approximately to scale. We shall solve both triangles.

$$\frac{b}{\sin B} = \frac{a}{\sin A} \qquad \text{or} \qquad \frac{\sin B}{b} = \frac{\sin A}{a} \qquad \text{or} \qquad \sin B = \frac{b \sin A}{a}$$

$$\sin B = \frac{125 \sin 25°}{80}$$

$$\begin{aligned} \log 125 &= 2.09691 \\ \log \sin 25° &= 9.62595 - 10 \\ \text{colog } 80 &= 8.09691 - 10 \\ \hline \log \sin B &= 19.81977 - 20 \\ B &= 41°19'34'' \end{aligned}$$

$$C = 180° - (25° + 41°19'34'') = 180° - 66°19'34'' = 113°40'26''$$

$$\frac{c}{\sin C} = \frac{a}{\sin A}$$

$$\frac{c}{\sin 113°40'26''} = \frac{80}{\sin 25°}$$

$$c = \frac{80 \sin 113°40'26''}{\sin 25°}$$

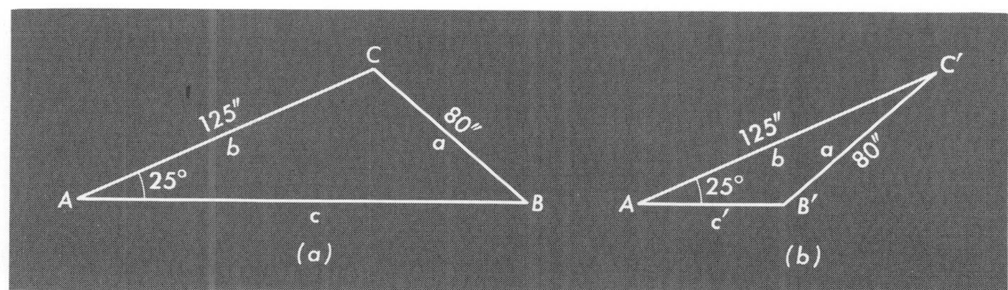

fig. 18·4

$$\log \sin 113°40'26'' = \log \sin (180° - 113°40'26'') = \log \sin 66°19'34''$$

$$\begin{aligned}
\log \sin 66°19'34'' &= 9.96182 - 10 \\
\log \sin 113°40'26'' &= 9.96182 - 10
\end{aligned}$$

$$\begin{aligned}
\log 80 \text{ in.} &= 1.90309 \\
\log \sin 113°40'26'' &= 9.96182 - 10 \\
\text{colog} \sin 25° &= \underline{0.37405} \\
\log c &= 12.23896 - 10 \\
c &= 173.36 \text{ in.}
\end{aligned}$$

$$B' = 180° - B = 180° - 41°19'34'' = 138°40'26''$$
$$C' = 180° - (138°40'26'' + 25°) = 16°19'34''$$

$$c' = \frac{a \sin C'}{\sin A} = \frac{80 \sin 16°19'34''}{\sin 25°}$$

$$\begin{aligned}
\log 80 \text{ in.} &= 1.90309 \\
\log \sin 16°19'34'' &= 9.44886 - 10 \\
\text{colog} \sin 25° &= \underline{0.37405} \\
\log c' &= 11.72600 - 10 \\
c' &= 53.211 \text{ in.}
\end{aligned}$$

EXERCISE 2

1. Redraw Figs. 18·2 and 18·3, and by the use of suitable construction lines prove that

$$\frac{b}{\sin B} = \frac{c}{\sin C}$$

2. In Fig. 18·5 prove that

$$2R = \frac{a}{\sin A} = \frac{b}{\sin B} = \frac{c}{\sin C}$$

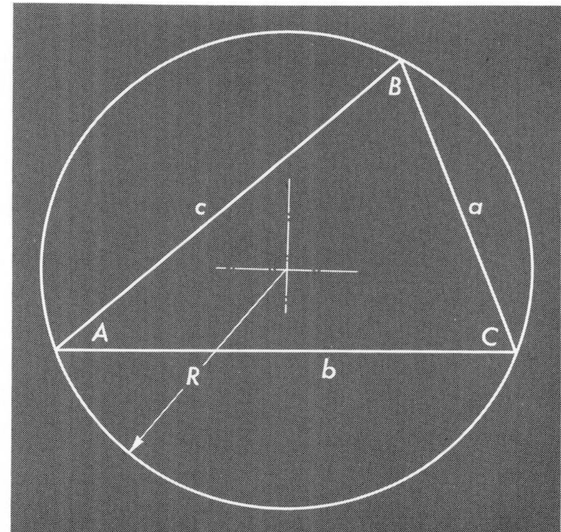

fig. 18·5

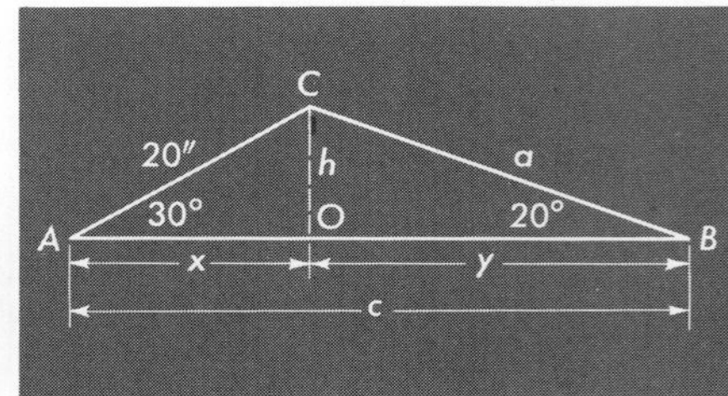

fig. 18·7

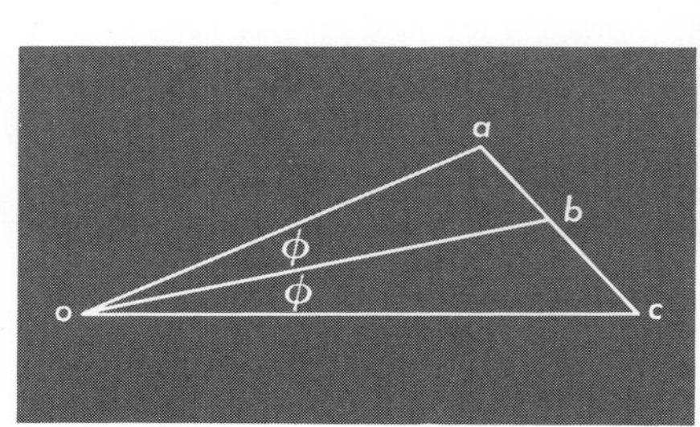

fig. 18·6

3. Rewrite Eq. (13) for the case in which $B = 90°$.
4. In a certain triangle, the angles A, B, and C are, respectively, as 3:4:5. Side a is 10.000 in. Find sides b and c.
5. The sides of a triangle a, b, and c are, respectively, 25, 38, and 51 in. The angles (not listed in the same order as the sides) are approximately 28°05′, 106°15′, and 45°40′. Identify the angles A, B, and C.
6. Given $a = 10\sqrt{2}$, $A = 30°$, and $C = 105°$, find b and c.
7. If $A = 45°$ and $B = 30°$, find the sides a and b when $c = 10$ in.
8. In Fig. 18·6 prove by the law of sines that

$$\frac{ab}{bc} = \frac{oa}{oc}$$

9. If $A = 30°$, $B = 120°$, and $c = 1{,}000$, find a, b, and the altitude drawn to c.
10. Referring to Fig. 18·7,
    (a) Find h, x, and $\angle ACO$.
    (b) Knowing h, find a, y, and $\angle BCO$.
    (c) Knowing x, y, $\angle ACO$, and $\angle BCO$, find C and side c.
11. (a) Angle A of a certain triangle is 17°27.7′, side a is 30 in., and angle B is 42°. Draw the triangle to scale and calculate side b.
    (b) If angle A is 162°32.3′, $a = 30$ in., and $B = 10°$, draw the triangle to scale and solve for side b.
12. The base of a triangle is 4,500 ft, and the angles at the base are 10°20.4′ and 15°34′. Find the unknown sides.

In the problems below solve for unknown sides to five figures and unknown angles to the nearest minute.

13.	$b = 1.5570$ ft	$A = 38°19'$	$C = 88°10'$
14.	$b = 3.3492$ ft	$B = 144°10'$	$C = 13°02'$
15.	$b = 4.1759$ in.	$A = 31°20'$	$C = 18°27'$
16.	$b = 4.2997$ in.	$A = 7°36'$	$C = 10°29'$
17.	$b = 6.8926$ ft	$A = 9°36'$	$C = 47°38'$

18. $a = 1.1831$ in. $B = 8°41'$ $C = 29°54'$
19. $c = 11.863$ in. $A = 5°24'$ $B = 83°50'$
20. $b = 3.8372$ in. $A = 25°26'$ $B = 124°36'$
21. $a = 6.3397$ in. $C = 26°23'$ $B = 49°07'$
22. $c = 10.165$ in. $B = 20°12'$ $C = 75°50'$
23. $c = 39.862$ in. $B = 39°11'$ $A = 12°37'$
24. $a = 2.7570$ ft $B = 43°7'$ $C = 35°14'$
25. $b = 1.7089$ in. $c = 1.2788$ in. $C = 48°21'$
26. $b = 4.8600$ ft $a = 3.5683$ ft $B = 68°01'$
27. $b = 7.2199$ ft $A = 57°37'$ $a = 6.5867$ ft
28. $a = 1.1690$ in. $c = .63966$ in. $C = 28°04'$
29. $b = 4.4682$ ft $A = 61°22'$ $a = 4.1244$ ft
30. $b = 1.0226$ ft $c = 1.3378$ ft $C = 70°14'$
31. $c = 3.7198$ in. $A = 62°31'$ $a = 3.3145$ in.
32. $b = 5.2979$ ft $A = 74°3'$ $C = 11°17'$
33. $a = 3.7956$ ft $B = 38°7'$ $C = 82°41'$
34. $b = 0.43972$ in. $A = 51°8'$ $C = 36°28'$

Find the unknown sides to five figures and the unknown angles to the nearest second, using the sine law, in the following problems.

35. $a = 17.230$ in. $A = 56°22'13''$ $C = 35°53'16''$
36. $c = 11.855$ in. $A = 7°30'47''$ $C = 47°36'12''$
37. $c = 133.70$ in. $A = 4°17'22''$ $B = 165°29'23''$
38. $b = 105.46$ in. $B = 85°10'31''$ $c = 105.09$ in.
39. $b = 145.70$ in. $a = 145.10$ in. $B = 85°09'55''$
40. $b = 16.683$ in. $A = 79°50'30''$ $a = 17.938$ in.
41. $c = 16.481$ in. $b = 32.675$ in. $B = 109°13'16''$
42. $c = 12.781$ in. $a = 12.412$ in. $C = 46°28'50''$
43. $a = 17.219$ in. $c = 19.751$ in. $C = 88°56'3''$
44. $a = 6.6435$ in. $B = 53°21'9''$ $C = 48°48'37''$
45. $a = 10.959$ in. $A = 80°43'53''$ $B = 33°24'58''$
46. $c = 30.361$ in. $A = 21°14'28''$ $B = 146°40'26''$
47. $a = 23.293$ in. $A = 24°15'35''$ $C = 25°25'25''$
48. $b = 10.878$ in. $A = 44°40'38''$ $B = 49°41'43''$
49. $b = 36.234$ in. $A = 20°6'20''$ $C = 48°16'42''$
50. $a = 11.306$ in. $A = 25°24'44''$ $B = 92°24'3''$
51. $a = 6527.6$ in. $B = 70°55'29''$ $C = 52°9'43''$
52. $c = 1004.0$ in. $A = 79°19'25''$ $B = 53°27'10''$
53. $b = 14.752$ in. $B = 13°19.7'$ $C = 59°13.6'$
54. $b = 999.90$ in. $A = 37°58.7'$ $C = 65°2.9'$
55. $a = 497.32$ in. $A = 10°36.4'$ $B = 46°37.9'$
56. $a = 832.76$ in. $A = 82°36'42''$ $B = 45°32'10''$
57. $a = 796.38$ in. $A = 99°36'24''$ $C = 49°37'45''$
58. $a = 827.56$ in. $C = 12°48.3'$ $B = 140°59.7'$
59. $a = 143.62$ in. $B = 37°42.7'$ $C = 28°26.5'$

18·3 The cosine law

This law is useful when two sides and the included angle are known or when three sides are known.

Referring to Fig. 18·1,

$$a^2 = b^2 + c^2 - 2 \times b \times c \times \cos A \quad \textbf{(15)}$$
$$b^2 = a^2 + c^2 - 2 \times a \times c \times \cos B \quad \textbf{(16)}$$
$$c^2 = a^2 + b^2 - 2 \times a \times b \times \cos C \quad \textbf{(17)}$$

If one of the angles in the triangle is obtuse, its cosine may be found by the rule below:

To find the cosine of an obtuse angle, subtract the obtuse angle from 180° and use the negative *of the cosine of the acute angle so found.* (See Sec. 17·8.)

In general, when the angle A is obtuse,

$$\cos A = -\cos (180° - A) \quad (18)$$

example 5 Find the cosine of 126°.

$$\cos 126° = -\cos (180° - 126°) = -\cos 54°$$

From the five-place tables,

$$\cos 54° = 0.58779$$

Therefore, $\cos 126° = -0.58779$

If the angle A, B, or C is obtuse, then Eqs. (15), (16), and (17) may be written

$$a^2 = b^2 + c^2 + 2 \times b \times c \times \cos (180° - A) \quad (19)$$
$$b^2 = a^2 + c^2 + 2 \times a \times c \times \cos (180° - B) \quad (20)$$
$$c^2 = a^2 + b^2 + 2 \times a \times b \times \cos (180° - C) \quad (21)$$

18·4 Derivation of the cosine law

Given the oblique triangle ABC in Fig. 18·8, where A, b, and c are known, and where A is an acute angle, find a formula for a in terms of A, b, and c.

Drop the perpendicular h from B to side b.

$$x = c \times \cos A \quad (22)$$
$$h = c \times \sin A \quad (23)$$
$$a^2 = h^2 + (b - x)^2 \quad (24)$$

But $h^2 = c^2 - x^2 \quad (25)$

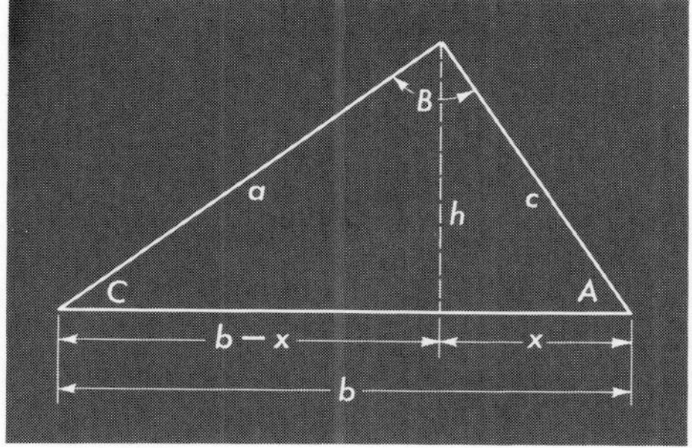

fig. 18·8

fig. 18·9

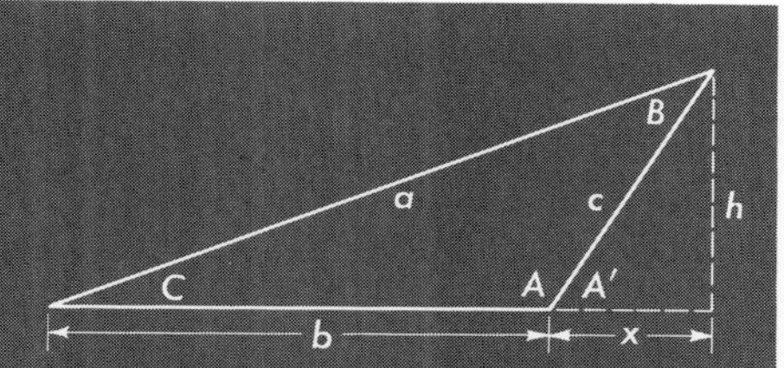

Substituting the above value of h^2 in Eq. (24), we obtain

$$a^2 = c^2 - x^2 + (b - x)^2 \quad (26)$$

or

$$a^2 = c^2 - x^2 + b^2 - 2bx + x^2 \quad (27)$$

or

$$a^2 = c^2 + b^2 - 2bx \quad (28)$$

But

$$x = c \cos A \quad (29)$$

Substituting the above value of x in Eq. (28),

$$a^2 = c^2 + b^2 - 2bc \cos A \quad (30)$$

Equations (16) and (17) can be derived in a similar way.

If the known angle is obtuse, the cosine law can be derived from Fig. 18·9. Here the angle A and the sides b and c are given. Angle A is obtuse.

Drop the perpendicular h from B to the side b extended.

$$h = c \sin A'$$

$$x = c \cos A'$$

$$a^2 = h^2 + (b + x)^2 \quad (31)$$

But

$$h^2 = c^2 - x^2 \quad (32)$$

Substituting the above value of h^2 in Eq. (31),

$$a^2 = c^2 - x^2 + (b + x)^2$$

$$a^2 = c^2 - x^2 + b^2 + 2bx + x^2$$

$$a^2 = c^2 + b^2 + 2bx$$

But

$$x = c \cos A'$$

Therefore,

$$a^2 = b^2 + c^2 + 2bc \cos A'$$

$$A' = 180° - A \quad (33)$$

and

$$a^2 = b^2 + c^2 - 2bc \cos A \quad (34)$$

Therefore the cosine law as stated in Eqs. (15) to (17) is valid for both acute and obtuse angles.

It is not at all unusual to encounter situations in which it is more convenient to use the acute exterior angle A' than to use the obtuse interior angle A (see Fig. 18·9). Such cases frequently occur in alternating-current problems and concurrent-force problems. In these problems the side b, the side c, and the angle A' would naturally appear in the data.

If the angles A', B', and C' are exterior angles corresponding to the interior angles A, B, and C, then the cosine law may be written

$$a^2 = b^2 + c^2 + 2bc \cos A' \tag{35}$$
$$b^2 = a^2 + c^2 + 2ac \cos B' \tag{36}$$
$$c^2 = a^2 + b^2 + 2ab \cos C' \tag{37}$$

As a special case, if $A' = 90°$, Eq. (35) becomes

$$a^2 = b^2 + c^2 + 2bc \cos 90°$$
$$a^2 = b^2 + c^2 + 2bc(0)$$
$$a^2 = b^2 + c^2$$

which is the Pythagorean theorem. The cosine law is sometimes called the *generalized Pythagorean theorem* because, with the ($\pm 2bc \cos A$) term included, the traditional Pythagorean theorem applies to all triangles.

example 6 Solve the triangle $a = 25$ in., $b = 56$ in., $C = 36°52'12''$.

$$c^2 = a^2 + b^2 - 2ab \cos 36°52'12''$$
$$c^2 = 25^2 + 56^2 - 2 \times 25 \times 56 \times 0.8$$
$$c^2 = 1{,}521$$
$$c = \sqrt{1{,}521} = 39$$

One of the unknown angles can now be computed by use of the sine law.

$$\frac{c}{\sin C} = \frac{b}{\sin B} \qquad \frac{39}{\sin 36°52'12''} = \frac{56}{\sin B}$$

$$\sin B = \frac{56 \sin 36°52'12''}{39}$$

$$\begin{aligned} \log 56 &= 1.74819 \\ \log \sin 36°52'12'' &= 0.77815 - 1 \\ \text{colog } 39 &= \underline{0.40894 - 2} \\ \log \sin B &= 0.93528 - 1 \end{aligned}$$

B would equal $59°29'26''$ *if B were acute.* However, from the scale drawing of the problem, B is obviously obtuse. Therefore

$$B = 180° - 59°29'26'' = 120°30'34''$$

example 7 Solve the triangle $a = 25.000$ in., $b = 16.000$ in., $C = 143°7'48''$.

Here the known angle is obtuse, and there are two ways of thinking when attacking the problem. Equation (37) can be used, and

$$c^2 = a^2 + b^2 + 2ab \cos (180° - 143°7'48'')$$
$$c^2 = a^2 + b^2 + 2ab \cos 36°52'12''$$
$$c^2 = 25^2 + 16^2 + 2 \times 25 \times 16 \times 0.8 = 1{,}521$$
$$c = \sqrt{1{,}521} = 39.000 \text{ in.}$$

Or the fact stated in Eq. (18) may be used, and, therefore,

$$\cos 143°7'48'' = -\cos(180° - 143°7'48'') = -\cos 36°52'12'' = -0.8$$

$$\begin{aligned} c^2 &= a^2 + b^2 - 2ab\cos C \\ c^2 &= 25^2 + 16^2 - 2 \times 25 \times 16(-0.8) \\ c^2 &= 25^2 + 16^2 + 2 \times 25 \times 16 \times 0.8 = 1{,}521 \\ c &= \sqrt{1{,}521} = 39 \end{aligned}$$

Angle B can be calculated by the sine law, which is here illustrated by the use of natural functions rather than log functions.

$$\frac{\sin B}{b} = \frac{\sin C}{c}$$

$$\frac{\sin B}{16} = \frac{\sin 143°7'48''}{39}$$

Referring to Eq. (5),

$$\sin 143°7'48'' = \sin(180° - 143°7'48'') = \sin 36°52'12'' = 0.60000$$

$$\sin B = \frac{16 \times 0.6}{39} = 0.24615$$

$$B = 14°15'$$

$$A = 180° - (14°15' + 143°7'48'') = 22°37'12''$$

The cosine law is also useful when three sides are known.

example 8 Solve for all the angles in the triangle $a = 13''$, $b = 21''$, $c = 20''$. (Data are known to five significant digits.)

Use Eqs. (15) to (17).

$$\begin{aligned} a^2 &= b^2 + c^2 - 2bc\cos A \\ 13^2 &= 21^2 + 20^2 - 2 \times 21 \times 20\cos A \\ 169 &= 441 + 400 - 840\cos A \\ 169 &= 841 - 840\cos A \end{aligned}$$

$$\cos A = 672/840 = 0.80000 \qquad \text{ANS.: } A = 36°52'11''$$

$$\begin{aligned} b^2 &= a^2 + c^2 - 2ac\cos B \\ 21^2 &= 13^2 + 20^2 - 2 \times 13 \times 20\cos B \\ 441 &= 169 + 400 - 520\cos B \\ 441 &= 569 - 520\cos B \\ \cos B &= 128/520 = 0.24615 \end{aligned} \qquad \text{ANS.: } B = 75°45'00''$$

$$\begin{aligned} c^2 &= a^2 + b^2 - 2ab\cos C \\ 20^2 &= 13^2 + 21^2 - 2 \times 13 \times 21\cos C \\ 400 &= 169 + 441 - 546\cos C \\ 400 &= 610 - 546\cos C \\ \cos C &= 210/546 = 0.38462 \end{aligned} \qquad \text{ANS.: } C = 67°22'47''$$

$$\text{CHECK: } = 179°59'58''$$

example 9 Find the angle C in the triangle $a = 78$ in., $b = 35$ in., $c = 97$ in. (Data are known to five significant digits.)

$$\begin{aligned} c^2 &= a^2 + b^2 - 2ab \cos C \\ 97^2 &= 78^2 + 35^2 - 2 \times 78 \times 35 \cos C \\ 9{,}409 &= 6{,}084 + 1{,}225 - 5{,}460 \cos C \\ 9{,}409 &= 7{,}309 - 5{,}460 \cos C \end{aligned}$$

Here C is obviously obtuse, since c^2 actually is larger than $a^2 + b^2$; in other words, c^2 actually is larger than it would be if C were 90°. A scale drawing would indicate the same fact. Also,

$$-\cos C = \frac{2{,}100}{5{,}460}$$

Therefore from Eq. (18), page 462, C must be obtuse.

$$\begin{aligned} \cos C &= -2{,}100/5{,}460 = -0.38462 \\ C &= 180° - 67°22'47'' = 112°37'13'' \end{aligned}$$

EXERCISE 3

1. Verify the following:

(a) $\cos 42° = 0.74314$ (b) $\cos 138° = -0.74314$
(c) $\cos 130° = -0.64279$ (d) $\cos 179° = -0.99985$

2. Given the cosine of the angle, verify the following:

(a) -0.89101 is the cosine of 153° (b) 0.89101 is the cosine of 27°
(c) -0.96126 is the cosine of 164° (d) 0.96126 is the cosine of 16°

3. Show that with proper regard to signs

$$a = b \cos C + c \cos B$$

whether B is acute or obtuse.

4. Prove that in a triangle with sides a, b, and c,

$$a^2 + b^2 + c^2 = 2(ab \cos C + bc \cos A + ca \cos B)$$

5. Show that if

$$\frac{\cos A}{b} = \frac{\cos B}{a}$$

the triangle is either an isosceles triangle or a right triangle.

6. Prove that

$$\frac{\cos A}{a} + \frac{\cos B}{b} + \frac{\cos C}{c} = \frac{a^2 + b^2 + c^2}{2abc}$$

7. Prove that

$$\frac{c^2}{b}\cos B + \frac{b^2}{a}\cos A + \frac{a^2}{c}\cos C = \frac{a^4 + b^4 + c^4}{2abc}$$

Also show that the equation is dimensionally correct.

Find the side opposite the given angle, using the cosine law.

8.	$a = 4.0000$ in.	$b = 5.0000$ in.	$C = 66°25'18''$
9.	$b = 7.0000$ in.	$c = 10.000$ in.	$A = 45°34'23''$
10.	$a = 20.000$ in.	$b = 35.000$ in.	$C = 60°$
11.	$a = 7.0000$ in.	$b = 12.000$ in.	$C = 123°22'02''$
12.	$c = 11.000$ in.	$b = 9.0000$ in.	$A = 31°47'19''$
13.	$a = 13.000$ in.	$b = 18.000$ in.	$C = 36°52'11''$
14.	$a = 5.0000$ in.	$b = 10.000$ in.	$C = 126°52'13''$
15.	$a = 15.000$ in.	$b = 22.000$ in.	$C = 130°32'30''$
16.	$a = 17.000$ in.	$b = 15.000$ in.	$C = 154°9'28''$
17.	$b = 10.000$ in.	$c = 20.000$ in.	$A = 36°52.2'$

Find all the angles. Make three separate calculations, one for each angle. Find angles to seconds.

18.	$a = 61.000$ in.	$b = 87.000$ in.	$c = 74.000$ in.
19.	$a = 65.000$ in.	$b = 87.000$ in.	$c = 44.000$ in.
20.	$a = 78.000$ in.	$b = 95.000$ in.	$c = 97.000$ in.
21.	$a = 25.000$ in.	$b = 28.000$ in.	$c = 17.000$ in.
22.	$a = 3.0000$ in.	$b = 4.0000$ in.	$c = 6.0000$ in.
23.	$a = 4.0000$ in.	$b = 5.0000$ in.	$c = 7.0000$ in.
24.	$a = 5.0000$ in.	$b = 7.0000$ in.	$c = 9.0000$ in.
25.	$a = 5.0000$ in.	$b = 6.0000$ in.	$c = 7.0000$ in.
26.	$a = 6.0000$ in.	$b = 9.0000$ in.	$c = 11.000$ in.
27.	$a = 13.000$ in.	$b = 16.000$ in.	$c = 19.000$ in.
28.	$a = 5.00000$ in.	$b = 8.0000$ in.	$c = 12.000$ in.
29.	$a = 5.8750$ in.	$b = 3.2500$ in.	$c = 8.5000$ in.

18·5 Other formulas

If we are given two sides of a triangle and the included angle and if we wish to find the unknown angles without first finding the third side, the formula derived below will be found convenient.

In Fig. 18·10 we have given the angle C and the sides a and b. We wish to find the angle A.

In this figure

$$Cd = a\cos C = a\sin C\cot C \tag{38}$$

$$Ad = h\cot A \tag{39}$$

but

$$h = a\sin C \tag{40}$$

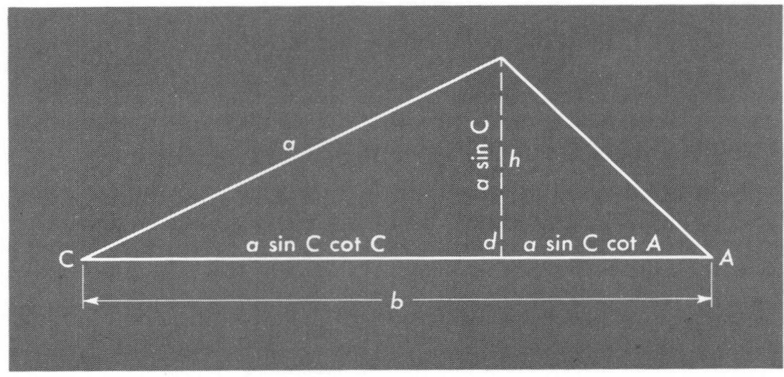

fig. 18·10

Therefore	$Ad = a \sin C \cot A$
Also	$b = Cd + dA$
Therefore	$b = a \cos C + a \sin C \cot A$
or	$b - a \cos C = a \sin C \cot A$
or	$\dfrac{b - a \cos C}{a \sin C} = \cot A$
or	$\dfrac{b}{a \sin C} - \cot C = \cot A$ **(41)**

example 10 Find the unknown angles in the triangle $a = 75.000$ in., $b = 136.00$ in., $C = 53°07'47''$.

Following Eq. (41),

$$\frac{136.00}{75.000 \sin 53°07'47''} - \cot C = \cot A$$

$$\log a = \log 75.000 = \underline{1}.87506$$
$$\log \sin C = \log \sin 53°07'47'' = \underline{1.90309}$$
$$\log (a \sin C) = 1.77815$$

$$\log b = \log 136.00 = 2.13354$$
$$\log (a \sin C) = \underline{1.77815}$$

$$\log \frac{b}{a \sin C} = 0.35539$$

$$\frac{b}{a \sin C} = 2.2667$$

$$\cot A = 2.2667 - \cot C = 2.2667 - 0.7500 = 1.5167$$
$$A = 33°23'53''$$
$$B = 180° - (53°07'47'' + 33°23'53'') = 93°28'20''$$

EXERCISE 4

Solve the following triangles assuming that the given angle is known to the nearest second. Express your answers to an appropriate number of significant digits consistent with the tables used.

1.	$B = 110°44'$	$c = 18.1419$	$a = 26.2635$
2.	$B = 74°30'$	$c = 113.031$	$a = 145.856$
3.	$A = 148°40'$	$b = 1.35482$	$c = 1.92802$
4.	$A = 7°36'$	$b = 21.1113$	$c = 76.3668$
5.	$A = 9°36'$	$b = 110.007$	$c = 131.919$
6.	$A = 25°26'$	$b = 12.1591$	$c = 76.8406$
7.	$A = 5°24'$	$b = 3.49028$	$c = 3.54202$
8.	$A = 26°23'$	$b = 19.1707$	$c = 37.5060$
9.	$A = 9°18'$	$b = 7.63674$	$c = 6.18797$
10.	$A = 27°12'46''$	$b = 378.95$	$c = 472.63$
11.	$A = 11°25'16''$	$b = 114.00$	$c = 101.00$
12.	$A = 14°15'$	$b = 93.000$	$c = 65.000$
13.	$A = 12°40'50''$	$b = 162.36$	$c = 285.88$
14.	$B = 143°7'48''$	$a = 0.61087$	$c = 0.76794$
15.	$A = 22°37'12''$	$b = 90.757$	$c = 57.596$

If we have three sides of a triangle given and wish to find an angle, the following variation of the cosine law is quite convenient since it is better adapted to logarithmic computation.

From Eq. (15) we have

$$a^2 = b^2 + c^2 - 2 \cdot b \cdot c \cdot \cos A$$

or

$$b^2 + c^2 - a^2 = 2 \cdot b \cdot c \cdot \cos A$$

By adding $2bc$ to both sides of the above equation, we obtain

$$b^2 + 2bc + c^2 - a^2 = 2bc + 2bc \cdot \cos A = 2bc(1 + \cos A)$$

or

$$\frac{(b + c + a)(b + c - a)}{2bc} = 1 + \cos A \qquad \textbf{(42)}$$

example 11 If the sides of a triangle are $a = 75.000$, $b = 86.000$, and $c = 97.000$, find the angle A to the nearest 0.1 min.

Following Eq. (42),

$$\frac{(86 + 97 + 75)(86 + 97 - 75)}{2 \times 86 \times 97} = 1 + \cos A$$

$$\frac{258 \times 108}{2 \times 86 \times 97} = 1 + \cos A$$

$$\begin{aligned}
\log 258 &= 2.41162 \\
\log 108 &= \underline{2.03342} \\
&\ 4.44504 = \log 258 \times 108
\end{aligned}$$

$$\begin{aligned}
\log 2 &= 0.30103 \\
\log 86 &= 1.93450 \\
\log 97 &= \underline{1.98677} \\
&\ 4.22230 = \log (2 \times 86 \times 97)
\end{aligned}$$

$$
\begin{aligned}
\log(258 \times 108) &= 4.44504 \\
\log(2 \times 86 \times 97) &= \underline{4.22230} \\
0.22274 &= \log(1 + \cos A) \\
1.6701 &= 1 + \cos A \\
\cos A &= 0.6701 \\
A &= 47°55.5'
\end{aligned}
$$

EXERCISE 5

1. If $a = 410.95$, $b = 469.23$, and $c = 389.76$, find angle A to the nearest 0.1 min.
2. If $a = 13.492$, $b = 15.786$, and $c = 10.387$, find angle B to the nearest 0.1 min.
3. If $a = 431.76$, $b = 609.95$, and $c = 710.89$, find angle C to the nearest 0.1 min.
4. If $a = 6.6168$, $b = 9.7161$, and $c = 15.688$, find angle B to the nearest 0.1 min.
5. If $a = 1.3701$, $b = 4.7503$, and $c = 5.4868$, find angle A to the nearest 0.1 min.

EXERCISE 6

1. Solve for x in Fig. 18·11.
2. Solve for x in Fig. 18·12.
3. Solve for x in Fig. 18·13.
4. Solve for x in Fig. 18·14.
5. Solve for x in Fig. 18·15.
6. Solve for x in Fig. 18·16.
7. Solve for x in Fig. 18·17.

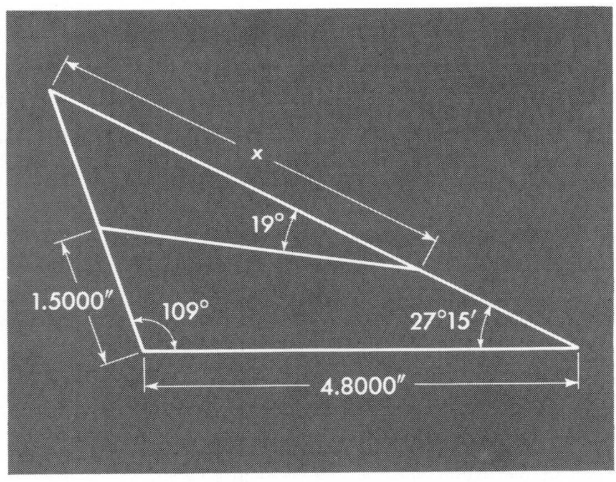

fig. 18·11

fig. 18·12

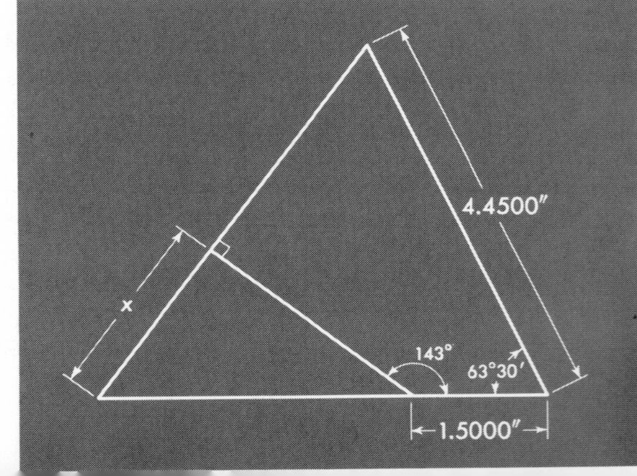

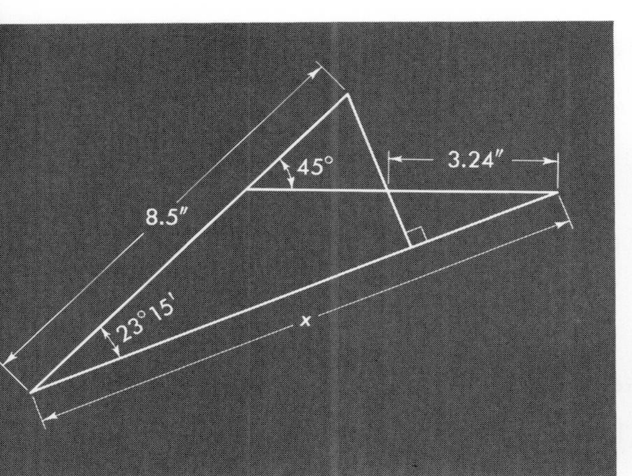

: 18·13

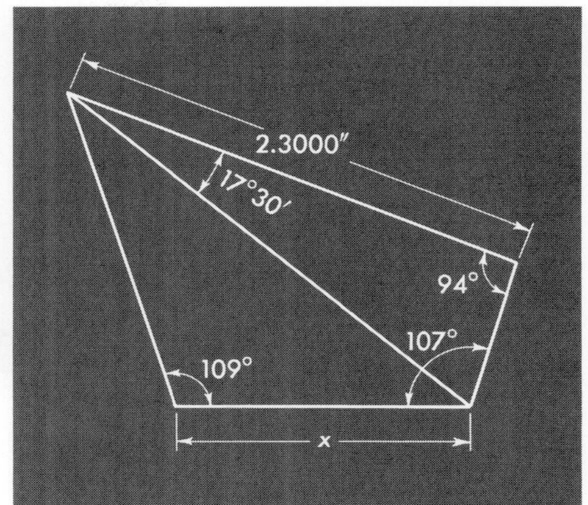

fig. 18·14

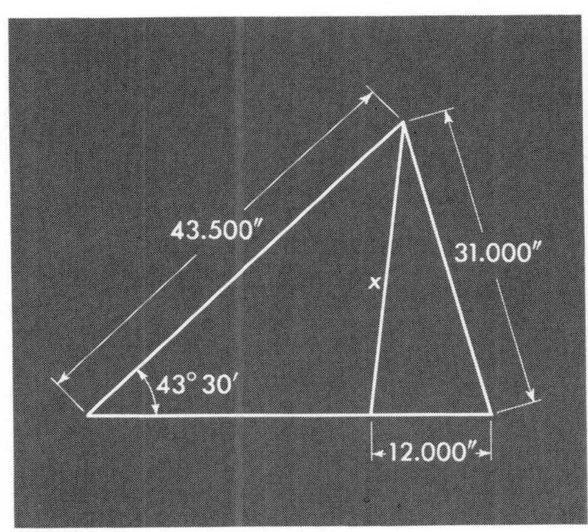

fig. 18·15

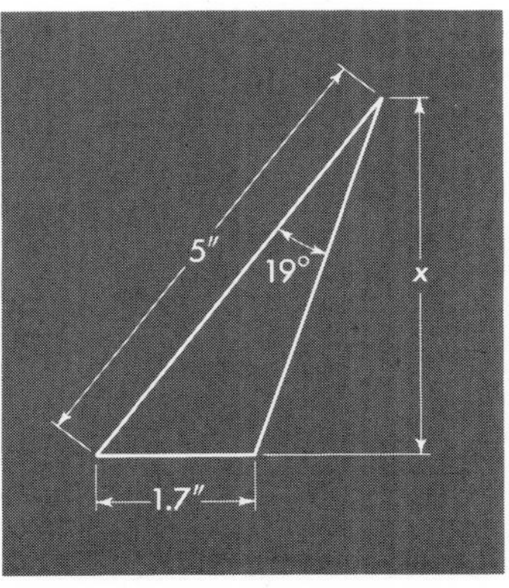

fig. 18·16

fig. 18·17

18·6 Areas of triangles (see Fig. 18·18)

Given the base and altitude

From geometry,

$$A_t = \tfrac{1}{2}bh \tag{43}$$

where

A_t = area of triangle
b = base of triangle
h = altitude of triangle

Given two sides and the included angle

Let the two known sides be c and b. Let the known angle be A.

$$h = c \sin A$$

Substituting the above value of h in Eq. (43)

$$A_t = \tfrac{1}{2}b \times c \sin A \tag{44}$$

Similarly,

$$A_t = \tfrac{1}{2}ab \sin C \tag{45}$$

$$A_t = \tfrac{1}{2}ac \sin B \tag{46}$$

Given two angles and any side

$$\frac{\sin A}{\sin B} = \frac{a}{b} \tag{47}$$

[See Eq. (2), page 455.]

$$b = \frac{a \sin B}{\sin A} \tag{48}$$

Substituting the value of b above in Eq. (45)

$$A_t = \frac{a^2 \sin B \times \sin C}{2 \sin A} \tag{49}$$

fig. 18·18

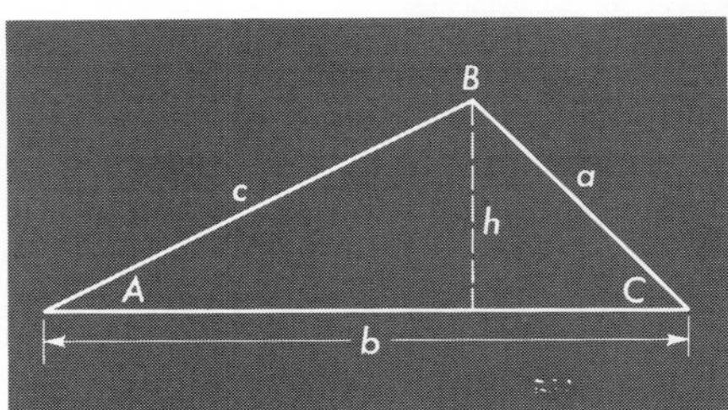

fig. 18·19

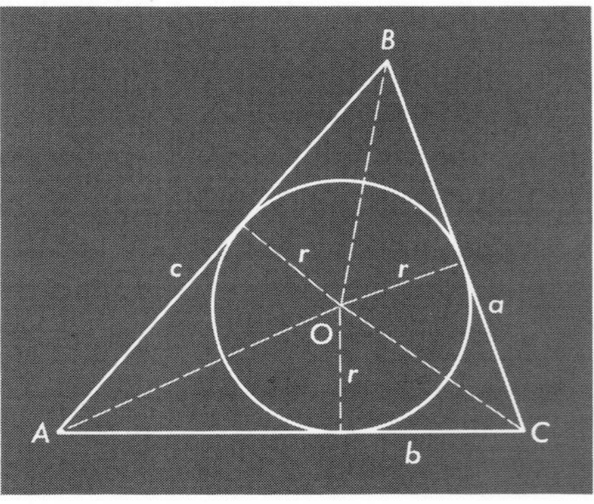

Similarly,

$$A_t = \frac{b^2 \sin A \times \sin C}{2 \sin B} \tag{50}$$

$$A_t = \frac{c^2 \sin A \times \sin B}{2 \sin C} \tag{51}$$

Given three sides

The area of triangle ABC (Fig. 18·19) is the sum of the areas of triangles AOB, BOC, and COA. Therefore, the total area A_t of triangle ABC is

$$A_t = \tfrac{1}{2}ra + \tfrac{1}{2}rb + \tfrac{1}{2}rc \tag{52}$$
$$A_t = \tfrac{1}{2}r(a + b + c) \tag{53}$$

If we let

$$s = \tfrac{1}{2}(a + b + c)$$

then

$$A_t = rs \tag{54}$$

In Exercise 3, Prob. 27, on page 551, the student will prove that referred to Fig. 18·19

$$r = \sqrt{\frac{(s-a)(s-b)(s-c)}{s}}$$

By substituting the above value of r in Eq. (54) we obtain

$$A_t = \sqrt{s(s-a)(s-b)(s-c)} \tag{55}$$

EXERCISE 7

Find the areas of the following triangles:

	a	b	c	A	B	C
1.	38.000		56		49°	
2.	15.000	12.000	13.000			
3.		65.000		36°	75°	
4.		48.000	84.000	73°		
5.	124.00				115°	26°
6.	34.000	36.000	38.000			
7.			682.00	56°32′	65°10′	
8.	26.800	9.7000				102°18′
9.	364.00	812.00	526.00			
10.	3.1420				31°9.7′	62°54.5′
11.	42.700	5.6000	38.500			
12.		103.00	264.00	18°42′16″		
13.			4,122.0		154°18′27″	12°12′12″
14.	56.240	43.290	27.570			
15.	3,721.0		4,609.0		27°8.7′	

18 · 7 Units of angular measure

Angles are commonly measured in either of two systems of units: the degree system or the radian system.

The degree system

The vector $\overrightarrow{OP}$ in Fig. 17·4 is shown in its initial position. If now it is rotated counterclockwise one complete revolution until it again coincides with its initial position, then, by definition, an angle of +360 degrees has been generated. The angle 360 degrees is usually written 360°. One degree is by definition 1/360 revolution.

The radian system

As the vector $\overrightarrow{OP}$ rotates, the point P moves in a circular path (see Fig. 18·20). If the arc length traversed by P is $\widehat{XP}$ (where $\widehat{XP}$ is measured in the same linear units as $\overrightarrow{OP}$), then ϕ measured in radians is

$$\phi_r = \frac{\widehat{XP}}{|OP|} \tag{56}$$

and

$$\widehat{XP} = |OP| \times \phi_r \tag{57}$$

or

$$l = r\,\phi_r \tag{58}$$

where l is the arc length traversed by P and the subscript r indicates that the angle is measured in radians rather than in degrees.

In other words, the quotient of the arc length divided by the radius is the measure of the central angle in radians.

If the vector $\overrightarrow{OP}$ makes one complete revolution, then the arc length becomes the circumference of the circle, and

$$\phi_r = \frac{2\pi|OP|}{|OP|} = 2\pi \tag{59}$$

There are 2π radians in one revolution, and 1 radian is $1/(2\pi)$ revolution.

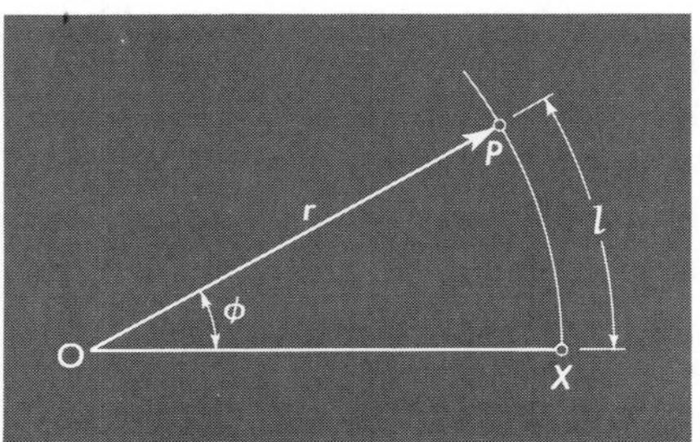

fig. 18·20

Since by definition one revolution of the vector is equivalent to an angle of 360°, and since by definition one revolution is also equivalent to 2π radians,

$$2\pi_{(r)} = 360°$$

$$\pi_{(r)} = 180°$$

$$1 \text{ radian} = \frac{180°}{\pi} = 57.2957795° \qquad \textbf{(60)}$$

$$1° = \frac{\pi}{180} = 0.01745329 \text{ radian} \qquad \textbf{(61)}$$

Ordinarily, fractions of a degree are not written in decimals, but rather in subunits called minutes and seconds. There are no subunits attached to radian measure. For purposes of numerical calculation in solving triangles, etc., the degree system is ordinarily used. In more analytical work the radian system is common.

For simplicity, we usually choose to write π radians rather than 3.14159 radians, $\pi/2$ radians rather than 1.57080 radians, $3\pi/2$ radians rather than 4.71239 radians, etc. In such cases it is easy to change from radian measure to degree measure by substituting for π radians the degree equivalent, 180°.

$$\pi_{(r)} = 180° \qquad (62)$$

$$\frac{\pi}{2}(r) = \frac{180°}{2} = 90° \qquad (63)$$

$$\frac{3\pi}{2}(r) = \frac{3 \times 180°}{2} = 270° \qquad (64)$$

example 12 Change 56.73° to radians.

Since by Eq. (61)

$$1° = \frac{\pi}{180} \text{ radians}$$

then

$$56.73° = 56.73 \times \frac{\pi}{180} = 0.99013 \text{ radian}$$

example 13 Change 0.792 radian to degrees. Leave the answer a decimal.

Since by Eq. (60)

$$1 \text{ radian} = \frac{180°}{\pi}$$

then

$$0.792 \text{ radian} = 0.792 \times \frac{180}{\pi} = \frac{0.792 \times 180}{\pi}$$

$$= 45.38°$$

example 14 How many degrees are there in $7\pi/15$ radians?

$$\pi \text{ radians} = 180°$$

$$\frac{7}{15}\pi \text{ radians} = \frac{7}{15} \times 180° = \frac{1{,}260}{15} = 84°$$

example 15 How many revolutions are there in an angle of 5π radians?

Since 1 revolution $= 2\pi$ radians, it follows that

$$5\pi \text{ radians} = \frac{5\pi}{2\pi} = 2.5 \text{ revolutions}$$

example 16 How many revolutions are there in 2.5 radians?

Since 1 revolution $= 2\pi$ or 6.2832 radians, it follows that

$$2.5 \text{ radians} = 2.5/6.2832 = 0.40 \text{ revolution}$$

example 17 Refer to Fig. 18·20. If $l = 5$ in. and $r = 3$ in., find the angle ϕ in radians.

Following Eq. (58), where

$$l = r\,\phi_r$$

it is evident that

$$5 = 3\phi_r$$

or

$$\phi_r = 5/3 \text{ radians}$$

example 18 What is the arc length which subtends a central angle of 2.36 radians in a circle whose radius is 4 in.?

Following Eq. (58),

$$l = 4 \times 2.36 = 9.44 \text{ in.}$$

example 19 How many revolutions are equivalent to 4,320°?

Since there are 360° in one revolution, we may write

$$4{,}320/360 = 12 \text{ revolutions}$$

EXERCISE 8

Convert into degrees, radians, and revolutions as indicated in the following tabulation:

	Radians	*Degrees*	*Revolutions*
1.	2.5		
2.			0.75
3.		1,000	
4.		2,000	
5.			400
6.	100		
7.	400π		
8.		30	
9.		315	
10.	$(3\pi)/2$		

EXERCISE 9

Referring to Fig. 18·20, find arc length, radius, or central angle as indicated in the following tabulation:

	Arc length, in.	*Radius, in.*	*Central angle*
1.		16	4 radians
2.	12		8 radians
3.	2.4	5	
4.		25	2 revolutions
5.	18		45°
6.	32	8	Find central angle in revolutions

18·8 Angular and linear velocity

In certain engineering applications we have to deal with physical phenomena which can be represented mathematically by rotating position vectors (see Sec. 22·4).

In Fig. 18·20, let us consider the point P to be moving with a uniform linear velocity v along the circular arc of radius r.

The linear velocity v is expressed in some such units as feet per second, feet per minute, or inches per second.

The central angle ϕ is consequently changing with a uniform angular velocity which we shall designate as ω. The angular velocity ω is measured in units such as radians per second, degrees per minute, or revolutions per minute.

If the position vector $\overrightarrow{OP}$ in Fig. 18·20 is rotating with a uniform angular velocity ω about the point O, the angle turned in time t is

$$\phi_r = \omega t \tag{65}$$

example 20 If the position vector $\overrightarrow{OP}$ in Fig. 18·20 is rotating with an angular velocity of 0.3 radian per sec, through what angle ϕ will it rotate in 5 sec?

Since

$$\phi_r = \omega t$$

in this case,

$$\phi_r = 0.3 \times 5 = 1.5 \text{ radians}$$

example 21 Express the angle ϕ_r in Example 20 in revolutions.

$$\phi_{\text{rev}} = \frac{1.5}{2\pi} = 0.2387 \text{ revolution}$$

Since by Eq. (58)

$$l = r\,\phi_r \tag{66}$$

by substituting in Eq. (65), we may write

$$\frac{l}{r} = \omega t \tag{67}$$

or

$$\frac{l}{t} = \omega r \tag{68}$$

But since l/t is by definition equal to linear velocity v, we may write

$$v = \omega r \tag{69}$$

example 22 A position vector $\overrightarrow{OP}$ has a length of 1.5 ft and rotates at the rate of 400 rpm. Find the linear velocity of point P in inches per second.

$$400 \text{ rpm} = 2\pi \times 400 = 800\pi \text{ radians/min}$$

or

$$\frac{800\pi}{60} \text{ radians/sec}$$

Furthermore,

$$1.5 \text{ ft} = 1.5 \times 12 = 18 \text{ in.}$$

Now, following Eq. (69),

$$v = \frac{800\pi}{60} \times 18 = 240\pi \text{ in./sec}$$

The use of a slide rule is suggested in Exercises 10 and 11.

EXERCISE 10

Find the central angle, angular velocity, or time in the units required as indicated in the following tabulation:

	Angular velocity	*Time*	*Central angle*
1.	3 rad/sec	16 sec	? radians
2.	? rad/sec	25 sec	80 radians
3.	15 rad/sec	12 sec	? revolutions
4.	? rad/sec	3 min	100 revolutions
5.	50 rad/sec	2.5 min	? radians
6.	12 rad/sec	? sec	50 radians
7.	? rad/sec	3 min	600 radians
8.	6 rev/sec	? min	400 radians
9.	12 rad/sec	? sec	600 revolutions
10.	4 rev/sec	? min	800π radians

EXERCISE 11

Find the linear velocity, angular velocity, or radius in the units required as indicated in the following tabulation:

	Linear velocity	*Angular velocity*	*Radius*
1.	? ft/sec	30 rad/sec	1.5 ft
2.	16 ft/sec	? rad/sec	2.5 ft
3.	210 in./min	35 rad/sec	? ft
4.	? in./sec	6 rev/sec	12 in.
5.	? in./sec	500 rpm	15 ft
6.	4 ft/sec	600 rpm	? in.
7.	5 ft/sec	? deg/sec	16 in.
8.	20 ft/sec	200 rpm	? ft

18·9 The ratio of sin ϕ to ϕ

At this point we can apply some of the formulas for the areas of triangles to develop an important and basic theorem. This theorem states that the ratio $(\sin \phi)/\phi$ approaches 1 as ϕ approaches zero. The theorem can be proved as follows:

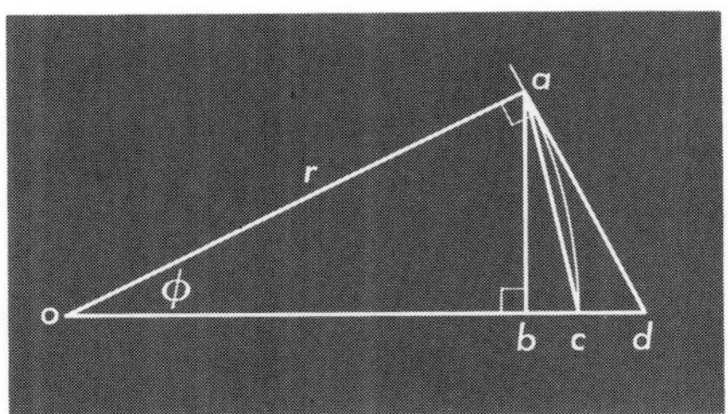

fig. 18·21

Let ϕ in Fig. 18·21 be measured in radians. Also let $+\pi/2 > \phi > -\pi/2$. The area of the triangle *oac* is

$$A_{oac} = \tfrac{1}{2}(oc)(ab) = \tfrac{1}{2}r \sin \phi \times r = \tfrac{1}{2}r^2 \sin \phi$$

The area of the sector *oac* is $\phi/2\pi \times \pi r^2$; therefore

$$A_{\text{sector } oac} = \tfrac{1}{2}r^2 \phi$$

The area of the triangle *oad* is

$$\begin{aligned} A_{oad} &= \tfrac{1}{2}r(ad) = \tfrac{1}{2}r \times r \times \tan \phi \\ &= \tfrac{1}{2}r^2 \tan \phi \end{aligned}$$

From the geometry of the figure, area of triangle *oad* > area of sector *oac* > area of triangle *oac*.

$$\tfrac{1}{2}r^2 \tan \phi > \tfrac{1}{2}r^2 \phi > \tfrac{1}{2}r^2 \sin \phi$$

Dividing by $r^2/2$,

$$\tan \phi > \phi > \sin \phi$$

But

$$\tan \phi = \frac{\sin \phi}{\cos \phi}$$

$$\frac{\sin \phi}{\cos \phi} > \phi > \sin \phi$$

Dividing by $\sin \phi$,

$$\frac{1}{\cos \phi} > \frac{\phi}{\sin \phi} > 1$$

As ϕ approaches zero, $\cos \phi$ approaches 1. Therefore,

$$\frac{1}{\cos \phi} \text{ approaches 1 as } \phi \text{ approaches zero}$$

but $\phi/\sin \phi$ remains between $1/\cos \phi$ and 1. Therefore $\phi/\sin \phi$ approaches 1 and $(\sin \phi)/\phi$ approaches 1 as ϕ approaches zero.

From Sec. 18·7,

$$\phi \text{ (in radians)} = \frac{\text{arc length } ac}{r}$$

$$\phi \text{ (in degrees)} = \frac{\text{arc length } ac}{r} \times 57.296$$

By definition,

$$\sin \phi = \frac{\overline{ab}}{r}$$

When ϕ is small, the arc length ac and the line ab are nearly equal. Therefore

$$\frac{\overline{ab}}{r} \approx \frac{\widehat{ac}}{r}$$

or

$$\sin \phi \approx \frac{\widehat{ac}}{r} \approx \phi \text{ (in radians)}$$

$$\sin \phi \approx \phi \times 0.01745 \text{ (in degrees)}$$

EXERCISE 12

1. Using a table of natural functions for angles in radians, plot $\sin \phi$ vertically and ϕ horizontally between $\phi = 0.1$ and $\phi = 1.0$. Calculate values of $(\sin \phi)/\phi$. Explain how this graph confirms the statement that as ϕ approaches zero, $(\sin \phi)/\phi$ approaches unity.

19 trigonometric applications and review

In this chapter we shall illustrate some of the applications of numerical trigonometry to civil- and mechanical-engineering problems.

19 · 1 Plane surveying

We shall limit any discussion of surveying to *plane surveying,* i.e., to surveys conducted on the assumption that the earth is flat over the area under consideration. The errors involved in this approximation are small, provided the area covered by the survey is small.

19 · 2 Measurement of angles

Angles are measured directly in the field with either of two instruments: the engineer's transit or the surveyor's compass. For the construction and operation of these instruments the student is referred to any standard surveying text.

19 · 3 Mapping

A typical problem of the land surveyor is to measure the length and direction of the boundary lines of a parcel of land in order to draw a scale map of the parcel and calculate the area.

Figure 19 · 1 shows the map of a small parcel of land plotted from the field notes shown in Table 19 · 1.

The surveyor started from point A and found by observation that the line AB makes an angle of $10°30'$ with the magnetic north. Furthermore, in moving along the line AB, he moves north and also west.

table 19·1

Course		
AB	N 10°30′W	500.00 ft
BC	N 41°45′W	410.00 ft
CD	S 00°00′W	797.00 ft
DA	S 90°E	364.00 ft

All bearings from magnetic north.

Hence the bearing is recorded North 10°30′ West. A property line is not completely described unless both *direction* and *length* are given. This particular property line was measured (probably with a tape) and found to be 500 ft long.

As the notes read, we may assume that the surveyor traversed this survey in a counterclockwise direction. Therefore, he moved west and north along *AB* and west and north also along *BC*. Along *CD* he moved directly south, and along *DA* he moved directly east, returning to the starting point.

We would be justified in assuming that he measured linear dimensions to the nearest 0.01 ft. For our purpose, we shall assume that bearings were measured to the nearest minute.

19·4 Latitudes and departures

In Fig. 19·1 the line *XB* is called the *departure* of the course *AB*. Since the point *B* is west of the point *X*, the line *XB* is a westerly departure.

Departure is defined as the distance by which the second extremity of a course is east or west of the first extremity.

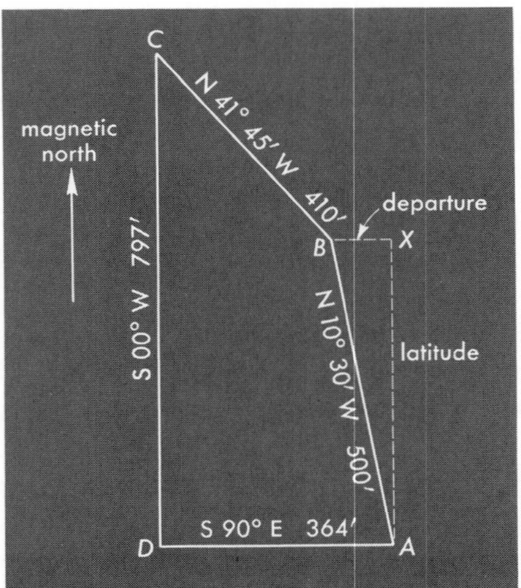

fig. 19·1

The departure of the course AB is

$$500 \sin 10°30' = 500 \times 0.18224 = 91.12 \text{ ft west}$$

The departure of the course BC is

$$410 \sin 41°45' = 410 \times 0.66588 = 273.01 \text{ ft west}$$

The departure of the course CD is zero, since in moving along this line the surveyor moves neither east nor west.

The departure of the course DA is 364 ft, since in moving along this line he moves directly east.

Adding the departures in a westerly direction, we find that the total westerly departure is

$$91.12 + 273.01 = 364.13 \text{ ft west}$$

In other words, if we take the survey notes at their face value, they indicate that the surveyor moved 364.13 ft westward and 364.00 ft eastward and arrived back at the starting point. This discrepancy may be explained by the fact that it is impossible to measure with absolute precision. Yet the departures check reasonably well.

If the survey had proceeded in a clockwise direction, then the departure of the course CB would have been an easterly departure, and the departure of the course BA would have been an easterly departure also.

In Fig. 19·1 the line AX is called the *latitude* of the course AB. Since the point X is north of the point A, the line AX is a northerly latitude.

Latitude is defined as the distance by which the second extremity of a course is north or south of the first extremity.

The latitude of the course AB is

$$500 \text{ ft} \cos 10°30' = 500 \text{ ft} \times 0.98325 = 491.62 \text{ ft north}$$

The latitude of the course BC is

$$410 \text{ ft} \cos 41°45' = 410 \text{ ft} \times 0.74606 = 305.88 \text{ ft north}$$

The latitude of the course CD is 797 ft south, since in moving along this line the surveyor moves directly south.

The latitude of the course DA is zero, since in moving along this line the surveyor moves neither north nor south.

Adding the northerly latitudes, we find that the total latitude is

$$491.62 \text{ ft} + 305.88 \text{ ft} = 797.50 \text{ ft north}$$

Again, if we take the survey notes at their face value, they indicate that the surveyor moved 797.5 ft north and 797.0 ft south. As before, we assume that this discrepancy occurs because we cannot measure bearings and lengths with absolute precision.

This suggests a method of checking the accuracy of the field work. We know that if the surveyor ended the survey at the starting point, he must have moved south exactly the same distance that he moved north. Also he must have moved east exactly the same distance as he moved west. Stated more formally, *if northerly latitudes and easterly departures are considered positive, and southerly latitudes and westerly departures are considered negative, the algebraic sum of the departures must be zero and the algebraic sum of the latitudes must be zero if the traverse is to close on itself.*

The linear error of closure is, by definition,

$$e = \sqrt{(\text{error in latitude})^2 + (\text{error in departure})^2} \tag{1}$$

The calculations for latitudes and departures are repeated below in tabular form. The linear error is also calculated. While the latitudes and departures are calculated here to the nearest 1/100 ft, a greater number of places may be retained in practical problems, depending on circumstances.

Course	*Bearing*	*Distance, ft*	*N lat, ft*	*S lat, ft*	*E dep, ft*	*W dep, ft*
AB	N 10°30′W	500	491.62			91.12
BC	N 41°45′W	410	305.88			273.01
CD	S 00°	797		797.00		
DA	S 90°00′E	364			364.00	
			797.50	797.00	364.00	364.13
			797.00			364.00
		Error in lat	0.50		Error in dep	0.13

Linear error $= \sqrt{0.50^2 + 0.13^2} = 0.52$

There are statistical methods of distributing the error of closure among the several courses. For our purpose such procedures would be of little importance.

19·5 Azimuth angles

The bearings of courses can be recorded in terms of *azimuth angles.* Azimuth angles are measured from some directional line of reference to the line in question. Usually zero degrees azimuth is taken to be true south. Azimuth angles are measured in a clockwise direction from true south. Angles are also measured from north in aviation, astronomy, and meteorology.

On maps and in field notes this fact should be recorded in some such fashion as "00°00′ azimuth true south." In terms of azimuth angles, the notes in Table 19·1 would be as follows:

Course	*Azimuth* 0° *true south*	*Distance, ft*
AB	169°30′	500
BC	138°15′	410
CD	00°00′	797
DA	270°00′	364

19·6 Interior angles

The sum of the interior angles of any polygon is $180°(n - 2)$. Therefore, if we subtract 2 from the number of courses and multiply by 180°, we obtain precisely the sum of the interior angles. This total can be compared with a similar total obtained from the field notes.

In Fig. 19·1 the interior angles are checked as follows:

$$\begin{aligned}
\angle DAB &= 90° - 10°30' &&= 79°30' \\
\angle CBA &= 180° - 41°45' + 10°30' &&= 148°45' \\
\angle DCB &= &&41°45' \\
\angle CDA &= &&90° \\
& &&\overline{358°120'} = 360°
\end{aligned}$$

The figure is a four-sided polygon, the sum of whose interior angles is $(4 - 2)\ 180° = 360°$. Thus the check is perfect.

EXERCISE 1

Plot the following traverses to a scale. Compute the error in latitudes and the error in departures, using five-place tables.

1.

Course	*Length, ft*	*Bearing*
AB	683.57	N 11°49′E
BC	221.63	N 53°40′W
CD	412.90	S 88°36′W
DE	513.27	S 1°00′E
EF	225.41	S 33°17′E
FA	330.79	S 74°30′E

2.

Course	*Length, ft*	*Bearing*
AB	4,181.5	N 10°08′E
BC	3,872.1	N 58°28′W
CD	4,747.0	S 41°15′W
DE	3,751.7	S 16°10′E
EA	4,762.8	N 77°30′E

3. Find the bearing and the length of the line *DA* in Prob. 1.

4. Plot the following traverse to scale. Calculate the error in the latitudes and departures.

Course	*Length, ft*	*Bearing*
AB	885.84	N 10°18′W
BC	542.67	S 69°45′W
CD	875.04	S 12°15′E
DE	230.77	S 84°00′E
EF	210.03	N 14°00′E
FG	162.70	N 86°20′E
GH	249.95	S 14°00′W
HA	245.00	N 24°00′E

5. Plot the following traverse to scale, and calculate the error in latitude and departure.

Course	*Length, ft*	*Azimuth* 0° *true south*
AB	578.63	265°45′
BC	206.30	174°36′
CD	250.22	106°20′
DE	452.51	226°30′
EF	137.00	180°00′
FG	524.86	91°45′
GA	792.18	8°45′

6. The owner of the tract of land described in Prob. 5 wishes to buy the triangular piece of land *CDE*. What is the length of the line *CE*, and what is its bearing? How much area would this purchase add to his land?
7. The owner of the tract of land described in Prob. 4 wishes to sell his holdings south of the line *FG*. Two new bounds *J* and *K* will have to be established. *J* will be at the intersection of the line *CD* and the westward extension of the line *FG*. *K* will be at the intersection of the line *BA* and the eastward extension of the line *FG*. Find the distance *CJ* and *BK*.

19·7 Calculation of areas

A useful method of finding the area enclosed by a traverse consisting of straight lines is illustrated below.

Ordinarily, it is more convenient to establish reference coordinates so that the entire survey is placed in one quadrant, say the northeast quadrant, as shown in Fig. 19·2. The corner points are numbered con-

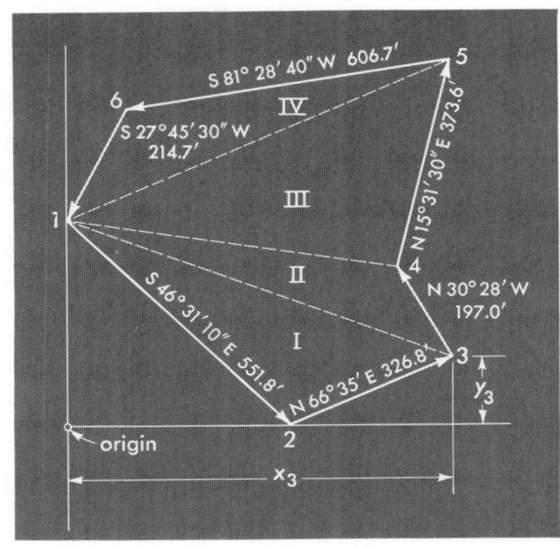

fig. 19·2

secutively around the traverse in a counterclockwise direction. The area is given by Eq. (2) below (see Sec. 6·14).

$$A_t = \tfrac{1}{2}[x_1(y_2 - y_6) + x_2(y_3 - y_1) + x_3(y_4 - y_2) + x_4(y_5 - y_3) + x_5(y_6 - y_4) + x_6(y_1 - y_5)] \tag{2}$$

To find the area enclosed by a traverse, multiply the x *distance of each corner by the difference between the* y *distance of the following corner and the* y *distance of the preceding corner. The sum of these products is twice the area.*

The following convention is sometimes used:

$$\text{Area} = \tfrac{1}{2}\left(\frac{x_1}{y_1} \times \frac{x_2}{y_2} \times \frac{x_3}{y_3} \times \frac{x_4}{y_4} \times \frac{x_5}{y_5} \times \frac{x_6}{y_6} \times \frac{x_1}{y_1}\right) \tag{3}$$

Here we multiply the coordinates connected by solid lines and separately multiply the coordinates connected by dotted lines. Then we find the sum of the solid-line products and the sum of the dotted-line products. The difference between these two sums is twice the area.

example 1 Find the area enclosed by the traverse shown in Fig. 19·2.

First we shall find the latitude and departure of each course by the methods already discussed in Sec. 19·2. A tabulation of the results is shown below:

Course	*Bearing*	*Distance, ft*	*N lat, ft*	*S lat, ft*	*E dep, ft*	*W dep, ft*
1–2	S 46°31′10″E	551.8		379.7	400.4	
2–3	N 66°35′E	326.8	129.8		298.5	
3–4	N 30°28′W	197.0	169.8			99.9
4–5	N 15°31′30″E	373.6	360.0		101.0	
5–6	S 81°28′40″W	606.7		89.9		600.1
6–1	S 27°45′30″W	214.7		190.0		100.0
			659.6	659.6	799.9	800.0

The latitudes check perfectly within the limits of the precision to which the data were obtained. The departures check within 0.1 ft. The coordinates of the several corners are found by reference to Fig. 19·2 and the tabulation above.

$$\begin{aligned} x_1 &= 000.0 & y_1 &= 379.7 \\ x_2 &= 400.4 & y_2 &= 000.0 \\ x_3 &= 698.9 & y_3 &= 129.8 \\ x_4 &= 599.1 & y_4 &= 299.6 \\ x_5 &= 700.1 & y_5 &= 659.6 \\ x_6 &= 100.0 & y_6 &= 569.7 \end{aligned}$$

Substituting the x and y values just found in Eq. (2),

$$\begin{aligned} A_t &= \tfrac{1}{2}[0(0 - 569.7) + 400.4(129.8 - 379.7) + 698.9(299.6 - 0) \\ &\qquad + 599.1(659.6 - 129.8) + 700.1(569.7 - 299.6) + 100(379.7 - 659.6)] \\ &= \tfrac{1}{2}(-400.4 \times 249.9 + 698.9 \times 299.6 + 599.1 \times 529.8 \\ &\qquad + 700.1 \times 270.1 - 100 \times 279.9) \\ A_t &= \tfrac{1}{2}(-100{,}060 + 209{,}390 + 317{,}403 + 189{,}097 - 27{,}990) \\ &= \tfrac{1}{2}(587{,}840) = 293{,}900 \text{ sq ft} \end{aligned}$$

to four significant figures.

Using Eq. (3),

$$A_t = \frac{1}{2}\left(\frac{0}{379.7} \times \frac{400.4}{0} \times \frac{698.9}{129.8} \times \frac{599.1}{299.6} \times \frac{700.1}{659.6} \times \frac{100.0}{569.7} \times \frac{0}{379.7}\right)$$

Carrying out the calculations indicated above,

$0 \times 569.7 = 00{,}000$	$100 \times 379.7 = 37{,}970$
$659.6 \times 100.0 = 65{,}960$	$700.1 \times 569.7 = 398{,}847$
$700.1 \times 299.6 = 209{,}750$	$599.1 \times 659.6 = 395{,}166$
$599.1 \times 129.8 = 77{,}763$	$698.9 \times 299.6 = 209{,}390$
$698.9 \times 0 = 00{,}000$	$129.8 \times 400.4 = 51{,}972$
$400.4 \times 379.7 = 152{,}032$	$0 \times 0 = 00{,}000$
$505{,}505$	$1{,}093{,}345$

$$A_t = \frac{1{,}093{,}345 - 505{,}505}{2}$$

$$= \frac{587{,}840}{2} = 293{,}900 \text{ sq ft}$$

to four significant figures.

EXERCISE 2

1. Find the area enclosed by the traverse shown in Fig. 19·1.
2. Find the area enclosed by the traverse described in Prob. 1 in Exercise 1.
3. Find the area enclosed by the traverse described in Prob. 2 in Exercise 1.

19·8 Measurement of distances in a vertical plane

Practically all the distances and angles used in surveying are measured in either a vertical or a horizontal plane.

The property line *ab* in Fig. 19·3 slopes uphill. However, the distance recorded for the length of this property line is not the actual length *ab* but the horizontal projection of the line *ab*, which is *ax*.

In general, the projection of one line on another is defined in Fig. 19·4. Here *gj* is the projection of the line *cf* on the line *mn*, and *de* is the projection of the line *hi* on the line *kl*. Notice the positions of the right angles.

Ordinarily in the field it is not difficult to measure the distance *ab* in Fig. 19·3; neither is it difficult to measure the difference in elevation between *a* and *b*. As a rule, it is a relatively simple matter to measure the vertical angle ϕ. It may, however, be somewhat more difficult to arrive at the distance *ax* by direct measurement in the field.

The distance *ax* in Fig. 19·3 can be calculated from field notes, provided that the length *ab* and the difference in elevation between *a* and *b* are known.

Following the Pythagorean theorem,

$$ax = \sqrt{(ab)^2 - (bx)^2} \tag{4}$$

If the angle ϕ is small, the approximation developed below may be perfectly satisfactory and will effect a considerable saving of time, particularly when there are many data to be reduced. Referring to Fig. 19·3,

$$xy = ab - ax \tag{5}$$

$$(bx)^2 = (ab)^2 - (ax)^2 = (ab - ax)(ab + ax) \qquad \text{[See Eq. (2), Sec. 4·17]}$$

$$ab - ax = \frac{(bx)^2}{ab + ax} \tag{6}$$

Substituting Eq. (6) in Eq. (5),

$$xy = \frac{(bx)^2}{ab + ax}$$

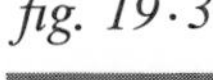

fig. 19·3

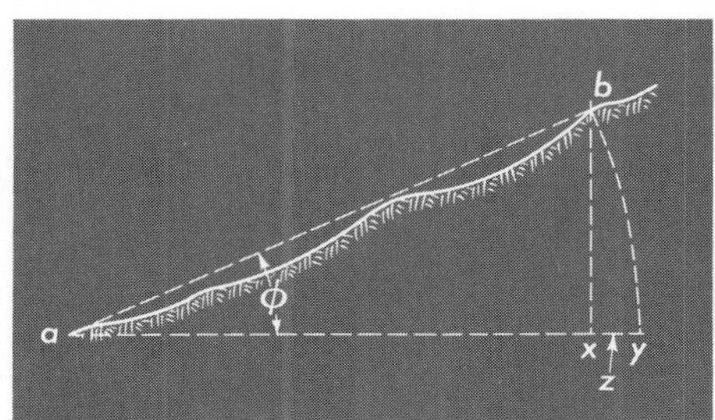

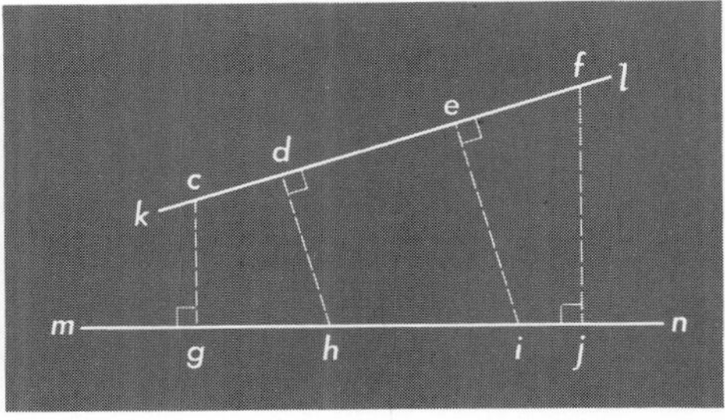

fig. 19·4

or if ab and ax are nearly equal, as they will be if ϕ is small,

$$xy \approx \frac{(bx)^2}{2(ab)} \tag{7}$$

The distance xy is the correction which, when subtracted from ab, gives the horizontal projection ax. Therefore,

$$ax \approx ab - \frac{(bx)^2}{2(ab)} \qquad \text{(See Table B·1, Appendix B)} \tag{8}$$

If the field notes give the angle ϕ instead of the difference in elevation between a and b and if ϕ is small, the correction bx can be found by the approximation developed below.

For small angles, the sine of the angle is very nearly proportional to the angle (see the last equation on page 480). That is,

$$\sin \phi \approx k\phi \tag{9}$$

where k is the proportionality constant.

Up to almost 8° in the five-place tables, each increase of 1′ increases the sine of the angle 0.00029. That is, within the limits of the five-place table and up to 7°48′,

$$\sin \phi \approx 0.00029\phi \tag{10}$$

where ϕ is measured in minutes. Or

$$\sin \phi \approx 0.00029 \times 60 \times \phi = 0.0174\phi \tag{11}$$

where ϕ is measured in degrees.

In Fig. 19·3,

$$bx = (ab) \sin \phi \tag{12}$$

or, substituting Eq. (11) in Eq. (12),

$$bx \approx 0.0174 \times ab \times \phi \tag{13}$$

where ϕ is measured in degrees.

Following Eq. (7),

$$xy \approx \frac{(bx)^2}{2(ab)} \approx \frac{0.0174^2 \times (ab)^2 \times \phi^2}{2(ab)} \tag{14}$$

$$xy \approx \frac{0.00030275 \times (ab) \times \phi^2}{2} \tag{15}$$

Within about 1 per cent, Eq. (16) is valid.

$$xy \approx 3/2 \times \phi^2 \times 10^{-4}(ab) \tag{16}$$

Another method may be used if a table of versines is available. By definition,

$$\text{vers } \phi = 1 - \cos \phi \tag{17}$$

In Fig. 19·3,

$$xy = ab - (ab)\cos\phi = (ab)(1 - \cos\phi) \tag{18}$$
$$xy = (ab)\text{ vers }\phi \tag{19}$$

example 2 In Fig. 19·3, if $ab = 375.00$ ft and $bx = 30.00$ ft, calculate ax, using both formulas

$$ax = \sqrt{(ab)^2 - (bx)^2}$$

and

$$ax \approx ab - \frac{(bx)^2}{2ab}$$

Using the Pythagorean theorem,

$$ax = \sqrt{375^2 - 30^2} = 373.80\text{ ft} \qquad \text{(to five figures)}$$

Using the approximate formula,

$$ax \approx 375 - \frac{30^2}{2 \times 375} = 375 - 1.20 = 373.80\text{ ft}$$

to five figures. Note that the accuracy required of this correction factor 1.20 is not beyond the capabilities of the slide rule.

19·9 Surveying around obstructions

Equation (11) is convenient in another connection (see Fig. 19·5). If ϕ is small and is measured in degrees,

$$a \approx 0.0174 \times c \times \phi \tag{20}$$

to a close approximation.

A problem sometimes arises in which it is desired to locate a point x (Fig. 19·6) on an extension of the line ab. The exact distance ax is not important, but the point x must be located so that the points a, b, and x are on the same straight line. Between b and x there are obstructions such as houses, trees, and boulders, so that a direct line of sight cannot be used. The distances bc, cd, de, and ex can be measured. Also the angles u, v, w, and y can be measured. The surveyor runs a traverse bc, cd, and de, and at the point e he sets the angle y at some convenient value. He wishes to find the distance ex such that x will fall on

fig. 19·5

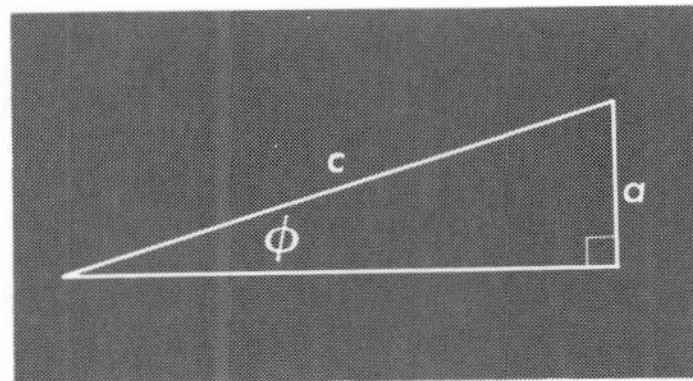

fig. 19·6

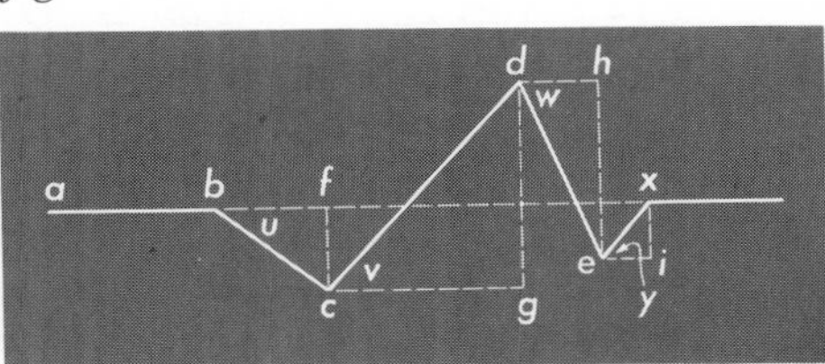

the continuation of the line ab. The offsets fc, gd, he, and ix can be calculated, to a close approximation, as follows:

$$fc \approx 0.0174(bc)u \tag{21}$$
$$gd \approx 0.0174(cd)v \tag{22}$$
$$he \approx 0.0174(de)w \tag{23}$$
$$ix \approx 0.0174(ex)y \tag{24}$$

If the offsets downward are considered to be negative and the offsets upward are considered to be positive, then from the geometry of the figure

$$fc + he = gd + ix \tag{25}$$

Substituting Eqs. (21) to (24) in Eq. (25) and dividing out the 0.0174,

$$(bc)u + (de)w = (cd)v + (ex)y \tag{26}$$

In Eq. (26) the angles u, w, v, and y may be in any units, but we shall use minutes. To find ex,

$$ex = \frac{(bc)u + (de)w - (cd)v}{y} \tag{27}$$

example 3 Find ex in Fig. 19·6 if $bc = 120$ ft, $cd = 375$ ft, $de = 500$ ft, $\angle u = 50'$, $\angle v = 200'$, $\angle w = 240'$, and $\angle y = 80'$.

Substituting in Eq. (27),

$$ex = \frac{(50 \times 120) + (240 \times 500) - (200 \times 375)}{80}$$
$$= 368 \text{ ft}$$

EXERCISE 3

1. Plot a graph of $\sin \phi$ vertically and ϕ in minutes horizontally for angles between $0'$ and $500'$.
   (a) What is the shape of this graph?
   (b) What is the slope?
   (c) Over this range about how much does $\sin \phi$ change for a change of each $60'$, in ϕ?
2. In Fig. 19·3, if $ab = 300.00$ ft and the difference in elevation between points a and b is 15 ft, find the distance ax, using Eq. (8). Find the percentage of error that results from using this approximation.
3. In Fig. 19·3 if $ab = 650.00$ ft and $\phi = 5°$, find ax, using Eq. (16).
4. Solve Prob. 3 using a table of versines (if possible) and Eq. (19).
5. In Fig. 19·6 find the distance ex if $bc = 100$ ft, $cd = 200$ ft, $de = 150$ ft, $\angle u = 1°$, $\angle v = 1°30'$, $\angle w = 2°$, and $\angle y = 45'$.

EXERCISE 4

The problems in this exercise have their application in measuring inaccessible distances, highway curves, etc. It is beyond the scope of this book to dwell in detail on the engineering principles involved, but the student should have no particular difficulty in sensing the general nature of the applications.

1. Referring to Fig. 19·7, prove that

$$h = \frac{b}{\cot A - \cot B}$$

2. If b in Prob. 1 is 362 ft, $A = 26°48'$, and $B = 48°32'$, find h.
3. In Fig. 19·8 show that

$$h = b(\tan B - \tan A)$$

4. At point e on the surface of the earth a satellite is observed directly overhead at point B (see Fig. 19·9). Find the altitude h of the satellite to the nearest mile. Use slide rule for multiplication and division.

fig. 19·8

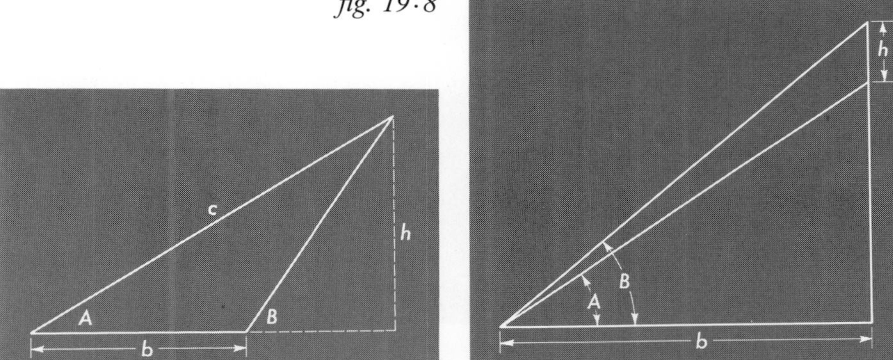

fig. 19·7

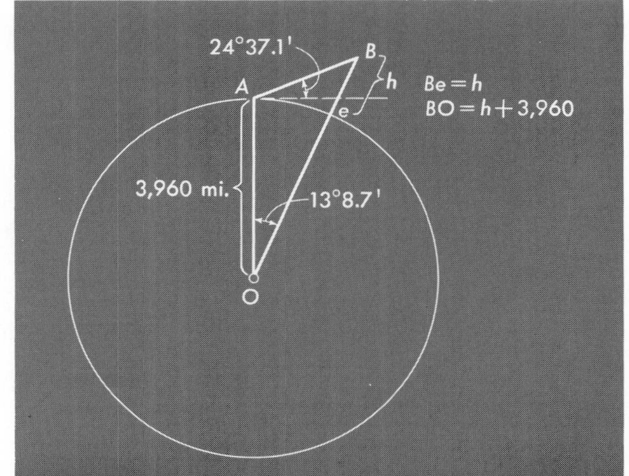

fig. 19·9

5. If in Prob. 3 the side $b = 986$ ft, angle $A = 15°46'$, and angle $B = 23°18'$, find h.
6. Find ϕ and x in Fig. 19·10.
7. In Fig. 19·11 find an expression for the length of the line ab in terms of the line ac and the angle ϕ.
8. Referring to Fig. 19·12, show that $R_1 - R_2 = a \cot(\phi/2)$.

The following problems may be done more conveniently by the use of the oblique-triangle formulas:

9. The inaccessible distance AB across the pond is to be found from the survey data shown in Fig. 19·13. The given distances were measured from point O by means of stadia.

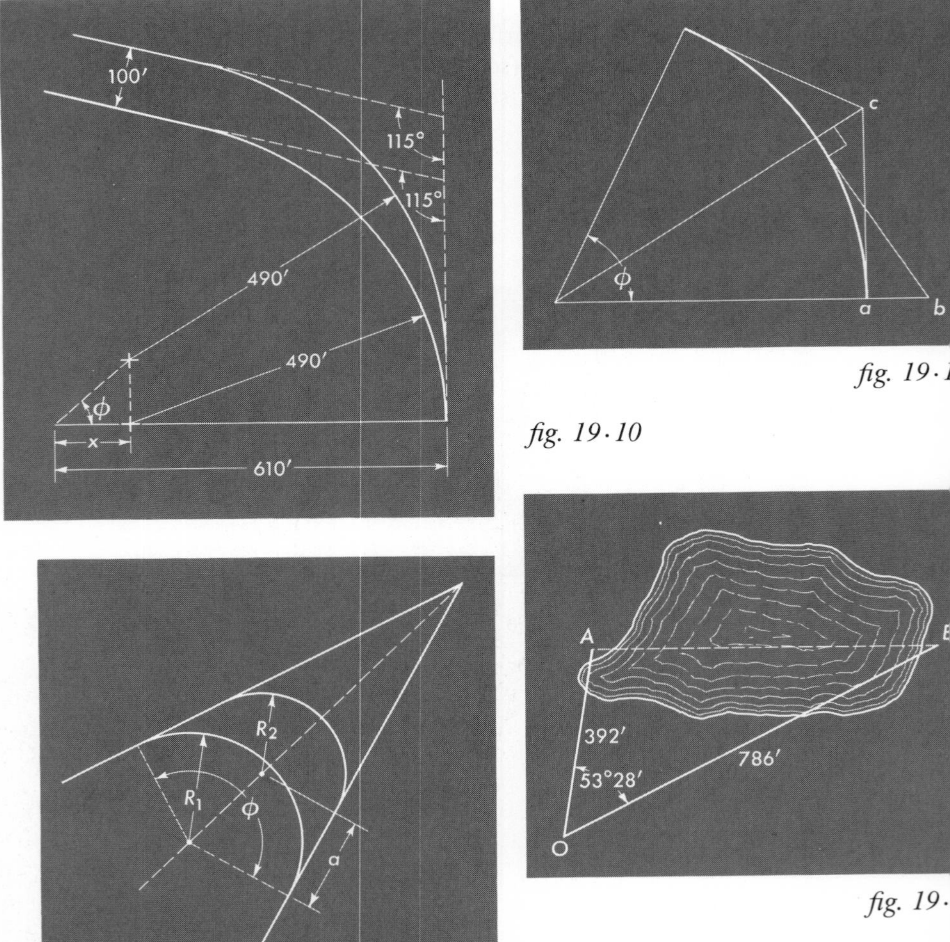

fig. 19·10

fig. 19·11

fig. 19·12

fig. 19·13

10. The points A and B in Fig. 19·14 are on opposite sides of the river and inaccessible from points x and y. Find the distance AB from the survey notes below:

$$
\begin{aligned}
xy &= 450 \text{ ft} \\
\angle Ayx &= 32^\circ \\
\angle Axy &= 129^\circ \\
\angle Bxy &= 43^\circ \\
\angle Byx &= 113^\circ
\end{aligned}
$$

11. An aircraft at d (Fig. 19·15) is located from two ground stations a and b by the following data:

$$
\begin{aligned}
\angle dac &= 25^\circ 37' \\
\angle dbc &= 30^\circ 40' \\
\angle cab &= 40^\circ 15' \\
ab &= 5{,}676 \text{ yd}
\end{aligned}
$$

Find da, ac, and bc.

12. Three equally spaced Telstar satellites are in equatorial, synchronous orbit. This means that the plane of the satellite orbit is the same as the plane of the equator and that the satellites orbit once in 24 hr; thus each appears to hover over one spot.
    (a) Find the degrees of longitude overlap in coverage at the equator. (This is the arc over which two satellites are in sight at the same time.)
    (b) Find the northern limit (°N Lat) of coverage.

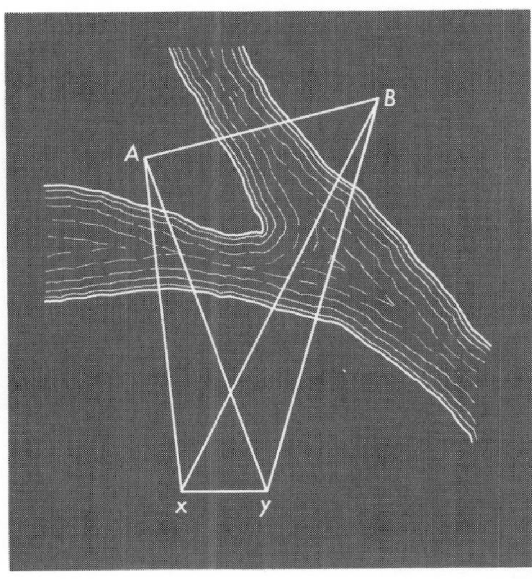

fig. 19·14

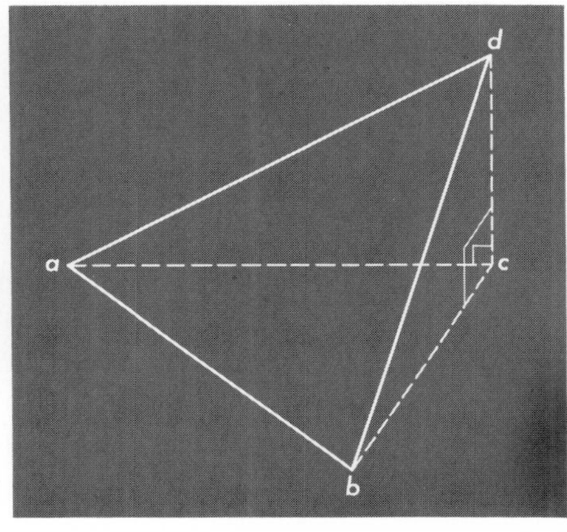

fig. 19·15

(c) How many minutes out of the 24 hr is a satellite in the earth's shadow?

The earth's radius is 3,960 miles, and the satellites orbit at an altitude of 22,300 miles.

19·10 Applications to machine- and tool-design problems

The problems in the following sections will be of particular interest to students of machine and tool design. Unfortunately, no definite rules can be given for solving this type of problem. The student will have to draw on his knowledge of basic mathematics and his own native ingenuity, building up experience as he goes along. However, the few general suggestions given below may be of some help.

In practically all the problems in Exercise 5, the student will have to draw certain construction lines. In general, it is suggested that he consider drawing these lines perpendicular or parallel to known dimensions. If there are arcs of circles involved, it may be helpful to connect the centers. Often it is helpful to draw a construction line from the center of curvature of one arc and tangent to another. Figure 19·16 is an idealized drawing of a situation frequently encountered, in which we are given *oa*, *ab*, and *bc*. It is required to find ϕ. The procedure in solving this problem is first to find the angle *boa*, using the sides *ab* and *oa*. Second, the side *ob* is calculated and used in connection with the side *bc* to find the angle *boc*. The angle ϕ will then be the sum of *aob* and *boc*. Illustrated below is a somewhat more direct method, in which the hypotenuse *ob* is not actually calculated.

fig. 19·16

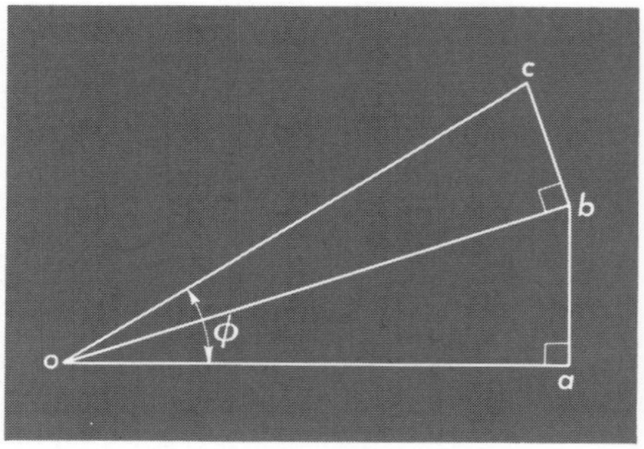

$$\tan boa = \frac{ba}{oa}$$

$$ob = \frac{oa}{\cos boa}$$

$$\tan cob = \frac{cb}{oa/\cos boa} = \frac{(cb)\cos boa}{oa}$$

$$\angle boa + \angle cob = \angle coa = \phi$$

fig. 19·18

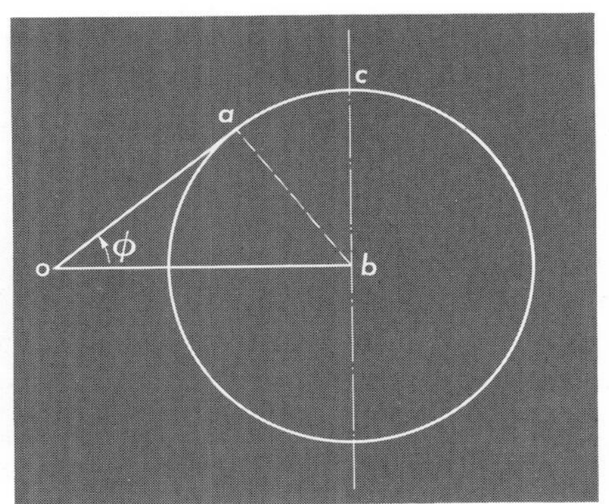

fig. 19·17

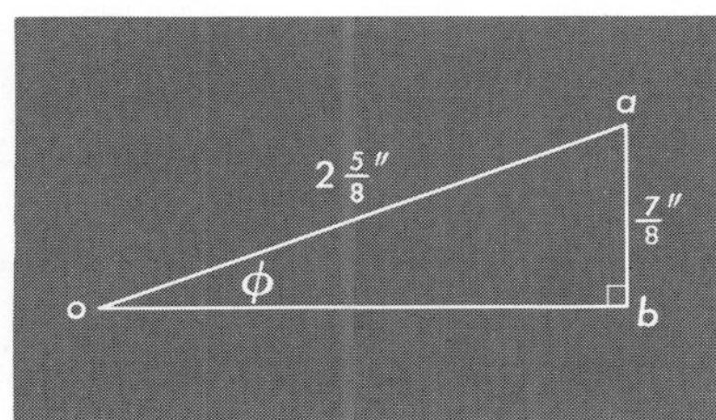

This method is particularly useful when *cb* and *oa* have common factors.

In Fig. 19·17 it is desired to calculate the angle by use of the sine. Decimal equivalents could be used, but common fractions make the problem much easier.

$$\sin \phi = \frac{7/8}{2\,5/8} = \frac{7}{8} \times \frac{8}{21} = \frac{1}{3} = 0.33333$$

If the side *ob* is to be calculated by means of the Pythagorean theorem, again decimal equivalents could be used, but it is much better to reason as follows: Use ⅛ in. as the basic unit in the problem. Hence the hypotenuse will be 21 units long, and the side *ab* will be 7 units long; therefore,

$$ob = \tfrac{1}{8}\sqrt{21^2 - 7^2} = \tfrac{1}{8}\sqrt{441 - 49} = \frac{19.799}{8} = 2.475 \text{ in.}$$

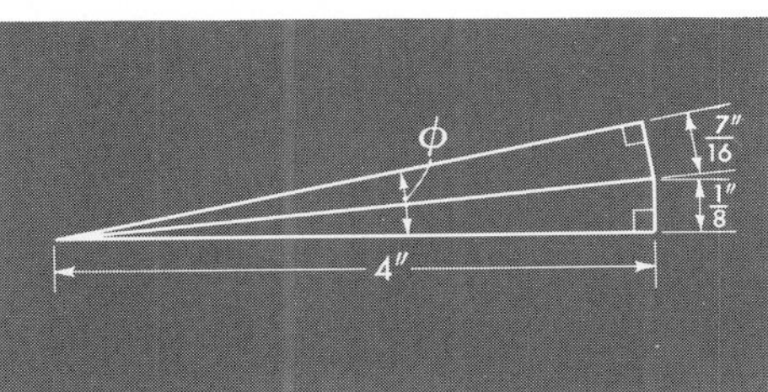

fig. 19·19

fig. 19·20

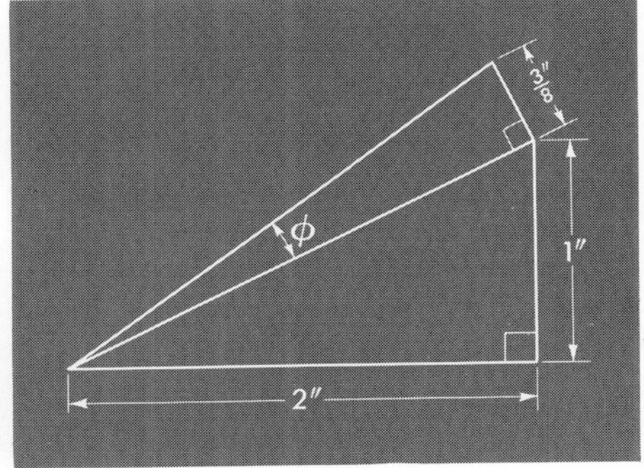

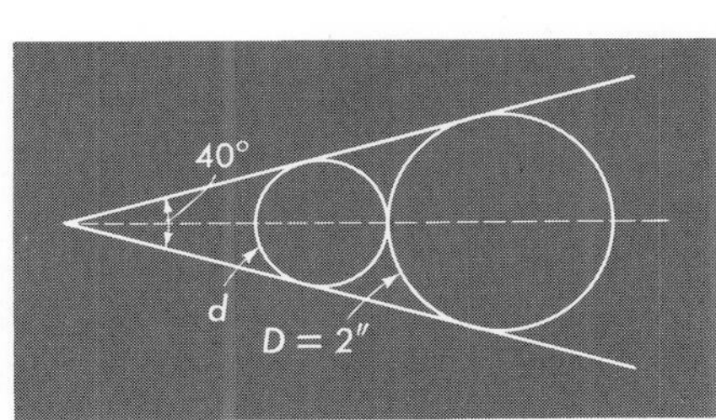

fig. 19·21

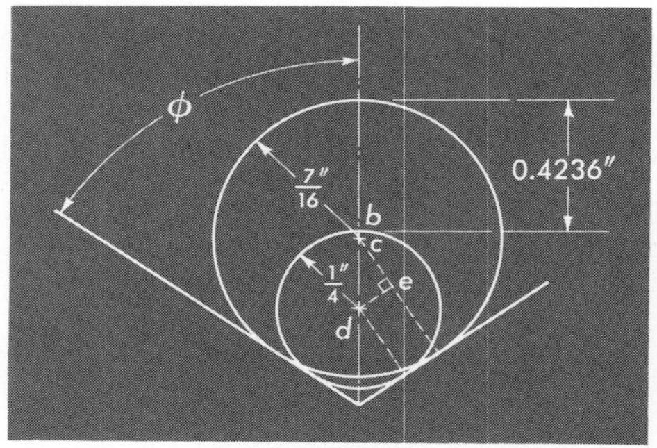

fig. 19·22

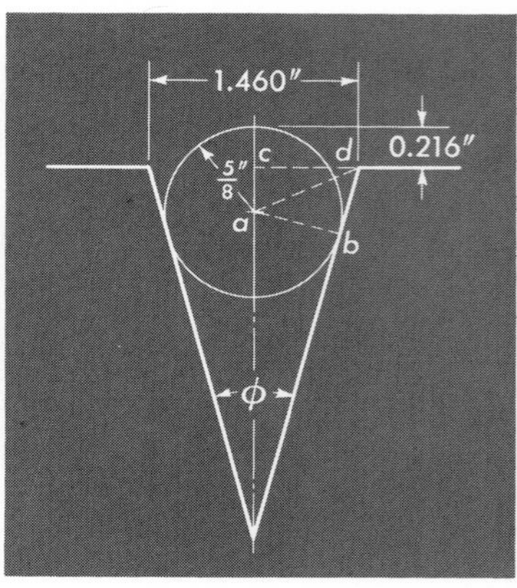

fig. 19·23

Figure 19·18 illustrates a type of problem which is very frequently done incorrectly. A solution is often attempted assuming that the figure *obc* is a right triangle. As a matter of fact, it is not even any kind of a triangle. A triangle is a figure formed by three intersecting straight lines. The line *oc* is not a straight line. It is a combination of the straight line *oa* and the arc of a circle *ac*; sin ϕ equals ab/ob and not bc/oc.

As far as tolerances and limits are concerned, no attempt is made to follow commercial shop practices in Exercise 5. Nominal dimensions are given on the drawings, and it will be assumed that their accuracy is consistent with the use of five-place tables. Angles will be computed either to tenths of minutes or to seconds at the discretion of the instructor. A deviation from the answer of three or four seconds is not usually significant.

EXERCISE 5

1. Find the angle ϕ in Fig. 19·19.
2. Find the angle ϕ in Fig. 19·20.
3. Find the diameter d in Fig. 19·21.
4. Find ϕ in Fig. 19·22.
5. Find ϕ in Fig. 19·23.
6. Find ϕ in Fig. 19·24.
7. Find ϕ in Fig. 19·25.

fig. 19·24

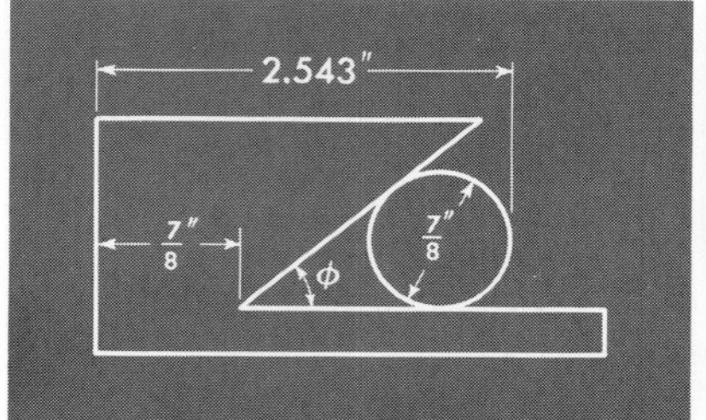

fig. 19·25

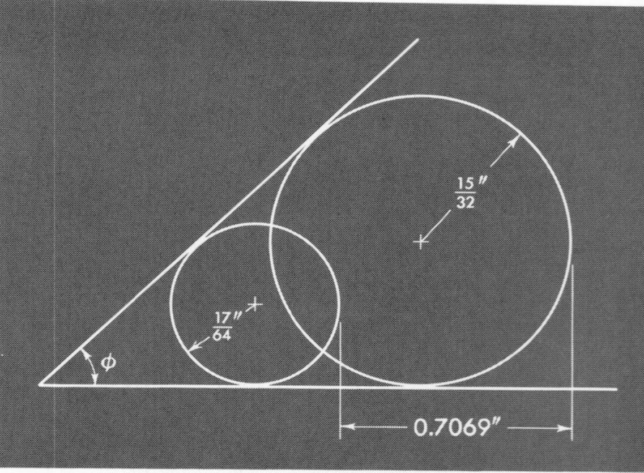

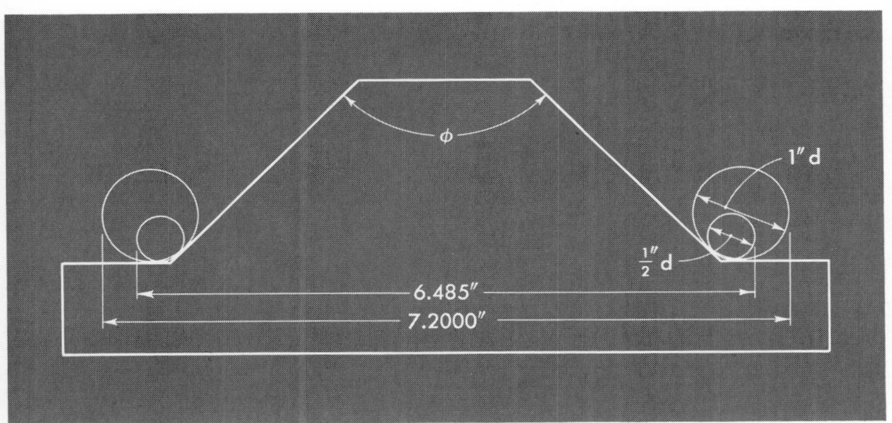

fig. 19·26

fig. 19·27

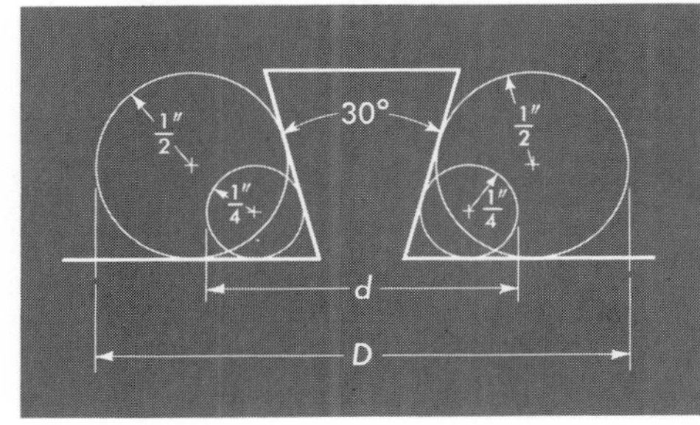

fig. 19·28

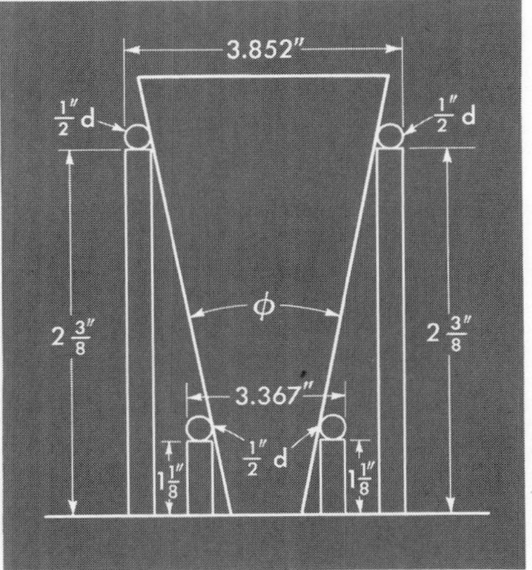

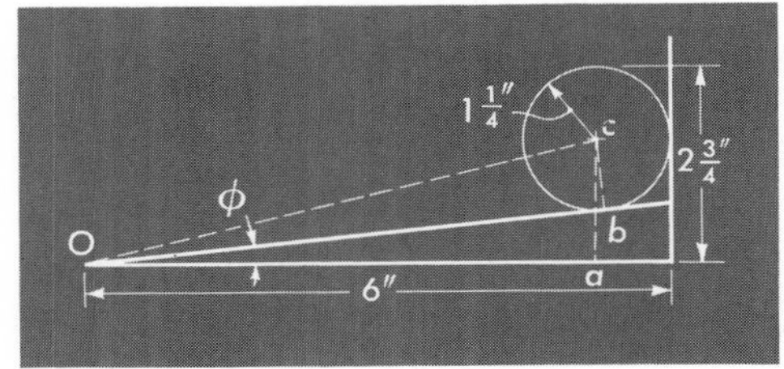

fig. 19·29

8. Find ϕ in Fig. 19·26.
9. Find the distance $(D - d)$ in Fig. 19·27.
10. Find ϕ in Fig. 19·28.
11. Find ϕ in Fig. 19·29.
12. Find R in Fig. 19·30.
13. Find R in Fig. 19·31.

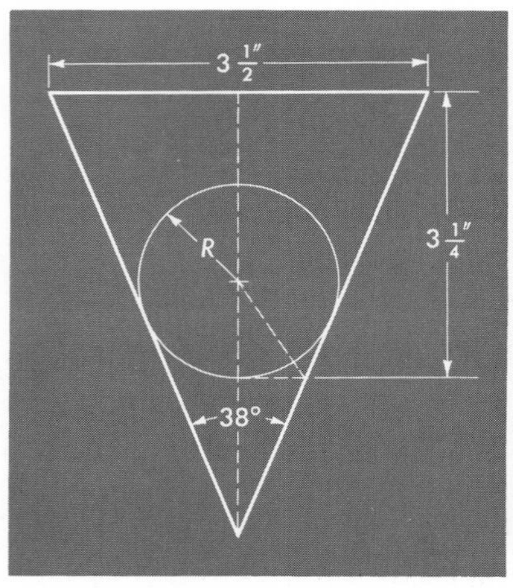

fig. 19·30

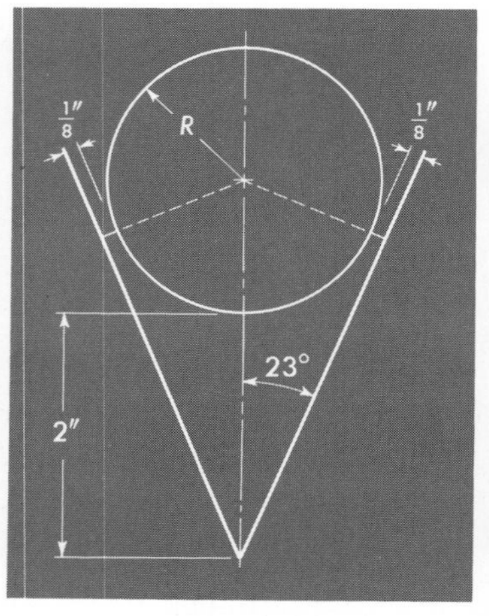

fig. 19·31

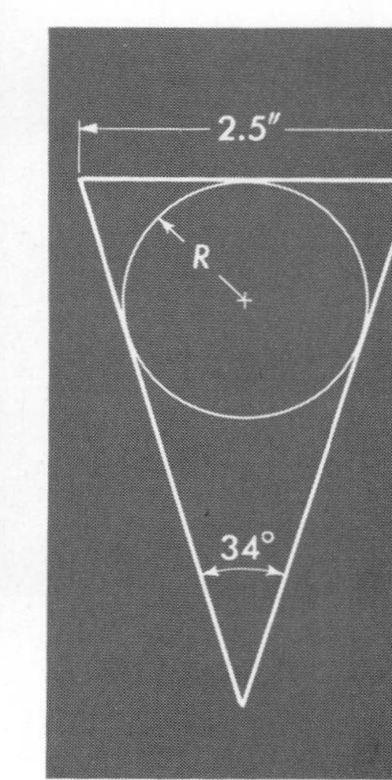

fig. 19·32

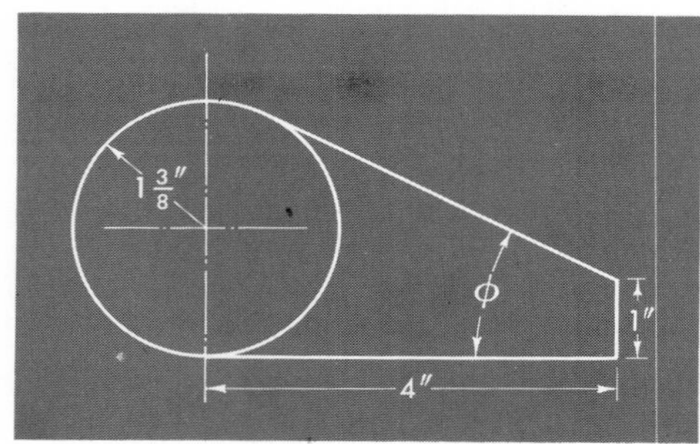

fig. 19·33

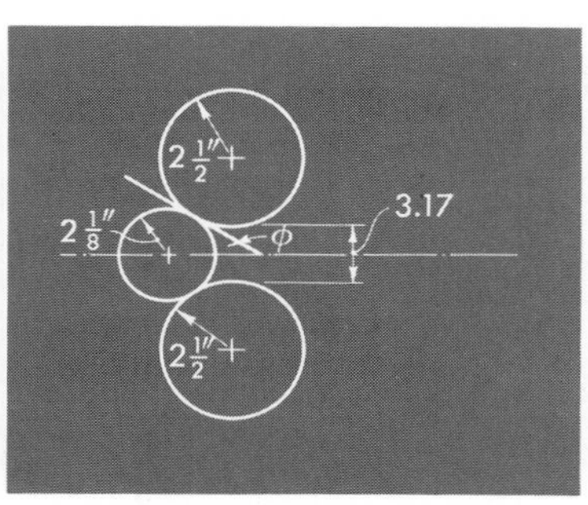

fig. 19·34

fig. 19·35

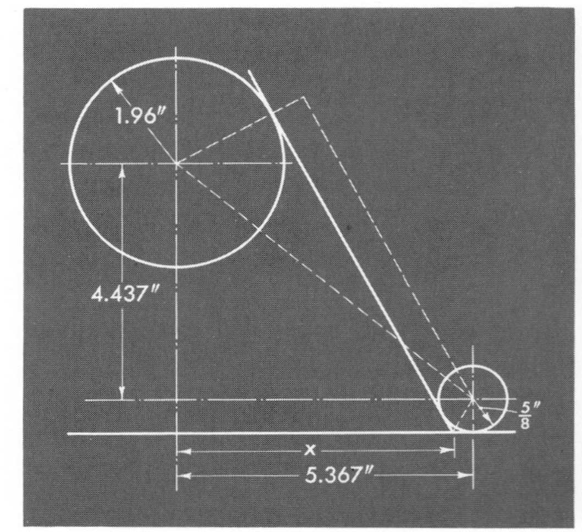

14. Find R in Fig. 19·32.
15. Find ϕ in Fig. 19·33.
16. Find ϕ in Fig. 19·34.
17. Find x in Fig. 19·35.

18. Find ϕ in Fig. 19·36.
19. Find ϕ in Fig. 19·37.
20. Find the angle ϕ and the lengths x and y in Fig. 19·38.

fig. 19·36

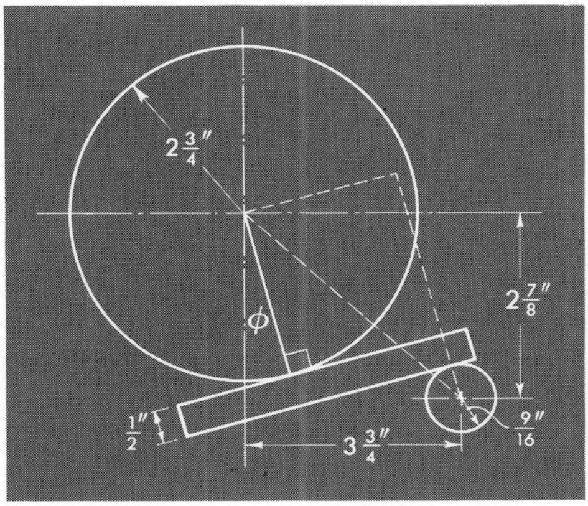

fig. 19·37

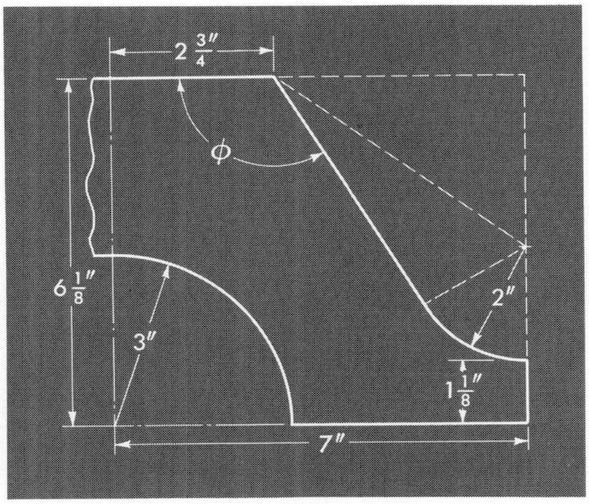

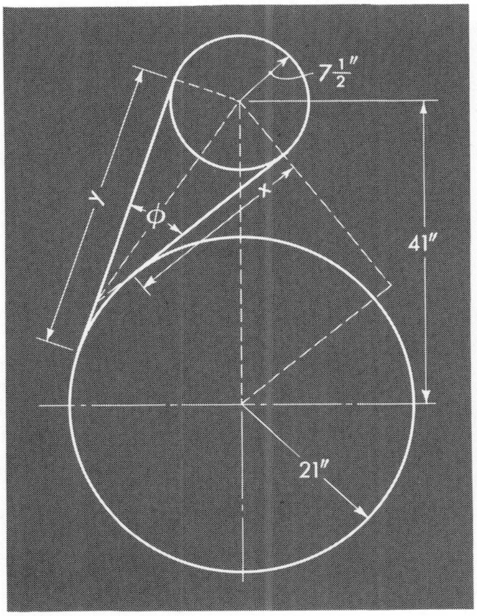

fig. 19·38

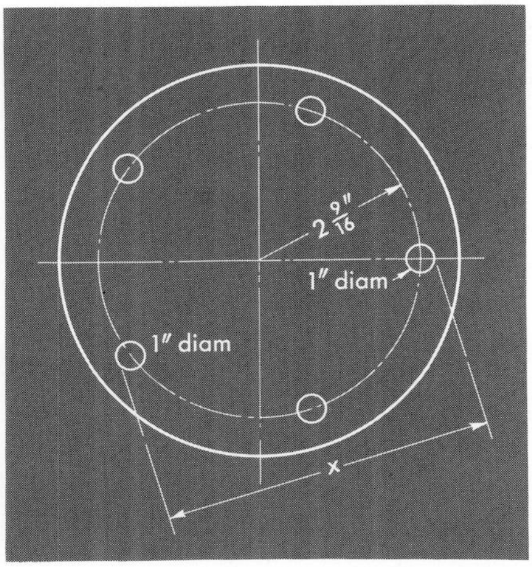

fig. 19·39

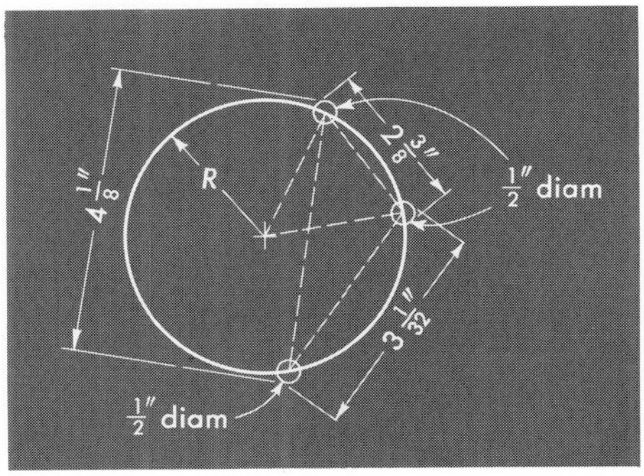

fig. 19·40

21. Find x in Fig. 19·39. The five holes in the 2$\frac{9}{16}$-in. circle are evenly spaced.
22. Find R in Fig. 19·40.
23. Find R in Fig. 19·41 if oa = 2.400 in., ob = 4.000 in., oc = 5.000 in., and $\angle aob = \angle boc$.
24. Find x and y in Fig. 19·42.
25. Find x and y in Fig. 19·43.
26. Find x in Fig. 19·44.

fig. 19·43

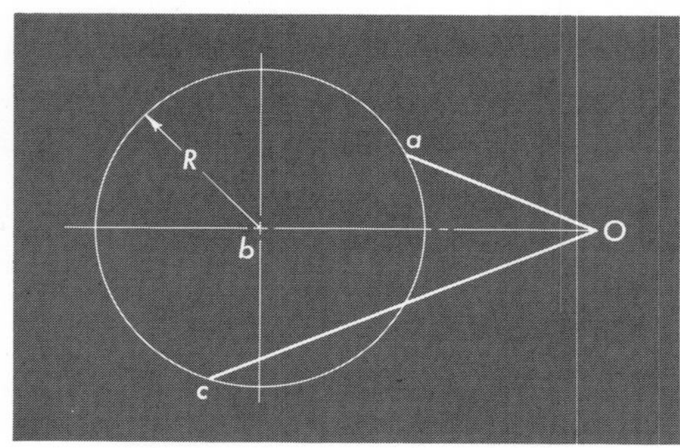

fig. 19·41

fig. 19·42

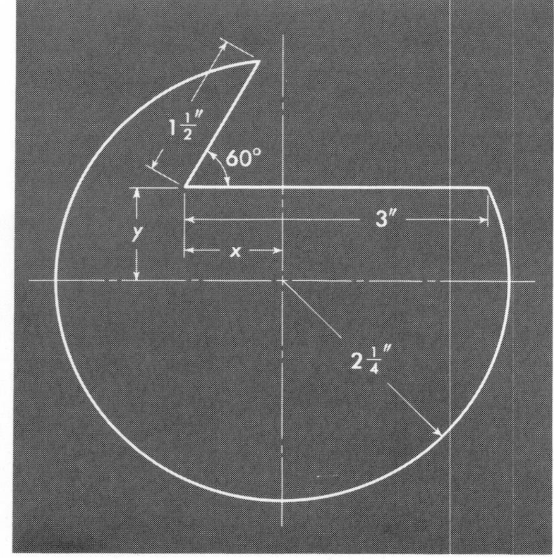

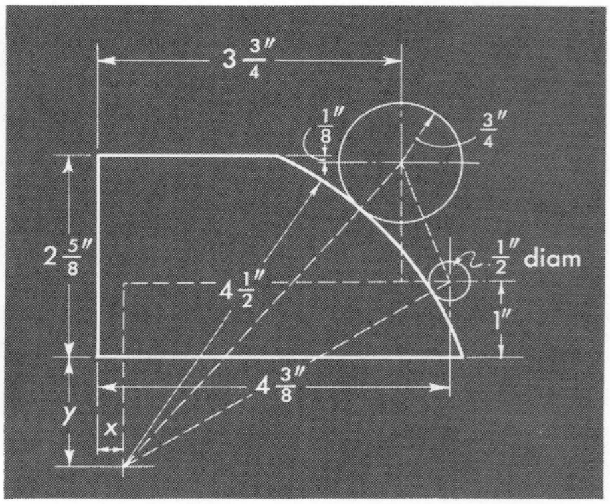

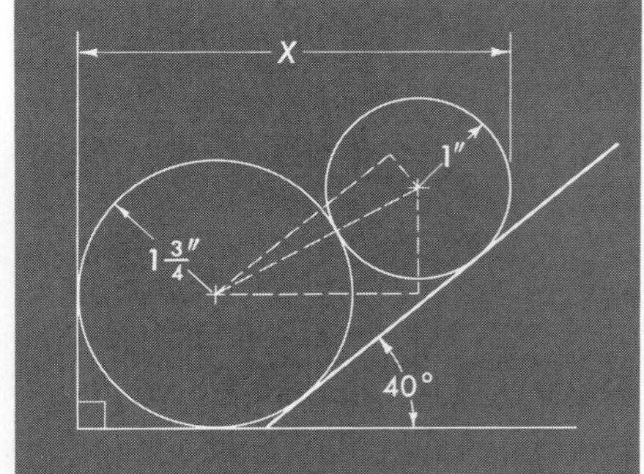

fig. 19·44

19·11 Solid figures

Many of the problems in this chapter have involved more than one triangle, but these triangles have usually been in the same plane.

There is a wide range of practical applications in which related triangles lie in different planes. The authors feel that a thorough treatment of this type of problem would consume an unwarranted amount of textbook space and classroom time. Therefore, the few problems which are given in this section are intended only to introduce the student to this highly specialized and restricted field of applications. The student who has reason to be interested in this particular type of problem is referred to Wolfe and Phelps' "Practical Shop Mathematics," vol. 2 (4th ed., McGraw-Hill Book Company, Inc., 1959).

Figures 19·45 and 19·46 illustrate two of several figures which, for this purpose, might be called basic. A typical problem in this type of work requires that one of the angles be calculated when certain other angles are given.

example 4 In Fig. 19·45 $\angle gch = 20°$ and $\angle bgc = 30°$ (note the positions of the 90° angles); find the angle *gbh*.

The data as given determine the *shape* of the figure, but since no linear dimensions are given, the *size* of the figure is not determined. However, this is beside the point, since the required answer is an angle and not a side.

The general procedure in the solution is as follows:

1. Locate the known triangles. In this problem they are the triangles *gch* and *bgc*.
2. Locate the side common to both these known triangles. In this problem this is the side *cg*. Let the length of this side be 1 unit.
3. Locate the unknown triangle. In this problem it is the triangle *bgh*.

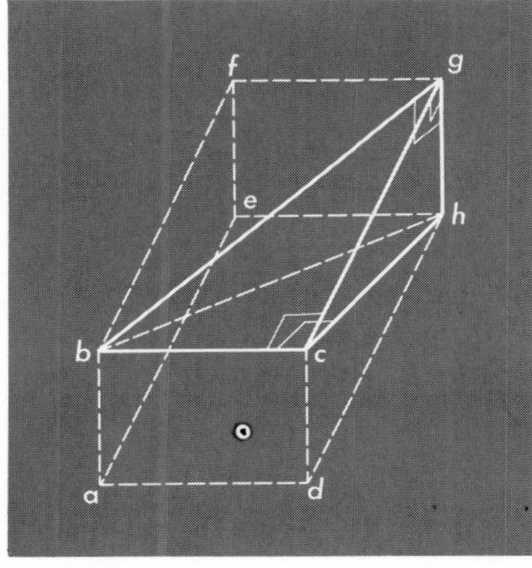

fig. 19·45

fig. 19·46

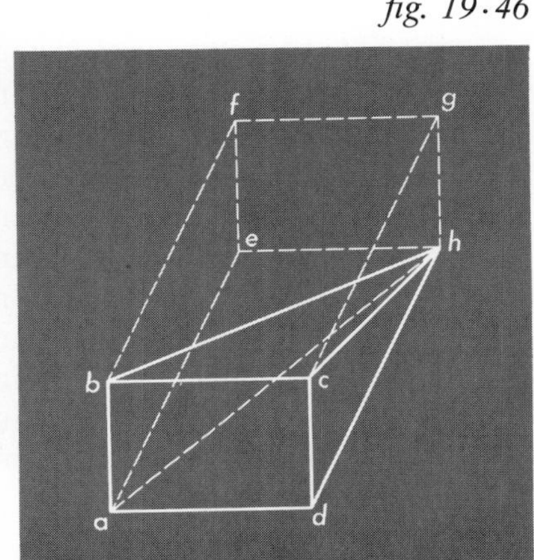

4. Locate the common sides between the unknown triangle and each of the known triangles.
5. Solve for the common sides found in step 4 in terms of functions of the known angles.
6. Solve for a function of the unknown angle in terms of the sides found in step 5.
7. Find the angle whose function was found in step 6. The arithmetical work involved in steps 5 to 7 follows:
8. In triangle *gch*,

$$gh = 1 \times \tan gch = \tan gch = \tan 20^\circ = 0.36397$$

9. In triangle *bgc*,

$$bg = 1 \times \sec bgc = \sec bgc = \sec 30^\circ = 1.1547$$

10. In triangle *gbh*,

$$\tan gbh = \frac{gh}{bg} = \frac{\tan 20^\circ}{\sec 30^\circ} = \frac{0.36397}{1.1547} = 0.31521$$

$$\angle gbh = 17^\circ 29' 43''$$

Since in general it is easier to multiply than it is to divide, the last equation probably should be altered to its equivalent:

$$\tan gbh = \tan 20^\circ \times \cos 30^\circ = 0.36397 \times 0.86603 = 0.31521$$
$$\angle gbh = 17^\circ 29' 43''$$

EXERCISE 6

1. Draw Figs. 19·45 and 19·46 in orthographic projection. Draw enough views, including auxiliaries, so that the triangles *bcg*, *bch*, *cgh*, and *bgh* may be seen in their true dimensions. Let $ad = 1$, $ab = 1\frac{1}{2}$, and $dh = 2$ in.
2. Referring to Fig. 19·45, write equations, involving multiplication only, which can be used as follows:

(a) Solve for $\angle gbh$ in terms of $\angle bgc$ and $\angle gch$.
(b) Solve for $\angle gbh$ in terms of $\angle bgc$ and $\angle hbc$.
(c) Solve for $\angle gbh$ in terms of $\angle gch$ and $\angle hbc$.
(d) Solve for $\angle bgc$ in terms of $\angle gch$ and $\angle hbc$.
(e) Solve for $\angle bgc$ in terms of $\angle gch$ and $\angle gbh$.
(f) Solve for $\angle bgc$ in terms of $\angle gbh$ and $\angle hbc$.
(g) Solve for $\angle gch$ in terms of $\angle gbh$ and $\angle bgc$.
(h) Solve for $\angle gch$ in terms of $\angle gbh$ and $\angle hbc$.
(i) Solve for $\angle gch$ in terms of $\angle bgc$ and $\angle hbc$.
(j) Solve for $\angle hbc$ in terms of $\angle gbh$ and $\angle bgc$.
(k) Solve for $\angle hbc$ in terms of $\angle gbh$ and $\angle ghc$.
(l) Solve for $\angle hbc$ in terms of $\angle bgc$ and $\angle ghc$.

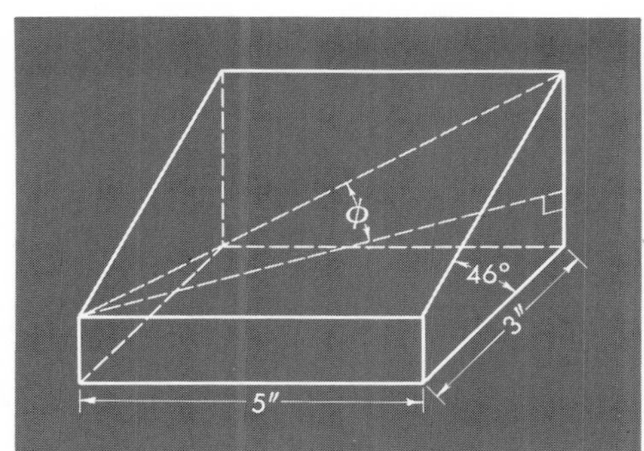

fig. 19·47

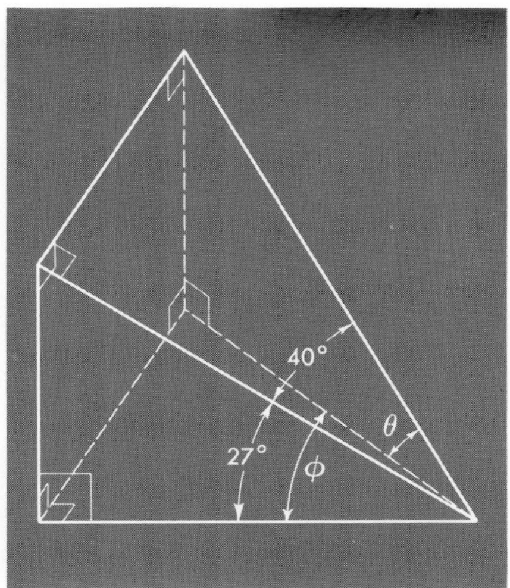

fig. 19·48

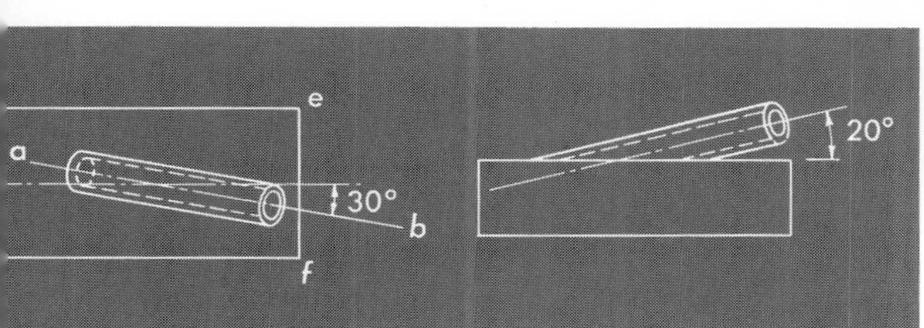

9·49

3. Prove that in Fig. 19·46 angle *bha* is less than angle *chd*.
4. Prove that in Fig. 19·46 angle *bhc* is less than angle *ahd*.
5. If in Fig. 19·46 $ad = 2$ in., $dh = 4$ in., and $ab = 3$ in., find $\angle bha$.
6. Referring to Fig. 19·46, write equations which can be used as follows:

   (a) Solve for $\angle bhc$ in terms of $\angle chd$ and $\angle ahd$.
   (b) Solve for $\angle bha$ in terms of $\angle chd$ and $\angle ahd$.
   (c) Solve for $\angle chd$ in terms of $\angle bha$ and $\angle bhc$.
   (d) Solve for $\angle ahd$ in terms of $\angle bhc$ and $\angle bha$.

7. Find the angle ϕ in Fig. 19·47.
8. Find the angles ϕ and θ in Fig. 19·48.
9. In Fig. 19·49 find the angle which the center line *ab* makes with the plane *cdef*.
10. Find ϕ in Fig. 19·50.
11. Find the angle ϕ in Fig. 19·51.
12. In Fig. 19·52 $gb = 3$, $ah = 1$, $ci = 1.3$, $gi = 4$, $gh = 3$, and $hi = 2$. Find $\angle bfg$.

19·50

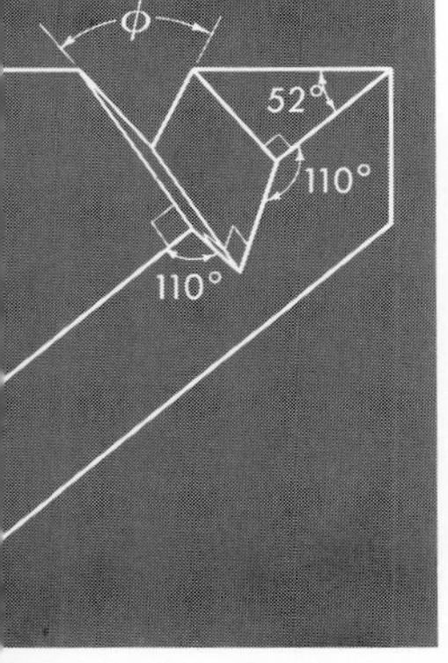

fig. 19·51

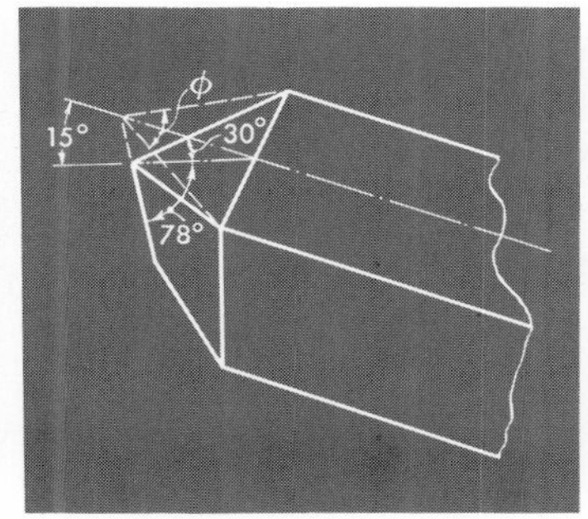

fig. 19·52

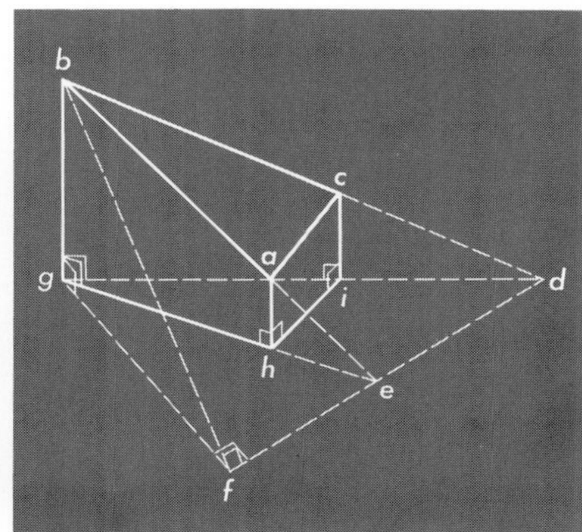

unit eight analytical trigonometry

this unit will be of particular interest to electrical and electronics students; it presupposes a study of units two to seven

20 vectors

In Sec. 17 · 1 we defined a vector as follows: A vector is a line segment, or simply a line, whose distinctive properties are length, direction, and sense. The length of a vector is the linear distance between the extremities. Direction is measured in terms of the angular orientation of the vector with respect to some reference line. If we consider the vector to have been generated by a moving point, the sense of the vector is determined by the order in which the point coincides with the extremities.

20 · 1 Some further notes on vectors and their projections

In Fig. 20 · 1 let the point P be any point in the coordinate plane. Its coordinates are x_P and y_P.

If we draw a line perpendicular to the X axis through the point P, then the point of intersection of this perpendicular with the X axis is called the *X projection of the point P*. The abscissa of this point is evidently x_P.

In a similar way, if we draw a perpendicular to the Y axis through the point P, then the point of intersection of this perpendicular with the Y axis is called the *Y projection of the point P*. The ordinate of this point is evidently y_P.

Now observe the vector $\overrightarrow{PQ}$ in Fig. 20 · 2. The sense of this vector is upward and to the right from point P toward point Q. Consequently we shall name the point P the *initial* point of the vector $\overrightarrow{PQ}$, and we shall name the point Q the *terminal* point of the vector $\overrightarrow{PQ}$. The X projection of the initial point of this vector is x_P. The X projection of the terminal point of this vector is x_Q.

The X projection of the *vector* $\overrightarrow{PQ}$ is defined as the *algebraic* difference obtained by subtracting the X projection of the initial point *from* the X projection of the terminal point. That is,

$$x_{PQ} = x_Q - x_P \tag{1}$$

where $x_{PQ} = X$ projection of *vector* $\overrightarrow{PQ}$

$x_Q = X$ projection of terminal point of $\overrightarrow{PQ}$

$x_P = X$ projection of initial point of $\overrightarrow{PQ}$

In a similar manner,

$$y_{PQ} = y_Q - y_P \tag{2}$$

where $y_{PQ} = Y$ projection of *vector* $\overrightarrow{PQ}$

$y_Q = Y$ projection of terminal point of $\overrightarrow{PQ}$

$y_P = Y$ projection of initial point of $\overrightarrow{PQ}$

The abscissa distances x_P and x_Q are, by the usual conventions of rectangular coordinates, signed numbers. Consequently, x_{PQ} is a signed number. *If the sign of* x_{PQ} *is positive, the sense of this projection is from the reader's left to his right as he observes Fig. 20·2. If the sign of* x_{PQ} *is negative, the sense of this projection is from the reader's right to his left as he observes Fig. 20·3. In a similar manner, if the sign of the Y projection of a vector is positive, the sense of that projection is away from the reader toward the top of the page as he observes Fig. 20·2. If the sign of the Y projection is negative, the sense of this projection is toward the reader as he observes Fig. 20·3.*

The student should be careful to verify these statements by a detailed study of Examples 1 through 4.

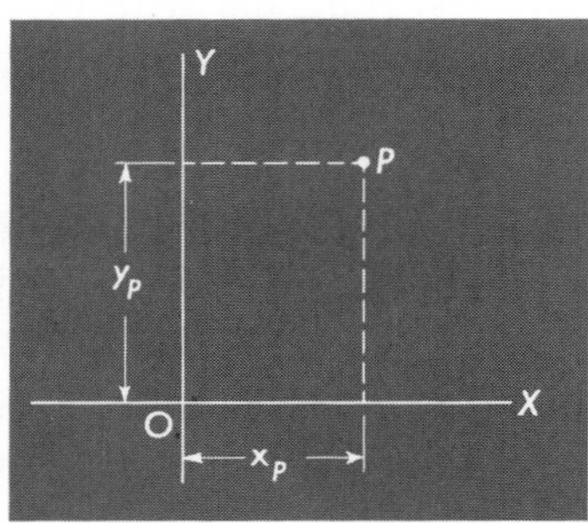

fig. 20·1

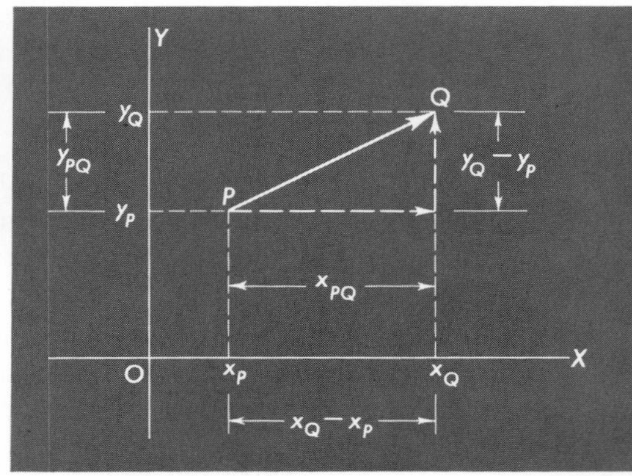

fig. 20·2

example 1 The coordinates of the initial point of a certain vector are $(+5,+9)$. The coordinates of the terminal point of the same vector are $(-3,+4)$. Sketch this vector, referred to a system of rectangular coordinates. Indicate the sense of the vector and its projections by arrows. Express the sense and magnitude of each projection by a signed number (see Fig. 20·4).

Following Eqs. (1) and (2),

$$\begin{aligned} X \text{ projection} &= (-3) - (+5) = -8 \\ Y \text{ projection} &= (+4) - (+9) = -5 \end{aligned}$$

example 2 The coordinates of the initial point of a certain vector are $(-3,+4)$. The coordinates of the terminal point of the same vector are $(+5,+9)$. Sketch this vector, referred to a system of rectangular coordinates. Indicate the sense of the vector and its projections by arrows. Express the sense and magnitude of each projection by a signed number (see Fig. 20·5).

Following Eqs. (1) and (2),

$$\begin{aligned} X \text{ projection} &= (+5) - (-3) = +8 \\ Y \text{ projection} &= (+9) - (+4) = +5 \end{aligned}$$

fig. 20·4

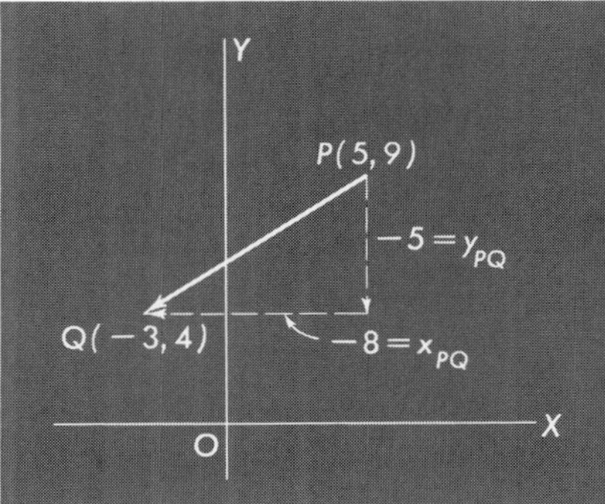

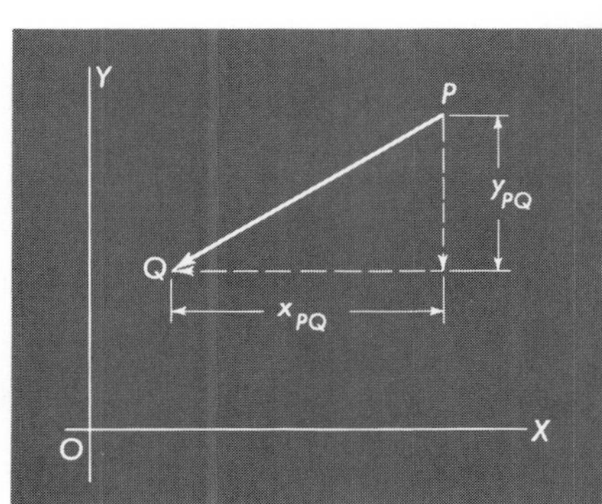

fig. 20·3

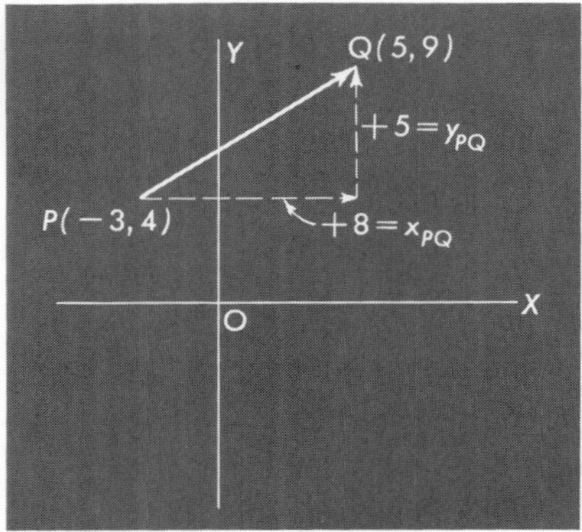

fig. 20·5

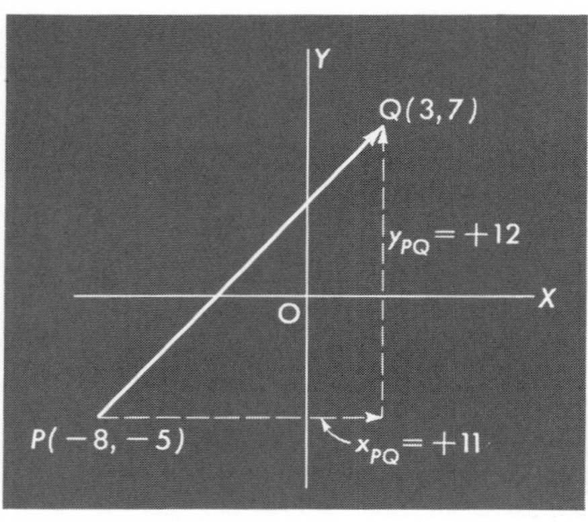

fig. 20·6

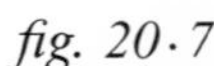

fig. 20·7

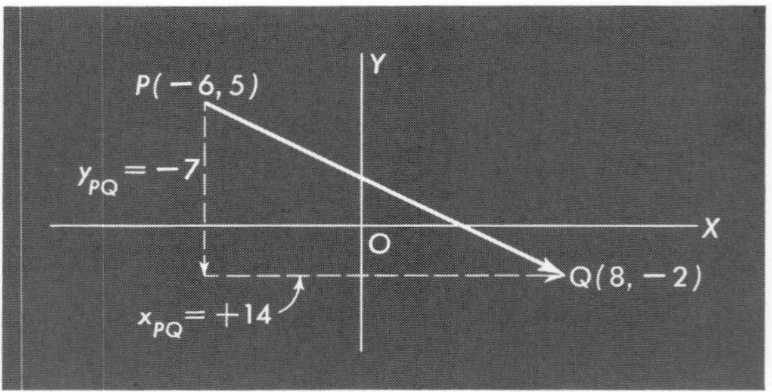

example 3 The coordinates of the initial point of a certain vector are $(-8, -5)$. The coordinates of the terminal point of the same vector are $(+3, +7)$. Sketch this vector, referred to a system of rectangular coordinates. Indicate the sense of the vector and its projections by arrows. Express the sense and magnitude of each projection by a signed number (see Fig. 20·6).

Following Eqs. (1) and (2),

$$X \text{ projection} = (+3) - (-8) = +11$$
$$Y \text{ projection} = (+7) - (-5) = +12$$

example 4 The coordinates of the initial point of a certain vector are $(-6, +5)$. The coordinates of the terminal point of the same vector are $(+8, -2)$. Sketch this vector, referred to a system of rectangular coordinates. Indicate the sense of the vector and its projections by arrows. Express the sense and magnitude of each projection by a signed number (see Fig. 20·7).

Following Eqs. (1) and (2),

$$X \text{ projection} = (+8) - (-6) = +14$$
$$Y \text{ projection} = (-2) - (+5) = -7$$

EXERCISE 1

Calculate the projections of the vectors described below. Draw a sketch of the vector in each case.

	Coordinates of initial point of vector	*Coordinates of terminal point of vector*
1.	+8, +15	+5, −5
2.	−8, −9	+2, +5
3.	+16, +20	−3, +4
4.	+9, +4	+6, −7
5.	+15, +20	+25, +10
6.	−6, +2	+5, +8
7.	+3, −4	+8, −1
8.	+17, −12	−4, −9
9.	0, −6	8, 0
10.	−10, 0	0, +7

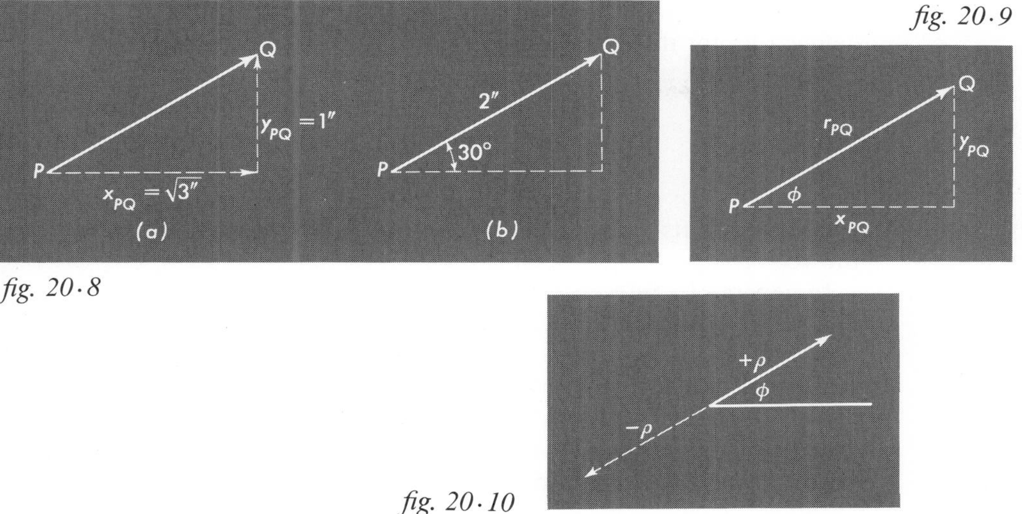

fig. 20·8

fig. 20·9

fig. 20·10

20·2 Polar and rectangular coordinates

Figure 20·8 shows two equal vectors, each designated as $\overrightarrow{PQ}$. The vector $\overrightarrow{PQ}$ in Fig. 20·8*a* is defined in terms of its X and Y projections. The same vector $\overrightarrow{PQ}$ in Fig. 20·8*b* is defined in terms of its length and reference angle. (The student should at this point review Sec. 16·14 to assure himself of the numerical equivalence between the data in this figure.)

When, as in Fig. 20·8*a*, we define a vector in terms of its projections, we are using *rectangular notation.*

When, as in Fig. 20·8*b*, we define a vector in terms of its length and reference angle, we are using *polar notation.*

As we discussed in the preceding section, when using rectangular notation, we designate the length of the projections and the length of the vector by x, y, and r, respectively, with some appropriate subscript where necessary (see Fig. 20·9).

Evidently, from Fig. 20·9, we may write

$$|\overrightarrow{PQ}| = r_{PQ} = \sqrt{x_{PQ}^2 + y_{PQ}^2} \tag{3}$$

where r_{PQ} is the absolute value of the length of the vector $\overrightarrow{PQ}$.

In polar notation the length of the vector is designated by the symbol ρ. The sign of ρ indicates the sense of the vector. If ρ is positive, the sense of the vector is away from the vertex along the terminal side of the reference angle. If ρ is negative, the sense of the vector is in the opposite direction (see Fig. 20·10).

There is a compact and generally understood symbolism used to define a vector in polar notation. It is, referred to Fig. 20·8*b*,

$$2\underline{/30^\circ}$$

or, in general,

$$\pm\rho\underline{/\phi} \tag{4}$$

where ρ (with its associated sign) defines both the length and sense of the vector.

In general, by reference to Fig. 20·9,

$$|\overrightarrow{PQ}| = \sqrt{x_{PQ}^2 + y_{PQ}^2} = r_{PQ} \tag{5}$$

$$\phi = \tan^{-1} \frac{y_{PQ}}{x_{PQ}} \tag{6}$$

We may define the vector $\overrightarrow{OP}$ in polar notation using data appropriate to rectangular notation as indicated in Eq. (7) below.

$$\sqrt{x_{PQ}^2 + y_{PQ}^2}\underline{/\tan^{-1} \frac{y_{PQ}}{x_{PQ}}} \tag{7}$$

We may define the vector $\overrightarrow{OP}$ in rectangular notation using data appropriate to polar notation as indicated in Eqs. (8) and (9) below.

$$x_{PQ} = |\overrightarrow{PQ}| \cos \phi \tag{8}$$

$$y_{PQ} = |\overrightarrow{PQ}| \sin \phi \tag{9}$$

Thus polar notation may be converted to rectangular notation, and vice versa, by Eqs. (5) through (9).

In Fig. 20·11, if $\overrightarrow{OP'} = -\overrightarrow{OP}$ and the rectangular coordinates of P are x_P and y_P, the rectangular coordinates of P' are $-x_{P'}$ and $-y_{P'}$. The magnitude of both $\overrightarrow{OP}$ and $\overrightarrow{OP'}$ in rectangular notation is

$$|\overrightarrow{OP}| = |\overrightarrow{OP'}| = \sqrt{x_{PQ}^2 + y_{PQ}^2} \tag{10}$$

The magnitude and sense of $\overrightarrow{OP}$ in polar notation is $+\rho$; the magnitude and sense of $\overrightarrow{OP'}$ in polar coordinates is $-\rho$. In polar notation (see Fig. 20·11),

$$\overrightarrow{OP} = +\rho\underline{/\phi} \tag{11}$$

In polar notation (see Fig. 20·11),

$$\overrightarrow{OP'} = -\rho\underline{/\phi} \tag{12}$$

or

$$\overrightarrow{OP'} = +\rho\underline{/\phi + 180^\circ} \tag{13}$$

or

$$\overrightarrow{OP'} = +\rho\underline{/\phi \pm 180^\circ} \tag{14}$$

That is, in polar notation the size of the angle shows how much the terminal side of the angle has been rotated, and the sign before ρ denotes the sense of the vector along that terminal side.

example 5 Find the X and Y projections of the vector $6\underline{/40^\circ}$.

$$X \text{ projection} = 6\cos 40^\circ = 6 \times 0.7660 = +4.596$$
$$Y \text{ projection} = 6\sin 40^\circ = 6 \times 0.6428 = +3.857$$

example 6 Find the X and Y projections of the vector $5\underline{/120^\circ}$.

$$X \text{ projection} = 5\cos 120^\circ = 5 \times (-0.5) = -2.5$$
$$Y \text{ projection} = 5\sin 120^\circ = 5 \times (+0.8660) = +4.330$$

example 7 Find the X and Y projections of the vector $3\underline{/260^\circ}$.

$$X \text{ projection} = 3\cos 260^\circ = 3 \times (-0.1737) = -0.5211$$
$$Y \text{ projection} = 3\sin 260^\circ = 3 \times (-0.9848) = -2.9544$$

example 8 Find the X and Y projections of the vector $2\underline{/-30^\circ}$.

$$X \text{ projection} = 2\cos(-30^\circ) = 2 \times 0.8660 = +1.732$$
$$Y \text{ projection} = 2\sin(-30^\circ) = 2 \times -0.5000 = -1.000$$

example 9 Find the X and Y projections of the vector $-4\underline{/120^\circ}$.

$$X \text{ projection} = -4\cos 120^\circ = -4 \times (-0.5) = +2.000$$
$$Y \text{ projection} = -4\sin 120^\circ = -4 \times (+0.8660) = -3.464$$

example 10 If the coordinates of P in Fig. 20·12 are (7,11) and the coordinates of

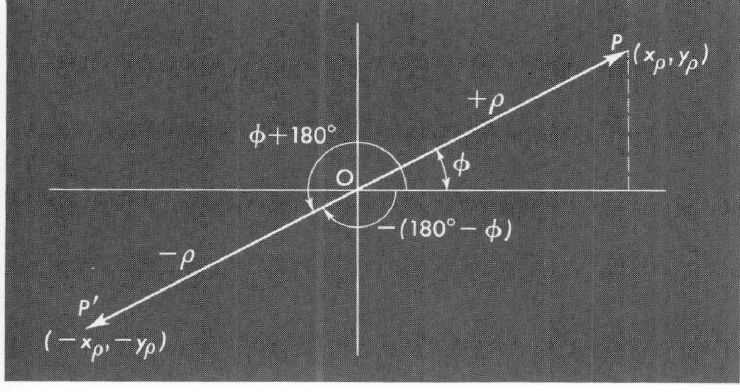

fig. 20·11

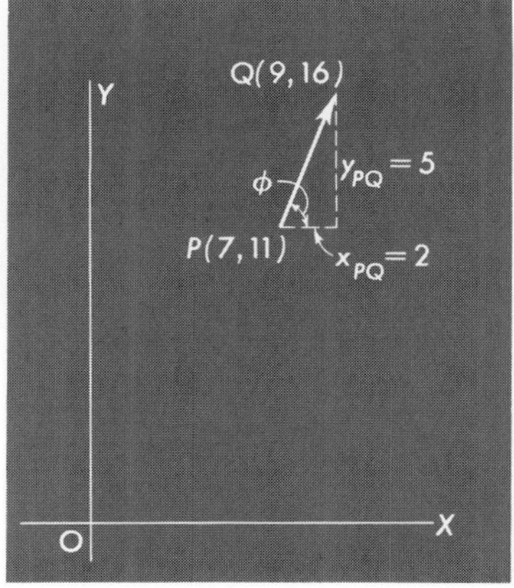

fig. 20·12

Q are (9,16), write the defining expression for the vector $\overrightarrow{PQ}$ in polar notation.

$$x_{PQ} = 9 - 7 = 2$$
$$y_{PQ} = 16 - 11 = 5$$

Following Eq. (7), page 514,

$$\begin{aligned}\text{polar notation} &= \sqrt{2^2 + 5^2}\underline{/\tan^{-1} 5/2} \\ &= \sqrt{29}\underline{/\tan^{-1} 5/2} \\ &= 5.385\underline{/\tan^{-1} 5/2} \\ &= 5.385\underline{/68°12'}\end{aligned}$$

example 11 If the rectangular coordinates of P in Fig. 20·13 are (3,15) and the coordinates of Q are (−2,19), write the defining expression for the vector $\overrightarrow{PQ}$ in polar notation.

$$\begin{aligned}x_{PQ} &= -2 - 3 = -5 \\ y_{PQ} &= 19 - 15 = 4 \\ r &= \sqrt{(-5)^2 + 4^2} = \sqrt{41} = 6.403 \\ \tan \phi &= 4/-5 = -0.80000 \\ \phi &= 141°20'\end{aligned}$$

In polar notation the vector can be expressed as

$$6.403\underline{/141°20'}$$

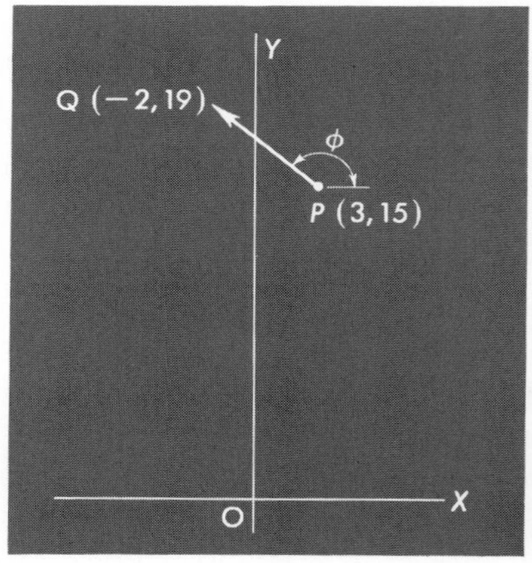

fig. 20·13

EXERCISE 2

1. Certain vectors are defined below in polar notation. Calculate the corresponding X and Y projections. Use a slide rule or a table of four-place natural functions.

(a) $3\underline{/27°}$ (b) $4\underline{/320°}$ (c) $-10\underline{/-30°}$

(d) $3\underline{/-270°}$ (e) $7\underline{/90°}$ (f) $5\underline{/160°}$

(g) $15\underline{/29°}$ (h) $15\underline{/-250°}$ (i) $20\underline{/-135°}$

(j) $-7\underline{/-90°}$ (k) $2\underline{/220°}$ (l) $10\underline{/-140°}$

(m) $3\underline{/270°}$ (n) $4\underline{/225°}$ (o) $5\underline{/1,470°}$

2. The coordinates of the terminal points of certain vectors are given below. The initial point is at the origin. In each case write the polar expression defining the vector. Use a slide rule or a four-place table of natural functions.

(a) (3,6)	(b) (2, −3)	(c) (−2, +2)
(d) (−4,4)	(e) (5, −6)	(f) $(\sqrt{3},1)$
(g) (−3, −2)	(h) (−5,6)	(i) $\left(\frac{\sqrt{2}}{2}, -\frac{\sqrt{2}}{2}\right)$
(j) $(a^2 - b^2, 2ab)$	(k) (6, −6)	(l) (5,0)

20·3 Vector operations

There are several recognized vector operations which are so well defined and so frequently used that they have been given names. These names are derived, by analogy, from the names of the fundamental algebraic operations: addition, subtraction, multiplication, and division. The analogy is by no means exact, however, since the nature of a vector is quite different from the nature of an algebraic number. Therefore vector addition, subtraction, multiplication, and division are quite different processes from algebraic addition, subtraction, multiplication, and division.

In this work we shall develop the consideration of vector operations along rather restricted lines. We shall name and define operations for which we have an immediate use, but we shall have to omit consideration of those vector processes appropriate to the more advanced fields of engineering.

The vector operations of addition and subtraction will be discussed in this chapter. In Chap. 23 we shall discuss certain aspects of vector multiplication and division.

20·4 Vector addition

Since vectors in a plane are so widely used in so many fields of engineering, each with its own professional nomenclature, we shall for reference adopt the conventional system of rectangular coordinates used in Chap. 6.

A general definition of vector addition is: *The sum of several vectors is a vector, each of whose projections is the algebraic sum of the corresponding projections of the several vectors.* The term composition of vectors is sometimes used synonymously with vector addition, particularly if the vectors represent forces.

If, for example, we wish to find the sum of several vectors such as $\overrightarrow{OM}$, $\overrightarrow{ON}$, $\overrightarrow{OP}$, and $\overrightarrow{OQ}$, we first find the X projection of each vector. We then add these X projections algebraically to find the X projection of the vector sum. Next we find the Y projection of each vector. Then we add these Y projections algebraically to find the Y projection of the vector sum.

If the vectors to be added are defined in rectangular notation, the process of finding the projections of the vector sum is one of simple algebraic addition.

If the vectors to be added are defined in polar notation, we must first calculate the respective X and Y projections and then proceed as above.

20·5 Polar and topographic diagrams

The purely algebraic method of adding vectors described in Sec. 20·4 should be supplemented by appropriate diagrams. Such diagrams are essential for an intelligent analysis of a practical problem and will help the student to avoid gross errors.

In a polar diagram each vector is drawn with its initial point at the origin of the reference axis. This is illustrated in Fig. 20·14, in which we propose to add the vectors $\overrightarrow{OP}$ and $\overrightarrow{OQ}$.

Let us now construct the line PS equal in magnitude and direction to the vector $\overrightarrow{OQ}$ and construct the line QS equal in magnitude and direction to the vector $\overrightarrow{OP}$. We have now completed the parallelogram $OPSQ$.

It is quite evident from the geometry of the figure that

$$x_{PS} = x_{OQ}$$

and

$$y_{PS} = y_{OQ}$$

Also,

$$y_{OS} = y_{OP} + y_{OQ}$$

and

$$x_{OS} = x_{OP} + x_{OQ}$$

Thus the vector $\overrightarrow{OS}$ is the vector whose projections are the sum of the corresponding projections of $\overrightarrow{OP}$ and $\overrightarrow{OQ}$. By definition, therefore, $\overrightarrow{OS}$ is the vector sum of $\overrightarrow{OP}$ and $\overrightarrow{OQ}$.

When a graphical method is sufficiently accurate (and there are many such situations), two vectors may be added simply by constructing a diagram to scale. The reference angle of the sum vector can be measured with a protractor, and the length of the sum vector can be measured with a ruler.

The polar diagram is perfectly practical for adding two vectors, but it becomes rather cumbersome when more than two vectors are to be added.

A topographic diagram is more suitable if more than two vectors are to be added. To construct a topographic diagram for the graphical addition of a series of vectors, we proceed as follows: Beginning at the origin of the coordinate system, we draw the first vector chosen with its initial point on the origin. Then we draw the second vector with its initial point on the terminal point of the first vector. Then we draw the third vector with its initial point on the terminal point of the second, and so on, until the last vector in the series has been plotted. The vector whose initial point is at the origin and whose terminal point is at the terminal point of the last vector plotted is the sum of the several vectors.

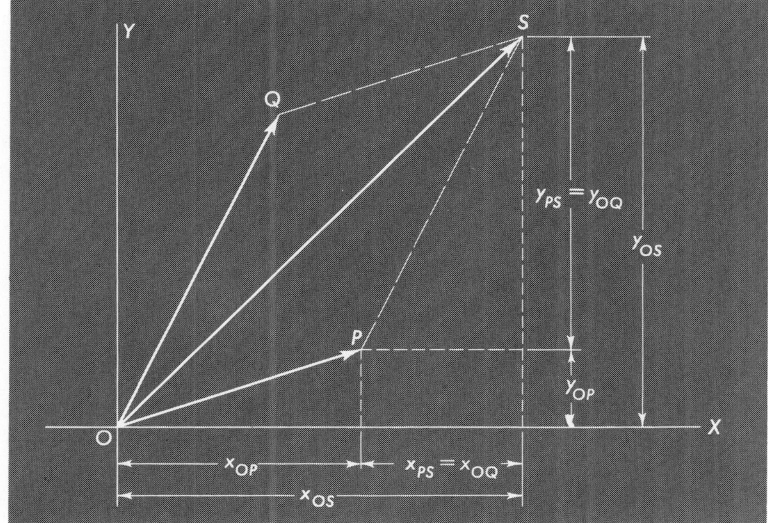

fig. 20·14

The student will find that a careful study of the examples below will be more profitable than the reading of further descriptive material.

example 12 Find the X and Y projections of the sum of the following vectors:

Vector	*X projection*	*Y projection*
$\overrightarrow{OA}$	+320	+200
$\overrightarrow{AB}$	−250	+100
$\overrightarrow{BC}$	−50	−500

The X projection of the vector sum is $(+320 - 250 - 50) = +20$. The Y projection of the vector sum is $(+200 + 100 - 500) = -200$.

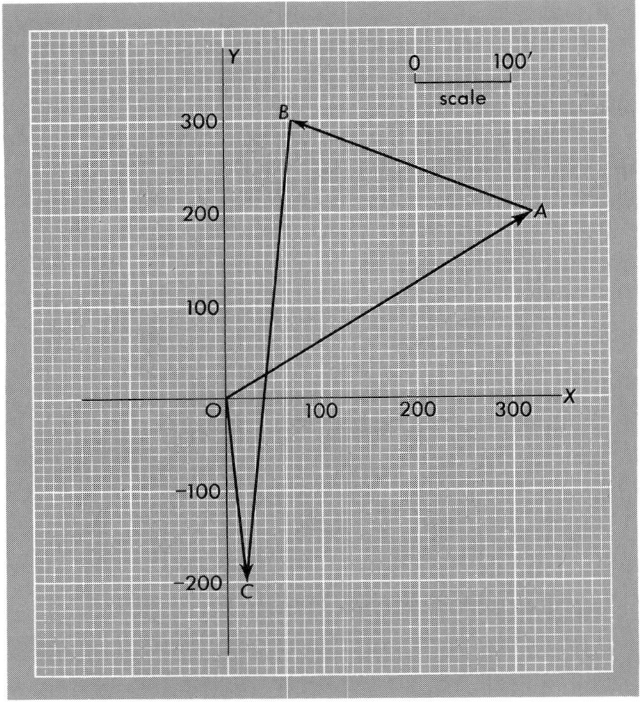

fig. 20·15

The vector sum is indicated as the vector $\overrightarrow{OC}$ in Fig. 20·15.

example 13 Find the X and Y projections of the sum of the following vectors:

Vector	*X projection*	*Y projection*
$\overrightarrow{OA}$	-4.7	-2.1
$\overrightarrow{AB}$	$+1.0$	$+5.0$
$\overrightarrow{BC}$	$+4.5$	$+2.0$

The sum of the vectors $\overrightarrow{OA}$, $\overrightarrow{AB}$, and $\overrightarrow{BC}$ is the vector whose X projection is $(-4.7 + 1.0 + 4.5) = +0.8$ and whose Y projection is $(-2.1 + 5.0 + 2.0) = +4.9$. This vector is designated as the vector $\overrightarrow{OC}$ in Fig. 20·16.

example 14 Find the sum of the following vectors graphically:

$$5\underline{/60°} + 2\underline{/210°} + 1\underline{/270°}$$

The three given vectors are plotted as $\overrightarrow{OA}$, $\overrightarrow{AB}$, and $\overrightarrow{BC}$ in Fig. 20·17. The vector $\overrightarrow{OC}$ is the sum of the given vectors. By scaling with

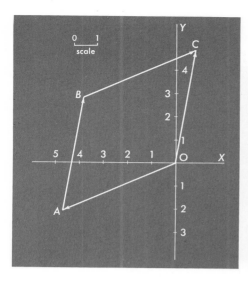

fig. 20·16

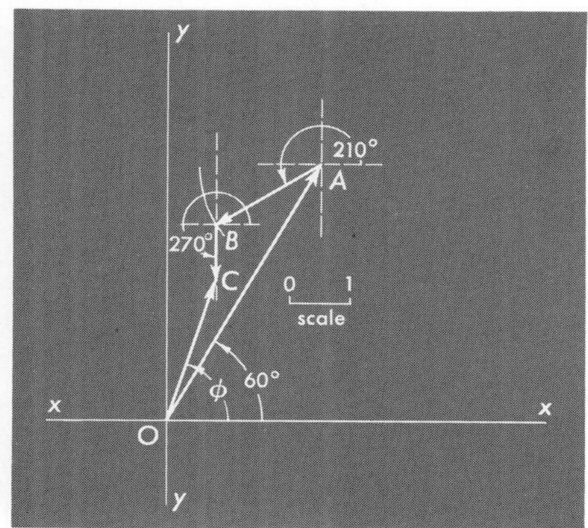

fig. 20·17

a ruler, $|OC| = 2.45$. By scaling with a protractor, $\phi = 72°$. Therefore,

$$\overrightarrow{OC} = 2.45\underline{/72°}$$

example 15 Perform the following vector addition:

$$2\underline{/20°} + 3\underline{/120°} + 4\underline{/250°} + 5\underline{/310°}$$

A topographic diagram illustrating this problem is shown in Fig. 20·18.

The work will be easier and the correct answer more certain if the solution is organized according to some orderly scheme, such as the arrangement in Table 20·1.

table 20·1

Vector	*cosine*	*X projection*		*sin*	*Y projection*	
		+	−		+	−
$2\underline{/20°}$	+0.9397	1.879		+0.3420	0.684	
$3\underline{/120°}$	−0.5000		1.500	+0.8660	2.598	
$4\underline{/250°}$	−0.3420		1.368	−0.9397		3.759
$5\underline{/310°}$	+0.6428	3.214	____	−0.7660	____	3.830
+*X* projection		5.093				
−*X* projection			2.868			
+*Y* projection					3.282	
−*Y* projection						7.589

Total *X* projection = 5.093 − 2.868 = 2.225

Total *Y* projection = 3.282 − 7.589 = −4.307

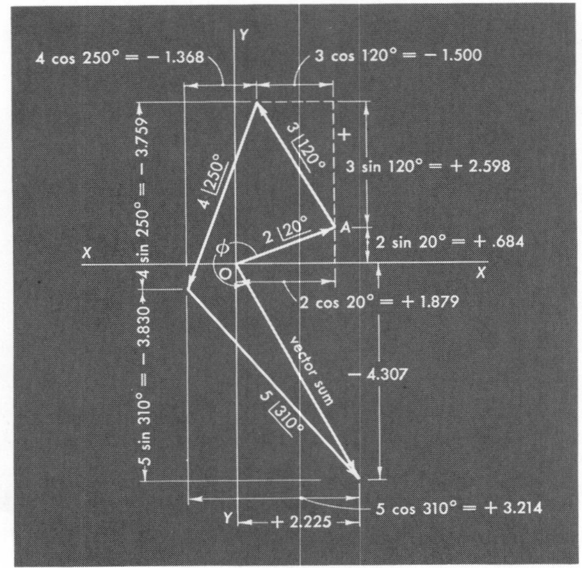

fig. 20·18

The magnitude of the vector sum is

$$r = \sqrt{2.225^2 + (-4.307)^2} = \sqrt{23.50} = 4.85$$

If ϕ is the reference angle of the vector sum,

$$\tan \phi = \frac{-4.307}{+2.225} = -1.936$$

$$\phi = 297°19'$$

In polar notation, the vector sum is $4.85\underline{/297°19'}$.

EXERCISE 3

1. The X and Y projections of each of several vectors are given below. Find the X and Y projections of the vector sums.

(a)

Vector	*X projection*	*Y projection*
$\overrightarrow{OA}$	+100′	+600′
$\overrightarrow{AB}$	+700′	−200′
$\overrightarrow{BC}$	+100′	−600′
$\overrightarrow{CD}$	−1,000′	−200′

(b)

Vector	*X projection*	*Y projection*
$\overrightarrow{OA}$	+200′	−200′
$\overrightarrow{AB}$	+100′	+200′
$\overrightarrow{BC}$	000′	+400′
$\overrightarrow{CD}$	−100′	−200′

(c)

Vector	X projection	Y projection
$\overrightarrow{OA}$	+100′	−200′
$\overrightarrow{AB}$	+100′	+400′
$\overrightarrow{BC}$	−200′	+300′
$\overrightarrow{CD}$	−100′	−300′
$\overrightarrow{DE}$	−300′	+200′
$\overrightarrow{EF}$	+100′	−200′
$\overrightarrow{FG}$	+500′	−800′

2. Plot the following vectors to scale using a protractor and ruler. Find, graphically, the reference angle and length of the vector sum.

(a) 250 ft/17°
175 ft/138°
160 ft/70°
400 ft/195°

(b) 175 ft/135°
240 ft/60°
250 ft/17°
180 ft/278°

(c) 260 ft/330°
210 ft/291°
230 ft/315°
450 ft/165°

(d) 410 ft/00°
175 ft/270°
230 ft/153°
360 ft/205°

(e) 200 ft/172°
240 ft/258°
250 ft/11°
150 ft/344°
100 ft/55°

3. Find the X and Y projections of the sums of the following vectors. Also find the length and reference angle of the vector sum. Use either a slide rule or table of four-place trigonometric functions as directed by the instructor.

	Vector	X projection	Y projection
(a)	$\overrightarrow{OA}$	3.6	−4.5
	$\overrightarrow{AB}$	−2.9	−8.4
	$\overrightarrow{BC}$	5.6	10.1
(b)	$\overrightarrow{OA}$	−9.8	3.5
	$\overrightarrow{AB}$	2.6	6.8
	$\overrightarrow{BC}$	5.8	−8.1
(c)	$\overrightarrow{OA}$	5.6	0.0
	$\overrightarrow{AB}$	0.0	5.6
	$\overrightarrow{BC}$	−3.0	3.0
	$\overrightarrow{CD}$	−5.8	7.2

(d)	$\overrightarrow{OA}$	-7.0	4.0
	$\overrightarrow{AB}$	0.0	2.0
	$\overrightarrow{BC}$	5.0	-2.0
(e)	$\overrightarrow{OA}$	5.0	0.0
	$\overrightarrow{AB}$	2.0	2.0
	$\overrightarrow{BC}$	-1.0	-5.0

4. Calculate the X and Y projections of the sums of the following vectors. Also calculate the length and reference angle of the vector sum. Use either a slide rule or a table of four-place trigonometric functions as directed by the instructor.

(a)	(b)	(c)	(d)
$15\underline{/25^\circ}$	$25\underline{/120^\circ}$	$3\underline{/0^\circ}$	$2\underline{/-30^\circ}$
$20\underline{/140^\circ}$	$10\underline{/-90^\circ}$	$4\underline{/90^\circ}$	$10\underline{/-90^\circ}$
$10\underline{/180^\circ}$	$10\underline{/300^\circ}$	$3\underline{/180^\circ}$	$5\underline{/120^\circ}$

(e) $10\underline{/42^\circ} + 20\underline{/140^\circ} + 30\underline{/240^\circ}$

(f) $5\underline{/180^\circ} + (-10)\underline{/30^\circ} + 20\underline{/-30^\circ}$

(g) $2\underline{/150^\circ} + 6\underline{/90^\circ} + 12\underline{/330^\circ} + 10\underline{/225^\circ}$

(h) $8\underline{/300^\circ} + 5\underline{/20^\circ} + 6\underline{/270^\circ} + 15\underline{/220^\circ}$

(i) $20\underline{/360^\circ} + 20\underline{/180^\circ} + 40\underline{/90^\circ}$

20·6 Vector subtraction

The process of vector subtraction may be described as follows: To subtract the vector $\overrightarrow{OQ}$ from the vector $\overrightarrow{OP}$, we subtract algebraically the projections of $\overrightarrow{OQ}$ from the corresponding projections of $\overrightarrow{OP}$ to obtain the projections of the vector difference. That is, if

$$\overrightarrow{OR} = \overrightarrow{OP} - \overrightarrow{OQ}$$

then
$$x_{OR} = x_{OP} - x_{OQ} \tag{15}$$

and
$$y_{OR} = y_{OP} - y_{OQ} \tag{16}$$

example 16 The vector $\overrightarrow{OA}$ has an X projection of 3 in. and a Y projection of 4 in. Another vector $\overrightarrow{OB}$ has an X projection of 6 in. and a Y projection of 2 in. Express in polar notation the vector $\overrightarrow{OR}$ if

$$\overrightarrow{OR} = \overrightarrow{OA} - \overrightarrow{OB}$$

Following Eq. (15),

$$X \text{ projection of } \overrightarrow{OR} = 3 - 6 = -3$$

Following Eq. (16),

$$Y \text{ projection of } \overrightarrow{OR} = 4 - 2 = +2$$

The magnitude of $\overrightarrow{OR}$ is

$$|OR| = \sqrt{(-3)^2 + 2^2} = \sqrt{13} = 3.61$$

$$\tan \phi_r = \frac{+2}{-3} = -0.6667$$

where ϕ_r = reference angle of $\overrightarrow{OR}$

$$\phi_r = 146°19'$$

In polar notation the value of $\overrightarrow{OR}$ is $3.61\underline{/146°19'}$.

The subtractions indicated in Eqs. (15) and (16) are conventional algebraic subtractions.

Furthermore, the student will note by reference to Fig. 20·11 that a reversal of the sense of a vector automatically reverses the signs of both projections.

Therefore, vector subtraction can be accomplished by reversing the sense of the vector subtrahend and proceeding as in vector addition. Thus, if

$$\overrightarrow{OR} = \overrightarrow{AB} - \overrightarrow{CD} \tag{17}$$

and if

$$\overrightarrow{CD'} = -\overrightarrow{CD} \tag{18}$$

then

$$\overrightarrow{OR} = \overrightarrow{AB} + \overrightarrow{CD'} \tag{19}$$

example 17 If $\overrightarrow{OR} = 5\underline{/20°} - 8\underline{/50°}$, express $\overrightarrow{OR}$ in polar notation.

Following Eqs. (17) to (19), we may write

$$\overrightarrow{OR} = 5\underline{/20°} + 8\underline{/230°}$$

Note that we have reversed the sense of the vector $-8\underline{/50°}$ and have changed the problem from a vector subtraction to a vector addition. The numerical solution is tabulated in Table 20·2.

table 20·2

Vector	*cosine*	*X projection* +	*X projection* −	*sine*	*Y projection* +	*Y projection* −
$5\underline{/20°}$	+0.940	4.70		0.342	1.71	
$8\underline{/230°}$	−0.643	—	5.144	−0.766	—	6.128
+X projection		4.70				
−X projection			5.144			
+Y projection					1.71	
−Y projection						6.128

$$\text{Total } X \text{ projection} = +4.70 - 5.144 = -0.444$$
$$\text{Total } Y \text{ projection} = +1.71 - 6.128 = -4.418$$
$$r_{OR} = \sqrt{(-0.444)^2 + (-4.418)^2} = 4.44$$
$$\tan \phi_{OR} = \frac{-4.418}{-0.444} = +9.95$$
$$\phi_{OR} = 264.3°$$
$$\overrightarrow{OR} = 4.44\underline{/264.3°}$$

EXERCISE 4

Use a slide rule or a four-place table of natural functions as directed by the instructor.

1. Find the X and Y projections of the vector difference obtained by subtracting the vector $\overrightarrow{OA}$ from the vector $\overrightarrow{OB}$. Also find the length and the reference angle of the vector difference.

	Vector	*X projection*	*Y projection*
(a)	$\overrightarrow{OA}$	+7	+5
	$\overrightarrow{OB}$	+2	+6
(b)	$\overrightarrow{OA}$	−3	−5
	$\overrightarrow{OB}$	+2	+8
(c)	$\overrightarrow{OA}$	+15	+20
	$\overrightarrow{OB}$	−20	+15
(d)	$\overrightarrow{OA}$	−20	−30
	$\overrightarrow{OB}$	−10	−10
(e)	$\overrightarrow{OA}$	−32	+42
	$\overrightarrow{OB}$	+26	−20

2. Perform the following vector operations, expressing the answer in polar notation.

(a) $30\underline{/45°} - 20\underline{/90°}$

(b) $20\underline{/36°} - 5\underline{/80°}$

(c) $15\underline{/160°} - 20\underline{/330°}$

(d) $90\underline{/220°} - 45\underline{/20°}$

(e) $25\underline{/110°} - 60\underline{/220°}$

(f) $20\underline{/45°} - 30\underline{/30°} + 10\underline{/225°}$

(g) $100\underline{/90°} + 200\underline{/180°} - 100\underline{/0°}$

(h) $-25\underline{/330°} + 40\underline{/160°} - 20\underline{/260°}$

(i) $15\underline{/60°} - 30\underline{/120°} + 50\underline{/330°}$

(j) $20\underline{/115°} - 15\underline{/250°} - 30\underline{/25°}$

20 · 7 Vector and scalar quantities

A *vector quantity* is a quantity whose pertinent characteristics can be represented by a vector.

Quantities which have no pertinent relation to direction and sense are called *scalar quantities.*

Examples of vector quantities are force, velocity, acceleration, voltage, current, and (more loosely) impedance.

Examples of scalar quantities are such quantities as arise in the process of simple enumeration. Other examples are volume, area, and prices.

EXERCISE 5

Which of the following quantities would you expect to be vector quantities, and which would you expect to be scalar quantities?

1. The path of an airplane in flight
2. The weight of an automobile
3. The stress in a member of a bridge truss
4. The area of a plot of land
5. A magnetic field
6. The salinity of sea water
7. The field strength of an antenna
8. The number of teeth on a gear

20·8 The product of a vector and a scalar quantity

The product of a scalar quantity U and a vector $\overrightarrow{OP}$ is, by definition, a vector whose magnitude is U times the magnitude $\overrightarrow{OP}$, whose direction is the same as the direction of $\overrightarrow{OP}$, and whose sense is either the same as or exactly opposite to the sense of $\overrightarrow{OP}$, according as U is positive or negative.

The quotient of a vector $\overrightarrow{OP}$ divided by a scalar quantity U is, by definition, a vector whose magnitude is $|OP|$ divided by U, whose direction is the same as the direction of $\overrightarrow{OP}$, and whose sense is either the same as or exactly opposite to the sense of $\overrightarrow{OP}$, according as U is positive or negative.

20·9 Velocity as a vector

The linear speed of a moving point is the straight-line distance over which the point moves per unit time, without regard to the sense of motion along that straight line. Velocity, on the other hand, is completely described only when speed, direction, and sense of motion are known. Velocity is a vector quantity; speed is a scalar quantity.

Suppose the propeller of an airplane is imparting a 200-mph north-

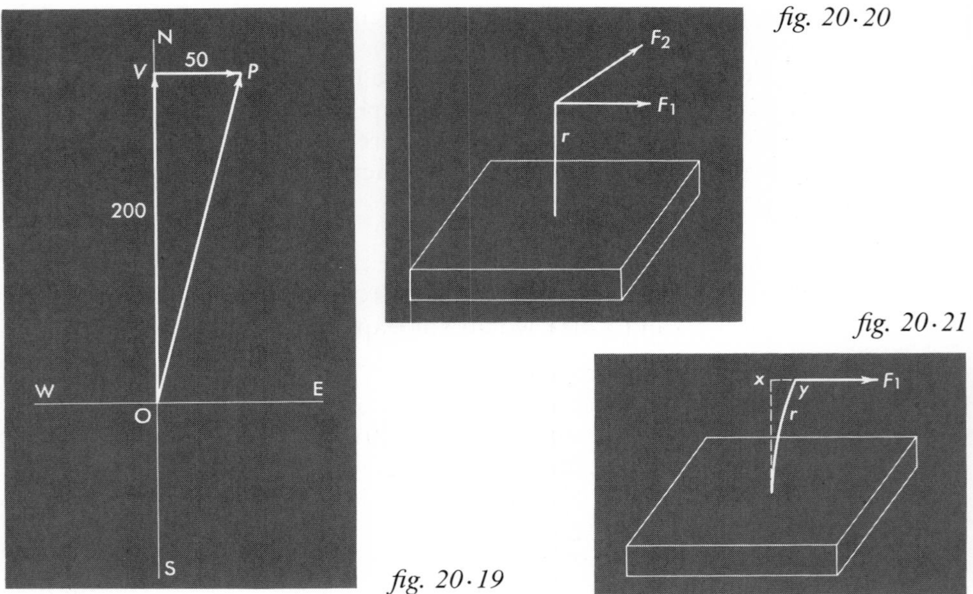

fig. 20·19

fig. 20·20

fig. 20·21

erly velocity to the plane while the plane is encountering a 50-mph cross wind blowing directly toward the east. Assuming that these velocities remain constant for 1 hr, at the end of 1 hr the plane will be 200 miles north and 50 miles east of the starting point.

A vector diagram of the distances will appear as in Fig. 20·19. The vector $\overrightarrow{OP}$ represents the course of the plane. The magnitude of $\overrightarrow{OP}$ represents the actual distance traveled in this hour.

The vectors $\overrightarrow{OV}$, $\overrightarrow{VP}$, and $\overrightarrow{OP}$ in Fig. 20·19 are distances. However, each of these vectors may be divided by the scalar quantity, time (in this case, 1 hr), so that a similar diagram in which the vectors represent velocities may be constructed. With this interpretation, Fig. 20·19 is identical in appearance with a corresponding velocity diagram.

20·10 Forces as vectors

When two forces act through a single point, as in Fig. 20·20, these forces are called *concurrent forces.*

In Fig. 20·20 the strings indicated as F_1 and F_2 will presently carry the forces F_1 and F_2, but we shall apply these forces one at a time. First let the elastic rod r be pulled a little by the force F_1; then the top of the rod will be displaced by a certain distance, say xy, as in Fig. 20·21. Now, while holding F_1 constant both as regards magnitude and direction, let us apply force F_2, as shown in Fig. 20·22. Now the rod r will be deflected by the further amount yz.

The top of the rod could have been made to occupy the position z by the action of a single force F_3 of some as yet undetermined magnitude acting along the line xz. This force F_3 is called the resultant of the forces F_1 and F_2.

If the deflections do not exceed the elastic limit of the rod, then it can be proved experimentally that the forces are proportional to the deflections they cause.

In Fig. 20·23 the vectors $\overrightarrow{xy}$, $\overrightarrow{yz}$, and $\overrightarrow{xz}$ are deflections, but if we divide all three vector deflections by the spring constant, which is a scalar, we arrive at the vector diagram shown in Fig. 20·24, in which the vectors represent forces.

While the amounts of the deflections $\overrightarrow{xy}$, $\overrightarrow{yz}$, and $\overrightarrow{xz}$ have not been stated, the student may be thinking of deflections in the order of an inch or two or perhaps more. However, the discussion would be just as valid if the deflections were a few thousandths of an inch or, for that matter, even less.

Therefore, in the vector solutions of force problems we ordinarily pay no attention to deflections, but instead deal directly with forces.

The process just described illustrates vector addition, or a problem in the *composition of forces*. In vector nomenclature we may write

$$\overrightarrow{F_1} + \overrightarrow{F_2} = \overrightarrow{F_3} \tag{20}$$

Problems dealing with concurrent forces can be solved either graphically or by computation. When solved graphically, the lengths of the

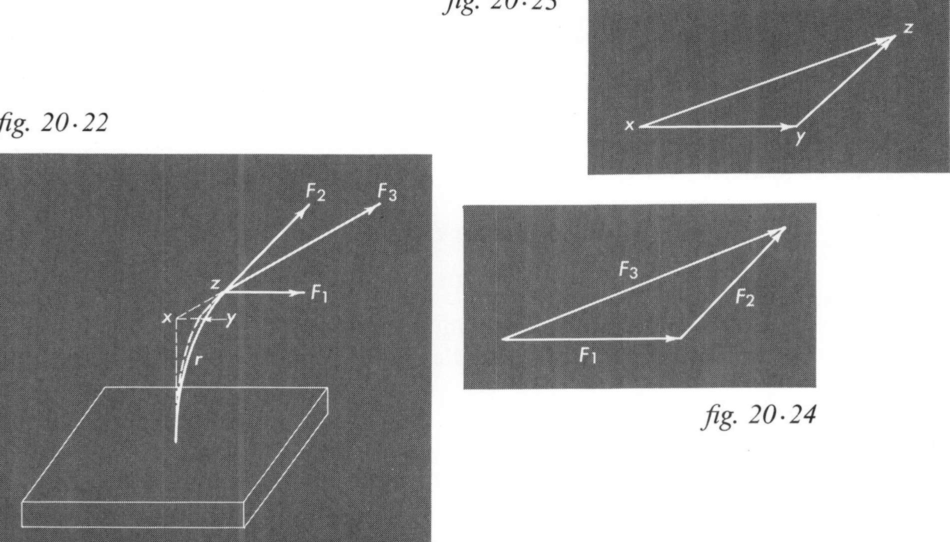

fig. 20·23

fig. 20·22

fig. 20·24

vectors $\overrightarrow{xy}$, $\overrightarrow{yz}$, and $\overrightarrow{xz}$ are plotted proportional to the magnitudes of F_1, F_2, and F_3, respectively. The angles on the scale drawing are the same as the angles between the respective forces.

The force F_3 in Fig. 20·22 is called the *resultant* of forces F_1 and F_2. A force which has the same magnitude and direction as F_3 but which is opposite in sense is called the *equilibrant* of F_1 and F_2.

20·11 Resolution of forces

In Fig. 20·25 it is given that $|F_3| = 10$ lb and its line of action makes an angle of 30° with the line of action of $\overrightarrow{F_1}$. Also, it is given that $\overrightarrow{F_1}$ and $\overrightarrow{F_2}$ are at right angles and that $\overrightarrow{F_3}$ is the resultant of $\overrightarrow{F_1}$ and $\overrightarrow{F_2}$. The problem is to find the magnitudes of $\overrightarrow{F_1}$ and $\overrightarrow{F_2}$.

Graphically, this can be done by drawing the figure to scale, as in Fig. 20·25. Now $|F_1|$ and $|F_2|$ can be measured. By calculation,

$$|\overrightarrow{F_2}| = 10 \sin 30° = 10 \times 0.5 = 5$$
$$\overrightarrow{F_2} = 5\underline{/90°}$$
$$|\overrightarrow{F_1}| = 10 \cos 30° = 10 \times 0.866 = 8.66$$
$$\overrightarrow{F_1} = 8.66\underline{/0°}$$

This process is called the *resolution* of the force $\overrightarrow{F_3}$ into two rectangular *components* $\overrightarrow{F_1}$ and $\overrightarrow{F_2}$.

If it is assumed that $\overrightarrow{F_2}$ is vertical and $\overrightarrow{F_1}$ is horizontal, then $\overrightarrow{F_2}$ is called the vertical component of $\overrightarrow{F_3}$, and $\overrightarrow{F_1}$ is called the horizontal component of $\overrightarrow{F_3}$.

20·12 Resolution of general vectors

Having been given the vector $\overrightarrow{OP}$ in Fig. 20·26, we may under certain conditions find it convenient to *resolve* the vector $\overrightarrow{OP}$ into its rectangular *components;* i.e., to find two vectors $\overrightarrow{Ox}$ and $\overrightarrow{Oy}$ which are mutually perpendicular and lie on the axes, such that

$$\overrightarrow{Oy} + \overrightarrow{Ox} = \overrightarrow{OP} \qquad (21)$$

Here the sum of the vectors $\overrightarrow{Oy}$ and $\overrightarrow{Ox}$ is identical with the single vector $\overrightarrow{OP}$.

In general, we can resolve any vector into its mutually perpendicu-

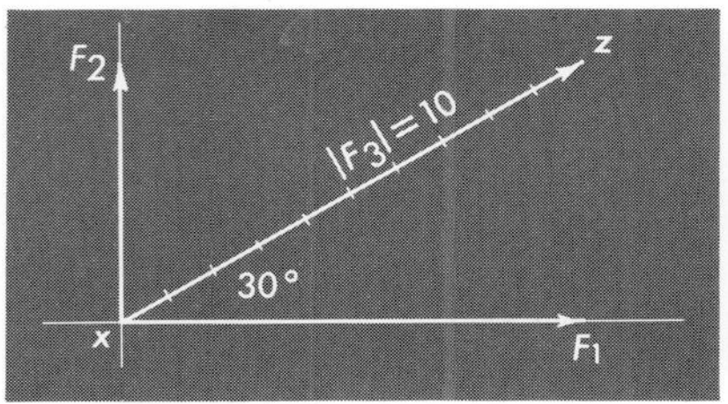

fig. 20·25

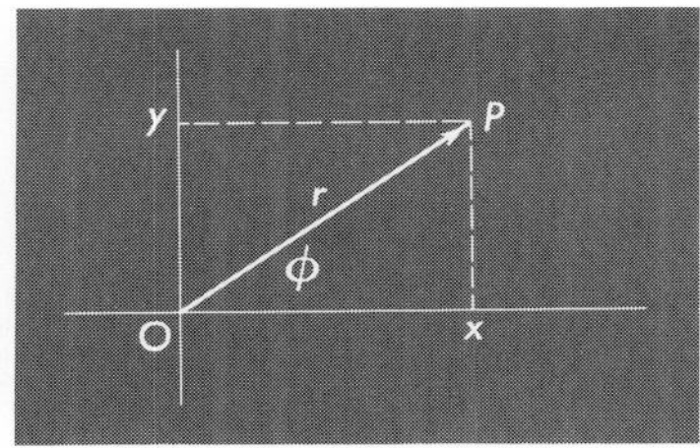

fig. 20·26

lar components if we know the direction and sense of the vector relative to the direction of the components. By reference to Fig. 20·26,

$$|\overrightarrow{OP}| = r = \sqrt{|Ox|^2 + |Oy|^2}$$
$$|\overrightarrow{Ox}| = r \cos \phi$$
$$|\overrightarrow{Oy}| = r \sin \phi$$

example 18 Find the resultant and the equilibrant of a force of 3 lb and a force of 4 lb acting at right angles.

Draw the vector forces to scale (see Fig. 20·27). The resultant appears to be 5 lb, as determined by measurement.

By calculation, since the angle $xyz = 90°$,

$$|xz| = \sqrt{3^2 + 4^2} = 5$$
$$\tan \phi = 3/4 = 0.75000$$
$$\phi = 36°52'$$

The resultant is, then, the vector force $5\underline{/36°52'}$, and the equilibrant is the vector force $-5\underline{/36°52'}$.

example 19 Two forces act on a single point. The angle between them is 60°, and the forces are 20 and 30 lb, respectively. Find the magnitude of the resultant and the equilibrant and the angles they make with the 30-lb force.

The problem can be diagrammed as shown in Fig. 20·28. Following Eq. (35), page 464,

$$|F| = \sqrt{30^2 + 20^2 + 2 \times 20 \times 30 \cos 60°} = 43.6 \text{ lb}$$

$$\sin \phi = \frac{20 \times \sin 60°}{43.6} = \frac{20 \times 0.866}{43.6} = 0.397$$

$$\phi = 23.4°$$

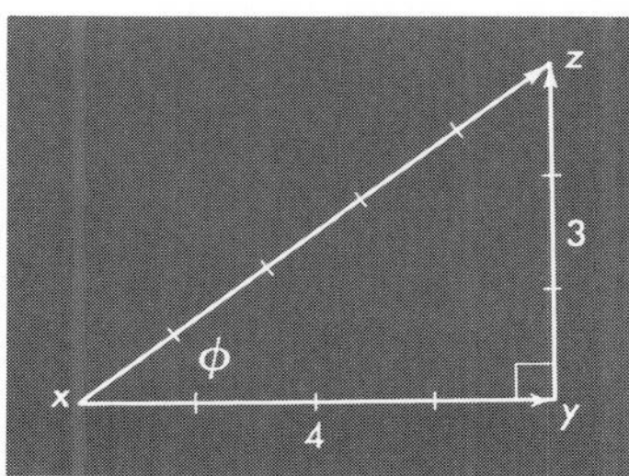

fig. 20·27

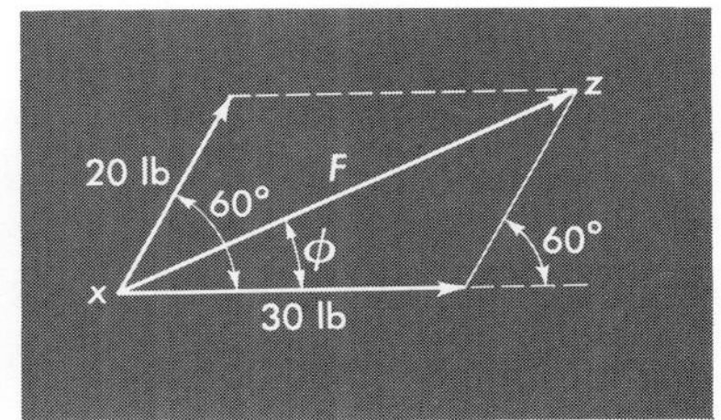

fig. 20·28

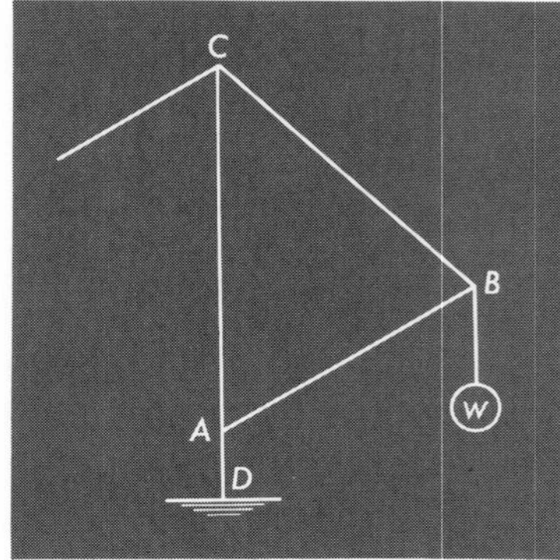

fig. 20·29

The resultant is a force whose magnitude is 43.6 lb in the direction *xz*. The equilibrant is a force whose magnitude is also 43.6 lb, but which acts in the direction *zx*.

EXERCISE 6

1. Find the resultant of two concurrent forces, one of 253 and the other of 578 lb, acting at an angle of 18°27′20″ with each other.
2. Two forces acting at right angles with each other have a resultant of 350 lb, and one of the forces is 270 lb. Find the other force and the angle it makes with the resultant.
3. Two forces, of 70 and 85 lb, have a resultant of 125 lb. Find the angle which each of the forces makes with the resultant.
4. Find the horizontal and vertical components of a force of 5,680 lb acting at an angle of 23°46′25″ with the horizontal.
5. A horse pulls a canalboat with a force of 425 lb on the end of a towline which makes an angle of 6° with the side of the canal. Find the force tending to urge the boat toward shore and the effective force which pulls the boat forward.
6. Two forces, of 3,600 and 5,300 lb, have a resultant of 7,500 lb. Find the angle which the resultant makes with each force.
7. A man pushes a floating plank with a force of 25 lb on the end of a pole which makes an angle of 53° with the surface of the water. What force tends to submerge the plank, and what to move it horizontally?
8. Three forces, of 125, 150, and 175 lb, are concurrent and in equilibrium. The first pulls toward the north, and the second in a general direction south of east. Find the direction of the third force.
9. In the derrick shown in Fig. 20·29 the mast *DC* is 45 ft high, the boom *AB* is 42 ft long, and pin *A* is 2 ft above *D*. *W* is a weight of 1,000 lb, and angle *CAB* is 44°. Find the length of the line *BC* and the force in *BC* and in *AB*.

21 trigonometric formulas, identities, and equations

In this chapter we shall derive some of the more fundamental relations between the trigonometric functions.

21·1 Some simple trigonometric relations

As a first step let us review the definitions of the trigonometric functions already familiar to the student.

We have already discussed the following definitions (see Fig. 21·1):

$$\sin \phi = \frac{y}{r} \tag{1}$$

$$\cos \phi = \frac{x}{r} \tag{2}$$

$$\tan \phi = \frac{y}{x} \tag{3}$$

$$\cot \phi = \frac{x}{y} \tag{4}$$

$$\sec \phi = \frac{r}{x} \tag{5}$$

$$\operatorname{cosec} \phi = \frac{r}{y} \tag{6}$$

A comparison between Eqs. (1) and (6) will show that

$$\sin \phi = \frac{1}{\operatorname{cosec} \phi} \qquad \operatorname{cosec} \phi = \frac{1}{\sin \phi} \tag{7}$$

A similar comparison between Eqs. (2) and (5) will show that

$$\cos \phi = \frac{1}{\sec \phi} \qquad \sec \phi = \frac{1}{\cos \phi} \tag{8}$$

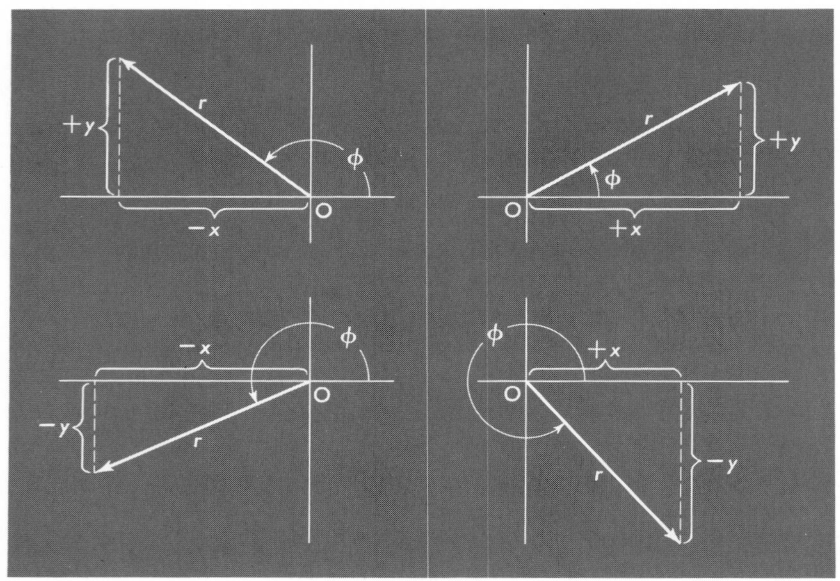

fig. 21·1

Also, a comparison between Eqs. (3) and (4) will show that

$$\tan\phi = \frac{1}{\cot\phi} \qquad \cot\phi = \frac{1}{\tan\phi} \tag{9}$$

Since $\sin\phi = y/r$ and $\cos\phi = x/r$, it follows that

$$\frac{\sin\phi}{\cos\phi} = \frac{y/r}{x/r} = \frac{y}{x} = \tan\phi \qquad \cos\phi \neq 0 \tag{10}$$

Applying Eq. (9) to Eq. (10),

$$\frac{\cos\phi}{\sin\phi} = \cot\phi \qquad \sin\phi \neq 0 \tag{11}$$

Referring to Fig. 21·1 and remembering the Pythagorean theorem,

$$r^2 = x^2 + y^2 \tag{12}$$

Dividing both sides of Eq. (12) by r^2, x^2, and y^2 in turn gives

$$\frac{r^2}{r^2} = \frac{x^2}{r^2} + \frac{y^2}{r^2} \tag{13}$$

$$1 = \cos^2\phi + \sin^2\phi \tag{14}$$

$$\frac{r^2}{x^2} = \frac{x^2}{x^2} + \frac{y^2}{x^2} \tag{15}$$

$$\sec^2\phi = 1 + \tan^2\phi \tag{16}$$

$$\frac{r^2}{y^2} = \frac{x^2}{y^2} + \frac{y^2}{y^2} \tag{17}$$

$$\operatorname{cosec}^2\phi = \cot^2\phi + 1 \tag{18}$$

Observe carefully that the symbol $\sin^2 \phi$ means "the square of the sine of the angle ϕ." It does not mean "the sine of the square of the angle ϕ." For example, $\sin 30° = 0.5$ and $\sin^2 30° = 0.25$. On the other hand, $\sin (30°)^2 = \sin 900° = \sin 180° = 0$. The expressions $(\sin \phi)^2$ and $\sin^2 \phi$ are identical.

Among other values of the above relations is their use in simplifying otherwise complicated expressions. Broadly speaking, simplification is the process of transforming a given expression so that the arithmetical work involved in evaluating the expression is as simple as possible.

example 1 By reference to appropriate trigonometric relationships given above, simplify the expression

$$\frac{1 - \operatorname{cosec} \phi + \cot^2 \phi}{1 - \sin \phi} \qquad \sin \phi \neq +1$$

Note that when $\phi = 90°$ the denominator becomes zero and the expression has no meaning. Values of ϕ which make the expression meaningless are specifically excluded.

Following Eq. (18), we may write

$$\frac{1 - \operatorname{cosec} \phi + \cot^2 \phi}{1 - \sin \phi} = \frac{\cot^2 \phi + 1 - \operatorname{cosec} \phi}{1 - \sin \phi} = \frac{\operatorname{cosec}^2 \phi - \operatorname{cosec} \phi}{1 - \sin \phi}$$

By factoring,

$$\frac{\operatorname{cosec} \phi \,(\operatorname{cosec} \phi - 1)}{1 - \sin \phi}$$

Following Eq. (7), we may write

$$\frac{\operatorname{cosec} \phi \left(\dfrac{1}{\sin \phi} - 1\right)}{1 - \sin \phi} = \frac{\operatorname{cosec} \phi \left(\dfrac{1 - \sin \phi}{\sin \phi}\right)}{1 - \sin \phi}$$

or

$$\frac{(\operatorname{cosec} \phi/\sin \phi)(1 - \sin \phi)}{1 - \sin \phi} = \frac{\operatorname{cosec} \phi}{\sin \phi} = \operatorname{cosec}^2 \phi$$

where $\sin \phi \neq +1$.

One of the best ways to check a simplification is to substitute the numerical value of any convenient angle, both in the original expression as it is written and in the simplification. We may then compare the numerical equivalence of the original expression with the numerical value of the simplification.

Let us check the simplification in Example 1 by substituting some convenient numerical value for ϕ in the original expression. For convenience let us choose a value of 30° for ϕ. Any other angle would do as well.

Remember that

$$\csc 30° = 2$$
$$\cot 30° = \sqrt{3}/1$$
$$\sin 30° = 1/2$$

Substituting in the original expression, we obtain

$$\frac{1 - 2 + 3}{1 - (1/2)} = \frac{2}{1/2} = 4$$

Since cosec 30° = 2, it follows that cosec² 30° = 4, and the simplification checks. The student should realize that it is possible that such a simplification may check and still be in error. However it is not likely.

EXERCISE 1

The work the student does in this exercise should, as in all other mathematical work, be arranged in a logical sequence of steps. Each step should clearly show that it may be justified in terms of the preceding steps. The student must provide a reason for each step.

By reference to appropriate trigonometric relations given in Eqs. (1) through (18), simplify the expressions below. If it is necessary to exclude certain values of the angle concerned in order to make the expression meaningful, tell what values of the angle must be excluded.

1. $\sin x (\sin x - 1) + \cos^2 x - 1$
2. $(1 - \sin A)(1 + \sin A) - \cos^2 A$
3. $3 \sin^2 B + 3 \cos^2 B - 2$
4. $\sin^2 A - 2 + \cos^2 A$
5. $\sin x + \cos^2 x - \sin x (1 - \sin x)$
6. $\cos x (\cos x - 1) + \sin^2 x + \cos x - 1$
7. $\dfrac{1 - \sin^2 A}{\cos A}$
8. $\dfrac{\cos \theta - \cos^3 \theta}{\sin^2 \theta}$
9. $\dfrac{\sin^2 A}{1 + \cos A}$
10. $\dfrac{1 - \cos^2 A}{\sin A}$
11. $\dfrac{\cos^2 A}{1 - \sin^2 A}$
12. $2 \sin x \cos x + (\sin x - \cos x)^2$
13. $\cos^2 x + 1 - \sin^2 x$
14. $\sin^2 \phi + (\cos \phi + 1)^2 - 2$
15. $\sin^3 x + \cos^2 x \sin x$
16. $1 - \sin^2 x + (1 - \sin x)^2 + 2 \sin x$
17. $\dfrac{(\cos M + \sin M)^2 - 2 \sin M \cos M}{\sin M}$
18. $\dfrac{\cos x \tan^2 x}{\sin^2 x}$
19. $\dfrac{\sin x \cos x \tan x}{1 + \cos x} - 1$
20. $\dfrac{1}{\sin^2 \theta} - \dfrac{\cos \theta}{\sin \theta \tan \theta}$
21. $\cos^3 x (\tan^2 x + 1)$
22. $\tan P \sin P \cos P + \cos^2 P$
23. $\dfrac{\sin x \cos x}{(1 - \sin x) \tan x}$

24. $\dfrac{\tan x\,(1 - \sin^2 x)}{\sin x \cos x}$

25. $\tan K \sin K + \cos K$

26. $(1 + \sin x)\left(\dfrac{1}{\cos x} - \tan x\right)$

27. $\dfrac{\tan^2 x + 1}{\sec^3 x}$

28. $\dfrac{2 \sin^2 M}{\sin M \cos M} - \tan M$

29. $\left(\dfrac{\sin x - \sin^3 x}{\sin x \cos x + \cos^2 x}\right)\left(\dfrac{1 + 2 \sin x \cos x}{\cos x \sin x}\right)$

30. $\dfrac{\sin x}{1 - \sin x} + \dfrac{\cos^2 x}{\sin x + 1} - \dfrac{1 + \sin x}{\cos^2 x}$

31. $\left(\dfrac{\sin x + \sin x \cos x}{1 - \sin x}\right)\left(\dfrac{\cos^2 x}{1 + \cos x} \csc x\right)$

32. $\dfrac{\sin x}{1 + \cos x} + \dfrac{\cos x}{\sin x}$

33. $\left(\dfrac{\sin^2 x + \sin x \cos x}{\cos x}\right)\left(\dfrac{1 - \sin^2 x}{\cos x - \sin x}\right)$

34. $\dfrac{\sin^2 x}{\cos x} + \cos x$

35. $\dfrac{\cos^2 x}{\sin^2 x - \sin^2 x \cos x} \div \dfrac{1 + \sin x}{(1 - \cos x)^2(1 + \cos x)}$

36. $\dfrac{\sin A + \cos A}{\sin A} - \dfrac{\cos A - \sin A}{\cos A}$

37. $\left(\dfrac{\cos x}{\sin x - 1} + \dfrac{\sin x}{\cos x}\right) \div \dfrac{1}{\sin x - 1}$

38. $\dfrac{\sin x + \sin x \cos x}{\sin x - \sin^2 x} \div \dfrac{1 + \cos x}{\cos^2 x}$

39. $\left(\dfrac{\sin x}{\cos x} + \dfrac{\cos x}{\sin x}\right)(1 - \sin^2 x)$

40. $\left(\dfrac{\sin x - \cos^2 x}{\sin x} - \sin x\right) \div \dfrac{\cos^2 x}{\sin x}$

41. $\dfrac{\sin x\,(\sin x - \cos x \tan x \cot^2 x)}{\cos x\,(\tan x + 1)} + \cos x$

42. $\dfrac{1 - 2\cos^2 x}{\sin x \cos x} + \cot x$

43. $\cot x \cos x + \sin x$

44. $(\cot^2 x + 1) \sin x$

45. $\dfrac{\sin x}{\cot x\,(1 - \cos x)} - 1$

46. $(\tan x + \cot x)^2 - (1 + \tan^2 x)$

47. $\cot x \cos x \sin x + \sin^2 x$

48. $\sin x \cos x\,(\tan x - \cot x) + 2 \cos^2 x$

49. $\dfrac{\cot A}{\sec A \sin A}$

50. $\dfrac{1}{\cot^2 x\,(\sec x - 1)}$

51. $\dfrac{\sec\theta}{\sin\theta\cot\theta}$

52. $\dfrac{\sec M - \cos M}{\sin M}$

53. $\left(\dfrac{\sec\phi}{\tan\phi} - \sin\phi\right)\sec\phi$

54. $\dfrac{(1 - \cos x)(1 + \cos x)\sec x}{\tan x}$

55. $\dfrac{\cot x - (\csc^2 x - 1)\sin x + \cos x\cot x}{\cot x}$

56. $\dfrac{\csc^2 x - \cot^2 x\csc^2 x}{\cot^2 x} + \csc^2 x$

57. $\left[\dfrac{\csc x\,(1 + \tan^2 x)}{\sec x}\csc x - \sec x\right]\sin x$

21 · 2 Trigonometric identities

A trigonometric equation which is true for all values of the angles involved for which both members of the equation are defined is called a trigonometric identity. Any value of an angle involved which leads to an indicated division by zero is not a permissible value of that angle.

In the course of analyzing practical problems mathematically, we sometimes encounter a trigonometric equation that we suspect—without being certain—may be an identity. In such cases it is important to verify the equation and determine whether or not it is an identity.

For example, suppose that in the process of developing a certain formula we arrive at the mathematical statement

$$\sin^2\phi = 1 - \cot^2\phi\sin^2\phi \qquad (19)$$

and we feel that while this equation is probably true, it would be advisable to prove it.

Two somewhat different methods of attack are illustrated in the examples below. Example 3 is, perhaps, somewhat more rigorous, but the authors have no objection to the method illustrated in Example 2. In any case, however, the identity must be proved in the precise form in which it appears. No terms may be shifted across the equal sign.

example 2 Prove that

$$\sin^2\phi = 1 - \cot^2\phi\sin^2\phi \qquad (20)$$

$$\cot\phi = \frac{x}{y} \qquad (21)$$

$$\sin\phi = \frac{y}{r} \qquad (22)$$

Substituting Eq. (21) in Eq. (20),

$$\sin^2 \phi = 1 - \frac{x^2}{y^2} \sin^2 \phi \tag{23}$$

Substituting Eq. (22) in Eq. (23),

$$\sin^2 \phi = 1 - \frac{x^2}{y^2}\frac{y^2}{r^2} = 1 - \frac{x^2}{r^2} = 1 - \cos^2 \phi \tag{24}$$

The expression $1 - \cos^2 \phi$ is recognized from Eq. (14) to be equal to $\sin^2 \phi$. Therefore

$$\sin^2 \phi = \sin^2 \phi \tag{25}$$

and the identity has been proved.

example 3 Prove the identity

$$\sin^2 \phi = 1 - \cot^2 \phi \sin^2 \phi \tag{26}$$

From Eq. (11) it appears that

$$\cot^2 \phi = \frac{\cos^2 \phi}{\sin^2 \phi} \tag{27}$$

Substituting Eq. (27) in Eq. (26),

$$\sin^2 \phi = 1 - \frac{\cos^2 \phi}{\sin^2 \phi} \sin^2 \phi = 1 - \cos^2 \phi \tag{28}$$

But from Eq. (14),

$$1 - \cos^2 \phi = \sin^2 \phi \tag{29}$$

Therefore,

$$\sin^2 \phi = \sin^2 \phi \tag{30}$$

and the identity has been proved.

EXERCISE 2

Verify the following assumed identities. It is left to the student to decide which of the assumed identities are true and which are false.

1. $1 - \sin^2 A - \cos^2 A = 0$
2. $2 \cos^2 x + 2 (\sin^2 x - 2) = -2$
3. $\sin^2 B + 2 \cos^2 B - 1 = \cos^2 B$
4. $\cos^2 x - (1 - \sin x)(1 + \sin x) = \sin x$
5. $\sin \theta (1 - \sin \theta) - \cos^2 \theta + 1 = \sin \theta$
6. $\sin^2 y + (\cos y + 1)(\sin y + \cos y) - 1 - \sin y - \cos y = \sin y (\cos y - 1)$
7. $\sin^2 M - 2 (\cos M - 1)(\cos M + 1) - 3 \sin^2 M = -4 \sin^2 M$
8. $\dfrac{\sin^3 A}{1 - \cos^2 A} = \sin A$
9. $\dfrac{\sin^2 A}{1 - \cos A} = 1 + \cos A$
10. $\dfrac{\cos^2 M - 1}{\sin M} = \cos M$
11. $\dfrac{\cos^2 A}{1 - \sin A} = 1 + \sin A$

12. $\dfrac{\cos^2 x}{\sin x - \sin^2 x} = \csc x + 1$

13. $(\sin B + \cos B)^2 - 2 \sin B \cos B = 1$

14. $1 - (\cos y - \sin y)^2 = \cos y \sin y$

15. $(\sin x + 1)^2 + \cos^2 x - 2 = 2 \sin x$

16. $\dfrac{\tan x\,(1 - \cos x)}{\sin x} + 1 = \cos x$

17. $\dfrac{\cos B}{\tan B} + \sin B = \csc B$

18. $\dfrac{\cos^2 x \tan x}{\sin x} = \cos x$

19. $\sin x \left(\dfrac{1}{\tan x} + \tan x\right) = \sec x$

20. $\dfrac{1 - \cos^2 x}{\cos x \sin x} = \tan x$

21. $\left(\dfrac{1}{\sin^2 x} - \dfrac{1}{\sin x \tan x}\right)(1 + \cos x) = 1$

22. $\dfrac{\cos^3 x}{\sin^3 x + \sin^4 x} \div \dfrac{1 - \sin x}{\sin^3 x} = \csc x$

23. $\dfrac{\cos^2 x}{\sin^2 x}\,\dfrac{(1 - \cos^2 x)}{(\sin^2 x - \sin x)} = 1 - \csc x$

24. $\cot A \sin A = \cos A$

25. $\cot x \dfrac{1}{\tan x} = 2 \cot x$

26. $\left(\dfrac{1}{\cos^2 x} - 1\right) \cot x = \tan x$

27. $\dfrac{\sin^2 x - \cos^2 x}{\sin^2 x\,(1 + \cot x)} = 1 - \cot x$

28. $\dfrac{\cot^2 x + 1}{\cot x} - \cot x = \tan x$

29. $\dfrac{\sin x\,(\cot^2 x - 1)}{\sin x - \cos x} = \cot x - 1$

30. $\dfrac{\cot x + \cos x}{\cos x} - \dfrac{1}{\sin x} = 1$

31. $\sin A \sec A \tan A = \tan^2 A$

32. $\dfrac{\tan^2 A}{\sec A + 1} = \sec A - 1$

33. $\sec A \cot A = \csc A$

34. $\dfrac{\tan A \csc A}{\sec A} = 1$

35. $\dfrac{\cos A \tan^2 A}{\sec A \sin A} = \sin A \cos A$

36. $\dfrac{\cos^2 \theta \tan \theta}{\sin \theta} + \dfrac{\sin^3 \theta \cot \theta}{\cos^2 \theta} = \sec \theta$

37. $\dfrac{2 \tan A\,(\tan A - \cot A)}{\tan^2 A - 1} = 2$

38. $\dfrac{\cot x \sin^3 x + \cos x\,(1 + \tan^2 x)}{\tan x \cos^2 x \sin x} - 1 = \cos^2 x \sin^2 x$

39. $\csc x\,(\sin^3 x + \sin x \cos^2 x + \sec x - \cos x) = 1 - \sec x$

40. $\dfrac{(\csc^2 x - 1) \sin^2 x + \sin x \cos^2 x}{\cos^2 x} = 1 + \sin x$

41. $\left(\dfrac{\sec^2 x}{2 + \tan^2 x}\right)(1 + \cos^2 x) = 1$

42. $\dfrac{\cos x \cot x - \tan x}{\csc x} + \dfrac{\sin^2 x}{\cos x} = \cos^2 x$

43. $\sec^2 x \csc^2 x = \sec^2 x + \csc^2 x$

44. $2 \csc x = \dfrac{\sin x}{1 + \cos x} + \dfrac{1 + \cos x}{\sin x}$

21 · 3 Standard trigonometric formulas

Before proceeding to the verification of more complicated trigonometric identities and to the solution of trigonometric equations, the student should become familiar with the standard formulas derived in the following sections.

The important formulas are designated by boldface type for the equation numbers.

21 · 4 The cosine of the difference of two angles

A common mistake made by students is to assume (quite erroneously) that the sine of the sum of two angles is equal to the sum of their sines. Let us put this erroneous notion to a numerical test.

We know that

$$\sin 45° = \frac{\sqrt{2}}{2}$$

and that

$$\sin 30° = \tfrac{1}{2}$$

Then

$$\sin 45° + \sin 30° = \frac{\sqrt{2} + 1}{2} = \frac{2.414}{2} = 1.207$$

However, the sine of $(45° + 30°) = \sin 75°$.

From a five-place table of trigonometric functions we find that

$$\sin 75° = 0.96593$$

Therefore we conclude that

$$\sin 45° + \sin 30° \neq \sin (45° + 30°)$$

In general,

$$\sin \phi + \sin \theta \neq \sin (\phi + \theta)$$

In the same way we can show that none of the trigonometric functions is additive in this way. That is,

$$\cos \phi + \cos \theta \neq \cos (\phi + \theta)$$
$$\cos \phi - \cos \theta \neq \cos (\phi - \theta)$$

and so on. Thus we need special formulas if we wish to find $\sin (\phi \pm \theta)$, $\cos (\phi \pm \theta)$, $\tan (\phi \pm \theta)$, etc.

We will find it convenient to first develop a formula for $\cos (\theta - \phi)$.

As we proceed with this and subsequent developments in this chapter, we do not restrict the angles involved to any particular quadrant. The relations which we shall develop hold for any angles.

Figure 21·2 shows a circle of unit radius drawn with its center at the origin of a rectangular coordinate system.

From Sec. 17·7 we see that the coordinates of point P are $(\cos \phi, \sin \phi)$ and that the coordinates of point Q are $(\cos \theta, \sin \theta)$.

Therefore from the distance formula [Eq. (12), page 124] we may write

$$d = \sqrt{(\cos \theta - \cos \phi)^2 + (\sin \theta - \sin \phi)^2} \tag{31}$$

By squaring both members of Eq. (31) we obtain

$$d^2 = (\cos \theta - \cos \phi)^2 + (\sin \theta - \sin \phi)^2$$

or

$$d^2 = \cos^2 \theta - 2 \cos \theta \cos \phi + \cos^2 \phi + \sin^2 \theta - 2 \sin \theta \sin \phi + \sin^2 \phi$$

or since $\cos^2 \phi + \sin^2 \phi = 1 = \cos^2 \theta + \sin^2 \theta$, we may write

$$d^2 = 2 - 2 \cos \phi \cos \theta - 2 \sin \phi \sin \theta \tag{32}$$

But, following the cosine law (see Sec. 18·4) applied to Fig. 21·2,

$$d^2 = 1^2 + 1^2 - 2 \cos (\theta - \phi) \tag{33}$$

Thus by solving Eqs. (32) and (33) simultaneously, we obtain

$$2 - 2 \cos (\theta - \phi) = 2 - 2 \cos \phi \cos \theta - 2 \sin \phi \sin \theta$$

or

$$\cos (\theta - \phi) = \cos \theta \cos \phi + \sin \theta \sin \phi \tag{34}$$

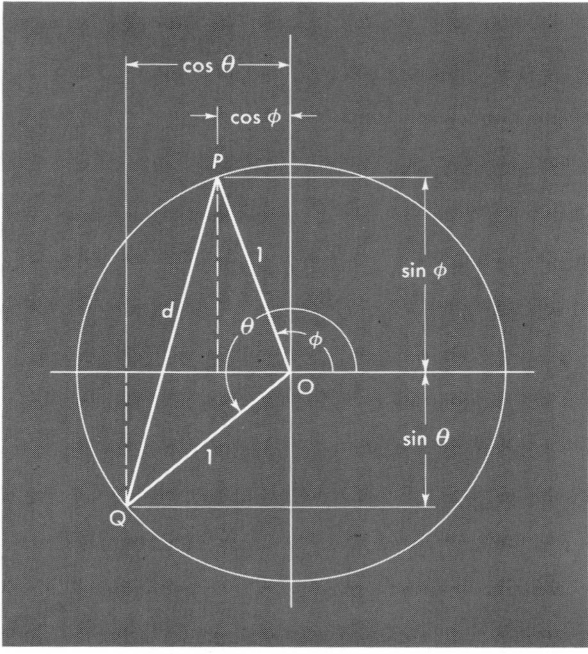

fig. 21·2

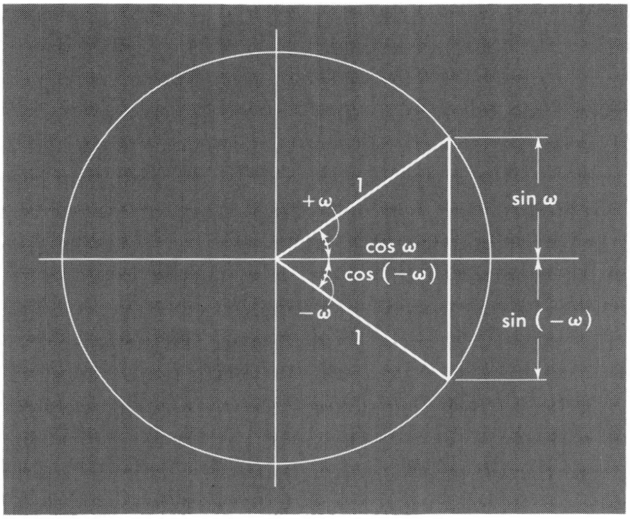

fig. 21·3

21·5 Some additional formulas

From Fig. 21·3 it seems intuitively evident that

$$\cos \omega = \cos(-\omega) \tag{35}$$

and that

$$-\sin \omega = \sin(-\omega) \tag{36}$$

However, we shall derive the above equations more formally.

If in Eq. (34) we let $\theta = 0$ and let $\phi = \omega$, we obtain

$$\cos(0 - \omega) = \cos 0^\circ \cos \omega + \sin 0^\circ \sin \omega$$

or since $\cos 0^\circ = 1$ and $\sin 0^\circ = 0$, we may write

$$\cos(-\omega) = \cos \omega \tag{37}$$

If in Eq. (34) we let $\theta = 90^\circ$ and let $\phi = -\omega$, we obtain

$$\cos[90^\circ - (-\omega)] = \cos 90^\circ \cos(-\omega) + \sin 90^\circ \sin(-\omega)$$

but since $\cos 90^\circ = 0$ and $\sin 90^\circ = 1$, we may write

$$\cos[90^\circ - (-\omega)] = \sin(-\omega)$$

or

$$\cos(90^\circ + \omega) = \sin(-\omega) \tag{38}$$

If in Eq. (34) we let $\theta = -90^\circ$ and let $\phi = \omega$, we obtain

$$\cos[(-90^\circ) - \omega] = \cos(-90^\circ) \cos \omega + \sin(-90^\circ) \sin \omega$$

but since $\cos(-90^\circ) = 0$ and $\sin(-90^\circ) = -1$, we may write

$$\cos[(-90^\circ) - \omega] = -\sin \omega$$

or

$$\cos[-(90^\circ + \omega)] = -\sin \omega \tag{39}$$

But, from Eq. (37) applied to Eqs. (38) and (39), we may write

$$\sin(-\omega) = -\sin\omega \tag{40}$$

If in Eq. (34) we let $\theta = 90°$ and let $\phi = \omega$, we obtain

$$\cos(90° - \omega) = \cos 90° \cos\omega + \sin 90° \sin\omega$$

but since $\cos 90° = 0$ and $\sin 90° = 1$, we may write

$$\cos(90° - \omega) = \sin\omega \tag{41}$$

If in Eq. (41) we replace ω by $(90° - \omega)$, we obtain

$$\cos[90° - (90° - \omega)] = \sin(90° - \omega)$$

or

$$\cos\omega = \sin(90° - \omega) \tag{42}$$

21·6 Functions of the sum of two angles

sin $(\phi + \theta)$

From Eq. (41) if we let $\omega = \phi + \theta$, we obtain

$$\begin{aligned}\sin(\phi + \theta) &= \cos[90° - (\phi + \theta)] = \cos[(90° - \phi) - \theta] \\ &= \cos(90° - \phi)\cos\theta + \sin(90° - \phi)\sin\theta\end{aligned}$$

and from Eqs. (41) and (42) we obtain

$$\sin(\phi + \theta) = \sin\phi\cos\theta + \cos\phi\sin\theta \tag{43}$$

cos $(\phi + \theta)$

If in Eq. (34) we replace θ by $-\theta$, we obtain

$$\cos(-\theta-\phi) = \cos\phi\cos(-\theta) + \sin\phi\sin(-\theta)$$

But from Eqs. (37) and (40) we may write

$$\cos(\phi + \theta) = \cos\phi\cos\theta - \sin\phi\sin\theta \tag{44}$$

tan $(\phi + \theta)$

Following Eq. (10),

$$\tan(\phi + \theta) = \frac{\sin(\phi + \theta)}{\cos(\phi + \theta)}$$

Substituting Eqs. (43) and (44) in the above equation,

$$\tan(\phi + \theta) = \frac{\sin\phi\cos\theta + \cos\phi\sin\theta}{\cos\phi\cos\theta - \sin\phi\sin\theta}$$

Dividing numerator and denominator by $\cos\phi\cos\theta$,

$$\tan(\phi+\theta) = \frac{\sin\phi/\cos\phi + \sin\theta/\cos\theta}{1 - (\sin\phi/\cos\phi)(\sin\theta/\cos\theta)}$$

$$\tan(\phi+\theta) = \frac{\tan\phi + \tan\theta}{1 - \tan\phi\tan\theta} \qquad \textbf{(45)}$$

cot $(\phi + \theta)$

Since the cotangent of an angle is the reciprocal of the tangent of that angle,

$$\cot(\phi+\theta) = \frac{1 - \tan\phi\tan\theta}{\tan\phi + \tan\theta}$$

and

$$\cot(\phi+\theta) = \frac{1 - 1/\cot\phi\cot\theta}{1/\cot\phi + 1/\cot\theta}$$

$$\cot(\phi+\theta) = \frac{\cot\phi\cot\theta - 1}{\cot\phi + \cot\theta} \qquad \textbf{(46)}$$

21·7 Functions of the difference of two angles

If in Eq. (43) we replace θ by $-\theta$, we obtain

$$\sin(\phi-\theta) = \sin\phi\cos(-\theta) + \cos\phi\sin(-\theta)$$

but from Eqs. (37) and (40) we may write

$$\sin(\phi-\theta) = \sin\phi\cos\theta - \cos\phi\sin\theta \qquad \textbf{(47)}$$

We have already derived the equation

$$\cos(\phi-\theta) = \cos\phi\cos\theta + \sin\phi\sin\theta \qquad (48)$$

tan $(\phi - \theta)$

$$\tan(\phi-\theta) = \frac{\sin(\phi-\theta)}{\cos(\phi-\theta)}$$

Substituting Eqs. (47) and (48) in the above equation,

$$\tan(\phi-\theta) = \frac{\sin\phi\cos\theta - \cos\phi\sin\theta}{\cos\phi\cos\theta + \sin\phi\sin\theta}$$

Dividing numerator and denominator by $\cos\phi\cos\theta$ gives

$$\tan(\phi-\theta) = \frac{\sin\phi\cos\theta/\cos\phi\cos\theta - \cos\phi\sin\theta/\cos\phi\cos\theta}{\cos\phi\cos\theta/\cos\phi\cos\theta + \sin\phi\sin\theta/\cos\phi\cos\theta}$$

$$= \frac{\sin\phi/\cos\phi - \sin\theta/\cos\theta}{1 + (\sin\phi/\cos\phi)(\sin\theta/\cos\theta)}$$

$$\tan(\phi-\theta) = \frac{\tan\phi - \tan\theta}{1 + \tan\phi\tan\theta} \qquad \textbf{(49)}$$

cot $(\phi - \theta)$

$$\cot(\phi - \theta) = \frac{1}{\tan(\phi - \theta)}$$

Following Eq. (49),

$$\cot(\phi - \theta) = \frac{1 + \tan\phi \tan\theta}{\tan\phi - \tan\theta}$$

$$= \frac{1 + 1/(\cot\phi \cot\theta)}{1/\cot\phi - 1/\cot\theta}$$

$$\cot(\phi - \theta) = \frac{\cot\phi \cot\theta + 1}{\cot\theta - \cot\phi} \tag{50}$$

21·8 Functions of twice an angle

sin 2ϕ

In Eq. (43) let $\theta = \phi$; then

$$\sin(\phi + \phi) = \sin 2\phi = \sin\phi \cos\phi + \sin\phi \cos\phi$$

$$\sin 2\phi = 2 \sin\phi \cos\phi \tag{51}$$

cos 2ϕ

In Eq. (44) let $\theta = \phi$; then

$$\cos(\phi + \phi) = \cos 2\phi = \cos\phi \cos\phi - \sin\phi \sin\phi$$

$$\cos 2\phi = \cos^2\phi - \sin^2\phi \tag{52}$$

tan 2ϕ

In Eq. (45) let $\theta = \phi$; then

$$\tan(\phi + \phi) = \tan 2\phi = \frac{\tan\phi + \tan\phi}{1 - \tan\phi \tan\phi}$$

$$\tan 2\phi = \frac{2\tan\phi}{1 - \tan^2\phi} \tag{53}$$

cot 2ϕ

In Eq. (46) let $\theta = \phi$; then

$$\cot(\phi + \phi) = \cot 2\phi = \frac{\cot\phi \cot\phi - 1}{\cot\phi + \cot\phi}$$

$$\cot 2\phi = \frac{\cot^2\phi - 1}{2\cot\phi} \tag{54}$$

21·9 Functions of half an angle

sin $\frac{\phi}{2}$

Following Eqs. (14) and (52),

$$\sin^2\frac{\phi}{2} + \cos^2\frac{\phi}{2} = 1 \tag{55}$$

$$-\sin^2\frac{\phi}{2} + \cos^2\frac{\phi}{2} = \cos\phi \tag{56}$$

Solving the above equations by subtraction,

$$2\sin^2\frac{\phi}{2} = 1 - \cos\phi \tag{56a}$$

$$\sin^2\frac{\phi}{2} = \frac{1-\cos\phi}{2}$$

$$\sin\frac{\phi}{2} = \pm\sqrt{\frac{1-\cos\phi}{2}} \tag{57}$$

where the choice of sign before the radical depends on the magnitude of $\phi/2$.

cos $\frac{\phi}{2}$

Solving Eqs. (55) and (56) simultaneously by addition gives

$$2\cos^2\frac{\phi}{2} = 1 + \cos\phi \tag{57a}$$

$$\cos^2\frac{\phi}{2} = \frac{1+\cos\phi}{2}$$

$$\cos\frac{\phi}{2} = \pm\sqrt{\frac{1+\cos\phi}{2}} \tag{58}$$

where the choice of sign before the radical again depends on the magnitude of $\phi/2$.

tan $\frac{\phi}{2}$

$$\tan\frac{\phi}{2} = \frac{\sin(\phi/2)}{\cos(\phi/2)}$$

If we multiply the numerator and denominator of the right member by $2\sin(\phi/2)$, we obtain

$$\tan\frac{\phi}{2} = \frac{2\sin^2(\phi/2)}{2\sin(\phi/2)\cos(\phi/2)}$$

or

$$\tan\frac{\phi}{2} = \frac{1-\cos\phi}{\sin\phi} \tag{59}$$

cot $\frac{\phi}{2}$

$$\cot \frac{\phi}{2} = \frac{1}{\tan (\phi/2)}$$

and from Eq. (59) above we may write

$$\cot \frac{\phi}{2} = \frac{\sin \phi}{1 - \cos \phi} \tag{60}$$

21·10 More complicated trigonometric identities

Before attempting the formal verification of a suspected trigonometric identity, it is often more efficient to see if it is true for a special angle. If it is not true for a particular angle, it is certainly not true generally, and there would be no point in carrying the investigation any further.

For example, suppose we suspect that the equation

$$\frac{1 + \cos \phi}{1 - \cos \phi} = \frac{1 - \cos (\phi/2)}{\sin (\phi/2)}$$

is an identity. Let us substitute $\phi = 60°$. Then

$$\frac{1 + \frac{1}{2}}{1 - \frac{1}{2}} \stackrel{?}{=} \frac{1 - \sqrt{3}/2}{\frac{1}{2}}$$

$$\frac{\frac{3}{2}}{\frac{1}{2}} \stackrel{?}{=} 2 - \sqrt{3}$$

$$3 \stackrel{?}{=} 2 - \sqrt{3}$$

Obviously the given equation is not true when $\phi = 60°$; therefore it is not an identity. There may, however, be other values which, if substituted for ϕ, would check.

There are three formal methods by which we may prove an identity. We can substitute the proper ratios for the functions themselves, as was done in Example 2. Sometimes we can prove a suspęcted identity by referring to an identity of which we are already sure. Again, we may resort to a geometrical proof, as was done in Sec. 21·4.

When we use algebraic methods in proving an identity, the identity should be verified in the precise form in which it appears. We can alter either or both sides by appropriate substitutions, but it is unwise to transpose any quantities across the equality sign.

example 4 Verify the identity

$$\tan \phi = \frac{2 \tan (\phi/2)}{1 - \tan^2 (\phi/2)}$$

First let us see if the identity is true when $\phi = 60°$:

$$\sqrt{3} \stackrel{?}{=} \frac{2 \times 1/\sqrt{3}}{1 - \frac{1}{3}}$$

$$\sqrt{3} \stackrel{?}{=} \frac{2/\sqrt{3}}{\frac{2}{3}} = \frac{2}{\sqrt{3}} \times \frac{3}{2} = \frac{3}{\sqrt{3}} = \frac{3\sqrt{3}}{3} = \sqrt{3}$$

We are now sure that the equation is true for at least one angle. Let us proceed with a more general check. A recommended arrangement of work is shown below:

$\tan \phi$	$\dfrac{2 \tan \frac{1}{2}\phi}{1 - \tan^2 \frac{1}{2}\phi}$
$\dfrac{\sin \phi}{\cos \phi}$	From Eq. (10), $\dfrac{2\dfrac{\sin (\phi/2)}{\cos (\phi/2)}}{1 - \dfrac{\sin^2 (\phi/2)}{\cos^2 (\phi/2)}}$
	or $\dfrac{2 \cos (\phi/2) \sin (\phi/2)}{\cos^2 \phi/2 - \sin^2 (\phi/2)}$
	From Eqs. (51) and (52) we obtain $\dfrac{\sin \phi}{\cos \phi}$

example 5 Verify the identity

$$\pm\sqrt{\frac{1 - \sin \beta}{1 + \sin \beta}} = \frac{1 - \sin \beta}{\cos \beta}$$

$\pm\sqrt{\dfrac{1 - \sin \beta}{1 + \sin \beta}}$	$\dfrac{1 - \sin \beta}{\cos \beta}$
Rationalize by multiplying numerator and denominator by $1 - \sin \beta$: $\pm\sqrt{\dfrac{(1 - \sin \beta)(1 - \sin \beta)}{(1 + \sin \beta)(1 - \sin \beta)}}$	↑
$\pm\sqrt{\dfrac{(1 - \sin \beta)^2}{1 - \sin^2 \beta}}$	
$\dfrac{1 - \sin \beta}{\cos \beta}$ ←	

example 6 Verify the identity

$$\pm\sqrt{\frac{1-\sin\omega}{1+\sin\omega}} = \frac{\cos\omega}{1+\sin\omega}$$

$$\pm\sqrt{\frac{1-\sin\omega}{1+\sin\omega}} \qquad \frac{\cos\omega}{1+\sin\omega}$$

Rationalize by multiplying numerator and denominator by $1 + \sin\omega$:

$$\pm\sqrt{\frac{(1-\sin\omega)(1+\sin\omega)}{(1+\sin\omega)^2}}$$

$$\pm\sqrt{\frac{1-\sin^2\omega}{(1+\sin\omega)^2}}$$

$$\frac{\cos\omega}{1+\sin\omega}$$

EXERCISE 3

Verify the following suspected identities. It is left to the student to determine which are identities and which are not.

1. $\sin^2\phi + \csc^2\phi = \dfrac{1+\sin^2\phi}{\sin^2\phi}$
2. $1 - \sin\phi = \dfrac{\cos^2\phi}{1+\sin\phi}$
3. $\cos^2\phi = 1 - 2\sin^2\phi$
4. $\sin 2\phi = \dfrac{2\tan\phi}{1+\tan^2\phi}$
5. $\sin 2\phi = \dfrac{1}{\tan\phi + \cot\phi}$
6. $\tan\phi = \dfrac{\sin\phi + \tan\phi}{\sin\phi\cos\phi + 1}$
7. $\sec\phi\csc\phi = \dfrac{\tan\phi - \cot\phi}{\sin^2\phi - \cos^2\phi}$
8. $\dfrac{\tan^2\phi - \sin^2\phi}{\tan^2\phi} = \dfrac{\sec^2\phi - 1}{1+\tan^2\phi}$
9. $\dfrac{1+\tan\phi}{1-\tan\phi} = \tan(45° + \phi)$
10. $\dfrac{\cot\phi + \sin\phi}{\cot\phi\cos\phi} = \tan\phi + \sec\phi$
11. $\dfrac{\sin\phi}{1-\cos\phi} + \dfrac{\sin\phi}{1+\cos\phi} = 2\cot\phi$
12. $\sec\phi = \tan\phi\sin\phi + \sin\phi$
13. $\sin\phi = \dfrac{2\tan\frac{1}{2}\phi}{1+\tan^2\frac{1}{2}\phi}$
14. $\sin\phi = \dfrac{\cos\phi - \sin\phi\tan\phi}{2\cot 2\phi}$
15. $\pm\sqrt{\dfrac{1-\cos\phi}{1+\cos\phi}} = \dfrac{\sin\phi}{1+\cos\phi}$
16. $\cot\frac{1}{2}\phi = \dfrac{\sin\phi}{1-\cos\phi}$
17. $4\sin^3\phi + \sin 3\phi = 3\sin\phi$
18. $(\sin x + \cos x)^2 = 1 + \sin 2x$
19. $\cos^4 x - \sin^4 x = \cos 2x$
20. $\dfrac{\sin^3 x - \cos^3 x}{\sin x - \cos x} = 1 + \dfrac{1}{2}\sin 2x$
21. $\operatorname{cosec} x \sin 3x = 2 + \sec x \cos 3x$
22. $\tan x = \dfrac{1-\cos 2x}{\sin 2x}$

23. $-\cos 2x = \dfrac{1 - \cot^2 x}{\operatorname{cosec}^2 x}$

24. $\cos 2x \cos 3x = \cos x - \sin 2x \sin 3x$

25. $\cot 2x = \dfrac{\cot x - \tan x}{2}$

26. $\dfrac{2 \tan A}{\sin 2A} = 1 + \tan^2 A$

27. This problem refers to Fig. 18·19 (also see Sec. 18·6).
(a) Show that in Fig. 18·19

$$2 \sin^2 \frac{A}{2} = \frac{(a + b - c)(a - b + c)}{2bc}$$

Hint: Use the cosine law and Eq. (56*a*).
(b) Show that

$$2 \cos^2 \frac{A}{2} = \frac{(a + b + c)(b + c - a)}{2bc}$$

Hint: Use the cosine law and Eq. (57*a*).
(c) Using the results obtained in (a) and (b) show that

$$\tan \frac{A}{2} = \frac{1}{s - a}\sqrt{\frac{(s - a)(s - b)(s - c)}{s}}$$

where $s = ½(a + b + c)$
(d) Using the results obtained in (c) show that referred to Fig. 18·19

$$r = \sqrt{\frac{(s - a)(s - b)(s - c)}{s}}$$

28. Let two wattmeter readings for a particular electric circuit be w_1 and w_2. Then the so-called "power factor" for the problem can be determined from these wattmeter readings by aid of the equation

$$\tan \theta = \frac{\sqrt{3}(w_2 - w_1)}{w_2 + w_1} = \frac{\sqrt{3}d}{s}$$

Show that $\cos \theta = 1/[1 + 3(d/s)^2]^{1/2}$.

29. The follower on a cam at a time t sec has for its abscissa $x = 5 \sin 2\pi\omega t$ in. and for its ordinate $y = 4 \cos 2\pi\omega t$ in. The quantity ω is a constant. Show that $x^2/25 + y^2/16$ always has the value $+1$, irrespective of the time.

30. It is necessary to make a table of values of the function

$$\frac{x}{(16 - 9x^2)^{1/2}}$$

for $x = 0, 0.1, 0.2, \ldots, 1.3$. Show that this computation may be accomplished readily by replacing $3x$ by $4 \sin \theta$ and then simplifying the given expression to $⅓ \tan \theta$. Make up the table of required values correct to four decimals.

31. A sphere weighing W lb rests between two smooth planes, as shown in Fig. 21·4. Figure 21·5 shows the weight of the sphere and the

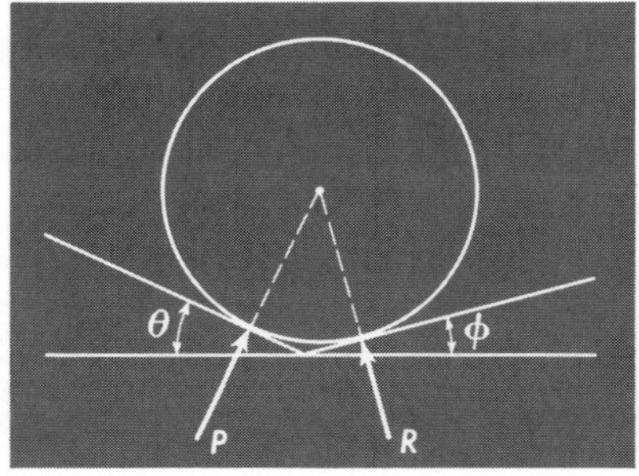

fig. 21·4

fig. 21·5

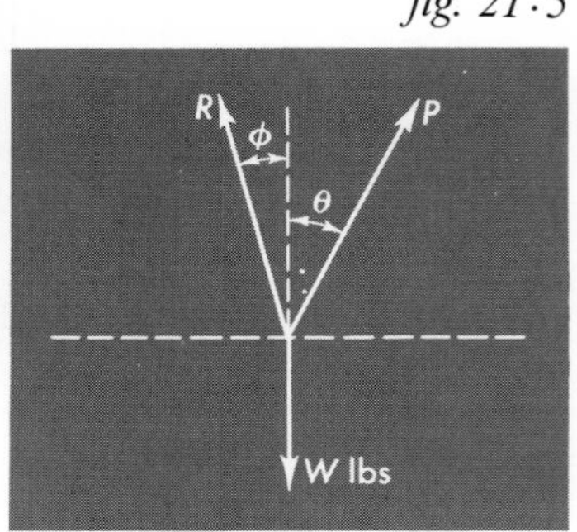

forces that the two planes exert upon the sphere. Since the algebraic sum of the horizontal components of the forces must be zero and the algebraic sum of the vertical forces must likewise be zero, we obtain

$$R \sin \phi - P \sin \theta = 0$$
$$R \cos \phi + P \cos \theta = W$$

Solve these two equations simultaneously for R and P in terms of W, θ, and ϕ and show that your results can be put in the form

$$P = \frac{W \sin \phi}{\sin (\theta + \phi)} \qquad R = \frac{W \sin \theta}{\sin (\theta + \phi)}$$

32. The period of vibration of a pendulum is given by the approximate formula

$$T = 2\pi \left(\frac{L}{g}\right)^{1/2} \left(1 + \frac{1}{4} \sin^2 \frac{\theta}{2} + \frac{9}{64} \sin^4 \frac{\theta}{2}\right)$$

which is much more accurate than the one customarily given in an elementary course in physics, namely, $T = 2\pi(L/g)^{1/2}$. L is the length of the pendulum and $g = 32.2$ ft per sec^2. θ is the angle that the pendulum makes with the vertical at the instant it is released.

(a) Evaluate the part in parentheses for $\theta = 2°$, $30°$, and $60°$

(b) Show that the quantity in parentheses can be written in the following form: $1 + {}^{91}\!/_{512} - {}^{25}\!/_{128} \cos \theta + {}^{9}\!/_{512} \cos 2\theta$.

33. The voltage in an electric circuit is

$$e = 40 \sin 120\pi t + 5 \sin 360\pi t \qquad \text{volts}$$

The current is

$$i = 4 \sin 120\pi t + 2 \sin 360\pi t \qquad \text{amp}$$

Determine an expression for the power $p = ei$ watts and leave your final result in a form free of powers and products of trigonometric functions.

34. Two voltages

$$e_1 = 40 \sin\left(120\pi t + \frac{\pi}{3}\right) \qquad \text{volts}$$

$$e_2 = 60 \sin\left(120\pi t - \frac{\pi}{4}\right) \qquad \text{volts}$$

are simultaneously impressed in series on an electric circuit. Combine these into a single voltage by performing the operation $e = e_1 + e_2$. Give your final result in the form $E \sin (120\pi t + \theta)$.

35. If the voltage in an electric circuit is

$$e = E_m \sin \alpha$$

and the current is

$$i = I_m \sin (\alpha + \theta)$$

show that the power, $p = ei$ watts, can be expressed in the form

$$p = \left(\frac{E_m I_m}{2}\right)[\cos \theta - \cos (2\alpha + \theta)]$$

This derivation is to be found in every text on a-c circuits.

36. The value of the voltage e in volts due to "amplitude modulation" is given by

$$e = 100(1 + 0.7 \cos 4{,}000t - 0.3 \cos 8{,}000t) \sin 4{,}000{,}000t$$

where t is in seconds. Show that this can be rewritten in a form free of products of trigonometric functions, i.e., as the sum of simple sine functions. Then determine the amplitude, period, and frequency for each of the resulting terms.

37. Figure 21·6 shows a connecting-rod, crank-arm mechanism from an engine.
(a) Show that

$$x = r \cos \theta + (L^2 - r^2 \sin^2 \theta)^{1/2}$$
$$= r \cos \theta + L\left(1 - \frac{r^2}{L^2} \sin^2 \theta\right)^{1/2}$$

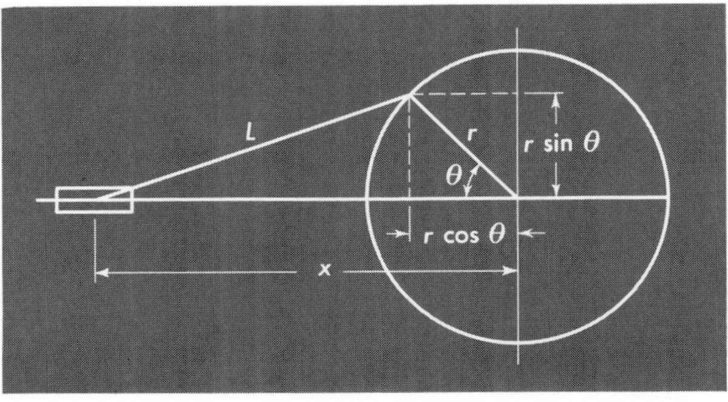

fig. 21·6

(b) Expand the binomial to four terms by aid of the binomial theorem and obtain

$$x = r\cos\theta + L - \frac{r^2\sin^2\theta}{2L} - \frac{r^4\sin^4\theta}{8L^3} - \frac{r^6\sin^6\theta}{16L^5} - \cdots$$

(c) Transform this expression so that there are no powers of trigonometric functions present and show that the result is

$$x = \left(L - \frac{r^2}{4L} - \frac{3r^4}{64L^3} - \frac{5r^6}{256L^5} - \cdots\right) + r\cos\theta$$

$$+ \cos 2\theta\left(\frac{r^2}{4L} + \frac{r^4}{16L^3} + \frac{13r^6}{512L^5} + \cdots\right)$$

$$- \cos 4\theta\left(\frac{r^4}{64L^3} + \frac{3r^6}{256L^5} + \cdots\right) + \cdots$$

(d) Simplify the preceding expression if $L/r = 5$.

(e) What would this last result be if you used only the first two terms of the binomial expansion?

The result in (e) is commonly used in engineering problems, since the coefficients of the higher harmonics are small ($L/r \geqq 5$). However, there are times when it is necessary to know something about the higher harmonics, and you obtained some of them in this problem.

38. Find $\sin^{-1} 0.999985$ using $\cos\theta = \sqrt{1 - \sin^2\theta}$.

21·11 Trigonometric equations

A conditional trigonometric equation or simply a trigonometric equation is an equation which is valid for some but not all of the possible values of the angles involved.

A solution of a trigonometric equation is a value of the angle, in degrees or radians, which satisfies the equation.

The three suggestions given below will take care of most cases but not all. Unfortunately no rules exist which will apply universally.

1. If only one function is involved, the equation can usually be solved algebraically (see Example 7).
2. If several functions of the same angle are involved, it is best to use some of the fundamental identities to express the entire equation in terms of a single function (see Example 8).

Very often it will be found that the equation will be easier to solve if the several functions are converted to sine and cosine functions.

3. If several angles are involved, it is usually best to express the entire equation in terms of functions of a single angle (see Example 9).

example 7 Solve the equation

$$15\cos^2\phi - 7\cos\phi - 2 = 0$$

This equation can be factored into

$$(3 \cos \phi - 2)(5 \cos \phi + 1) = 0$$

Therefore,
$$3 \cos \phi = 2$$
$$\cos \phi = 2/3$$

and
$$5 \cos \phi = -1$$
$$\cos \phi = -1/5$$

The quadratic formula could also have been used, and

$$\cos \phi = \frac{7 \pm \sqrt{49 + 120}}{30} = \frac{7 \pm \sqrt{169}}{30} = \frac{7 \pm 13}{30}$$

$$\cos \phi = 2/3 \text{ and } -1/5$$

When $\cos \phi = 2/3$
$$\phi = 48°11' \text{ (to the nearest minute)}$$

or
$$\phi = 311°49' \text{ (to the nearest minute)}$$

When $\cos \phi = -1/5$
$$\phi = 101°32'$$

or
$$\phi = 258°28'$$

To complete the problem the results should be substituted in the original equation to eliminate any extraneous roots which may have been introduced in the process of solving.

Substituting $\cos \phi = 2/3$,

$$15 \times 4/9 - 7 \times 2/3 - 2 \stackrel{?}{=} 0$$
$$60/9 - 14/3 - 2$$
$$60/9 - 42/9 - 2$$
$$18/9 - 2$$
$$2 - 2 = 0 \qquad \text{(check)}$$

Substituting $\cos \phi = -1/5$,

$$15 \times 1/25 + 7 \times 1/5 - 2 \stackrel{?}{=} 0$$
$$3/5 + 7/5 - 2 = 0$$
$$10/5 - 2 = 0 \qquad \text{(check)}$$

example 8 Solve the equation

$$2 \sin \phi = \cos \phi$$

or
$$2 = \frac{\cos \phi}{\sin \phi} = \cot \phi$$

By consulting the tables of trigonometric functions, we find that

$$\phi = 26°34' \text{ and } 206°34'$$

example 9 Solve the equation

$$\sin 2\phi = \tan \phi$$

$$2 \sin \phi \cos \phi = \frac{\sin \phi}{\cos \phi}$$

Multiply both sides by $\cos \phi$:

$$\begin{aligned} 2 \sin \phi \cos^2 \phi &= \sin \phi \qquad \cos \phi \neq 0 \\ 2 \sin \phi \cos^2 \phi - \sin \phi &= 0 \\ \sin \phi(2 \cos^2 \phi - 1) &= 0 \\ \sin \phi &= 0 \\ 2 \cos^2 \phi &= 1 \\ \cos^2 \phi &= ½ \\ \cos \phi &= \pm\frac{1}{\sqrt{2}} = \pm\frac{\sqrt{2}}{2} \end{aligned}$$

When $\sin \phi = 0$,

$$\phi = 0° \text{ and } 180°$$

When $\cos \phi = +\sqrt{2}/2$,

$$\phi = 45° \text{ and } 315°$$

When $\cos \phi = -\sqrt{2}/2$,

$$\phi = 135° \text{ and } 225°$$

Check in the original problem:
When $\phi = 0°$,

$$\begin{aligned} \sin (2 \times 0)° &\stackrel{?}{=} \tan 0° \\ 0 &= 0 \qquad \text{(check)} \end{aligned}$$

when $\phi = 180°$,

$$\begin{aligned} \sin (2 \times 180)° &\stackrel{?}{=} \tan 180° \\ 0 &= 0 \qquad \text{(check)} \end{aligned}$$

when $\phi = 45°$,

$$\begin{aligned} \sin (2 \times 45)° &\stackrel{?}{=} \tan 45° \\ \sin 90° &\stackrel{?}{=} \tan 45° \\ 1 &= 1 \qquad \text{(check)} \end{aligned}$$

when $\phi = 315°$,

$$\begin{aligned} \sin (2 \times 315)° &\stackrel{?}{=} \tan 315° \\ \sin 630° &\stackrel{?}{=} \tan 315° \\ \sin 270° &\stackrel{?}{=} \tan 315° \\ -1 &= -1 \qquad \text{(check)} \end{aligned}$$

when $\phi = 135°$,

$$\begin{aligned} \sin (2 \times 135)° &\stackrel{?}{=} \tan 135° \\ \sin 270° &\stackrel{?}{=} \tan 135° \\ -1 &= -1 \qquad \text{(check)} \end{aligned}$$

when $\phi = 225°$,

$$\sin(2 \times 225)° \stackrel{?}{=} \tan 225°$$
$$\sin 450° \stackrel{?}{=} \tan 225°$$
$$\sin 90° \stackrel{?}{=} \tan 225°$$
$$+1 = +1 \qquad \text{(check)}$$

EXERCISE 4

Find all positive angles less than 360° which satisfy each of the following equations.

1. $\sqrt{2}\sin x = 1$
2. $\cos x - 1 = 0$
3. $\sec x - 2 = 0$
4. $5\sin x - 2 = 0$
5. $\sqrt{3}\tan x + 1 = 0$
6. $3\operatorname{cosec} x - 7 = 0$
7. $\tan^2 x = \tan x$
8. $5\cot x = 2(-\cot x)$
9. $2\cos x\sin x + \cos x = 0$
10. $\sqrt{3}\cos x + 2\cos^2 x = 0$
11. $2\cos x + \cot x = 0$
12. $2\sin^2 x = \cos x\tan x$
13. $\sqrt{3}\sec x\sin x = \tan^2 x$
14. $2\cot x = \operatorname{cosec}^2 x - 1$
15. $\cos x + \sin^2 x = 1$
16. $\operatorname{cosec}^2 x = 1 + 3\cos x\operatorname{cosec} x$
17. $\sqrt{3}\operatorname{cosec}^2 x = 2\sin x + \sqrt{3}\cot^2 x$
18. $\sin^2 x\cos x - \sin x\cos x = 0$
19. $2\sin^3 x\sec x + 3\tan x = 0$
20. $2\tan^2 x\cos x - \sin x = 0$
21. $\sin\phi = \cos 2\phi$
22. $\sin\phi = \dfrac{\tan\phi}{2}$
23. $\sin\phi = \dfrac{\sec\phi}{2}$
24. $\sin\phi - \cos 2\phi = 1$
25. $\tan\phi + \cot\phi = 1$
26. $\cos^2\phi + \cos 2\phi = 1$
27. $\dfrac{\tan\phi}{\sin\phi} = 5$
28. $\cos^2(\phi - 30°) = 1$
29. $3\operatorname{cosec}^2\phi = 9$
30. $\sin 3\phi + 2\sin\phi = 1$

31. The relation between the size of feed b, the space between the rolls $2a$, the radius of the rolls r, and the angle of "nip" $N°$ is

$$\cos\left(\frac{N}{2}\right) = \frac{r + a}{r + b}$$

(a) Derive this equation from Fig. 21·7.
(b) What is the relation for N in terms of r, a, and b? For r in terms of N, a, and b?

32. Figure 21·8 shows four circles that possess the indicated tangency properties. The radii of three circles are known: $\overline{OC} = 5$ in., $\overline{AB} = 3$ in., and $\overline{ED} = 2$ in. Determine the coordinates of the center P and the radius r of the circle BCD, this fourth circle being tangent to each of the three given circles.

Suggestion: Angle θ is common to the two triangles OAP and EAP, and the dimensions of the sides of both these triangles can be determined in terms of r.

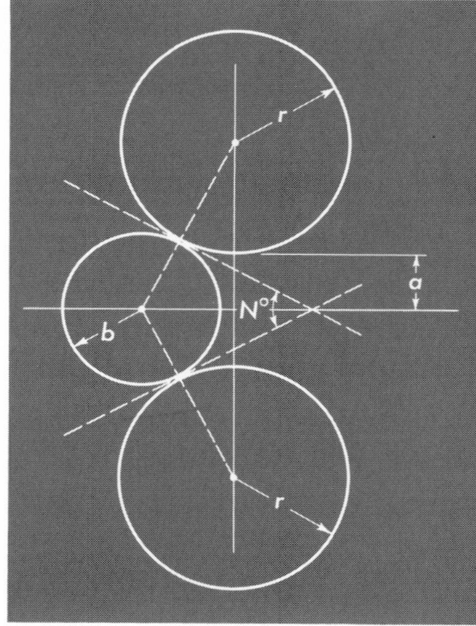

fig. 21·7

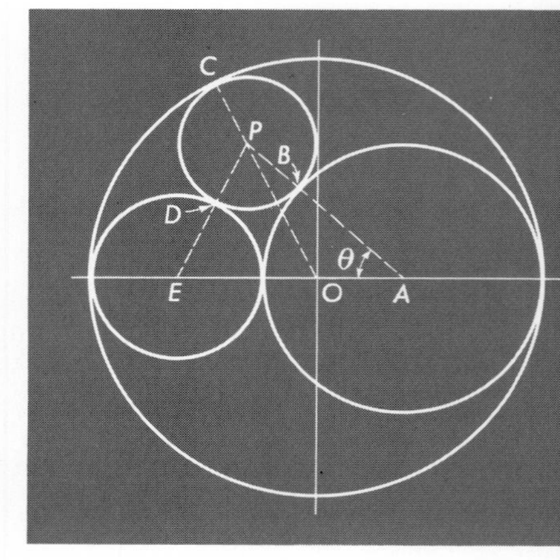

fig. 21

33. When a block of weight W lb is pulled up an inclined plane by a horizontally directed force (P lb), the angle θ which the plane makes with the horizontal will make the efficiency a maximum if

$$\sin 2(\theta + \phi) = \sin 2\theta$$

Mechanical efficiency is defined as the ratio of the useful work performed to the total energy expended (see Fig. 21·10). Tan ϕ is a measure of the friction between the block and the plane. Solve for the smallest acute angle θ if $\tan \phi = 0.347$ (the proper value if the block is made of cast iron and the plane of steel).

34. A ski jumper starts down a hill from the point marked A (Fig. 21·9). The cross section of the hill is a circle of radius R. It can be shown, by methods of physics and mechanics, that the radius to the point at which he will leave the surface of the hill (neglecting friction, which is

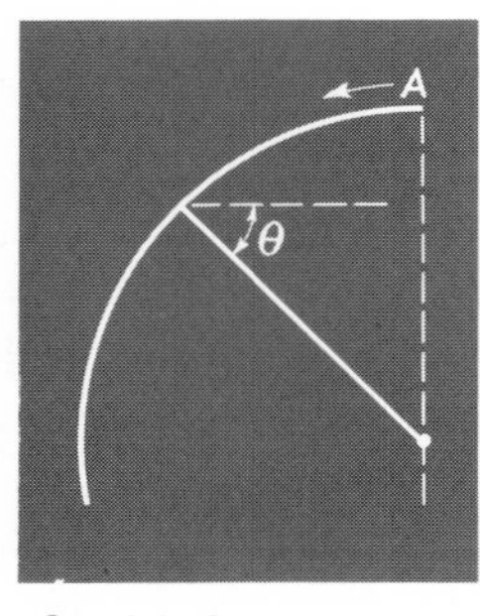

fig. 21·9

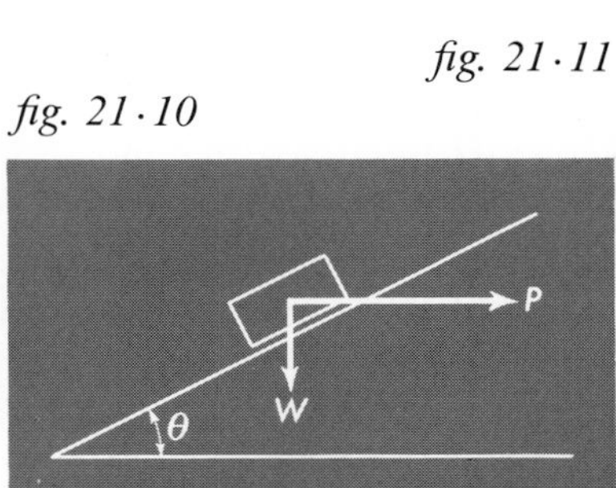

fig. 21·10

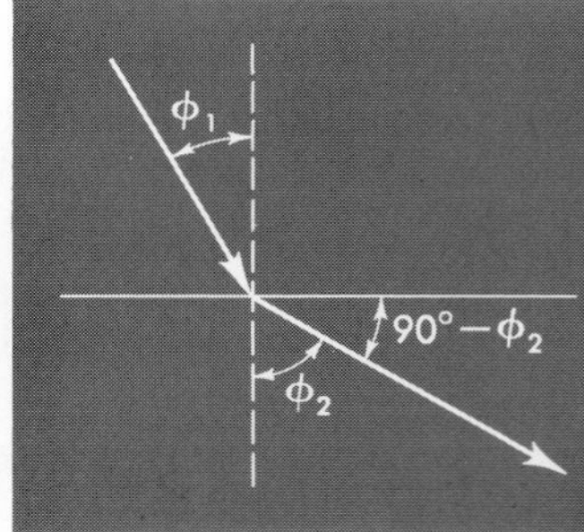

fig. 21·11

small) will make an angle θ with the horizontal, where

$$\sin \theta = 2(1 - \sin \theta)$$

Determine this angle.

35. A body weighing W lb rests on a rough plane inclined at an angle θ with the horizontal (Fig. 21·10). To determine the force P lb that will just cause the body to begin to slide up the hill, one applies methods of mechanics to obtain the following equations:

$$P \cos \theta - W \sin \theta = F \qquad N - W \cos \theta = P \sin \theta \qquad F = N \tan \phi$$

where $\tan \phi$ is a measure of the friction between the body and the plane and F is the frictional force. Solve these three equations simultaneously for P and obtain $P = W \tan (\theta + \phi)$.

36. The equation

$$\frac{\tan \alpha_2}{\tan \alpha_1} = \frac{u_1}{u_2}$$

is used in electrical engineering to determine the change in direction when magnetic lines pass from one medium to another. A special case yields

$$\tan \alpha_{\text{air}} = 1{,}000 \tan \alpha_{\text{iron}}$$

Compute α_{air} in degrees correct to the nearest minute when $\alpha_{\text{iron}} = 0°$, 0.1°, 1°, 15°, 30°, and 60°.

37. Snell's law from physics is

$$\frac{\sin \phi_1}{\sin \phi_2} = \frac{n_2}{n_1}$$

where n_1 and n_2 are the indices of refraction for two mediums through which light is passing, and ϕ_1 and ϕ_2 are the corresponding angles. Let

$$n_1 = \text{index of refraction of water} = 1.33$$
$$n_2 = \text{index of refraction of air} = 1.000{,}292$$

then we may write

$$\frac{\sin \phi_{\text{water}}}{\sin \phi_{\text{air}}} = \frac{1.000{,}292}{1.33}$$

If ϕ_{air} takes on successive values of 0°, 1°, 10°, 30°, 45°, 60°, and 90°, tabulate corresponding values of ϕ_{water}.

22

graphs of the trigonometric functions

In this chapter we shall graph each of the six trigonometric functions. By observing the nature of the graphs, we can deduce many of the properties of the functions themselves.

In addition to such theoretical uses, the graphs of the functions, particularly those of the sine and cosine, are very convenient devices to use in the analysis and solution of certain engineering problems.

Figure 22 · 1 shows the graphs of the six trigonometric equations:

$$y = \sin \phi \tag{1}$$
$$y = \cos \phi \tag{2}$$
$$y = \tan \phi \tag{3}$$
$$y = \cot \phi \tag{4}$$
$$y = \sec \phi \tag{5}$$
$$y = \operatorname{cosec} \phi \tag{6}$$

While it is true that the choice of scale is to a certain extent arbitrary, we do obtain a somewhat more characteristic shape of the graphs if we use the same scale on both axes and plot the angles in radians rather than in degrees. Figure 22 · 1 is plotted in this way.

However, in technology the theoretical advantage gained by using radian measure rather than degree measure does not ordinarily outweigh the disadvantage of using the irrational number π.

22 · 1 Some periodic functions

One of the most important characteristics of the trigonometric functions is their repetitive nature.

A study of Fig. 22 · 1 will show that as the angle increases, the six functions undergo certain characteristic changes. As the angle indefi-

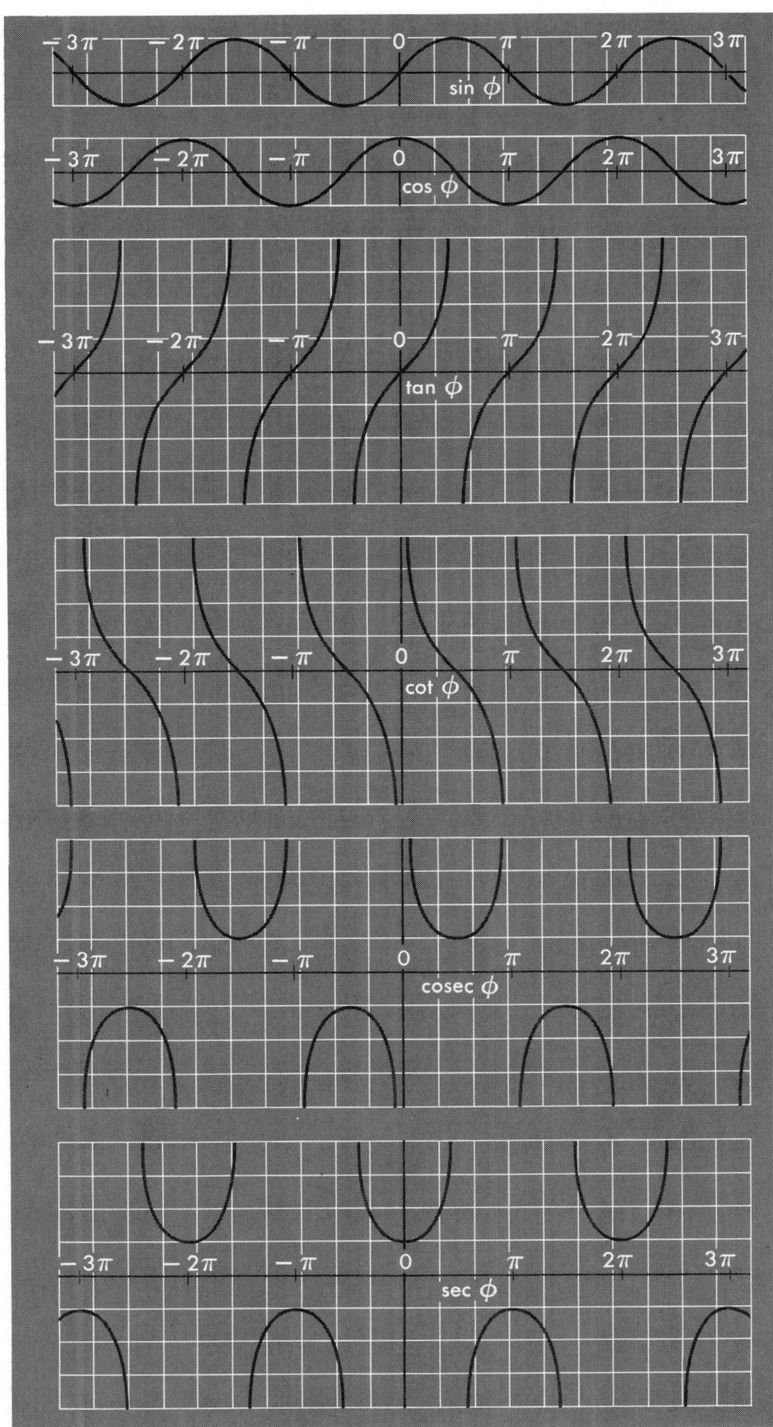

fig. 22·1

nitely increases, these changes repeat periodically. The trigonometric functions are therefore called *periodic functions*. One *cycle* has elapsed when a function has traversed once all the variations of which that particular function is capable.

The *angular period* of any of the trigonometric functions is the angular interval required for the completion of one cycle.

Beginning at $\phi = 0$, let us trace the characteristic changes of the sine function. From $\phi = 0$ to $\phi = \pi/2$ radians, the sine increases from 0 to 1; from $\pi/2$ radians to π radians, the sine decreases from 1 to 0; from π radians to $3\pi/2$ radians, the sine decreases from 0 to -1; from $3\pi/2$ radians to 2π radians, the sine increases from -1 to 0. As ϕ begins to increase beyond 2π radians, the cycle begins to repeat. Thus the angular period of the sine function is 2π radians, or 360°.

The period of the tangent function is π radians. Over the interval $\phi = -\pi/2$ to $\phi = 0$, the tangent increases from $-\infty$ to 0. As the angle increases from 0 to $+\pi/2$ radians, the tangent increases from 0 to $+\infty$. If ϕ increases beyond $\pi/2$ radians, the tangent again traverses the complete array of values from $-\infty$ to $+\infty$, repeating the variation which took place in the previous angular period of π radians.

EXERCISE 1

1. In the equation $y = 5 \sin \beta$, find y from the tables when β is 10°, 50°, 160°, 250°, and 300°.
2. On a common area, plot the six trigonometric functions between 0° and 360°.
3. Read the graph in Prob. 2 to verify the answers to Probs. 22, 23, 25, 27, and 29 in Exercise 4, Chap. 21. Also use the same graph to verify the answers to Probs. 1 through 6 in Exercise 5, Chap. 17.
4. On the same axes plot the curves of $y = \sin \beta$ and $y = \tan \beta$. Use radian measure rather than degree measure, and plot over the interval $\beta = 0$ radians to $\beta = 0.02$ radian. What is the approximate slope of the graphs in this region? What would you expect the slope to be when $\beta = 0$? For any given angle in this region, which is greater, the sine or the tangent?

22·2 Sine and cosine graphs

For our immediate purpose, the graphs of the sine and cosine are by far the most important.

Since the period of a sine or cosine curve is 2π radians or 360°, we usually plot only in the interval between $\phi = 0$ and $\phi = 2\pi$ radians. All the characteristic changes of these functions appear in this region.

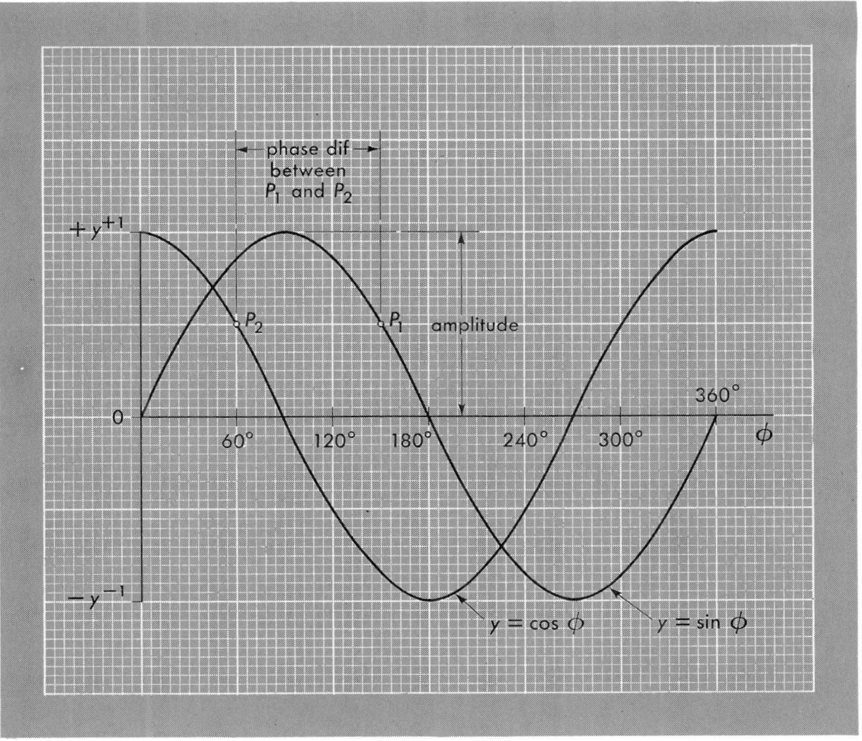

fig. 22·2

Figure 22·2 shows a plot of the equations

$$y = \sin \phi \tag{7}$$
$$y = \cos \phi \tag{8}$$

The horizontal axis is calibrated in degrees rather than in radians. A comparison between the shapes of the graphs of these functions in Figs. 22·1 and 22·2 will show the practical equivalence of the two plots.

Notice that the sine and cosine curves in Fig. 22·2 have exactly the same shape, but the cosine curve is displaced 90° to the left with respect to the sine curve.

The *amplitude* of a sine or cosine curve is the absolute value of the maximum and minimum ordinates. In Fig. 22·2 the amplitude of both curves is 1.

The *phase* of a point on the graph is defined as the abscissa of that point, and it may be measured in degrees or radians. The phase of point P_1 on the sine curve is 150°. The phase of the corresponding point P_2 on the cosine curve is 60°.

The *phase difference* between two points on a sine or cosine curve is the difference between their abscissas measured in degrees or radians.

The term *phase difference* may be applied to points on different sine or cosine curves, provided both curves are referred to the same zero reference angle.

The phase difference between P_1 and P_2 in Fig. 22·2 is $150° - 60° = 90°$. The same phase difference exists between any other pair of corresponding points. In fact, all the characteristic changes in the cosine functions of ϕ occur at angles differing by 90° from the corresponding changes in the sine functions of ϕ. Therefore, a cosine function of ϕ is said to have a 90° phase difference when compared to a sine function of ϕ. Since, in scanning the curve from left to right in the direction of increasing angles, we observe points on the cosine curve before we observe the corresponding points on the sine curve, we say that the cosine function *leads* the sine function.

The above facts may be written in the form of equations:

$$\cos \phi = \sin (\phi + 90°) \tag{9}$$
$$\sin \phi = \cos (\phi - 90°) \tag{10}$$

The equations for the sine and cosine functions may be generalized as

$$y = k \sin (\phi + \psi) \tag{11}$$

and

$$y = k \cos (\phi + \psi) \tag{12}$$

where k and ψ are constants.

When $(\phi + \psi) = 90°$ in Eq. (11), the ordinate of the sine curve is a maximum and equal to k. When $(\phi + \psi) = 0°$ in Eq. (12), the ordinate of the cosine curve is a maximum and also equal to k. The factor k is called the *amplitude* of the curve and is numerically equal to the maximum value of the function.

The constant angle ψ is known as the *phase constant* and has the effect of shifting the graphs of the equations

$$y = k \sin \phi$$

or

$$y = k \cos \phi$$

to the right or left along the ϕ axis. The curve is shifted to the left when ψ is positive and to the right when ψ is negative. The effect of k and ψ is illustrated in Fig. 22·3.

EXERCISE 2

1. The amplitude of a sine curve is 25. What is the ordinate of the curve at the following positions in its cycle?

(a) 20° (b) 90° (c) 130° (d) 180°
(e) 210° (f) 270° (g) 300° (h) 360°

2. Write an equation for a sine function in which the amplitude is 23 and the phase constant is +56°.

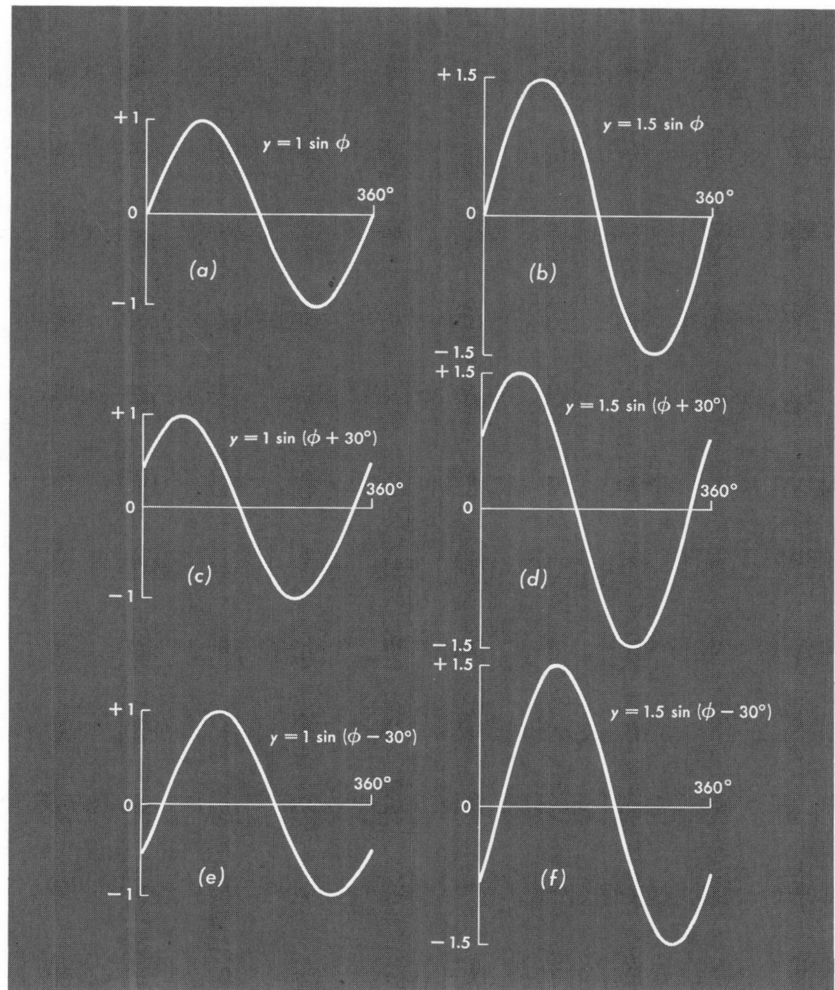

fig. 22·3

3. Plot the following curves on common axes:

(a) $y = \sin \phi$ (b) $y = \sin (\phi - 90°)$
(c) $y = \sin (\phi - 60°)$ (d) $y = \sin (\phi - 30°)$
(e) $y = \sin (\phi + 30°)$ (f) $y = \sin (\phi + 60°)$
(g) $y = \sin (\phi + 90°)$

4. Plot the following curves on common axes:

(a) $y = \cos \phi$ (b) $y = \cos (\phi - 90°)$
(c) $y = \cos (\phi - 60°)$ (d) $y = \cos (\phi - 30°)$
(e) $y = \cos (\phi + 30°)$ (f) $y = \cos (\phi + 60°)$
(g) $y = \cos (\phi + 90°)$

5. The ordinate of a sine curve is +25 when 100° of its cycle has been completed. Find the amplitude.
6. The ordinate of a sine curve is 15 when 80° of its cycle has been completed. What is the ordinate when 300° has been completed?
7. At what positive angles less than 360° will the absolute value of the ordinate of a cosine curve be 70 per cent of its amplitude?
8. The amplitude of a sine curve is 15. Find the ordinate at a phase 20° after its minimum.
9. What is the phase difference between the curves of the functions $y = 3 \sin \phi$ and $y' = 7 \sin (\phi + 40°)$?
10. If $y = 100 \sin (\phi + \psi)$ and $y' = 100 \sin (\phi + \psi')$, sketch each graph on the same coordinate axes where $y = y' = 76.6$ when $\phi = 20°$.

    Also plot on the same coordinate axes the graph of $y'' = 100 \sin \phi$.

    Find the absolute value of the phase difference in degrees between the graph of y'' and y. Find the absolute value of the phase difference in degrees between the graph of y'' and y' if $\psi > \psi'$.
11. If $y_1 = 50 \sin (\phi + \psi_1)$ and $y_1' = 50 \sin (\phi + \psi_1')$ where $y_1 = y_1' = 32.15$ when $\phi = 60°$, sketch y_1 and y_1' on the same coordinate axes.

    On the same coordinate axes as above, sketch the graphs of $y_2 = 25 \sin (\phi + \psi_2)$ and $y_2' = 25 \sin (\phi + \psi_2')$ where $y_2 = y_2' = 12.5$ when $\phi = 30°$.

    Find the absolute value of the phase difference in degrees between the graphs of y_1 and y_2, between the graphs of y_1 and y_2', between the graphs of y_1' and y_2, and between the graphs of y_1' and y_2'. Let $\psi_1 < \psi_1'$ and let $\psi_2' > \psi_2$.
12. A curve whose equation is in the form $y = k \sin (\theta + \psi)$ passes through the points ($\theta = 30°, y = 20$) and ($\theta = 40°, y = 28$). Determine the constants k and ψ.

22·3 Plotting the sine and cosine functions by geometric methods

Thus far we have plotted the sine and cosine curves by the use of tables. There is a geometric method which is extremely useful in the analysis of certain problems. This method is illustrated in Fig. 22·4*a*. First a base line *ox* of arbitrary length is established. Then a circle is drawn with its center (C) on an extension of *ox*. The radius of this circle is the amplitude of the sine curve to be plotted. The length *ox* is to scale numerically equal to the angular measure of one period.

The circle is divided into a convenient number of equal arcs, and the line *ox* is calibrated with the same number of equally spaced angle markers.

The points *a*, *b*, *c*, *d*, etc., are projected from the circle parallel to *ox*. The points *a'*, *b'*, *c'*, *d'*, etc., are projected vertically from the *ox* axis. Points on the sine curve are found at the intersection of corresponding projections.

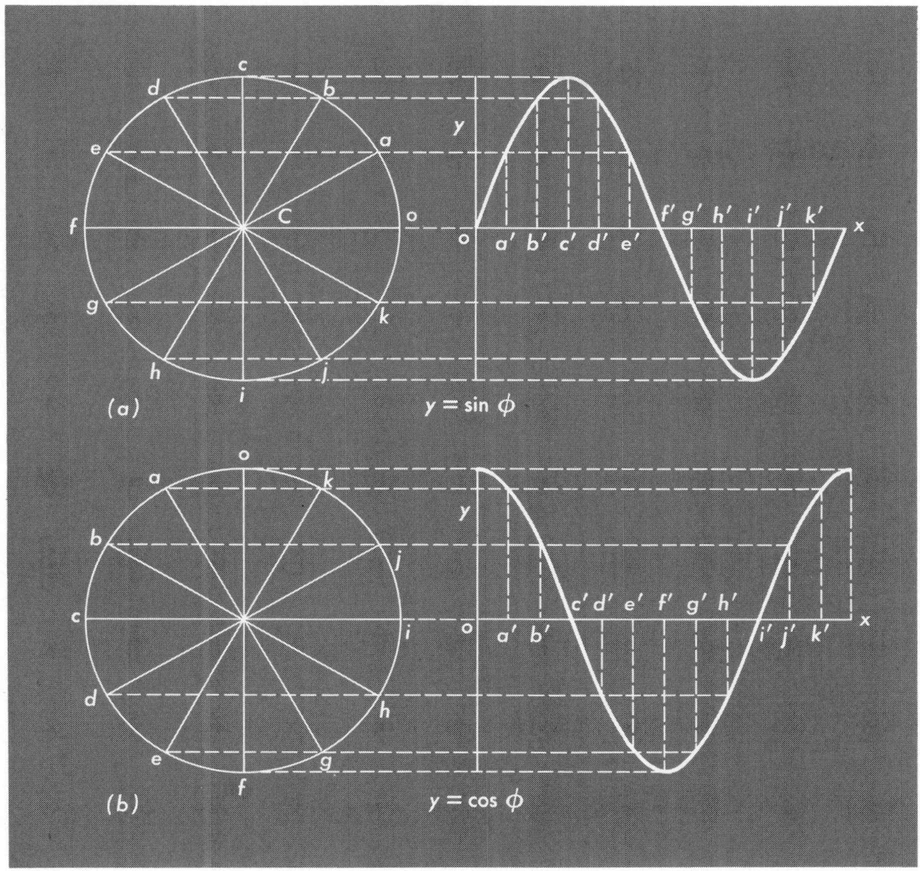

fig. 22·4

Figure 22·4*b* is a similar construction of a cosine curve. Note that the reference point *o* on the circle has been advanced 90° counterclockwise.

22·4 Phasors

The geometric method of plotting sine functions discussed in Sec. 22·3 is highly important in explaining the procedure used in solving many important engineering problems.

For these applications we shall consider the radii in Fig. 22·5 to represent successive, momentary positions of a rotating position vector.

We impose four critical conditions on such a rotating position vector:

1. It rotates with a constant angular velocity.
2. It is of constant length.

3. It rotates in a coordinate plane about the origin of the coordinate system.
4. It rotates in a counterclockwise direction.

A rotating position vector is sometimes called a *phasor*.

Referring to Fig. 22·5*a*, we note that this figure is similar to Fig. 22·4*a*. However, certain very important differences do exist. The phasors $\overrightarrow{OR_0}$, $\overrightarrow{OR_1}$, $\overrightarrow{OR_2}$, etc., represent successive positions of the rotating phasor $\overrightarrow{OR}$ at times t_0, t_1, t_2, etc. The horizontal axis of the sine curve is calibrated with equally spaced *time* markers rather than with equally spaced angle markers. The ordinate of the sine curve at t_0, t_1, t_2, t_3, etc., is the momentary vertical projection of the position vector $\overrightarrow{OR}$ at that time.

During each revolution the position vector $\overrightarrow{OR}$ rotates through 360°, or 2π radians. The sequence of events which takes place during one revolution of the position vector is called a *cycle.*

The number of cycles taking place in 1 sec is called the *frequency*. The time in seconds required for the completion of 1 cycle is called the *time period* or simply the *period.*

From these definitions the following relations appear:

$$\phi = 360° \times f \times t \qquad \text{(in degrees)} \tag{13}$$

$$\phi = 2\pi \times f \times t \qquad \text{(in radians)} \tag{14}$$

$$T = \frac{1}{f} \tag{15}$$

where ϕ = momentary reference angle of position vector, referred to its position when we choose to begin to count time
f = frequency, cps
t = time during which position vector has been rotating from some arbitrary zero time-reference position, sec
T = period, sec

The zero reference position R_0 can be rotated either clockwise or counterclockwise, as shown in Fig. 22·5*b* and *c*. In such cases we introduce the phase constant ψ. The momentary reference angle of the position vector now becomes $(\phi - \psi)$ or $(\phi + \psi)$, according as R_0 has been rotated clockwise or counterclockwise.

The general equation for the ordinate of the sine curve as a function of time is

$$y = Y \sin (2\pi ft \pm \psi) \tag{16}$$

or

$$y = Y \sin (360° ft \pm \psi) \tag{17}$$

The term $2\pi f$ or $360° f$ is in the nature of angular velocity.

Ordinarily we let

$$\omega = 2\pi f \tag{18}$$

(when measuring ω in radians per second) or

$$\omega = 360^\circ f \tag{19}$$

fig. 22·5

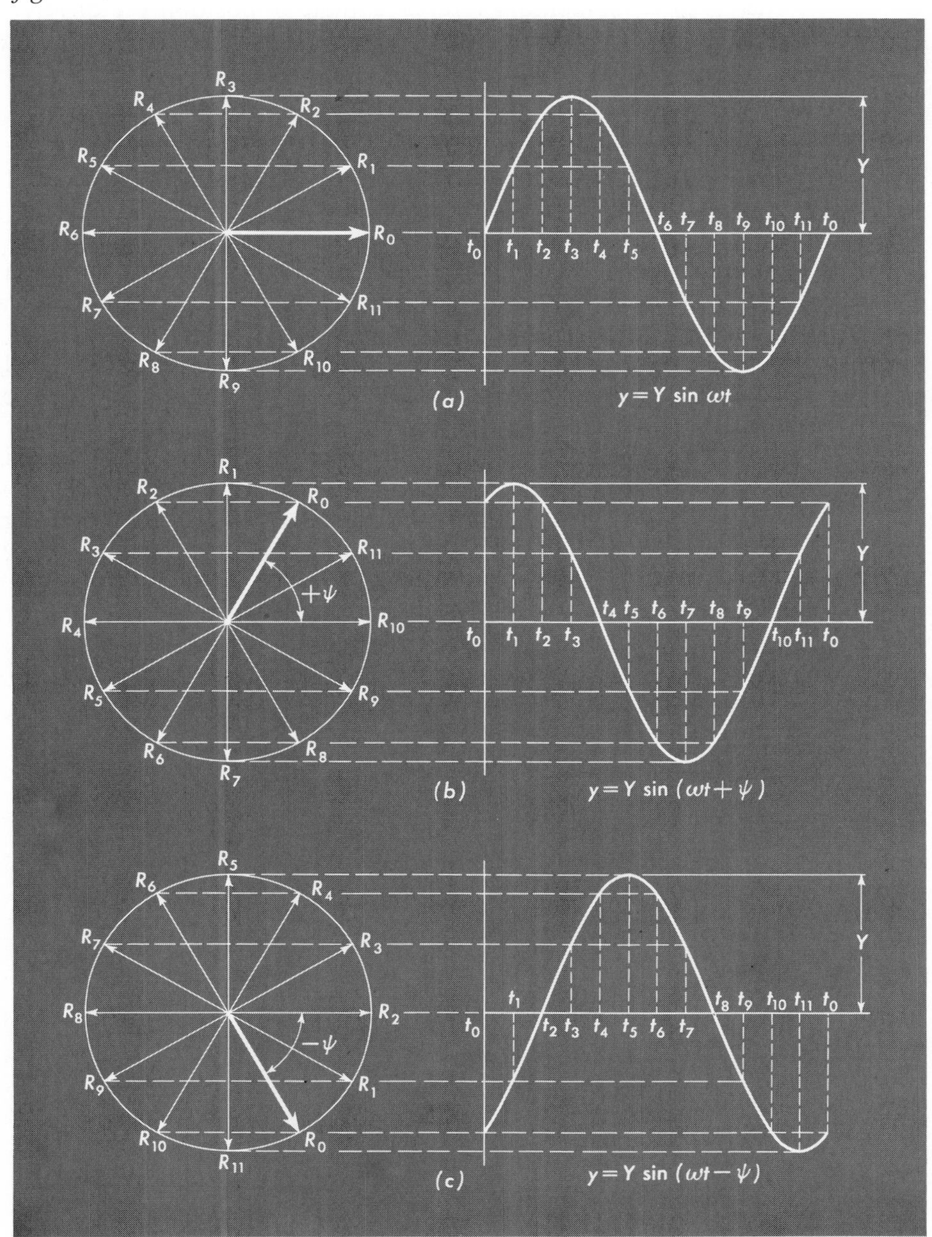

(when measuring ω in degrees per second). Equation (16) then becomes

$$y = Y \sin(\omega t \pm \psi) \tag{20}$$

where Y = constant amplitude
ω = angular velocity, radians or degrees per sec
t = time, sec
ψ = phase constant measured in same angular units as ωt
$(\omega t \pm \psi)$ = momentary reference angle of position vector referred to conventional reference position of system of rectangular coordinates

As a matter of expediency, we usually plot y against the angle ωt rather than against t itself. However, if after plotting y against ωt, it seems worth while to show the plot of y against t, the horizontal scale can be altered to read directly in time units.

The terms *amplitude, frequency, angular velocity, period,* and *phase constant* have been defined. Now let us interpret these terms in relation to specific quantities appearing in the general equation for a sine function.

With reference to Eq. (20), the constant Y is the amplitude. A change in Y alters each ordinate of the sine curve, but does not destroy the characteristic shape of the sine curve. A comparison of Fig. 22·3*a*, *c*, and *e* with Fig. 22·3*b*, *d*, and *f*, respectively, should illustrate this.

The phase constant ψ has no effect on the amplitude or the shape of the curve, but does have the effect of shifting the whole curve to the right or left along the time axis. A comparison among Fig. 22·3*a*, *c*, and *e* should illustrate this fact.

The constant ω or $2\pi f$ has no effect on either the amplitude or the relative position of the curve along the time axis. The constant ω or $2\pi f$ determines the number of cycles occurring in a given time interval. Figure 22·6 shows four curves all having the same amplitude and

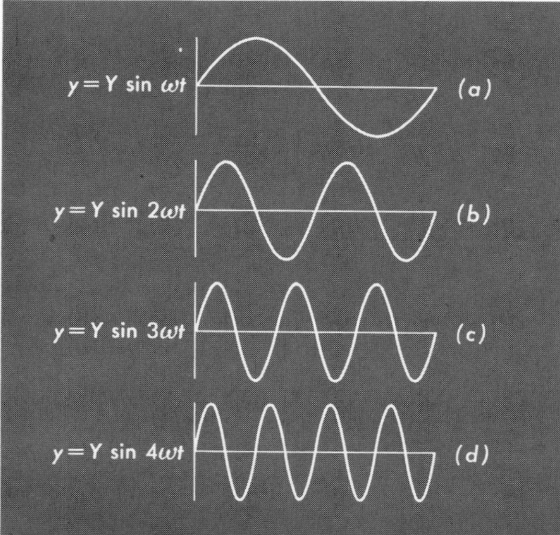

fig. 22·6

phase constant. In this case the phase constant is zero. The ω in curve a has been replaced by 2ω, 3ω, and 4ω in curves b, c, and d, respectively. This means that, referred to curve a, curve b has twice the frequency, curve c has 3 times the frequency, and curve d has 4 times the frequency.

When the frequency of one sine function occurs as an integral multiple of the frequency of another sine function, these two functions are said to be *harmonically* related.

Referred to Fig. 22·6, the function $y = \sin \omega t$ is called the *fundamental* frequency. The function $y = 2\omega t$ is called the *second harmonic* of the fundamental frequency.

The third and fourth harmonics of the function $y = \sin \omega t$ are illustrated in Fig. 22·6c and d.

EXERCISE 3

1. On the same axes plot the following equations. Use y as the ordinate and ωt measured in degrees as the abscissa. Plot over an interval of one cycle.

   (a) $y = \sin \omega t$ (b) $y = 2 \sin \omega t$
   (c) $y = 3 \sin \omega t$ (d) $y = 4 \sin \omega t$

2. Plot the following equations as instructed in Prob. 1:

   (a) $y = \cos \omega t$ (b) $y = 2 \cos \omega t$
   (c) $y = 3 \cos \omega t$ (d) $y = 4 \cos \omega t$

3. Plot the following equations as instructed in Prob. 1:

   (a) $y = \sin \omega t$ (b) $y = \sin 2\omega t$
   (c) $y = \sin 3\omega t$ (d) $y = \sin 4\omega t$

4. Plot the following curves as instructed in Prob. 1:

   (a) $y = \cos \omega t$ (b) $y = \cos 2\omega t$
   (c) $y = \cos 3\omega t$ (d) $y = \cos 4\omega t$

5. Plot as instructed in Prob. 1:

   (a) $y = \sin (\omega t + 30°)$ (b) $y = 3 \sin (\omega t + 60°)$
   (c) $y = 3 \sin \omega t$ (d) $y = \sin (\omega t - 30°)$
   (e) $y = \sin (\omega t - 60°)$

6. In the following equations find the amplitude, frequency, period, angular velocity, and phase constant. Express angular velocity in both radians per second and degrees per second; also express the phase constant in both radians and degrees. Note carefully when the data are given in radians and when in degrees.

   (a) $y = 23 \sin (314.16t + \pi/6)$
   (b) $y = 144 \sin (157.08t - \pi)$

(c) $y = 77 \sin (251.327t + 2\pi/7)$
(d) $y = 100 \sin (9 \times 10^5 t + 45°)$
(e) $y = 15 \sin (3.76992 \times 10^8 t - 3\pi/5)$
(f) $y = 147 \sin (21600t + 60°)$
(g) $y = 200 \sin (6.2832t - 2\pi/5)$
(h) $y = 300 \sin (1.6588 \times 10^{12} t + \pi/2)$

7. Using radian measure, write the equation for each of the sine curves described below:

	Amplitude	*Frequency*	*Phase constant*
(a)	200	30	$-50°$
(b)	150	3.0×10^8	00°
(c)	5	10^{12}	$\pi/2$
(d)	9	60	00°
(e)	10	1,000	$-45°$
(f)	20	500	30°
(g)	20	25	00°
(h)	115	40	-2π
(i)	100	50	90°

22·5 The sum of two sine functions of the same frequency

One of the typically characteristic problems in alternating-current electricity, vibrating mechanical bodies, certain types of wave motion, etc., involves the addition of two sine functions of the same frequency. If, for example,

$$y_1 = Y_1 \sin \omega t \tag{21}$$

and

$$y_2 = Y_2 \sin (\omega t + \psi) \tag{22}$$

let us investigate the properties of y_3, where

$$y_3 = y_1 + y_2 \tag{23}$$

That is to say, let us investigate some of the properties of the function

$$y_3 = Y_1 \sin \omega t + Y_2 \sin (\omega t + \psi) \tag{24}$$

where Y_1, Y_2, ω, and ψ are constants.

Figure 22·7 is a plot of Eqs. (21) and (22). In that figure we have arbitrarily let

$$Y_1 = 2$$
$$Y_2 = 3$$
$$\psi = 60°$$

The points on y_1 and y_2 were located by the geometric method discussed in Sec. 22·3. In Fig. 22·7 the phasors Y_1 and Y_2 are shown in their zero-reference position.

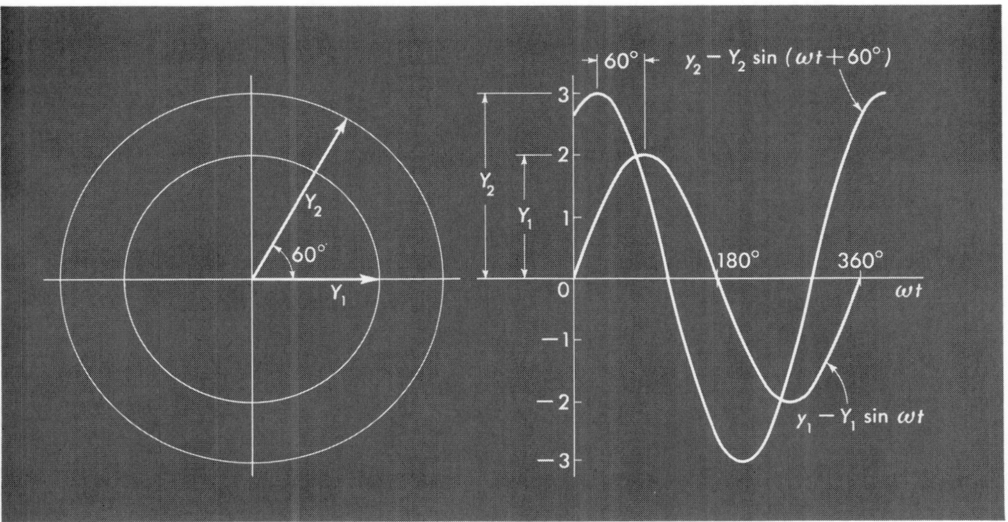

fig. 22·7

For any given value of ωt the ordinate of the graph of y_3 will be equal to the sum of the ordinates of y_1 and y_2. This is illustrated in Fig. 22·8. In this figure a succession of ordinates of y_1 and y_2 have been added to obtain a succession of points on the graph of y_3.

The shape of the graph of y_3 suggests that it may itself be a sine function. This fact will be demonstrated later.

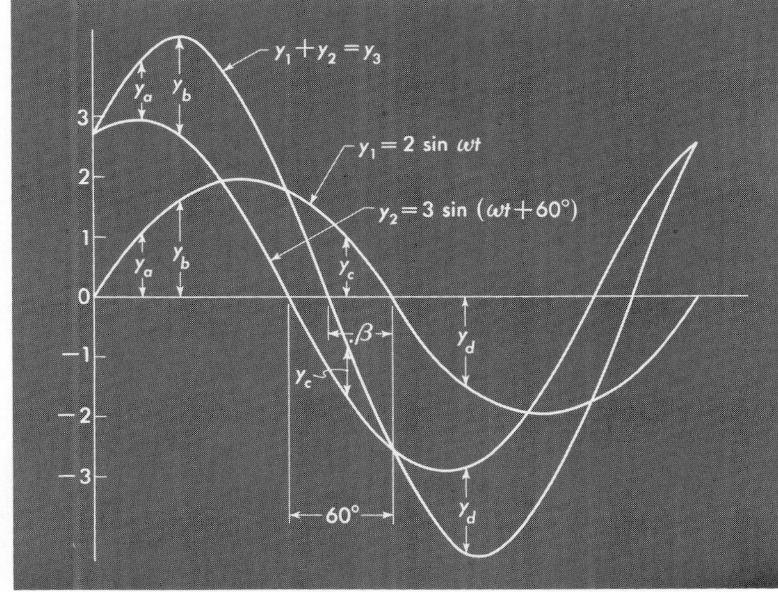

fig. 22·8

Within the limits to which we can plot the graph it would appear that the amplitude of y_3 is in the vicinity of 4.4 and that the phase of y_3 referred to y_1 is about 36°.

While this method of analysis has certain merits in describing the nature of y_3, it is quite cumbersome and its accuracy is limited by the strictly geometrical treatment.

A much more practical geometry is illustrated in Fig. 22·9. Here we have shown the three graphs plotted in Fig. 22·8, but we have also shown the phasors Y_1 and Y_2 which generated these curves, oriented in accordance with a randomly chosen value of ωt.

Now let us draw the line P_1P_3 parallel to Y_2. Also let us draw the line P_2P_3 parallel to Y_1, thus forming the parallelogram $OP_1P_3P_2$.

By the conditions of the problem, the lengths of Y_1 and Y_2 remain constant. Therefore the parallelogram $OP_1P_3P_2$ remains constant regardless of ωt.

Now let us draw the line OP_3 and designate it as Y_3. From the geometry of the figure it is quite evident that

$$P_3a = Y_2 \sin(\omega t + \psi) \tag{25}$$

and

$$ab = Y_1 \sin \omega t \tag{26}$$

Accordingly,

$$P_3b = Y_1 \sin \omega t + Y_2 \sin(\omega t + \psi) \tag{27}$$

However,

$$P_3b = Y_3 \sin(\omega t + \beta) \tag{28}$$

where β is indicated on the diagram. The evaluation of β will be discussed presently.

fig. 22·9

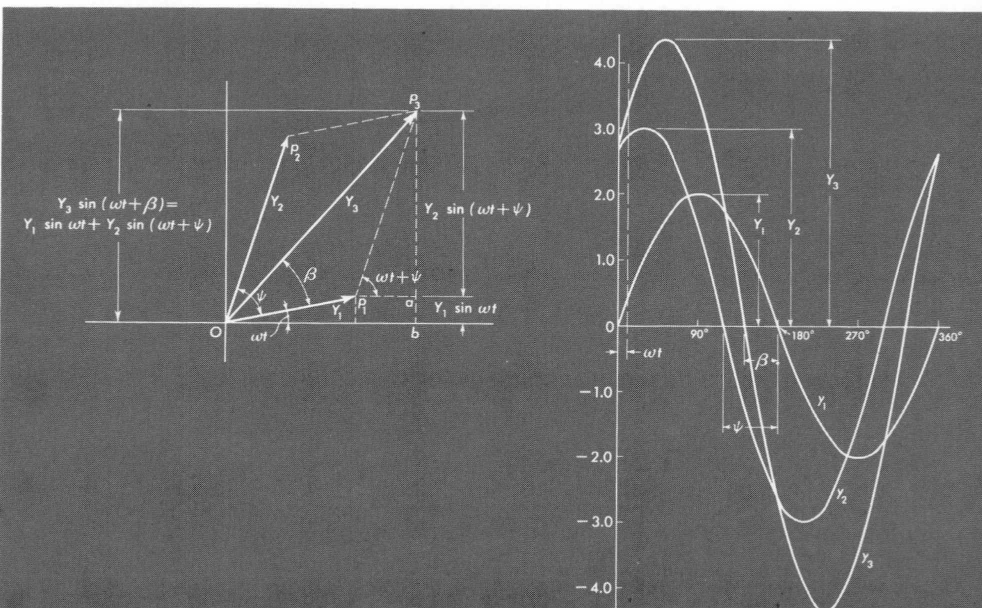

Therefore,

$$Y_3 \sin(\omega t + \beta) = Y_1 \sin \omega t + Y_2 \sin(\omega t + \psi) \tag{29}$$

The form of Eq. (29) shows that the sum of two sine functions of the same frequency is itself a sine function of that frequency.

A particularly important problem involving this area of mathematics is illustrated below.

example 1 If $y_1 = 2 \sin \omega t$ and $y_2 = 3 \sin(\omega t + \psi)$ and if $y_3 = y_2 + y_1$, find the amplitude of y_3 and the phase of y_3 referred to y_1, where $\psi = 60°$.

If we let Y_3 be the amplitude of y_3, and if we let β be the phase angle of y_3 referred to the phase of y_1, we can solve for Y_3 and β by reference to Fig. 22·10. We do this rather than to go through the somewhat unsatisfactory procedure of plotting all three graphs.

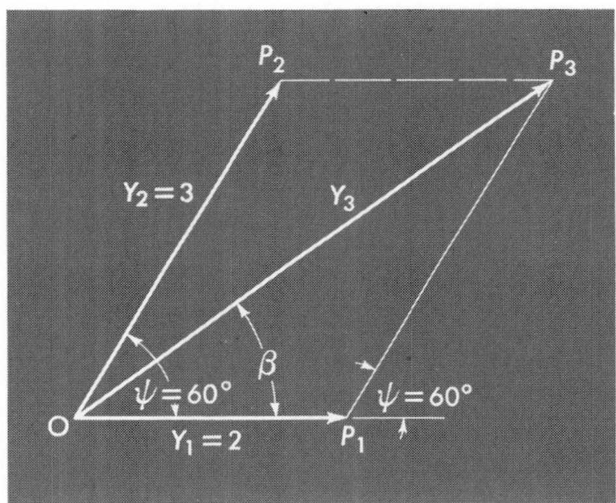

fig. 22·10

The student will observe that we can solve the triangle OP_3P_1 in Fig. 22·10 by the cosine law discussed in Secs. 18·3 and 18·4. That is,

$$Y_3^2 = Y_1^2 + Y_2^2 + 2Y_1Y_2 \cos \psi \tag{30}$$

$$Y_3^2 = 2^2 + 3^2 + 2 \times 2 \times 3 \cos 60°$$

$$= 4 + 9 + 6 = 19$$

$$Y_3 = \sqrt{19} = 4.359 \qquad \text{(ANS.)}$$

$$\frac{\sin \beta}{3} = \frac{\sin 120°}{4.359}$$

$$\sin \beta = 3 \times \frac{0.86603}{4.359} = 0.5960$$

$$\beta = 36°35' \qquad \text{(ANS.)}$$

EXERCISE 4

Find the amplitude of the sum of the two sine functions given in Probs. 1 through 5. Also find the phase angle of the sum referred to y_1. It is suggested that the computations be done on a slide rule.

1. $y_1 = 65 \sin \omega t \qquad y_2 = 44 \sin (\omega t + 75.75°)$
2. $y_1 = 3 \sin \omega t \qquad y_2 = 4 \sin (\omega t + 62.7°)$
3. $y_1 = 5 \sin \omega t \qquad y_2 = 4 \sin (\omega t + 78.5°)$
4. $y_1 = 7 \sin \omega t \qquad y_2 = 5 \sin (\omega t - 84.2°)$
5. $y_1 = 5 \sin \omega t \qquad y_2 = 8 \sin (\omega t - 46.56°)$

6. Given the equation $5 \sin \theta + 8 \cos \theta = 9$, write it as

$$5 \sin \theta + 8 \sin (\theta + 90°) = 9$$

and solve for θ.

7. A typical frequency-modulated carrier wave might be represented by the equation $E = D \sin (2\pi \cdot 100{,}000t + a \sin 2\pi \cdot 400t)$. Sketch the curve over a domain wide enough to show the important characteristics of this function.
8. A typical amplitude-modulated carrier wave might be represented by the equation $E = D(1 + 0.3 \sin 2\pi \cdot 400) \sin (2\pi \cdot 1{,}000{,}000t)$. Sketch the curve over a domain wide enough to show the important characteristics of this function.

23

complex numbers and position vectors

It has been discovered that complex numbers (see Sec. 8·16), the base of natural logarithms (see Sec. 11·4), the trigonometric functions, and position vectors (see Sec. 17·2) have certain related properties.

By taking advantage of these related properties we can develop some tremendously powerful mathematical tools with which to attack many important engineering problems.

In this chapter we shall relate some of the mathematical properties of exponential functions, complex numbers, trigonometric functions, and position vectors.

Unless otherwise stated or implied, the data in the examples and problems of this chapter are assumed to have an accuracy appropriate to a slide-rule solution.

23·1 The series expansion of $e^{j\alpha}$

In Sec. 11·3 we developed the series expansion of e^x where x is a real number. In Sec. 11·9 we began to study some of the properties of the series obtained when x is replaced by the imaginary number jx (where $j^2 = -1$).

Equation (2) of Sec. 11·3 is repeated below for reference.

$$e^x = 1 + x + \frac{x^2}{2!} + \frac{x^3}{3!} + \frac{x^4}{4!} + \frac{x^5}{5!} + \cdots \qquad (1)$$

Now as in Sec. 11·9 let us replace the real number x by an imaginary number. In this chapter a slightly different nomenclature will be convenient and for the imaginary exponent we shall use $j\alpha$, where α is a real number. Thus we may write

$$e^{j\alpha} = 1 + j\alpha + \frac{j^2\alpha^2}{2!} + \frac{j^3\alpha^3}{3!} + \frac{j^4\alpha^4}{4!} + \cdots \qquad (2)$$

23·2 Some properties of $e^{j\alpha}$

Again following Sec. 11·9 we note that Eq. (2) above may be written as

$$e^{j\alpha} = 1 + j\alpha - \frac{\alpha^2}{2!} - \frac{j\alpha^3}{3!} + \frac{\alpha^4}{4!} + \frac{j\alpha^5}{5!}\cdots \tag{3}$$

It can be proved that the terms in this particular series can be combined to yield (4) below:

$$e^{j\alpha} = \left(1 - \frac{\alpha^2}{2!} + \frac{\alpha^4}{4!}\cdots\right) + j\left(\alpha - \frac{\alpha^3}{3!} + \frac{\alpha^5}{5!}\cdots\right) \tag{4}$$

Now we shall let A designate the limit of the series

$$1 - \frac{\alpha^2}{2!} + \frac{\alpha^4}{4!} - \frac{\alpha^6}{6!}\cdots \tag{5}$$

and let B designate the limit of the series

$$\alpha - \frac{\alpha^3}{3!} + \frac{\alpha^5}{5!} - \frac{\alpha^7}{7!}\cdots \tag{6}$$

Then we may write

$$e^{j\alpha} = A + jB. \tag{7}$$

Observe that both A and B are real numbers. In a more advanced treatment of infinite series, it can be shown that by multiplying as

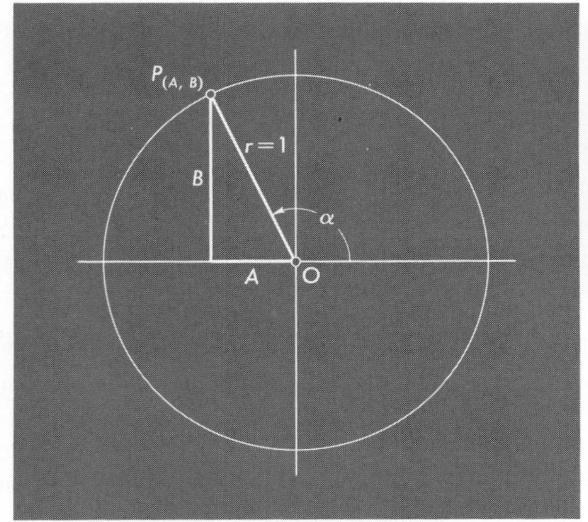

fig. 23·1

fig. 23·2

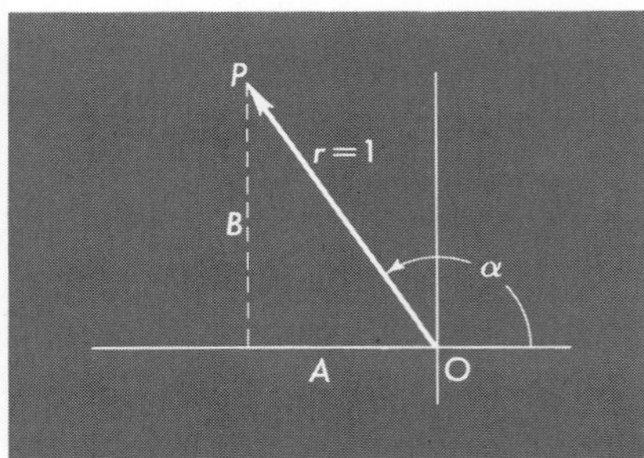

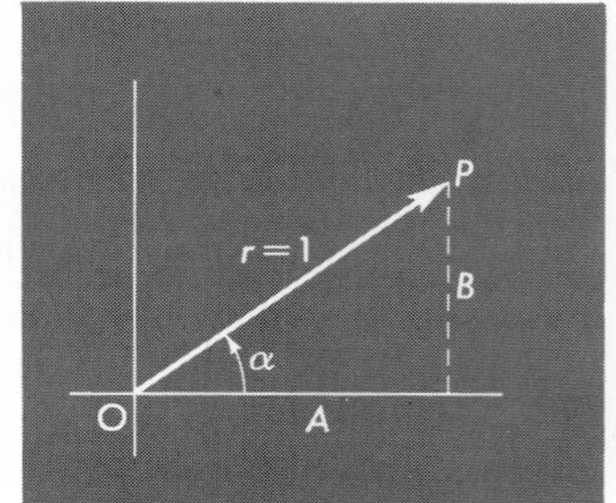

fig. 23·3

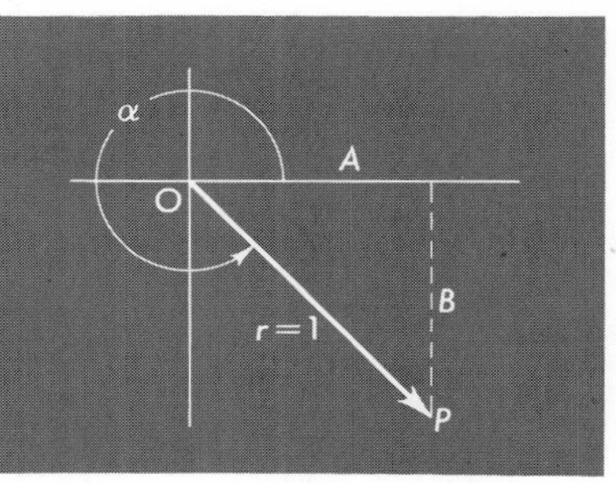

fig. 23·5

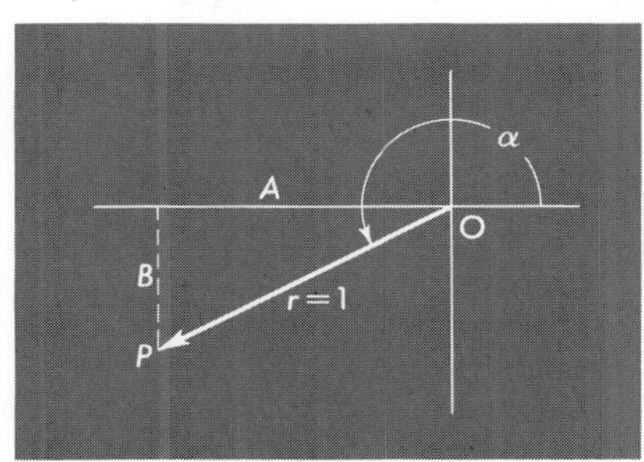

fig. 23·4

is done in Sec. 11·9, we may obtain the series for A^2 and B^2. Thus

$$A^2 = 1 - \alpha^2 + \frac{\alpha^4}{3} - \frac{2\alpha^6}{45} \cdots \tag{8}$$

and

$$B^2 = \alpha^2 - \frac{\alpha^4}{3} + \frac{2\alpha^6}{45} \cdots \tag{9}$$

Therefore, we may write

$$A^2 + B^2 = \left(1 - \alpha^2 + \frac{\alpha^4}{3} - \frac{2\alpha^6}{45} \cdots\right) + \left(\alpha^2 - \frac{\alpha^4}{3} + \frac{2\alpha^6}{45} \cdots\right) \tag{10}$$

By simplifying Eq. (10) we obtain

$$A^2 + B^2 = 1 \tag{11}$$

which the student will recognize as the equation for a circle of unit radius drawn with its center at the origin of the coordinate axes.

Thus any point on the circumference of the unit circle see (Fig. 23·1) will have coordinates (A,B) and the magnitude of the position vector $\overrightarrow{OP}$ is

$$|\overrightarrow{OP}| = 1 \tag{12}$$

(See also Figs. 23·2 through 23·5.)

23·3 The trigonometric functions

When we assign an arbitrary value to α in $e^{j\alpha}$, we thereby determine the projections A and B of a position vector whose magnitude is 1. Thus we also determine the reference angle of this unit position vector.

It seems reasonable, therefore, to consider α to be a measure of the vector reference angle.

Referring to Fig. 23 · 1 and according to our earlier geometric definitions of the trigonometric functions,

$$\sin \alpha = \frac{B}{r} \tag{13}$$

$$\cos \alpha = \frac{A}{r} \tag{14}$$

In Fig. 23 · 1, $r = 1$; therefore we may write

$$\sin \alpha = B \tag{15}$$

and

$$\cos \alpha = A \tag{16}$$

where α is measured in *radians*. (The student will have an opportunity to confirm this choice of angular units by arithmetical substitution in Exercise 1 below.)

From Eqs. (15), (16), and (7) we may write

$$e^{j\alpha} = \cos \alpha + j \sin \alpha \tag{17}$$

This is known as Euler's equation. It is sometimes abbreviated to

$$e^{j\alpha} = \text{Cis } \alpha \tag{18}$$

where the letters C, i, and s stand for the first letters in the words "cosine," "imaginary," and "sine."

By substituting (6) into (15) and (5) into (16) we find

$$\cos \alpha = 1 - \frac{\alpha^2}{2!} + \frac{\alpha^4}{4!} - \frac{\alpha^6}{6!} + \frac{\alpha^8}{8!} \cdots \tag{19}$$

and

$$\sin \alpha = \alpha - \frac{\alpha^3}{3!} + \frac{\alpha^5}{5!} - \frac{\alpha^7}{7!} + \frac{\alpha^9}{9!} \cdots \tag{20}$$

where α is measured in radians.

If as is customary in more advanced mathematics we take Eqs. (19) and (20) as the defining equations for the sine and cosine of the angle α, we find that these functions are now defined in arithmetic terms, independent of geometry.

The geometric definitions of the trigonometric functions used in more elementary treatment of trigonometry now cease to be basic definitions, and instead become subordinate properties of an infinite series.

EXERCISE 1

Evaluate as indicated in the following problems. Unless otherwise indicated the angles are in radians. Check your answers in a table of five-place trigonometric functions.

By using Table 23 · 1 much of the arithmetical labor can be eliminated. Evaluate to six decimal places:

1. $\sin \pi/3$	2. $\cos \pi/3$	3. $\sin \pi/4$
4. $\cos \pi/4$	5. $\sin 2\pi/3$	6. $\cos 2\pi/3$
7. $\sin 300°$	8. $\cos 300°$	9. $\sin 270°$

Hint: $300° = -\pi/3$ radians; also $270° = -\pi/2$ radians.

table 23·1

$\frac{\pi^1}{1!} = 3.1415927$	$\frac{\pi^{10}}{10!} = 0.0258069$
$\frac{\pi^2}{2!} = 4.9348022$	$\frac{\pi^{11}}{11!} = 0.0073704$
$\frac{\pi^3}{3!} = 5.1677128$	$\frac{\pi^{12}}{12!} = 0.0019296$
$\frac{\pi^4}{4!} = 4.0587121$	$\frac{\pi^{13}}{13!} = 0.0004663$
$\frac{\pi^5}{5!} = 2.5501640$	$\frac{\pi^{14}}{14!} = 0.0001046$
$\frac{\pi^6}{6!} = 1.3352628$	$\frac{\pi^{15}}{15!} = 0.0000219$
$\frac{\pi^7}{7!} = 0.5992645$	$\frac{\pi^{16}}{16!} = 0.0000043$
$\frac{\pi^8}{8!} = 0.2353306$	$\frac{\pi^{17}}{17!} = 0.0000008$
$\frac{\pi^9}{9!} = 0.0821459$	

23·4 A more general expression

In our discussion so far we have been dealing with the relation

$$e^{j\alpha} = A + jB \tag{21}$$

where

$$A = \cos\alpha$$
$$B = \sin\alpha$$

Thus the magnitudes of A and B are restricted to the range -1 to $+1$.

We can generalize Eq. (21) somewhat while still preserving an equivalence between the exponential and complex forms.

Let us multiply both members of Eq. (21) by the constant r whose numerical magnitude is unrestricted. We obtain

$$re^{j\alpha} = rA + jrB = r\cos\alpha + jr\sin\alpha \tag{22}$$

or

$$re^{j\alpha} = r(\cos\alpha + j\sin\alpha) = r\,\text{Cis}\,\alpha \tag{23}$$

Just as Eq. (21) has a geometric application to the unit circle (see Figs. 23·1 through 23·5), so, as we shall see presently, Eqs. (22) and (23) have an application to a circle of any radius (see Figs. 23·6 and 23·7).

If we let

$$a = r\cos\alpha \tag{24}$$

and

$$b = r\sin\alpha \tag{25}$$

where $a = X$ projection of position vector $\overrightarrow{OP}$

$b = Y$ projection of position vector $\overrightarrow{OP}$

$r =$ length of position vector $\overrightarrow{OP}$

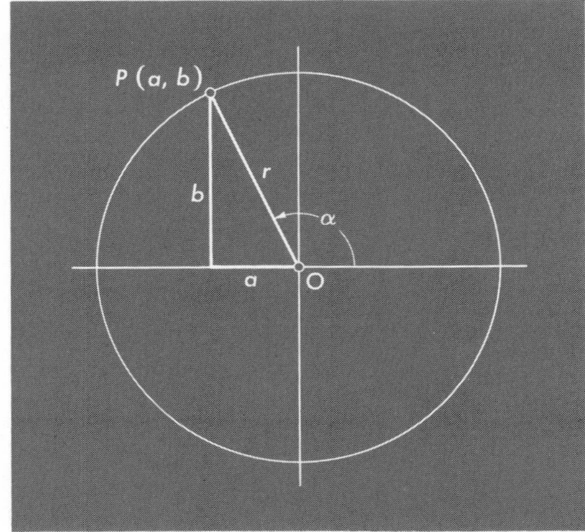

fig. 23·6

we may write

$$re^{j\alpha} = a + jb \tag{26}$$

The non-negative, real number r is called the *modulus* or the *absolute value* of the complex number $a + jb$. Thus we may write

$$r = |a + jb| = \sqrt{a^2 + b^2} \tag{27}$$

The angle α in Eq. (26) above is called the *argument* of the complex number $a + jb$.

fig. 23·7

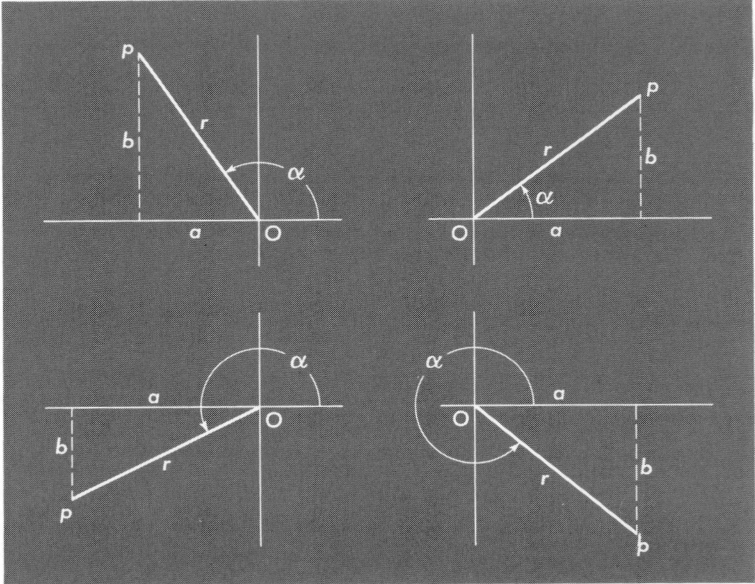

Thus we are no longer limited to the consideration of position vectors of unit length. We can define any position vector $\overrightarrow{OP}$ in the coordinate plane by a function expressed either in the form

$$\overrightarrow{OP} = re^{j\alpha} \tag{28}$$

or

$$\overrightarrow{OP} = a + jb \tag{29}$$

23·5 The reference position vector

Thus far we have discussed some of the related properties of exponential functions, complex numbers, and the trigonometric functions as they apply to position vectors. In the treatment so far we have emphasized the exponential forms.

In this section we shall begin to explore some of the ways in which we can involve position vectors more closely with the general complex number in the form $a + jb$.

As a first step we shall make certain basic definitions and agree on nomenclature. The axes in the rectangular coordinate system of Fig. 23·8 have been renamed for convenience the j axis and the R axis. Vectors drawn on these axes are defined below:

$+a$ = vector a units long drawn to right on R axis
$-a$ = vector a units long drawn to left on R axis
$+jb$ = vector b units long drawn upward on j axis
$-jb$ = vector b units long drawn downward on j axis

Therefore vector quantities such as $+2$, $+j3$, -4, $-j5$, etc., have a unique significance illustrated in Fig. 23·9.

fig. 23·9

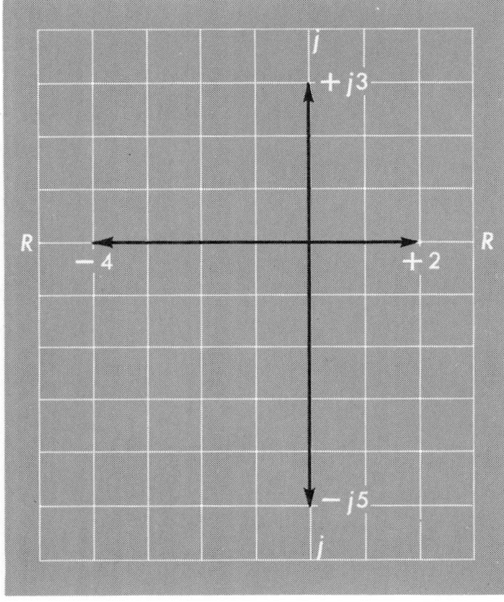

fig. 23·8

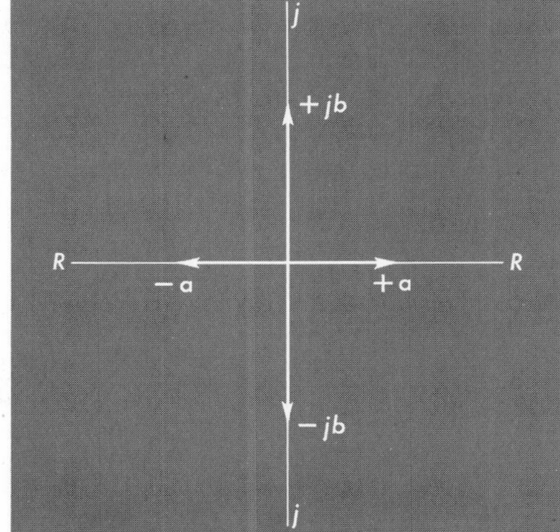

As in Fig. 23·9, "imaginary" numbers are plotted along the j axis and "real" numbers are plotted along the R axis.

It is important to notice two aspects of this notation.

1. The presence or absence of the "imaginary" unit j indicates the direction of the vector.
2. The sign before the "real" or "imaginary" number indicates the sense of the vector.

23·6 Addition of the reference vectors

The point P in Fig. 23·10 may be reached from O by moving a units in the positive direction along the R axis and, *in addition,* by moving b units in the positive direction referred to the j axis. The point P could also have been reached by moving along the vector $\overrightarrow{OP}$. The equivalence between these two traverses is indicated by the equation

$$\overrightarrow{OP} = a + jb \tag{30}$$

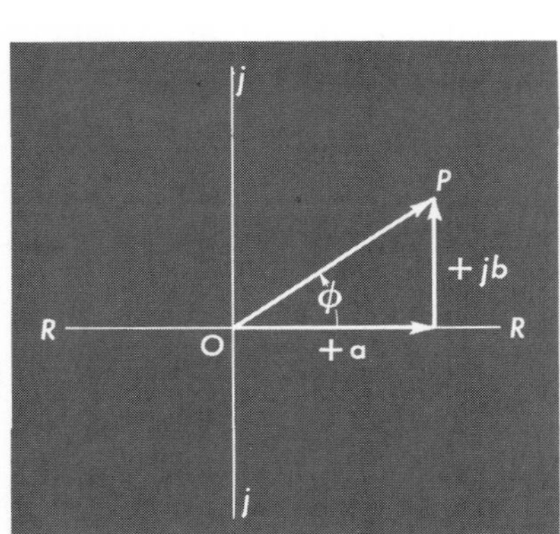

fig. 23·10

Hereafter in this chapter, when we encounter an expression in the form $a + jb$, we shall understand that a vector is indicated. If the vector a in Eq. (30) is drawn in a positive sense, it is customary to omit the plus sign before it. Several vectors are shown in Fig. 23·11, together with the complex numbers which represent them.

From the geometry of Fig. 23·10 it has become conventional to write

$$|\overrightarrow{OP}| = \sqrt{a^2 + b^2} \tag{31}$$

and

$$\tan \phi = \frac{b}{a} \tag{32}$$

However, as used in Eqs. (31) and (32), the quantities a and b are algebraic numbers, not vectors. Observe that the characteristic vector symbol j is missing from both equations. Furthermore, the multiplication involved in obtaining a^2 and b^2 in Eq. (31) is not a vector multiplication. Neither is the division in Eq. (32) a vector division.

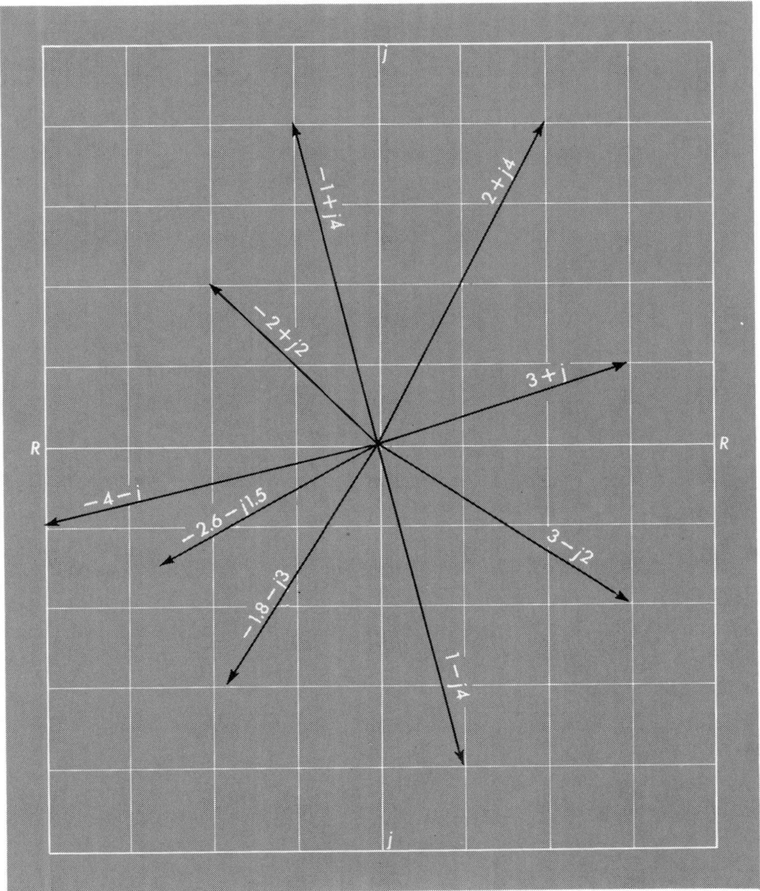

fig. 23·11

Equation (30) expresses the vector $\overrightarrow{OP}$ in terms of its rectangular components. The corresponding polar form is

$$\overrightarrow{OP} = \sqrt{a^2 + b^2}\,\underline{/\tan^{-1}\frac{b}{a}} \tag{33}$$

example 1 Plot the vector $2 + j9$, and calculate its magnitude and reference angle. Also express the vector in polar form.

The vector $2 + j9$ is plotted in Fig. 23·12.

$$|OP| = \sqrt{2^2 + 9^2} = \sqrt{4 + 81} = \sqrt{85} = 9.22$$
$$\tan \phi = 9/2 = 4.5$$
$$\phi = 77.5°$$
$$\overrightarrow{OP} = 9.22\underline{/77.5°}$$

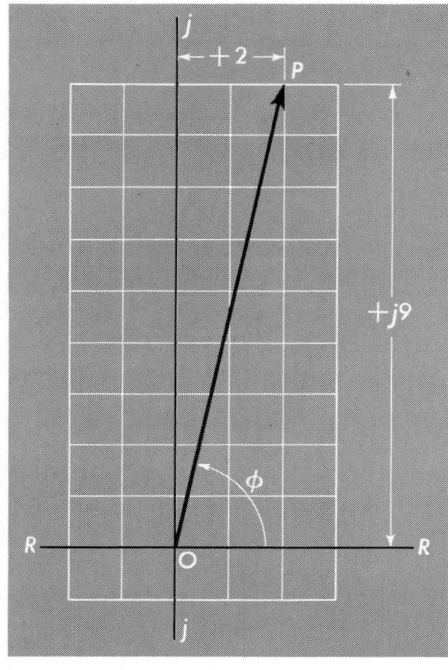

fig. 23·12

EXERCISE 2

Plot the following vectors, and calculate the magnitude and reference angle of each:

1. $3 + j4$	2. $6 - j2$	3. $-3 + j7$	4. $-2 - j6$
5. $3 - j4$	6. $4 + j2$	7. $-5 - j3$	8. $6 + j7$
9. $-2 + j2$	10. $3 - j2$	11. $-2 - j2$	12. $7 - j6$

23·7 Addition of position vectors in a complex plane

In this section we shall demonstrate that if $\overrightarrow{OS} = \overrightarrow{OP} + \overrightarrow{OQ}$, and if $\overrightarrow{OP} = a + jb$ and $\overrightarrow{OQ} = c + jd$, then the *algebraic* sum of $(a + jb)$ and $(c + jd)$ is a complex number defining the *vector* sum of $\overrightarrow{OP}$ and $\overrightarrow{OQ}$.

1. By definition of vector addition (referred to Fig. 23·13), the R projection of $\overrightarrow{OS}$, $(a + c)$, is the algebraic sum of the R projections of $\overrightarrow{OP}$ and $\overrightarrow{OQ}$. The j projection of $\overrightarrow{OS}$, $(b + d)$, is the algebraic sum of the j projections of $\overrightarrow{OP}$ and $\overrightarrow{OQ}$.

2. If we let

$$\overrightarrow{OP} = a + jb$$

and

$$\overrightarrow{OQ} = c + jd$$

then

$$\overrightarrow{OS} = (a + jb) + (c + jd)$$

$$\overrightarrow{OS} = (a + c) + j(b + d) \qquad \textbf{(34)}$$

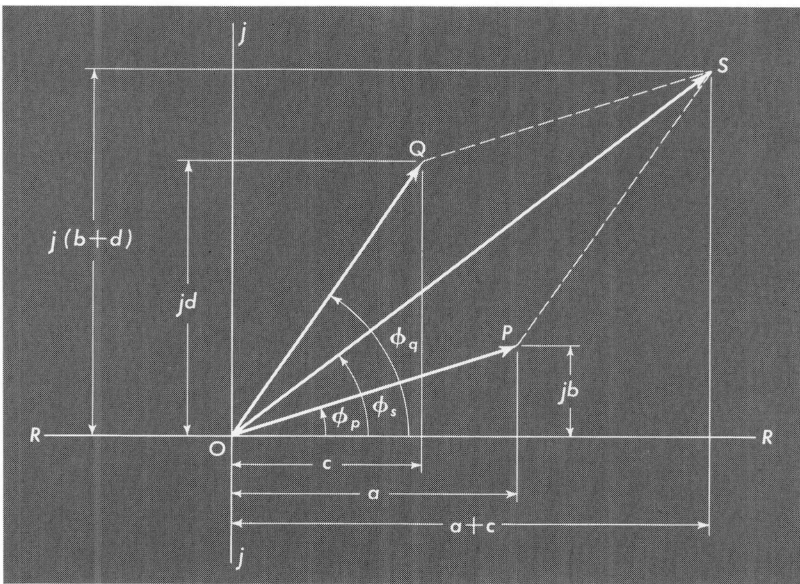

fig. 23·13

Part 1 above is a definitive statement for the *vector* sum of $\overrightarrow{OP}$ and $\overrightarrow{OQ}$. Equation (34) is the result of the *algebraic* addition of $(a + jb)$ and $(c + jd)$. The definitive statement above and Eq. (34) correspond. Therefore, we may conclude that *vector* addition may be accomplished by the *algebraic* addition of the complex numbers representing the vectors.

Observe that in vector addition we need not take advantage of the unique properties of j. As far as this operation is concerned, the symbol j is used simply to signal that its coefficient is the magnitude of a vector perpendicular to the vector whose magnitude is the real part of the complex number.

example 2 Add the vectors $(3 + j4)$ and $(2 + j5)$ and express the sum in polar form.

Let

$$\overrightarrow{OS} = (3 + j4) + (2 + j5)$$

$$\overrightarrow{OS} = 5 + j9$$

Then

$$|\overrightarrow{OS}| = \sqrt{5^2 + 9^2} = \sqrt{106} = 10.30$$

$$\tan \psi = 9/5 = 1.8$$

where ψ = reference angle of $\overrightarrow{OS}$
$= 60.9°$

$$\overrightarrow{OS} = 10.30\underline{/60.9°}$$

example 3 Add the vectors $(2 + j5)$ and $(-6 - j7)$. Express the sum in polar form.

Let

$$\overrightarrow{OS} = (2 + j5) + (-6 - j7)$$
$$\overrightarrow{OS} = -4 - j2$$
$$|\overrightarrow{OS}| = \sqrt{4^2 + 2^2} = \sqrt{16 + 4} = \sqrt{20} = 4.47$$
$$\tan \psi = \frac{-2}{-4} = +0.5$$

where ψ = reference angle of $\overrightarrow{OS}$

$\psi = 26.6° + 180° = 206.6°$

$$\overrightarrow{OS} = 4.47\underline{/206.6°}$$

example 4 Express the vector $10\underline{/30°}$ in complex notation.

$$R \text{ projection} = 10 \cos 30°$$
$$j \text{ projection} = 10 \sin 30°$$

Therefore we may write

$$\begin{aligned} 10\underline{/30°} &= 10 \cos 30° + j10 \sin 30° \\ &= 10 \times 0.866 + j10 \times 0.5 \\ &= 8.66 + j5 \end{aligned}$$

example 5 Add the vectors $5\underline{/150°}$ and $10\underline{/45°}$. Express the sum in polar form.

Let

$$\overrightarrow{OS} = 5\underline{/150°} + 10\underline{/45°}$$

$$\begin{aligned} \overrightarrow{OS} &= (5 \cos 150° + j5 \sin 150°) + (10 \cos 45° + j10 \sin 45°) \\ &= 5(-0.866) + (j5 \times 0.5) + (10 \times 0.707) + (j10 \times 0.707) \\ &= -4.33 + j2.5 + 7.07 + j7.07 \\ &= 2.74 + j9.57 \end{aligned}$$
$$|\overrightarrow{OS}| = \sqrt{2.74^2 + 9.57^2} = \sqrt{7.5 + 91.6} = 9.95$$
$$\tan \psi = \frac{9.57}{2.74} = 3.49$$
$$\overrightarrow{OS} = 9.95\underline{/74.0°}$$

EXERCISE 3

Perform the following vector additions, and express the sums in polar form:

1. $(2 + j3) + (4 + j5)$
2. $(5 + j7) + (-6 + j5)$
3. $(9 + j2) + (-3 + j2)$
4. $(8 + j7) + (-2 - j3)$
5. $(6 + j10) + (-9 - j5)$
6. $(4 + j3) + (-8 - j6)$

7. $(7 + j9) + (4 - j5)$
8. $(2 + j3) + (5 - j8)$
9. $(-5 + j2) + (-2 + j6)$
10. $(-2 + j5) + (-4 - j1)$
11. $(-3 + j8) + (-4 - j12)$
12. $(-5 + j12) + (3 - j4)$
13. $(-2 + j10) + (1 - j15)$
14. $(-2 + j2) + (6 - j5)$
15. $(-5 - j9) + (-2 - j6)$
16. $(-2 - j8) + (1 - j2)$
17. $(-5 - j10) + (10 - j5)$
18. $(3 - j2) + (7 - j5)$

Perform the following vector additions, and express the sums in complex form:

19. $6\underline{/40^\circ} + 10\underline{/70^\circ}$
20. $3\underline{/30^\circ} + 10\underline{/160^\circ}$
21. $15\underline{/20^\circ} + 20\underline{/100^\circ}$
22. $20\underline{/50^\circ} + 2\underline{/200^\circ}$
23. $20\underline{/20^\circ} + 10\underline{/150^\circ}$
24. $5\underline{/80^\circ} + 2\underline{/200^\circ}$
25. $5\underline{/40^\circ} + 2\underline{/205^\circ}$
26. $13\underline{/15^\circ} + 2\underline{/340^\circ}$
27. $25\underline{/10^\circ} + 25\underline{/300^\circ}$
28. $15\underline{/140^\circ} + 20\underline{/120^\circ}$
29. $10\underline{/170^\circ} + 5\underline{/260^\circ}$
30. $8\underline{/160^\circ} + 2\underline{/240^\circ}$

23·8 Subtraction of position vectors in a complex plane

In this section we shall demonstrate that if $\overrightarrow{OS} = \overrightarrow{OP} - \overrightarrow{OQ}$, and if $\overrightarrow{OP} = a + jb$ and $\overrightarrow{OQ} = c + jd$, then the *algebraic* difference between $a + jb$ and $c + jd$ is a complex number defining the *vector* difference between $\overrightarrow{OP}$ and $\overrightarrow{OQ}$ (see Fig. 23·14).

1. By definition of vector subtraction (referred to Fig. 23·14), the R projection of $\overrightarrow{OS}$, $(a - c)$, is the algebraic difference between the R

fig. 23·14

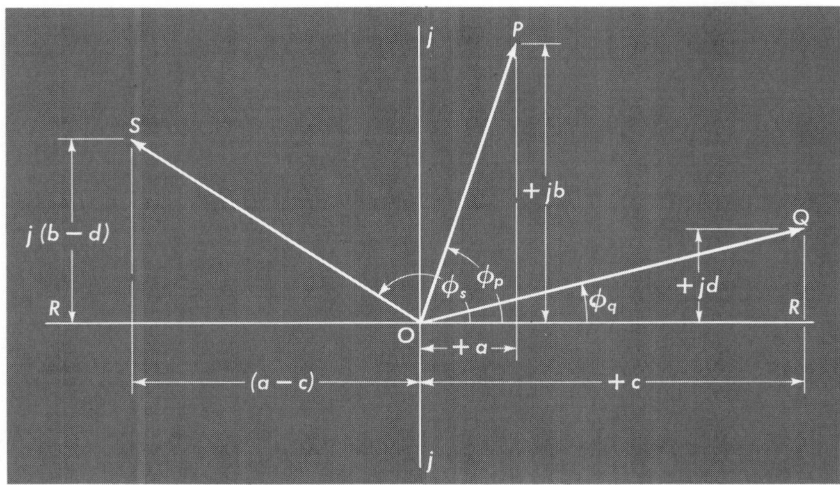

projections of $\overrightarrow{OP}$ and $\overrightarrow{OQ}$. The j projection of $\overrightarrow{OS}$ is the algebraic difference between the j projections of $\overrightarrow{OP}$ and $\overrightarrow{OQ}$.

2. If we let

$$\overrightarrow{OP} = a + jb$$

and

$$\overrightarrow{OQ} = c + jd$$

then

$$\overrightarrow{OS} = (a + jb) - (c + jd)$$

$$\overrightarrow{OS} = a + jb - c - jd = a - c + jb - jd$$

$$\overrightarrow{OS} = (a - c) + j(b - d) \tag{35}$$

Part 1 above is a definitive statement of the *vector* difference between $\overrightarrow{OP}$ and $\overrightarrow{OQ}$. Equation (35) is the result of the *algebraic* subtraction of $(c + jd)$ from $(a + jb)$. The definitive statement above and Eq. (35) correspond. Therefore, we may conclude that vector subtraction may be accomplished by the algebraic subtraction of the complex numbers representing the vectors.

Observe that in vector subtraction we need not take advantage of the unique properties of j. As far as this operation is concerned, the symbol j is used simply as a signal that its coefficient is the magnitude of a vector perpendicular to the vector whose magnitude is the real part of the complex number.

example 6 Subtract the vector $5 + 3j$ from the vector $2 - 6j$.

Let

$$\overrightarrow{OS} = (2 - 6j) - (5 + 3j)$$

$$= -3 - 9j$$

$$|\overrightarrow{OS}| = \sqrt{3^2 + 9^2} = \sqrt{9 + 81} = \sqrt{90} = 9.49$$

$$\tan \psi = \frac{-9}{-3} = +3$$

where ψ = reference angle of $\overrightarrow{OS}$
= 251.6°

$$\overrightarrow{OS} = 9.49\underline{/251.6^\circ}$$

example 7 Subtract the vector $30\underline{/60^\circ}$ from the vector $10\underline{/30^\circ}$.

Let

$$\overrightarrow{OS} = 10\underline{/30^\circ} - 30\underline{/60^\circ}$$

$$30\underline{/60^\circ} = 30 \cos 60^\circ + j30 \sin 60^\circ$$

$$= (30 \times 0.5) + (j30 \times 0.866)$$

$$= 15 + j26.0$$

$$
\begin{aligned}
10\underline{/30^\circ} &= 10 \cos 30^\circ + j10 \sin 30^\circ \\
&= (10 \times 0.866) + (j10 \times 0.5) \\
&= 8.66 + j5 \\
\overrightarrow{OS} &= (8.66 + j5) - (15 + j26.0) \\
&= -6.34 - j21.0 \\
|\overrightarrow{OS}| &= \sqrt{6.34^2 + 21.0^2} = 21.9 \\
\tan \psi &= \frac{-21.0}{-6.34} = +3.31 \\
\psi &= 253.2^\circ \\
OS &= 21.9\underline{/253.2^\circ}
\end{aligned}
$$

EXERCISE 4

Perform the following vector subtractions, and record the vector difference in both complex and polar forms:

1. $(3 + j5) - (2 - j3)$
2. $(4 + j6) - (10 - j9)$
3. $(-2 + j5) - (3 + j4)$
4. $(10 - j3) - (6 + j8)$
5. $(-1 + j2) - (-4 + j2)$
6. $10\underline{/42^\circ} - 30\underline{/160^\circ}$
7. $3\underline{/100^\circ} - 4\underline{/340^\circ}$
8. $2\underline{/250^\circ} - 3\underline{/40^\circ}$
9. $6\underline{/300^\circ} - 8\underline{/125^\circ}$
10. $3\underline{/270^\circ} - 2\underline{/180^\circ}$

23·9 Other operations with position vectors

In Sec. 23·4, Eq. (29), we showed how complex numbers can be used to define uniquely position vectors in a complex plane. In Secs. 23·7 and 23·8 we showed how we can use complex notation in vector addition and subtraction according to the definitions of these vector operations previously given.

Up to this point we have not defined the operations of multiplication, division, raising to powers, extracting roots, or obtaining the reciprocal as applied to position vectors. These operations will be discussed in the following sections.

23·10 The product of two position vectors

Let us now develop the significance of the multiplication of two position vectors. Let these position vectors be expressible in the form

$$\overrightarrow{OA} = r_a e^{j\phi_a} \tag{36}$$

and

$$\overrightarrow{OB} = r_b e^{j\phi_b} \tag{37}$$

where r_a = magnitude of position vector $\overrightarrow{OA}$

r_b = magnitude of position vector $\overrightarrow{OB}$

ϕ_a = reference angle of position vector $\overrightarrow{OA}$

ϕ_b = reference angle of position vector $\overrightarrow{OB}$

By multiplying Eq. (36) by Eq. (37), we obtain

$$\overrightarrow{OA} \times \overrightarrow{OB} = r_a r_b e^{j(\phi_a + \phi_b)} \tag{38}$$

But from Eq. (23) we may write

$$\overrightarrow{OA} \times \overrightarrow{OB} = r_a r_b[\cos(\phi_a + \phi_b) + j \sin(\phi_a + \phi_b)] \tag{39}$$

Thus the product of two position vectors $\overrightarrow{OA}$ and $\overrightarrow{OB}$ is a position vector $\overrightarrow{OC}$ such that the magnitude of $\overrightarrow{OC}$ is the product of the magnitudes of $\overrightarrow{OA}$ and $\overrightarrow{OB}$ and such that the reference angle of $\overrightarrow{OC}$ is the sum of the reference angles of $\overrightarrow{OA}$ and $\overrightarrow{OB}$.

23 · 11 The quotient of two position vectors

Let us now develop the significance of the division of two position vectors. Let these position vectors be expressible in the form

$$\overrightarrow{OA} = r_a e^{j\phi_a} \tag{40}$$

and

$$\overrightarrow{OB} = r_b e^{j\phi_b} \tag{41}$$

where r_a = magnitude of position vector $\overrightarrow{OA}$

r_b = magnitude of position vector $\overrightarrow{OB}$

ϕ_a = reference angle of position vector $\overrightarrow{OA}$

ϕ_b = reference angle of position vector $\overrightarrow{OB}$

By dividing Eq. (40) by Eq. (41), we obtain

$$\frac{\overrightarrow{OA}}{\overrightarrow{OB}} = \frac{r_a}{r_b} e^{j(\phi_a - \phi_b)} \tag{42}$$

But from Eq. (23) we may write

$$\frac{\overrightarrow{OA}}{\overrightarrow{OB}} = \frac{r_a}{r_b}[\cos(\phi_a - \phi_b) + j \sin(\phi_a - \phi_b)] \tag{43}$$

Thus the quotient of two position vectors $\overrightarrow{OA}$ and $\overrightarrow{OB}$ is a position vector $\overrightarrow{OC}$ such that the magnitude of $\overrightarrow{OC}$ is the quotient of the magnitudes of $\overrightarrow{OA}$ and $\overrightarrow{OB}$ and such that the reference angle of $\overrightarrow{OC}$ is the difference between the reference angles of $\overrightarrow{OA}$ and $\overrightarrow{OB}$.

23·12 Multiplication and division of position vectors in a real plane

The mathematical work in Sec. 23·10 culminating in Eq. (39) and the mathematical work in Sec. 23·11 culminating in Eq. (43) were done to establish a rationale for the processes of multiplication and division of position vectors. We based those discussions on position vectors expressed in the exponential form. The worded definitions which necessarily follow Eqs. (39) and (43) apply, however, regardless of the mathematical form used to express these vectors.

23·13 The product of two position vectors in a real plane

From the definition of vector multiplication of position vectors discussed in Sec. 23·10 it is evident that (see Fig. 23·15) if

$$\overrightarrow{OP} = |OP| \underline{/\phi_p} \tag{44}$$

$$\overrightarrow{OQ} = |OQ| \underline{/\phi_q} \tag{45}$$

$$\overrightarrow{OR} = |OR| \underline{/\phi_r} \tag{46}$$

and if

$$\overrightarrow{OR} = \overrightarrow{OP} \times \overrightarrow{OQ} \tag{47}$$

then

$$|\overrightarrow{OR}| \underline{/\phi_r} = |\overrightarrow{OP}| \times |\overrightarrow{OQ}| \underline{/\phi_p + \phi_q} \tag{48}$$

$$|\overrightarrow{OR}| = |\overrightarrow{OP}| \times |\overrightarrow{OQ}| \tag{49}$$

and

$$\phi_r = \phi_p + \phi_q \tag{50}$$

fig. 23·15

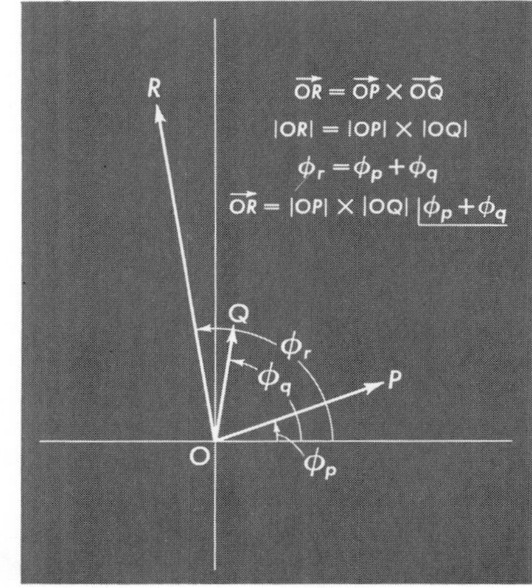

The multiplication of position vectors in a real plane can be accomplished directly when the data are given in polar notation. If the data are given in rectangular notation, they must be converted to polar notation before multiplying or dividing, unless we resort to the method outlined in Sec. 23·15.

example 8 If the vector $\overrightarrow{OR} = 2\underline{/17^\circ} \times 5\underline{/180^\circ}$, find the magnitude and reference angle of $\overrightarrow{OR}$.

Following Eq. (49),

$$|\overrightarrow{OR}| = 2 \times 5 = 10$$

Following Eq. (50),

$$\phi_r = 17^\circ + 180^\circ = 197^\circ$$

Then $$\overrightarrow{OR} = 10\underline{/197^\circ}$$

example 9 Find $\overrightarrow{OR}$ in polar notation if $\overrightarrow{OR} = \overrightarrow{OA} \times \overrightarrow{OB}$, where the X projection of $\overrightarrow{OA}$ is 2, the Y projection of $\overrightarrow{OA}$ is 3, the X projection of $\overrightarrow{OB}$ is 5, and the Y projection of $\overrightarrow{OB}$ is -4.

$$|\overrightarrow{OA}| = \sqrt{2^2 + 3^2} = \sqrt{4 + 9} = \sqrt{13} = 3.61$$
$$\tan \phi_a = 3/2 = 1.5$$
$$\phi_a = 56.3^\circ$$
$$|\overrightarrow{OB}| = \sqrt{5^2 + 4^2} = \sqrt{25 + 16} = \sqrt{41} = 6.40$$
$$\tan \phi_b = \frac{-4}{5} = -0.8$$
$$\phi_b = -38.66^\circ$$
$$|\overrightarrow{OR}| = 3.61 \times 6.40 = 23.1$$
$$\phi_r = 56.3^\circ + (-38.66^\circ) = 17.64^\circ$$
$$\overrightarrow{OR} = 23.1\underline{/17.64^\circ}$$

EXERCISE 5

Solve the following vector equations for ρ and ϕ. Draw a scale diagram to illustrate each problem.

1. $\rho\underline{/\phi} = 2\underline{/20^\circ} \times 3\underline{/-30^\circ}$
2. $\rho\underline{/\phi} = 4\underline{/300^\circ} \times 5\underline{/60^\circ}$
3. $\rho\underline{/\phi} = 5\underline{/160^\circ} \times 4\underline{/-90^\circ}$
4. $\rho\underline{/\phi} = 3\underline{/225^\circ} \times 2\underline{/40^\circ}$
5. $\rho\underline{/\phi} = 6\underline{/159^\circ} \times 4\underline{/340^\circ}$
6. $\rho\underline{/\phi} = 25\underline{/-120^\circ} \times 50\underline{/120^\circ}$

Find the vector product of each set of vectors given below. Express the products in polar form.

	Vector	*X projection*	*Y projection*
7.	$\overrightarrow{OA}$	+3	+2
	$\overrightarrow{OB}$	−2	+7
8.	$\overrightarrow{OA}$	+4	+5
	$\overrightarrow{OB}$	+1	+2
9.	$\overrightarrow{OA}$	−6	−5
	$\overrightarrow{OB}$	−2	−3
10.	$\overrightarrow{OA}$	+5	−1
	$\overrightarrow{OB}$	−3	+2

23·14 The quotient of two position vectors in a real plane

From the definition of vector division as applied to position vectors, discussed in Sec. 23·11, it is evident that (see Fig. 23·16) if

$$\overrightarrow{OP} = |OP| \underline{/\phi_p} \tag{51}$$

$$\overrightarrow{OQ} = |OQ| \underline{/\phi_q} \tag{52}$$

$$\overrightarrow{OR} = |OR| \underline{/\phi_r} \tag{53}$$

and if

$$\overrightarrow{OR} = \overrightarrow{OP} \div \overrightarrow{OQ} \tag{54}$$

then

$$|\overrightarrow{OR}| \underline{/\phi_r} = \frac{|\overrightarrow{OP}|}{|\overrightarrow{OQ}|} \underline{/\phi_p - \phi_q} \tag{55}$$

The division of position vectors in a real plane can be accomplished directly when the data are given in polar notation. If the data are given in rectangular notation, they must be converted to polar notation before multiplying or dividing, unless we resort to the method outlined in Sec. 23·16.

fig. 23·16

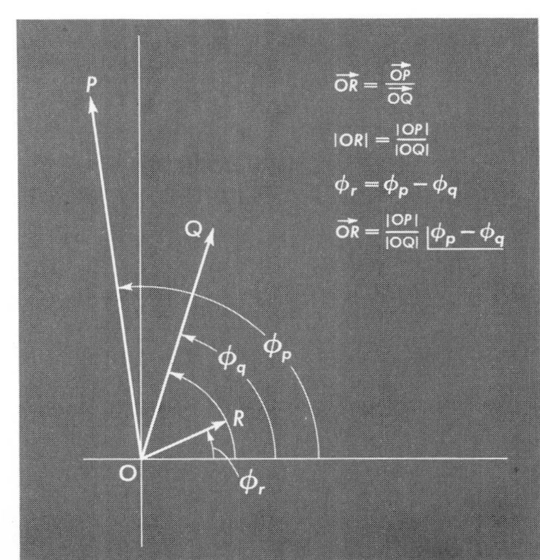

example 10 If the vector $\overrightarrow{OR} = 16\underline{/40^\circ}/2\underline{/-20^\circ}$, find the magnitude of $\overrightarrow{OR}$ and the reference angle of $\overrightarrow{OR}$.

Following Eq. (55),

$$\overrightarrow{OR} = 16/2\underline{/40^\circ - (-20^\circ)}$$
$$\overrightarrow{OR} = 8\underline{/60^\circ}$$

example 11 Find $\overrightarrow{OR}$ in polar notation if $\overrightarrow{OR} = \overrightarrow{OA}/\overrightarrow{OB}$, where the X projection of $\overrightarrow{OA}$ is 2, the Y projection of $\overrightarrow{OA}$ is 3, the X projection of $\overrightarrow{OB}$ is 5, and the Y projection of $\overrightarrow{OB}$ is -4.

$$|\overrightarrow{OA}| = \sqrt{2^2 + 3^2} = \sqrt{4 + 9} = \sqrt{13} = 3.61$$
$$\tan \phi_a = 3/2 = 1.5$$
$$\phi_a = 56.3^\circ$$
$$|\overrightarrow{OB}| = \sqrt{5^2 + (-4)^2} = \sqrt{25 + 16} = \sqrt{41} = 6.40$$
$$\tan \phi_b = \frac{-4}{5} = -0.8$$
$$\phi_b = -38.66^\circ$$
$$|\overrightarrow{OR}| = \frac{3.61}{6.40} = 0.564$$
$$\phi_r = 56.3^\circ - (-38.66^\circ) = 95.0^\circ$$
$$\overrightarrow{OR} = 0.564\underline{/95.0^\circ}$$

example 12 Solve for ρ and ϕ in the equation

$$\rho\underline{/\phi} = \frac{3\underline{/45^\circ} + 2\underline{/30^\circ}}{5\underline{/60^\circ} - 4\underline{/30^\circ}}$$

The addition and subtraction may be performed in rectangular notation. We shall simplify the numerator of the given equation first and express this numerator as a single vector in polar form. The X projection of the vector sum of the numerator is

$$\begin{aligned} x_n &= 3 \cos 45^\circ + 2 \cos 30^\circ \\ &= 3 \times 0.707 + 2 \times 0.866 \\ &= 2.12 + 1.732 = +3.85 \end{aligned}$$

The Y projection of the vector sum of the numerator is

$$\begin{aligned} y_n &= 3 \sin 45^\circ + 2 \sin 30^\circ \\ &= 3 \times 0.707 + 2 \times 0.5 \\ &= 2.12 + 1.00 = 3.12 \end{aligned}$$

The magnitude of the vector sum of the numerator is

$$\rho_n = \sqrt{3.85^2 + 3.12^2} = 4.96$$

The tangent of the numerator reference angle ϕ_n is

$$\tan \phi_n = \frac{3.12}{3.85} = 0.810$$

$$\phi_n = 39.0°$$

We shall now simplify the denominator of the given equation and express this denominator as a single vector in polar form.

The X projection of the vector sum of the denominator is

$$\begin{aligned} x_d &= 5 \cos 60° - 4 \cos 30° \\ &= 5 \times 0.5000 - 4 \times 0.8660 \\ &= 2.500 - 3.464 = -0.964 \end{aligned}$$

The Y projection of the vector sum of the denominator is

$$\begin{aligned} y_d &= 5 \sin 60° - 4 \sin 30° \\ &= 5 \times 0.866 - 4 \times 0.500 \\ &= 4.33 - 2.00 = +2.33 \end{aligned}$$

The magnitude of the vector sum of the denominator is

$$\rho_d = \sqrt{(-0.964)^2 + 2.330^2} = \sqrt{6.36} = 2.52$$

The tangent of the denominator reference angle ϕ_d is

$$\tan \phi_d = \frac{2.330}{-0.964} = -2.42$$

$$\phi_d = 180° - 67.55° = 112.45°$$

The original equation may now be written

$$\rho\underline{/\phi} = \frac{4.96\underline{/39.0°}}{2.52\underline{/112.45°}}$$

Following Eq. (55),

$$\rho\underline{/\phi} = \frac{4.96}{2.52}\underline{/39.0° - 112.45°} = 1.97\underline{/-73.45°}$$

or

$$\rho\underline{/\phi} = 1.97\underline{/286.55°}$$

EXERCISE 6

Solve for ρ and ϕ:

1. $\rho\underline{/\phi} = 6\underline{/75°} \div 2\underline{/15°}$
2. $\rho\underline{/\phi} = 15\underline{/150°} \div 3\underline{/50°}$
3. $\rho\underline{/\phi} = 25\underline{/300°} \div 10\underline{/-20°}$
4. $\rho\underline{/\phi} = 90\underline{/-27°} \div 10\underline{/-50°}$

5. $\rho/\!\underline{\phi} = -100/\!\underline{300^\circ} \div 20/\!\underline{-50^\circ}$

6. Find the polar form of the vector quotient of the vectors $\overrightarrow{OA}/\overrightarrow{OB}$ for Prob. 7 in Exercise 5.
7. Find the polar form of the vector quotient of the vectors $\overrightarrow{OA}/\overrightarrow{OB}$ for Prob. 8 in Exercise 5.
8. Find the polar form of the vector quotient of the vectors $\overrightarrow{OA}/\overrightarrow{OB}$ for Prob. 9 in Exercise 5.
9. Find the polar form of the vector quotient of the vectors $\overrightarrow{OA}/\overrightarrow{OB}$ for Prob. 10 in Exercise 5.

Solve for ρ and ϕ:

10. $\rho/\!\underline{\phi} = \dfrac{3/\!\underline{60^\circ} \times 7/\!\underline{50^\circ}}{3/\!\underline{20^\circ}}$

11. $\rho/\!\underline{\phi} = \dfrac{4/\!\underline{76^\circ} \times 10/\!\underline{120^\circ}}{3/\!\underline{40^\circ} + 7/\!\underline{82^\circ}}$

12. $\rho/\!\underline{\phi} = \dfrac{6/\!\underline{200^\circ} \times 3/\!\underline{-20^\circ}}{5/\!\underline{45^\circ} + 7/\!\underline{30^\circ}}$

13. $\rho/\!\underline{\phi} = \dfrac{10/\!\underline{20^\circ} \times 20/\!\underline{50^\circ}}{10/\!\underline{20^\circ} + 20/\!\underline{50^\circ}}$

14. $\rho/\!\underline{\phi} = \dfrac{32/\!\underline{150^\circ} \times 20/\!\underline{320^\circ}}{32/\!\underline{150^\circ} + 20/\!\underline{320^\circ}}$

15. $\rho/\!\underline{\phi} = \dfrac{50/\!\underline{75^\circ} \times 10/\!\underline{25^\circ}}{50/\!\underline{75^\circ} + 10/\!\underline{25^\circ}}$

16. $\rho/\!\underline{\phi} = \dfrac{30/\!\underline{60^\circ} \times 30/\!\underline{30^\circ}}{30/\!\underline{60^\circ} + 30/\!\underline{30^\circ}}$

17. $\rho/\!\underline{\phi} = \dfrac{25/\!\underline{-30^\circ} \times -50/\!\underline{120^\circ}}{25/\!\underline{-30^\circ} + -50/\!\underline{120^\circ}}$

23 · 15 Multiplication of position vectors in a complex plane

In this section we shall demonstrate that if $\overrightarrow{OS} = \overrightarrow{OP} \times \overrightarrow{OQ}$, and if $\overrightarrow{OP} = a + jb$ and $\overrightarrow{OQ} = c + jd$, then the *algebraic* product of $a + jb$ and $c + jd$ is a complex number defining the *vector* product of $\overrightarrow{OP}$ and $\overrightarrow{OQ}$ (see Fig. 23 · 17).

1. By definition,

$$\overrightarrow{OS} = |\overrightarrow{OP}| \times |\overrightarrow{OQ}|/\!\underline{\phi_p + \phi_q} \tag{56}$$

where ϕ_p = reference angle of $\overrightarrow{OP}$

ϕ_q = reference angle of $\overrightarrow{OQ}$

2. If we let

$$\overrightarrow{OP} = a + jb$$

and

$$\overrightarrow{OQ} = c + jd$$

then

$$\begin{aligned}\overrightarrow{OS} &= (a + jb) \times (c + jd) \\ &= (ac - bd) + j(bc + ad) \qquad (57) \\ |\overrightarrow{OS}| &= \sqrt{(ac - bd)^2 + (bc + ad)^2}\end{aligned}$$

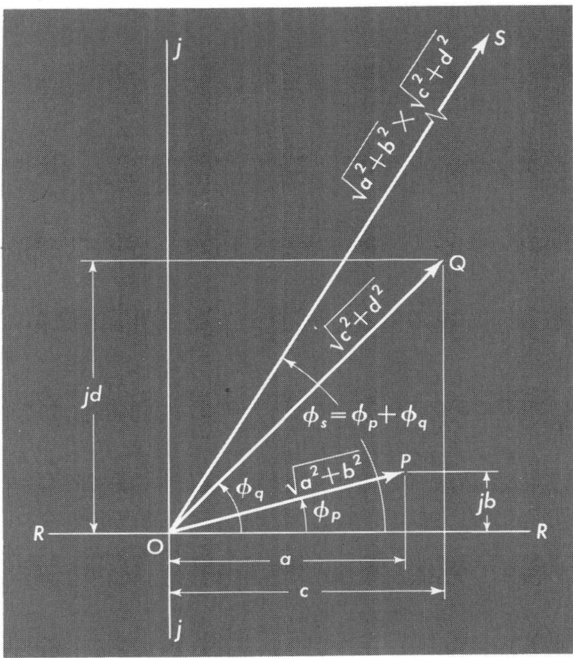

fig. 23·17

(See Example 56, page 198.)

$$
\begin{aligned}
|OS| &= \sqrt{a^2c^2 - 2abcd + b^2d^2 + b^2c^2 + 2abcd + a^2d^2} \\
&= \sqrt{a^2c^2 + b^2d^2 + b^2c^2 + a^2d^2} \\
&= \sqrt{(a^2 + b^2)(c^2 + d^2)} \\
&= \sqrt{a^2 + b^2} \times \sqrt{c^2 + d^2}
\end{aligned}
$$

but $$\sqrt{a^2 + b^2} = |OP|$$

and $$\sqrt{c^2 + d^2} = |OQ|$$

Therefore, $$|\overrightarrow{OS}| = |\overrightarrow{OP}| \times |\overrightarrow{OQ}| \tag{58}$$

From Eq. (57),

$$\tan \phi_s = \frac{bc + ad}{ac - bd} \tag{59}$$

where ϕ_s is the reference angle of $\overrightarrow{OS}$.

Dividing numerator and denominator of Eq. (59) by ac,

$$\tan \phi_s = \frac{bc/ac + ad/ac}{ac/ac - bd/ac} = \frac{b/a + d/c}{1 - (b/a)(d/c)}$$

But $$\frac{b}{a} = \tan \phi_p$$

$$\frac{d}{c} = \tan \phi_q$$

Therefore,
$$\tan \phi_s = \frac{\tan \phi_p + \tan \phi_q}{1 - \tan \phi_p \tan \phi_q} \tag{60}$$

From Eq. (45), page 545, we recognize that if Eq. (60) is valid, then

$$\phi_s = \phi_p + \phi_q \tag{61}$$

Therefore from Eqs. (58) and (61),

$$\overrightarrow{OS} = |\overrightarrow{OP}| \times |\overrightarrow{OQ}| \underline{/\phi_p + \phi_q} \tag{62}$$

Equation (56) is a definitive statement of the *vector* product of $\overrightarrow{OP}$ and $\overrightarrow{OQ}$. Equation (62) is the result of the *algebraic* multiplication of $(a + jb)$ and $(c + jd)$. These two equations are identical. Therefore, we may conclude that *vector* multiplication may be accomplished by the *algebraic* multiplication of the complex numbers representing the vectors.

example 13 Solve for $\overrightarrow{OR}$ in polar notation if

$$\overrightarrow{OR} = (2 + j3) \times (5 - j4)$$

$$\begin{array}{l} 2 + j3 \\ \underline{5 - j4} \\ 10 + j15 - j8 + 12 \end{array}$$

$$\overrightarrow{OR} = 22 + j7$$

$$\overrightarrow{OR} = \sqrt{22^2 + 7^2} \underline{/\tan^{-1} 7/22}$$

$$|\overrightarrow{OR}| = \sqrt{484 + 49}$$

$$|\overrightarrow{OR}| = \sqrt{533} = 23.1$$

$$\overrightarrow{OR} = 23.1 \underline{/17.65^\circ}$$

Compare with Example 9, page 594.

EXERCISE 7

Using complex notation, perform the following vector multiplications and compare with Probs. 7 to 10, page 595. Express the answers in polar form.

1. $(3 + j2)(-2 + j7)$
2. $(4 + j5)(1 + j2)$
3. $(-6 - j5)(-2 - j3)$
4. $(5 - j1)(-3 + j2)$

Multiply the following vectors and leave the answers in rectangular form. Sketch each vector, including the product, approximately to scale.

5. $(2 + j5)(3 + j7)$
6. $(-4 + j2)(3 + j6)$
7. $(-3 - j4)(3 + j5)$
8. $(7 - j3)(3 + j2)$
9. $(3 + j7)(-2 + j5)$
10. $(-4 + j2)(-3 + j6)$
11. $(-3 - j4)(-3 + j5)$
12. $(7 - j3)(-3 + j2)$
13. $(3 + j7)(2 - j5)$
14. $(-4 + j2)(3 - j6)$
15. $(-3 - j4)(3 - j5)$
16. $(7 - j3)(3 - j2)$
17. $(3 + j7)(-2 - j5)$
18. $(-4 + j2)(-3 - j6)$
19. $(-3 - j4)(-3 - j5)$
20. $(7 - j3)(-3 - j2)$

23·16 Division of position vectors in a complex plane

In this section we shall demonstrate that if $\overrightarrow{OS} = \overrightarrow{OP}/\overrightarrow{OQ}$ and if $\overrightarrow{OP} = a + jb$ and $\overrightarrow{OQ} = c + jd$, then the *algebraic* quotient of $a + jb$ divided by $c + jd$ is a complex number defining the *vector* quotient of $\overrightarrow{OP}$ and $\overrightarrow{OQ}$ (see Fig. 23·18).

1. By definition,

$$\overrightarrow{OS} = \frac{|OP|}{|OQ|} \underline{/\phi_p - \phi_q} \tag{63}$$

where ϕ_p = reference angle of $\overrightarrow{OP}$

ϕ_q = reference angle of $\overrightarrow{OQ}$

fig. 23·18

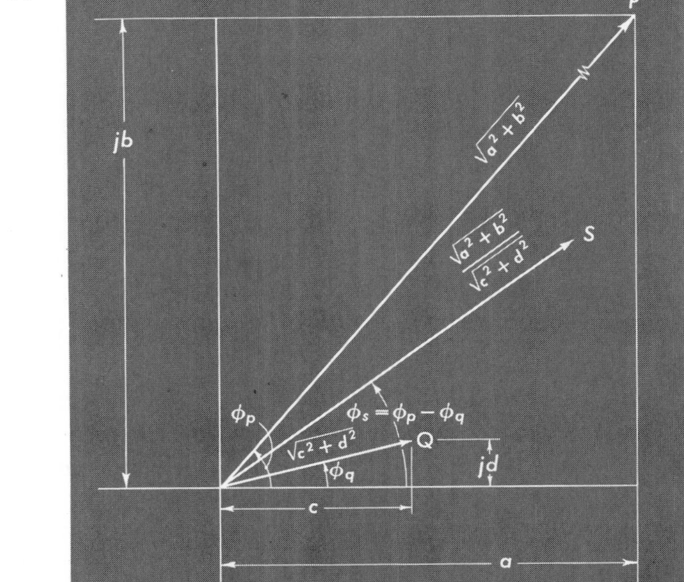

2. If we let

$$\overrightarrow{OP} = a + jb$$

and
$$\overrightarrow{OQ} = c + jd$$

then
$$\overrightarrow{OS} = (a + jb) \div (c + jd)$$

$$\overrightarrow{OS} = \frac{(a + jb)}{(c + jd)}$$

Rationalizing the denominator (see Sec. 8·16 and Example 58, page 199),

$$\overrightarrow{OS} = \frac{(a + jb)(c - jd)}{c^2 + d^2} = \frac{ac + bd}{c^2 + d^2} + j\,\frac{bc - ad}{c^2 + d^2} \tag{64}$$

$$|\overrightarrow{OS}| = \sqrt{\left(\frac{ac + bd}{c^2 + d^2}\right)^2 + \left(\frac{bc - ad}{c^2 + d^2}\right)^2}$$

$$|\overrightarrow{OS}| = \sqrt{\frac{a^2c^2 + 2abcd + b^2d^2 + b^2c^2 - 2abcd + a^2d^2}{(c^2 + d^2)^2}}$$

$$|\overrightarrow{OS}| = \frac{1}{c^2 + d^2}\sqrt{a^2c^2 + b^2d^2 + b^2c^2 + a^2d^2}$$

$$|\overrightarrow{OS}| = \frac{1}{c^2 + d^2}\sqrt{a^2 + b^2}\,\sqrt{c^2 + d^2}$$

$$|\overrightarrow{OS}| = \frac{\sqrt{a^2 + b^2}}{\sqrt{c^2 + d^2}}$$

But
$$\sqrt{a^2 + b^2} = |\overrightarrow{OP}|$$

and
$$\sqrt{c^2 + d^2} = |\overrightarrow{OQ}|$$

Therefore,
$$|\overrightarrow{OS}| = \frac{|\overrightarrow{OP}|}{|\overrightarrow{OQ}|} \tag{65}$$

From Eq. (64),

$$\tan \phi_s = \frac{(bc - ad)/(c^2 + d^2)}{(ac + bd)/(c^2 + d^2)} = \frac{bc - ad}{ac + bd} \tag{66}$$

where ϕ_s is the reference angle of $\overrightarrow{OS}$.

Dividing numerator and denominator of Eq. (66) by ac,

$$\tan \phi_s = \frac{bc/ac - ad/ac}{ac/ac + bd/ac} = \frac{b/a - d/c}{1 + (b/a)(d/c)}$$

But
$$\frac{b}{a} = \tan \phi_p$$

and
$$\frac{d}{c} = \tan \phi_q$$

Therefore,
$$\tan \phi_s = \frac{\tan \phi_p - \tan \phi_q}{1 + \tan \phi_p \tan \phi_q} \tag{67}$$

From Eq. (49), page 545, we recognize that if Eq. (67) is valid, then

$$\phi_s = \phi_p - \phi_q \tag{68}$$

Therefore, from Eqs. (65) and (68),

$$\overrightarrow{OS} = \frac{|\overrightarrow{OP}|}{|\overrightarrow{OQ}|} \underline{/\phi_p - \phi_q} \tag{69}$$

Equation (63) is a definitive statement of the *vector* quotient of $\overrightarrow{OP}$ and $\overrightarrow{OQ}$. Equation (69) is the result of the *algebraic* division of $(a + jb)$ by $(c + jd)$. These two equations are identical. Therefore, we may conclude that the *vector* division may be accomplished by the *algebraic* division of the complex numbers representing the vectors.

example 14 Find $\overrightarrow{OR}$ in polar form if

$$\overrightarrow{OR} = \frac{2 + j3}{5 - j4}$$

$$\overrightarrow{OR} = \frac{(2 + j3)(5 + j4)}{(5 - j4)(5 + j4)}$$

Here we have multiplied both numerator and denominator of the given ratio by the complex conjugate of the denominator (see Example 58, page 199). The complex conjugate of $(a + jb)$ is, by definition, $(a - jb)$. The product of a complex number and its conjugate is always a real number. The multiplications are written out below:

$$\begin{array}{l} \quad 2 + j3 \\ \quad \underline{5 + j4} \\ \quad 10 + j15 + j8 + j^2 12 \\ = 10 + j15 + j8 - 12 \\ = -2 + j23 = \text{numerator} \end{array}$$

$$\begin{array}{l} \quad 5 - j4 \\ \quad \underline{5 + j4} \\ \quad 25 - j20 + j20 - j^2 16 \\ = 25 - j20 + j20 + 16 \\ = 25 + 16 \\ \qquad 41 = \text{denominator} \end{array}$$

Therefore,

$$\overrightarrow{OR} = \frac{2 + j3}{5 - j4} = \frac{-2 + j23}{41}$$

$$= \frac{-2}{41} + j\frac{23}{41}$$

$$= -0.0488 + j0.561$$

The magnitude of the vector quotient will be

$$|\overrightarrow{OR}| = \sqrt{(-0.0488)^2 + 0.561^2} = 0.563$$

$$\overrightarrow{OR} = 0.563\underline{/\tan^{-1}\frac{0.561}{-0.0488}}$$

$$\tan \phi_r = -11.5$$

where ϕ_r = reference angle of $\overrightarrow{OR}$
$\phi_r = 95.0°$

$$\overrightarrow{OR} = \underline{0.563/95.0°}$$

(Compare with Example 11, page 596.)

EXERCISE 8

1. Using complex notation, find the quotients of the following vectors. Express the answers in both polar and rectangular forms. Compare these problems with Probs. 6 to 9, page 598.

(a) $\frac{3 + j2}{-2 + j7}$ (b) $\frac{4 + j5}{1 + j2}$ (c) $\frac{-6 - j5}{-2 - j3}$ (d) $\frac{5 - j1}{-3 + j2}$

In the following problems, divide as indicated:

2. $\frac{3 + j7}{2 + j5}$ 3. $\frac{-4 + j2}{3 + j6}$ 4. $\frac{-3 - j4}{3 + j5}$ 5. $\frac{7 - j3}{3 + j2}$

6. $\frac{3 + j7}{-2 + j5}$ 7. $\frac{-4 + j2}{-3 + j6}$ 8. $\frac{-3 - j4}{-3 + j5}$ 9. $\frac{7 - j3}{-3 + j2}$

10. $\frac{3 + j7}{2 - j5}$ 11. $\frac{-4 + j2}{3 - j6}$ 12. $\frac{-3 - j4}{3 - j5}$ 13. $\frac{7 - j3}{3 - j2}$

14. $\frac{3 + j7}{-2 - j5}$ 15. $\frac{-4 + j2}{-3 - j6}$ 16. $\frac{-3 - j4}{-3 - j5}$ 17. $\frac{7 - j3}{-3 - j2}$

EXERCISE 9

Using complex notation exclusively, solve the following vector equations. Leave the answers in rectangular form.

1. $\overrightarrow{OP} = \frac{(4 + j7)(3 - j6)}{(4 + j7) + (3 - j6)}$

2. $\overrightarrow{OP} = \frac{(146 - j248)(320 - j480)}{(146 - j248) + (320 - j480)}$

3. $\overrightarrow{OP} = \frac{(3.6 - j4.7)(7.9 + j5.6)}{(3.6 - j4.7) + (7.9 + j5.6)}$

4. $\overrightarrow{OP} = \frac{(27.6 - j38.5)(27.9 + j35.8)}{(27.6 - j38.5) + (27.9 + j35.8)}$

5. $\overrightarrow{OP} = \dfrac{(7.8 + j3.8)(4.6 + j3.5)}{(7.8 + j3.8) + (4.6 + j3.5)}$

6. $\overrightarrow{OP} = \dfrac{(2.4 + j3.7)(2.5 + j7.6)}{(2.4 + j3.7) + (2.5 + j7.6)}$

7. $\overrightarrow{OP} = \dfrac{(25.8 - j36.4)(48.7 + j32.9)}{(25.8 - j36.4) + (48.7 + j32.9)}$

8. $\overrightarrow{OP} = \dfrac{(-20 + j27)(30 - j20)}{(-20 + j27) + (30 - j20)}$

23·17 Demoivre's theorem

Equation (23) is repeated below for reference:

$$re^{j\alpha} = r(\cos\alpha + j\sin\alpha) \tag{70}$$

Now let us raise the expression $re^{j\alpha}$ to the nth power, obtaining

$$r^n e^{jn\alpha} \tag{71}$$

From Eq. (70), it is evident that

$$r^n e^{jn\alpha} = r^n(\cos n\alpha + j\sin n\alpha) \tag{72}$$

However, by raising both members of Eq. (70) to the nth power, we obtain

$$r^n e^{jn\alpha} = r^n(\cos\alpha + j\sin\alpha)^n \tag{73}$$

Now by equating the right members of Eqs. (72) and (73), we obtain

$$(\cos\alpha + j\sin\alpha)^n = (\cos n\alpha + j\sin n\alpha) \tag{74}$$

Equation (74) is known as *Demoivre's theorem.*

If we let the position vector

$$\overrightarrow{OP} = |OP|(\cos\alpha + j\sin\alpha) \tag{75}$$

then

$$\overrightarrow{OP^n} = |OP|^n(\cos n\alpha + j\sin n\alpha) \tag{76}$$

Stated in words (see Figs. 23·19 to 23·21): The nth power of the vector $\overrightarrow{OP}$ is the vector whose magnitude is the arithmetic nth power of the magnitude of $\overrightarrow{OP}$ and whose reference angle is n times the refer-

fig. 23·19

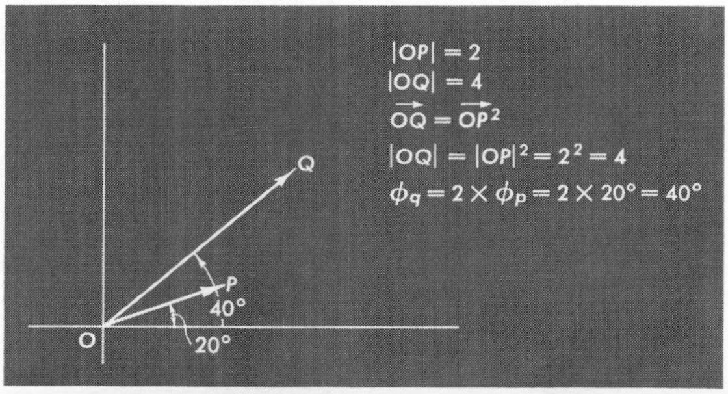

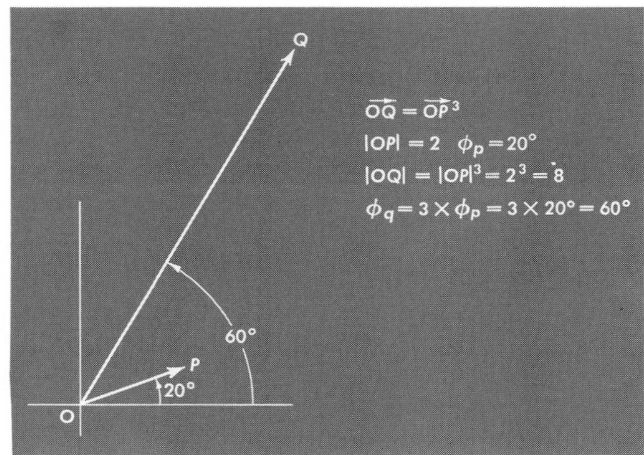

Q
OQ = OP³
|OP| = 2 φp = 20°
|OQ| = |OP|³ = 2³ = 8
φq = 3 × φp = 3 × 20° = 60°
60°
P
20°
O

fig. 23·20

ence angle of $\overrightarrow{OP}$. (This is a special form of the rule for multiplication. See Sec. 23·10.) That is,

$$\overrightarrow{OP}^n = |OP|^n \underline{/n\phi_p} \tag{77}$$

where ϕ_p = reference angle of $\overrightarrow{OP}$
n = any real number

or, following the principle illustrated in Eq. (76),

$$\overrightarrow{OP}^n = |OP|^n(\cos n\phi_p + j \sin n\phi_p) \tag{78}$$

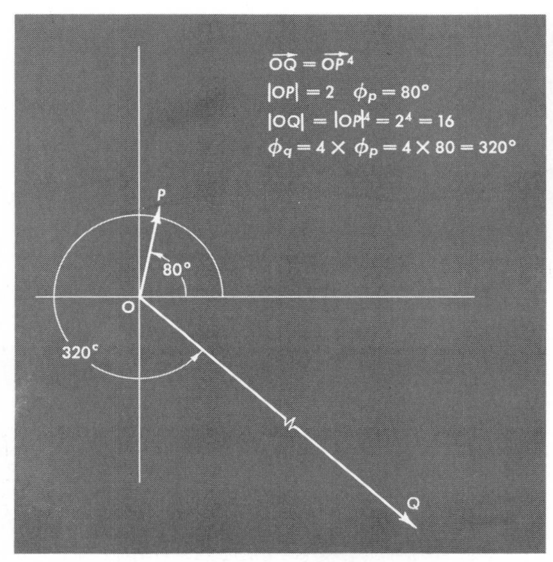

fig. 23·21

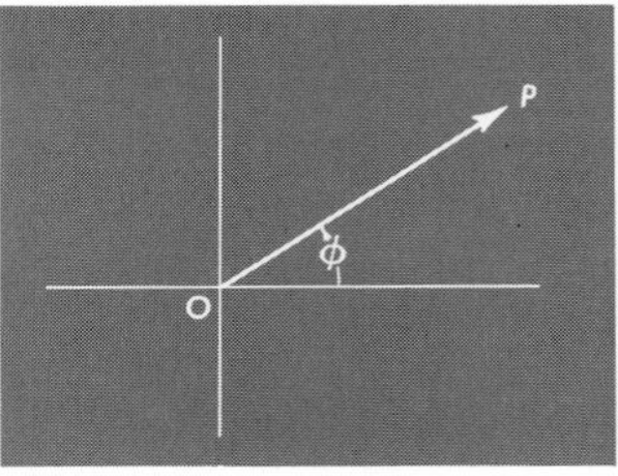

fig. 23·22

EXERCISE 10

1. If $\overrightarrow{OP} = 5\underline{/20°}$, find $\overrightarrow{OP}^3$.
2. If $\overrightarrow{OP} = 3\underline{/120°}$, find $\overrightarrow{OP}^2$.
3. If $\overrightarrow{OP} = 2\underline{/150°}$, find $\overrightarrow{OP}^4$.
4. If $\overrightarrow{OP} = 22\underline{/360°}$, find $\overrightarrow{OP}^2$.
5. If $\overrightarrow{OP} = 5\underline{/90°}$, find $\overrightarrow{OP}^4$.

23 · 18 The *n*th root of a position vector

From Eq. (74), we may conclude that

$$(\cos \alpha + j \sin \alpha)^{1/n} = \left(\cos \frac{\alpha}{n} + j \sin \frac{\alpha}{n}\right) \tag{79}$$

If we let

$$\overrightarrow{OP} = |OP|(\cos \alpha + j \sin \alpha) \tag{80}$$

then

$$\overrightarrow{OP}^{1/n} = |OP|^{1/n}\left(\cos \frac{\alpha}{n} + j \sin \frac{\alpha}{n}\right) \tag{81}$$

Stated in words: The *n*th root of the position vector $\overrightarrow{OP}$ is a position vector whose magnitude is the real *n*th root of $|OP|$ and whose reference angle is $1/n$ times the reference angle of $\overrightarrow{OP}$.

Usually we express the direction of a vector in terms of an angle less than 360°, or 2π radians, as in Fig. 23 · 22. However, we can express the same direction as $(\phi + 2\pi k)$ in radians or as $(\phi + 360°k)$ in degrees, where k is any integer including zero (see Fig. 23 · 23).

fig. 23 · 23

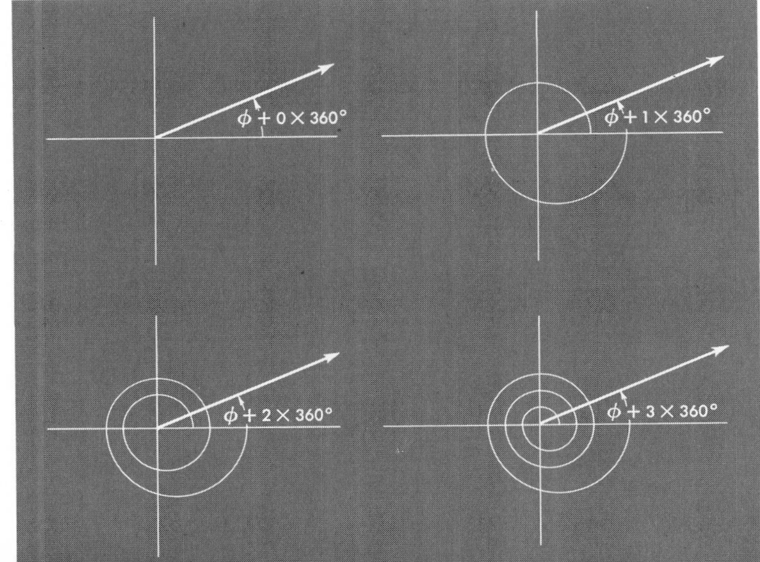

Such nomenclature ordinarily serves no useful purpose, but in the present instance we shall have need for it. We shall indicate the nth roots of $\overrightarrow{OP}$ as follows:

$$\sqrt[n]{\overrightarrow{OP}} = \sqrt[n]{|OP|} \angle \frac{\phi_p + 360^\circ k}{n} \tag{82}$$

Now let us tabulate the angle $(\phi_p + 360^\circ k)/n$ for various values of k:

k	$\dfrac{\phi_p + 360^\circ k}{n}$
0	$\dfrac{\phi_p}{n}$
1	$\dfrac{\phi_p}{n} + \dfrac{360^\circ}{n}$
2	$\dfrac{\phi_p}{n} + \dfrac{2 \times 360^\circ}{n}$
3	$\dfrac{\phi_p}{n} + \dfrac{3 \times 360^\circ}{n}$
4	$\dfrac{\phi_p}{n} + \dfrac{4 \times 360^\circ}{n}$
5	$\dfrac{\phi_p}{n} + \dfrac{5 \times 360^\circ}{n}$
$n - 1$	$\dfrac{\phi_p}{n} + \dfrac{(n-1)360^\circ}{n} = \dfrac{\phi_p}{n} - \dfrac{360^\circ}{n} + 360^\circ$
n	$\dfrac{\phi_p}{n} + \dfrac{n360^\circ}{n} = \dfrac{\phi_p}{n} + 360^\circ$
$n + 1$	$\dfrac{\phi_p}{n} + \dfrac{360^\circ}{n} + 360^\circ$
$n + 2$	$\dfrac{\phi_p}{n} + \dfrac{2 \times 360^\circ}{n} + 360^\circ$
$n + 3$	$\dfrac{\phi_p}{n} + \dfrac{3 \times 360^\circ}{n} + 360^\circ$
$n + 4$	$\dfrac{\phi_p}{n} + \dfrac{4 \times 360^\circ}{n} + 360^\circ$
$n + 5$	$\dfrac{\phi_p}{n} + \dfrac{5 \times 360^\circ}{n} + 360^\circ$

In the above series observe that the respective reference angles increase by steps of $360^\circ/n$. When n steps have been completed, the reference angle has increased by

$$\frac{n \times 360^\circ}{n} = 360^\circ$$

or one complete revolution. At this point a sequence of vectors begins which will be superimposed on those already found. Thus, when $k > (n - 1)$, no new vector roots are discovered.

In general, there are n and only n nth roots of a vector.

The position vector obtained from Eq. (82) when $k = 0$ is called the *principal* nth root of $\overrightarrow{OP}$.

By the principle illustrated in Eq. (77), Eq. (82) may be written

$$\sqrt[n]{\overrightarrow{OP}} = \sqrt[n]{|OP|\underline{/\phi_p}} = \sqrt[n]{|OP|}\left(\cos\frac{\phi_p + 360°k}{n} + j\sin\frac{\phi_p + 360°k}{n}\right) \tag{83}$$

example 15 Find the five fifth roots of the vector $32\underline{/30°}$ (see Fig. 23·24).

Applying Eq. (82),

$$\sqrt[5]{32\underline{/30°}} = \sqrt[5]{32}\,\underline{\Big/\frac{30° + 360°k}{5}}$$

$$= 2\,\underline{\Big/\frac{30° + 360°k}{5}}$$

Let us tabulate the angles $(30° + 360°k)/5$ for a succession of values of k:

k	$\frac{30° + 360°k}{5}$	
0	$\frac{30°}{5} = 6°$	(this is the reference angle of the principal 5th root)
1	$\frac{30° + 360°}{5} = 78°$	
2	$\frac{30° + 720°}{5} = 150°$	
3	$\frac{30° + 1{,}080°}{5} = 222°$	
4	$\frac{30° + 1{,}440°}{5} = 294°$	
5	$\frac{30° + 1{,}800°}{5} = 366°$, or a reference angle of 6°	
6	$\frac{30° + 2{,}160°}{5} = 438°$, or a reference angle of 78°	
7	$\frac{30° + 2{,}520°}{5} = 510°$, or a reference angle of 150°	
8	$\frac{30° + 2{,}880°}{5} = 582°$, or a reference angle of 222°	

Observe that Fig. 23·24 could be constructed by first locating the principal fifth root of $\overrightarrow{OP}$ ($2\underline{/6°}$) and then constructing the other four fifth roots of equal magnitude and spaced equally by a constant angular difference (360°/5 or 72°).

From this series of reference angles we can distinguish five and only

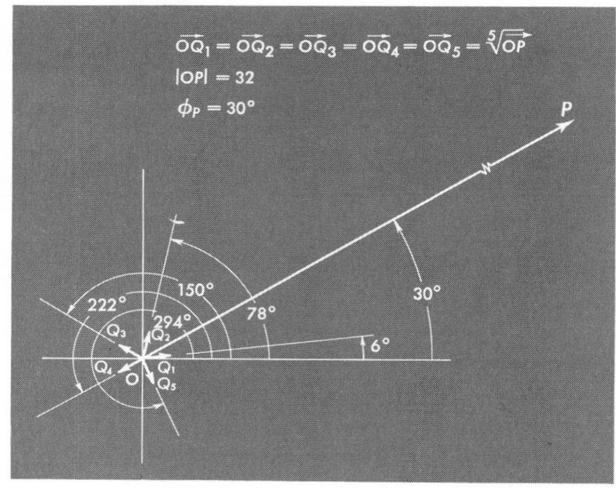

fig. 23·24

five fifth roots of the vector $32\underline{/30°}$. These roots are referred to Fig. 23·24:

$$\begin{aligned}\vec{OQ_1} &= 2\underline{/6°}\\ \vec{OQ_2} &= 2\underline{/78°}\\ \vec{OQ_3} &= 2\underline{/150°}\\ \vec{OQ_4} &= 2\underline{/222°}\\ \vec{OQ_5} &= 2\underline{/294°}\end{aligned}$$

Subsequent roots found by making $k > (n - 1)$ (in this case, making $k > 4$) merely duplicate those already found.

EXERCISE 11

Find all the indicated roots of the following vectors. Plot the vector roots to scale.

1. $\sqrt[3]{8\underline{/30°}}$
2. $\sqrt[3]{27\underline{/180°}}$
3. $\sqrt[2]{4\underline{/0°}}$
4. $\sqrt[2]{9\underline{/210°}}$
5. $\sqrt[4]{81\underline{/280°}}$
6. $\sqrt[10]{1{,}024\underline{/330°}}$

23·19 The *n*th roots of real numbers

From the conventions which apply to position vectors in a complex plane it is evident that any positive real number N can be expressed as $|N|\underline{/0°}$ and any negative real number N can be expressed as $|N|\underline{/180°}$.

Accordingly, following Eq. (83), when $N > 0$ we may write

$$\sqrt[n]{N} = \sqrt[n]{|N|\underline{/0°}} = \sqrt[n]{|N|}\left(\cos\frac{0° + 360°k}{n} + j\sin\frac{0° + 360°k}{n}\right)$$

When $N < 0$,

$$\sqrt[n]{N} = \sqrt[n]{|N|\angle 180^\circ} = \sqrt[n]{|N|}\left(\cos\frac{180^\circ + 360^\circ k}{n} + j\sin\frac{180^\circ + 360^\circ k}{n}\right)$$

example 16 Find the three cube roots of 1.

When $k = 0$,

$$\sqrt[3]{1} = \sqrt[3]{|1|}\left(\cos\frac{360^\circ \times 0}{3} + j\sin\frac{360^\circ \times 0}{3}\right)$$

$$= 1(\cos 0^\circ + j\sin 0^\circ) = 1 + 0 = +1$$

When $k = 1$,

$$\sqrt[3]{1} = \sqrt[3]{|1|}\left(\cos\frac{360^\circ}{3} + j\sin\frac{360^\circ}{3}\right)$$

$$= 1(\cos 120^\circ + j\sin 120^\circ)$$

$$= 1\left(-\frac{1}{2} + j\frac{\sqrt{3}}{2}\right) = -\frac{1}{2} + j\frac{\sqrt{3}}{2}$$

When $k = 2$,

$$\sqrt[3]{1} = \sqrt[3]{|1|}\left(\cos\frac{360^\circ \times 2}{3} + j\sin\frac{360^\circ \times 2}{3}\right)$$

$$= 1(\cos 240^\circ + j\sin 240^\circ)$$

$$= 1\left(-\frac{1}{2} - j\frac{\sqrt{3}}{2}\right) = -½ - j\frac{\sqrt{3}}{2}$$

These roots can also be found by the algebraic solution of the equation

$$x^3 - 1 = 0$$

Factoring, $$(x - 1)(x^2 + x + 1) = 0$$

When $$x - 1 = 0$$
$$x = 1$$

When $$x^2 + x + 1 = 0$$

$$x = \frac{-1 \pm \sqrt{1 - 4}}{2}$$

$$= -\frac{1}{2} \pm \frac{j\sqrt{3}}{2}$$

That these roots are in fact cube roots of 1 can be verified by multiplication. By elementary algebra,

$$\sqrt[3]{1} \times \sqrt[3]{1} \times \sqrt[3]{1} = 1$$

Also

$$\begin{array}{l}
-\frac{1}{2} + j\frac{\sqrt{3}}{2} \\
\underline{-\frac{1}{2} + j\frac{\sqrt{3}}{2}} \\
+\frac{1}{4} - j\frac{\sqrt{3}}{4} - j\frac{\sqrt{3}}{4} + j^2\frac{3}{4} = -\frac{1}{2} - j\frac{\sqrt{3}}{2} \\
\qquad\qquad\qquad\qquad\qquad\qquad \underline{-\frac{1}{2} + j\frac{\sqrt{3}}{2}} \\
\qquad\qquad\qquad\qquad\qquad\qquad \frac{1}{4} + j\frac{\sqrt{3}}{4} - j\frac{\sqrt{3}}{4} - j^2\frac{3}{4} = 1
\end{array}$$

and

$$\begin{array}{l}
-\frac{1}{2} - j\frac{\sqrt{3}}{2} \\
\underline{-\frac{1}{2} - j\frac{\sqrt{3}}{2}} \\
+\frac{1}{4} + j\frac{\sqrt{3}}{4} + j\frac{\sqrt{3}}{4} + j^2\frac{3}{4} = -\frac{1}{2} + j\frac{\sqrt{3}}{2} \\
\qquad\qquad\qquad\qquad\qquad\qquad \underline{-\frac{1}{2} - j\frac{\sqrt{3}}{2}} \\
\qquad\qquad\qquad\qquad\qquad\qquad +\frac{1}{4} - j\frac{\sqrt{3}}{4} + j\frac{\sqrt{3}}{4} - j^2\frac{3}{4} = 1
\end{array}$$

EXERCISE 12

1. Find the two square roots of 1.
2. Find the four fourth roots of 1.
3. Find the five fifth roots of 1.
4. Show that the sum of the five fifth roots of 1 is zero.
5. Prove that, in general, the sum of the n nth roots of 1 is zero.
6. Draw a scale vector diagram to illustrate Probs. 1 to 4.

example 17 Find the five fifth roots of 32.000.

$$\sqrt[5]{32\underline{/0^\circ}} = \sqrt[5]{|32|}\left(\cos\frac{360^\circ k}{5} + j\sin\frac{360^\circ k}{5}\right)$$

When $k = 0$,

$$\begin{aligned}\sqrt[5]{32\underline{/0^\circ}} &= 2(\cos \tfrac{0}{5} + j\sin \tfrac{0}{5}) \\ &= 2(1 + 0) = 2\end{aligned}$$

When $k = 1$,

$$\begin{aligned}\sqrt[5]{32\underline{/0^\circ}} &= 2\left(\cos\frac{360^\circ}{5} + j\sin\frac{360^\circ}{5}\right) \\ &= 2(\cos 72^\circ + j\sin 72^\circ) = 2(0.30902 + j0.95106) \\ &= 0.61804 + j1.90212\end{aligned}$$

When $k = 2$,

$$\sqrt[5]{32\angle 0^\circ} = 2\left(\cos\frac{720^\circ}{5} + j\sin\frac{720^\circ}{5}\right)$$

$$= 2(-0.80902 + j0.58779) = -1.61804 + j1.17558$$

When $k = 3$,

$$\sqrt[5]{32\angle 0^\circ} = 2\left(\cos\frac{1{,}080^\circ}{5} + j\sin\frac{1{,}080^\circ}{5}\right)$$

$$= 2(\cos 216^\circ + j\sin 216^\circ)$$

$$= 2(-0.80902 - j0.58779) = -1.61804 - j1.17558$$

When $k = 4$,

$$\sqrt[5]{32\angle 0^\circ} = 2\left(\cos\frac{1{,}440^\circ}{5} + j\sin\frac{1{,}440^\circ}{5}\right)$$

$$= 2(\cos 288^\circ + j\sin 288^\circ)$$

$$= 2(+0.30902 - j0.95106) = +0.61804 - j1.90212$$

EXERCISE 13

1. Find the three cube roots of 27.
2. Find the four fourth roots of -81.
3. Find the six sixth roots of 729.
4. Show that the square of one of the complex sixth roots of 729 is a cube root of 729.

23·20 Rotating position vectors

In Sec. 22·4 we discussed rotating position vectors and showed how a rotating position vector could be described, in terms of one of its projections, by an equation in the form

$$y = E\sin(\omega t + \psi) \tag{84}$$

In Sec. 23·4 we developed another nomenclature which can be used to describe a vector; for example,

$$\overrightarrow{OA} = E(\cos\alpha + j\sin\alpha) \tag{85}$$

The angle α may be a variable and a function of time. Therefore, we may let

$$\alpha = \omega t \tag{86}$$

To make the situation general, we shall introduce the phase constant ψ, and

$$\overrightarrow{OA} = E[\cos(\omega t + \psi) + j\sin(\omega t + \psi)] \tag{87}$$

Also in Sec. 23·4 we developed an equivalent expression with which we may describe the same rotating vector as

$$\overrightarrow{OA} = Ee^{j\alpha} \tag{88}$$

If α is a function of time, we may let $\alpha = \omega t$ and write

$$\overrightarrow{OA} = Ee^{j(\omega t + \psi)} \tag{89}$$

where ψ is a phase constant.

In Eqs. (84), (87), and (89), E is the amplitude of the function, ω is the angular velocity of the rotating vector, t is time, and ψ is a constant phase angle.

Any of these three forms may be used to describe a rotating vector. However, it may very well be that in some specific application one of these three forms is more convenient to use than the others. All three are in common use.

Equation (84) is more convenient to use when we are plotting a projection of the rotating vector. Equation (87) is more convenient when we wish to combine rotating vectors by addition, subtraction, multiplication, or division. Equation (89) is more convenient when transient terms are present.

EXERCISE 14

Find the amplitude, frequency, period, and phase constant for the following functions:

1. $v = 10 \sin (120\pi t + 60^\circ)$
2. $v = 10[\cos (120\pi t + 60^\circ) + j \sin (120\pi t + 60^\circ)]$
3. $v = 10e^{j(120\pi t + 60^\circ)}$
4. $i = 15\left[\cos\left(628.32t + \frac{\pi}{2}\right) + j \sin\left(628.32t + \frac{\pi}{2}\right)\right]$
5. $i = 25e^{j(2513.27t)}$
6. $v = 25 \sin (2513.27t)$

unit nine an introduction to calculus

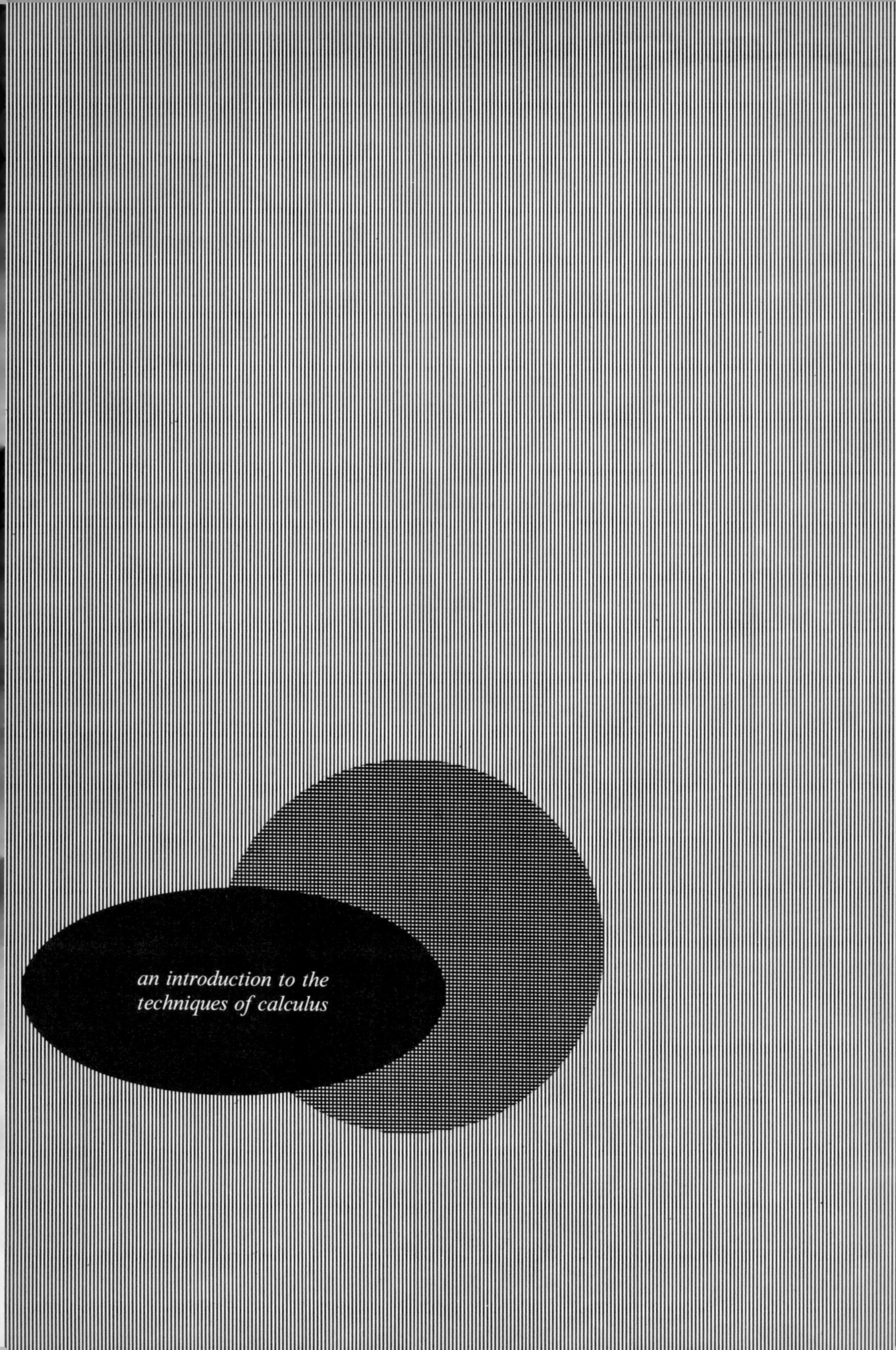
an introduction to the
techniques of calculus

24 graphical methods of calculus

Without trying to define "calculus" we can at least say that it is a branch of mathematics particularly useful in problems involving motion and other kinds of change.

In this chapter we shall lean heavily on the graphical aspects of calculus, not only because graphical methods of analysis furnish the easiest approach to the subject but also because they are important in their own right (see Chap. 6).

24·1 The slope of a linear graph

In Chap. 6 we learned that if we are given the graph of a linear function f, the slope of the graph between any two distinct points P_1 and P_2 on the graph (see Fig. 24·1) is

$$\text{Slope} = \frac{f(x_1 + \Delta x) - f(x_1)}{\Delta x} \tag{1}$$

where the meaning of x_1, Δx, $f(x_1)$, and $f(x_1 + \Delta x)$ is illustrated in Fig. 24·1.

The slope of the graph of a function is a measure of what we understand to be the *rate of change in the value of the function* with respect to the independent variable.

24·2 Slopes of nonlinear graphs

Figure 24·2 is the graph of a certain nonlinear function.

Intuitively, we can see that as x increases, the "slope" of the graph increases. That is, the curve rises "faster" as we scan it from left to right. Of course, the graph also rises higher as we progress to the right, but that is beside the point at the moment. The essential point is that the slope of the curve is not, in general, the same between different pairs of points on the graph.

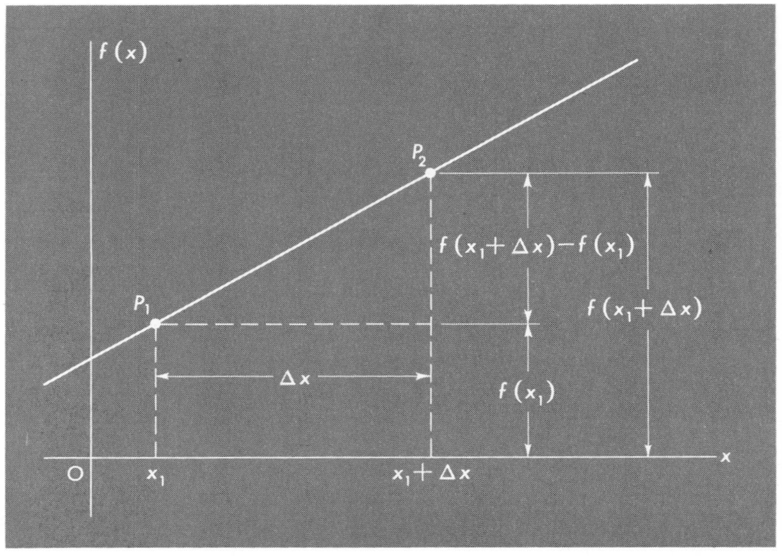

fig. 24·1

What, then, shall we consider to be the slope of a nonlinear graph?

In Fig. 24·2 the tangent line AB is drawn to the curve at point P_1. It seems quite proper to let the slope of AB be a measure of what we intuitively think of as "the slope of the graph at point P_1."

However, we shall have to describe in more detail just what we mean by a "tangent."

In Fig. 24·2 the line DE is called a secant. A secant is a line of unlimited length cutting a curve. The line segment P_1P_2 is a part of the secant DE and is called a chord. One extremity of this chord will be fixed at P_1.

Now if the secant DE is rotated clockwise while always passing through P_1, the other end of the chord will pass through P_2, P_3, P_4, P_5, etc., as well as intermediate points. The chord will then progressively decrease in length.

Finally, at one particular position (when the secant coincides with the line P_1B), the chord will disappear altogether. If the secant were rotated beyond this position, a chord would appear to the left of P_1. There is then a unique position of the secant DE where the length of the chord is zero.

The tangent to the curve at a given point is therefore "the unique limiting position of the secant passing through that point as the length of the chord approaches zero."

To draw a tangent to a curve at a given point, therefore, we keep the edge of a straight edge through the point and adjust the direction of the straight edge until the chord appears to vanish. The slope of this straight edge is now a graphical approximation to the slope of the curve at the point under consideration.

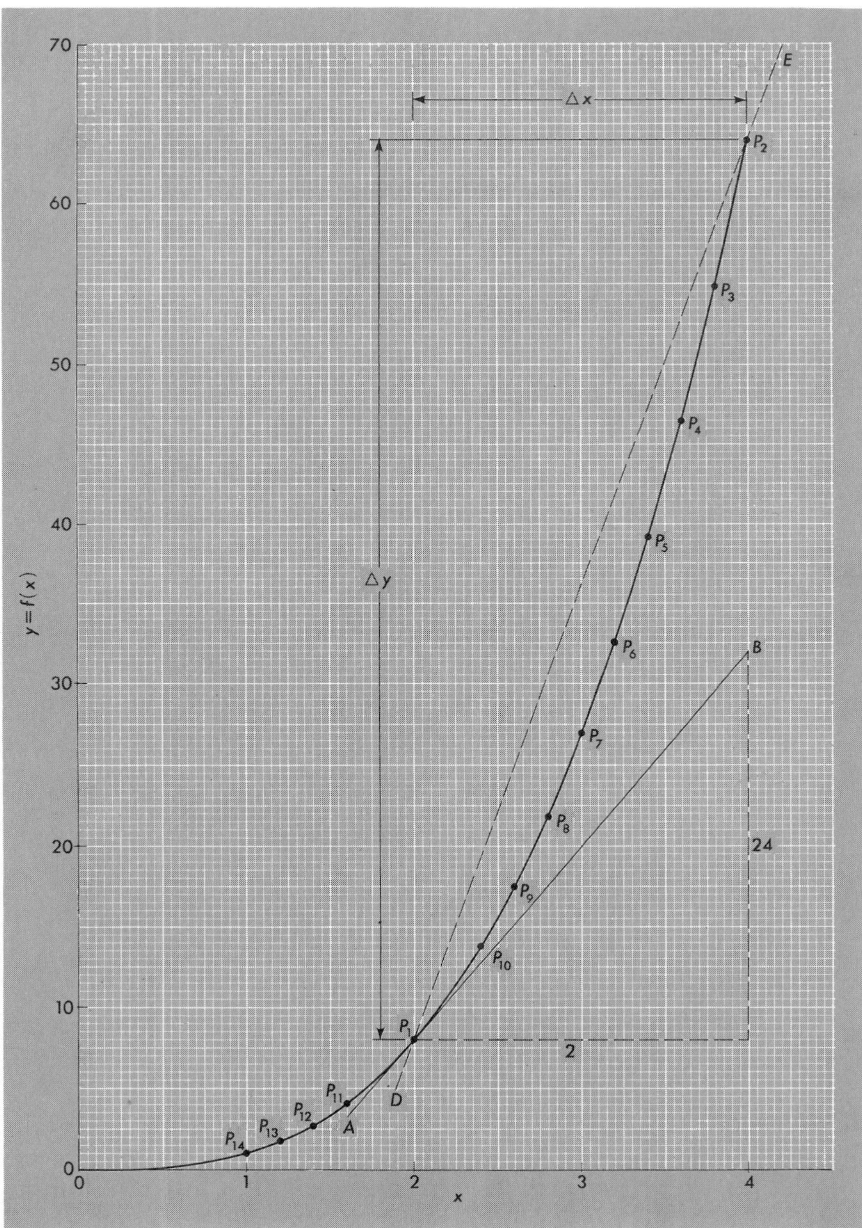
70
60
50
40
30
20
10
0
y = f(x)
0
1
2
3
4
x
Δx
Δy
E
B
D
A
24
2
P_1
P_2
P_3
P_4
P_5
P_6
P_7
P_8
P_9
P_{10}
P_{11}
P_{12}
P_{13}
P_{14}

fig. 24·2

24·3 Average and instantaneous slopes and rates

In dealing with the graphs of nonlinear functions we distinguish between *average* and *instantaneous* slopes.

The average slope of the nonlinear graph illustrated in Fig. 24·2 between the point P_1 (whose x coordinate is x_1) and another point P_2 on the graph (whose x coordinate is $x_1 + \Delta x$) is given by

$$\begin{pmatrix} \text{Average slope} \\ \text{between } P_1 \text{ and } P_2 \end{pmatrix} = \frac{f(x_1 + \Delta x) - f(x_1)}{\Delta x} \tag{2}$$

By reading the graph we find that in this case

$$\begin{aligned} f(x_1) &= 8 \\ f(x_1 + \Delta x) &= 64 \\ \Delta x &= 2 \end{aligned}$$

Then

$$\begin{pmatrix} \text{Average slope} \\ \text{between } P_1 \text{ and } P_2 \end{pmatrix} = \frac{64 - 8}{2} = 28$$

We may also say that the average rate of change in the value of this function with respect to x between x_1 and $x_1 + \Delta x$ is 28 when $x_1 = 2$ and $x_1 + \Delta x = 4$.

The *instantaneous* slope of the graph at P_1 is the slope of the tangent to the graph at P_1, and

$$\begin{pmatrix} \text{Instantaneous} \\ \text{slope at } P_1 \end{pmatrix} = \frac{24}{2} = 12$$

Also, the instantaneous rate of change in the value of the function with respect to x is 12 when $x = 2$.

If we let

$$y = f(x)$$

it is quite common to let

$$\Delta y = f(x_1 + \Delta x) - f(x_1)$$

Then we may write

$$\frac{\Delta y}{\Delta x} = \begin{pmatrix} \text{average slope } \textit{between} \text{ two points} \\ P_1 \text{ and } P_2 \text{ on the graph} \end{pmatrix}$$

It is very important that the student observe that we speak of the *average* slope *between two points* and the *instantaneous* slope *at one single point.* Let us investigate the matter still further. We shall calculate the slopes of lines connecting P_1 and P_2, P_3, P_4, P_5, etc., in Fig. 24·2 and tabulate them in Table 24·1. The values $\Delta y = f(x_1 + \Delta x) - f(x_1)$ were read from a much larger graph than the one presented here. However, the student can verify them approximately.

The values of Δx and $\Delta y/\Delta x$ are plotted in Fig. 24·3. As we scan this graph from right to left, we note that the trend of the graph is directly toward the point (0,12).

table 24·1

Between points	$f(x_1)$	Δx	$f(x_1+\Delta x)$	$f(x_1+\Delta x)-f(x_1)=\Delta y$	$\dfrac{f(x_1+\Delta x)-f(x_1)}{\Delta x}=\dfrac{\Delta y}{\Delta x}$
P_1 and P_2	8.000	2.0	64.000	56.000	+28.00
P_1 and P_3	8.000	1.8	54.872	46.872	+26.04
P_1 and P_4	8.000	1.6	46.656	38.656	+24.16
P_1 and P_5	8.000	1.4	39.304	31.304	+22.36
P_1 and P_6	8.000	1.2	32.768	24.768	+20.64
P_1 and P_7	8.000	1.0	27.000	19.000	+19.00
P_1 and P_8	8.000	0.8	21.952	13.952	+17.44
P_1 and P_9	8.000	0.6	17.576	9.576	+15.96
P_1 and P_{10}	8.000	0.4	13.824	5.824	+14.56
P_1 and P_{11}	8.000	−0.4	4.096	−3.904	+ 9.76
P_1 and P_{12}	8.000	−0.6	2.744	−5.256	+ 8.76
P_1 and P_{13}	8.000	−0.8	1.728	−6.272	+ 7.84
P_1 and P_{14}	8.000	−1.0	1.000	−7.000	+ 7.00

As we pass the vertical axis and continue on toward the left, we note that it would appear that the graph had passed through 12 on the vertical axis.

However, $\Delta y/\Delta x$ is indeterminate when Δx is precisely zero, since division by zero is indeterminate. This is indicated on the graph by the circle whose center is at (0,12).

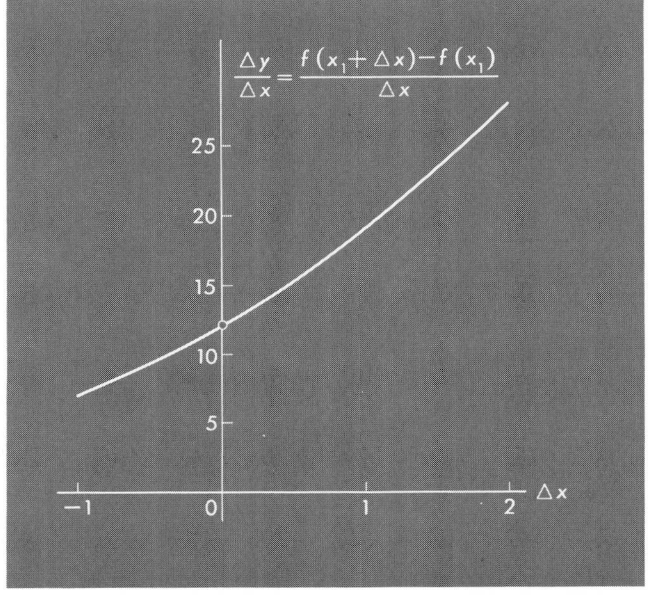

fig. 24·3

Let us be satisfied to see what $\Delta y/\Delta x$ *approaches* as Δx *approaches* zero. We have observed from this graphical work that $\Delta y/\Delta x$ (the average slope) approaches 12 (the instantaneous slope) as Δx approaches zero. The symbol $\Delta y/\Delta x$ indicates the *actual* change in y divided by the *corresponding* actual change in x. This is an *average* slope.

For the present we shall let the instantaneous slope be designated by the symbol dy/dx. In Chap. 25 we shall consider a more fundamental concept of this symbol.

In the case of the straight line

$$\frac{\Delta y}{\Delta x} = \frac{dy}{dx}$$

In the case of a curve

$$\frac{\Delta y}{\Delta x} \neq \frac{dy}{dx}$$

The symbol dy/dx is called the "derivative of y with respect to x" and will be discussed somewhat superficially in the following section.

24·4 The Derivative

The relation between $\Delta y/\Delta x$ and Δx is exhibited in Fig. 24·2, Table 24·1, and Fig. 24·3 with reference to point P_1 in Fig. 24·2.

The derivative is "the limit which $\Delta y/\Delta x$ approaches as Δx approaches zero." This symbol is written

$$\frac{dy}{dx} = \lim_{\Delta x \to 0} \frac{\Delta y}{\Delta x}$$

In the function represented in Fig. 24·2, therefore, the derivative of y with respect to x is 12 when $x = 2$, or

$$\lim_{\Delta x \to 0} \frac{\Delta y}{\Delta x} = 12$$

Thus

$$\frac{dy}{dx} = 12$$

example 1 What is the instantaneous rate of change in y with respect to x when $x = 0.2$ in Fig. 24·4?

The instantaneous rate of change in y with respect to x is numerically equal to the slope of the curve at any given point.

To find the slope of the curve at $x = 0.2$, a straight edge was placed on the point where the curve passes through the ordinate erected at $x = 0.2$. This straight edge was adjusted until it appeared to be tangent to the curve. The slope of the tangent is

$$\frac{5}{0.2} = 25$$

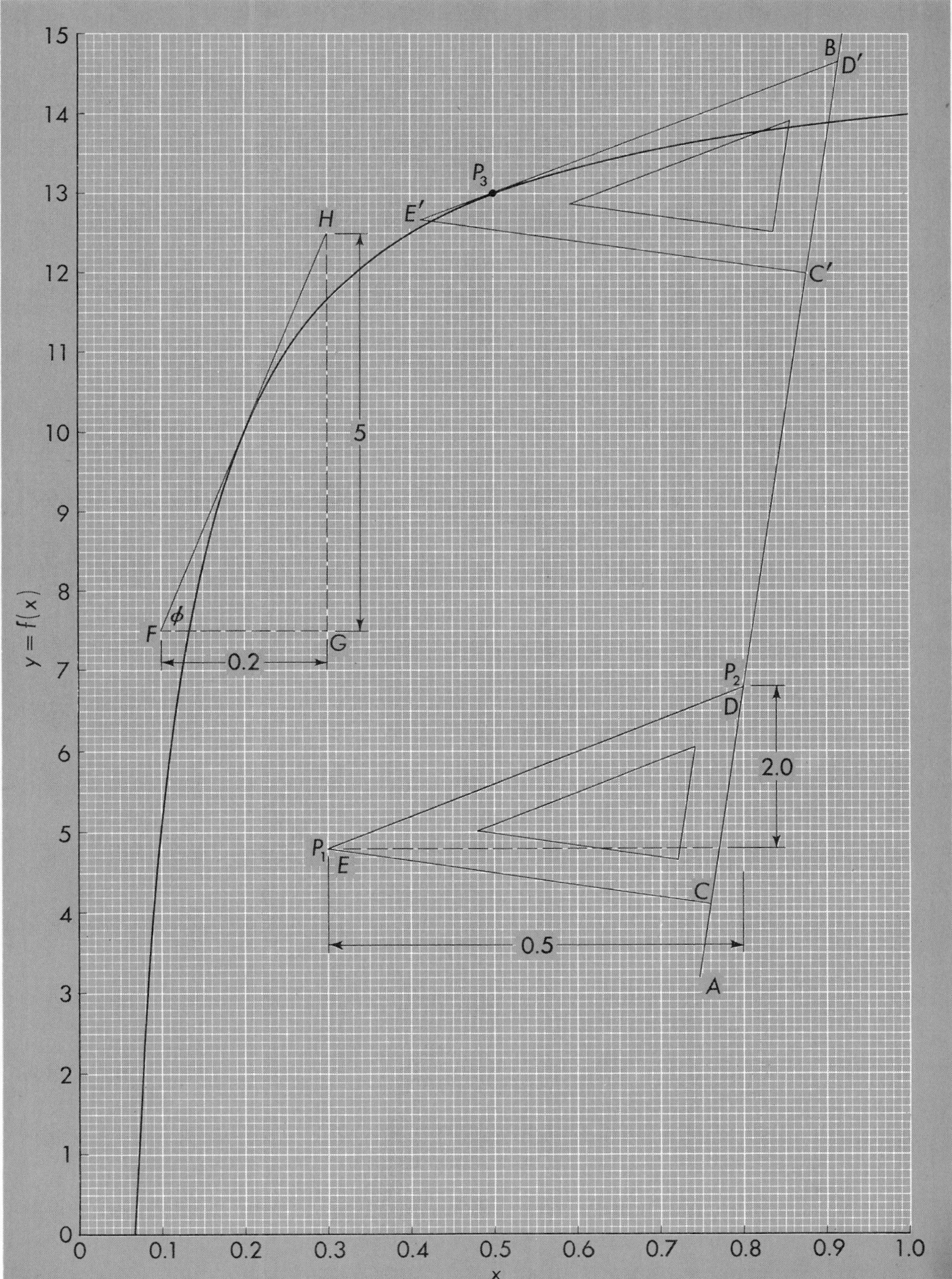

15
14
13
12
11
10
9
8
7
6
5
4
3
2
1
0
0
0.1
0.2
0.3
0.4
0.5
0.6
0.7
0.8
0.9
1.0
x
y = f(x)
B
D′
P3
E′
H
C′
5
F
ϕ
G
0.2
P2
D
2.0
P1
E
C
0.5
A

fig. 24·4

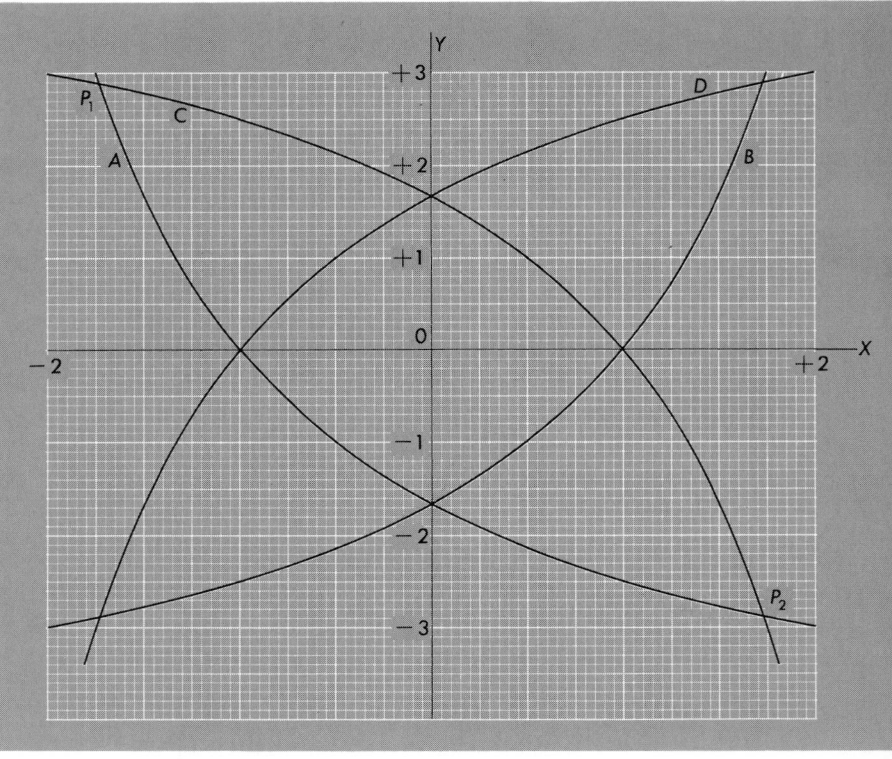

fig. 24·5

example 2 In Fig. 24·5 (curve *A*) find the average rate of change in y with respect to x between $x = -1.73$ and $+1.73$.

$$\frac{\Delta y}{\Delta x} = \frac{2.89 - (-2.89)}{-1.73 - (+1.73)} = \frac{+5.78}{-3.46} = -1.67$$

Thus the average rate of change in y with respect to x between $x = -1.73$ and $x = +1.73$ is -1.67. Observe also that these two points P_1 and P_2 are at the intersections of curves *A* and *C*. Therefore the *average* rate of change in y with respect to x is the same for both curves between these two points.

Thus, over a relatively large Δx the *average* slope is not necessarily very descriptive of the actual path of the curve throughout that interval.

example 3 In Fig. 24·4 find the coordinates of the point at which the instantaneous slope is $+4$.

A pair of convenient points such as P_1 and P_2 are located on the same coordinate system as the graph, such that the slope of the straight line between them is $+4$. Then one edge of a triangle, ED, is placed so that the edge of the triangle passes through P_1 and P_2.

A straight edge, AB, is pressed against another side of the triangle, CD.

The triangle is then moved along the straight edge until the side ED becomes tangent to the curve as shown by the position $(E'D')$.

The point of tangency P_3 has the coordinates (0.5,13.00).

Thus the coordinates of the point at which the instantaneous slope is $+4$ are (0.5,13.00).

example 4 What is the angle ϕ in Fig. 24·4?

The angle ϕ is called the *inclination* of the tangent line FH. The inclination of a line is defined as "the smallest angle measured from the positive part of the X axis to the line." Angles measured in a counter-clockwise direction from the X axis are positive angles. Angles measured in a clockwise direction from the X axis are negative angles.

This angle is one angle of the triangle FGH. The length of the side opposite this angle is 5 units long and the side adjacent is 2 units long. Therefore the tangent of the angle is

$$\tan \phi = \frac{5}{2} = 2.5$$

and

$$\phi = 68^\circ \qquad \text{(approximately)}$$

Observe that in finding the tangent of the angle, the *same* scale is used for the opposite and adjacent sides, not the scales used on the axes. Therefore the tangent of the angle and the slope of the curve are identical *only* when the same scale is used on the vertical and horizontal axes.

24·5 Approximate increments

Suppose we wished to find how much y increased when x increased from 0.2 to 0.2001 in Fig. 24·4. Of course it would be impossible to read this small increment directly from the graph. But from Example 1 above, we find that when $x = 0.2$ the rate of change of y with respect to x is 25. Now it is true that the rate of change of y with respect to x will be a little different at $x = 0.2001$ from what it was at exactly $x = 0.2000$, but not much different. Over this small interval we shall be approximately correct to assume that the rate is constant.

Therefore, we can say that if Δx is *small*, the *instantaneous* rate of change of y with respect to x is *approximately* the same as the average rate of change of y with respect to x at all points within the interval.

In mathematical symbols

$$\frac{dy}{dx} \approx \frac{\Delta y}{\Delta x} \qquad \text{(when } \Delta x \text{ is small)} \tag{3}$$

In the present example

$$\frac{dy}{dx} = 25$$

and $\Delta x = 0.0001$. Therefore,

$$\frac{\Delta y}{0.0001} \approx 25$$

$$\Delta y \approx 0.0025$$

and y increases approximately 0.0025 unit when x increases 0.0001 unit from $x = 0.2000$ to $x = 0.2001$.

EXERCISE 1

The following problems all refer to Fig. 24·5.

1. For curve B of Fig. 24·5, find the average rate of change of y with respect to x between $x = -1.5$ and $x = 0$.
2. Find the instantaneous rate of change of y with respect to x for curve B when $x = -1.5$.
3. Find the average slope of curve B between $x = +1$ and $x = +1.5$.
4. Find the instantaneous slope of curve B when $x = +1$.
5. Find $\Delta y/\Delta x$ between $x = -0.5$ and $x = +0.5$ for curve C.
6. Find dy/dx at $x = 0$ for curve A.
7. For curve D find the coordinates of the point where the instantaneous slope is $+5/8$.
8. Find the angle which the tangent drawn to the curve C makes with the horizontal when $x = 0$.
9. Find the approximate change in y when x changes from -1.5 to -1.499 for curve B (see Prob. 2 above). Does y increase or decrease?
10. Find the approximate change in y when x changes from 1 to 1.03 for curve B (see Prob. 4 above). Does y increase or decrease?
11. Find the approximate change in y when x changes from 0 to 0.02 for curve A (see Prob. 6 above). Does y increase or decrease?

24·6 Area under a straight-line graph

As we mentioned in Sec. 6·18 the "area under a straight-line graph" refers to the area between the graph and the X axis (see Figs. 24·6, 24·7, and Sec. 6·18).

The arithmetic average of y_1 and y_2 is called the *average ordinate* ($\bar{y}$) of the graph between ordinates erected at x_1 and x_2. Thus

$$\bar{y} = \frac{y_2 + y_1}{2} \tag{4}$$

and

$$A = \bar{y}(x_2 - x_1) \tag{5}$$

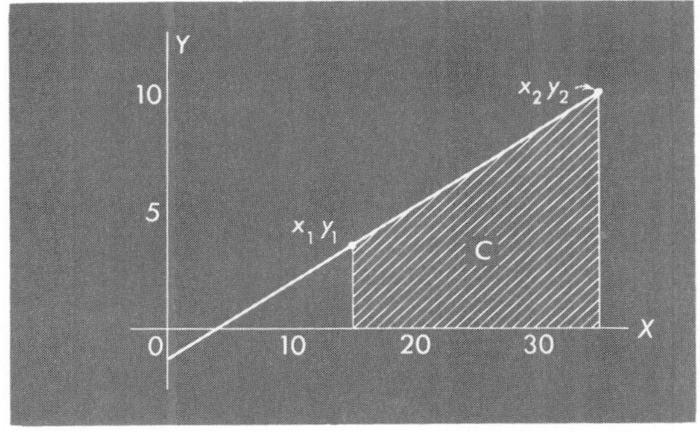

fig. 24·6

fig. 24·7

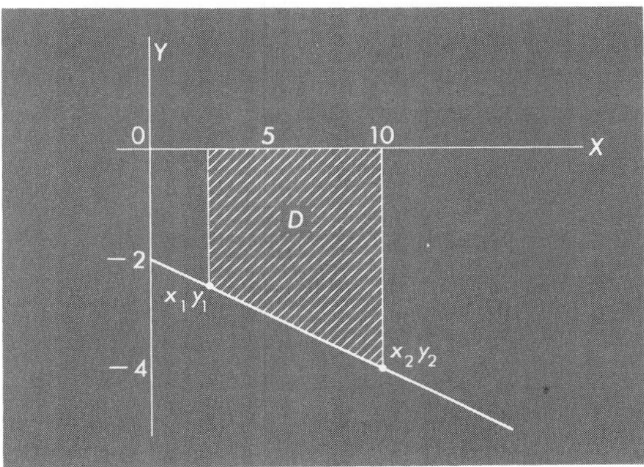

or

$$\bar{y} = \frac{A}{x_2 - x_1} \tag{6}$$

where A = area under the graph between ordinates erected at x_1 and x_2
$\bar{y}$ = average ordinate between ordinates erected at x_1 and x_2

If we have given a linear graph, we can read x_1, x_2, y_1, and y_2 directly from the graph and calculate the area between x_1 and x_2 from Eqs. (4) and (5) as was done in Sec. 6·18. However, in preparation for work with nonlinear graphs which follows, we shall discuss the "narrow strip" method (see Fig. 24·8).

The area under this linear graph has been divided into relatively narrow strips. The area of each strip (see Fig. 24·9) is given by

$$\Delta A = \bar{y}_s(\Delta x)$$

where ΔA = area of each strip
$\bar{y}_s$ = average ordinate of each strip
Δx = width of each strip

The total area under the graph in Fig. 24·8, between x_1 and x_2, is the sum of the areas of the individual strips. In Table 24·2 the average ordinate of each strip as read directly from the graph is listed in the $\bar{y}_s$

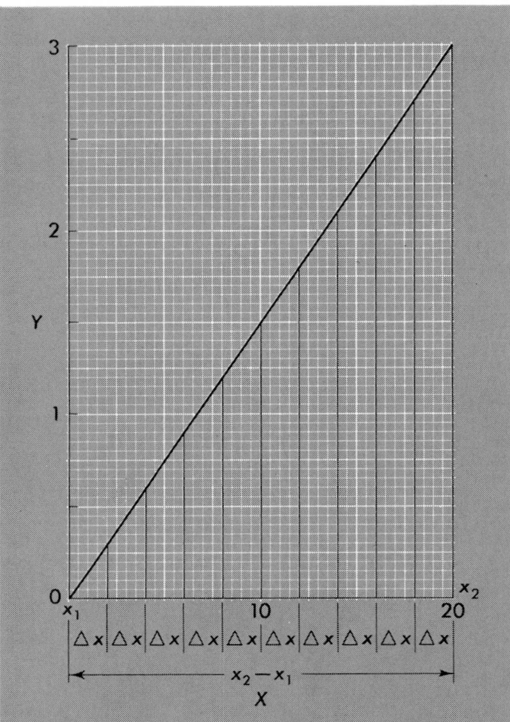

fig. 24·8

fig. 24

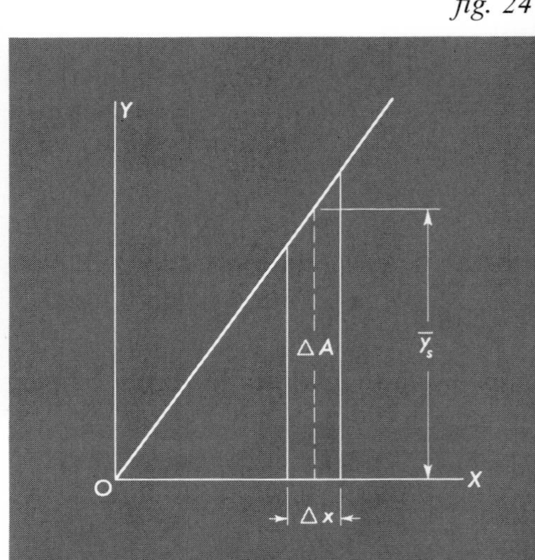

table 24·2

$\bar{y}_s$	Δx	ΔA
0.15	2	0.30
0.45	2	0.90
0.75	2	1.50
1.05	2	2.10
1.35	2	2.70
1.65	2	3.30
1.95	2	3.90
2.25	2	4.50
2.55	2	5.10
2.85	2	5.70
		30.00 = total area A

column in order. The width Δx of each strip is 2 units and is tabulated in the Δx column. The area of each strip is listed in the ΔA column. The area under the graph between x_1 and x_2 is the sum of the entries in the ΔA column.

By reference to Table 24·2 and following Eq. (6) the average ordinate $\bar{y}$ between $x = 0$ and $x = 20$ is

$$\bar{y} = \frac{A}{x_2 - x_1} = \frac{30}{20} = 1.5$$

The dimensions attached to the area under a graph depend on the physical units used to calibrate the axes (see Sec. 6·18).

Figure 6·32 is repeated here for reference as Fig. 24·10. It shows the graph of the force (F) required to elongate a certain spring by the amount (e) inches. Thus the dimensions of the area under the graph are

$$\text{Force} \times \text{distance} = \text{work}$$

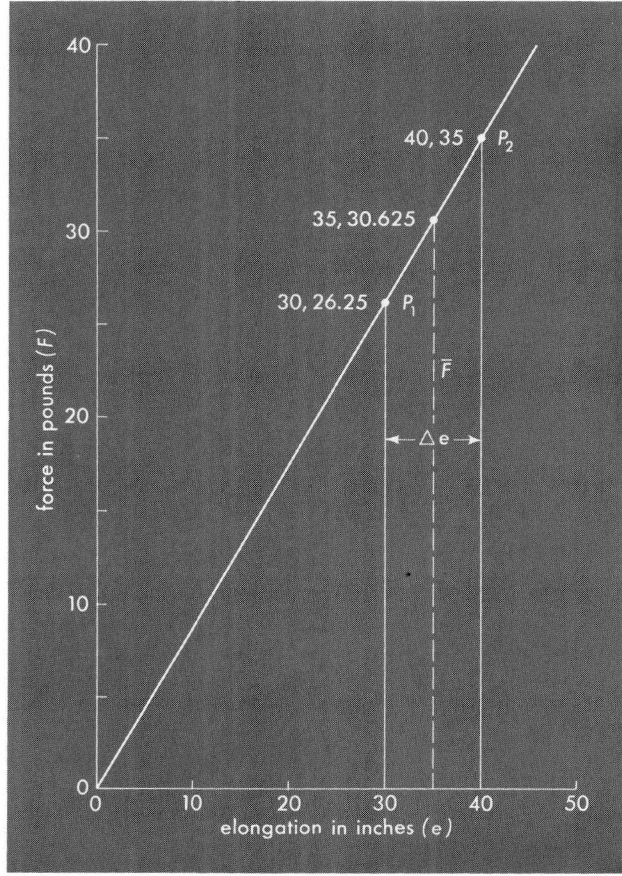

fig. 24·10

Observe that if ΔW = the work done between an elongation of 30 in. and an elongation of 40 in., then

$$\Delta W = \overline{F}(\Delta e) = 30.625 \times 10 = 306.25 \text{ in.-lb}$$

example 5 Show that for the graph shown in Fig. 24·11

$$W = \frac{0.875e^2}{2}$$

where W = work done in inch-pounds to elongate the spring by an amount e from its relaxed length
e = elongation in inches

We find by direct reading that the slope of this graph is 35/40 or 0.875 lb/in. This is called the *spring constant.* Thus the equation for the graph in Fig. 24·11 is

$$F = 0.875e$$

Following Eq. (4) and the above equation

$$\overline{F} = \frac{F - 0}{2} = \frac{F}{2} = \frac{0.875e}{2}$$

Following Eq. (5)

$$W = \frac{0.875e}{2}(e - 0) = \frac{0.875e^2}{2}$$

or in general

$$W = \frac{(\text{spring constant})e^2}{2}$$

24·7 Calculation of work from a force-distance graph

Disregarding, for the time being the implications of Example 5 above let us investigate by the "narrow strip" method the work done in elongating the spring whose force-elongation characteristics are illustrated in Fig. 24·11.

The area under this graph is divided into vertical strips, each 2 units wide.

The average height of each strip is indicated by the dotted lines. The student can verify, precisely by calculation or approximately by direct reading of the graph, the average ordinates in the $\overline{F}$ column in Table 24·3. The strips are lettered alphabetically from left to right. The Δe column indicates 2 units throughout. The width of all strips is identical.

The ΔW column (Table 24·3) indicates the work done in the corresponding interval; that is, $\overline{F}\,\Delta e$. While the elongation is identical for each interval, the average force required to produce this elongation varies progressively as the elongation increases. Therefore the work ex-

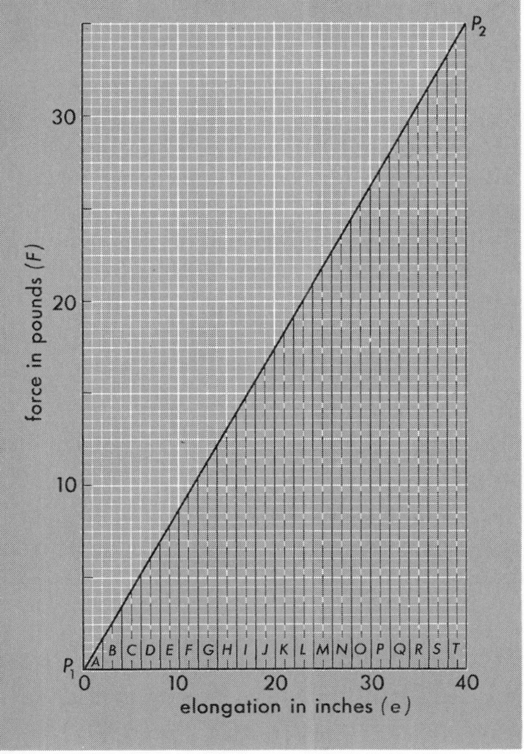

fig. 24·11

fig. 24·12

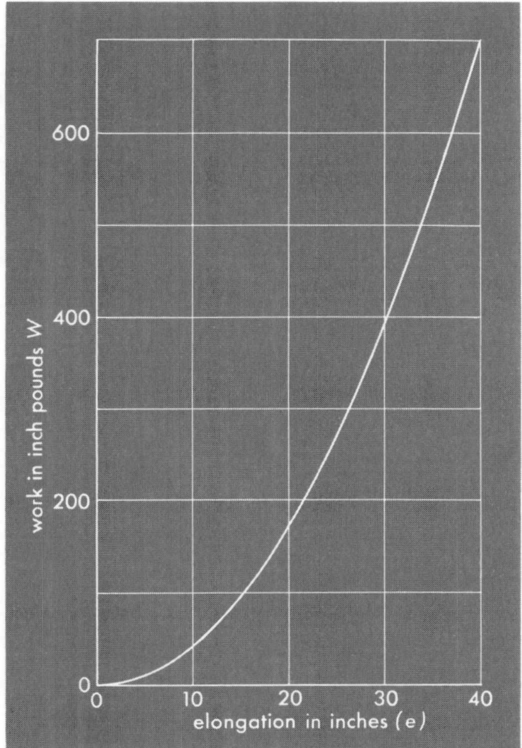

table 24·3

Strip	e	$\overline{F}$	Δe	ΔW	W
A	2	0.875	2	1.75	1.75
B	4	2.625	2	5.25	7.00
C	6	4.375	2	8.75	15.75
D	8	6.125	2	12.25	28.00
E	10	7.875	2	15.75	43.75
F	12	9.625	2	19.25	63.00
G	14	11.375	2	22.75	85.75
H	16	13.125	2	26.25	112.00
I	18	14.875	2	29.75	141.75
J	20	16.625	2	33.25	175.00
K	22	18.375	2	36.75	211.75
L	24	20.125	2	40.25	252.00
M	26	21.875	2	43.75	295.75
N	28	23.625	2	47.25	343.00
O	30	25.375	2	50.75	393.75
P	32	27.125	2	54.25	448.00
Q	34	28.875	2	57.75	505.75
R	36	30.625	2	61.25	567.00
S	38	32.375	2	64.75	631.75
T	40	34.125	2	68.25	700.00

pended to produce each increment of elongation also progressively increases.

The column headed W indicates the total amount of work expended in elongating the spring from 0 in. to the elongation at the end of the interval in question. For example, 63 in.-lb of work were expended in elongating the spring from 0 to 12 in., the end of the F interval. Figure 24·12 is a plot of W with respect to elongation. Note that we plot W against the elongation at the *end* of the interval in question.

EXERCISE 2

1. The relation between the force and the corresponding elongation of a spring is illustrated by Fig. 24·13.
   (a) Find the work done over the interval between $e = 1$ and $e = 3$.
   (b) Find the average force over this interval.
2. Plot a curve of work done versus elongation between $e = 0$ in. and $e = 4$ in.
   Note: See Exercise 12 in Chap. 6.

24·8 Calculation of distance from a speed-time graph

If we have given a graph of the speed versus time for a moving object, we can calculate the distance covered in a way exactly analogous to the calculation of work from a force-distance plot (see Sec. 24·7).

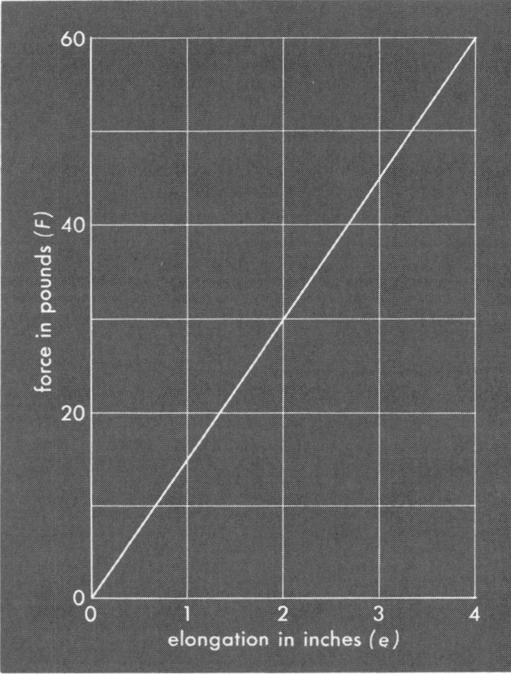

fig. 24·13

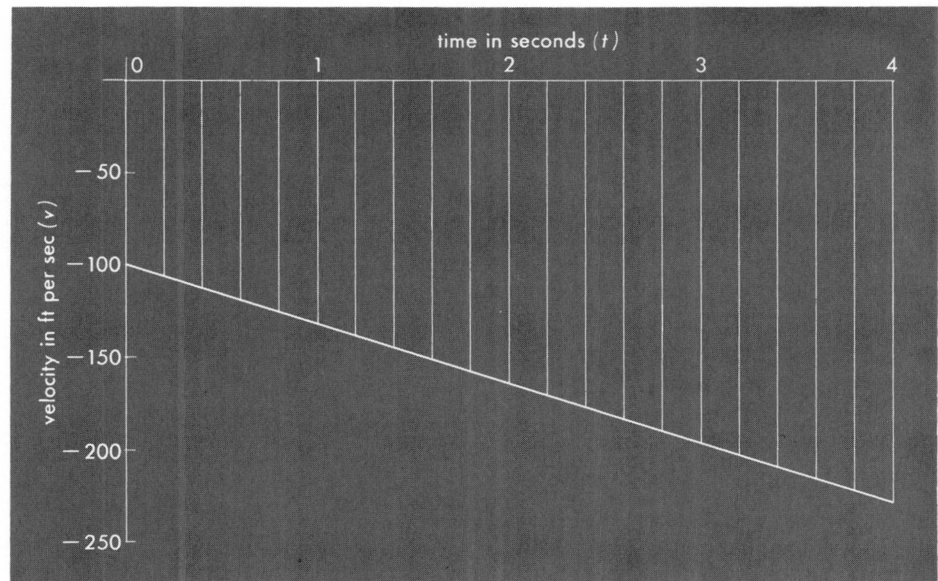

fig. 24·14

Figure 24·14 shows the graph of speed for a freely falling body with an initial downward velocity of 100 fps.

It will be noted that this area carries a negative sign. The reason is that velocities in a downward direction are conventionally negative.

The area under this graph is proportional to the product of a negative velocity and a positive time interval. The product is negative (see Fig. 24·7 and Sec. 24·6).

EXERCISE 3

1. Find the distance the object falls for each strip in Fig. 24·14.
2. Plot the distance the object falls versus time.
3. Plot a curve of altitude versus time. The object was thrown downward from a height of 800 ft.
4. When does the object hit the ground?
5. Show that the area under the graph of $y = mx + b$ between $x = 0$ and $x = x_1$ is

$$A = \frac{m}{2}x_1^2 + bx_1$$

6. Using the derivation in Prob. 5 above, find the equation for the graph in Fig. 24·12.
7. Find the equation for the plot required in Prob. 3 above.
8. From Fig. 24·12 find graphically dW/de for e equals 10 in., 20 in., 30 in., and 40 in. Compare with the force F at corresponding values of e.
9. Using the curve plotted in Prob. 3 above find graphically dh/dt (where h is altitude in feet) when t is 1, 2, 3, and 4 sec. Compare with the velocity (v) at these times.

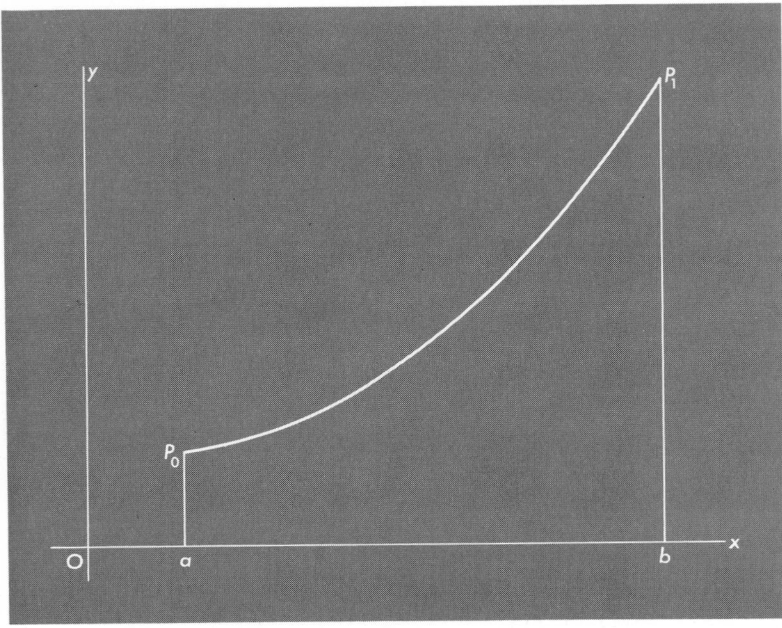

fig. 24·15

24·9 Area under a nonlinear graph

In Sec. 24·6 we discussed what we mean by "area under a straight-line graph." The student should review that section before proceeding with the present discussion.

In Sec. 24·6 we were concerned only with the areas of relatively simple geometric figures, specifically with rectangles, triangles, and trapezoids.

The problem of finding the area under a *curve* is more difficult because we have not as yet given meaning to the area of a plane figure, any of whose sides is a *curved* line (see area aP_0P_1b in Fig. 24·15).

To develop methods of finding this sort of area, let us suppose that the curve shown in Fig. 24·15 is the plot of a certain function which is defined, continuous, and positive-valued over the domain $a \leq x \leq b$. The area under this graph between $x = a$ and $x = b$ is shown as the area aP_0P_1b.

To calculate this area approximately, we divide it into narrow strips by lines drawn perpendicular to the X axis, as shown in Fig. 24·16. In this case we show ten strips numbered from 1 to 10.

Although it is not entirely necessary, we have, as a convenience, used strips of equal width.

Now as in Fig. 24·17 we shall construct rectangles whose width is the width of each strip and whose height y' is the *minimum* ordinate of each strip.

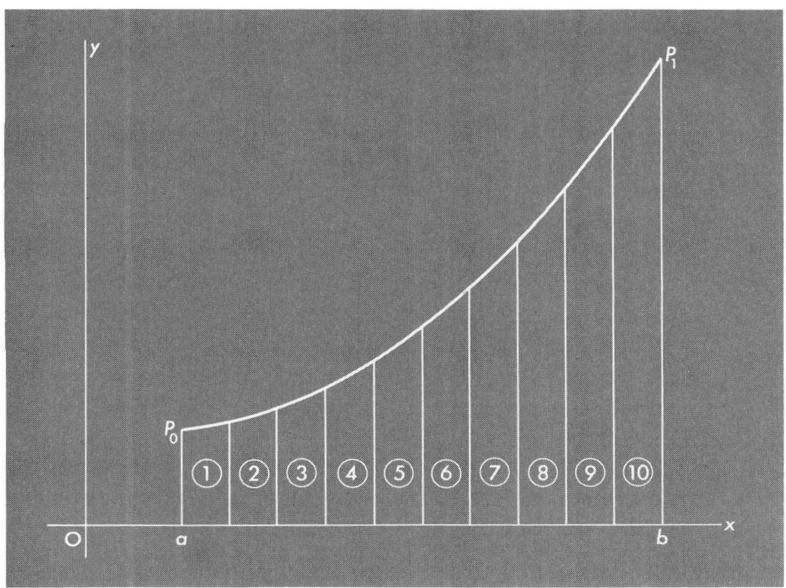

fig. 24·16

The area of each rectangle approximates the area of its corresponding strip. However, as we see in Fig. 24·17, the area of each rectangle is actually *less* than the area of the corresponding strip. This difference can be reduced as much as we please by making each strip sufficiently narrow and by increasing the number of strips.

As we use more and narrower strips, the total of the areas of their corresponding rectangles approaches closer and closer to the area aP_0P_1b.

fig. 24·17

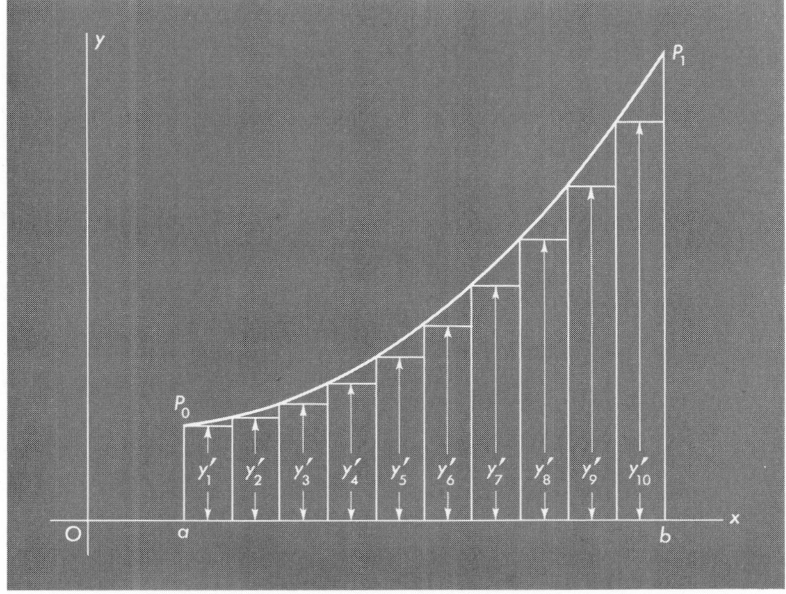

We could also have reasoned from a drawing such as Fig. 24·18. Here we approximate the area of each strip by a rectangle of the same width whose ordinate y'' is the *maximum* ordinate of the strip. In this case, of course, the sum of the areas of the rectangles is *greater* than the area aP_0P_1b.

However, as we again use more and narrower strips, the total of their areas approaches closer and closer to the area aP_0P_1b.

If, instead of using either the maximum ordinate y'' or the minimum ordinate y', we were to use some intermediate ordinate y^* (see Fig. 24·19), we would find that the limit which the sum of the areas of these rectangles approaches as the number of rectangles increases indefinitely is also the area of aP_0P_1b.

If we divide the area aP_0P_1b into n equal strips (in this case $n = 10$) and make each strip Δx units wide, the area under the graph between $x = a$ and $x = b$ can be approximated by

$$A_a{}^b \approx y_1^*(\Delta x) + y_2^*(\Delta x) + y_3^*(\Delta x) \cdots + y_n^*(\Delta x) \tag{7}$$

where $A_a{}^b$ = area aP_0P_1b
$\Delta x = (b - a)/n$
y_1^* = any ordinate erected within first interval
y_2^* = any ordinate erected within second interval
y_3^* = any ordinate erected within third interval
y_n^* = any ordinate erected within nth interval

fig. 24·18

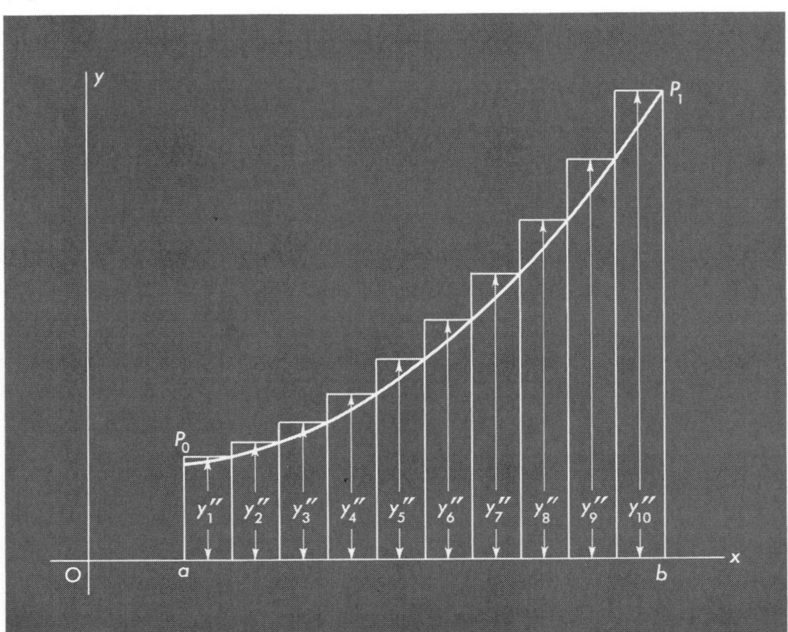

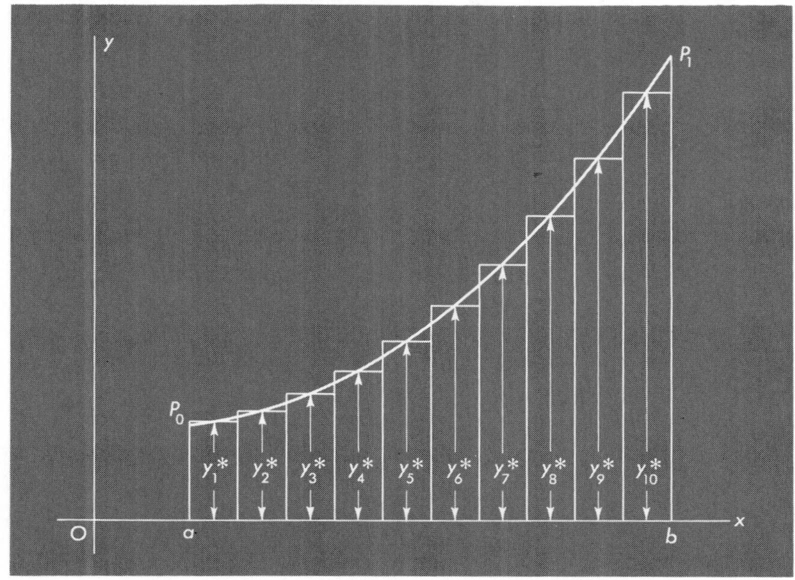

fig. 24·19

We can express this idea somewhat more concisely by writing

$$A_a{}^b \approx \sum_1^n y_k{}^* (\Delta x) \tag{8}$$

where the symbol $\sum_1^n y_k(\Delta x)$ designates "the sum whose typical (or kth) term is $y_k^*(\Delta x)$, where k may take on in turn any integral value between 1 and n."

As n is made larger (and consequently Δx becomes smaller), the approximation in Eq. (8) becomes closer.

We can usually approximate the area of each strip more closely by using good judgment in locating y^*. In Fig. 24·20 it should be intuitively

fig. 24·20

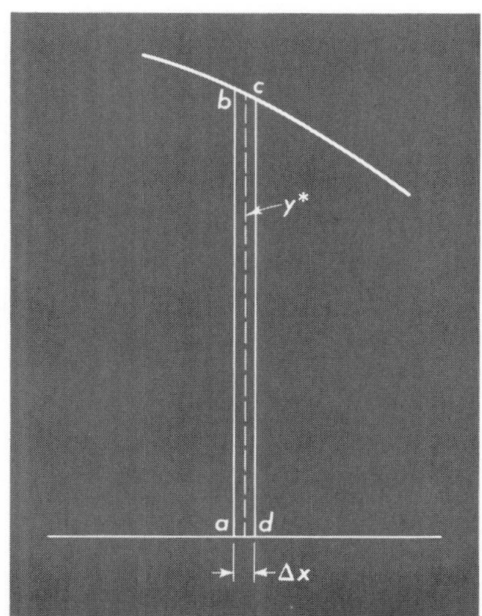

evident that we can obtain a better approximation by placing y^* about midway of the strips than if we located it near either boundary. No generally applicable rule can be given, but the student's judgment in this matter will probably be much better than he may think.

As an example, let us find the area under the graph shown in Fig. 24·21 between $x = 0$ and $x = 6.8$.

We first divide this area into equal strips, each strip being 0.4 unit wide. Thus Δx in Eq. (8) is 0.4. There are 17 strips; consequently n in Eq. (8) is 17.

table 24·4

Strip	x	y^*	*Width* (Δx)	ΔA	$\Sigma y^*(\Delta x)$
1	0.4	100.0	0.4	40.0	40.0
2	0.8	99.6	0.4	39.8	79.8
3	1.2	99.0	0.4	39.6	119.4
4	1.6	98.0	0.4	39.2	158.6
5	2.0	96.8	0.4	38.7	197.3
6	2.4	95.2	0.4	38.1	235.4
7	2.8	93.2	0.4	37.3	272.7
8	3.2	91.0	0.4	36.4	309.1
9	3.6	88.4	0.4	35.3	344.4
10	4.0	85.6	0.4	34.2	378.6
11	4.4	82.4	0.4	32.9	411.5
12	4.8	78.8	0.4	31.5	443.0
13	5.2	75.0	0.4	30.0	473.0
14	5.6	70.8	0.4	28.3	501.3
15	6.0	66.4	0.4	26.6	527.9
16	6.4	61.6	0.4	24.6	552.5
17	6.8	56.4	0.4	22.6	575.1
				575.1	

The calculations involved are tabulated in Table 24·4.

The ordinate y^* for each strip is read directly from the graph about midway of each strip. The approximate area of each strip (ΔA) is found by multiplying y^* for that strip by 0.4. Each entry in the $\Sigma y^*(\Delta x)$ column of the table includes the approximate area of the corresponding strip as well as the approximate areas of all strips to the left. The total area is

$$A_0{}^{6.8} \approx 575.1 \text{ square units}$$

Find the area under the graph shown in Fig. 24·21 between ordinates erected at $x = 4$ and $x = 6$.

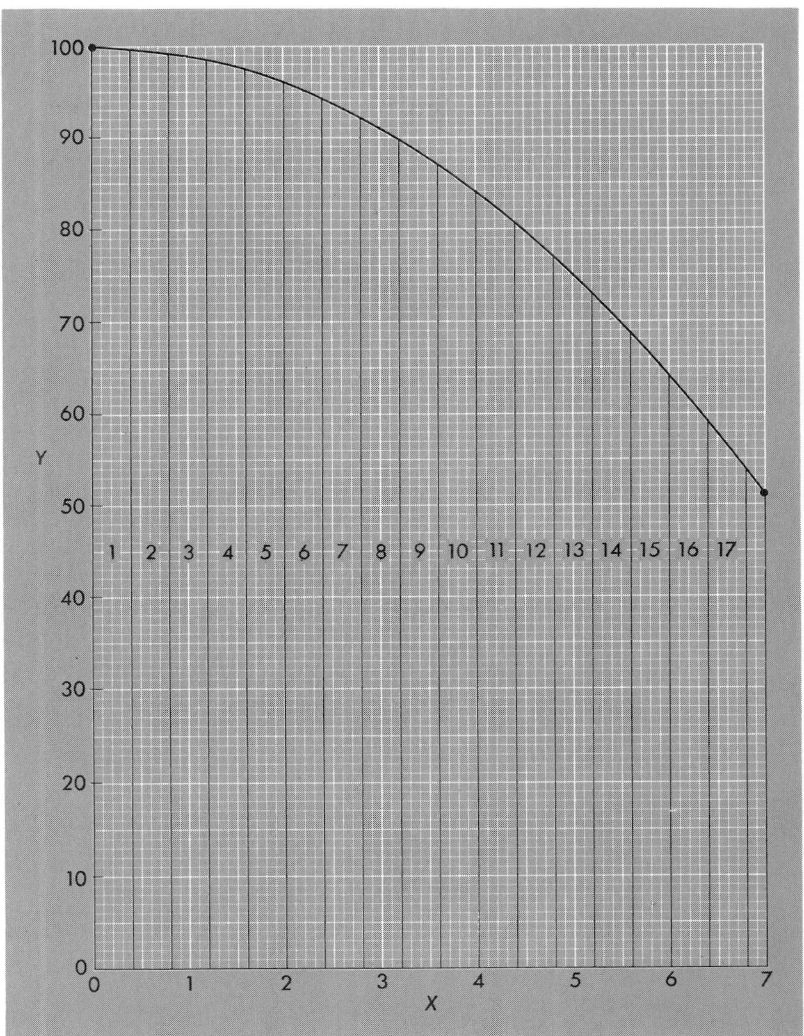

fig. 24·21

By reference to Table 24·4 we see that the area between $x = 0$ and $x = 6$ is 527.9. The area between $x = 0$ and $x = 4$ is 378.6. Therefore the area between $x = 4$ and $x = 6$ is

$$A_4{}^6 = 527.9 - 378.6 = 149.3$$

24·10 Average or mean ordinates of curves

Figure 24·22 shows the graph of a function which is continuous and positive-valued on the closed interval with end points at $x = a$ and $x = b$. Now, leaning heavily on geometric intuition, it seems plausible

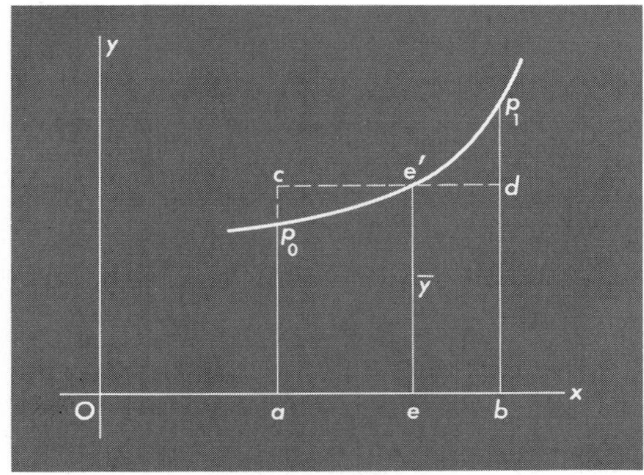

fig. 24·22

that there is a point *e* between *a* and *b* on the *X* axis at which an ordinate $\bar{y}$ can be erected such that

$$\bar{y} = \frac{A_a{}^b}{b - a} \tag{9}$$

where $A_a{}^b$ = area bounded above by the curve, below by the *X* axis, on the left by the ordinate erected at $x = a$, and on the right by the ordinate erected at $x = b$.

$\bar{y}$ = mean ordinate of the graph between *a* and *b*. Note that $\bar{y}$ is defined by Eq. (9) above. It is not necessarily the arithmetic average of the ordinates erected at *a* and *b*, as was the case with linear graphs.

example 7 Find the mean ordinate of the graph shown in Fig. 24·21 between $x = 0$ and $x = 6.8$.

In this case referred to Eq. (9), $a = 0$ and $b = 6.8$. From Table 24·4 $A_0{}^{6.8} = 575.1$. Therefore, from Eq. (9) the average ordinate or the mean ordinate between $x = 0$ and $x = 6.8$ is

$$\bar{y} = \frac{575.1}{6.8 - 0} = 84.6$$

EXERCISE 4

1. Find the average height of the curve in Fig. 24·2 between $x = 2$ and $x = 3\frac{1}{2}$. In doing this problem, divide the area under the curve into strips such that $\Delta x = 0.3$.

EXERCISE 5

Figure 24·23 shows the cross-sectional area of a cone versus the distance from the apex.

1. Find *a* when $h = 20$.
2. Find da/dh when $h = 20$. Also find dh/da.
3. Find da/dh when $a = 100$. Also find dh/da.
4. Find the area *a* when $da/dh = 5$.
5. Find the average rate of change of area with respect to distance between $h = 5$ and $h = 25$.

6. Find the average slope between $h = 15$ and $h = 20$.
7. Find the average slope between $a = 25$ and $a = 100$.
8. Find the instantaneous slope at $h = 22$.
9. Find the instantaneous slope at $a = 100$.
10. How fast is ordinate changing with distance at 12 ft?
11. How fast is ordinate changing with distance at 75 sq ft?
12. How much does ordinate change when distance changes from 10 to 20 ft?
13. How much does distance change when ordinate changes from 25 to 50 sq ft?
14. About how much does ordinate increase when h increases from 10 to 10.001?
15. Find the average ordinate of the curve between $h = 10$ and $h = 20$.
16. Find the average ordinate of the curve between $a = 50$ and $a = 100$.

fig. 24·23

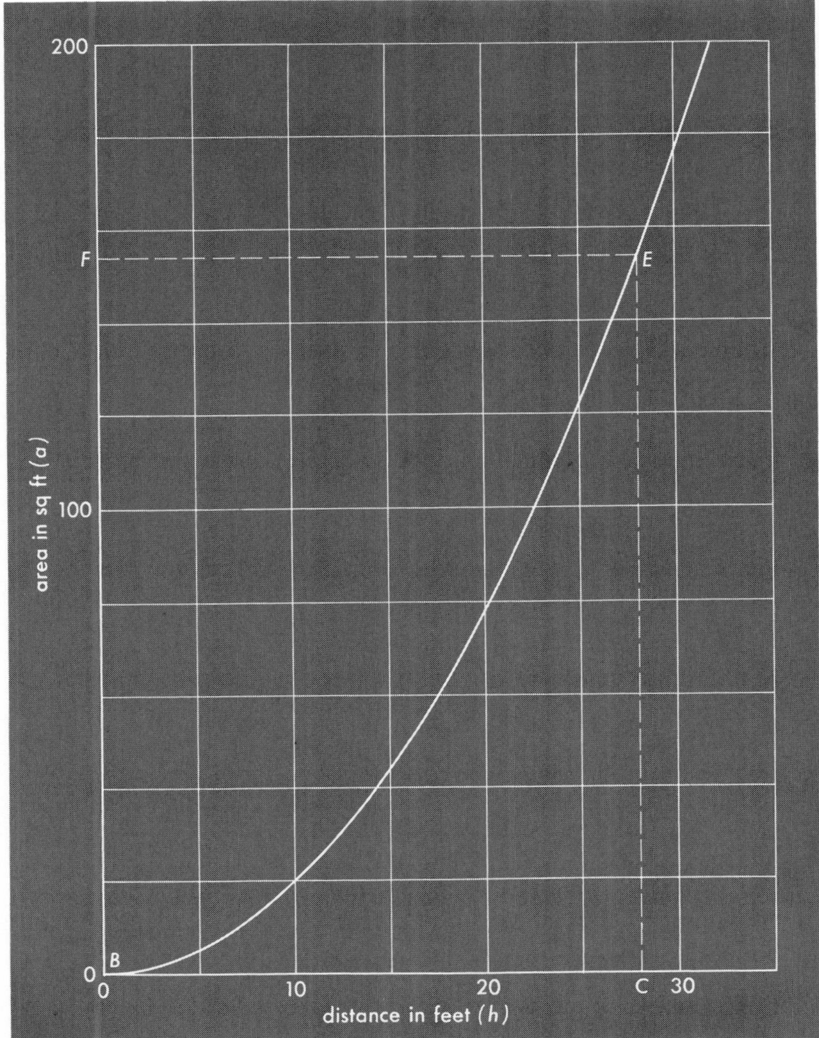

17. What volume is included between the levels $h = 15$ and $h = 25$? Check by the formula for the frustum of a cone.
18. (a) If the area of *BEC* represents the volume of the cone, what does the area of *BFEC* represent?
    (b) What does the area of *FEB* represent?

EXERCISE 6

The temperature change of a warm object in cooler surroundings versus time is illustrated in Fig. 24·24.

1. Find dT/dt when $t = 10$.
2. Find dt/dT when $t = 10$.
3. Find dT/dt when $T = 10$.
4. Find dt/dT when $T = 10$.

fig. 24·24

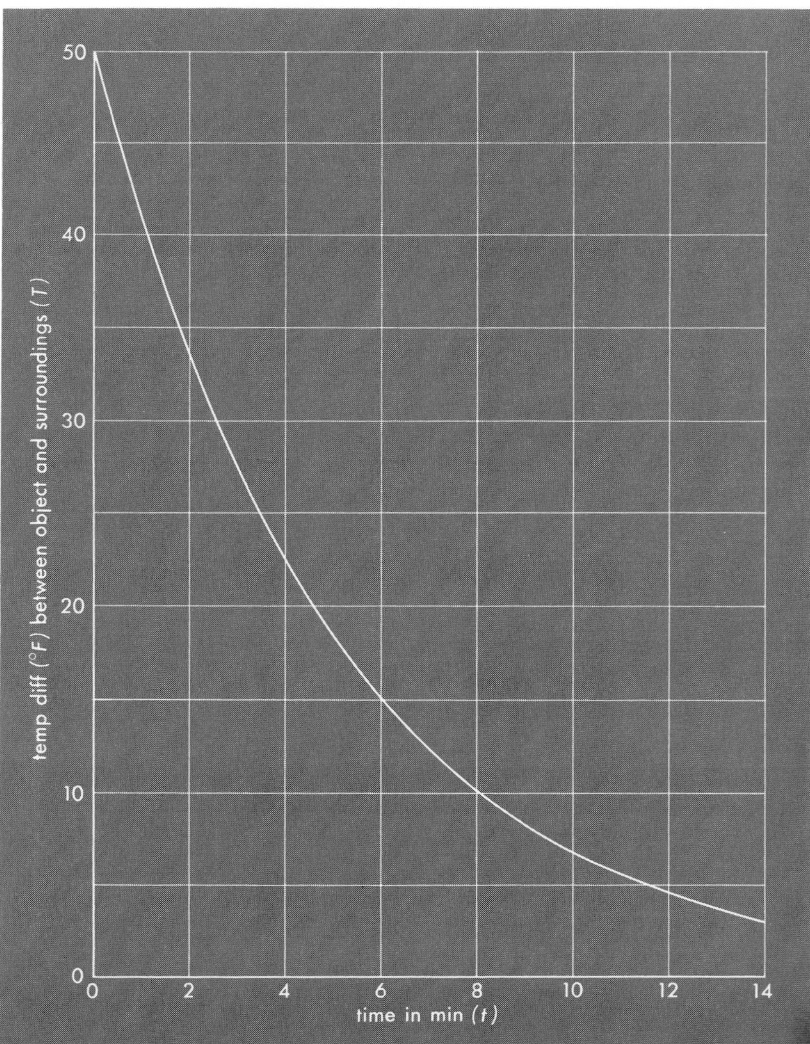

5. Find t when $dT/dt = -5.0°$ per min.
6. Find T when $dT/dt = -2.5°$ per min.
7. Find the average rate of change of T with respect to t between $t = 2$ and $t = 8$.
8. Find the average slope between $t = 6$ and $t = 10$.
9. Find the average slope between $T = 30$ and $T = 10$.
10. Find the instantaneous slope at $t = 6$.
11. Find the instantaneous slope at $T = 30$.
12. How fast is T changing with t at $t = 10$?
13. How much does T change when t changes from 4 to 8?
14. How much does t change when T changes from 40 to 10?
15. About how much does T decrease when t increases from 3.99 to 4.00?
16. Find the area under the curve between $t = 4$ and $t = 8$.
17. Find the average height of the curve between $t = 4$ and $t = 8$.
18. Find the average ordinate of the curve between $t = 4$ and $t = 8$.
19. Find the average T from 3 to 6 min.
20. Find the average rate of change of T between 3 to 6 min.
21. Find the instantaneous rate of temperature change at 4.5 min.
22. When is the rate of change of temperature difference equal to $-4°$ per min?
23. Approximately how long will it take for the temperature difference to go from 10° to 9.98°?
24. Approximately what will be the change in temperature difference between 2.0 and 2.06 min?
25. What is the rate of change of temperature difference when the temperature difference is 50°, 40°, 30°, 20°, 10°? Plot these rates against corresponding temperature differences. What relationship is revealed by this plot?
26. When will the temperature difference be reduced to ½, ¼, ⅛, and 1/16 of the original value? What relationship is revealed?
27. Figure 24·24 was plotted from an equation in the form

$$T = ke^{mt}$$

where k and m are arbitrary constants and e is the base of natural logarithms. From your solution to Probs. 25 and 26 above, try to surmise some of the properties of relationship.

EXERCISE 7

The force on a piston versus the distance from one end of the cylinder is illustrated in Fig. 24·25.

1. How fast does the force decrease with distance when the distance is 4 ft?
2. What is the rate of change in force with respect to distance when the force is 6 lb?
3. Find dF/dD when $D = 5$ ft, where F = force in pounds and D = distance in feet.
4. Find dD/dF when $D = 5$ ft.

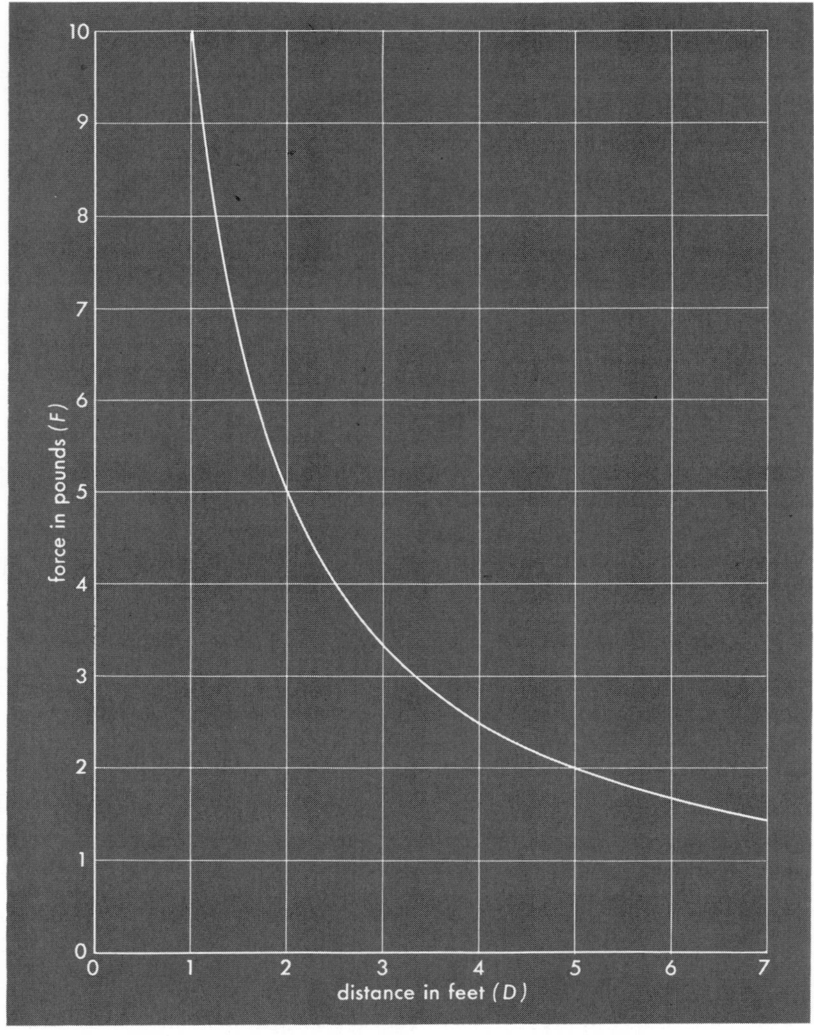

fig. 24·25

5. Find $\Delta F/\Delta D$ between $D = 2$ and $D = 3$. Also find $\Delta D/\Delta F$.
6. Find the average force between $D = 2$ and $D = 4$.
7. Plot a curve of work versus distance between $D = 1$ and $D = 6$.
8. For what force is the rate of change of force with respect to distance equal to -2 lb per ft?
9. Find the average rate of change in force with respect to distance between 1 and 4 ft.
10. Find the instantaneous rate of change in force with respect to distance when the distance is $3\frac{1}{3}$ ft.
11. Find the approximate change in force when the distance changes from $2\frac{1}{2}$ to 2.507 ft.

24·11 Maxima and minima

Suppose we have a function f for which $y = f(x)$. This function is said to have a *relative maximum* at $x = a$ if $f(a)$ is equal to or greater than any other $f(x)$ in the immediate vicinity (see Fig. 24·26).

Similarly, this function is said to have a *relative minimum* at $x = b$ if $f(b)$ is equal to or less than any other $f(x)$ in the immediate vicinity (see Fig. 24·26).

A point whose ordinate is a maximum value of a function is called a maximum point. Similarly, a point whose ordinate is the minimum value of a function is called a minimum point.

We distinguish between relative maxima and minima as described above and *absolute* maxima and minima which are illustrated in Fig. 24·27. If a function is defined for the domain $a \leq x \leq b$ (see Fig. 24·27) and if $f(a)$ is greater than any other $f(x)$ for this domain, then the function is said to have an *absolute* maximum at $x = a$. This function is shown to have an *absolute* minimum at $x = b$ (see Fig. 24·27).

A function may have relative maxima and minima of the type illustrated in Fig. 24·28, although we shall have little to do with such situations.

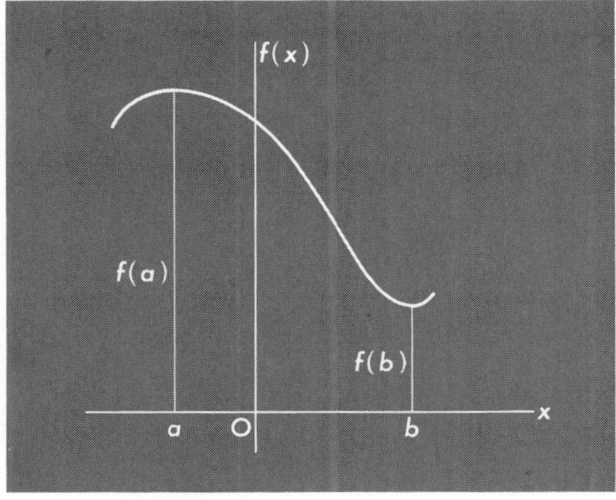

fig. 24·26

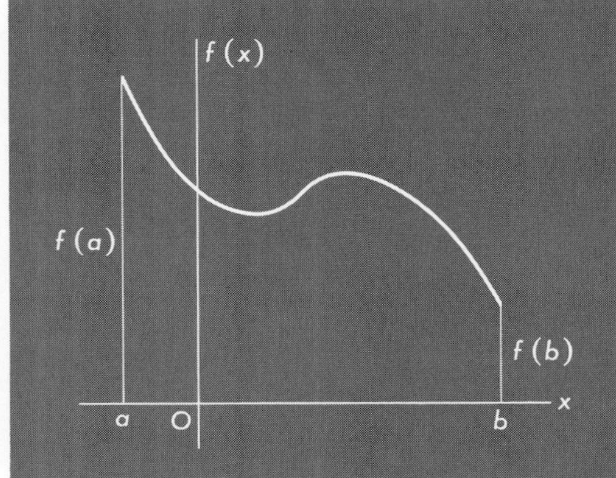

fig. 24·27

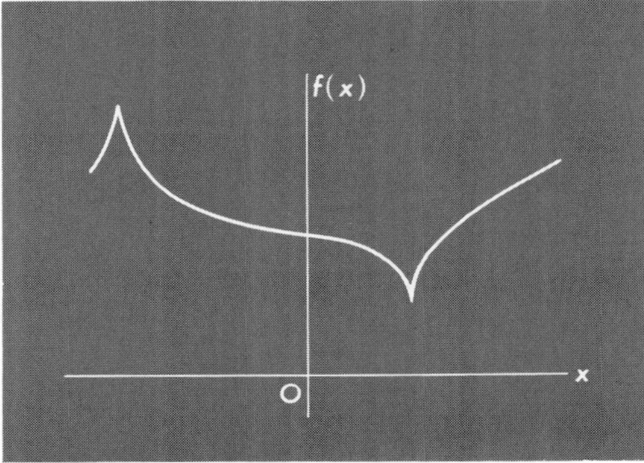

fig. 24·28

Hereafter, when we use the words "maximum" and "minimum" without further qualification, we shall mean the sort of relative maximum or minimum illustrated in Fig. 24·26.

There are four important characteristics of relative maximum and minimum points.

1. If a graph has a relative maximum or minimum point in a certain vicinity, and if a tangent whose slope is a finite real number can be drawn at this point, then the slope of this tangent must be zero.
2. A maximum point is higher than any other point in the immediate vicinity, and a minimum point is lower than any other point in the immediate vicinity.
3. In passing through a maximum point, if we scan the graph in the direction of increasing abscissa (that is, as we scan the graph from left to right), we find a positive slope, a zero slope, and a negative slope, *in that order.*
4. In passing through a minimum point, if we scan the graph in the direction of increasing abscissa, we find a negative slope, a zero slope, and a positive slope, *in that order.*

Consider the maximum point P_1 (Fig. 24·29*a*). At the point P_1 the slope is zero. The point P_1 is higher than any other point in the immediate vicinity. Immediately to the left the slope is positive, and immediately to the right the slope is negative.

A similar situation exists about the minimum point P_2. At the point P_2 the slope is zero. This point is lower than any other point in the immediate vicinity, and the slope is negative to the left of P_2 and positive to the right of P_2.

As we scan the graph from left to right, if the sign of the slope is in the sequence

$$\text{Positive} \longrightarrow \text{zero} \longrightarrow \text{negative}$$

the point is at a *maximum.*

If the sequence is

$$\text{Negative} \longrightarrow \text{zero} \longrightarrow \text{positive}$$

the point is at a *minimum.*

If the sequence is

$$\text{Negative} \longrightarrow \text{zero} \longrightarrow \text{negative}$$

or

$$\text{Positive} \longrightarrow \text{zero} \longrightarrow \text{positive}$$

the point is at neither a maximum nor a minimum.

Thus we cannot assume that just because the slope of a graph is zero at a critical point either a maximum or a minimum must exist at that point.

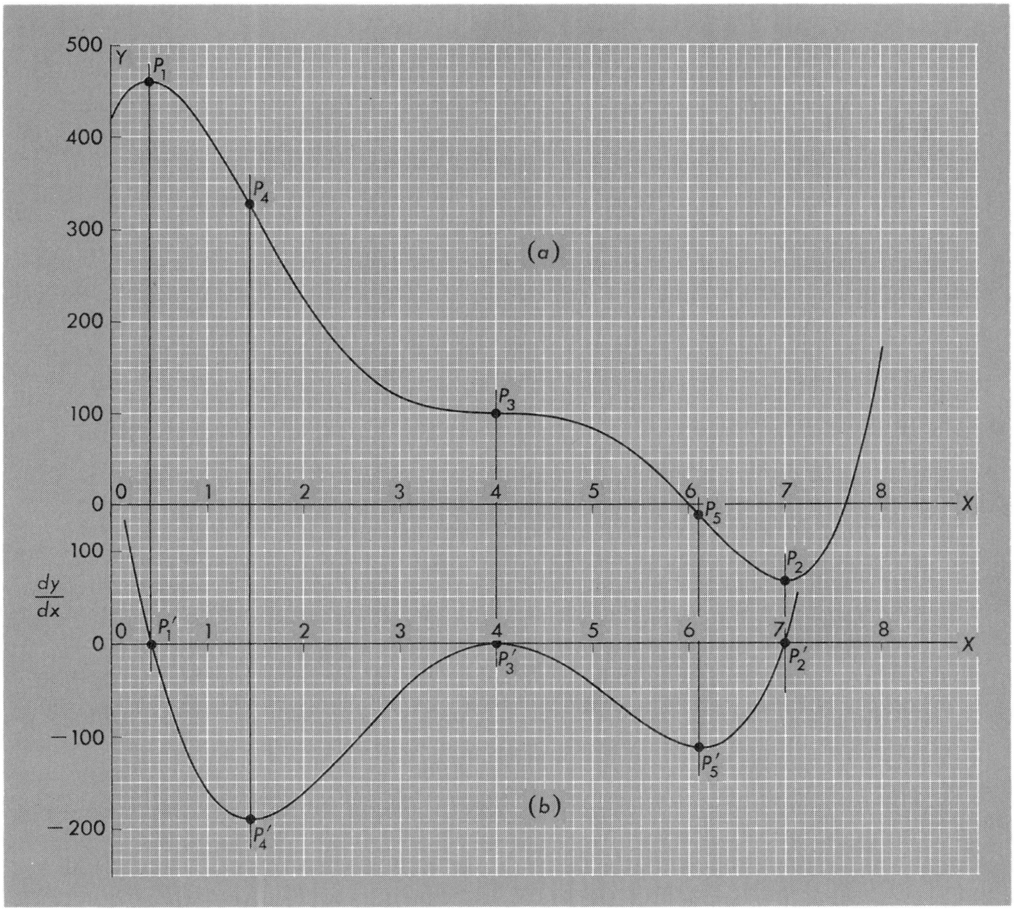

fig. 24·29

24·12 Points of inflection

Refer to Fig. 24·30. Consider the reverse curve *ABC* to be a map of a road. As we drive an automobile along the road from *A* toward *B* we are steering to the right. When we reach point *B* we must steer to the left. At point *B* the curvature *reverses.*

fig. 24·30

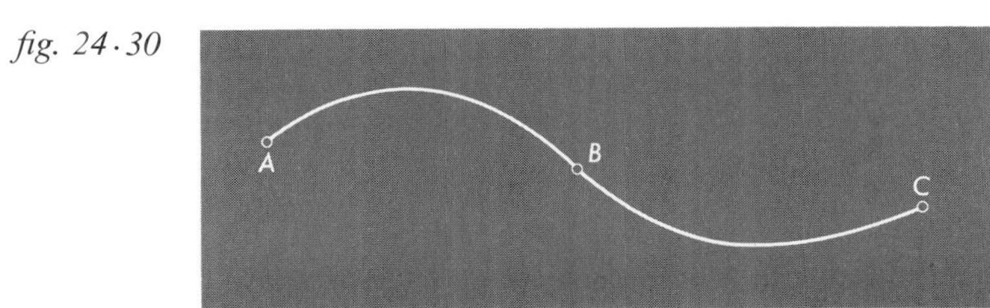

Any point on a graph where the curvature reverses is called a *point of inflection.*

Applying this notion to Fig. 24·29*a*, we note that points of inflection occur at P_3, P_4, and P_5. True, the slope at P_3 is zero, but this is not a necessary condition for a point of inflection. The slopes at the other two points of inflection, P_4 and P_5, are not zero.

It is a characteristic of a point of inflection having a horizontal tangent (such as P_3) that as we scan the graph in either direction the slope passes through zero but *does not change sign.*

Thus a point of horizontal tangency may be a maximum, a minimum, or simply a point of inflection.

24·13 Derived curves

Figure 24·29*b* is a plot of dy/dx versus x, that is, for a given value of x, the numerical value of the slope in Fig. 24·29*a* is the ordinate of Fig. 24·29*b*.

For example, we can see that the slope in Fig. 24·29*a* is zero at P_1 because the tangent to the curve at that point is horizontal. The corresponding point P_1' in Fig. 24·29*b* shows that at this point $dy/dx = 0$. Precisely the same information in this respect is obtained from either graph.

Observe points P_2 and P_3 together with their corresponding points in Fig. 24·29*b* (P_2' and P_3'). In each case the slope of Fig. 24·29*a* and its synonym dy/dx are shown to be zero.

If we scan Fig. 24·29*a* from P_1 toward the right, we note that the slope decreases (increases numerically but in a negative direction). The slope continues to decrease until we reach P_4, a point of inflection.

Subsequently, the graph flattens out and the slope becomes zero again at P_3, which is another point of inflection. Considering signs, then, the slope at P_4 is a minimum. Now notice that a minimum dy/dx occurs at P_4' in Fig. 24·29*b*.

Observe that the slope is again a minimum at the point of inflection P_5 and is so indicated at P_5'.

The slope is at a maximum at P_3 and is also so indicated at P_3'. However, the student should be careful to notice that the point P_3 corresponds to a maximum slope in Fig. 24·29*a*. It does not correspond to a maximum ordinate on Fig. 24·29*a*.

EXERCISE 8

1. By laying a straight edge against the curve in Fig. 24·29*a* find the slope of this curve at the following values of x: 0.4, 1.0, 2.5, 4.0, 4.5, 5.0, 6.0, 6.1, 6.5, 7.0.
2. (a) Compare the slopes found in Prob. 1 with the corresponding ordinates in Fig. 24·29*b*.

fig. 24·31

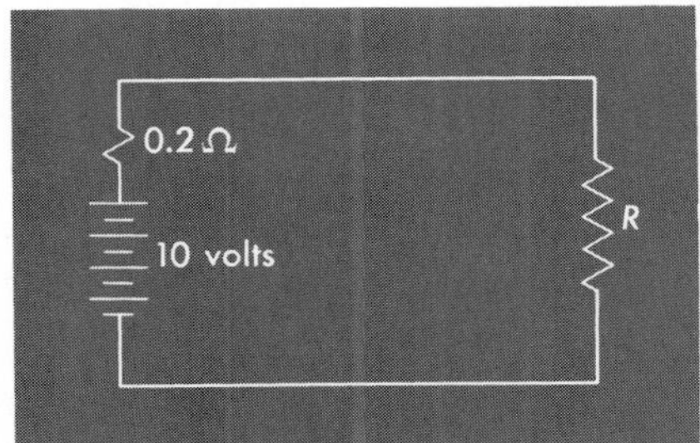

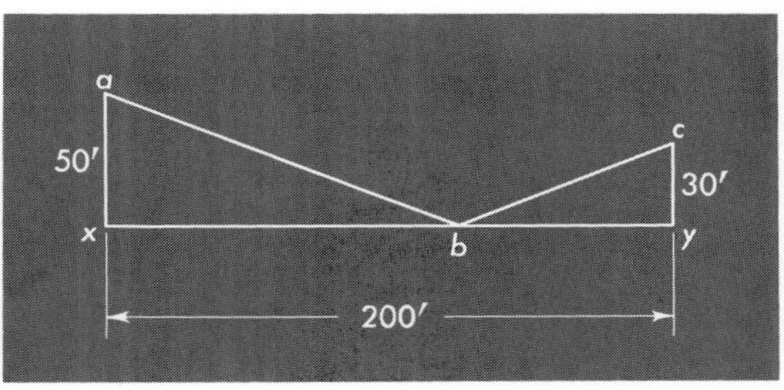

fig. 24·32

(b) Find where the slope of Fig. 24·29*a* is a maximum. A minimum.

(c) Find where the slope of Fig. 24·29*b* is a maximum; a minimum.

3. Find the maximum speed in Fig. 24·34.
4. When was the speed a maximum in Fig. 24·34?
5. A rectangle has a perimeter of 40 in. Plot the area of this rectangle against the length of a side. Find the dimensions of the rectangle to give the greatest area.
6. The power lost in resistance R is given by the equation

$$P = \frac{(10 - 0.2i)^2}{R}$$

Also

$$i = \frac{10}{R + 0.2}$$

Plot P against R and find the value of R such that the power dissipated in R is a maximum (see Fig. 24·31).

7. The tops of two vertical poles ax and cy are connected by a rope abc. Plot the length of the rope against the distance xb and find the length of xb for a minimum length of the rope (see Fig. 24·32).
8. A sheet-iron trough is to be made by bending up two edges so as to give a rectangular cross-section area. The width of the sheet is 20 in. Therefore 20 in. $= x + 2y$. Plot the cross-section area against y and find y to give a maximum cross-section area (see Fig. 24·33).

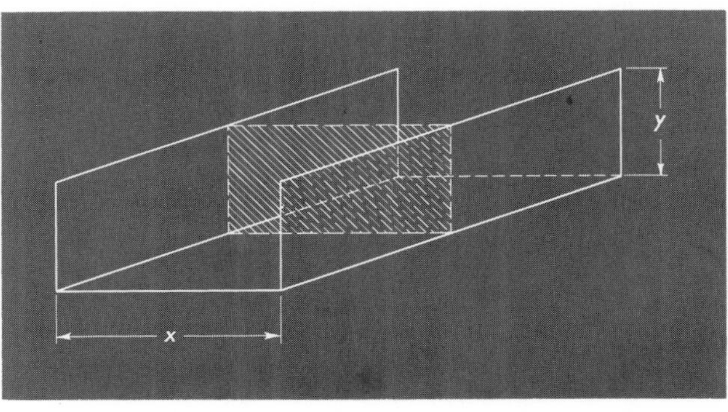

fig. 24·33

EXERCISE 9

The tangential speed of a point on the tread of an automobile tire during one revolution versus time is shown in Fig. 24·34.

1. Find the average acceleration of the point between $t = 0.02$ and $t = 0.03$. (Acceleration is the rate of change in velocity.)
2. Find the instantaneous acceleration at $t = 0.03$.
3. Find the time and value of the maximum speed.
4. Find the speed of the car.
5. Find the outside diameter of the tire.
6. Find the distance the point moves through space between $t = 0$ sec and $t = \frac{1}{8}$ sec.

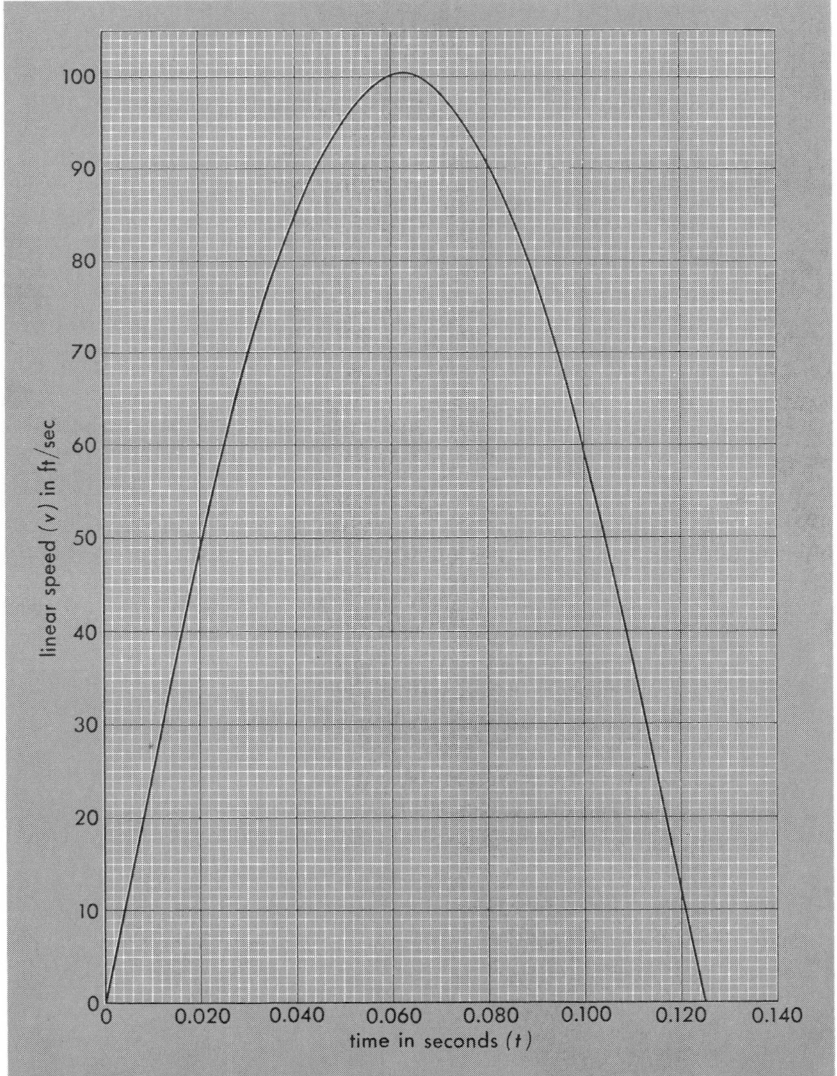

fig. 24·34

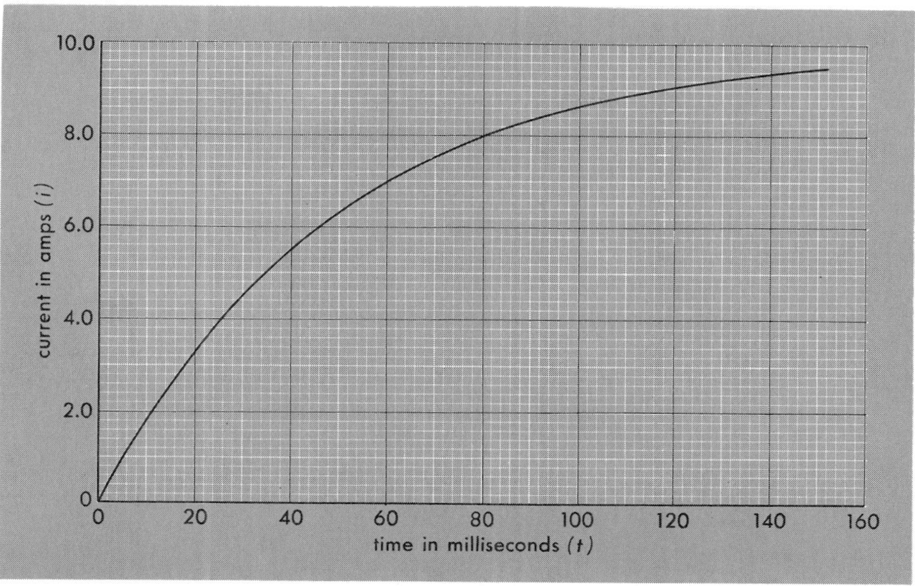

fig. 24·35

EXERCISE 10

The graph in Fig. 24·35 shows the relation between current and time in a certain series circuit containing inductance and resistance. The inductance is 0.75 henry, the resistance is 15 ohms. A battery of 150 volts is connected across this series combination when $t = 0$. Thereafter the current rises as shown in the curve.

1. Find di/dt, where t is in seconds, for 0, 0.02, 0.04, 0.06, 0.08, 0.10, and 0.12 sec.
2. What is the "maximum" current?
3. If the current increased at the constant rates found in Prob. 1, how long would it take for the current to reach the maximum in each case?
4. Compare the values found in Prob. 3 with the ratio L/R.
5. Plot di/dt versus i between 0 and 120 msec.

EXERCISE 11

1. Complete the computations which have been started on Table 24·5. This table is an idealized set of trajectory data for a sounding rocket fired in an upward direction when $T = 0$.
2. Plot these data as indicated in the sketch (see Fig. 24·36).
3. Explain the physical significance of the shape of the acceleration curve.
4. Find the vertical distance covered between 120 and 140 sec (a) from velocity curve, (b) from height curve.
5. Find the vertical distance covered between 180 and 230 sec (a) from

table 24·5

Time, sec	Velocity,* fps	Average*† velocity, fps	Average*‡ acceleration, ft/sec²	Change† in altitude Δh, ft	Cumulative altitude, ft
0	0				0
		200	40	2,000	
10	400				2,000
		725	65	7,250	
20	1,050				9,250
		1,410	72	14,100	
30	1,770				23,350
		2,145	75	21,450	
40	2,520				44,800
50	3,270				
60	4,020				
62	4,168				
64	4,308				
66	4,348				135,520
68	4,292				
70	4,220				
80	3,870				
90	3,530				
100	3,200				263,772
120	2,580				
140	1,980				
160	1,380				
180	780				
200	180				431,972
220	−420				
240	−1,040				
260	−1,660				
280	−2,280				
300	−2,760				298,172
320	−2,960				
340	−2,860				
360	−2,520				
380	−2,080				
400	−1,640				
420	−1,200				17,372

* All references to acceleration and velocity are in terms of their vertical components.

† Do not plot. Used only to calculate cumulative altitude.

‡ Plot against midpoint of time interval.

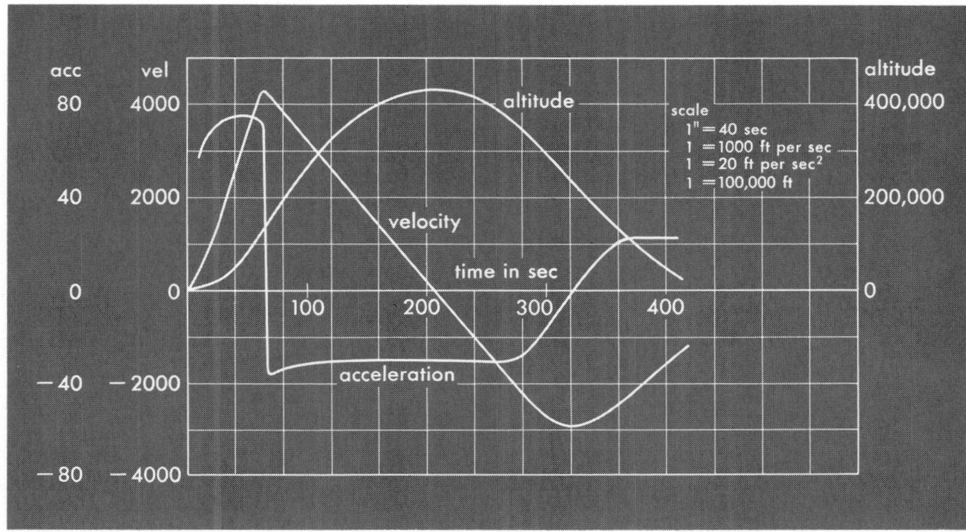

fig. 24·36

velocity curve, (b) from height curve. (c) What would be the significance of a zero answer?

6. Find the average velocity from 260 sec to 270 sec (a) using velocity curve, (b) using height curve.
7. Repeat Prob. 6 for interval 300 to 360 sec.
8. Use height curve to find velocity at 250 sec. Check by reading from velocity curve.
9. What was the probable time of impact?
10. What was the probable velocity of impact?
11. Find the acceleration at 42 sec (a) from velocity curve, (b) from acceleration curve.
12. Find the average acceleration from 260 to 290 sec (a) from acceleration curve, (b) from velocity curve.
13. Find time of maximum upward velocity, (a) using velocity curve, (b) using height curve, (c) using acceleration curve. (d) Find value of maximum upward velocity.
14. Answer the same questions as in Prob. 13 for the maximum downward velocity.
15. Find the time of maximum height (a) from height curve, (b) from velocity curve.
16. Find the probable value of the maximum height.
17. Calculate each of the following by the best method; also indicate (without calculating) an alternative method of doing the same thing: (a) velocity at 50 sec, (b) average velocity from 54 to 96 sec, (c) acceleration at 290 sec, (d) average acceleration from 42 to 58 sec, (e) actual distance covered from 160 to 250 sec.

25 differentiation

In Chap. 24 we discussed methods of finding the average and the instantaneous rates of change in the value of certain functions when these functions are represented by graphs.

In this chapter we shall discuss methods of expressing the average and the instantaneous rates of change in the value of certain functions when these functions are represented by equations.

25 · 1 Average rates of change: nonlinear functions

In Chap. 24 we learned that if we are given a certain function f, and if we wish to find an average rate of change in $f(x)$, we start with a definite value of x which we designate as x_1 and let x change by a certain amount Δx. Then the *average* rate of change in $f(x)$ with respect to x is

$$\begin{pmatrix}\text{Average rate of}\\ \text{change of } f(x)\\ \text{with respect to } x\end{pmatrix} = \frac{f(x_1 + \Delta x) - f(x_1)}{\Delta x} \tag{1}$$

If we let

$$y = f(x) \tag{2}$$

then we may let

$$\Delta y = f(x_1 + \Delta x) - f(x_1) \tag{3}$$

and

$$\begin{pmatrix}\text{Average rate of}\\ \text{change of } f(x)\\ \text{with respect to } x\end{pmatrix} = \begin{pmatrix}\text{average rate of}\\ \text{change of } y \text{ with}\\ \text{respect to } x\end{pmatrix} = \frac{\Delta y}{\Delta x}$$

$$= \frac{f(x_1 + \Delta x) - f(x_1)}{\Delta x} \tag{4}$$

example 1 Find an expression for the average rate of change in the value of the function defined by

$$y = f(x) = x^3 \tag{5}$$

This is the equation of the graph plotted in Fig. 24·2 over the domain $0 \leq x \leq +4$.

Following Eq. (3),

$$\Delta y = (x_1 + \Delta x)^3 - (x_1)^3 \tag{6}$$

$$\Delta y = x_1^3 + 3x_1^2(\Delta x) + 3x_1(\Delta x)^2 + (\Delta x)^3 - x_1^3$$

$$\Delta y = 3x_1^2(\Delta x) + 3x_1(\Delta x)^2 + (\Delta x)^3 \tag{7}$$

and

$$\frac{\Delta y}{\Delta x} = 3x_1^2 + 3x_1(\Delta x) + (\Delta x)^2 \tag{8}$$

example 2 Find the average slope of the graph of $y = x^3$ between $x_1 = 2$ and $x_1 + \Delta x = 2.5$.

In this case $\Delta x = 2.5 - 2 = 0.5$ and $x_1 = 2$. Substituting these values in Eq. (8),

$$\frac{\Delta y}{\Delta x} = 3(2)^2 + 3 \cdot 2 \cdot 0.5 + 0.5^2$$

$$\frac{\Delta y}{\Delta x} = 12 + 3 + 0.25 = 15.25 \tag{9}$$

Check this value of average slope directly from Fig. 24·2.

example 3 Find an expression for the average rate of change of y with respect to x if

$$y = f(x) = 5x^2 + 3$$

Following Eq. (3),

$$\Delta y = 5(x_1 + \Delta x)^2 + 3 - (5x_1^2 + 3)$$

$$\Delta y = 5x_1^2 + 10x_1(\Delta x) + 5(\Delta x)^2 + 3 - 5x_1^2 - 3$$

$$\Delta y = 10x_1(\Delta x) + 5(\Delta x)^2$$

$$\frac{\Delta y}{\Delta x} = 10x_1 + 5(\Delta x)$$

Observe that the added constant 3 subtracts out in the course of doing the problem.

example 4 Find the equation for the average rate of change in y with respect to x if $y = 1/x^2$.

$$\Delta y = \frac{1}{(x_1 + \Delta x)^2} - \frac{1}{x^2}$$

$$\Delta y = \frac{1}{x_1^2 + 2x_1(\Delta x) + (\Delta x)^2} - \frac{1}{x_1^2}$$

$$= \frac{x_1^2 - x_1^2 - 2x_1(\Delta x) - (\Delta x)^2}{x_1^2[x_1^2 + 2x_1(\Delta x) + (\Delta x)^2]}$$

$$\frac{\Delta y}{\Delta x} = \frac{-2x_1 - \Delta x}{x_1^2[x_1^2 + 2x_1(\Delta x) + (\Delta x)^2]}$$

EXERCISE 1 Find the equation for the average rate of change in the dependent variable with respect to the independent variable in the following problems.

1. $y = 5x^3$
2. $y = 5x^3 + 8$
3. $y = 7x^2 + 3$
4. $y = x^3 - 2x$
5. $w = u^2 - 3u - 18$
6. $w = 3/u$
7. $w = 1 + 2z - \frac{1}{z}$
8. $g = \frac{t}{t + 3}$
9. $w = \sqrt{x}$
10. $A = \pi R^2$
11. $V = \frac{4}{3}\pi R^3$
12. Find ΔA in Prob. 10 if R increases from 5 to 5.2 in.
13. Confirm your answers to Probs. 10 and 11 by geometry.

25·2 Limits and continuity

The concepts of limits and continuity are two of the most fundamental concepts in calculus. However, a rigorous treatment of them is somewhat beyond the scope of this book.

The more intuitive approach which we shall discuss below is entirely adequate for the needs of the student at present.

The statement that $f(x)$ approaches the number L as a limit when x approaches the number a is symbolized as

$$\lim_{x \to a} f(x) = L \tag{10}$$

This means that

(1) if $|f(x) - L|$ can be made arbitrarily small
(2) by making $|x - a|$ smaller and smaller (but still greater than zero)
(3) we may say that $f(x)$ approaches L as x approaches a
(4) and L is the limit which $f(x)$ approaches as x approaches a.

The above assumes, of course, that x remains within the domain of definition of the function.

table 25·1

x	$\lvert x-3\rvert$	$f(x)$	$\lvert f(x)-6\rvert$
3.05	0.05	6.05	0.05
3.04	0.04	6.04	0.04
3.03	0.03	6.03	0.03
3.02	0.02	6.02	0.02
3.01	0.01	6.01	0.01
3.00	0.00	6.00	0.00
2.99	0.01	5.99	0.01
2.98	0.02	5.98	0.02
2.97	0.03	5.97	0.03
2.96	0.04	5.96	0.04
2.95	0.05	5.95	0.05

For example, if $f(x) = x + 3$, let us see what limit if any $f(x)$ approaches as x approaches 3. Here the number 3 corresponds to a in Eq. (10). It seems intuitively evident that as x approaches 3, then $f(x)$ approaches 6. However, let us illustrate some of our ideas of limits by Table 25·1. Here we have calculated $|x - 3|$ and $|f(x) - 6|$ for a sequence of values of x. Note that 6 in this example corresponds to L in Eq. (10).

Thus we see that (1) as we make the absolute value $|x - 3|$ smaller and smaller, (2) the absolute value $|f(x) - 6|$ becomes smaller and smaller, (3) and we say that $f(x)$ approaches 6 as x approaches 3; (4) thus 6 is the limit that $f(x)$ approaches as x approaches 3.

example 5 What limit if any does

$$y = f(x) = \frac{x^2 - 9}{x - 3}$$

approach as x approaches 3?

First let us form a table of values from which we can plot the graph of $f(x)$ versus x.

The graph of $f(x)$ versus x is plotted in Fig. 25·1. Note that $f(x)$ is

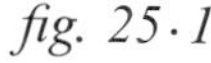
fig. 25·1

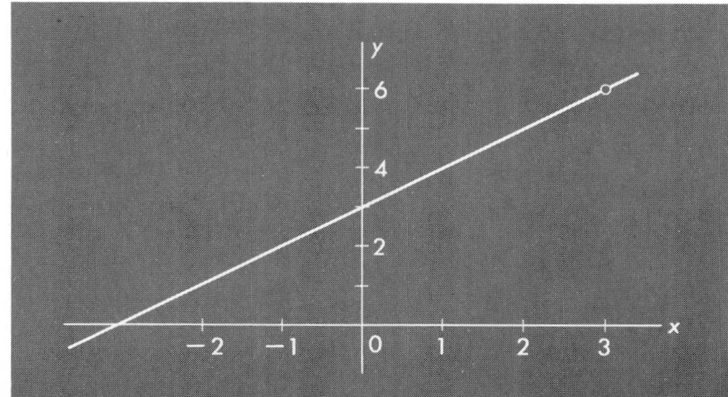

not defined for $x = 3$. This is indicated on the graph by the circle with its center at the point (3,6).

Even so we see from Table 25·2 that (1) as we make the absolute value $|x - 3|$ smaller and smaller, (2) the absolute value $|f(x) - 6|$ becomes smaller and smaller, (3) and we may say that $f(x)$ approaches 6 as x approaches 3; (4) thus 6 is the limit that $f(x)$ approaches as x approaches 3, even though $f(x)$ is undefined *at* $x = 3$.

table 25·2

x	$\|x - 3\|$	$f(x)$	$\|f(x) - 6\|$
5	2	8	2
4	1	7	1
3	0	Undefined	Undefined
2	1	5	1
1	2	4	2
0	3	3	3

A somewhat more direct approach would be to factor the numerator of $(x^2 - 9)/(x - 3)$, obtaining

$$\frac{(x-3)(x+3)}{x-3} = x + 3 \qquad x \neq 3$$

Though this equality does not hold for $x = 3$, it does hold for all other values of x, including those as close to 3 as we choose. Thus we may write

$$\lim_{x\to 3} \frac{x^2 - 9}{x - 3} = \lim_{x \to 3} (x + 3) = 6 \qquad x \neq 3$$

Observe that the function is undefined for $x = 3$, even though $f(x)$ approaches 6 as x approaches 3.

example 6 If $y = f(x) = 1/x$ what limit, if any, does $f(x)$ approach when x approaches zero?

We can see intuitively that as the difference between x and 0 becomes less and less in absolute value, then $f(x)$ becomes larger and larger in absolute value without bound.

In symbols we may write

$$1/x \to \infty \qquad \text{as} \qquad x \to 0$$

The student should not be misled into thinking of the symbol ∞ as some enormous number called "infinity." It is not. It is simply used in this context to indicate that, as x approaches a fixed value (in this case 0), then $1/x$ increases (or decreases) without bound.

On account of the notation used in Eq. (10) we sometimes write

$$\lim_{x \to 0} \frac{1}{x} = \infty$$

However, since ∞ is not a real number, it is not, strictly speaking, a limit in the real-number system with which we are concerned at present.

Sometimes it is desirable to distinguish whether x approaches 0 while always remaining positive or approaches 0 while always remaining negative. In such cases we may write

$$\lim_{x \to 0} \frac{1}{x} = \infty + \qquad (\text{for } 0 < x) \tag{11}$$

or

$$\lim_{x \to 0} \frac{1}{x} = \infty - \qquad (\text{for } 0 > x) \tag{12}$$

Equation (11) means that as x approaches zero while always remaining a positive number, $1/x$ increases without bound. Equation (12) means that as x approaches zero while always remaining a negative number, $1/x$ decreases without bound.

example 7 If $y = f(x) = 1/x$, what limit if any does y approach as x approaches infinity (that is, as x becomes larger and larger without bound)?

The student should have no difficulty in discovering for himself that we can bring the absolute value of y as near to 0 as we please by taking the absolute value of x large enough. Thus for this function we may write

$$\lim_{x \to \infty} \frac{1}{x} = 0$$

just as in Example 6 we can distinguish between the effect of positive and negative values of x by the following symbolism:

$$\lim_{x \to \infty} \frac{1}{x} = 0+ \qquad (\text{for } 0 < x)$$

and

$$\lim_{x \to \infty} \frac{1}{x} = 0- \qquad (\text{for } 0 > x)$$

example 8 If $y = f(x) = x^2 + x - 2$, what limit if any does $f(x)$ approach as x approaches 5?

The student should have no difficulty in discovering for himself that $f(x)$ approaches 28 as x approaches 5.

example 9 What limit if any does $y = f(x) = (8x^2 - 1)/(x^2 + 2)$ approach as x approaches infinity?

In this case, a direct substitution leads to the indeterminate form ∞/∞, and we would not know whether this function approaches any finite limit, and if so, what that limit is.

However, we can divide both numerator and denominator by x^2, obtaining

$$\frac{8 - \dfrac{1}{x^2}}{1 + \dfrac{2}{x^2}} \qquad x^2 \neq 0$$

Now it appears that

$$\lim_{x\to\infty} \frac{8x^2 - 1}{x^2 + 2} = \lim_{x\to\infty} \frac{8 - \dfrac{1}{x^2}}{1 + \dfrac{2}{x^2}} = 8$$

Now we shall briefly consider the matter of *continuity*.

A fairly satisfactory intuitive idea of continuity is expressed by the following statement.

If we can draw the graph of a function over a given interval without lifting the pencil from the paper, we say that the function is continuous over that interval.

Although the engineering technician will usually find this notion of continuity quite adequate for ordinary situations, there are occasions when he will need more precise ideas. Therefore, without attempting a high order of mathematical rigor, let us investigate the matter in more detail.

A function f for which $y = f(x)$ is said to be continuous for $x = a$ if all three of the following conditions are satisfied:

1. The value of the function is defined for $x = a$. That is,

$$f(a) \text{ is defined}$$

2. The value of the function approaches a definite limit as x approaches a. That is,

$$\lim_{x\to a} f(x) \text{ exists}$$

3. This limit is the value of the function when $x = a$. That is,

$$\lim_{x\to a} f(x) = f(a)$$

A function f for which $y = f(x)$ is said to be discontinuous for $x = a$ if any of these conditions are not satisfied.

A function is said to be continuous over an interval if it is continuous for all points within that interval.

For example, the function for which $f(x) = x + 3$ is continuous at $x = 3$ because (1) $f(x)$ is defined for $x = 3$, since $f(3) = 6$, and (2) as x

approaches 3, $f(x)$ approaches a definite limit (in this case the limit is 6), and (3) $\lim_{x \to 3} f(x) = f(3)$.

In Example 5 the function for which $f(x) = \dfrac{x^2 - 9}{x - 3}$ is *not* continuous for $x = 3$ because (1) $f(x)$ is not defined for $x = 3$.

We could, if we wished, extend the original definition of $f(x)$ to read

$$f_1(x) = \begin{cases} \dfrac{x^2 - 9}{x - 3} & x \neq 3 \\ 6 & x = 3 \end{cases}$$

Now $f_1(3)$ is defined, and $f_1(x)$ is continuous for $x = 3$. On the other hand, we could extend the original definition of $f(x)$ to read

$$f_2(x) = \begin{cases} \dfrac{x^2 - 9}{x - 3} & x \neq 3 \\ 10 & x = 3 \end{cases}$$

Then, $f_2(x)$ is not continuous at $x = 3$ because while (1) $f_2(x)$ is defined at $x = 3$, and (2) when x approaches 3, $f_2(x)$ does approach a definite limit (which in this case is 6), (3) this limit is *not* the value of the function when $x = 3$.

EXERCISE 2

Evaluate the limits indicated below when such limits exist. Discuss the continuity of each function, and sketch its graph near any points of discontinuity that you may discover.

1. If $f(x) = (x^3 + 6x^2 - 16)$, find $\lim_{x \to -2} f(x)$.
2. If $f(x) = \dfrac{2x^2 - x - 10}{x + 2}$, find $\lim_{x \to -2} f(x)$.
3. If $f(x) = \dfrac{x + 5}{x + 2}$, find $\lim_{x \to 3} f(x)$.
4. If $f(x) = \dfrac{x^2 - x - 20}{x - 5}$, find $\lim_{x \to 5} f(x)$.
5. If $f(x) = \dfrac{3(x^2 - 1)}{x + 1}$, find $\lim_{x \to -1} f(x)$.
6. If $f(x) = \dfrac{3x + 8}{x + 3}$, find $\lim_{x \to -3} f(x)$.
7. If $f(x) = \dfrac{x - 9}{3(\sqrt{x} - 3)}$, find $\lim_{x \to 9} f(x)$.
8. If $f(x) = x\sqrt{x - 3}$, find $\lim_{x \to 0} f(x)$.
9. If $f(x) = \dfrac{5^{1/x} - 1}{5^{1/x} + 1}$, find $\lim_{x \to 0} f(x)$.
10. If $f(x) = \dfrac{x^2 - 5x}{2x^2 - 4}$, find $\lim_{x \to \infty} f(x)$.

25·3 The Derivative

By finding the limit (if one exists) that

$$\frac{f(x_1 + \Delta x) - f(x_1)}{\Delta x}$$

approaches as Δx approaches zero, we may find the *instantaneous* rate of change in y with respect to x at $x = x_1$ [see Eq. (4)].

This limit is called the *derivative* of y with respect to x or the derivative of $f(x)$ with respect to x.

The derivative can be designated as $f'(x)$, dy/dx, and sometimes in other ways. From Eq. (4) and the above we may write

$$\left(\begin{array}{c}\text{Derivative of } y \\ \text{with respect to } x\end{array}\right) = f'(x) = \frac{dy}{dx} = \lim_{\Delta x \to 0} \frac{\Delta y}{\Delta x} = \lim_{\Delta x \to 0} \frac{f(x_1 + \Delta x) - f(x_1)}{\Delta x} \tag{13}$$

provided this limit exists.

Thus far we have used the subscript 1 to emphasize the fact that x is held constant at the value x_1 while Δx varies and approaches zero. If we remember the above and also that most of the functions found in this book do have derivatives for all but perhaps a few values of the independent variable, we may omit the subscript 1 and write

$$\left(\begin{array}{c}\text{Derivative of } y \\ \text{with respect to } x\end{array}\right) = f'(x) = \frac{dy}{dx} = \lim_{\Delta x \to 0} \frac{\Delta y}{\Delta x} = \lim_{\Delta x \to 0} \frac{f(x + \Delta x) - f(x)}{\Delta x} \tag{14}$$

and understand that the symbol (x) so used represents any of the nonexceptional values of x.

The symbol dy/dx as it is used here *does not mean that some number* dy *is to be divided by some number* dx. It simply means

$$\lim_{\Delta x \to 0} \frac{\Delta y}{\Delta x} = \frac{dy}{dx}$$

A somewhat different interpretation will be made in Sec. 25·25.

Now let us return to Example 1. In this example we found an expression for the average rate of change in $f(x)$ with respect to x when $f(x) = y = x^3$ [See Eq. (8)]. This function was plotted in Fig. 24·2. The student should refer to this graph frequently in order to gain a graphical concept of the algebraic operations below.

Equation (8) is repeated below for reference, with the subscript 1 omitted:

$$\frac{\Delta y}{\Delta x} = 3x^2 + 3x(\Delta x) + (\Delta x)^2 \tag{15}$$

In Example 2 we calculated the average rate of change in the value of this function between $x = 2$ and $x + \Delta x = 2.5$. Now as a specific example, let us compute Δy when x changes from 2 to a few other values in the vicinity of 2. When $x = 2$, Eq. (7) can be written as

$$\Delta y = 12\,\Delta x + 6(\Delta x)^2 + (\Delta x)^3$$

When $\Delta x = +0.1$

$$\Delta y = 1.2 + 0.06 + 0.001 = 1.261$$

When $\Delta x = +0.01$

$$\Delta y = 0.12 + 0.0006 + 0.000001 = 0.120601$$

When $\Delta x = -0.1$

$$\Delta y = -1.2 + 0.06 - 0.001 = -1.141$$

Column 2 of Table 25·3 was calculated in this way.

The ratio $\Delta y/\Delta x$ can be calculated by dividing each value of Δy above by the corresponding value of Δx. The ratio $\Delta y/\Delta x$ can also be calculated by direct substitution in Eq. (15). Let us adopt the first method.

When $\Delta x = +0.1$

$$\frac{\Delta y}{\Delta x} = \frac{1.261}{0.1} = 12.61$$

When $\Delta x = +0.01$

$$\frac{\Delta y}{\Delta x} = \frac{0.120601}{0.01} = 12.0601$$

When $\Delta x = -0.1$

$$\frac{\Delta y}{\Delta x} = \frac{-1.141}{-0.1} = 11.41$$

Column 3 of Table 25·3 was calculated in this way.

table 25·3

(1) Δx	(2) Δy	(3) $\Delta y/\Delta x$
+0.1	+1.261	+12.61
+0.01	+0.120601	+12.0601
+0.001	+0.012006001	+12.006001
+0.0001	+0.001200060001	+12.00060001
+0.00001	+0.000120000600001	+12.0000600001
+0.000001	+0.000012000006000001	+12.000006000001
+0.0000001	+0.000001200000060000001	+12.0000006000000001
0.00000000	0.0000000000000000000000	Indeterminate
−0.0000001	−0.000001199999940000001	+11.9999994000000001
−0.000001	−0.000011999994000001	+11.999994000001
−0.00001	−0.000119999400001	+11.9999400001
−0.0001	−0.001199940001	+11.99940001
−0.001	−0.011994001	+11.994001
−0.01	−0.119401	+11.9401
−0.1	−1.1414	+11.41

As we scan Table 25·3 from either the top or bottom, toward the center of the table, we observe that as Δx *approaches* zero, Δy also *approaches* zero. However, their ratio $\Delta y/\Delta x$ approaches the finite constant 12. But if we let $\Delta x = 0$, then the quotient $\Delta y/\Delta x$ becomes meaningless.

This is also indicated in Fig. 25·2. In this figure we show a graph of the equation

$$\frac{\Delta y}{\Delta x} = 3x^2 + 3x(\Delta x) + (\Delta x)^2$$

where $x = 2$, (Δx) is the independent variable, and $\Delta y/\Delta x$ is the dependent variable.

We note that $\Delta y/\Delta x$ is not defined when $\Delta x = 0$ and have indicated this fact by the small circle with its center at the point (0,12). Therefore we rest with the statement

$$\lim_{\Delta x \to 0} \frac{\Delta y}{\Delta x} = 12 \tag{16}$$

which we read: "The limit which $\Delta y/\Delta x$ approaches as Δx approaches zero is 12."

As we stated in Eq. (13), this limit is denoted by dy/dx and

$$\frac{dy}{dx} = \lim_{\Delta x \to 0} \frac{\Delta y}{\Delta x} \tag{17}$$

where dy/dx is called "the derivative of y with respect to x."

If y is the ordinate of a curve and x is the abscissa of the same curve, then dy/dx is the instantaneous slope of the curve.

The process of finding the derivative of a function is called *differentiation.*

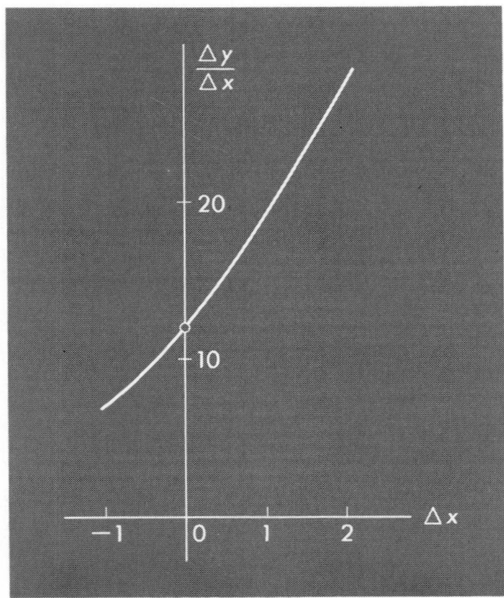

fig. 25·2

example 10 Find the derivative of y with respect to x if $y = x^2$.

$$\Delta y = (x + \Delta x)^2 - x^2$$
$$\Delta y = x^2 + 2x(\Delta x) + (\Delta x)^2 - x^2$$
$$\Delta y = 2x(\Delta x) + (\Delta x)^2$$
$$\frac{\Delta y}{\Delta x} = 2x + \Delta x$$
$$\lim_{\Delta x \to 0} \frac{\Delta y}{\Delta x} = \frac{dy}{dx} = 2x$$

The same answer would have been required if the problem had been stated in any of the following ways:

1. Differentiate $y = x^2$ with respect to x.
2. Find $\frac{d(x^2)}{dx}$ if $y = x^2$.
3. Find y' if $y = x^2$.
4. Find dy/dx if $y = x^2$.
5. Find the equation for the rate of change in y with respect to x if $y = x^2$.
6. Find the equation for the instantaneous slope of the graph of $y = x^2$.
7. Find the equation for the slope of any tangent to the graph of $y = x^2$.

EXERCISE 3

1. The cost of publishing a certain pamphlet is given by the following equation:

$$C = \$10.00 + 0.05n$$

where C = total cost, dollars
n = number of pamphlets published

(a) Calculate the total cost of publishing 10, 100, 1,000, 10,000, 100,000, 1,000,000, and ∞ pamphlets.
(b) Divide the total cost as determined in (a) by the corresponding number of pamphlets to determine the cost per pamphlet.
(c) What limit does the cost per pamphlet approach as the number of pamphlets approaches ∞?
(d) Point out the fallacy in the following statement: "The cost per pamphlet when an infinite number are published is \$0.05 per pamphlet."

Differentiate the following (also see Exercise 1):

2. $y = 5x^3$
3. $y = 5x^3 + 8$
4. $y = 7x^2 + 3$
5. $y = x^3 - 2x$
6. $w = u^2 - 3u - 18$
7. $w = 3/u$
8. $w = 1 + 2z - \frac{1}{z}$
9. $g = \frac{t}{t + 3}$
10. $u = \sqrt{x}$

25·4 General rule for differentiating $y = kx^n$

In this section we shall develop a formula by which we can find dy/dx if $y = kx^n$ without using the rather laborious Δ method. In the development of this rule we shall restrict n to positive integers. However, it can be shown in a somewhat more advanced textbook on calculus that this rule applies also when n is any rational number. In an advanced calculus textbook based on an extensive consideration of the real-number system, it can be proved that the rule below applies when n is any real number.

Let us begin by finding dy/dx if

$$y = x^n \tag{18}$$

Following Eq. (3),

$$\Delta y = (x + \Delta x)^n - x^n \tag{19}$$

We can expand the right-hand member of Eq. (19) by the binomial theorem [see Eq. (1), page 203].

$$\Delta y = x^n + nx^{n-1}\,\Delta x + \frac{n(n-1)x^{n-2}(\Delta x)^2}{2!} + \frac{n(n-1)(n-2)x^{n-3}\,(\Delta x)^3}{3!} + \cdots + (\Delta x)^n - x^n \tag{20}$$

By simplifying Eq. (20) we obtain

$$\Delta y = nx^{n-1}\,\Delta x + \frac{n(n-1)x^{n-2}(\Delta x)^2}{2!} + \frac{n(n-1)(n-2)x^{n-3}(\Delta x)^3}{3!} + \cdots + (\Delta x)^n \tag{21}$$

Dividing Eq. (21) by Δx,

$$\frac{\Delta y}{\Delta x} = nx^{n-1} + \frac{n(n-1)x^{n-2}\,\Delta x}{2!} + \frac{n(n-1)(n-2)x^{n-3}(\Delta x)^2}{3!} + \cdots + (\Delta x)^{n-1} \tag{22}$$

Now observe that all terms on the right-hand side of Eq. (22) except the first contain the factor Δx. Therefore, as Δx approaches zero, all terms on the right-hand side of (22) except the first also approach zero and

$$\lim_{\Delta x \to 0} \frac{\Delta y}{\Delta x} = nx^{n-1}$$

or

$$\frac{dy}{dx} = nx^{n-1}$$

Therefore, if

$$y = x^n \tag{23}$$

where n is a positive integer, then

$$\frac{dy}{dx} = nx^{n-1} \tag{24}$$

As we mentioned before, Eq. (24) is actually valid when n is any real number.

Equations (23) and (24) can be summarized as

$$\frac{d(x^n)}{dx} = nx^{n-1} \tag{25}$$

RULE 1 *To find the derivative of* x *with a constant exponent, multiply this constant exponent by a new power of* x *whose exponent is one less than the original exponent.*

Now let us find dy/dx if $y = kx^n$. Following Eq. (3), we may write

$$\Delta y = k(x + \Delta x)^n - kx^n$$

We can expand the right member of the above equation by the binomial theorem, obtaining

$$\Delta y = k\left[x^n + nx^{n-1}\,\Delta x + \frac{n(n-1)x^{n-2}(\Delta x)^2}{2!} + \frac{n(n-1)(n-2)x^{n-3}\,(\Delta x)^3}{3!} + \cdots + (\Delta x)^n\right] - kx^n$$

By simplifying the above equation we obtain

$$\Delta y = nkx^{n-1}\,\Delta x + \frac{kn(n-1)x^{n-2}(\Delta x)^2}{2!} + \frac{kn(n-1)(n-2)x^{n-3}(\Delta x)^3}{3!} + \cdots + k(\Delta x)^n$$

Dividing the above equation by Δx gives

$$\frac{\Delta y}{\Delta x} = nkx^{n-1} + \frac{kn(n-1)x^{n-2}\,\Delta x}{2!} + \frac{kn(n-1)(n-2)x^{n-3}(\Delta x)^2}{3!} + \cdots + k(\Delta x)^{n-1} \tag{26}$$

Now observe that all terms on the right-hand side of Eq. (26) except the first contain the factor Δx. Therefore, as Δx approaches zero, all terms on the right-hand side of (26) except the first also approach zero and

$$\lim_{\Delta x \to 0} \frac{\Delta y}{\Delta x} = nkx^{n-1}$$

or

$$\frac{dy}{dx} = nkx^{n-1}$$

or

$$\frac{d(kx^n)}{dx} = nkx^{n-1} \tag{27}$$

RULE 2 *To find the derivative of the product of a constant factor and a variable with a constant exponent, multiply the derivative of the variable with the constant exponent by the constant factor.*

For example, if

$$y = x^3$$

then $$\frac{dy}{dx} = 3x^2$$

but if $$y = 5x^3$$

then $$\frac{dy}{dx} = 5 \cdot 3x^2 = 15x^2$$

It is important to note that in Eq. (27) it is the *independent variable itself* that is raised to the nth power. A very different situation exists for a function such as

$$y = (x^2 + 7)^n + C \tag{28}$$

Here it is not the independent variable itself that is raised to the nth power. Differentiating Eq. (28) requires a somewhat different approach, which will be discussed in Sec. 25·6.

In Examples 11 through 19 be sure to notice the different forms in which the result may be written.

example 11 Differentiate $y = 3x^5$.

$$\frac{dy}{dx} = 15x^4$$

$$y' = 15x^4$$

$$\frac{d(3x^5)}{dx} = 15x^4$$

example 12 Differentiate $y = 3x^{-5}$.

$$\frac{dy}{dx} = -15x^{-6}$$

$$y' = -15x^{-6}$$

$$\frac{d(3x^{-5})}{dx} = -15x^{-6}$$

example 13 Differentiate $y = -3x^{-5}$.

$$\frac{dy}{dx} = +15x^{-6}$$

$$y' = +15x^{-6}$$

$$\frac{d(-3x^{-5})}{dx} = +15x^{-6}$$

example 14 Differentiate $y = 5x^{7/4}$.

$$\frac{dy}{dx} = \frac{35}{4}x^{3/4}$$

$$y' = \frac{35}{4}x^{3/4}$$

$$\frac{d(5x^{7/4})}{dx} = \frac{35}{4}x^{3/4}$$

example 15 Differentiate $y = x$.

$$\frac{dy}{dx} = 1$$

$$y' = 1$$

$$\frac{d(x)}{dx} = 1$$

example 16 Differentiate $y = 5x^{1/3}$.

$$\frac{dy}{dx} = \frac{5}{3}x^{-2/3}$$

$$y' = \frac{5}{3}x^{-2/3}$$

$$\frac{d(5x^{1/3})}{dx} = \frac{5}{3}x^{-2/3}$$

example 17 Differentiate $y = 7x^{-1/2}$.

$$\frac{dy}{dx} = -\frac{7}{2}x^{-3/2}$$

$$y' = -\frac{7}{2}x^{-3/2}$$

$$\frac{d(7x^{-1/2})}{dx} = -\frac{7}{2}x^{-3/2}$$

example 18 Differentiate $y = 6x^{\pi}$.

$$\frac{dy}{dx} = 6\pi x^{\pi-1}$$

$$y' = 6\pi x^{\pi-1}$$

$$\frac{d(6x^{\pi})}{dx} = 6\pi x^{\pi-1}$$

example 19 Differentiate $a = \frac{\pi}{16}h^2$.

$$\frac{da}{dh} = \frac{\pi}{8}h$$

$$a' = \frac{\pi}{8}h$$

$$\frac{d\left(\frac{\pi}{16}h^2\right)}{dh} = \frac{\pi}{8}h$$

example 20 Differentiate $y = 5\sqrt{x}$.

Before we can apply Eq. (27) to this problem, we must convert the given equation to the form

$$y = 5x^{1/2}$$

Then $$\frac{dy}{dx} = \frac{1}{2}(5)\,x^{-1/2} = \frac{5}{2\sqrt{x}}$$

example 21 Differentiate $y = 5(3x)^2$.

Referring to Eq. (27), we note that there it is *the independent variable itself* that is raised to a power. In the present example we have the product of the independent variable and a constant raised to a power. Therefore, before we can apply Eq. (27) we must alter the given equation to

$$y = 5 \cdot 3^2 \cdot x^2 = 45x^2$$

Then $$\frac{dy}{dx} = 90x$$

example 22 Differentiate $F = 10/D$.

Again, before we can apply Eq. (27) directly, we alter the given equation to

$$F = 10D^{-1}$$

Then $$\frac{dF}{dD} = -10D^{-2} = -\frac{10}{D^2}$$

example 23 Express the derivative in Example 22 in terms of F.

From the original equation

$$D = \frac{10}{F}$$

Therefore $$\frac{dF}{dD} = -\frac{10}{(10/F)^2} = -\frac{F^2}{10}$$

example 24 If $F = 10/D$, find dD/dF.

From the given equation we note that

$$D = \frac{10}{F} = 10F^{-1}$$

Then
$$\frac{dD}{dF} = -10F^{-2} = -\frac{10}{F^2}$$

Compare with Example 23.

example 25 Find the slope of the tangent to the graph of $F = 10/D$ drawn through the point on the graph where $D = 2$. This is the equation for the graph shown in Fig. 24·25.

From Example 22 we find that the slope of any tangent to the graph is, in general,

$$\frac{dF}{dD} = -\frac{10}{D^2}$$

At $D = 2$,

$$\frac{dF}{dD} = -\frac{10}{2^2} = -\frac{10}{4} = -2.5$$

The student should verify the above slope graphically from Fig. 24·25.

example 26 Find the equation of the tangent to the graph of $F = 10/D$ through the point whose abscissa is 2.

In Example 25 we find that the slope of the tangent is -2.5. The equation for this tangent is (see Sec. 6·8)

$$F = mD + b$$

where
$$m = \text{slope}$$
$$b = \text{the } F \text{ intercept}$$

In this example $F = {}^{10}\!/_{2} = 5$ when $D = 2$. Thus we may write

$$5 = -2.5 \times 2 + b$$

and
$$b = 10$$

Then the equation for this tangent is

$$F = -2.5D + 10$$

EXERCISE 4

Differentiate the following:

1. $y = 3x^2$
2. $y = cx^3$
3. $y = 10x^9$
4. $y = 3x^{-2}$
5. $y = 3/x^2$
6. $y = {}^4\!/_3\pi x^3$
7. $y = 12x^{2/3}$
8. $y = 14x^{-1}$

9. $y = 14/x$
10. $y = 6x^{1/2}$
11. $y = 6\sqrt{x}$
12. $y = \sqrt{6x}$
13. $y = -8x^{-1/2}$
14. $y = -8/\sqrt{x}$
15. $y = 10x^{1/4}$
16. $y = 10\sqrt[4]{x}$
17. $y = \dfrac{a}{b}x^4$
18. $y = \dfrac{a}{bx}$
19. $y = 2x^{-3/4}$
20. $y = 2/\sqrt[4]{x^3}$
21. $y = 2/\sqrt[4]{7x^3}$
22. $y = 5x$
23. $y = 5$
24. $y = x^5$

The graph shown in Fig. 24·23 was plotted from the equation $a = (\pi/16)h^2$ where a is the area of cross section of a right circular cone and h is the distance between the apex of the cone and the cross-section area a. Using the above equation rather than the graph, solve Probs. 25 through 37 below.

25. Derive an equation for da/dh in terms of h. In terms of a. Also derive an equation for dh/da in terms of h. In terms of a.
26. Find da/dh when $h = 20$. Also find dh/da when $h = 20$.
27. Find da/dh when $a = 100$. Also find dh/da when $a = 100$.
28. Find the area a when $da/dh = 5$.
29. Find the average rate of change of area with respect to distance between $h = 5$ and $h = 25$.
30. Find the average slope of the graph between $h = 15$ and $h = 20$.
31. Find the average slope of the graph between $a = 25$ and $a = 100$.
32. Find the instantaneous slope of the graph at $h = 22$.
33. Find the instantaneous slope of the graph at $a = 100$.
34. How fast is the area changing with respect to distance at 75 sq ft?
35. How fast is the area changing with respect to distance at 12 ft?
36. How much does the area change when distance changes from 10 to 20 ft?
37. Find the equation for the tangent to the graph at the point whose h coordinate is 20.
38. Compare the a intercept of the tangent with the a coordinate of the point of tangency.
39. Compare the h intercept of the tangent with the h coordinate of the point of tangency.

The graph shown in Fig. 24·25 was plotted from the equation $F = 10/D$, where F is the force on a piston and D is the distance between the piston and one end of the cylinder. Using the above equation rather than the graph, solve Probs. 40 through 46.

40. Derive the equation for dF/dD in terms of F. In terms of D. Also derive the equation for dD/dF in terms of F. In terms of D.
41. What is the rate of change in force with respect to distance when F is 6 lb?
42. Find dF/dD when $D = 5$ ft.

43. Find dD/dF when $D = 5$ ft.
44. Find $\Delta F/\Delta D$ between $D = 2$ and $D = 3$. Also find $\Delta D/\Delta F$ between $D = 2$ and $D = 3$.
45. For what force is the rate of change of force with respect to distance equal to -2 lb per ft?
46. Find the instantaneous rate of change in force with respect to distance when distance is 3⅓ ft.

25·5 Some further rules for differentiation

If $y = c$ where c is some constant, then y does not change at all, and its derivative with respect to any varying quantity is zero.

RULE 3 *The derivative of a constant is zero.*

That is, if $y = c$ where c is a constant, then

$$\frac{dy}{dx} = 0$$

Now let us differentiate $y = x^2 + x^3$ by the Δ method

$$y = x^2 + x^3$$

$$\Delta y = x^2 + 2x\,\Delta x + (\Delta x)^2 + x^3 + 3x^2(\Delta x) + 3x(\Delta x)^2 + (\Delta x)^3 - x^2 - x^3$$

$$\Delta y = 2x\,\Delta x + (\Delta x)^2 + 3x^2(\Delta x) + 3x(\Delta x)^2 + (\Delta x)^3$$

$$\frac{\Delta y}{\Delta x} = 2x + \Delta x + 3x^2 + 3x\,\Delta x + (\Delta x)^2$$

$$\frac{dy}{dx} = 2x + 3x^2$$

Following Eqs. (23) and (24), we note that the derivative of x^2 is $2x$. Also, the derivative of x^3 is $3x^2$. Thus it seems plausible that rule 4 below is valid.

RULE 4 *The derivative of the sum of any finite number of differentiable functions is the sum of their derivatives.*

example 27 Differentiate $y = \frac{5}{3x} + x^2 + C$.

$$y = \frac{5}{3}x^{-1} + x^2 + C$$

$$\frac{dy}{dx} = -\frac{5}{3}x^{-2} + 2x = -\frac{5}{3x^2} + 2x$$

example 28 Differentiate $y = 2x^{-6} + 5^e$ (note that 5^e is a constant).

$$\frac{dy}{dx} = -12x^{-7} = -\frac{12}{x^7}$$

example 29 Differentiate $y = \dfrac{a}{bx} + bx^{-2} - 3\pi x$.

By convention the first letters of the alphabet are usually used to represent constants. Therefore we shall consider a and b to be constants.

$$y = \frac{a}{b}x^{-1} + bx^{-2} - 3\pi x$$

$$\frac{dy}{dx} = -\frac{a}{b}x^{-2} - 2bx^{-3} - 3\pi = -\frac{a}{bx^2} - \frac{2b}{x^3} - 3\pi$$

example 30 Differentiate $y = \dfrac{3}{4x} + 2x^3$.

$$y = \frac{3}{4}x^{-1} + 2x^3$$

$$\frac{dy}{dx} = -\frac{3}{4}x^{-2} + 6x^2 = -\frac{3}{4x^2} + 6x^2$$

example 31 Figure 25·3 shows two parabolas. The equation for one is

$$y = \tfrac{1}{2}x^2$$

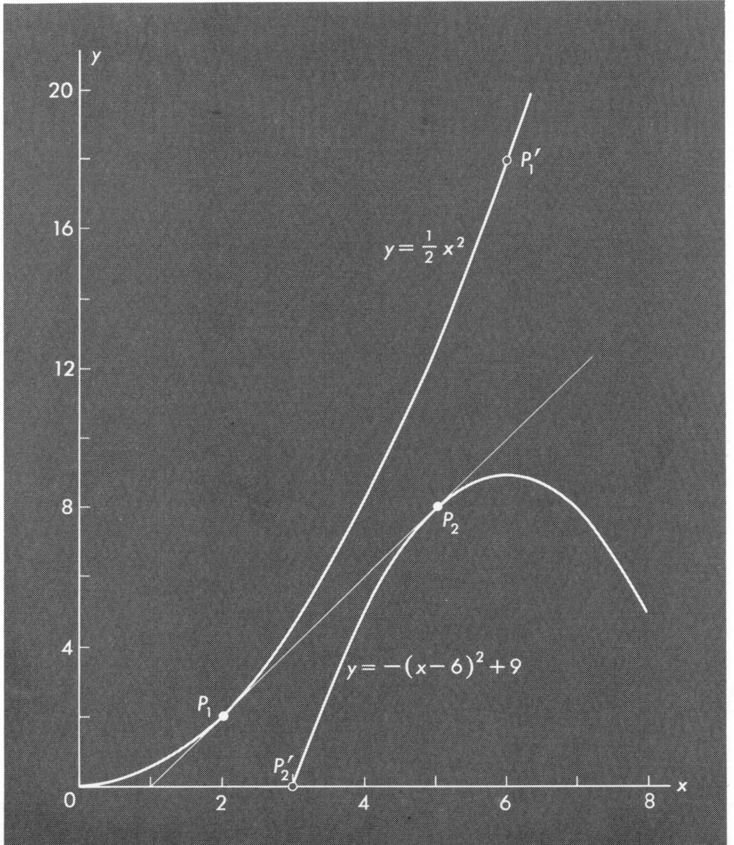

fig. 25·3

The equation for the other is

$$y = -(x - 6)^2 + 9$$

Find the coordinates of points on these curves through which a straight line may be drawn tangent to both curves.

The value of the slope of the first curve is

$$\frac{dy}{dx} = \frac{d(\tfrac{1}{2}x^2)}{dx} = x$$

The value of the slope of the second curve is

$$\frac{dy}{dx} = \frac{d[-(x - 6)^2 + 9]}{dx} = \frac{d(-x^2 + 12x - 27)}{dx} = -2x + 12$$

Let a tangent common to both curves be drawn through points P_1 and P_2 (see Fig. 25·3). Let the x coordinate of P_1 be x_1 and the x coordinate of P_2 be x_2.

Since the slope of both curves must be the same at these points of tangency, we may write

$$x_1 = -2x_2 + 12$$

From Eq. (1), page 111, the slope of the tangent through P_1 and P_2 is

$$\frac{y_2 - y_1}{x_2 - x_1} = \frac{-(x_2 - 6)^2 + 9 - \tfrac{1}{2}x_1^2}{x_2 - x_1} = \frac{-x_2^2 + 12x_2 - 27 - \tfrac{1}{2}x_1^2}{x_2 - x_1}$$

where x_1 and y_1 are the coordinates of P_1 and x_2 and y_2 are the coordinates of P_2.

After replacing x_1 by its equivalent $(-2x_2 + 12)$ and simplifying, we obtain

$$\frac{y_2 - y_1}{x_2 - x_1} = \frac{-x_2^2 + 12x_2 - 33}{x_2 - 4}$$

But since the slope can also be expressed as

$$-2x_2 + 12$$

we may write

$$\frac{-x_2^2 + 12x_2 - 33}{x_2 - 4} = -2x_2 + 12$$

or $$-x_2^2 + 12x_2 - 33 = -2x_2^2 + 20x_2 - 48$$

or $$x_2^2 - 8x_2 + 15 = 0$$

and $$(x_2 - 3)(x_2 - 5) = 0$$

Therefore $$x_2 = +5 \text{ or } +3$$

When $x_2 = 5$,

$$y_2 = -(5 - 6)^2 + 9 = +8$$

and $$x_1 = -2(5) + 12 = +2$$

Also $$y_1 = \tfrac{1}{2}(2)^2 = +2$$

Thus one tangent passes through points $P_1(2,2)$ and $P_2(5,8)$.

When $x_2 = 3$

$$y_2 = -(3 - 6)^2 + 9 = 0$$

and $$x_1 = -2(3) + 12 = +6$$

Also $$y_1 = \tfrac{1}{2}(6)^2 = +18$$

Thus another tangent passes through the points $P_1'(6,18)$ and $P_2'(3,0)$.

example 32 Figure 25·4 shows the graph of the equation

$$y = \tfrac{1}{4}(x - 3)^2 + 2 = 0.25x^2 - 1.5x + 4.25$$

A tangent is drawn through the point P whose x coordinate is $+5.4$. The line segment y_0P is drawn perpendicular to this tangent through the point P. The y coordinate of point Q is 5. Find the length of the line segment PQ.

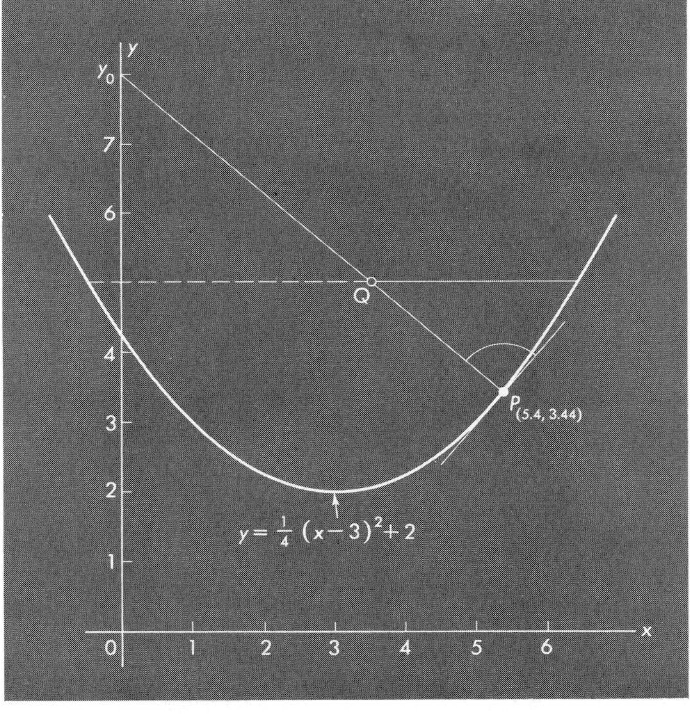

fig. 25·4

The y coordinate of point P is

$$y_P = 0.25(5.4)^2 - 1.5(5.4) + 4.25 = 3.44$$

Thus the coordinates of P are (5.4,3.44).

The slope of a tangent drawn to the curve is, in general,

$$\text{Slope of tangent} = \frac{d(0.25x^2 - 1.5x + 4.25)}{dx} = 0.5x - 1.5$$

In particular, the slope of the tangent at P where $x = 5.4$ is

$$\text{Slope at } P = 0.5 \cdot 5.4 - 1.5 = 1.2 = 6/5$$

From Eq. (11), page 123,

$$\text{Slope of } y_0P = -\frac{1}{6/5} = -\frac{5}{6}$$

The equation for the line y_0P is then in the form

$$y = -5/6x + y_0$$

But since the coordinates of P are (5.4,3.44), we may write

$$3.44 = -5/6(5.4) + y_0$$

and

$$y_0 = 7.94$$

Therefore the equation of the line y_0P is

$$y = -5/6x + 7.94$$

The y coordinate of point Q is given as 5; therefore

$$5 = -5/6x_Q + 7.94$$

and

$$x_Q = 3.53$$

From Eq. (12), page 124,

$$PQ = \sqrt{(5.4 - 3.53)^2 + (3.44 - 5)^2} = 2.44$$

EXERCISE 5

Differentiate the following:

1. $y = ax^2 + bx + c$
2. $y = \dfrac{4x^3 - 7x + 8}{x}$
3. $y = (2x - 5)(3x + 1)$
4. $y = \dfrac{4}{\sqrt{x}} - 4\sqrt{x}$
5. $y = \dfrac{1}{3x^2} - \dfrac{5}{2x}$
6. $y = \dfrac{ab}{x} - \dfrac{x}{b} + \dfrac{b}{ax}$
7. $y = \sqrt[n]{x^{n-1}}$
8. $y = (1/9)x^6$
9. $y = 3x^{-4} + \pi$
10. $y = -\dfrac{2x^{-4}}{3} - 10^2$

11. $y = \frac{26}{x^4} - 3$

12. $y = \frac{-3}{5x^{20}} + \pi^2$

13. $y = kx^{-3} + 15$

14. $y = \frac{\pi}{2x^3} - 26$

15. $y = e^2 + 3x^5 + k$

16. $y = 3x^5 - \frac{10}{x^2}$

17. $y = \pi x^2 + 30$

18. $y = 26/10^4$

19. $y = \frac{\pi}{x^2} - \frac{e}{x^3}$

20. Power is defined as the rate of doing work with respect to time. If W denotes work, t time, and P power, give the mathematically equivalent definition of power.
21. Using the conclusion in Prob. 20, find the power at $t = 2$ sec if the work being done by a force is $W = 3t^2 + 4t + 6$, where W is in foot-pounds.
22. If specific heat is defined to be dQ/dt, where Q is the quantity of heat necessary to raise the temperature of 1 g of a substance from 0 to t°C and if for ethyl alcohol

$$Q = 0.5068t + 0.00143t^2 + 0.0000018t^3$$

(valid for the range from 0 to 60°C), determine the specific heats of ethyl alcohol at $t = 10, 20, 30, 40$, and 50°C.
23. A parabolic arch is 10 ft high and 20 ft wide, as shown in Fig. 25·5. A brace AB is inserted as shown in the figure. Find its length.

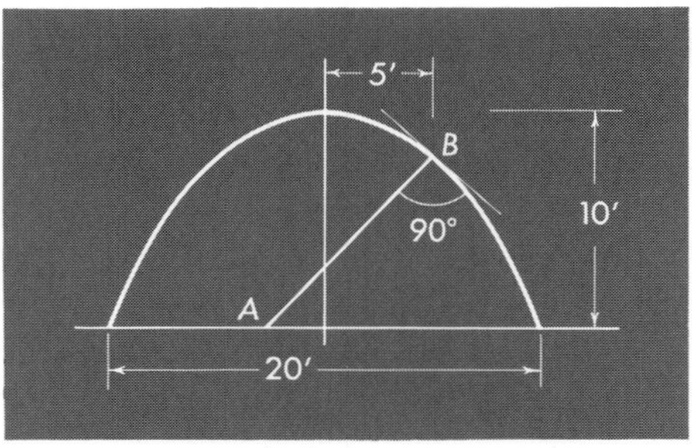

fig. 25·5

24. Euler's column formula from studies of strength of materials is

$$\frac{P}{A} = \frac{\pi^2 E}{(L/r)^2}$$

where P is the total load, A is the cross-section area of the column, E is a property of the material from which the column is made (the modulus of elasticity), L is the length of the column, and r depends on the shape of the cross section.
(a) Sketch a graph of P/A as a function of L/r. E is a positive quantity.
(b) Determine the equation of the tangent to this curve at the point where $L/r = (3\pi^2 E/p)^{1/2}$, $P/A = p/3$.

REMARK: p is the load required to crush the column. Your resulting straight-line equation is known as the *straight-line column formula.*

25. In constructing a certain type of cam for accelerating a lift, it is necessary to find two parabolas that have a common tangent at points on two given abscissas. Find a and b so that the tangent to $x^2 = ay$ at $x = 2$ shall coincide with the tangent to $(x - 10)^2 = b(y - 8.5)$ at $x = 9$.
26. Devise a graphical solution for the common tangent line in Prob. 25 based on the following theorem for parabolas. Also prove the theorem:

THEOREM: *The tangent at the vertex of a parabola bisects the segment of any other tangent which is included by the principal axes and the point of tangency.*

27. If $V = dM/dx$ and if

$$M = \frac{2Px}{7} \qquad \text{for } 0 < x < 10 \qquad (P \text{ is a positive constant})$$

$$M = 10P - \frac{5Px}{7} \qquad \text{for } 10 < x < 14$$

(a) Sketch a graph of M/P as a function of x for x from 0 to 14.
(b) Determine V for $0 < x < 10$ and for $10 < x < 14$. Then sketch the graph for V/P as a function of x for x from 0 to 14.
(c) Does the graph of V as a function of x have a discontinuity in the range $0 < x < 14$?

REMARK: The beam and loading for this problem are shown in Fig. 25·6. The mathematical analysis of such beams gives a shear graph (V as a function of x) with discontinuities at each point where there was a concentrated load. The mathematical analysis of such problems assumes that the concentrated load is applied *at a point* (which is physically impossible). However, the results from this analysis are accurate enough for most purposes.

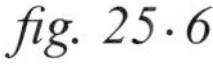
fig. 25·6

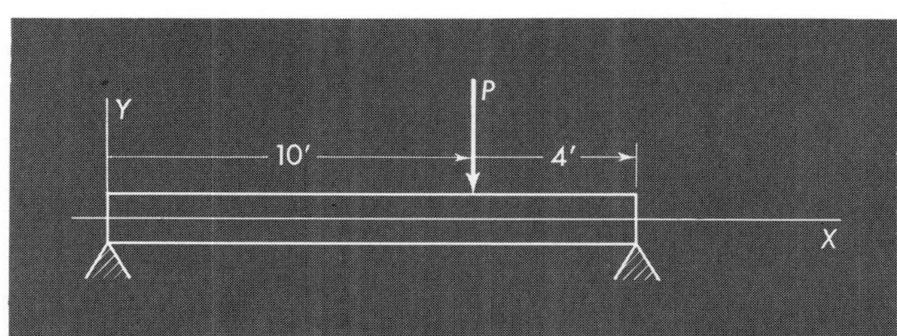

28. A cantilever beam of length L ft bears a uniform load of w lb per ft for the length $L/2$ ft next to the wall as shown in Fig. 25·7. The equation for this part of the curve of the beam is

$$EIy = -\frac{wx^4}{24} + \frac{wLx^3}{12} - \frac{wL^2x^2}{16} + \frac{wL^3x}{24} - \frac{wL^4}{48}$$

that is, this equation is valid for x between $L/2$ and L. If the weight of the beam itself is neglected, the part of the beam to the left of this load will be straight and will be along the tangent to the preceding curve at the point whose abscissa is $x = L/2$.

Determine the maximum deflection; that is, find the largest numerical value of y in the entire range (which is clearly the ordinate at $x = 0$).

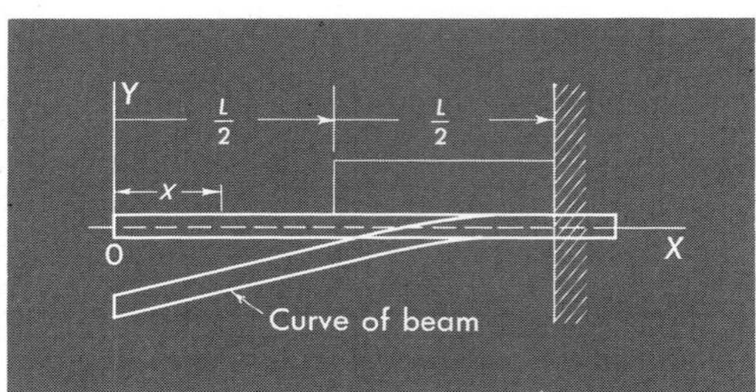

fig. 25·7

25·6 Composite functions

Thus far we have discussed methods of finding the derivative with respect to x of the sum of various powers of x. For example, we can find the derivative of y with respect to x if

$$y = x^2 + 3x + 5 \tag{29}$$

However, without multiplying out we cannot find the derivative of y with respect to x if

$$y = (x^2 + 3x + 5)^3 \tag{30}$$

because as the equation stands it is not expressed as the sum of powers of x [also see Eq. (28)].

Fortunately, a method does exist for differentiating Eq. (30) as it stands. This method depends upon the theorem:

THEOREM: *If* y *is the value of a differentiable function of* u, *and* u *is the value of a differentiable function of* x, *then* y *is the value of a differentiable function of* x, *and*

$$\frac{dy}{dx} = \frac{dy}{du}\frac{du}{dx} \tag{31}$$

Since y depends on u, and u depends on x, we sometimes call y the value of a *composite* function.

A rigorous proof of the above theorem is quite involved and will not be presented here. However, the interested student can easily find such a proof in almost any textbook devoted entirely to calculus.

Let us proceed to differentiate Eq. (30) directly by use of Eq. (31). If

$$y = (x^2 + 3x + 5)^3 \tag{32}$$

and if we let

$$u = x^2 + 3x + 5 \tag{33}$$

then

$$y = u^3 \tag{34}$$

and

$$\frac{dy}{du} = 3u^2 \tag{35}$$

Substituting (33) in (35) gives

$$\frac{dy}{du} = 3(x^2 + 3x + 5)^2 \tag{36}$$

Now from (33) we may write

$$\frac{du}{dx} = 2x + 3 \tag{37}$$

By substituting (37) and (36) in (31) we obtain

$$\frac{dy}{dx} = 3(x^2 + 3x + 5)^2 (2x + 3) \tag{38}$$

Thus we obtain the derivative of y with respect to x.

In general, if

$$y = u^n \tag{39}$$

where u is the value of a differentiable function of x, then

$$\frac{dy}{dx} = nu^{n-1}\frac{du}{dx} \tag{40}$$

or

$$\frac{d(u^n)}{dx} = nu^{n-1}\frac{du}{dx} \tag{41}$$

EXERCISE 6

Differentiate the following functions with respect to the independent variable.

1. $y = (3x^2 + 2x + 5)^4$
2. $y = (7x^3 - 5x^2 + 2x)^{-3/4}$
3. $z = \sqrt[3]{(-5x^2 + 3x)}$
4. $w = \sqrt{3t + 7}$
5. $v = \sqrt[4]{6 - 7t^2}$
6. $w = 37/\sqrt{6 - t^2}$
7. $y = -2/\sqrt[4]{(1 - t^2)^3}$
8. $y = (4 - x^2)^3$
9. $y = \sqrt{2t} + 2\sqrt[3]{t}$
10. $R = 5/\sqrt[3]{3t^2 - 6t}$
11. $S = 2\sqrt[3]{(1 + y^2)^2}$
12. $y = \dfrac{1}{8(3 - 2t)^2}$

13. $y = \dfrac{4}{1 - x^3}$

14. $y = \dfrac{4}{(1 - x)^3}$

15. $x = 4\sqrt[5]{5t^3 - t^5}$

16. Sketch the graph of $y = \dfrac{10}{3 - x} - 5$ between $x = -2$ and $x = +2$. Compare with Fig. 24·5, curve *B*. Find the equation for dy/dx. Find dy/dx when $x = -1.5$. Check graphically from Fig. 24·5.

17. Sketch the graph of $y = \dfrac{10}{3 + x} - 5$ between $x = -2$ and $x = +2$. Compare with Fig. 24·5, curve *A*. Find the equation for dy/dx. Find dy/dx when $x = 0$. Check graphically from Fig. 24·5.

18. Sketch the graph of $y = 5 - \dfrac{10}{x + 3}$ between $x = -2$ and $x = +2$. Compare with Fig. 24·5, curve *D*. Find the equation for dy/dx. Find x and y when $dy/dx = 5/8$. Check graphically from Fig. 24·5 as far as possible. Explain the two answers.

NOTE: Some of the work in Sec. 25·22 will be based on the problems below which can be done by direct application of Eq. (31).

19. Show that $\dfrac{d(y^2)}{dx} = 2y\dfrac{dy}{dx}$.

20. Show that $\dfrac{d(x^2)}{dx} = 2x$.

21. Show that $\dfrac{d(x^5)}{dx} = 5x^4$.

22. Show that $\dfrac{d(7y^5)}{dx} = 35y^4\dfrac{dy}{dx}$.

25·7 The derivative of a product and a quotient

If u and v are the values of differentiable functions of x, we shall now develop a formula for $d(u \cdot v)/dx$.

We shall let

$$y = u \cdot v \tag{42}$$

Now if x changes by some amount Δx, then u will change by some amount Δu, and v will change by some amount Δv. Also y will change by another amount Δy; then

$$y + \Delta y = (u + \Delta u)(v + \Delta v)$$

or, multiplying the factors on the right together,

$$y + \Delta y = uv + v\,\Delta u + u\,\Delta v + \Delta u\,\Delta v \tag{43}$$

Subtracting (42) from (43)

$$\Delta y = v\,\Delta u + u\,\Delta v + \Delta u\,\Delta v$$

Dividing both sides by Δx and reversing the positions of the first two terms on the right,

$$\frac{\Delta y}{\Delta x} = u\frac{\Delta v}{\Delta x} + v\frac{\Delta u}{\Delta x} + \frac{\Delta u}{\Delta x}\Delta v \tag{44}$$

As Δx approaches zero, the quantity $\Delta u/\Delta x$ may very well approach some finite value. But as Δx approaches zero, Δv also approaches zero; therefore the product of $\Delta u/\Delta x$ and Δv will approach zero. Consequently, when we approach the limits

$$\frac{dy}{dx} = u\frac{dv}{dx} + v\frac{du}{dx}$$

or

$$\frac{d(u \cdot v)}{dx} = u\frac{dv}{dx} + v\frac{du}{dx} \tag{45}$$

RULE 5 *The derivative of a product is the first factor multiplied by the derivative of the second factor plus the second factor multiplied by the derivative of the first factor.*

In Example 33 below we have chosen, for illustration, to use the product of two rather simple algebraic functions. However, Eq. (45) applies generally, and we shall have occasion to use it in connection with more complicated algebraic functions as well as for logarithmic and trigonometric functions.

example 33 Find dy/dx if $y = (3x + 5)^2 (2x^2 - 7)$.

Following Eq. (45),

$$\frac{d[(3x + 5)^2(2x^2 - 7)]}{dx} = (3x + 5)^2\frac{d(2x^2 - 7)}{dx} + (2x^2 - 7)\frac{d(3x + 5)^2}{dx}$$

$$= (3x + 5)^2 \cdot 4x + (2x^2 - 7) \cdot 2(3x + 5) \cdot 3$$

$$= (9x^2 + 30x + 25) \cdot 4x + 6(2x^2 - 7)(3x + 5)$$

$$= 36x^3 + 120x^2 + 100x + 6(6x^3 - 21x + 10x^2 - 35)$$

$$= 72x^3 + 180x^2 - 26x - 210$$

The student should verify the above answer by multiplying the given factors and differentiating term by term.

In a similar way we can develop a formula for $\dfrac{d(u/v)}{dx}$. Let

$$y = \frac{u}{v} \tag{46}$$

Now let x increase by the amount Δx, and as a consequence u will change by the amount Δu, v will change by the amount Δv, and y will change by the amount Δy.

Accordingly

$$y + \Delta y = \frac{u + \Delta u}{v + \Delta v} \tag{47}$$

Subtracting (46) from (47) gives

$$\Delta y = \frac{u + \Delta u}{v + \Delta v} - \frac{u}{v} \tag{48}$$

or, by combining the right-hand side of (48)

$$\Delta y = \frac{uv + v\,\Delta u - uv - u\,\Delta v}{v(v + \Delta v)}$$

or

$$\Delta y = \frac{v\,\Delta u - u\,\Delta v}{v(v + \Delta v)} \tag{49}$$

Dividing both sides of (49) by Δx,

$$\frac{\Delta y}{\Delta x} = \frac{v(\Delta u/\Delta x) - u(\Delta v/\Delta x)}{v(v + \Delta v)} \tag{50}$$

Now as Δx approaches zero, the denominator of (50) approaches v^2, and in the limit

$$\frac{dy}{dx} = \frac{v(du/dx) - u(dv/dx)}{v^2}$$

or

$$\frac{d(u/v)}{dx} = \frac{v(du/dx) - u(dv/dx)}{v^2} \tag{51}$$

RULE 6 *The derivative of a quotient is the denominator times the derivative of the numerator minus the numerator times the derivative of the denominator divided by the denominator squared.*

example 34 If $y = \dfrac{5x^2 - 3}{x + 1}$, find dy/dx.

By rule 6 above,

$$\frac{dy}{dx} = \frac{(x + 1)(10x) - (5x^2 - 3)(1)}{(x + 1)^2}$$

$$= \frac{10x^2 + 10x - 5x^2 + 3}{(x + 1)^2}$$

$$= \frac{5x^2 + 10x + 3}{(x + 1)^2}$$

We may also use rule 5 by first writing

$$y = (5x^2 - 3)(x + 1)^{-1}$$

Then

$$\frac{dy}{dx} = (5x^2 - 3)(-1)(x + 1)^{-2} + (x + 1)^{-1}(10x)$$

or

$$\frac{dy}{dx} = \frac{-(5x^2 - 3)}{(x + 1)^2} + \frac{10x}{x + 1}$$

$$= \frac{-5x^2 + 3 + 10x^2 + 10x}{(x + 1)^2}$$

$$= \frac{5x^2 + 10x + 3}{(x + 1)^2}$$

In this case we can avoid the use of either rule 5 or rule 6 by dividing as indicated:

$$y = \frac{5x^2 - 3}{x + 1} = 5x - 5 + \frac{2}{x + 1}$$
$$= 5x - 5 + 2(x + 1)^{-1}$$

The actual division is shown below.

$$\begin{array}{r} 5x - 5 \\ x + 1 \overline{)\, 5x^2 - 3} \\ \underline{5x^2 + 5x } \\ -5x - 3 \\ \underline{-5x - 5} \\ +2 \end{array}$$

Then
$$\frac{dy}{dx} = 5 - 2(x + 1)^{-2} = 5 - \frac{2}{(x + 1)^2}$$
$$= \frac{5x^2 + 10x + 5 - 2}{(x + 1)^2}$$
$$= \frac{5x^2 + 10x + 3}{(x + 1)^2}$$

example 35 If $y = \sqrt{(3t^2 + 2)/(t^2 - t)}$, find dy/dt.

If we first write

$$y = \frac{(3t^2 + 2)^{1/2}}{(t^2 - t)^{1/2}}$$

and apply Eq. (51), we obtain

$$\frac{dy}{dt} = \frac{(t^2 - t)^{1/2}(\tfrac{1}{2})(3t^2 + 2)^{-1/2}(6t) - (3t^2 + 2)^{1/2}(\tfrac{1}{2})(t^2 - t)^{-1/2}(2t - 1)}{t^2 - t}$$
$$= \frac{3t}{(t^2 - t)^{1/2}(3t^2 + 2)^{1/2}} - \frac{(2t - 1)(3t^2 + 2)^{1/2}}{2(t^2 - t)^{3/2}} = \frac{-3t^2 - 4t + 2}{2(t^2 - t)^{3/2}(3t^2 + 2)^{1/2}}$$

EXERCISE 7

By use of Eq. (45) or Eq. (51) find the derivative of the following functions with respect to the independent variable.

1. $y = x\sqrt{3 + x^2}$
2. $y = x^2\sqrt{6 - x^2}$
3. $y = (x + 5)^2(3x^3 - 7)^3$
4. $y = \dfrac{2x + 5}{x^2 - 2}$
5. $y = \left(\dfrac{x + 5}{x - 2}\right)^2$
6. $y = \dfrac{x}{x^3 - 5}$
7. $y = \dfrac{x + 1/x}{2x^2 + 5}$
8. $y = x^3(3x^2 + 5)^{-2}$
9. $y = \dfrac{2x}{\sqrt{4x^2 - 9}}$
10. $y = \dfrac{(x^2 - 1)^{3/2}}{x^2}$

Problems 11 through 14 involve the verification of the rules for relative error of products, quotients, powers, and roots given in Secs. B·12 through B·15. (The factor 100 is used to convert to per cent.)

11. Show that if $p = uv$ then

$$100\frac{\Delta p}{p} \approx 100\frac{\Delta u}{u} + 100\frac{\Delta v}{v}$$

12. Show that if $q = u/v$ then

$$100\frac{\Delta q}{q} \approx 100\frac{\Delta u}{u} - 100\frac{\Delta v}{v}$$

13. Show that if $y = x^n$ then

$$100\frac{\Delta y}{y} \approx n(100)\frac{\Delta x}{x}$$

14. Show that if $y = \sqrt[k]{x} = x^{1/k}$ then

$$100\frac{\Delta y}{x} \approx \frac{1}{k}(100)\frac{\Delta x}{x}$$

25·8 Maxima and minima

The subject of maxima and minima was introduced in Sec. 24·11. The student should review that section before proceeding with the discussion below.

In Sec. 24·11 and in Exercise 8 of Chap. 24 we considered relative maxima and minima in connection with certain graphs. We noted that these maximum and minimum points are transition points between rising and falling portions of a graph.

We also noted in Sec. 24·11 that there may be exceptional cases as illustrated by the "cusp" type of relative maximum and minimum shown in Fig. 24·28.

In general, if $y = f(x)$ is defined over a certain interval and if y has a relative maximum or minimum within that interval at, for example, $x = c$ and if dy/dx exists at $x = c$, then

$$\frac{dy}{dx} = 0$$

at $x = c$.

The statement above specifically avoids mention of situations

1. Involving the end points of the interval of definition of the function
2. Involving points for which the derivative does not exist

Furthermore, the fact that the derivative is zero for a certain value of the function does not guarantee the occurrence of either a maximum or minimum. Note, for example, the point P_3 in Fig. 24·29.

If $y = f(x)$, we shall call the value of x_1 for which

$$\frac{dy}{dx} = 0$$

a *critical* value.

As we learned in Sec. 24·12, the derivative may be zero for a point of inflection.

The procedure for identifying maxima and minima will be illustrated in the following examples.

example 36 Find what values of x will make y maximum or minimum if

$$y = x^3 - 3x^2 - 9x + 10$$

Differentiating, we obtain

$$\frac{dy}{dx} = 3x^2 - 6x - 9 = 3(x - 3)(x + 1) \tag{52}$$

Any maximum or minimum values must occur when $dy/dx = 0$. Accordingly, setting $dy/dx = 0$, we obtain

$$0 = 3(x - 3)(x + 1)$$

whereby $$x = 3, -1$$

In order to explore the properties of the curve at $x = 3$ and $x = -1$ we shall compute the values of the slope at various points:

x	-2	-1	0	$+3$	$+4$
$\frac{dy}{dx}$	$+15$	0	-9	0	$+15$

In this example let us draw possible tangents whose slopes are in the order positive, zero, negative, zero, and positive. We shall then roughly sketch a reasonable curve to fit these tangents. This is done in Fig. 25·8. Thus we have indicated a maximum at $x = -1$ and a minimum at $x = 3$.

fig. 25·8

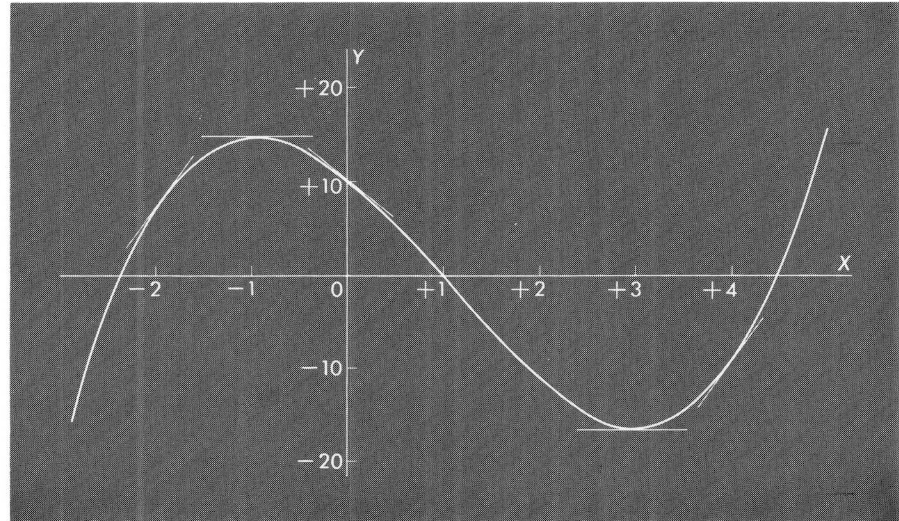

We might confirm this conclusion by substituting values of x in the original equation, noting how y varies in the vicinity of $x = 3$ and $x = -1$. This is done as follows:

x	-3	-2	-1	0	1	2	3	4	5
y	-17	$+8$	$+15$	$+10$	-1	-12	-17	-10	$+15$

At $x = 3$, where $y = -17$, we have a minimum, this point being the lowest point in the immediate vicinity. Likewise at $x = -1, y = 15$, we have a maximum point, this point being the highest point in the immediate vicinity.

The labor involved in identifying a critical point as a maximum, a minimum, or a point of inflection can be reduced considerably by simply investigating the signs of the derivative in the vicinity of the critical points without actually calculating the numerical value of the derivative.

If the sign of the derivative is in the sequence

Positive ⟶	zero ⟶	negative
for $x < +3$	for $x = +3$	for $x > +3$

the value of the function has a maximum at $x = +3$.

If the sign of the derivative is in the sequence

Negative ⟶	zero ⟶	positive
for $x < +3$	for $x = +3$	for $x > +3$

the value of the function has a minimum at $x = +3$.

When x *is near* $+3$

The first and third factors of Eq. (52), that is, 3 and $(x + 1)$, are obviously positive if x is near $+3$. However, if x is a little less than $+3$, say $+2.999$, then the second factor is negative, the product of all factors is negative, and dy/dx is *negative.*

If x is a little *more* than $+3$, say, $+3.0001$, then the second factor is positive, the product of all factors is positive, and dy/dx is *positive.*

As x increases, then, in the vicinity of $x = +3$, the sign of the derivative traverses the following sequence:

Negative ⟶ zero ⟶ positive

and we have a *minimum.*

When x *is near* -1

The first factor, 3, is obviously positive, and the second factor, $(x - 3)$, is obviously negative.

However, if x is a little less than -1, say, -1.0001, then the third factor is negative, the product of all the factors is positive, and dy/dx is *positive.*

If x is a little *more* than -1, say, -0.9999, then the third factor is positive, the product of all factors is negative, and dy/dx is *negative.*

As x increases in the vicinity of $x = -1$, the sign of the derivative traverses the following sequence:

$$\text{Positive} \rightarrow \text{zero} \rightarrow \text{negative}$$

and we have a *maximum.*

example 37 Find the critical values of x, and identify them, if

$$y = 3x^2 - 2x + 7$$

Differentiating the above equation,

$$\frac{dy}{dx} = 6x - 2 = 2(3x - 1)$$

Setting this equation equal to zero

$$0 = 2(3x - 1)$$

and the critical value of x is

$$x = +\tfrac{1}{3}$$

When x is a little less than $\frac{1}{3}$, the derivative is negative; when x is just $\frac{1}{3}$, the derivative is 0; when x is a little more than $\frac{1}{3}$, the derivative is positive. Therefore we can identify the point at which $x = \frac{1}{3}$ as a *minimum* point.

example 38 A uniform bar weighing 1½ lb per ft is to be used to lift a 100-lb load as shown in Fig. 25·9. What length of bar will require the minimum force, and what is the force?

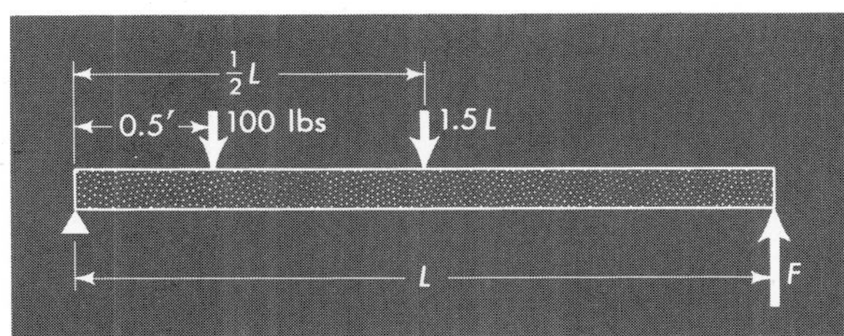

fig. 25·9

We have two clockwise-force moments 100(0.5) due to the load and $(1.5L)(L/2)$ due to the weight of the bar itself. These are balanced by the moment FL. Accordingly we may write

$$FL = 100(0.5) + 1.5L\,\frac{L}{2}$$

or
$$F = \frac{50}{L} + 0.75L$$

Differentiating,
$$\frac{dF}{dL} = -\frac{50}{L^2} + 0.75$$

Equating the derivative to zero,
$$0 = -\frac{50}{L^2} + 0.75$$

or
$$L = 8.16 \text{ ft}$$

and
$$F = \frac{50}{8.16} + 0.75(8.16) = 12.25 \text{ lb}$$

The student should convince himself that when $L = 8.16$ ft, the force is actually a minimum and not a maximum.

example 39 Given $y = x^3 - 6x^2 + 12x - 20$.

Let us investigate any horizontal slopes as we did in the preceding examples. In this example we obtain
$$\frac{dy}{dx} = 3x^2 - 12x + 12$$

Equating to zero and solving, we obtain
$$x = 2, 2 \qquad \text{(thus the two roots are identical)}$$

If we calculate values of the slope and tabulate, we have

x	$+4$	$+3$	$+2$	$+1$	0
$\frac{dy}{dx} = 3x^2 - 12x + 12$	$+12$	$+3$	0	$+3$	$+12$

Graphically, this is shown in Fig. 25·10 and we have neither a maximum nor a minimum but a point of inflection or reversal of curvature (see Sec. 24·12).

example 40 Locate and identify the critical points on the graph of
$$y = 2\sqrt{3x^3 - 16x + 20} \qquad \text{(see Fig. 25·11)}$$

Change to the form
$$y = 2(3x^3 - 16x + 20)^{1/2} \tag{53}$$

Then
$$\frac{dy}{dx} = (3x^3 - 16x + 20)^{-1/2}(9x^2 - 16)$$

or
$$\frac{dy}{dx} = \frac{9x^2 - 16}{\sqrt{3x^3 - 16x + 20}} \tag{54}$$

Values of x for which $\sqrt{3x^3 - 16x + 20}$ is either imaginary or zero are excluded.

It can be found by solving

$$3x^3 - 16x + 20 = 0$$

that when $x = -2.785$ (approximately), the quantity

$$\sqrt{3x^3 - 16x + 20} = 0$$

fig. 25·10

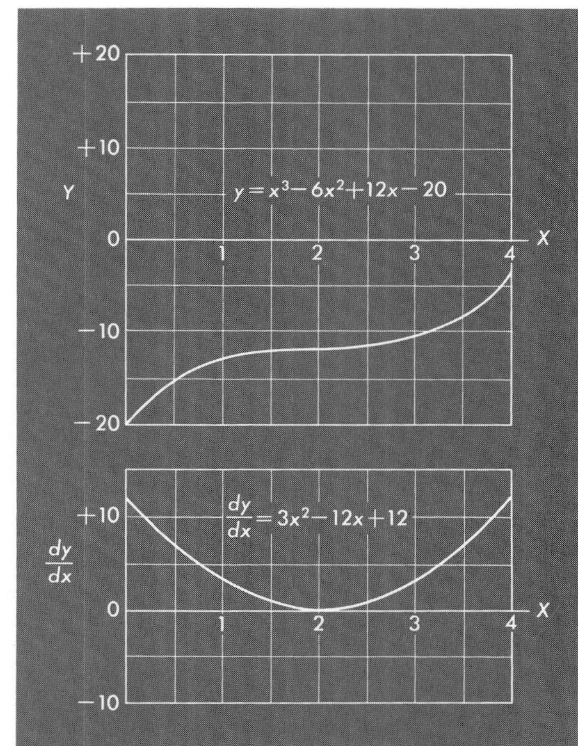

fig. 25·11

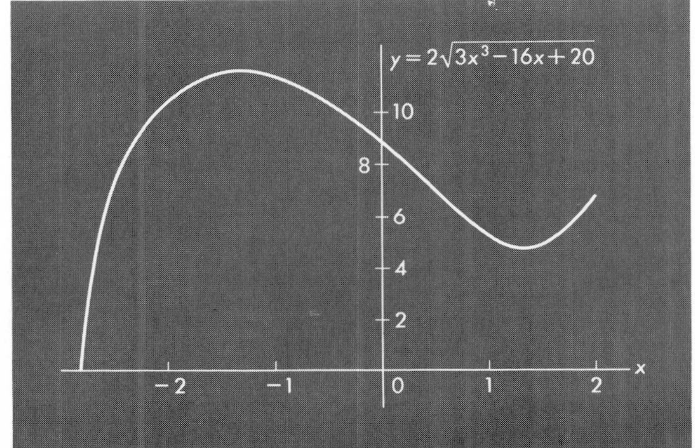

Also for values of x less than -2.785 the quantity $\sqrt{3x^3 - 16x + 20}$ is imaginary. Therefore values of x equal to or less than -2.785 are excluded, and the derivative is undefined for these values.

Now let us find values of x for which $dy/dx = 0$. From Eq. (54) $dy/dx = 0$ when

$$9x^2 - 16 = 0 \tag{55}$$

Solving (55), we obtain

$$x^2 = 16/9$$
$$x = \pm 4/3$$

Since the above values of x are not excluded, we shall investigate the sign of the derivative in Eq. (54) in the vicinity of $x = +4/3$ and $x = -4/3$ in order to identify the corresponding critical points.

The sign of the derivative in Eq. (54) is determined entirely by the sign of the numerator. The denominator is positive anyway. The numerator can be written

$$(3x + 4)(3x - 4) \tag{56}$$

When x is in the vicinity of $+4/3$, the left-hand factor of expression (56) is positive and the sign of the numerator of Eq. (54) will be governed by the sign of the quantity $3x - 4$.

When x is a little less than $+4/3$, the expression $3x - 4$ is negative. When x is a little more than $4/3$, the expression $3x - 4$ is positive.

Thus, as x traverses through this critical point in an increasing direction, the signs of the derivative are in the sequence

Negative → zero → positive

and this critical point is a *minimum*.

The student should justify for himself that when $x = -4/3$, the given function is a maximum.

example 41 Locate and identify the critical points if

$$y = x^{2/3}(x - 4)^2 \tag{57}$$

Equation (57) may be written

$$y = x^{8/3} - 8x^{5/3} + 16x^{2/3}$$

and

$$\frac{dy}{dx} = \frac{8}{3}x^{5/3} - \frac{40}{3}x^{2/3} + \frac{32}{3}x^{-1/3}$$

or

$$\frac{dy}{dx} = \frac{8}{3}x^{-1/3}(x^2 - 5x + 4)$$

or

$$\frac{dy}{dx} = \frac{8}{3\sqrt[3]{x}}(x - 4)(x - 1) \qquad x \neq 0$$

Therefore, $dy/dx = 0$ when $x = +4$ and when $x = +1$. By testing for the sign of the derivative in the vicinity of these critical values as we have done in the previous examples, we find that $x = 1$ corresponds to a relative maximum, and $x = 4$ corresponds to a relative minimum.

However, it is important to investigate the behavior of the function in the vicinity of $x = 0$ since for this value of x the derivative is not defined.

The plot of Eq. (57) is shown in Fig. 25·12. From this figure it is evident that when $x = 0$, we have a cusp minimum which we would have overlooked had we failed to investigate.

Thus we have a relative maximum at $x = 1$ and *two* relative minima, one at $x = 4$ and another at $x = 0$.

EXERCISE 8

Locate and identify any points where the tangent is horizontal.
* Hint: Divide out before differentiating.

1. $y = 2x^3 + 9x^2 - 24x + 12$
2. $y = -x^4 + 24x^2 + 2$
3. $y = x + \dfrac{9}{x}$
4. *$y = \dfrac{x^2 + 4}{x}$

fig. 25·12

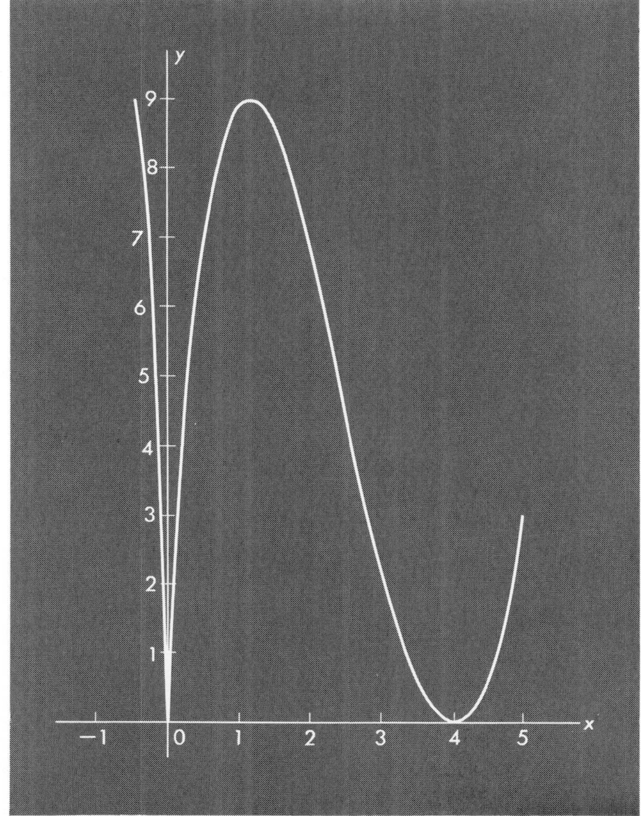

5.* $y = \frac{x^3 - 16}{x}$

6. $y = \sqrt{3x^3 - 4x + 11}$

7. $y = \frac{5}{2x^4 - 9x^2}$

8. The sum of two numbers is 12, and their product is to be a maximum. Find the numbers.
9. One of the factors considered in choosing the size of wire for a transmission circuit is cost. The larger the cross-section area, the greater will be the first cost and hence also the annual charges for interest, taxes, and depreciation. At the same time the larger the cross-section area, the lower will be the cost of lost power since the heating losses will be lower. For bare wire the investment is directly proportional to the area, and the lost power is inversely proportional to the area; hence the total part of the line cost depending on wire size can be written as $C = k_1a + k_2/a$, where a is the area and k_1 and k_2 are positive constants.

   Show that the area of the wire which makes C a minimum is that for which the two terms are equal, that is, that for which $k_1a = k_2/a$. Illustrate by sketching the two components and their sum, all on the same axes.

   REMARK: The basic law as stated in this problem is known as Kelvin's law.

10. A rectangle has a perimeter of 40 ft. Find the dimensions of the rectangle to give the greatest area.
11. A sheet iron trough is to be made by bending up two edges so as to give a rectangular cross-section area. The width of the sheet is 20 in. Therefore $20 = x + 2y$. Find y to give the maximum cross-section area (see Fig. 25·13).
12. A utility company wishes to determine the size wire to be used on a power transmission line for maximum economy. Initial cost and investment charges may be expressed by the equation $s_1 = ka + b$, where s_1 is the cost, a is the cross-section area of the wire, and k and b are constants. The energy loss may be written $s_2 = c/a$, where s_2 is the cost of lost power and c is a constant. If $k = 0.18$, $b = 15{,}000$, and $c = 40$, find the optimum cross-section area. (This is total area and may be distributed among n wires.)

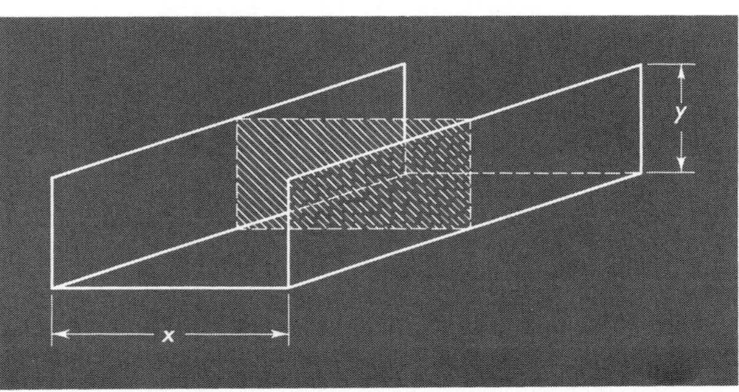

fig. 25·13

13. The total cost of operating a pipe line may be expressed as $C = Ad^2 + B/d^5$, where d is the diameter of the pipe, and A and B are positive and are substantially constants for a given range of diameter values. Determine the diameter for minimum cost.
14. An electric battery whose internal electromotive force is E_g volts and whose internal resistance is r ohms has the terminal voltage $E = E_g - Ir$ volts, the output power $P = E_gI - I^2r$, and the efficiency $\eta = P/(E_gI)$ as functions of the current I amp. Sketch the graphs of E, P, and η, each in terms of I in the range from open circuit ($I = 0$) to short circuit ($E = 0$). Determine by inspection the largest and smallest values of E, P, and η that occur at the end points of this range and whether any occur at intermediate points. Then differentiate to determine the latter. Tabulate all such values together with the values of I at which they occur. (Notice that the "maximums" for E and I actually occur, while the "maximum" for η does not, since it arises as an indeterminate form.)
15. The total cost of manufacturing a certain article is fixed by:
(a) The fixed organization cost which is \$90 per day.
(b) The unit production cost of each article which is \$0.09.
(c) The cost of repairs, maintenance, etc., which is $x^2/10{,}000$ per day (in dollars) as estimated by past records. x is the number of articles produced per day.
(1) Show that the total cost for each article in dollars is

$$U = \frac{90}{x} + 0.09 + \frac{x}{10{,}000}$$

(2) Determine the number of articles to be produced each day to make the unit cost least.
16. A rectangular package has square ends. If the sum of the girth and length may not exceed 80 in., what dimensions will correspond to the maximum volume?
17. A rectangular open-top box is to be made from a sheet of copper 8 by 15 in. by cutting a square from each corner and turning up the sides. What size squares must be cut out to make the capacity of the box a maximum?
18. Find the dimensions of the largest rectangle that can be contained in a right triangle whose sides are 3, 4, and 5 in.
19. It is desired to determine the optimum number of checks on the quality of a finished product. It is assumed that the cost of checking one unit is proportional to the number of checks; that is, $y_1 = kn$. It is further assumed that the cost of errors and defective units becomes progressively less with more frequent checks but can never be eliminated entirely. It has been found that the formula $y_2 = b/(n + a)$ applies, where a and b are constants. To summarize,

$$E = kn + \frac{b}{n + a}$$

where E = total cost of checks and errors—to be made a minimum
k = constant = \$0.13
n = number of checks
b = constant = \$1.36
a = constant = 0.32

Find the number of checks for a minimum total cost E. What is the minimum E?

20. A man is able to hire one dump truck at \$4 per hour for truck and driver. The truck takes half an hour to deliver a load of sand and return. It takes 4 man-hours to load the truck. Laborers get \$1 an hour whether they are loading the truck or standing around idle while waiting for the truck to return. How many laborers should be hired to realize the minimum cost per load? What is the minimum cost?
21. Two lights whose intensities are as 1:4 are 100 ft apart. How far from the weaker light is the point of minimum total illumination? (Intensity of illumination at any point varies as i/l^2, where i is the intensity of the light source, and l is the distance from the point to the light source.)
22. Three towns are to be served by a high-voltage line which takes the form of a letter Y 16 miles high and 12 miles across the top. Find the length of the stem of the Y for a minimum length of wire.
23. What are the dimensions of a covered gallon cylindrical container which will make its total surface a minimum?
24. A cylindrical cup is to be made of sheet metal. Find the ratio of height to diameter that will require the least material.
25. A totally enclosed cylindrical can is to be made of sheet metal. Find the ratio of height to diameter that will give a maximum volume for a given amount of material.
26. The hourly cost of operating a ship, in dollars per hour, is $c = 120 + 0.02v^3$, where v equals speed in miles per hour. Find the speed corresponding to a minimum cost per mile.
27. The tops of two vertical poles ax and cy are connected by a rope abc. Plot the length of the rope against the distance xb and find the length of xb for a minimum length of the rope (see Fig. 25 · 14).
28. Let c = cost of one Mazda lamp plus installation charge in cents
b = cost of power for lamp in cents per kilowatthour
V = actual operating voltage
V_0 = rated voltage for lamp
P_0 = watts input at voltage V_0
F_0 = luminous output in lumens at voltage V_0

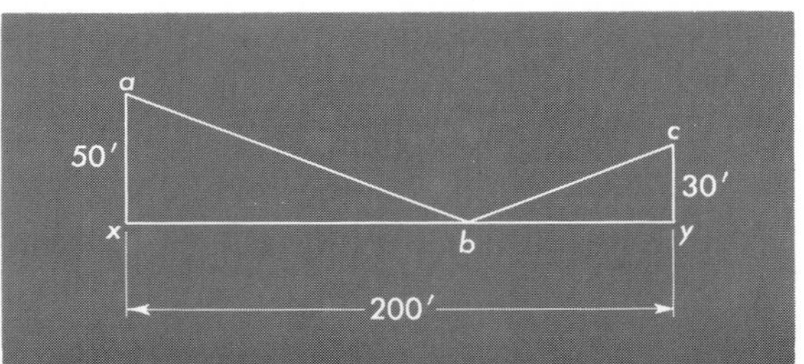

fig. 25 · 14

The cost per lumen for 1,000 hr (assuming 1,000 hr of life on the rated voltage of the lamp) is

$$y = \frac{c}{F_0}\left(\frac{V}{V_0}\right)^{B_5-B_2} + \frac{bP_0}{F_0}\left(\frac{V}{V_0}\right)^{B_3-B_2}$$

where the B's are constants that are determined experimentally.

(a) Determine the value of $x = V/V_0$ that makes y a minimum.

(b) For Mazda-C lamps from 60 to 150 watts: $B_2 = 3.613$; $B_3 = 1.523$; $B_5 = 13.50$. If $b = 6$ cents per kilowatthour, $P_0 = 100$ watts, and $c = 20$ cents, determine $x_{\min}$, and hence determine the best value for the rated voltage V_0 if the operating voltage V is 120 volts.

29. Determine the value of $x = p_2/p_1$ that will make the expression $y = (p_2/p_1)^{2/k} - (p_2/p_1)^{(k+1)/k}$, $k > 1$, a maximum and thus determine p_2 in terms of p_1 when y is a maximum. What is the value of the coefficient of p_1 in your result if $k = 1.4$?

REMARK: This problem occurs in thermodynamics in the study of flow in a nozzle.

30. The study of the formation of producer gas in chemical engineering leads to the equation

$$(b - a)v = x - x^{b/a}$$

where b and a are constants that depend on the process. x is the proportion of residual water remaining undecomposed, and v is the corresponding value for the amount of carbon dioxide.

(a) Determine a relation for the maximum value for v (amount of carbon dioxide), assuming that b is larger than a.

(b) If $a = 3.17$ and $b = 4.18$, determine the maximum value for v correct to slide-rule accuracy.

31. The fuel tank of an experimental rocket is a cylinder 40 ft long, and it flies with the axis of the tank vertical. The tank has a uniform cross-section area of 5 sq ft. It is filled with liquid fuel weighing 50 lb per cu ft. As the fuel is consumed, the joint center of gravity of the vertical tank and the remaining fuel will move along the axis of the tank. What depth of fuel will correspond to the minimum distance between the center of gravity and the bottom of the tank? The empty tank weighs 500 lb.

25·9 The derivative of sin x

In this section we shall develop formulas for dy/dx when $y = \sin x$ and when $y = \cos x$.

First, we shall recall from Sec. 18·9 that

$$\lim_{\phi \to 0} \frac{\sin \phi}{\phi} = 1 \tag{58}$$

Now we shall show that

$$\lim_{\phi \to 0} \frac{\cos \phi - 1}{\phi} = 0 \tag{59}$$

To justify Eq. (59) we shall operate on the given expression by the rules of elementary mathematics in the hope of finding some equivalent form in which the limit, if any, is more easily detected.

It has been found profitable in this case to multiply

$$\frac{\cos \phi - 1}{\phi}$$

by $(\cos \phi + 1)/(\cos \phi + 1)$, obtaining

$$\left(\frac{\cos \phi + 1}{\cos \phi + 1}\right) \frac{\cos \phi - 1}{\phi} = \frac{\cos^2 \phi - 1}{\phi(\cos \phi + 1)} = \frac{-sin^2 \phi}{\phi(\cos \phi + 1)}$$

Thus

$$\frac{\cos \phi - 1}{\phi} = -\frac{\sin \phi}{\phi} \frac{\sin \phi}{\cos \phi + 1} \tag{60}$$

As ϕ approaches zero, by Eq. (58) the factor $-\dfrac{\sin \phi}{\phi}$ of (60) approaches -1. As ϕ approaches zero, we see by inspection that the factor $\dfrac{\sin \phi}{\cos \phi + 1}$ of Eq. (60) approaches 0/2.

Thus it seems intuitively evident (and it can be proved rigorously in more advanced work on limit theory) that

$$\lim_{\phi \to 0} \frac{\cos \phi - 1}{\phi} = (-1)\frac{0}{2} = 0 \tag{61}$$

It is important to note that in all formulas for differentiation and integration the angles involved are measured in radians unless there is some specific indication to the contrary.

We shall now develop the formula for dy/dx when $y = \sin x$.

If we let x change by some amount Δx, then y will, in general, change by some amount Δy.

Then

$$\Delta y = \sin (x + \Delta x) - \sin x$$

$$\frac{\Delta y}{\Delta x} = \frac{\sin (x + \Delta x) - \sin x}{\Delta x}$$

or from Eq. (43), Chap. 21,

$$\frac{\Delta y}{\Delta x} = \frac{\sin x \cos \Delta x + \cos x \sin \Delta x - \sin x}{\Delta x}$$

$$\frac{\Delta y}{\Delta x} = \sin x \frac{\cos \Delta x - 1}{\Delta x} + \frac{\sin \Delta x}{\Delta x} \cos x$$

From Eqs. (58) and (61) above,

$$\lim_{\Delta x \to 0} \frac{\Delta y}{\Delta x} = \frac{dy}{dx} = (\sin x)0 + 1 \cos x = \cos x \tag{62}$$

Therefore, if

$$y = \sin x \tag{63}$$

then

$$\frac{dy}{dx} = \cos x \tag{64}$$

or

$$\frac{d(\sin x)}{dx} = \cos x \qquad (x \text{ in radians}) \tag{65}$$

25·10 The derivative of sin u, cos x, and cos u

If

$$y = \sin u$$

and u is the value of a differentiable function of x, we may from Eqs. (65) and (31) write

$$\frac{dy}{dx} = \cos u \frac{du}{dx}$$

or

$$\frac{d(\sin u)}{dx} = \cos u \frac{du}{dx} \tag{66}$$

and

$$\frac{d(k \sin u + C)}{dx} = k \cos u \frac{du}{dx} \tag{67}$$

example 42 If $y = \sin (4\pi\theta - \pi/2)$, find $dy/d\theta$.

Following Eq. (66),

$$\frac{dy}{d\theta} = \left[\cos\left(4\pi\theta - \frac{\pi}{2}\right)\right]4\pi$$

example 43 If $y = \sin \theta^{(t-1)/t}$, find $dy/d\theta$ where t is a constant.

The problem can be simplified somewhat by restating.

$$y = \sin \theta^{1-1/t}$$

Following Eqs. (66) and (27),

$$\frac{dy}{d\theta} = (\cos \theta^{1-1/t})\left(1 - \frac{1}{t}\right)\theta^{-1/t}$$

example 44 If $y = \sin^2 4\theta$, find $dy/d\theta$.

$$y = (\sin 4\theta)^2$$

Following Eqs. (66) and (27),

$$\frac{dy}{d\theta} = 2[(\sin 4\theta)(\cos 4\theta)]4$$

From Eq. (51), Chap. 21, we may write

$$\frac{dy}{d\theta} = 8 \sin 4\theta \cos 4\theta = 4 \sin 8\theta$$

example 45 If $y = \sin (4\theta)^2$, find $dy/d\theta$.

Restate the problem to make the expression for the angle match Eq. (27).

$$y = \sin 16\theta^2$$

$$\frac{dy}{d\theta} = (\cos 16\theta^2)32\theta$$

example 46 If $y = -\sin (4\pi\theta^2 - \pi/2)$, find $dy/d\theta$.

Following Eq. (66),

$$\frac{dy}{d\theta} = -\left[\cos\left(4\pi\theta^2 - \frac{\pi}{2}\right)\right]8\pi\theta = -\ 8\pi\theta \sin 4\pi\theta^2$$

Now let us develop a formula for dy/dx if $y = \cos x$.

From Eq. (42), Chap. 21,

$$\cos x = \sin (90° - x)$$

Thus

$$\frac{d(\cos x)}{dx} = \frac{d[\sin (90° - x)]}{dx} \tag{68}$$

From Eq. (66),

$$\frac{d[\sin (90° - x)]}{dx} = [\cos (90° - x)](-1) = -\cos (90° - x)$$

From Eq. (41), Chap. 21,

$$\begin{aligned} -\cos (90° - x) &= -(\cos 90° \cos x + \sin 90° \sin x) \\ &= -(0 + \sin x) = -\sin x \end{aligned} \tag{69}$$

Thus

$$\frac{d(\cos x)}{dx} = -\sin x \tag{70}$$

If

$$y = \cos u$$

and u is the value of a differentiable function of x, we may, from Eqs. (70) and (31), write

$$\frac{dy}{dx} = -\sin u \frac{du}{dx}$$

or

$$\frac{d(\cos u)}{dx} = -\sin u \frac{du}{dx} \tag{71}$$

and

$$\frac{d(k \cos u + C)}{dx} = -k \sin u \frac{du}{dx} \tag{72}$$

example 47 If $y = \cos(4\pi\theta - \pi/2)$, find $dy/d\theta$.

Following Eq. (72),

$$\frac{dy}{d\theta} = \left[-\sin\left(4\pi\theta - \frac{\pi}{2}\right)\right]4\pi$$

example 48 If $y = \cos \theta^{(t-1)/t}$, find $dy/d\theta$ where t is a constant.

The problem can be simplified somewhat by restating, as

$$y = \cos \theta^{1-1/t}$$

Following Eqs. (72) and (27),

$$\frac{dy}{d\theta} = (-\sin \theta^{1-1/t})\left(1 - \frac{1}{t}\right)\theta^{-1/t}$$

example 49 If $y = \cos^2 4\theta$, find $dy/d\theta$.

$$y = (\cos 4\theta)^2$$

Following Eqs. (27) and (72),

$$\frac{dy}{d\theta} = (2 \cos 4\theta)(-\sin 4\theta)4 = -8 \cos 4\theta \sin 4\theta = -4 \sin 8\theta$$

[Eq. (51), page 546]

example 50 If $y = \cos(4\theta)^2$, find $dy/d\theta$.

To make the expression for the angle match Eq. (27), we can restate the problem as

$$y = \cos 16\theta^2$$

Then

$$\frac{dy}{d\theta} = (-\sin 16\theta^2)32\theta$$

25·11 The derivative of secant u and cosecant u

Since

$$\sec u = \frac{1}{\cos u} = (\cos u)^{-1}$$

$$\frac{d(\sec u)}{dx} = \frac{d(1/\cos u)}{dx} = \frac{d(\cos u)^{-1}}{dx}$$

$$= -(\cos u)^{-2}(-\sin u)\frac{du}{dx}$$

or $$\frac{d(\sec u)}{dx} = \frac{\sin u}{(\cos u)^2}\frac{du}{dx} = \tan u \sec u \frac{du}{dx} \tag{73}$$

Also since

$$\operatorname{cosec} u = \frac{1}{\sin u} = (\sin u)^{-1}$$

$$\frac{d(\operatorname{cosec} u)}{dx} = \frac{d(1/\sin u)}{dx} = \frac{d(\sin u)^{-1}}{dx}$$

$$= -(\sin u)^{-2} \cos u \frac{du}{dx}$$

or $$\frac{d(\operatorname{cosec} u)}{dx} = \frac{-\cos u}{(\sin u)^2}\frac{du}{dx} = -\cot u \operatorname{cosec} u \frac{du}{dx} \tag{74}$$

example 51 If $y = \sqrt{3} \sec 2\pi\phi^2$, find $dy/d\phi$.

From Eq. (73),

$$\frac{dy}{d\phi} = \sqrt{3} \tan 2\pi\phi^2 \sec 2\pi\phi^2 \cdot 4\pi\phi$$

$$= 4\pi\sqrt{3}\, \phi \tan 2\pi\phi^2 \sec 2\pi\phi^2$$

example 52 If $y = \operatorname{cosec}^2 4\phi$, find $dy/d\phi$.

From Eq. (74),

$$\frac{dy}{d\phi} = (2 \operatorname{cosec} 4\phi)(-\cot 4\phi \operatorname{cosec} 4\phi)4$$

$$= -8 \operatorname{cosec}^2 4\phi \cot 4\phi$$

25·12 The derivative of tan u and cot u

Since

$$\tan u = \frac{\sin u}{\cos u}$$

by following Eq. (51) we may write

$$\frac{d(\tan u)}{dx} = \frac{\cos u \cos u \dfrac{du}{dx} - \sin u(-\sin u)\dfrac{du}{dx}}{\cos^2 u}$$

or $$\frac{d(\tan u)}{dx} = \frac{\cos^2 u + \sin^2 u}{\cos^2 u}\frac{du}{dx}$$

$$= \frac{1}{\cos^2 u}\frac{du}{dx} = \sec^2 u \frac{du}{dx} \tag{75}$$

Similarly, since

$$\cot u = \frac{\cos u}{\sin u}$$

by following Eq. (51) we may write

$$\frac{d(\cot u)}{dx} = \frac{\sin u(-\sin u)\dfrac{du}{dx} - \cos u \cos u \dfrac{du}{dx}}{\sin^2 u}$$

$$\frac{d(\cot u)}{dx} = -\frac{\sin^2 u + \cos^2 u}{\sin^2 u}\frac{du}{dx}$$

$$= -\frac{1}{\sin^2 u}\frac{du}{dx} = -\operatorname{cosec}^2 u \frac{du}{dx} \tag{76}$$

example 53 If $y = 4 \tan [(\theta/2) - (\pi/3)]$, find $dy/d\theta$.

By Eq. (75),

$$\frac{dy}{d\theta} = \left[4 \sec^2\left(\frac{\theta}{2} - \frac{\pi}{3}\right)\right]\frac{1}{2} = 2 \sec^2\left(\frac{\theta}{2} - \frac{\pi}{3}\right)$$

example 54 If $y = 3 \cot (1 - \phi^2)$, find $dy/d\phi$.

From Eq. (76),

$$\frac{dy}{d\phi} = [-3 \operatorname{cosec}^2 (1 - \phi^2)](-2\phi) = 6\phi \operatorname{cosec}^2 (1 - \phi^2)$$

example 55 If $y = \cos 2\theta \tan \theta$, find $dy/d\theta$.

$$\frac{dy}{d\theta} = \cos 2\theta \sec^2 \theta - 2 \sin 2\theta \tan \theta$$

$$= (2 \cos^2 \theta - 1)\left(\frac{1}{\cos^2 \theta}\right) - 4 \sin \theta \cos \theta \frac{\sin \theta}{\cos \theta} = 2 - \frac{1}{\cos^2 \theta} - 4 \sin^2 \theta$$

EXERCISE 9

Differentiate the following:

1. $y = \sin x^4$
2. $y = (\sin x)^4$
3. $y = \sin^4 x$
4. $u = \sin (2/\phi)$
5. $y = -6 \sin \phi^{3/4}$
6. $w = \sin\sqrt{\theta}$
7. $z = 25\sqrt{\sin x}$
8. $y = \sin^2 (\phi - 1)$
9. $y = \sqrt{3} \cos \sqrt[3]{\phi}$
10. $E = 10 \sin\left(\omega t + \frac{\pi}{2}\right)$
11. $y = 3 \cos \frac{2}{\phi}$
12. $y = 3 \cos\sqrt{x}$
13. $y = \cos\left(x - \frac{1}{x}\right)$
14. $u = \cos^2 (x - 1)$
15. $y = \tan^4 x$
16. $z = 3 \tan^{2/3} x$
17. $y = \tan\left(x + \frac{1}{x}\right)$
18. $y = \cot^2 (\phi - 1)$
19. $w = \cot\sqrt{\theta}$
20. $u = \cot^4 x$
21. $s = 25\sqrt{\sec x}$
22. $y = -6 \sec x^{3/4}$
23. $y = 3 \sec\sqrt{x}$
24. $y = \operatorname{cosec}\left(1 - \frac{1}{x}\right)$
25. $w = 4 \operatorname{cosec} (3\phi + 2)$
26. $u = 4 \operatorname{cosec}^2\left(x + \frac{1}{x}\right)$

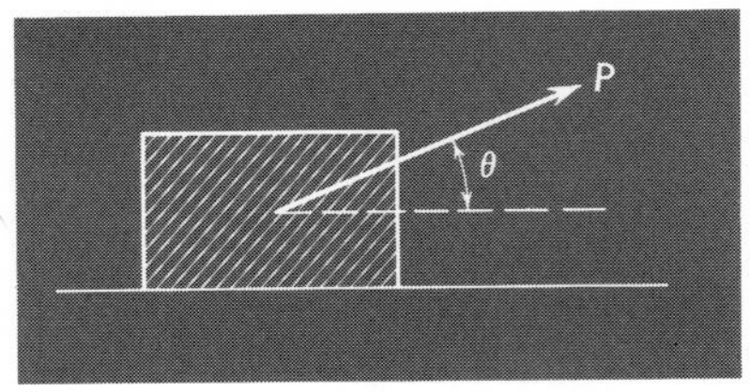

fig. 25·15

27. A block that weighs 100 lb rests on a horizontal surface for which the coefficient of friction is μ. A force of P lb acts on the block as shown in Fig. 25·15, the action line of the force making an *acute* angle θ with the horizontal. The force just necessary to start this block in motion can be shown, by methods of physics and mechanics, to be

$$P = \frac{100\mu}{\cos\theta + \mu \sin\theta}$$

If $\mu = 0.2$, determine the smallest value for P. Can you give a physical interpretation for your result?

28. Given $y = 6 \sin(\pi t/2)$, where the angle is in radians, find the smallest positive value of t for which $dy/dt = 0$.

29. The linear speed of a point on the tread of an automobile tire is given by the equation $v = 32\pi \sin(8\pi t)$, where v is in feet per second and t is in seconds (see Fig. 24·34 and Exercise 9, Chap. 24).
    (a) What significance if any can be attached to the above equation when $\frac{1}{4} > t > \frac{1}{8}$?
    (b) What time is required for one revolution?

30. From the equation in Prob. 29 find the following:
    (a) The average acceleration from $t = 0.02$ to $t = 0.03$. (Acceleration is the rate of change in velocity.)
    (b) The instantaneous acceleration at $t = 0.03$.
    (c) The maximum speed of the point.
    (d) The speed of the car.
    (e) The outside diameter of the tire.
    (f) When the acceleration is zero.

31. The equation

$$e = \tan\lambda \frac{\cos\phi - f\tan\lambda}{\cos\phi \tan\lambda + f}$$

gives the efficiency e for a worm drive which has a lead angle λ, a pressure angle ϕ, and friction f.
    (a) Show that the given equation can be rewritten in the form

$$\frac{2f}{1-e} = \cos\phi \sin 2\lambda + f + f\cos 2\lambda$$

    (b) Show that the value of λ that makes the efficiency e a maximum is given by $\tan 2\lambda = \cos\phi/f$.

NOTE: The result in (a) will facilitate the solution to (b).

25·13 The derivatives of arcsin u, arccos u, and arctan u

Consider the functions defined by

$$x = \sin \phi$$
$$x = \cos \phi$$
$$x = \tan \phi$$

In these equations ϕ is regarded as the independent variable, and x is regarded as the dependent variable.

With certain restrictions to be discussed below, we may reverse the roles of x and ϕ. We may regard ϕ as the dependent variable and x as the independent variable. Accordingly, we shall introduce the notation (see Sec. 17·9)

$$\phi = \arcsin x$$
$$\phi = \arccos x$$
$$\phi = \arctan x$$

in which the symbol "arcsin x" means *the radian measure of the angle whose sine is* x. Similarly, we interpret the symbol "arccos x" to mean *the radian measure of the angle whose cosine is* x, and the symbol "arctan x" to mean *the radian measure of the angle whose tangent is* x. In Fig. 25·16 we display the graphs of $\phi = \arcsin x$, $\phi = \arccos x$, and $\phi = \arctan x$ without indicating any restrictions on the range of ϕ. Without such restrictions, it is evident that there are infinitely many values of ϕ corresponding to any of the permissible values of x.

To avoid this multiplicity of values of ϕ we ordinarily do restrict the range of ϕ and define:

1. Arcsin x as the number ϕ for which $-\pi/2 \leq \phi \leq \pi/2$ and $\sin \phi = x$, where $|x| \leq 1$
2. Arccos x as the number ϕ for which $0 \leq \phi \leq \pi$ and $\cos \phi = x$, where $|x| \leq 1$
3. Arctan x as the number ϕ for which $-\pi/2 < \phi < \pi/2$ and $\tan \phi = x$

In accordance with the restrictions above, the heavy lines in Fig. 25·16 indicate the graphs of arcsin x, arccos x, and arctan x.

The arccot x, arcsec x, and arccosec x are so seldom encountered in practice that we shall omit further discussion of them here. Now let

$$\phi = \arcsin x$$

Then, from the above definitions,

$$x = \sin \phi \qquad -\frac{\pi}{2} \leq \phi \leq +\frac{\pi}{2} \tag{77}$$

By differentiating with respect to x we obtain

$$\frac{dx}{dx} = 1 = \cos \phi \frac{d\phi}{dx} \tag{78}$$

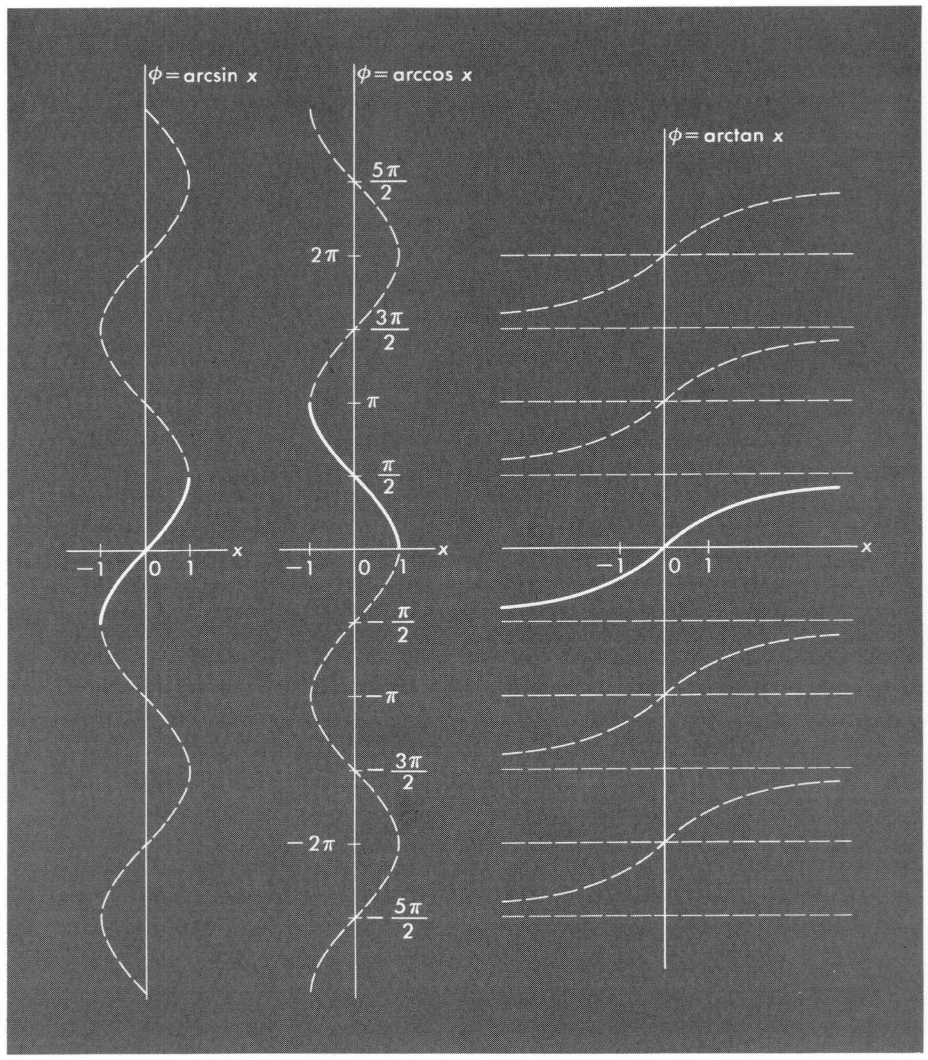

fig. 25·16

or
$$\frac{d\phi}{dx} = \frac{1}{\cos \phi} \qquad -\frac{\pi}{2} < \phi < +\frac{\pi}{2} \tag{79}$$

Observe that in Eq. (79) the derivative $d\phi/dx$ is undefined for $\phi = \pm\pi/2$. Now from the relation

$$\sin^2 \phi + \cos^2 \phi = 1$$

we may write

$$\cos \phi = \pm\sqrt{1 - \sin^2 \phi} \qquad -\frac{\pi}{2} \leq \phi \leq +\frac{\pi}{2} \tag{80}$$

However, for the range

$$-\frac{\pi}{2} \leq \phi \leq +\frac{\pi}{2}$$

$\cos \phi$ is always non-negative, and we may write

$$\cos \phi = \sqrt{1 - \sin^2 \phi} \qquad -\frac{\pi}{2} \leq \phi \leq +\frac{\pi}{2} \tag{81}$$

but since

$$\sin \phi = x$$

we may write

$$\cos \phi = \sqrt{1 - x^2} \tag{82}$$

By substituting Eq. (82) in Eq. (79) we obtain

$$\frac{d\phi}{dx} = \frac{1}{\sqrt{1 - x^2}} \tag{83}$$

or since $\phi = \arcsin x$,

$$\frac{d(\arcsin x)}{dx} = \frac{1}{\sqrt{1 - x^2}} \qquad |x| < 1 \tag{84}$$

By a similar argument we could show that

$$\frac{d(\arccos x)}{dx} = -\frac{1}{\sqrt{1 - x^2}} \qquad |x| < 1 \tag{85}$$

and

$$\frac{d(\arctan x)}{dx} = \frac{1}{1 + x^2} \tag{86}$$

From Sec. 25·6, if u is the value of a differentiable function of x, we may write

$$\frac{d(\arcsin u)}{dx} = \frac{1}{\sqrt{1 - u^2}} \frac{du}{dx} \qquad |u| < 1 \tag{87}$$

$$\frac{d(\arccos u)}{dx} = \frac{-1}{\sqrt{1 - u^2}} \frac{du}{dx} \qquad |u| < 1 \tag{88}$$

$$\frac{d(\arctan u)}{dx} = \frac{1}{1 + u^2} \frac{du}{dx} \tag{89}$$

example 56 Find $d\phi/dx$ if $\phi = \arcsin x^2$.

From Eq. (87),

$$\frac{d\phi}{dx} = \frac{2x}{\sqrt{1 - x^4}}$$

example 57 Find dx/dy if $x = \arccos \sqrt{y}$.

From Eq. (88),

$$\frac{dx}{dy} = \frac{-1}{\sqrt{1-y}}\frac{1}{2}y^{-1/2} = -\frac{1}{2\sqrt{y-y^2}}$$

example 58 Find $d\phi/dx$ if $\phi = \arctan(1/x)$.

From Eq. (89),

$$\frac{d\phi}{dx} = \frac{1}{1+(1/x^2)}\left(-\frac{1}{x^2}\right) = \frac{-1}{x^2+1}$$

EXERCISE 10

Differentiate the following:

1. $y = 3 \arcsin(x/3)$
2. $\phi = \arcsin 4x$
3. $\phi = \arccos x^5$
4. $y = \arctan(2x+5)$
5. $\phi = \arccos(4-2y)$
6. $y = \arctan 25x$

25·14 The derivative of $\log_b x$

Consider the function $y = \log_b x$. Recall from Sec. 10·1 that $b > 0$ and $b \neq 1$. Also, following Sec. 10·1, we shall for the present consider that $x > 0$.

Now if $y = \log_b x$ and if we let x change by some amount Δx, then, in general, y will change by some amount Δy, and

$$\frac{\Delta y}{\Delta x} = \frac{\log_b(x+\Delta x) - \log_b x}{\Delta x} \tag{90}$$

From Sec. 10·5 we may rewrite the numerator of Eq. (90) as

$$\frac{\Delta y}{\Delta x} = \frac{\log_b \dfrac{(x+\Delta x)}{x}}{\Delta x} \tag{91}$$

As Eq. (91) is written, it is by no means evident what if any limit is approached as Δx approaches zero. However, by a certain amount of algebraic manipulation as indicated below, we can make the situation clearer.

$$\frac{\Delta y}{\Delta x} = \frac{x}{x}\frac{1}{\Delta x}\log_b\left(1+\frac{\Delta x}{x}\right) = \frac{1}{x}\frac{x}{\Delta x}\log_b\left(1+\frac{\Delta x}{x}\right)$$

From Sec. 10·5 we may write

$$\frac{\Delta y}{\Delta x} = \frac{1}{x}\log_b\left(1+\frac{\Delta x}{x}\right)^{x/\Delta x}$$

If we let

$$m = \frac{x}{\Delta x}$$

we may write

$$\frac{\Delta y}{\Delta x} = \frac{1}{x} \log_b \left(1 + \frac{1}{m}\right)^m$$

Now as Δx approaches zero, m becomes larger and larger without limit. We have had occasion (see Sec. 11·3) to present an argument showing that

$$\lim_{m \to 0} \left(1 + \frac{1}{m}\right)^m = 2.7183 \ldots = e$$

Thus we may write

$$\lim_{x \to 0} \frac{\Delta y}{\Delta x} = \frac{dy}{dx} = \frac{1}{x} \log_b e$$

In Sec. 10·11 we showed that

$$\log_e e = 1$$

Therefore, if we choose to use the natural logarithm system, we find that if

$$y = \ln x$$

then

$$\frac{dy}{dx} = \frac{1}{x}$$

or

$$\frac{d(\ln x)}{dx} = \frac{1}{x} \tag{92}$$

and

$$\frac{d(k \ln x + C)}{dx} = \frac{k}{x} \qquad x \neq 0 \tag{93}$$

example 59 Differentiate the function $y = \ln x^6$.

$$y = 6 \ln x$$

and

$$\frac{dy}{dx} = \frac{6}{x}$$

EXERCISE 11

Differentiate the following:

1. $y = \ln x$
2. $y = 3 \ln x$
3. $y = \ln x^5$
4. $y = \ln \theta^6 - 3 \sin \theta + e^\theta$
5. $y = \ln 6x - \ln (5/x^2)$
6. $y = 2 \ln x - 3 \ln x + \ln x - ⅕ \sin x + 10e^x$
7. $y = 15 \ln x^{10}$

25·15 The derivative of the natural and common logarithm of u. If

$$y = \ln u \tag{94}$$

and u is the value of a differentiable function of x, we may from Eqs. (92) and (31) write

$$\frac{dy}{dx} = \frac{1}{u}\frac{du}{dx} \tag{95}$$

or

$$\frac{d(\ln u)}{dx} = \frac{1}{u}\frac{du}{dx} \tag{96}$$

and we may write

$$\frac{d(k \ln u + C)}{dx} = \frac{k}{u}\frac{du}{dx} \qquad 0 < u \tag{97}$$

From Eq. (5), page 254, we observe that

$$\log u = 0.4343 \ln u$$

Therefore

$$\frac{d(k \log u + C)}{dx} = \frac{0.4343k}{u}\frac{du}{dx} \tag{98}$$

example 60 Differentiate the function $y = \log x^6$.

Following Eq. (98),

$$y = 0.4343 \ln x^6$$

or

$$y = 0.4343(6) \ln x = 2.6058 \ln x$$

Therefore

$$\frac{dy}{dx} = \frac{2.6058}{x}$$

example 61 If $y = 5 \ln (x^2 - 7)$, following Eq. (96)

$$\frac{dy}{dx} = \frac{5}{x^2 - 7} 2x = \frac{10x}{x^2 - 7}$$

example 62 If $y = \ln [1/(1 - x^2)]$, find dy/dx.

First we may rearrange the expression $\ln [1/(1 - x^2)]$, obtaining

$$\ln 1 - \ln (1 - x^2) = 0 - \ln (1 - x^2) = - \ln (1 - x^2)$$

Then, if $y = - \ln (1 - x^2)$,

$$\frac{dy}{dx} = -\frac{1}{1 - x^2}(-2x) = \frac{2x}{1 - x^2}$$

example 63 If $y = \log_{10} [(4 - x^2)/(6 - 2x)]$, find dy/dx.

We may convert to the base e as follows:

$$y = 0.4343[\ln (4 - x^2) - \ln (6 - 2x)]$$

Then

$$\frac{dy}{dx} = 0.4343\left[\frac{1}{4 - x^2}(-2x) - \frac{1}{6 - 2x}(-2)\right] = 0.4343\left(\frac{2x}{x^2 - 4} + \frac{2}{6 - 2x}\right)$$

example 64 If $y = \ln^2 (25 - x^2)$, find dy/dx.

$$y = [\ln (25 - x^2)]^2$$

$$\frac{dy}{dx} = 2[\ln (25 - x^2)]\frac{1}{25 - x^2}(-2x) = \frac{4x \ln (25 - x^2)}{x^2 - 25}$$

EXERCISE 12

Differentiate the following:

1. $y = \ln (x^2 + 2)$
2. $y = \ln \sqrt{x^2 - 1}$
3. $y = \ln (x^2 + 3)^4$
4. $y = \ln (1/x)$
5. $z = \ln \sqrt[3]{4 - 3x}$
6. $z = \ln \dfrac{1}{4 - y}$
7. $y = \log (4 - x^2)$
8. $y = \log (4 - x)^2$
9. $y = \log \dfrac{1}{\sqrt{9 - x^2}}$
10. $z = \log \dfrac{2x + 5}{x - 3}$
11. $y = \log \dfrac{4x^2 - 9}{2x + 3}$
12. $y = \ln \left(x - \dfrac{1}{x}\right)$
13. $z = \ln^2 (x^3 - 8)$
14. $y = \ln^4 \sqrt{9 - x^2}$
15. $y = \log \sin (\theta + \pi)$
16. $y = \log \cos \left(2\theta - \dfrac{\pi}{2}\right)$

25·16 The derivative of e^x

If

$$y = e^x \tag{99}$$

where e is the base of natural logarithms, then from Eq. (1), page 209,

$$x = \ln y$$

Since both members of this equation are equal for all permissible values of the variables involved, the derivatives of both members with respect to x must be equal.

Differentiating both members with respect to x, we obtain on the left

$$\frac{dx}{dx} = 1 \qquad \text{(see Example 15)}$$

and on the right

$$\frac{d(\ln y)}{dx} = \frac{1}{y}\frac{dy}{dx} \qquad \text{[see Eq. (96)]}$$

Consequently we may write

$$1 = \frac{1}{y}\frac{dy}{dx} \tag{100}$$

or
$$\frac{dy}{dx} = y \tag{101}$$

By substituting Eq. (99) in Eq. (101) we obtain

$$\frac{dy}{dx} = e^x$$

or
$$\frac{d(e^x)}{dx} = e^x \tag{102}$$

25 · 17 The derivative of e^u

If
$$y = e^u$$

and u is the value of a differentiable function of x, we may from Eqs. (31) and (102) write

$$\frac{dy}{dx} = e^u \frac{du}{dx} \tag{103}$$

or
$$\frac{d(e^u)}{dx} = e^u \frac{du}{dx} \tag{104}$$

and we may write

$$\frac{d(ke^u + C)}{dx} = ke^u \frac{du}{dx} \tag{105}$$

example 65 If $y = 3e^{1/x}$, find dy/dx.

According to Eq. (105),

$$\frac{dy}{dx} = 3e^{1/x}\left(-\frac{1}{x^2}\right) = -\frac{3e^{1/x}}{x^2}$$

example 66 If $y = (3e^{\sqrt{x}})^2$, find dy/dx.

Squaring, as indicated, we obtain

$$y = 9e^{2\sqrt{x}}$$

Hence

$$\frac{dy}{dx} = 9e^{2\sqrt{x}}(2)\left(\frac{1}{2}\right)\left(\frac{1}{\sqrt{x}}\right) = \frac{9e^{2\sqrt{x}}}{\sqrt{x}}$$

example 67 Find the derivative of $y = A_1e^{k_1x} + A_2e^{k_2x}$.

Following Eq. (105),

$$\frac{dy}{dx} = A_1k_1e^{k_1x} + A_2k_2e^{k_2x}$$

example 68 Find the derivative of $z = A_1k_1e^{k_1x} + A_2k_2e^{k_2x}$.

Following Eq. (105),

$$\frac{dz}{dx} = A_1k_1^2e^{k_1x} + A_2k_2^2e^{k_2x}$$

EXERCISE 13

Differentiate:

1. $y = e^{5x^2}$
2. $y = e^{\sqrt{x}}$
3. $y = e^{x+8}$
4. $y = e^{(2-x)/x}$
5. $y = e^{\sqrt{1-x}}$
6. $y = \sin e^t$

7. The graph shown in Fig. 24·24 was plotted from the equation $T = 50e^{-0.2t}$ where T is the temperature difference between a warm body and its surroundings and t is time in minutes. Using the above equation rather than the graph:
(a) Find dT/dt when $t = 10$.
(b) Find dt/dT when $t = 10$.
(c) Find dT/dt when $T = 10$.
(d) Find dt/dT when $T = 10$.
(e) Find t when $dT/dt = -5.0°$ per min.
(f) Find T when $dT/dt = -2.5°$ per min.
(g) Find the average rate of change of T with respect to t between $t = 2$ and $t = 8$.
(h) Find the average slope between $t = 6$ and $t = 10$.
(i) Find the average slope between $T = 30$ and $T = 10$.
(j) Find the instantaneous slope at $t = 6$.
(k) Find the instantaneous slope at $T = 30$.
(l) How fast is T changing with t at $t = 10$?

8. From Prob. 7 write the equation for dT/dt in terms of T. If dT/dt were plotted against T, what is the shape of the plot?

9. Sketch the graph of $i = \frac{E}{R}(1 - e^{-Rt/L})$

where $E = 150$ volts
$R = 15$ ohms
$L = 0.75$ henry
$i =$ amperes
$t =$ seconds

This is an equation giving the relation between current and time in a certain series circuit containing inductance and resistance. The inductance is 0.75 henry, the resistance is 15 ohms. A battery of 150 volts is connected across this series combination when $t = 0$. Thereafter the current rises in accordance with the above equation. Compare your sketch with Fig. 24·35.
(a) Find di/dt when $t = 0$.
(b) Find the "maximum" value of current. When will it be reached?
(c) If the current increased at the rate it was increasing when $t = 0$, how long would it take for the current to reach its "maximum" value?

(d) Compare the value found in part (c) with the ratio L/R where L is inductance and R is resistance. This ratio is called the "time constant of the circuit."

(e) Find the rate of change of current with respect to time at frequent points between $t = 0$ and $t = 150$ msec. Plot a graph of di/dt versus i between $t = 0$ and $t = 150$ msec.

Problems 10 and 11 use the symbol ϵ to designate the base of natural logarithms to avoid confusion with the symbol e used here to designate a voltage.

10. In a resistance of r ohms the current i amp is given in terms of the voltage (e volts) by the equation (Ohm's law) $i = e/r$. In a capacitor (C farads) the relation (on discharge) is $i = -C(de/dt)$.
    If $e = E_0\epsilon^{-t/Cr}$, determine equations for i in terms of t for the case of a resistance and for the case of a capacitor (C, r, and E are constants).
    Sketch graphs of e as a function of t/Cr, i as a function of t/Cr for both the resistance and capacitor cases.
11. If the current in an electric circuit is given by $i = I\epsilon^{-at}$, where I and a are positive constants, determine the length of the subtangent to this curve at the time $t = 0$. (The subtangent is the difference between the x intercept of the tangent and the abscissa of its point of tangency.)

REMARK: This result is of importance in electrical engineering. It is called the *time constant* T of the electric circuit and has the following properties:

1. It is the length of the subtangent at $t = 0$.
2. It is the time required for the ordinate (current) to change from an arbitrary value A to the value A/ϵ (a decrease of about 60 per cent). In an interval equal to $3T$ the ordinate decreases from A to A/ϵ^3, that is, to about 5 per cent of the value at A. Five time constants of time would reduce the current to about 0.67 per cent of the value at the beginning of that time interval. Since this last result is often negligible as compared with the starting value by ordinary standards of engineering accuracy, the following statement is apparent: "The duration of the current, if of exponential form, is five time constants."
3. The time constant is the time it would take i to reduce to zero if i decreased at a constant rate equal to the rate at which i is decreasing when $t = 0$.
4. The area of the rectangle whose base is the time constant and whose altitude is along the i axis from $i = 0$ to $i = I$ is equal to the area under the curve $i = I\epsilon^{-at}$ in the first quadrant.

Prove that properties 2 and 3 are true. Property 4 can be established after you have studied integral calculus.

12. A catenary is the curve that a cable assumes when hanging between two supports. If the two supports are of equal height and are at $x = -a$ and

$x = +a$, the equation for the curve is

$$y = c + k \cosh \frac{x}{a} = c + \left(\frac{k}{2}\right)(e^{x/a} + e^{-x/a})$$

Determine an expression for the angle that the cable makes with the vertical support at $x = +a$.

25·18 The derivative of a^x

If

$$y = a^x \tag{106}$$

where a is any positive real number other than 1, then from Eq. (4), page 213,

$$x \ln a = \ln y$$

Now remembering that $\ln a$ is a constant, we may as in Sec. 25·16 differentiate both members of the above equation with respect to x, obtaining on the left

$$\frac{d[x(\ln a)]}{dx} = \ln a$$

and on the right

$$\frac{d(\ln y)}{dx} = \frac{1}{y}\frac{dy}{dx}$$

or

$$\ln a = \frac{1}{y}\frac{dy}{dx}$$

Thus

$$\frac{dy}{dx} = y \ln a \tag{107}$$

By substituting Eq. (106) in Eq. (107) we obtain

$$\frac{dy}{dx} = a^x \ln a$$

or

$$\frac{d(a^x)}{dx} = a^x \ln a \qquad 0 < a,\ a \neq 1 \tag{\textbf{108}}$$

25·19 The derivative of a^u

If

$$y = a^u \tag{109}$$

and u is the value of a differentiable function of x, we may from Eq. (108) write

$$\frac{dy}{dx} = a^u(\ln a)\frac{du}{dx} \tag{110}$$

or

$$\frac{d(a^u)}{dx} = a^u(\ln a)\frac{du}{dx} \tag{\textbf{111}}$$

and

$$\frac{d(ka^u + C)}{dx} = ka^u(\ln a)\frac{du}{dx} \qquad \textbf{(112)}$$

example 69 If $y = (3^{x^2+2x})/4$, find dy/dx.

According to Eq. (112),

$$\frac{dy}{dx} = \frac{1}{4}3^{x^2+2x}(2x + 2)\ln 3$$

$$= \frac{x + 1}{2}(3)^{x^2+2x}\ln 3$$

example 70 If $y = 3 \ln^x 4$ this equation can be rewritten as

$$y = 3\,(\ln 4)^x$$

Now following Eq. (112),

$$\frac{dy}{dx} = (3 \ln^x 4)(1)[\ln(\ln 4)]$$

By using some of the principles illustrated in this and the preceding three sections we can differentiate many nonlogarithmic functions which would be rather awkward or even impossible to differentiate otherwise.

example 71 Differentiate $y = x^x$ where $x > 0$.

Observe that in this case both the base and the exponent are variables. None of the differentiation formulas previously given cover this case. However, by writing the given equation in an equivalent logarithmic form we obtain

$$\ln y = x \ln x \qquad x > 0$$

Then
$$\frac{1}{y}\frac{dy}{dx} = x\frac{1}{x} + \ln x = 1 + \ln x$$

or
$$\frac{dy}{dx} = y(1 + \ln x) = x^x(1 + \ln x)$$

example 72 Differentiate

$$y = x^{x^2} \qquad x > 0$$

Again, none of the differentiation formulas previously given will apply since both the base and the exponent are variables. However,

$$\ln y = x^2 \ln x \qquad x > 0$$

and
$$\frac{1}{y}\frac{dy}{dx} = x^2\frac{1}{x} + (\ln x)(2x) = x + 2x \ln x$$

and
$$\frac{dy}{dx} = y(x + 2x \ln x) = x^{x^2}(x + 2x \ln x)$$

example 73 Differentiate

$$y = \sqrt{\frac{x^4 - 1}{x^4 + 1}}$$

Although this function can be differentiated by rules already discussed, it can probably be more easily differentiated by the use of logarithms. We may write

$$\ln y = \frac{1}{2}\ln\frac{x^4 - 1}{x^4 + 1} = \frac{1}{2}[\ln (x^4 - 1) - \ln (x^4 + 1)]$$

$$= \frac{1}{2}\ln (x^4 - 1) - \frac{1}{2}\ln (x^4 + 1)$$

$$\frac{1}{y}\frac{dy}{dx} = \frac{1}{2(x^4 - 1)}(4x^3) - \frac{1}{2(x^4 + 1)}(4x^3)$$

$$= \frac{2x^3}{x^4 - 1} - \frac{2x^3}{x^4 + 1}$$

$$\frac{dy}{dx} = y\left(\frac{2x^3}{x^4 - 1} - \frac{2x^3}{x^4 + 1}\right)$$

$$= y\frac{4x^3}{(x^4 - 1)(x^4 + 1)}$$

$$= \frac{(x^4 - 1)^{1/2}}{(x^4 + 1)^{1/2}}\frac{4x^3}{(x^4 - 1)(x^4 + 1)}$$

$$\frac{dy}{dx} = \frac{4x^3}{\sqrt{x^4 - 1}\,(x^4 + 1)^{3/2}}$$

EXERCISE 14

Differentiate the following by use of Eq. (112):

1. $y = a^x$ where a is constant
2. $y = a^{1/2}$ where a is constant
3. $z = 2^{\sqrt{x}}$
4. $y = 5^{e(x+1)}$ where e is constant

Differentiate the following by rewriting the given equation in an equivalent logarithmic form.

5. $y = kx^n$
6. $y = kuv$ where u and v are functions of x
7. $y = k\frac{u}{v}$ where u and v are functions of x
8. $y = ke^u$ where u is a function of x
9. $y = ka^u$ where u is a function of x
10. $y = a^{3x^2}$
11. $y = x^2 \cdot 3^x$
12. $y = ae^{-b^2x^2}$
13. $y = \sqrt{(3t^2 + 2)/(t^2 - t)}$ (Compare with Example 35, page 685.)
14. $y = \frac{3e^{(3x^2-1)}}{x\sqrt{x}}$
15. $y = \frac{x}{x^3 - 2}$

16. $y = 3x^2(x^3 - 1)^4$

17. $y = \dfrac{x^3}{x^5 + 3}$

18. $y = e^{2x}\sqrt{1 - x^3}$

19. $y = \dfrac{e^x}{4 + x}$

20. $y = x^{2\sqrt{x}}$

21. $y = \sqrt{x} \cdot e^{2x}$

22. $y = (x + 2)^x$

23. $y = x^{\sin x}$

EXERCISE 15

Differentiate the following:

1. $y = e^x \cos 2x$
2. $y = 3e^{-t} \sin t$
3. $y = \sin 3\theta \cos 3\theta$
4. $y = (x^2 + 3x) \ln x^2$
5. $y = x \ln x - x^2$
6. $y = (2x^3 + 5)^{2/3}\, x^{-1/5}$
7. $z = 3 \sin 2\phi \tan 4\phi$
8. $w = 5 \cos^2 2\phi \cos(-2\phi)$
9. $s = 5 \tan^2 x \cdot e^{3x^2}$
10. $y = (x^2 - 3)^{1/2} \ln 3x^5$
11. $y = \sqrt{2x^3 + 3x} \sin^2(7x^3 + 5)$
12. $y = \ln x^2 \tan x^2$
13. $y = 3e^{2x} \ln \dfrac{1}{x}$
14. $w = (x^2 + 3)^{1/2} \tan 4x$
15. $y = x^{-1/2} \cos \sqrt{x}$
16. $y = 3 \cos 3\phi \ln(3\phi + 5)$
17. $y = \dfrac{\sin x}{e^{2x}}$
18. $y = \dfrac{e^x + e^{-x}}{e^x - e^{-x}} + x$
19. $y = -\dfrac{x}{9\sqrt{x^2 - 9}}$
20. $y = \dfrac{\sin 3\phi}{\cos(\phi/2)}$
21. $y = \dfrac{x^2 + 3x}{\ln x^2}$
22. $y = \dfrac{5 \tan^2 x}{e^{3x^2}}$
23. $w = \dfrac{(x^2 + 3)^{1/2}}{\tan 4x}$
24. $y = \dfrac{3e^{2x}}{\ln(1/x)}$
25. $y = \dfrac{3 \cos 3x}{\ln(3x - 6)}$
26. $y = \dfrac{(x^2 + 5x)^{1/2}}{\ln 3x^5}$

Differentiate the following in preparation for Exercise 19:

27. $y = \dfrac{100x}{(x + 0.2)^2}$
28. $y = 5x(x^2 + 100)^{-3/2}$
29. $y = \dfrac{Ax}{Ax + C + Bx^2}$ where A, B, and C are constants
30. $y = \dfrac{A}{B} \cos \phi \sin^2 \phi$
31. $y = \dfrac{100x - 5x^2}{x + 0.8}$
32. $y = 3 \sin 3t + \dfrac{3 \sin 6t}{\sqrt{A - \sin^2 3t}}$ where A is a constant

The following problems are inserted here as a general review of differentiation formulas.

EXERCISE 16

Differentiate and simplify the following:

1. $y = \ln \sin x$
2. $y = \ln \cos x$
3. $q = \sin^3 5x$
4. $y = \sqrt{\sin 4x^2}$
5. $y = -\dfrac{1}{ax} + \dfrac{b}{a^2} \ln \left(\dfrac{a + bx}{x}\right)$
6. $y = \ln (x + \sqrt{x^2 - a^2})$
7. $y = \sqrt{x^2 + a^2} + \dfrac{a^2}{\sqrt{x^2 + a^2}}$
8. $y = \sin 3\theta \cos 3\theta$
9. $y = \dfrac{x}{x^3 - 4}$
10. $y = (x^2 + 3x) \ln x^2$
11. $y = \dfrac{\sin x}{e^{2x}} + e^{2x}$
12. $y = 5 \ln e^{2x} - e^2$
13. $y = \dfrac{e^x + e^{-x}}{e^x - e^{-x}}$
14. $y = \log (x^2 - 4x + 4)$
15. $y = \dfrac{5x}{(x - 1)^2} - \dfrac{5}{x - 1}$
16. $y = \dfrac{\sqrt{1 - x^2}}{1 - x}$
17. $y = \dfrac{\sqrt{x^2 - 1}}{x}$
18. $y = x \ln x - x$
19. $y = \frac{1}{2}[x\sqrt{x^2 + a^2} + a^2 \ln (x + \sqrt{x^2 + a^2})]$
20. $y = -\dfrac{x^2}{9\sqrt{x^2 - 9}}$
21. $y = \dfrac{x}{16\sqrt{16 - x^2}}$
22. $y = \dfrac{\sqrt{x^2 - a^2}}{a^2 x}$
23. $y = -\dfrac{\sqrt{8x - 2x^2}}{4x}$
24. $y = -\frac{1}{5}(x^2 + 6)(9 - x^2)^{3/2}$
25. $y = \frac{1}{2}x + \frac{1}{4} \sin 2x$
26. $y = \ln \tan \left(\dfrac{\pi}{4} + \dfrac{x}{2}\right)$
27. $y = \dfrac{x^2}{4} - \dfrac{x \sin 2x}{4} - \dfrac{\cos 2x}{8}$
28. $y = \tan \dfrac{x}{2}$
29. $y = \tan x - x$
30. $y = \frac{1}{2} \tan^2 \theta + \ln \cos \theta$
31. $y = \cos x + x \sin x$

25·20 Repeated differentiation

If we are given

$$y = x^5 - 19.25x^4 + 130x^3 - 352x^2 + 224x + 420 \tag{113}$$

which we shall call the *primary* equation, we may differentiate to obtain dy/dx or y'. Thus

$$y' = \frac{dy}{dx} = 5x^4 - 77x^3 + 390x^2 - 704x + 224 \tag{114}$$

This is called the *first* derivative. We can differentiate again to obtain the *second* derivative which we shall designate as y'' or d^2y/dx^2. Thus

$$y'' = \frac{d^2y}{dx^2} = 20x^3 - 231x^2 + 780x - 704 \tag{115}$$

We can differentiate a third time to obtain the *third* derivative designated as y''' or d^3y/dx^3. Thus

$$y''' = \frac{d^3y}{dx^3} = 60x^2 - 462x + 780 \qquad (116)$$

The *fourth* derivative is

$$\frac{d^4y}{dx^4} = 120x - 462 \qquad (117)$$

the *fifth* derivative is

$$\frac{d^5y}{dx^5} = 120 \qquad (118)$$

and the *sixth* derivative is

$$\frac{d^6y}{dx^6} = 0 \qquad (119)$$

In Fig. 25·17 graph A is plotted from Eq. (113), graph B from Eq. (114), graph C from Eq. (115), graph D from Eq. (116), and graph E from Eq. (117).

EXERCISE 17

Solve the following problems by direct reading of the graphs shown in Fig. 25·17 rather than by algebraic methods. Observe the vertical "tie lines" connecting corresponding points on successive curves.

1. Read the value of x on curve B for which curve A has a maximum. What is the sign of the second derivative for this value of x? Is the first derivative in this region increasing or decreasing?
2. Read the value of x on curve B for which curve A has a minimum. What is the sign of the second derivative for this value of x? Is the first derivative increasing or decreasing in this region?
3. Read the value of x on curve C for which curve B has a maximum. What is the sign of the third derivative for this value of x? Is the second derivative in this region increasing or decreasing?
4. Read the values of x on curve C for which curve B has a minimum. What are the signs of the third derivative for these values of x? Is the second derivative in this region increasing or decreasing?
5. Read the value of x on curve D for which curve C has a maximum. What is the sign of the fourth derivative for this value of x? Is the third derivative increasing or decreasing in this region?
6. Read the value of x on curve D for which curve C has a minimum. What is the sign of the fourth derivative for this value of x? Is the third derivative increasing or decreasing in this region?
7. For what values of x does graph A have a maximum slope? A minimum slope?

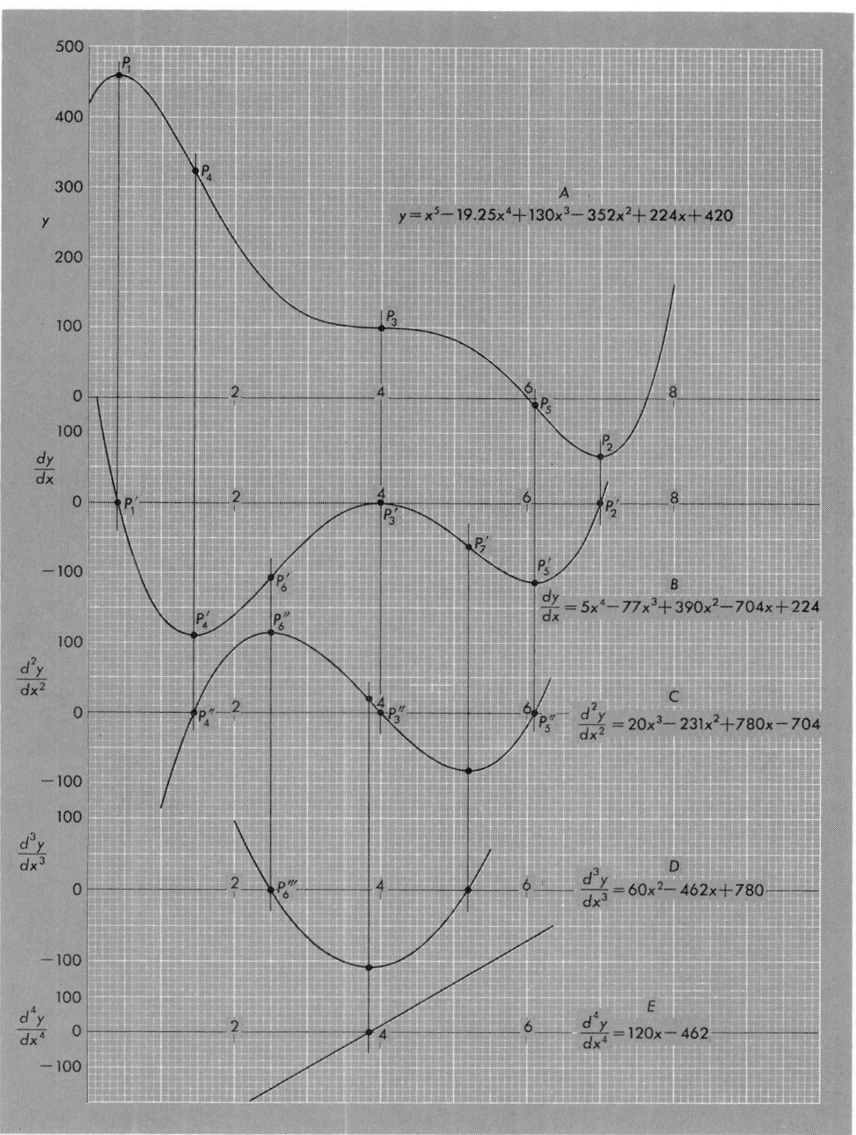

fig. 25·17

8. For what values of x does graph B have a maximum slope? A minimum slope?
9. For what values of x does graph C have a maximum slope? A minimum slope?
10. For what values of x does graph D have a maximum slope? A minimum slope?

25·21 Tests for maxima and minima by use of the second derivative

From Exercise 17 we note that at least for the functions involved, if a maximum occurs at x_m, then the sign of the second derivative at x_m is *negative.* If a minimum occurs at x_m, then the sign of the second derivative at x_m is positive.

This is actually a general principle. Without formal proof we shall assume that $y = f(x)$ has a relative maximum at $x = x_m$, provided that $dy/dx = 0$ at $x = x_m$ and that $d^2y/dx^2 < 0$ when $x = x_m$. Also, $f(x)$ will have a relative minimum at $x = x_m$, provided that $dy/dx = 0$ at $x = x_m$ and $d^2y/dx^2 > 0$ at $x = x_m$.

Sometimes it is more convenient to test critical values for maxima and minima by use of the second derivative rather than by the methods illustrated in Sec. 25·8.

example 74 Find the value of x at P_1, P_2, and P_3 in curve A of Fig. 25·17. At these points the curve has a zero slope.

The ordinate of curve A is given by

$$y = x^5 - 19.25x^4 + 130x^3 - 342x^2 + 224x + 420 \qquad (120)$$

Then

$$\frac{dy}{dx} = 5x^4 - 77x^3 + 390x^2 - 704x + 224 \qquad (121)$$

Zero slopes occur for values of x such that

$$0 = 5x^4 - 77x^3 + 390x^2 - 704x + 224 \qquad (122)$$

The algebra involved in solving Eq. (122) is quite laborious, even though elementary. However, from curve B the roots of this equation appear to be 4, 7, and 0.4. That these roots are precise can be verified by direct substitution in Eq. (122).

In Example 75 below we shall identify these roots as the abscissas of maximum points or minimum points, or as points of inflection.

example 75 By means of the second derivative, identify the roots found in Example 74 as values of x for which y is either a maximum or a minimum or for which x is the abscissa of a point of inflection.

The second derivative of the primary equation is [see Eq. (115)]

$$y'' = 20x^3 - 231x^2 + 780x - 704 \qquad (123)$$

When $x = 4$,

$$y'' = 20(4)^3 - 231(4)^2 + 780(4) - 704 \qquad (124)$$

$$y'' = 1{,}280 - 3{,}696 + 3{,}120 - 704 = 4{,}400 - 4{,}400 = 0 \qquad (125)$$

Since the second derivative is zero, its sign is neither positive nor negative, and $x = 4$ corresponds to neither a maximum nor a minimum. In this case it corresponds to a point of inflection.

When $x = 0.4$,

$$y'' = 20(0.4)^3 - 231(0.4)^2 + 780(0.4) - 704 \tag{126}$$
$$y'' = 1.280 - 36.96 + 312.00 - 704.00 \tag{127}$$
$$y'' = -427.68 \tag{128}$$

Since the sign of the second derivative is negative, $x = 0.4$ is the abscissa of a maximum point.

When $x = 7$,

$$y'' = 20(7)^3 - 231(7)^2 + 780(7) - 704 \tag{129}$$
$$y'' = 6{,}860 - 11{,}319 + 5{,}460 - 704 = +297 \tag{130}$$

Since the sign of the second derivative is positive, $x = 7$ is the abscissa of a minimum point.

example 76 Find the values of x for which the slope of curve A of Fig. 25·17 is a maximum or minimum. Remember that the ordinate of curve B is numerically equal to the slope of curve B.

The ordinate of curve B is given by

$$y' = \frac{dy}{dx} = 5x^4 - 77x^3 + 390x^2 - 704x + 224 \tag{131}$$

and

$$y'' = \frac{d^2y}{dx^2} = 20x^3 - 231x^2 + 780x - 704 \tag{132}$$

The slope of curve A may be a maximum or minimum when

$$0 = 20x^3 - 231x^2 + 780x - 704 \tag{133}$$

The algebra in solving Eq. (133) is quite laborious although elementary. However, it can be found that $x = 4$, $x = 1.440343$, and $x = 6.109657$ are all solutions of Eq. (133).

example 77 By means of the second derivative, identify the roots found in Example 76 as values of x for which y is either a maximum or a minimum or for which x is the abscissa of a point of inflection.

Considering

$$y' = 5x^4 - 77x^3 + 390x^2 - 704x + 224 \tag{134}$$

as the primary equation for these two examples, the second derivative of this primary equation is

$$\frac{d^3y}{dx^3} = 60x^2 - 462x + 780 \tag{135}$$

When $x = 4$,

$$\frac{d^3y}{dx^3} = 60 \cdot 16 - 462 \cdot 4 + 780 = -108 \tag{136}$$

Since the sign of the second derivative of the primary equation is negative, $x = 4$ is the abscissa of a maximum point on the graph.

When $x = 1.440343$, the substitution would be quite laborious. However, as a practical matter 1.4 or 1.5 would probably be a good enough approximation for our purpose.

Let us use $x = 1.5$. Then

$$\frac{d^3y}{dx^3} = 60 \cdot 2.25 - 462 \cdot 1.5 + 780 = +222$$

Since the second derivative of the primary equation is positive, $x = 1.440343$ is the abscissa of a minimum point on the graph.

Again, when $x = 6.109657$ the substitution would be quite laborious. However, as a practical matter in this case $x = 6.1$ is probably a satisfactory approximation for our purpose.

Let us use $x = 6.1$. Then

$$\frac{d^3y}{dx^3} = 60 \cdot 37.21 - 462 \cdot 6.1 + 780 = +194.4$$

Since the second derivative of the primary equation is positive, $x = 6.109657$ is the abscissa of a minimum point on the graph.

example 78 If y is given by Eq. (120), find the value of x for which d^2y/dx^2 is a maximum or a minimum.

In this case

$$\frac{d^2y}{dx^2} = 20x^3 - 231x^2 + 780x - 704 \qquad \text{(see graph } C \text{ in Fig. 25}\cdot\text{17)}$$

The above equation will be a maximum or minimum when $d^3y/dx^3 = 0$.

$$\frac{d^3y}{dx^3} = 60x^2 - 462x + 780 \tag{137}$$

Set the above equation to zero, and solve for x.

$$0 = 60x^2 - 462x + 780$$

or

$$0 = x^2 - 7.7x + 13$$

and

$$x = \frac{7.7 \pm \sqrt{(7.7)^2 - 4 \times 13}}{2} \tag{138}$$

$$= \frac{7.7 \pm \sqrt{59.29 - 52}}{2} \tag{139}$$

$$= \frac{7.7 \pm \sqrt{7.29}}{2} = \frac{7.7 \pm 2.7}{2} = \frac{5}{2}, \frac{10.4}{2}$$

$$x = 2.5 \text{ (max)}, 5.2 \text{ (min)}$$

The student will observe that the second derivative of the primary curve in this problem is $120x - 462$. When $x = 2.5$, the sign of this quantity is negative. When $x = 5.2$, the sign of the same quantity is positive. Consequently, $x = 5.2$ corresponds to a minimum, and $x = 2.5$ corresponds to a maximum.

EXERCISE 18

In Probs. 1 through 17, sketch the graph of the given equation. Then

(a) Sketch the graph of the first and second derivatives if they exist.

(b) Find the value of the independent variable for which the primary curve has a maximum, a minimum, or a point of inflection if such exists.

(c) Identify the critical values found in (b) above by means of the second derivative where practical.

(d) Find the slope of the primary curve for each point of inflection.

1. $y = \frac{4}{3}\pi x^3$ $\qquad 0 \leq x \leq +10$
2. $y = x^3 - x + 1$ $\qquad -1 \leq x \leq +1$
3. $y = x^3 - 6x^2 + 8$ $\qquad -1 \leq x \leq +5$
4. $y = x^4 - 4x^2 - 21$ $\qquad -3 \leq x \leq +3$
5. $z = 7x^2 - 8\sqrt{x}$ $\qquad 0 \leq x \leq +2$
6. $y = 3x^2 - 5x + 7 - \dfrac{4}{x}$ $\qquad -2 \leq x \leq +2$
7. $y = x^2 - \dfrac{1}{x^2}$ $\qquad -3 \leq x \leq +3$
8. $y = \dfrac{4x}{x^2 + 1}$ $\qquad -3 \leq x \leq +3$
9. $y = \cos 2x$ $\qquad 0 \leq x \leq +\pi$
10. $y = \sin x + \cos 2x$ $\qquad 0 \leq x \leq 2\pi$
11. $y = \frac{1}{4} \cos^2 \theta + \sin^2 \theta$ $\qquad 0 \leq \theta \leq 2\pi$
12. $y = \sin^2 \theta$ $\qquad 0 \leq \theta \leq 2\pi$
13. $y = \ln (2/x)$ $\qquad 0 < x \leq +3$
14. $y = \ln x^4$ $\qquad 0 < x \leq +3$
15. $y = x \ln x - x$ $\qquad 0 \leq x \leq +4$
16. $y = 3e^{2t}$ $\qquad -0.5 \leq t \leq +1$
17. $y = e^{-0.1x} \sin x$ $\qquad 0 \leq x \leq 2\pi$
18. $y = \sin 2x + 2 \sin x$ $\qquad 0 \leq x \leq 2\pi$

EXERCISE 19

1. If the height of a ball at any time t is given by the equation $h = 72t - 16t^2$, find the velocity and acceleration at any time.
2. Repeat Prob. 1, if $h = 120 + 72t^2 + t^3$. How fast is the acceleration changing at $t = 2$?

3. The distance traveled by a moving object is $d = 20t^4 - t^5$. Find when the acceleration is changing most rapidly.
4. The distance traveled by a moving object is given by the equation $d = 10t^3 - t^4$. Find when the speed is a maximum. Also find when the acceleration is a maximum.
5. A solenoid has a fixed internal diameter D and has a laminated core of the form shown in Fig. 25·18. Determine the dimension s and t of the core so that the cross-section area of the core will be a maximum.
6. The electric field intensity on the axis of a uniformly charged ring is found to be $E = Qx/(x^2 + a^2)^{3/2}$, where Q is the total charge on the ring. Also, a and Q are constants (see Fig. 25·19).
   (a) Sketch E as a function of x.
   (b) At what value of x is E a maximum?
   (c) What is the value of x which makes d^2E/dx^2 zero?
7. Find the dimensions of the largest rectangle that can be inscribed in a semicircle of diameter 24 ft.

   Referring to Fig. 25·20, the area of this rectangle can be expressed as

(a) $$A = 2h\sqrt{144 - h^2}$$

or

(b) $$A = (12 \sin \theta)(12 \cos \theta) \cdot 2$$

Find the required dimensions by use of (a) and again by use of (b).

fig. 25·18

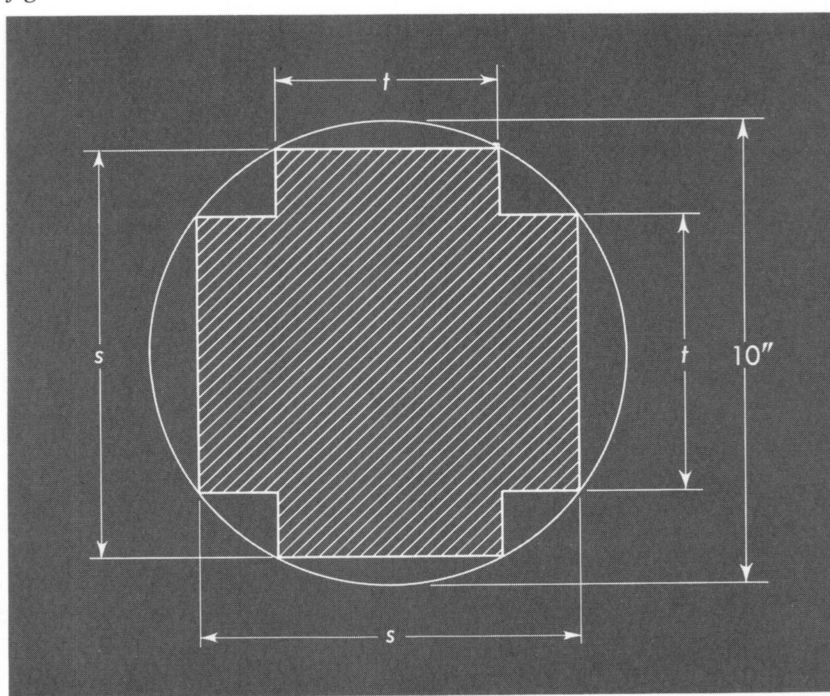

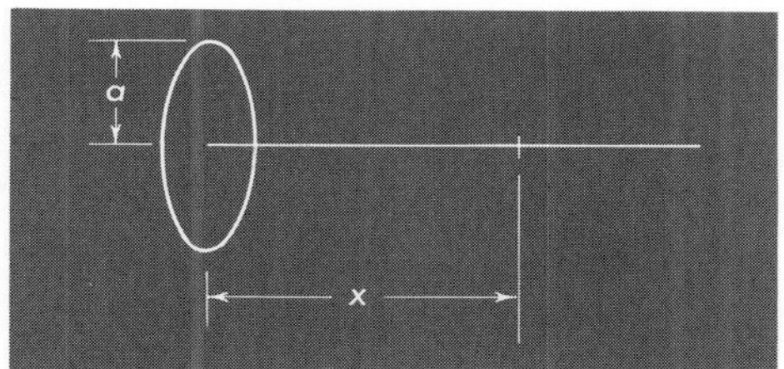

fig. 25·19

fig. 25·20

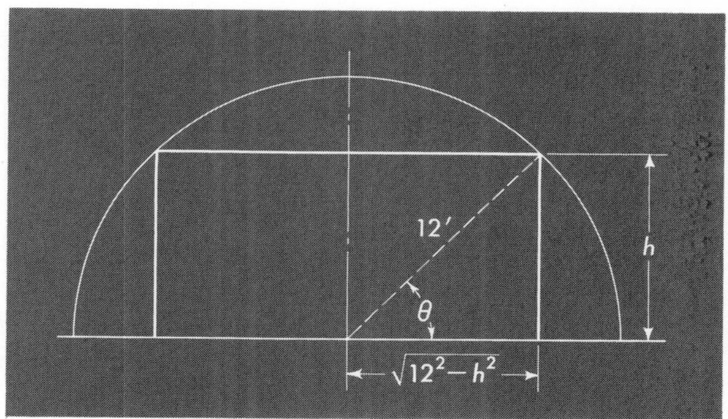

8. Find the dimensions of the largest rectangle which can be inscribed in a circle 20 in. in diameter.
9. The beam in Fig. 25·21 supports a uniform load of w lb per ft of beam. If axes are chosen as indicated, the equation of the curve of the beam is

$$EIy = \frac{wLx^3}{12} - \frac{wx^4}{24} - \frac{wL^3x}{24}$$

where E, I, w, and L = positive constants.

Studies of the strength of materials show that the bending moment is given by $M = EI(d^2y/dx^2)$, the shear by $V = dM/dx$, and the load

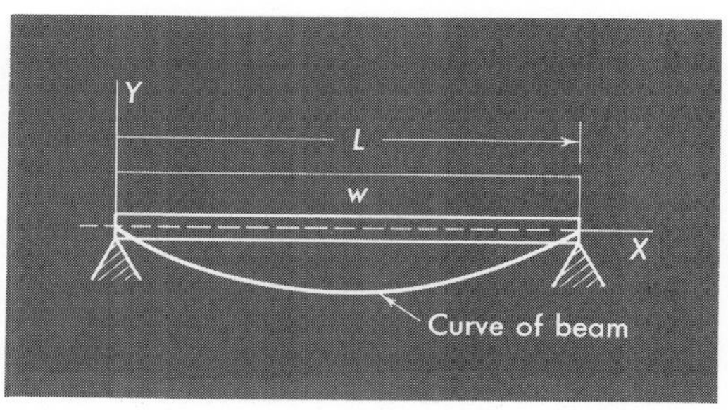

fig. 25·21

by $EI(d^4y/dx^4)$. Determine M, V, and $EI(d^4y/dx^4)$ for this beam, and sketch these three curves (these variables as functions of x) on the same graph.

10. The power lost in resistor R (see Fig. 25·22) is given by the equation

$$P = \frac{(10 - 0.2i)^2}{R}$$

where
$$i = \frac{10}{R + 0.2}$$

Find the value of R such that the power dissipated in R is a maximum.

11. A source of light is to be placed directly over the center of a circular table of diameter 20 ft. The intensity of illumination at any point on the circumference of the table varies directly as the cosine of the angle between the vertical and the light ray, and inversely as the square of the distance of the point from the light. How high should the light be placed above the table to obtain the maximum intensity at the edge of the table?
    (a) Express the light intensity I in terms of the height h and a constant of proportionality k before differentiating.
    (b) Express I in terms of trigonometric functions of the angle ϕ between the vertical and the light ray and a proportionality constant k before differentiating.

12. The turning effect of a ship's rudder may be shown theoretically to be $k \sin^2 \theta \cos \theta$, where θ is the angle the rudder makes with the keel and k is a constant. At what value of θ is the rudder most effective?

13. The power output of an electric generator is EI, where E is the constant terminal voltage and I the current. The power loss in the generator is the sum of a constant component P_0 and a variable component (due to heating loss) I^2R, R being the internal resistance of the generator. The efficiency of the generator may be written

$$\eta = \frac{\text{output}}{\text{input}} = \frac{\text{output}}{\text{output} + \text{losses}} = \frac{EI}{EI + P_0 + I^2R}$$

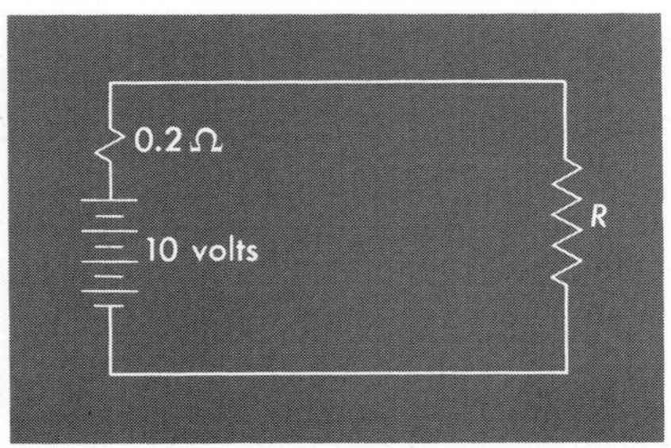

fig. 25·22

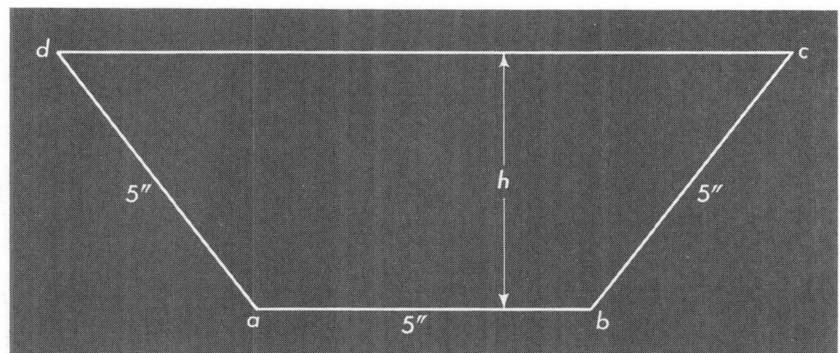

fig. 25·23

Determine the maximum value for the efficiency as the current I varies and express the result in terms of E, R, and P_0. Also give the relation between the fixed and variable losses (P_0 and I^2R) when the efficiency is a maximum.

14. Given a sphere of radius 10 in., find:
    (a) The altitude of an inscribed right cylinder of maximum volume.
    (b) The altitude of an inscribed right cylinder of maximum total surface.
    (c) The altitude of an inscribed right cone of maximum volume.
15. Write the equation for the area of the trapezoid shown in Fig. 25·23 in terms of h, and find h to give a maximum area.
16. It has been determined that a painter will paint 100 sq ft of surface per hour at the beginning of a day and that his rate decreases by 10 sq ft per hr as the day progresses. Allowing 0.4 hr for work preparations and another 0.4 hr to clean up at the end of the day, what total time, including preparation and clean up, will result in a maximum overall square feet per hour?
17. A minor sector is removed from a disk of brass. The remaining major sector is formed into a cone. Find the central angle of the minor sector required to make the capacity of the cone a maximum.
18. It has been determined that the cutting rate of a tool will diminish linearly to 98 per cent of its original value on 1 hr of use. Loss of 0.2 hr operating time occurs each time the tool is sharpened, and 100 hr total time is available for the job. How often during this interval should the tool be sharpened for maximum output?
19. Figure 25·24 shows a crank arm OA, which revolves at the constant rate of ω radians per sec and has a length of r ft. The connecting rod AB has a length of L ft. B is a piston which moves along the horizontal axis.
    (a) Show that $x = r(1 - \cos \omega t) + L - (L^2 - r^2 \sin^2 \omega t)^{1/2}$.
    (b) Expand the binomial to two terms by aid of the binomial theorem and obtain the approximate expression for x:

$$x = r(1 - \cos \omega t) + \left(\frac{r^2}{4L}\right)(1 - \cos 2\omega t)$$

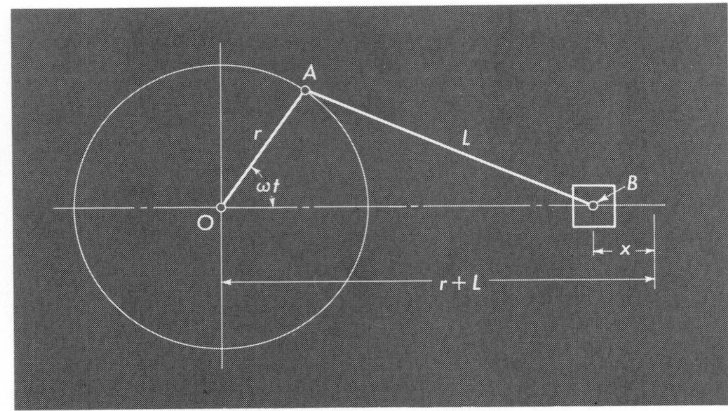

fig. 25·24

(c) Determine dx/dt and d^2x/dt^2, using both the original and the approximate expressions for x.

(d) Tabulate the values for dx/dt and d^2x/dt^2 from both results in (c) when $\omega t = 0$, $\pi/4$, $\pi/2$, π, and $3\pi/2$. Assume that $r = 1$ ft, $L = 5$ ft, and $\omega = ½$ radian per sec.

(e) When is the acceleration of the piston a maximum and hence what is the maximum inertia force which the piston can transmit? (The maximum inertia force is given by $F = ma$, where m is the mass of the piston, and a is the maximum acceleration.) Use the approximate expression for d^2x/dt^2 to answer this question.

20. The mechanism shown in Fig. 25·25 is an air compressor. The displacement of the piston from its position when the crank arm AB is vertical is given by $x = r \cos \omega t$, where r is the length of the crank arm, and the crank arm is rotating at ω radians per sec.

fig. 25·25

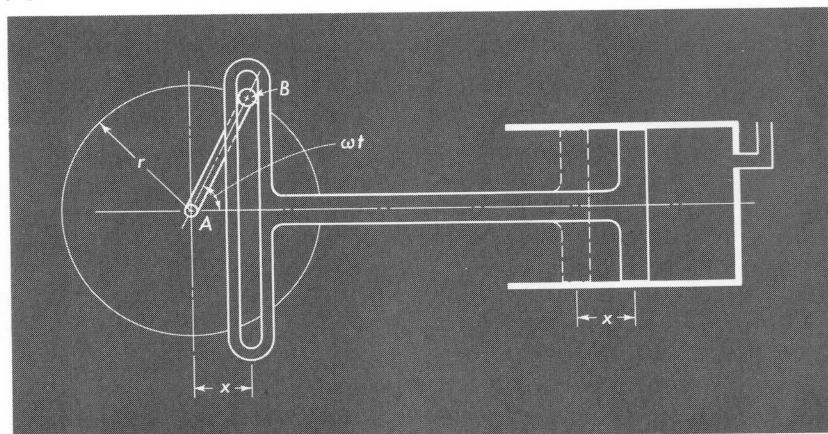

(a) If $r = 0.8$ ft and $\omega = 4\pi$ radians per sec, sketch the space-time, velocity-time, and acceleration-time graphs, and label the amplitude and period of each.
(b) If the weight of the piston and connecting rod is 100 lb, what is the force transmitted to the piston when $\omega t = \pi/6$? (Use force = mass × acceleration; the mass = $^{100}/_{32}$, approximately.)
(c) What is the maximum inertia force which the piston can transmit to the crank arm and connecting rod?

25·22 Implicit differentiation

Thus far we have differentiated functions in the form

$$y = f(x) \tag{140}$$

where x and y are related by an equation such as

$$y = 3x^2 + 2x + 5 \tag{141}$$

in which we regard the dependent variable y as being directly expressed in terms of the independent variable x. Such functions are commonly called *explicit* functions.

Quite often we have occasion to differentiate functions in the form

$$F(x,y) = 0 \tag{142}$$

in which two variables x and y are related by means of an equation such as

$$y^2 + x^2 - 36 = 0 \tag{143}$$
$$x^5 + 5xy^3 - 7y^5 = 0 \tag{144}$$

where both x and y are involved in the same equation but neither is explicitly expressed in terms of the other.

After studying equations such as (143) and (144) above, the student may surmise that by implication y must be a function of x in each of them.

Sometimes this surmise can be verified by solving the equation for y, although such a solution may yield just one, more than one, or possibly no explicit function of x.

A study into the matter of when and in what sense there is an explicit function in the form of $y = f(x)$ corresponding to a given implicit function in the form $F(x,y) = 0$ is beyond the scope of this book. In fact, it is ordinarily beyond the scope of an introductory textbook in calculus at any level. The interested student may consult one of the many excellent textbooks in advanced calculus when he is ready.

In any event, in this book the student will not be confronted with an implicit function expressed in the form $F(x,y) = 0$ which cannot be expressed as an explicit differentiable function of x (or perhaps one of several explicit functions of x) in the form $y = f(x)$.

The student may proceed on these assumptions for the rest of this book.

To calculate dy/dx when y is a differentiable function of x given implicitly by an equation in x and y, we differentiate with respect to x by rules already given. Then we solve for dy/dx in terms of x and y.

This process is called *implicit differentiation.*

example 79 In Eq. (143) find dy/dx.

Differentiating with respect to x, we find

$$\frac{d(y^2)}{dx} + \frac{d(x^2)}{dx} - \frac{d(36)}{dx} = \frac{d(0)}{dx} \tag{145}$$

From Prob. 19, Exercise 6, we know that

$$\frac{d(y^2)}{dx} = 2y\frac{dy}{dx} \tag{146}$$

From Prob. 20, Exercise 6, we know that

$$\frac{d(x^2)}{dx} = 2x\frac{dx}{dx} \tag{147}$$

But from Example 15 we know that

$$\frac{dx}{dx} = 1 \tag{148}$$

By substituting Eqs. (146), (147), and (148) in Eq. (145) we obtain

$$2y\frac{dy}{dx} + 2x = 0$$

or

$$\frac{dy}{dx} = -\frac{x}{y} \tag{149}$$

By solving the equation

$$y^2 + x^2 - 36 = 0$$

for y, we find

$$y = \pm\sqrt{36 - x^2} \tag{150}$$

Thus Eq. (150) yields two explicit, single-valued functions of x. One function is represented by the equation

$$y_1 = +\sqrt{36 - x^2} \tag{151}$$

and the other by the equation

$$y_2 = -\sqrt{36 - x^2} \tag{152}$$

Since we are dealing with only real numbers, x is restricted such that

$$-6 \leq x \leq 6 \tag{153}$$

The plot of Eq. (151) is a semicircle entirely above the x axis with its center at the origin.

The plot of Eq. (152) is the lower half of the same circle.

In a specific practical problem we would have to have more information about the problem in order to determine whether Eq. (151) or Eq. (152) would apply.

If we substitute Eq. (151) in Eq. (149), we find

$$\frac{dy}{dx} = -\frac{x}{\sqrt{36 - x^2}} \tag{154}$$

If we substitute Eq. (152) in Eq. (149), we find

$$\frac{dy}{dx} = +\frac{x}{\sqrt{36 - x^2}} \tag{155}$$

From Eq. (154) and (155) we note a further precaution necessary when working with these equations. Since division by zero is undefined, $x \neq \pm 6$.

example 80 In Eq. (144) find dy/dx.

By differentiating with respect to x we obtain

$$\frac{d(x^5)}{dx} + \frac{d(5xy^3)}{dx} - \frac{d(7y^5)}{dx} = \frac{d(0)}{dx} \tag{156}$$

From Prob. 21, Exercise 6,

$$\frac{d(x^5)}{dx} = 5x^4\frac{dx}{dx} = 5x^4 \tag{157}$$

Following Eq. (45), we obtain

$$\frac{d(5xy^3)}{dx} = 5x(3y^2)\frac{dy}{dx} + 5y^3\frac{dx}{dx} = 15xy^2\frac{dy}{dx} + 5y^3 \tag{158}$$

In Prob. 22, Exercise 6,

$$\frac{d(7y^5)}{dx} = 35y^4\frac{dy}{dx} \tag{159}$$

Substituting Eqs. (157), (158), and (159) in Eq. (156), we obtain

$$5x^4 + 5y^3 + \frac{dy}{dx}(15xy^2 - 35y^4) = 0 \tag{160}$$

By rearranging Eq. (160) we obtain

$$\frac{dy}{dx}(15xy^2 - 35y^4) = -5x^4 - 5y^3 \tag{161}$$

or

$$\frac{dy}{dx} = \frac{5x^4 + 5y^3}{35y^4 - 15xy^2} = \frac{x^4 + y^3}{7y^4 - 3xy^2} \tag{162}$$

EXERCISE 20

In Probs. 1 to 9 find dy/dx by differentiating implicitly.

1. By differentiating implicitly show that if $x^2 + y^2 = -1$, $dy/dx = -(x/y)$. Also show why this derivative is meaningless.

2. $x^2 + y^2 = K^2$ 3. $5x^2 + 3y^2 = 25$ 4. $x^2 - y^2 = 10$
5. $y^2 = 15x$ 6. $xy - y - 3x = 8$ 7. $x^3 + 3y^2 = y$
8. $2x^3 + 3xy^2 + 5y^3 = 15$ 9. $x^5y^5 = x^5 + y^5$

25·23 Related rates

Let us consider a specific problem.

example 81 A spherical balloon is being inflated at the rate of 15 cfpm. How fast is the radius increasing when the radius is 6 ft?

In this problem, the volume and the radius are varying quantities but for all permissible values of time they are related by the equation

$$V = \tfrac{4}{3}\pi r^3 \tag{163}$$

Since V and r are both functions of time, we may differentiate Eq. (163) with respect to time, obtaining

$$\frac{d(V)}{dt} = \frac{4}{3}\pi\frac{d(r^3)}{dt} = 4\pi r^2\frac{dr}{dt}$$

Now by using the given data we may write

$$15 = 4\pi \cdot 36\frac{dr}{dt}$$

or

$$\frac{dr}{dt} = \frac{5}{48\pi} = 0.0332 \text{ ft/min}$$

EXERCISE 21

1. A ladder 10 ft long rests against a vertical wall. If the foot of the ladder is moved horizontally at the rate of 5 fpm, how fast is the top of the ladder moving downward when the foot of the ladder is 8 ft from the base of the building?
2. A spherical balloon is being inflated by pumping gas into it at the rate of 12 cfpm. How fast is the radius of the balloon increasing when it is 0.5 ft in radius?
3. A particle A moves along the x axis at a constant rate of 3 fps while a particle B moves along the y axis with a constant speed of -5 fps. How fast is the distance between them changing when A is at (1,0) and B is at (0,12)?
4. A conical tank has an altitude of 15 ft and a diameter at the top of 15 ft. Water is flowing out of the apex (at the bottom) at the rate of 5 cu ft per hr. How fast is the water level dropping when it is 10 ft above the apex?
5. A particle moves in a circular path according to the equation $x^2 + y^2 = 4$. If the x component of velocity is y, find the y component of velocity.
6. A crankshaft (see Fig. 25·24) turns at the rate of 900 rpm. Find the speed of the piston dx/dt when $\omega t = \pi/2$ radians. Let $r = 1'$ and $L = 5'$.

7. If the quantity of wood in a tree is approximately proportional to the cube of the diameter at its base and if the diameter increases approximately 0.8 in. per year, what is the approximate rate of change in the volume? Give your result in terms of the constant of variation and the radius of the tree.
8. A given quantity of gas is expanding according to the adiabatic law $pV^{1.4} = k =$ constant. If the volume is 10 cu in. when the pressure is 20 psi and if the pressure is increased at the constant rate of 0.5 psi per sec, what is the rate of change of the volume when the volume is 5 cu in.?
9. The relation between altitude above sea level (h ft) and the pressure (p lb per sq ft) at a certain place on the earth and at a certain time of year is given by

$$p = 2{,}140e^{-0.000{,}035h}$$

If an airplane is climbing at this particular spot on the earth and at the stated time at the rate of 200 mph, what is the rate of change of the pressure due to change in altitude when the airplane is 3 miles up?
10. A boat is pulled in by means of a rope wound around a windlass on the dock which is 20 ft above the deck of the boat. If the windlass is pulling the rope in at 10 fps, determine, when there is 100 ft of rope out:
(a) The speed of the boat
(b) The acceleration of the boat

25·24 Approximate increments

We have become accustomed to the type of thinking that is involved in the equation

$$\lim_{\Delta x \to 0} \frac{\Delta y}{\Delta x} = \frac{dy}{dx} \tag{164}$$

For small values of x it appears evident that $\Delta y/\Delta x$ and its limit dy/dx are nearly equal. That is,

$$\frac{\Delta y}{\Delta x} \approx \frac{dy}{dx} \tag{165}$$

For a discussion of the error involved in this approximation the student is referred to a more advanced textbook in calculus.

example 82 The diameter of a sphere changes from 10 to 10.02 in. Approximately what is the change in volume?

The volume of a sphere is given by the formula

$$V = \tfrac{4}{3}\pi r^3$$

$$\frac{dV}{dr} = 4\pi r^2$$

When $r = 10$, $dV/dr = 400\pi$, and this quantity can be evaluated easily from the number tables.

$$\frac{dV}{dr} = 400\pi = 1{,}257 \qquad \text{(to four significant digits)} \tag{166}$$

From Eq. (166),

$$\frac{\Delta V}{\Delta r} \approx 1{,}257$$

and
$$\Delta V \approx 1{,}257 \cdot \Delta r$$

But
$$\Delta r = 0.02$$

Thus $\quad \Delta V \approx 1{,}257 \times 0.02 = 25.1 \qquad$ (to three significant digits)

By the far more laborious operation of evaluating the equation

$$\Delta V = \frac{4}{3}\pi(10.02^3 - 10^3)$$

we obtain

$$\Delta V = 25.2 \qquad \text{(to three significant digits)}$$

If this accuracy is sufficient in a particular problem, the first method is to be preferred because it involves less work.

EXERCISE 22

1. If a circle has a radius of 7 in., approximately what changes in radius will result from a change in area of 3 sq in.?
2. A cube expands so that its edge increases from 5 to 5.04 in. What is the approximate change in volume?
3. To three significant digits, what is the actual change in volume in Prob. 2 above?
4. A cylinder exactly 15 in. high has a nominal radius of 8 in., but the radius is 0.05 in. oversize. Find the approximate error this causes in (a) the volume and (b) the lateral surface.
5. If the radius of a sphere increases slightly, show that the increase in volume is approximately proportional to the surface area.
6. A sphere is to be fired (baked) out of a certain kind of clay that has a linear shrinkage of 4 per cent. Determine the approximate radius of the sphere before firing (baking) if the final radius is to be 6 in. Determine the approximate change in volume.
7. The heat Q required to raise the temperature T of a certain liquid 1°K (one degree on the Kelvin or absolute centigrade scale) is given by $Q = a + bT + cT^2$. Determine an expression for the amount of heat necessary to heat the material from $T = 300.0$ to $T = 300.1$°K.
8. Determine the approximate change in $\tan\theta$ if θ increases from 45°10′ to 45°11′. Then check with your tables.

9. If $y = \sin x$, and x is to increase by 1 min, determine the value of x that makes the largest change in y. Then refer to your tables and check.
10. Bernoulli's equation from fluid mechanics may be written

$$p + \frac{\rho v^2}{2} = H$$

where p is pressure, ρ is the constant density of the fluid, v is velocity, and H is a constant. Obtain an approximate formula for the change in pressure Δp due to a small change in velocity Δv.
11. If two resistors R_1 and R_2 are connected in parallel, the equivalent resistance R of the combination is given by the equation

$$R = \frac{R_1 \times R_2}{R_1 + R_2}$$

If the nominal value of R_1 is 5 ohms, and the nominal value of R_2 is 10 ohms, what would be the change in R if R_2 were increased by 0.5 ohm?
12. In Example 6, page 464, find the approximate error in the length of side c if $36°52''$ is used for angle C instead of $36°52'12''$. Find the equivalent per cent error.
13. The equation of the LL-3 scale on a 10-in. log log slide rule is

$$y \text{ in.} = 10 \log_{10} (\log_e x)$$

where the numbers that appear on the scale are values of x, and y is measured from the left-hand side of the rule. Use differentials to determine the approximate distance in inches (Δy) between the numbers marked $x = 3$ and $x = 3.2$.

NOTE: The true length is 25 cm.

25·25 Differentials

We remember that the symbol dy/dx has been used to designate the derivative of y with respect to x. Where it is used in this sense we have given meaning to dy/dx only when this symbol is considered as a whole. We have not, thus far, given meaning to dy and dx when they are considered separately.

We can, however, interpret dy and dx in such a way that they do have meaning when considered separately. When we do so we call them *differentials.* Thus dy is called the *differential* of y, and dx is called the *differential* of x.

Suppose that we are given a function f for which $y = f(x)$ and that this function has a derivative for each value of x with which we are concerned. Now let dx be any increment of x (of course, $dx \neq 0$). Then dy is defined by

$$dy = f'(x)\, dx \tag{167}$$

where $f'(x)$ = derivative of y with respect to x

We can divide both sides of Eq. (167) by the differential of x, that is, dx, obtaining

$$\frac{dy}{dx} = f'(x) \tag{168}$$

We note that Eq. (168) has a familiar appearance. However, there is this new concept involved in it. In Eq. (168) we have given *separate meanings to* dy *and* dx *so that now* dy/dx *is considered to be a quotient.*

From now on, in situations where it is convenient to do so, we may consider a derivative to be the quotient of two differentials.

It is sometimes convenient to give a geometric interpretation to differentials.

In Fig. 25·26 Δx is the increment of x between P_1 and P_2, and Δy is the corresponding increment in y. The quotient $\Delta y/\Delta x$ is the average slope of the graph between P_1 and P_2.

If we let $\Delta x = dx$, then dy is the corresponding increment in the tangent ab.

The quotient of the differentials dy and dx is then the slope of the tangent drawn to the graph through the point P_1.

Throughout this chapter we have, from time to time, introduced cer-

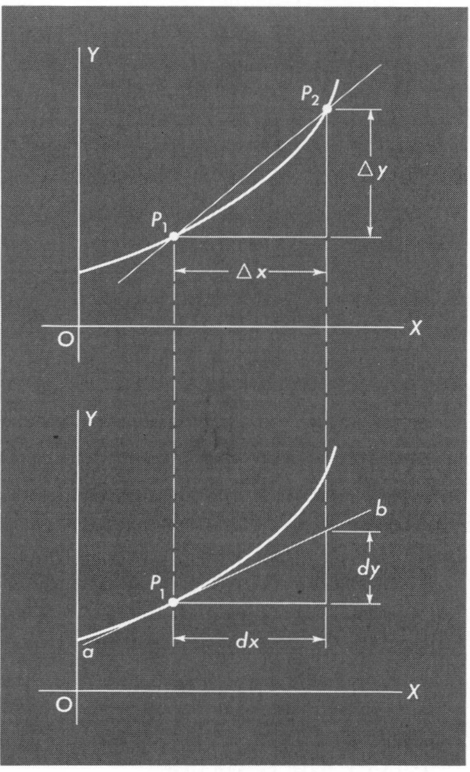

fig. 25·26

tain formulas for derivatives. We can now present corresponding formulas for differentials.

For example, from Eq. (27),

$$\frac{d(kx^n)}{dx} = nkx^{n-1}$$

Now we may write the differential of kx^n as

$$d(kx^n) = nkx^{n-1}\,dx$$

From Eq. (41) if

$$\frac{d(u^n)}{dx} = nu^{n-1}\frac{du}{dx}$$

then

$$d(u^n) = nu^{n-1}\,du \tag{169}$$

Also, if

$$\frac{d(ku^n)}{dx} = knu^{n-1}\frac{du}{dx}$$

then

$$d(ku^n) = knu^{n-1}\,du \tag{170}$$

In the special case where $n = 1$, we may write

$$d(ku) = k\,du \tag{171}$$

From rule 4, page 673,

$$\frac{d(u+v)}{dx} = \frac{du}{dx} + \frac{dv}{dx}$$

Then

$$d(u+v) = du + dv \tag{172}$$

From Eq. (45),

$$\frac{d(uv)}{dx} = u\frac{dv}{dx} + v\frac{du}{dx}$$

Then

$$d(uv) = u\,dv + v\,du \tag{173}$$

From Eq. (51),

$$\frac{d(u/v)}{dx} = \frac{v(du/dx) - u(dv/dx)}{v^2} \tag{174}$$

Then

$$d\left(\frac{u}{v}\right) = \frac{v\,du - u\,dv}{v^2} \tag{175}$$

From Eq. (66),

$$\frac{d(\sin u)}{dx} = \cos u\frac{du}{dx}$$

Then

$$d(\sin u) = \cos u\,du \tag{176}$$

From Eq. (71),

$$\frac{d(\cos u)}{dx} = -\sin u\frac{du}{dx}$$

Then

$$d(\cos u) = -\sin u\,du \tag{177}$$

From Eq. (96),

$$\frac{d(\ln u)}{dx} = \frac{1}{u}\frac{du}{dx}$$

Then

$$d(\ln u) = \frac{1}{u}\,du = u^{-1}\,du \tag{178}$$

From Eq. (104),

$$d(e^u) = e^u\,du \tag{179}$$

EXERCISE 23 Find the differential of y in the following problems. The letters a and b represent constants.

1. $y = \frac{1}{3}\arccos\frac{3}{x}$
2. $y = \frac{1}{a}\arctan\frac{x}{a}$
3. $y = \frac{2}{3b}\sqrt{(a+bx)^3}$
4. $y = \frac{1}{2b}\ln\left(x^2 + \frac{a}{b}\right)$
5. $y = \frac{1}{b^2}\left[-\frac{1}{a+bx} + \frac{a}{2(a+bx)^2}\right]$
6. $y = \frac{1}{5a}\ln\frac{x^5}{a+bx^5}$
7. $y = \frac{\sqrt{x^2-a^2}}{2a^2x^2} + \frac{1}{2a^3}\arccos\frac{a}{x}$
8. $y = -\frac{1}{a}\ln\frac{a+\sqrt{a^2+x^2}}{x}$
9. Van der Waals' equation for real gases is

$$\left(p + \frac{a}{v^2}\right)(v - b) = nRT$$

where a, b, n, R are constants; p is pressure; v is volume; and T is temperature.
(a) Determine an equation for dv if T is a constant.
(b) Determine an equation for dv if p is constant.

25·26 Newton's method of approximating a root

An important problem in engineering technology is to find to any desired accuracy the real roots of an equation (either polynomial or transcendental) which cannot be solved by elementary means. An excellent method for accomplishing this was developed by Sir Isaac Newton.

Essentially, the process depends upon obtaining a rough idea of the root graphically. This value is then substituted in the given function and in its derivative. Thus we can obtain the x intercept of the tangent. Thus this is a typical iterative or "feedback" process which will be a closer approximation of the root than the first. The process may be repeated as many times as desired.

We shall illustrate the method by finding the approximate root of the equation $e^{-x} = \frac{1}{2}x - 1$.

If we rearrange the equation to read $e^{-x} - \frac{1}{2}x + 1 = 0$ and sketch the curve $y = e^{-x} - \frac{1}{2}x + 1$, we find an x intercept or root between +2 and +2.5 (see Fig. 25·27).

Let us take 2.25 as our first approximation. We shall call this a_1. Substituting 2.25 for x in the original equation, we obtain

$$f(a_1) = f(2.25) = -0.01960$$

$$dy/dx = -e^{-x} - \tfrac{1}{2}$$

and

$$f'(a_1) = f'(2.25) = -0.60540$$

The x intercept (a_2) of this tangent is given by

$$-0.01960/(2.25 - a_2) = -0.60540$$

or $a_2 = 2.2176$, our second approximation of the root.

We now repeat the process for a closer approximation. Substituting $x = 2.2176$ in the original expression $e^{-x} - \frac{1}{2}x + 1$, we obtain $f(a_2) = 0.00007$, and the substitution of 2.2176 in the derivative $dy/dx = -e^{-x} - \frac{1}{2}$ gives us

$$f'(a_2) = \frac{0.00007}{2.2176 - a_3} = -0.6089$$

$$a_3 = 2.2176 - \frac{0.00007}{-0.6089} = 2.2177$$

for a third approximation of the root.

The method may be summarized as follows:

$$a_2 = a_1 - \frac{f(a_1)}{f'(a_1)} \qquad a_3 = a_2 - \frac{f(a_2)}{f'(a_2)} \qquad \text{etc.}$$

fig. 25·27

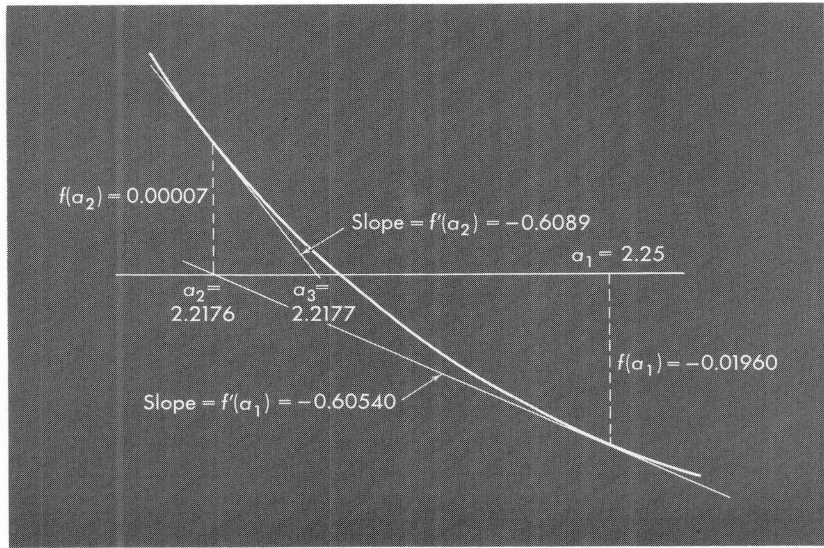

NOTE: If in seeking an intercept at B (Fig. 25·28) we were unfortunate enough to select A as a starting point, we could well become involved in a fruitless search since the first tangent would lead us in the wrong direction. In fact, it is often advisable to first sketch the curve. In addition to using the sketching principles described in Chap. 13, it would be helpful to determine the properties of the first and second derivatives in the area being investigated.

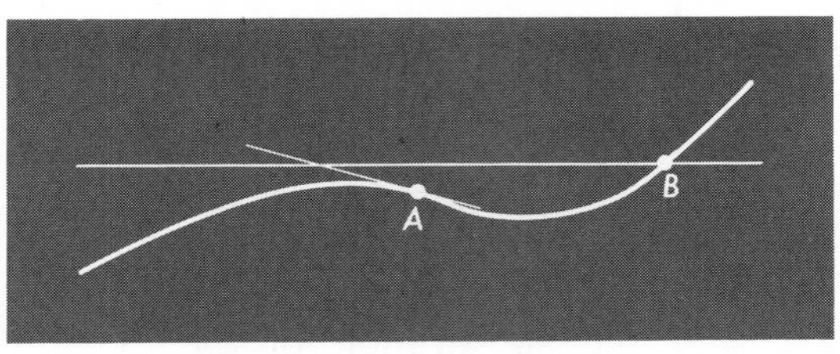

fig. 25·28

example 83 One root of the equation $x^5 - 4.5x^4 - 6x^3 + 30.5x^2 + 15x - 20 = 0$ has been found graphically to lie between 0 and +1. Determine the root correct to three significant figures.

If $y = x^5 - 4.5x^4 - 6x^3 + 30.5x^2 + 15x - 20$ and $f(a_1) = f(1) = 16$, then

$$\frac{dy}{dx} = 5x^4 - 18x^3 - 18x^2 + 61x + 15$$

and $f'(a_1) = f'(1) = 45$. Hence $a_2 = 1 - 16/45 = 0.645$.

$$f(a_2) = f(0.645) = 0.08653 \qquad \text{and} \qquad f'(a_2) = f'(0.645) = 42.89$$

It follows that $a_3 = 0.645 - 0.08653/42.89 = 0.643$.

example 84 One root of the equation $\sin x = -2x + 3$ is approximately 1.1. Determine the root correct to four decimal places.

If we set $y = 2x - 3 + \sin x$, where x is in radians,

$$\frac{dy}{dx} = 2 + \cos x$$

$$f(a_1) = f(1.1) = 2(1.1) - 3 + \sin 1.1 = 2.2 - 3 + 0.89121 = 0.09121$$

$$f'(a_1) = f'(1.1) = 2 + \cos 1.1 = 2 + 0.45360 = 2.4536$$

$$a_2 = 1.1 - \frac{0.09121}{2.4536} = 1.06283$$

$$f(1.06283) = 2(1.06283) - 3 - \sin 1.06283 = -0.00061$$

$$f'(1.06283) = 2.48639$$

$$a_3 = 1.06283 - \frac{-0.00061}{2.48639} = 1.0631$$

For additional references to Newton's and other approximation methods, see:

Fehr, H. F.: "Secondary Mathematics: a Functional Approach for Teachers," D. C. Heath and Company, Boston, 1951.
Smail, L. L.: "Analytic Geometry and Calculus," Appleton-Century-Crofts, Inc., New York, 1953.
Willers, F. A.: "Practical Analysis," Dover Publications, Inc., New York, 1948.
Love, C. E., and E. D. Rainville: "Differential and Integral Calculus," The Macmillan Company, New York, 1954.

EXERCISE 24

Solve the following by Newton's method, finding the indicated root correct to four significant figures:

1. $x^3 - 5x + 4 = 0$ (root between 1 and 2)
2. $2x^3 - 3x^2 - 6 = 0$ (root between 2 and 3)
3. $x^4 - x^2 - 6 = 0$ (find largest positive root)
4. $\sqrt[5]{30}$ (Hint: $x^5 - 30 = 0$)

Check your answers to Probs. 1, 3, and 4 by another method.

5. $e^x - 2x = 3$ (largest root)
6. $e^{-x} - \sin x = 0.5$ (smallest positive root)
7. $1 + \ln x = \frac{1}{2}x$ (largest positive root)
8. $\tan x = x + 1$ (smallest positive root)
9. A spherical segment of one base has its volume V given by

$$v = \frac{\pi h^2}{3}(3r - h)$$

where h = height. Find h if r (radius of sphere) = 4 in. and v = 20 cu in. (This problem arises in displacement of water by a floating sphere.)

10. A metal sphere of radius 2 in. is recast in the form of a cone of height 2 in. surmounted by a hemisphere of the same radius as the cone. Find the radius of the cone.
11. An integration led to the equation

$$\frac{1}{x}\ln\frac{3x - 1}{2x - 1} = 0.096$$

Find, to four significant figures, a root which is between 4 and 5.

12. The relationship between the pressure P and the volume V (in cubic centimeters per gram-mole) of a nonideal gas at a Kelvin (centigrade absolute) temperature T is given by

$$P = \frac{RT}{V - b} - \frac{a}{V^2}$$

where R, a, and b are constants. At a temperature of 27°C, 1 g-mole of

CO_2 is at a pressure of 4 atm. Compute to two significant figures the volume in cubic centimeters of gram-mole, assuming:

$$a = 3.60 \times 10^6 \left(\frac{\text{cc}}{\text{mole}}\right)^2 \text{atm}$$

$$b = 42.8 \text{ cc per g-mole}$$

$$R = 82 \frac{(\text{cc})(\text{atm})}{(\text{g-mole})(^\circ\text{K})}$$

NOTE: Since $V \approx 22{,}400/4 = 5{,}000^+$ we may neglect term $-a/V^2$ as a first approximation.

13. The emission current for a heated filament is given by the equation

$$i = AT^2e^{-B/T}$$

where i is expressed in amperes, A is a constant equal to 60, B is a constant equal to 52.4×10^3 for a tungsten filament, T is the temperature in degrees Kelvin, and $i = 0.114$ ampere. ($1000 < T < 2500$.) Find T (see Prob. 7, page 256).

14. Given:

$$i = \frac{E}{R}(1 - e^{-Rt/L})$$

where $i = 0.054$, $E = 10$, $L = 0.9$, $t = 0.005$. Solve for R.

15.
$$Q = 3.33b[(H + h)^{3/2} - h^{3/2}]$$

The above is Francis' formula for the discharge Q in cubic feet per second over a rectangular, suppressed weir b ft in width due to a head H ft over the crest, considering the velocity head h ft due to the velocity of approach. If $b = 5$, $Q = 20$, $H = 1.0$, find h, where

$$0.1 \leq h \leq 0.2$$

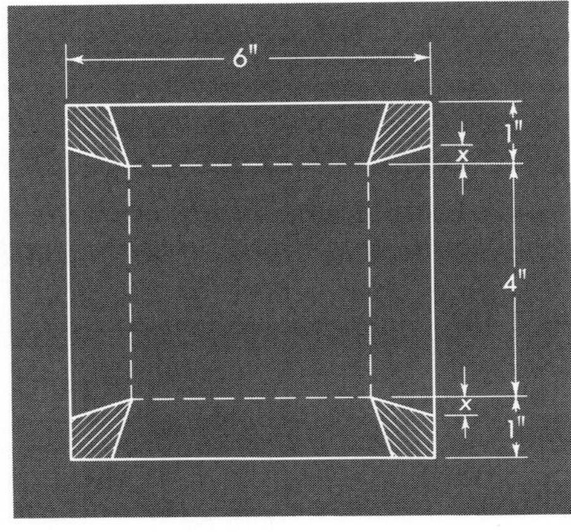

fig. 25·29

16. A 6-in. square of stainless steel has notches cut out of the corners, as shown in Fig. 25·29. The remaining tabs are bent up along the dotted lines to form a square tray with flaring sides. The equation for x leading to maximum capacity is found by differentiation to be

$$3x^3 + 12x^2 + 10x - 6 = 0$$

Find x to 0.01 in.

26
integration

In Chap. 25 we considered the problem of finding the derivative of a given function. The process involved is called differentiation.

We shall begin this chapter by considering the problem of reconstructing a function when its derivative is given. This process is called *antidifferentiation* or *indefinite integration.*

The appropriateness of the word "indefinite" when used in this context will be discussed in Sec. 26·2.

In Secs. 26·11 and 26·13 we shall discuss some further aspects of integration leading to the notion of the *definite integral.*

26·1 Introduction to integration

Differentiation is an orderly, algebraic process based on the Δ method (see Sec. 25·3). Indefinite integration is largely a matter of trial and memory.

Suppose we are given the equation

$$\frac{dy}{dx} = 15x^4 \tag{1}$$

An equation such as Eq. (1) is called a *differential* equation. A differential equation is an equation that relates variables with their derivatives. The differential equations which we shall consider here are, of course, very special ones and very simple ones.

Now suppose we are asked to solve Eq. (1). To solve this differential equation means to find some y value such that

$$\frac{dy}{dx} = 15x^4$$

From our experience with differentiation (see Example 11, page 668) we recall that *one* possible solution is

$$y = 3x^5$$

In general, if two functions F and f have the property that

$$\frac{d[F(x)]}{dx} = f(x) \tag{2}$$

then $F(x)$ is called a solution of this differential equation. $F(x)$ is also called an antiderivative of $f(x)$ or an indefinite integral of $f(x)$.

In the above example

$$f(x) = 15x^4 \tag{3}$$

and

$$F(x) = 3x^5 \tag{4}$$

This, of course, assumes that $F(x)$ is differentiable over the range of interest and that both $F(x)$ and $f(x)$ are continuous over this range. From Sec. 25·5, rules 3 and 4, we observe that if $F(x)$ is an integral of $f(x)$, then $F(x) + C$ is also an integral of $f(x)$. For example, $3x^5 + 8$, $3x^5 + \pi$, $3x^5 + e$, or $3x^5 +$ (any constant) will satisfy Eq. (1).

The elongated s written $\int$ is the symbol which designates the process of integration. It is customary to use differential notation (see Sec. 25·25) in connection with the symbol $\int$ to indicate this process. Thus

$$\int 15x^4\,dx = 3x^5 + C \tag{5}$$

is read "The indefinite integral of $15x^4$ with respect to x is $3x^5 + C$."

Similarly, if we wish to indicate that $F(x)$ is an antiderivative, or an indefinite integral of $f(x)$, we may write

$$\int f(x)\,dx = F(x) + C \tag{6}$$

In Eq. (5) the expression $15x^4\,dx$ is called the *integrand*, and C is called the *constant of integration.*

26·2 The indefinite integral

There is a certain "indefiniteness" about the above problem. If all we know about a function is its derivative then we do not know what the added constant is. Consequently, an integral in the form of Eq. (6) is called an *indefinite* integral.

26·3 Some important integration formulas

The formulas listed below are basic and will be used frequently in the work to follow. The symbols k, K, m, n, and C designate constants.

$$\int u^n\,du = \frac{u^{n+1}}{n+1} + C \qquad n \neq -1 \tag{7}$$

This can be verified by differentiating as follows:

$$\frac{d\left(\dfrac{u^{n+1}}{n+1} + C\right)}{du} = \frac{(n+1)u^{n+1-1}}{n+1} = u^n$$

For example,

$$\int u^4\, du = \frac{u^5}{5} + C$$

By differentiation we obtain

$$\frac{d\left(\frac{u^5}{5} + C\right)}{du} = \frac{5u^4}{5} = u^4$$

$$\int ku^n\, du = \frac{ku^{n+1}}{n+1} + C \qquad n \neq -1 \tag{8}$$

This can be verified by differentiation. Thus

$$\frac{d\left(\frac{ku^{n+1}}{n+1} + C\right)}{du} = \frac{k(n+1)u^n}{n+1} = ku^n \tag{9}$$

By comparing Eqs. (7) and (8) it seems plausible that

$$\int ku^n\, du = k\int u^n\, du \tag{10}$$

or, somewhat more generally,

$$\int kf(u)\, du = k\int f(u)\, du \tag{11}$$

From rule 4, page 673, we note that the derivative of the sum of any finite number of differentiable functions is the sum of their derivatives. Therefore, we are led to write

$$\int [f(u) + g(u)]\, du = \int f(u)\, du + \int g(u)\, du \tag{12}$$

For example,

$$\int \left(-\frac{5}{3u^2} + 2u\right) du = \int -\frac{5}{3u^2}\, du + \int 2u\, du \tag{13}$$

$$= \int -\frac{5}{3}u^{-2}\, du + \int 2u\, du$$

$$= -\frac{5}{3}\cdot\frac{u^{-1}}{-1} + C_1 + \frac{2u^2}{2} + C_2 \tag{14}$$

If we let

$$C_1 + C_2 = C$$

$$\int \left(-\frac{5}{3u^2} + 2u\right) du = \frac{5}{3}u^{-1} + u^2 + C = \frac{5}{3u} + u^2 + C \tag{15}$$

To verify the above by differentiation, see Example 27, page 673. Thus we conclude that the integral of the sum of a finite number of terms is the sum of their integrals.

The question frequently arises, Is integration unique? That is, for example, if

$$\frac{dy}{du} = 10u$$

can y be expressed by an equation (perhaps a very complicated one), other than

$$y = 5u^2 + \text{an arbitrary constant}$$

Without attempting a rigorous proof, suppose for a moment that z is the value of a function such that

$$\frac{dy}{du} = \frac{dz}{du} \tag{16}$$

Since the above derivatives are equal, it means that the rate of change of both y and z with respect to u is the same. Hence the difference between y and z does not change but remains constant. Thus y and z can differ only by an arbitrary constant.

Therefore functions defined by

$$y = 5u^2 + C \tag{17}$$

(where C is a constant) are the only functions which if differentiated will yield

$$\frac{dy}{du} = 10u \tag{18}$$

In a more advanced work, it can be proved rigorously that any two antiderivatives of the same function differ only by a constant.

Figure 26·1 illustrates the graphs of four equations. The only differ-

fig. 26·1

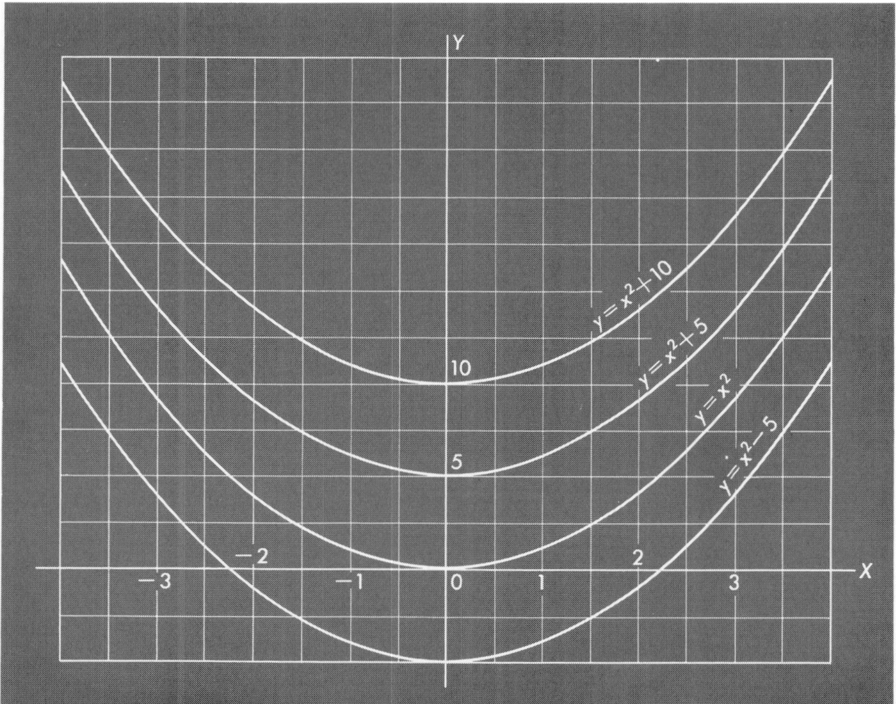

ence in these equations is in the added constant. The effect of the added constant is simply to raise or lower the graph. It has no effect whatever on the *shape* of the graph. It is the *shape* of the graph that determines the derivative. Therefore the added constant has no effect on the derivative.

EXERCISE 1

Verify the following indefinite integrals:

1. $\int 3x^5\,dx = \frac{3x^6}{6} + C = \frac{1}{2}x^6 + C$

2. $\int 2x^{5/3}\,dx = \frac{3}{4}x^{8/3} + C$

3. $\int 7x^{-5}\,dx = -\frac{7}{4}x^{-4} + C$

4. $\int 3x^{-1/2}\,dx = 6x^{1/2} + C$

5. $\int 8x^{-8/5}\,dx = -\frac{40}{3x^{3/5}} + C$

6. $\int -\frac{7}{8}x^{3/2}\,dx = -\frac{7x^{5/2}}{20} + C$

7. $\int 4\sqrt[3]{x^2}\,dx = \frac{12x^{5/3}}{5} + C$

8. $\int -32dx = -32x + C$

Find the indefinite integrals in Probs. 9 and 10 below.

9. $\int(x^3 - 6x^2 + 500x + 7)\,dx$
10. $\int(x^{3/4} - 2x^{-5/6} + 2\sqrt[3]{x^2} + \pi)\,dx$

In Probs. 11 through 18 find $F(x)$ as illustrated in Eq. (6).

11. $f(x) = \frac{5}{6}\sqrt{x}$

12. $f(x) = -\frac{3}{4}\sqrt[3]{x}$

13. $f(x) = (3x^2 + \sqrt{2})$

14. $f(x) = x^{-10}$

15. $f(x) = \frac{1}{x^5}$

16. $f(x) = \frac{k}{x^5}$

17. $f(x) = (\pi + 3x^{5/7})$

18. $f(x) = (3e + 5\sqrt{x^7})$

Solve the following differential equations.

19. $dy/dx = 2x$
20. $dy/dx = 3x^2$
21. $dy/dx = x$
22. $dy/dx = 10$
23. $dy/dx = -2$
24. $dy/dx = x^{5/2}$
25. $dy/dx = x^{1/3}$
26. $dy/dx = x^{-1/3}$
27. $dy/dx = 3x^{-1/2}$

26·4 Evaluating the constant of integration

As we mentioned in Sec. 26·2, the integral expressed in the form of Eq. (6) has a certain "indefiniteness" about it. Equation (6) is indefinite to the extent that the constant is not known. As a matter of fact, it could be anything, including zero. If the constant C is to be evaluated, the problem must contain more information than merely to give the derivative of the function. For example, if we have given that

$$dy = 10x\,dx \tag{19}$$

and we wish to find the value of y, we would naturally write

$$y = \int 10x\,dx \tag{20}$$

and according to Eq. (8)

$$y = 5x^2 + C \tag{21}$$

Now let us suppose that it is also given in the problem that when x is 2, y is 35; then we may write

$$35 = 5(2^2) + C \tag{22}$$

As a consequence,

$$35 = 20 + C \tag{23}$$

and

$$C = 15 \tag{24}$$

Therefore, with this bit of added information, commonly called a *boundary condition,* we can evaluate the constant of integration and find that

$$y = 5x^2 + 15$$

example 1 We have given that

$$\frac{d^2y}{dx^2} = 6x + 2 \qquad \text{(also see Sec. 25·20)}$$

Also we have given the boundary conditions that $dy/dx = 20$ when $x = 2$ and that $y = 0$ when $x = -10$. Find the equation for y in terms of x.

By integrating once, we obtain

$$\frac{dy}{dx} = 3x^2 + 2x + C_1$$

From the first boundary condition we know that

$$20 = 3 \cdot (2)^2 + 2 \cdot 2 + C_1$$
$$20 = 12 + 4 + C_1 = 16 + C_1$$
$$C_1 = 4$$

Therefore

$$\frac{dy}{dx} = 3x^2 + 2x + 4$$

By integrating again we obtain

$$y = x^3 + x^2 + 4x + C_2$$

From the second boundary condition we may write

$$0 = (-10)^3 + (-10)^2 + 4(-10) + C_2$$

or

$$0 = -1{,}000 + 100 - 40 + C_2 = -940 + C_2$$

Therefore

$$C_2 = 940$$

and

$$y = x^3 + x^2 + 4x + 940$$

This equation can be verified by calculating the second derivative of y with respect to x.

example 2 We have given that

$$\frac{d^4y}{dx^4} = 120x$$

Also we have given the following boundary conditions:

(a) When $x = 3$, $\frac{d^3y}{dx^3} = 552$ (25)

(b) When $x = 0$, $\frac{d^2y}{dx^2} = 6$ (26)

(c) When $x = 0$, $y = 0$ (27)

(d) When $x = 2$, $y = 0$ (28)

Find the equation for y in terms of x.

By integrating once we obtain

$$\frac{d^3y}{dx^3} = 60x^2 + C_1$$

From boundary condition (a)

$$552 = 60(3)^2 + C_1 = 540 + C_1$$

$$C_1 = 12$$

and $$\frac{dy^3}{dx^3} = 60x^2 + 12$$

By integrating again we obtain

$$\frac{d^2y}{dx^2} = 20x^3 + 12x + C_2$$

From boundary condition (b)

$$6 = 0 + 0 + C_2$$

and $$C_2 = 6$$

Therefore $$\frac{d^2y}{dx^2} = 20x^3 + 12x + 6 \tag{29}$$

By integrating again we obtain

$$\frac{dy}{dx} = 5x^4 + 6x^2 + 6x + C_3 \tag{30}$$

Here we have no boundary condition explicitly involving dy/dx. However, in this case, as we shall see below, there are enough data so that C_3 can still be evaluated.

By integrating again we obtain

$$y = x^5 + 2x^3 + 3x^2 + C_3x + C_4$$

From boundary condition (c) it is quite evident that $C_4 = 0$. Therefore

$$y = x^5 + 2x^3 + 3x^2 + C_3x$$

From boundary condition (d) we may write

$$0 = (2)^5 + 2(2)^3 + 3(2)^2 + 2C_3 = 32 + 16 + 12 + 2C_3$$
$$C_3 = -30$$

and $$y = x^5 + 2x^3 + 3x^2 - 30x$$

EXERCISE 2

In Probs. 1 through 9 below find the equation for y. The boundary conditions in each problem are that $y = 20$ when $x = 4$ (see Exercise 1, Probs. 19 through 27).

1. $y = \int 2x\,dx$
2. $y = \int 3x^2\,dx$
3. $y = \int x\,dx$
4. $y = \int 10dx$
5. $y = \int -2dx$
6. $y = \int x^{5/2}\,dx$
7. $y = \int x^{1/3}\,dx$
8. $y = \int x^{-1/3}\,dx$
9. $y = \int 3x^{-1/2}\,dx$

10. A simply supported beam is loaded with a load w in pounds per foot that varies directly as the distance from the left support, as indicated in Fig. 26·2. Given, from studies of strength of materials,

$$EI\frac{d^4y}{dx^4} = -w = -100x$$

where $E = 200{,}000{,}000$ lb per sq ft, $I = 0.00800$ ft^4, and y is the ordinate to the curve of the beam at abscissa x ft from the left support.

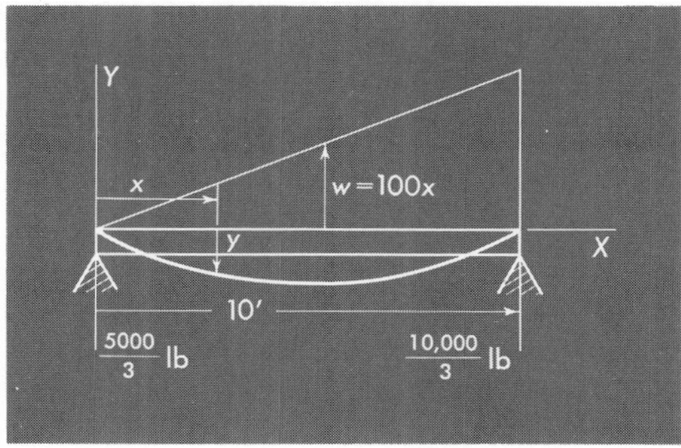

fig. 26·2

Given $(d^3y/dx^3)EI = 5{,}000/3$ when $x = 0$, $d^2y/dx^2 = 0$ when $x = 0$, and $y = 0$ when $x = 0$ and when $x = L$. Determine the equation for y as a function of x, that is, the curve of the beam.

11. Determine the maximum deflection of the beam from a horizontal position in Prob. 10.
12. A wooden beam is 12 ft long, 4 in. wide, and 8 in. deep and is loaded with a uniform load of 400 lb per ft, as shown in Fig. 26·3. From

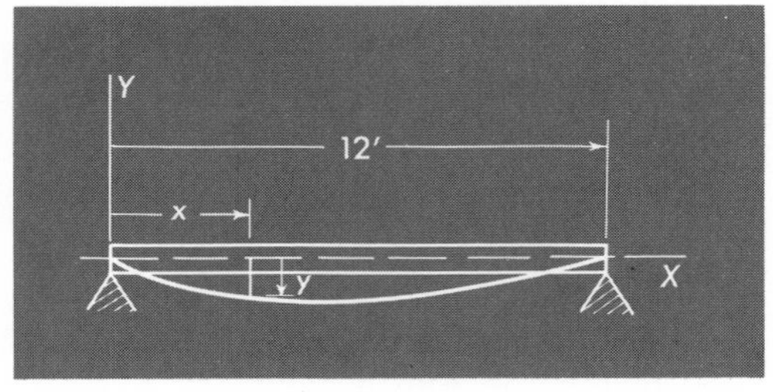

fig. 26·3

studies of strength of materials one can obtain the equation

$$\frac{d^2y}{dx^2} = 0.00204x - 0.000{,}170x^2$$

where x and y are in feet.

Determine the equation for y in terms of x and also determine the minimum value of y, that is, the largest deflection of the beam.

13. Given the equation $mv(dv/dx) = -mkx$, where m is a constant mass and k is a constant of variation. Integrate this equation and transpose all variable terms to the left-hand side. If kinetic energy (energy due to motion) is $mv^2/2$ and if potential energy (energy due to position) is $mkx^2/2$, what does your resulting equation state?

26·5 Integration by substitution

As we mentioned in Sec. 26·1, indefinite integration is largely a matter of trial and memory. It involves reconstructing a function whose differential is the given integrand.

In the discussion immediately to follow we shall lean heavily on Eq. (8). However, it is very common to find that although a given integrand may not be in such a form that we can apply Eq. (8) directly, it may be possible, by making suitable substitutions, to reduce the integrand to a form such that Eq. (8) is directly applicable.

For example, let us find

$$\int 5(4x^2 + 3x + 8)^2(8x + 3)\,dx \tag{31}$$

Observe that, if we let

$$u = 4x^2 + 3x + 8 \tag{32}$$

then

$$du = (8x + 3)\,dx \tag{33}$$

and (31) may be written as

$$\int 5u^2\,du \tag{34}$$

Also

$$\int 5u^2\,du = \tfrac{5}{3}u^3 + C \tag{35}$$

We may now substitute Eqs. (32) and (33) in (35) to obtain

$$\int 5u^2\,du = \int 5(4x^2 + 3x + 8)^2(8x + 3)\,dx \tag{36}$$

$$= \tfrac{5}{3}(4x^2 + 3x + 8)^3 + C \tag{37}$$

Of course, after a certain amount of practice, the student will learn to do most of this work mentally. Having been given the integrand in (31), he will be able to write the integral in (37) by inspection.

example 3 Find

$$\int(3x^2 + 5)^2 x\, dx \tag{38}$$

Here we let

$$u = (3x^2 + 5) \tag{39}$$

Then $$du = 6x\, dx$$

and (38) does *not* contain *du exactly*. However, we may multiply and divide by 6 without changing the value of (38) and write the equivalent of (38) as

$$\int \tfrac{1}{6}(3x^2 + 5)^2\, 6x\, dx \tag{40}$$

Now Eq. (8) does apply directly and

$$\begin{aligned} \int(3x^2 + 5)^2\, x\, dx &= \int \tfrac{1}{6}(3x^2 + 5)^2\, 6x\, dx \\ &= \tfrac{1}{18}(3x^2 + 5)^3 + C \end{aligned} \tag{41}$$

EXERCISE 3

Evaluate the following indefinite integrals.

1. $\int(3 - t)^4\, dt$
2. $\int(3 - 5x)^{-6}\, dx$
3. $\int\sqrt{4 - m}\, dm$
4. $\int\sqrt{4\phi - 1}\, d\phi$
5. $\int t^3(3 - t^4)^5\, dt$
6. $\displaystyle\int\frac{\phi^3}{(2 - \phi^4)^6}\, d\phi$
7. $\displaystyle\int\frac{t + 1}{\sqrt{t^2 + 2t}}\, dt$
8. $\int(r - 3)\sqrt{r^2 - 6r - 7}\, dr$
9. $\int 15x(4x^2 - 9)^{3/2}\, dx$

26·6 Accelerated motion

In this section it is assumed that the student has had a course in general physics and is therefore familiar with the elementary notions of distance, velocity, and acceleration.

We shall limit ourselves to bodies moving in a straight line and to some of the more elementary aspects of rotary motion.

We learn from mechanics that velocity is the time rate of change in distance. That is,

$$v = \frac{ds}{dt} \tag{42}$$

where v = velocity
s = distance
t = time

We also learn from mechanics that acceleration is the time rate of change in velocity. That is,

$$a = \frac{dv}{dt} \tag{43}$$

where a = acceleration.

In general, then, we may write

$$v = \int a\,dt \tag{44}$$

and

$$s = \int v\,dt \tag{45}$$

In accordance with engineering expediency, the data for any particular problem may be based on acceleration or velocity or distance in terms of time. Therefore, the student will be well advised to avoid relying entirely on memorized formulas which apply only to strictly limited situations.

example 4 The velocity in feet per second of a certain body moving in a straight line and starting from rest at $t = 0$ is given by

$$v = 3t^2 + 4t$$

(a) Find the acceleration at $t = 3$. (b) Find the distance moved between $t = 0$ and $t = 3$.

$$\text{Acceleration} = a = \frac{dv}{dt} = 6t + 4$$

At $t = 3$,

$$a = 6 \cdot 3 + 4 = 22 \text{ ft per sec}^2$$
$$\text{Distance} = \int v\,dt = \int (3t^2 + 4t)\,dt = t^3 + 2t^2 + C$$

When $t = 0$, $d = 0$ and $C = 0$; therefore

$$d = t^3 + 2t^2$$

When $t = 3$,

$$d = 3^3 + 2 \cdot 9 = 27 + 18 = 45 \text{ ft}$$

example 5 An automobile moves along a straight, level road with a speed of v_0 fps. The operator applies the brakes at $t = 0$ in such a way as to bring the automobile to a stop with a constant, negative acceleration in 6 sec. The distance required to stop the automobile is 270 ft. Find the constant acceleration and v_0.

The velocity at any time is given by

$$v = \int a\,dt = at + C_1$$

When $t = 0$, $v = v_0$; therefore $C_1 = v_0$, and

$$v = at + v_0$$

When $t = 6$, $v = 0$ and $v_0 = -at = -6a$. Therefore $v = at - 6a$. Distance is given by

$$d = \int v\,dt = \frac{a}{2}t^2 - 6at + C_2$$

But when $t = 0$, $d = 0$ and $C_2 = 0$; therefore

$$d = \frac{a}{2}t^2 - 6at$$

When $t = 6$, $d = 270$ ft; therefore

$$270 = \frac{a}{2}6^2 - 6 \cdot a \cdot 6 = 18a - 36a = -18a$$

Then $$a = -270/18 = -15 \text{ ft/sec}^2$$

and $$v_0 = -6(-15) = 90 \text{ fps}$$

example 6 A flywheel is turning at the rate of ω_0 rpm at the instant the power is turned off. Over the next 5 sec the angular speed is given by

$$\omega = 100 - 15t + t^2$$

where ω is the angular speed in revolutions per minute. (a) Find ω_0. (b) Find the number of revolutions that the flywheel makes in the first 2 sec. (c) Find the angular acceleration at $t = 2$ sec.

From the given equation we see by inspection that $\omega_0 = 100$. The angular acceleration is given by

$$\alpha = \frac{d\omega}{dt} = -15 + 2t$$

At $t = 2$,

$$\alpha = -15 + 4 = -11 \text{ rev/sec}^2$$

The number of revolutions is given by

$$\text{rev} = \int \omega\,dt = \int (100 - 15t + t^2)\,dt$$

$$= 100t - 7.5t^2 + \frac{t^3}{3} + C$$

By the conditions of the problem $C = 0$.

From $t = 0$ to $t = 2$,

$$\text{rev} = 100 \cdot 2 - 7.5 \cdot 4 + 8/3 = 172.7$$

EXERCISE 4

1. A ship, while being launched, started from rest at $t = 0$ and slipped down the skids with a constant acceleration. The ship slid the first foot in 10 sec. That is, $s = 1$ ft when $t = 10$ sec, where s is the distance moved from the rest position. How long did it take the ship to slip 400 ft along the skids from the rest position?

2. The ram of a pile driver hits a pile at $t = 0$ and travels with it. The pile is driven 4 in. before coming to rest at $t = 0.05$ sec. Assuming the deceleration of the driver to be constant, find the speed of the ram (v_0 in. per sec) at the instant of impact.
3. An automobile is moving along a straight road at a speed v_0 of 60 mph when the driver decides to stop the car. The brakes are applied at $t = 0$ and slow the car down with a constant deceleration. The car comes to rest at $d = 75$ ft, where d is measured from the position of the car when $t = 0$. What is the deceleration, and how long does it take to stop the car?
4. During the 4-sec interval after the current is shut off at $t = 0$ the angular speed ω of a certain electric motor is given with sufficient accuracy for engineering purposes by the equation

$$\omega = 200 - 20t + 0.5t^2 \qquad \text{radians per sec}$$

where t is the time in seconds since the current was turned off.
(a) What was the angular speed at $t = 0$?
(b) What was the angular acceleration α at $t = 3$ sec?
(c) How many revolutions did the motor make between $t = 0$ and $t = 4$ sec?
(d) Does the angular acceleration increase or decrease during the interval between $t = 0$ and $t = 4$? Why?
5. The driver of a truck increases the power output of the engine by depressing the accelerator. The tractive effort on the road increases at a uniform rate of 24 lb per sec. The truck weighs 16,100 lb, and the frictional resistance to motion is always 400 lb. Determine the distance (s ft) that the truck moves in terms of time (t sec) since the driver started to increase power at $t = 0$. The speed of the truck at $t = 0$ was 10 fps.

Solution: By aid of Newton's second law of motion,

Total horizontal force = (mass)(acceleration in horizontal direction)

Hence

$$24t - 400 = \frac{16{,}100}{32.2}\frac{d^2s}{dt^2}$$

6. The braking resistance of a truck is 200 lb for each 1,000 lb of weight. If a truck weighs 15,000 lb and is traveling at a speed v_0 of 24 mph, determine the time t required to stop the truck and the distance s it will travel (in a horizontal direction) from its position at $t = 0$. Hint: From Newton's second law applied to this problem,

$$-200 \cdot 15 = \frac{15{,}000}{32.2}\frac{d^2s}{dt^2}$$

26 · 7 Freely falling bodies

It has been found that bodies falling freely near the earth's surface have, to a satisfactory approximation, a constant acceleration. This, of course, neglects air resistance.

It has been found that the acceleration of gravity is approximately

$$a = -32 \text{ ft/sec}^2$$

The negative sign appears because, conventionally, distances measured toward the center of the earth are considered to be negative whereas distances measured away from the center of the earth are considered to be positive.

From Eq. (43) it follows that

$$\frac{dv}{dt} = -32 \text{ ft/sec}^2 \tag{46}$$

or

$$v = \int -32\, dt \tag{47}$$

and

$$v = -32t + C_1 \tag{48}$$

Evidently C_1 is the velocity when $t = 0$. This is called the *initial* velocity and may also be designated as v_0. Thus Eq. (48) may be written

$$v = -32t + v_0 \tag{49}$$

Since

$$\frac{ds}{dt} = v$$

where s = the distance measured from some arbitrary zero reference point, we may write

$$s = \int v\, dt = \int(-32t + v_0)\, dt$$
$$s = -16t^2 + v_0 t + C_2 \tag{50}$$

example 7 A stone is dropped from a height of 288 ft. Write the equation for acceleration, velocity, and distance fallen.

This is a freely falling body; therefore acceleration is

$$a = -32 \text{ ft/sec}^2$$

Following Eq. (49),

$$v = -32t + v_0 \tag{51}$$

Since the stone was dropped and not thrown, its initial velocity v_0 is zero, and

$$v = -32t$$

From Eq. (50) where $v_0 = 0$,

$$s = -16t^2 + C_2$$

The constant C_2 is the distance when $t = 0$. In this case when $t = 0$, s is also zero, and therefore $C_2 = 0$. Consequently,

$$s = -16t^2$$

When dealing with freely falling bodies, it is perhaps more natural to write Eq. (50) with the following symbols:

$$h = -16t^2 + v_0t + h_0 \tag{52}$$

where h = altitude of freely falling body measured from surface of earth at time t
t = time measured from zero reference time t_0
v_0 = velocity at $t = 0$ (initial velocity)
h_0 = altitude when $t = 0$ (initial altitude)

Incidentally, the term "free fall" applies to upward motion as well as to downward motion.

Since in this example the initial velocity $v_0 = 0$ and the initial altitude $h_0 = 288$, the equation for altitude may be written

$$h = -16t^2 + 288$$

example 8 In Example 7 find the velocity with which the stone hit the ground.

The stone hit the ground when $h = 0$. Therefore

$$0 = -16t^2 + 288$$

or

$$16t^2 = 288$$

and

$$t = \pm\sqrt{288/16} = 1/4\sqrt{288} = \pm 1/4 \times 16.97 = \pm 4.24 \text{ sec}$$

We shall reject the negative root as physically meaningless in this particular problem.

The stone hit the ground when $t = 4.24$ sec. The equation for velocity is

$$v = -32t$$

Therefore, when the stone hit the ground,

$$v = -32 \times 4.24 = -135.7 \text{ fps}$$

example 9 A stone is thrown straight up from a roof 288 ft high with an initial speed of 48 fps. Find the equations for acceleration, velocity, and altitude.

As is always the case with a freely falling body,

$$a = -32$$

From Eq. (49) applied to this problem

$$v = -32t + 48$$

Note that since the initial velocity is in a positive direction, the sign of the initial velocity (in this case 48 fps) is positive.

From Eq. (52) applied to this problem

$$h = -16t^2 + 48t + 288$$

example 10 Find the velocity of the stone in Example 9 when $t = 1$ and when $t = 2$.

When $t = 1$,

$$v = -32(1) + 48 = +16 \text{ fps}$$

When $t = 2$,

$$v = -32(2) + 48 = -16 \text{ fps}$$

Since the sign of the velocity when $t = 1$ is positive, we know that the direction of motion at that time is upward. Since the sign of the velocity is negative when $t = 2$, we know that the direction of motion at that time is downward.

example 11 Find the altitude in Example 9 when $t = 1$ and when $t = 2$.

When $t = 1$,

$$h = -16(1)^2 + 48(1) + 288 = 320 \text{ ft}$$

When $t = 2$,

$$h = -16(2)^2 + 48(2) + 288 = 320 \text{ ft}$$

In other words, the stone passes the 320-ft line, going up when $t = 1$. It passes the same level going down when $t = 2$.

example 12 Find the maximum altitude attained by the stone in Example 9.

The maximum altitude occurs when the velocity is zero, that is, when

$$0 = -32t + 48$$

or

$$t = 48/32 = 1.5$$

When $t = 1.5$, the altitude is

$$h = -16(1.5)^2 + 48(1.5) + 288 = -16(2.25) + 48(1.5) + 288 = 324 \text{ ft (max)}$$

example 13 With what velocity did the stone hit the ground in Example 9?

The stone hit the ground when $h = 0$. Therefore we shall find what value of t makes the altitude zero.

$$0 = -16t^2 + 48t + 288$$
$$0 = -t^2 + 3t + 18$$
$$0 = (-t + 6)(t + 3)$$

or

$$t = 6, -3$$

Discarding the root $t = -3$ as physically meaningless for this particular problem, we substitute $t = 6$ in the equation for velocity, obtaining

$$v = -32(6) + 48 = -192 + 48 = -144 \text{ fps}$$

example 14 If a stone is thrown upward from ground level with an initial speed of 144 fps, when will it reach a velocity of +48 fps?

$$48 = -32t + 144$$
$$32t = 96$$
$$t = 3 \text{ sec}$$

Compare with the rejected root in Example 13.

example 15 What maximum altitude will the stone in Example 14 reach?

Maximum altitude occurs when $v = 0$.

$$0 = -32t + 144$$
$$t = 4.5 \text{ sec}$$
$$h_{\text{max}} = -16(4.5)^2 + 144(4.5) = -16 \times 20.25 + 144 \times 4.5$$
$$= -324 + 648 = +324$$

(Compare with Example 12.)

example 16 If the stone had been thrown straight down with a speed of 48 fps from a height of 288 ft, find the equation for acceleration, velocity, and altitude.

As is always the case with a freely falling body

$$a = -32 \text{ ft/sec}^2$$

From Eq. (49) applied to this problem

$$v = -32t - 48$$

Note that, since the initial velocity is in a negative direction, the sign of the initial velocity (in this case 48 fps) is negative.

From Eq. (52) applied to this problem

$$h = -16t^2 - 48t + 288$$

example 17 With what velocity will the stone hit the ground in Example 16?

$$0 = -16t^2 - 48t + 288$$
$$0 = -t^2 - 3t + 18$$
$$0 = (-t + 3)(t + 6)$$
$$t = 3, -6$$

We shall reject the root $t = -6$ as physically meaningless in this problem. The stone hit the ground when $t = 3$, and

$$v = -32(3) - 48 = -144$$

Compare with the velocity found in Example 13. Explain.

Figure 26·4 is a plot of the equation

$$h = -16t^2 + 48t + 288$$

Observe that the region of the graph between $t = 0$ and $t = 6$ applies to Examples 9, 10, and 11.

Note that from the symmetry of the graph, the slope at $t = 1$ and $t = 2$ must be equal in magnitude and opposite in sign (see Example 10).

The axis of symmetry of the graph is at $t = 1.5$, and at this time the altitude is 324 ft, which is the maximum altitude (see Example 12).

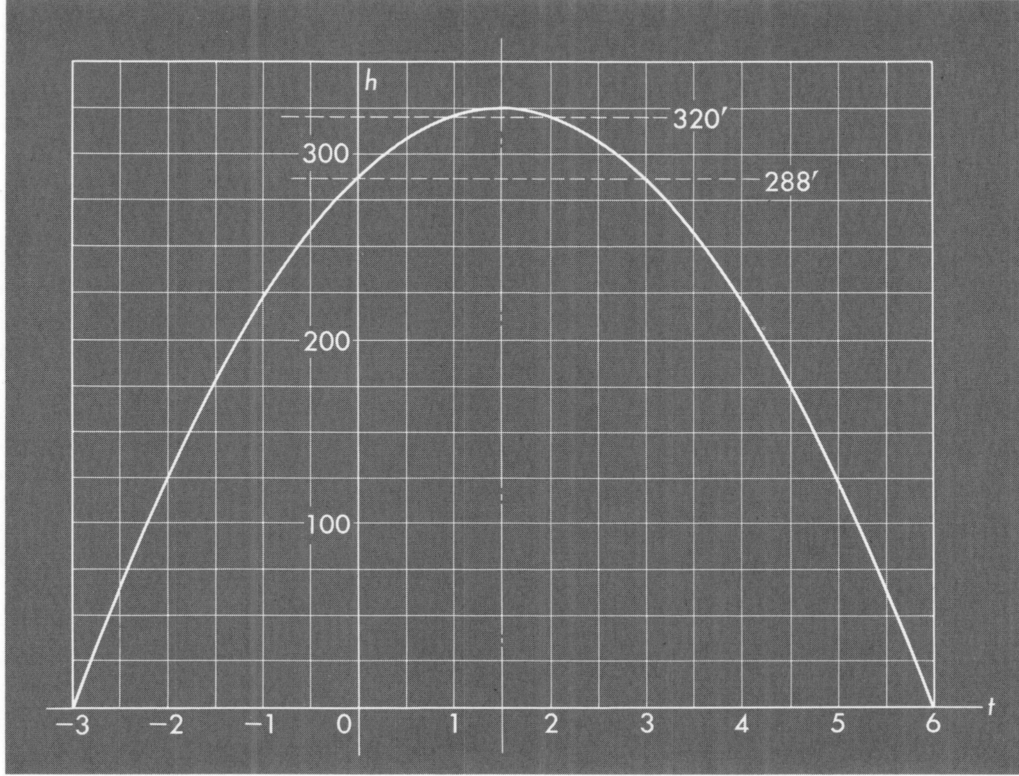

fig. 26·4

Considering only the mathematical relationship in the above equation, we find that $h = 0$ when $t = -3$ and when $t = +6$. Within the physical limitations imposed by the wording of Example 9, the root of $t = -3$ is meaningless (see Example 13).

However, if a stone had been thrown directly upward, 3 sec before our arbitrarily chosen zero reference time, with sufficient velocity to pass the 288-ft level with a velocity of +48 fps, the subsequent trajectory would be identical with the one prescribed by the statement of Example 9 (see Examples 14 and 15).

Observe that at the 288-ft level there are two velocities, equal in magnitude and opposite in sign, one occurring at $t = 0$ and the other occurring at $t = 3$. Considering, for example, the negative velocity when $t = +3$, it makes no difference to the subsequent trajectory whether this velocity is caused by a momentary thrust as is indicated in Example 16 or whether it is the cumulative effect of the force of gravity (see Examples 9, 10, 11, 12, and 13).

example 18 A ball is thrown horizontally from the top of a building 288 ft high with a speed of 50 fps (see Examples 7 and 8).

(a) How long did it take for the ball to reach the ground?

(b) What was the vertical component of velocity v_v at impact with the ground?
(c) What was the horizontal component of velocity v_h at impact?
(d) What was the angle between the impact velocity and the vertical?
(e) What was the absolute value of the impact velocity $|v|$?

It is shown in mechanics that if a projectile is thrown in a horizontal direction from a height h above ground, the horizontal component of velocity is constant and equal to the initial horizontal velocity. This is, of course, an approximation based on certain simplifying assumptions, one of which is the neglect of air resistance.

The vertical component of velocity is the same at any time t as it would be had the projectile been dropped instead of having been thrown in a horizontal direction. Therefore the situation discussed in Examples 7 and 8 is descriptive of the vertical component of the trajectory of the ball in this example. From Example 8, the time of flight is 4.24 sec.

The horizontal distance the ball travels in air is

$$d_h = v_h t = 50 \times 4.24 = 212 \text{ ft}$$

From Example 8 the vertical component of velocity v_v at impact is -135.7 fps.

If ϕ is the angle that the trajectory of the ball makes with the vertical at impact,

$$\cot \phi = \frac{135.7}{50} = 2.714$$

$$\phi = 20.2^\circ$$

The absolute value of the total velocity v_t at impact is

$$|v| = \sqrt{v_h^2 + v_v^2} = \sqrt{50^2 + (-135.7)^2} = 144.6 \text{ fps}$$

EXERCISE 5

1. A stone is dropped from a certain height h_0. Write the equation for its velocity and altitude in terms of time.
2. A stone is thrown downward with a velocity of 100 fps from a height of 192 ft. Write the equation for its velocity and altitude in terms of time.
3. A stone is thrown upward with a velocity of 100 fps from a height of 192 ft. Write the equation for its velocity and altitude as a function of time.
4. How long did it take the stone to reach the ground in Prob. 2? In Prob. 3?
5. With what velocity did the stone hit the ground in Prob. 2? In Prob. 3?
6. A ball is thrown upward from a roof 96 ft high with an initial speed of 80 fps. (a) When was the maximum altitude reached? (b) What was the maximum altitude? (c) When did the ball impact with the ground? (d) What was the speed at impact? (e) When was the ball 150 ft high

(two answers)? (f) Find the arithmetic average of the altitudes in part (e). On the same coordinate axes plot $y_1 = -16t^2, y_2 = 80t$, and $y_3 = 96$. By adding these ordinates, produce the graph of altitude versus time.

7. How long will it take for a stone to reach the ground if it is dropped from a height of 1,024 ft?

8. A bomber is traveling horizontally at a height of h ft with a speed of 300 mph = 440 fps. Neglecting air resistance, etc., determine how far ahead of a target the bomb should be released if (a) $h = 10{,}000$ ft; (b) $h = 20{,}000$ ft; (c) $h = 30{,}000$ ft. Also, compute for each case the angle that the bomb makes with the vertical on impact with a horizontal target. What is the theoretical speed of the bomb for each of these three cases just before impact?

The following table gives the *observed* striking speeds and angles of impact:

Altitude, ft	*Striking speed, mph*	*Angle of impact with vertical, deg*
2,000	540	50
4,000	620	40
6,000	690	34
8,000	750	30
10,000	790	26
12,000	830	24
15,000	870	21
20,000	940	17

26·8 Area under graphs

One of the most important uses for the integration process is in finding the area under curvilinear graphs (see also Sec. 24·9).

Suppose we have given a function f where $y = f(x)$ such as the one illustrated in Fig. 26·5, which is continuous and positive valued over the domain $a \leq x \leq b$. We wish to find the area aP_1P_2b.

To develop a technique for finding such areas we shall make free use of geometric intuition. Therefore, the details of the argument which we shall present will depend on the appearance of the graphs we have chosen to use.

In Fig. 26·6 we think of the ordinate y as a movable ordinate sweeping over a portion of the area involved and now momentarily occupying the position shown in Fig. 26·6. The momentary value of the area passed over by the moving ordinate depends on the momentary value of x.

Let the area passed over by the moving ordinate y between $x = a$ and some value of x equal to or greater than a be designated as $A_a{}^x$. Then the area $A_a{}^x$ is a variable area bounded by the arc P_1P_2, the fixed ordinate aP_1, that portion of the x axis between a and x, and the movable ordinate y.

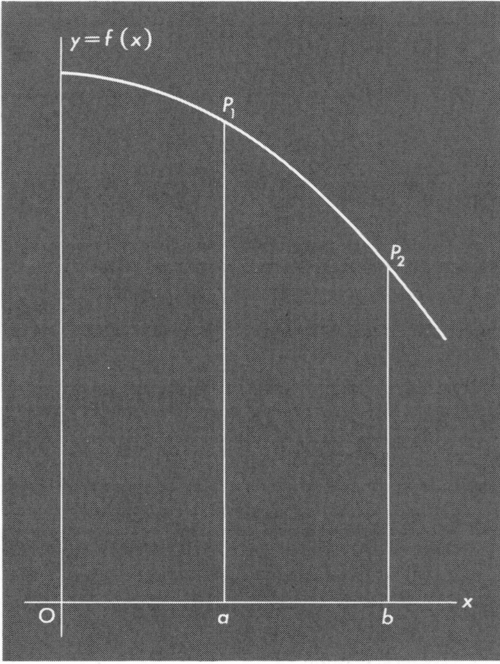

fig. 26·5

fig. 26·6

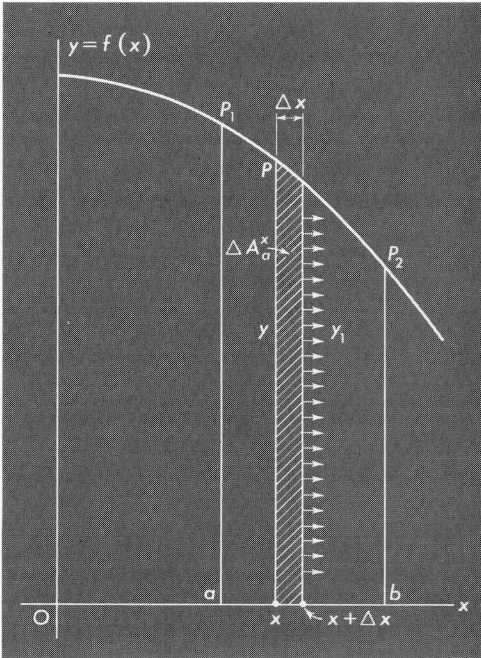

Now let us move the ordinate y to the right, Δx units, so that it then occupies position y_1, thereby increasing $A_a{}^x$ by the amount $\Delta A_a{}^x$.

Note that the motion along the x axis is in the direction conventionally considered to be positive. Consequently, Δx is considered to be positive.

Now see Fig. 26·7. In this figure we shall assume what is intuitively obvious, that there is an ordinate y^* which can be constructed between the ordinates y and y_1 such that

$$\Delta A_a{}^x = y^* \, \Delta x \tag{53}$$

Then

$$\frac{\Delta A_a{}^x}{\Delta x} = y^* \tag{54}$$

Now from Sec. 25·3 the limit which $\Delta A_a{}^x/\Delta x$ approaches as Δx approaches zero is $dA_a{}^x/dx$. By observing Fig. 26·7 we see that as Δx approaches zero, the ordinate y_1 is moved to the left in such a way that y^* approaches the length y. It is therefore appropriate to write

$$\lim_{\Delta x \to 0} \frac{\Delta A_a{}^x}{\Delta x} = \frac{dA_a{}^x}{dx} = y \tag{55}$$

Thus while we have not yet found an explicit equation for $A_a{}^x$ in terms of x, we have found a differential equation which $A_a{}^x$ must satisfy.

This differential equation shows that the rate of change in $A_a{}^x$ equals the ordinate of the *right-hand* boundary of the area $A_a{}^x$. This rate depends not at all on the choice of the *left-hand* boundary. However, the importance of the left-hand boundary will be made evident in Example 19 below.

From Eq. (55) we may write

$$dA_a{}^x = y\,dx \tag{56}$$

or

$$A_a{}^x = \int y\,dx$$

It is also common to designate the area involved simply as A, without explicitly indicating the boundaries. Therefore, we may write

$$A_a{}^x = A = \int y\,dx \tag{57}$$

When actually doing area problems where there is no need for considering the details of the theory involved, we frequently work from simplified drawings such as Fig. 26·8. Here we sometimes speak of the very narrow strip shown as having an area dA, an altitude y, and a width dx, where

$$dA = y\,dx$$

thus suggesting Eq. (57) above.

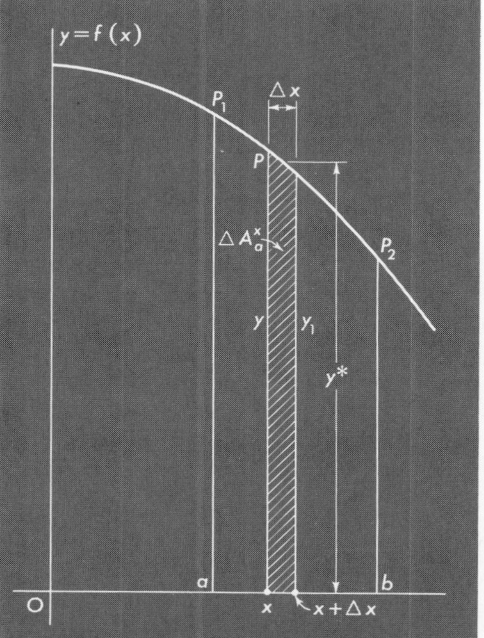

fig. 26·7

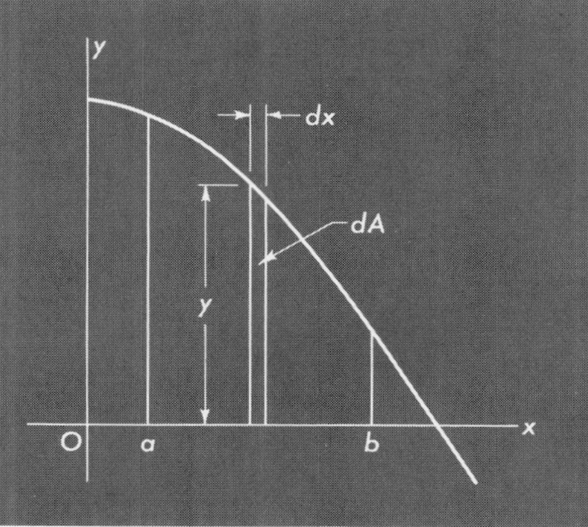

fig. 26·8

If $y = f(x)$ we may, following Eq. (57), write

$$A_a{}^x = \int f(x)\,dx \tag{58}$$

In Sec. 26·9 we shall find it convenient to use the symbolism shown in Eq. (6) and write Eq. (58) as

$$A_a{}^x = \int f(x)\,dx = F(x) + C \tag{59}$$

example 19 Find the area under the graph of $y = 100 - x^2$ between $x = 3$ and $x = 6$ (see Fig. 26·9).

Following Eq. (57),

$$A_a{}^x = \int y\,dx = \int(100 - x^2)\,dx = 100x - \frac{x^3}{3} + C \tag{60a}$$

Now let $A_3{}^x$ designate the area under the curve between the ordinate erected at $x = 3$ and any ordinate erected at some abscissa distance equal to or greater than 3. Then we may write

$$A_3{}^x = 100x - \frac{x^3}{3} + C$$

The problem now is to evaluate the constant of integration. As we indicated in Sec. 26·4, this is done in accordance with some known boundary condition. The appropriate boundary condition to use here is that at the left-hand boundary of the area under consideration (namely, $x = 3$); the area is zero. Therefore we may write

$$A_3{}^3 = 0 = 100 \cdot 3 - \frac{3^3}{3} + C \tag{60b}$$

and

$$0 = 300 - 9 + C = 291 + C \tag{60c}$$

and

$$C = -291 \tag{60d}$$

Substituting the value of the constant found above, we obtain

$$A_3{}^x = 100x - \frac{x^3}{3} - 291 \tag{60e}$$

Equation (60*e*) gives the area under the graph of $y = 100 - x^2$ between an ordinate erected at $x = 3$ and an ordinate erected at some arbitrary value of x equal to or greater than 3, say at $x = b$. Of course, over the interval $a \rightarrow b$ it is understood that the graph is everywhere continuous and non-negative.

When $x = 6$, we have

$$A_3{}^6 = 100 \cdot 6 - \frac{6^3}{3} - 291 = 600 - 72 - 291 = 237 \tag{60f}$$

Observe that in the above argument we have restricted Δx to positive values. That is, we have considered the moving ordinate always to move from left to right. We could as well have adopted the opposite convention of motion. The same result is obtained in either case. The only difference would be in a reversal of certain signs in the course of the argument.

Let us now apply Eq. (57) to the equation given in Example 20 below.

example 20 Find the area under the graph of $y = -100 + x^2$ between $x = 3$ and $x = 6$ (see Fig. 26·10).

Following Eq. (57),

$$A_a{}^x = \int y\,dx = \int(-100 + x^2)\,dx = -100x + \frac{x^3}{3} + C \qquad (61a)$$

From the left-hand boundary condition,

$$0 = A_3{}^3 = -100\cdot 3 + \frac{3^3}{3} + C = -300 + 9 + C \qquad (61b)$$

$$0 = -291 + C \qquad (61c)$$

and

$$C = +291 \qquad (61d)$$

Consequently,

$$A_3{}^x = -100x + \frac{x^3}{3} + 291 \qquad (61e)$$

When $x = 6$, we have

$$A_3{}^6 = -100\cdot 6 + \frac{6^3}{3} + 291 = -600 + 72 + 291 = -237 \qquad (61f)$$

If we compare Eq. (60*f*) and Fig. 26·9 with Eq. (61*f*) and Fig. 26·10, it would appear that in this context we may consider a region which lies below the x axis as having a "negative" area.

example 21 Find the area under the graph of $y = 25 - x^2$ between $x = 3$ and $x = 5$ (see Fig. 26·11).

Following Eq. (57),

$$A_a{}^x = \int y\,dx = \int(25 - x^2)\,dx = 25x - \frac{x^3}{3} + C \qquad (62a)$$

From the left-hand boundary condition,

$$0 = A_3{}^3 = 25\cdot 3 - \frac{3^3}{3} + C \qquad (62b)$$

$$0 = 25\cdot 3 - \frac{3^3}{3} + C = 75 - 9 + C \qquad (62c)$$

and

$$C = -66 \qquad (62d)$$

Consequently,

$$A_3{}^x = 25x - \frac{x^3}{3} - 66 \qquad (62e)$$

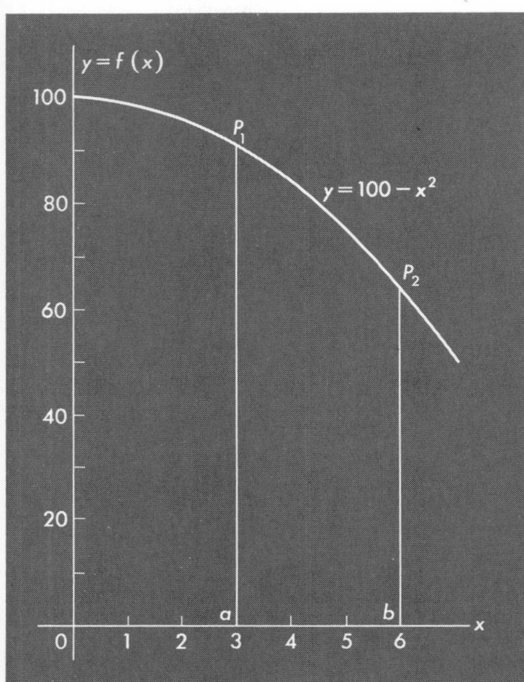

fig. 26·9

fig. 26·10

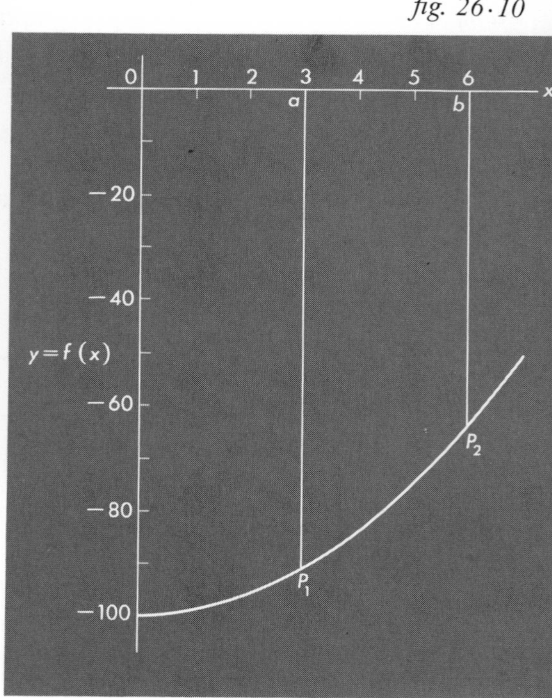

fig. 26·11

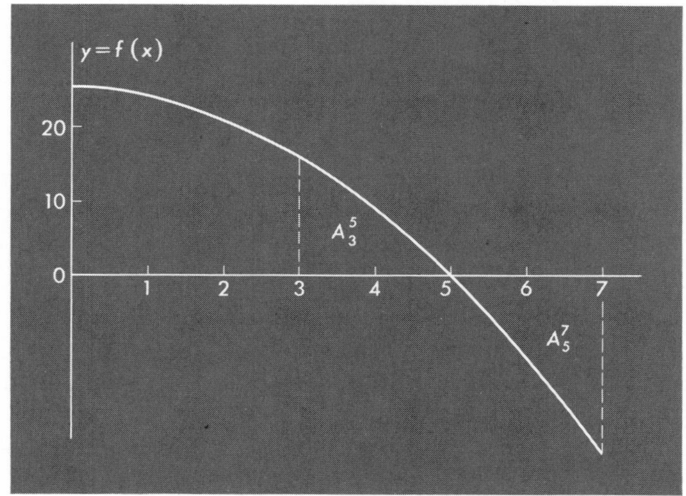

When $x = 5$, we have

$$A_3{}^5 = 25 \cdot 5 - \frac{5^3}{3} - 66 = 125 - 41\tfrac{2}{3} - 66 = 17\tfrac{1}{3} \tag{62f}$$

example 22 Find the area under the graph of $y = 25 - x^2$ between $x = 5$ and $x = 7$ (see Fig. 26·11).

Following Eq. (57),

$$A_a{}^x = \int y\,dx = \int (25 - x^2)\,dx = 25x - \frac{x^3}{3} + C \tag{63a}$$

From the left-hand boundary condition,

$$0 = A_5{}^5 = 25 \cdot 5 - \frac{5^3}{3} + C = 125 - 41\tfrac{2}{3} + C \tag{63b}$$

and

$$0 = 83\tfrac{1}{3} + C \tag{63c}$$

and

$$C = -83\tfrac{1}{3} \tag{63d}$$

Consequently, $A_5{}^x = 25x - \dfrac{x^3}{3} - 83\tfrac{1}{3}$ (63e)

When $x = 7$, we have

$$A_5{}^7 = 25 \cdot 7 - \frac{7^3}{3} - 83\tfrac{1}{3} = 175 - 114\tfrac{1}{3} - 83\tfrac{1}{3} = -22\tfrac{2}{3} \tag{63f}$$

example 23 Find the area under the graph of $y = 25 - x^2$ between $x = 3$ and $x = 7$ (see Fig. 26·11).

Following Eq. (57),

$$A_a{}^x = \int y\,dx = \int (25 - x^2)\,dx = 25x - \frac{x^3}{3} + C \tag{64a}$$

From the left-hand boundary condition,

$$0 = A_3{}^3 = 25 \cdot 3 - \frac{3^3}{3} + C = 75 - 9 + C \tag{64b}$$

and

$$0 = 66 + C \tag{64c}$$

$$C = -66 \tag{64d}$$

Consequently, $A_3{}^x = 25x - \dfrac{x^3}{3} - 66$ (64e)

When $x = 7$,

$$A_3{}^7 = 25 \cdot 7 - \frac{7^3}{3} - 66 = 175 - 114\tfrac{1}{3} - 66 = -5\tfrac{1}{3} \tag{64f}$$

We note here that within the context of our present discussion the process of integration automatically counts the area of a region above the x axis as positive and the region below the x axis as negative.

The result is the algebraic sum of these areas. That is, from Examples 21, 22, and 23 referred to Fig. 26·11:

$$A_3{}^7 = A_3{}^5 + A_5{}^7 = 17\tfrac{1}{3} + (-22\tfrac{2}{3}) = -5\tfrac{1}{3}$$

If the graph crosses the x axis between $x = a$ and $x = b$, say, for example, at $x = c$, and if we want the absolute value of the area (sometimes called the geometric area) between ordinates erected at $x = a$ and $x = b$, we integrate between $x = a$ and $x = c$ to find $A_a{}^c$. We integrate again between $x = c$ and $x = b$ to find $A_c{}^b$. Then

$$|A_a{}^b| = |A_a{}^c| + |A_c{}^b| \tag{65}$$

example 24 Find the area under the graph of $y = \tfrac{1}{2}x - 6$ between $x = 0$ and $x = 12$ (see Fig. 26·12).

$$A = \int y\,dx = \int \left(\frac{1}{2}x - 6\right) dx = \frac{x^2}{4} - 6x + C \tag{66}$$

When $x = 0$, $A = 0$, and $C = 0$; therefore

$$A_0{}^x = \frac{x^2}{4} - 6x \tag{67}$$

When $x = 12$,

$$A_0{}^{12} = {}^{144}\!/\!_4 - 72 = 36 - 72 = -36$$

example 25 Find the area under the graph $y = \tfrac{1}{2}x - 6$ between $x = 12$ and $x = 24$ (see Fig. 26·12).

$$A = \frac{x^2}{4} - 6x + C$$

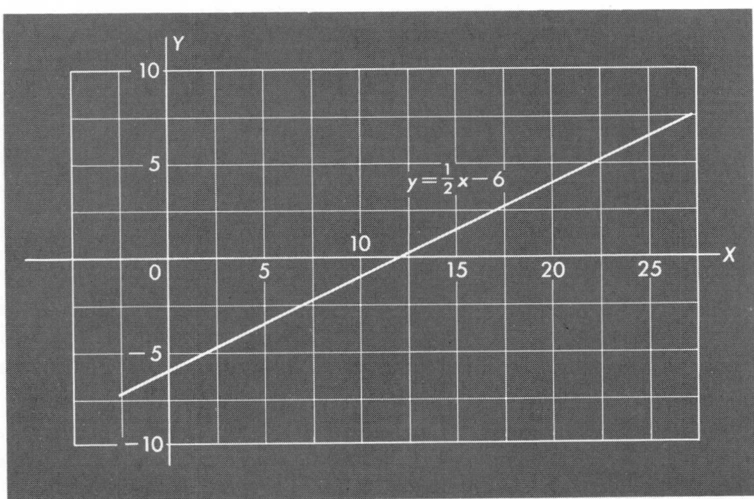

fig. 26·12

When $x = 12$, $A = 0$, and

$$0 = \frac{12^2}{4} - 6(12) + C = 36 - 72 + C$$
$$C = +36$$
$$A_{12}^{24} = {}^{576}\!/\!_4 - 144 + 36 = 144 - 144 + 36 = 36$$

example 26 Find the area under the graph of $y = \frac{1}{2}x - 6$ between $x = 0$ and $x = 24$.

$$A_0^x = \frac{x^2}{4} - 6x \qquad \text{[see Eq. (67)]}$$
$$A_0^{24} = {}^{576}\!/\!_4 - 144 = 144 - 144 = 0$$

From an observation of Fig. 26·12 we can see the reason for the zero answer. The area between $x = 0$ and $x = 12$ is -36. The area between $x = 12$ and $x = 24$ is $+36$. The sum of these two areas is (algebraically) zero.

However, the absolute value of A_0^{24} is

$$|A_0^{24}| = |A_0^{12}| + |A_{12}^{24}| = |-36| + |+36| = 72$$

example 27 Find the absolute value of the area under the graph of $y = 100 - x^2$ between $x = 5$ and $x = 15$.

Let us find what value of x makes y equal to zero.

$$0 = 100 - x^2$$
$$x^2 = 100$$
$$x = \pm 10$$

The root $x = +10$ occurs between the two boundary ordinates of the problem. (The boundary ordinates occur at $x = +5$ and $+15$.)

As a first step we shall find the area under the graph between $x = 5$ and $x = 10$. Then we shall find the area between $x = 10$ and $x = 15$.

$$A = \int y\,dx = \int (100 - x^2)\,dx = 100x - \frac{x^3}{3} + C$$

When $x = 5$, $A = 0$; therefore

$$0 = 500 - \frac{125}{3} + C = \frac{1{,}500 - 125}{3} + C$$
$$C = -\frac{1{,}375}{3}$$
$$A_5^x = 100x - \frac{x^3}{3} - \frac{1{,}375}{3} \qquad (68)$$
$$A_5^{10} = 1{,}000 - \frac{1{,}000}{3} - \frac{1{,}375}{3} = \frac{625}{3}$$

Now let us find the area under the graph between $x = 10$ and $x = 15$. When $x = 10$, $A = 0$; therefore

$$0 = 1{,}000 - \frac{1{,}000}{3} + C$$

$$C = -\frac{2{,}000}{3}$$

$$A_{10}{}^{x} = 100x - \frac{x^3}{3} - \frac{2{,}000}{3}$$

$$A_{10}{}^{15} = \frac{4{,}500 - 3{,}375 - 2{,}000}{3} = -\frac{875}{3}$$

The *absolute* value of the required area is

$$|A_5{}^{15}| = \frac{625}{3} + \frac{875}{3} = \frac{1{,}500}{3} = 500$$

Had we integrated directly over the entire region between $x = 5$ and $x = 15$, we would have substituted $x = 15$ in Eq. (68), obtaining

$$A_5{}^{15} = 1{,}500 - \frac{3{,}375}{3} - \frac{1{,}375}{3} = \frac{4{,}500 - 3{,}375 - 1{,}375}{3} = -\frac{250}{3} \qquad (69)$$

Observe that the *algebraic* sum of the area between $x = 5$ and $x = 10$ added to the area between $x = 10$ and $x = 15$ is

$$625/3 - 875/3 = -250/3$$

which agrees with Eq. (69).

example 28 Find the area under the graph of $y = 3\sqrt{x}$ between $x = +9$ and $x = +36$.

$$A = \int y\,dx = \int 3\sqrt{x}\,dx = \int 3x^{1/2}\,dx = 2x^{3/2} + C$$

When $x = +9$, $A = 0$, and

$$0 = 2(9)^{3/2} + C$$
$$C = -54$$

Then

$$A_9{}^{x} = 2x^{3/2} - 54$$
$$A_9{}^{36} = 2(36)^{3/2} - 54 = 432 - 54 = 378$$

example 29 Find the area under the graph of $y = 6/x^2$ between $x = 2$ and $x = \infty$.

$$A = \int y\,dx = \int \frac{6}{x^2}\,dx = \int 6x^{-2}\,dx = -6x^{-1} + C = -\frac{6}{x} + C$$

When $x = 2$, $A = 0$, and

$$0 = -6/2 + C$$

$$C = +3$$

$$A_2{}^x = -\frac{6}{x} + 3$$

$$A_2{}^\infty = -\frac{6}{\infty} + 3 = 0 + 3 = 3$$

EXERCISE 6

Find the areas under the following curves between the specified limits:

1. $y = x^2/4$ between $x = 4$ and $x = 10$
2. $y = 6\sqrt{x}$ between $x = 4$ and $x = 9$
3. $y = 9 - x^2$ between $x = -3$ and $x = +3$
4. $y = x^2 - 4$ between $x = -2$ and $x = +2$
5. $y = 16/x^3$ between $x = 1$ and $x = 4$
6. $y = 8/x^2$ between $x = 1$ and $x = \infty$
7. $y = \sqrt{x + 9}$ between $x = 0$ and $x = 16$
8. Find the area under the graph of $y = mx + b$ between $x = 0$ and $x = h$. Show that your answer confirms the formula for the area of a trapezoid.
9. Figure 24·23 was plotted from the equation $a = (\pi/16)h^2$. Confirm your answer to Prob. 17, Exercise 5, Chap. 24, by integration.
10. If the area under the graph of $y = 6\sqrt{x}$ is 108 between $x = 4$ and $x = b$, find b.

26·9 The definite integral

Let us approach the problem of finding the area under a curve in a somewhat different way.

example 30 Find the area under the graph of $y = f(x)$ between $x = a$ and $x = b$ (see Fig. 26·9).

The student will find it profitable to compare the following steps with those in Examples 19, 20, and 21.

Following Eq. (58),

$$A_a{}^x = \int f(x)\,dx \tag{70}$$

For the work to follow, it will be convenient to adopt the symbolism of Eq. (6) and let

$$\int f(x)\,dx = F(x) \tag{71}$$

[The constant of integration which the student might expect to see in the above equation will be incorporated in Eq. (72) below.] Then

$$A_a{}^x = F(x) + C \tag{72}$$

Compare with Eqs. (60*a*), (61*a*), and (62*a*) in Examples 19, 20, and 21.

However, from the left-hand boundary condition, $A = 0$ when $x = a$. We may now write

$$0 = F(a) + C \tag{73}$$

or

$$C = -F(a) \tag{74}$$

Then Eq. (72) becomes

$$A_a{}^x = F(x) - F(a) \tag{75}$$

which is a formula for the area A between the ordinate erected at $x = a$ and the ordinate erected at any x_1 such that $x_1 \geq x$. In particular, for this example,

$$A_a{}^b = F(b) - F(a) \tag{76}$$

Equation (76) above is particularly important. The value of $A_a{}^b$ is obtained by integrating $f(x)$ to obtain $F(x)$. Then x is replaced in $F(x)$ by b and a in turn. The final result is obtained by subtracting $F(a)$ from $F(b)$.

Where $F(x)$ is an indefinite integral of $f(x)$, we commonly express $F(b) - F(a)$ by the symbol $\int_a^b f(x)\,dx$. Thus

$$\int_a^b f(x)\,dx = F(b) - F(a) \tag{77}$$

where $\int_a^b f(x)\,dx$ is called the *definite integral* of $f(x)$ between the limits $x = a$ and $x = b$.

By reference to Eqs. (77) and (58) we see that we may write

$$A_a{}^b = \int_a^b f(x)\,dx \tag{78}$$

If we let

$$y = f(x)$$

then we may write Eq. (78) as

$$A_a{}^b = \int_a^b y\,dx \tag{79}$$

The problem layout for Example 19, using the definite integral techniques, would be constructed as shown below.

$$A_3{}^6 = \int_3^6 y\,dx \tag{80}$$

In this case $y = 100 - x^2$. Therefore we may write

$$A_3{}^6 = \int_3^6 (100 - x^2)\,dx = \left[100x - \frac{x^3}{3}\right]_3^6$$

$$= \left(100 \cdot 6 - \frac{6^3}{3}\right) - \left(100 \cdot 3 - \frac{3^3}{3}\right)$$

$$= (600 - 72) - (300 - 9) = 528 - 291 = 237$$

example 31 Find the area under the graph of $y = \frac{1}{2}x + 2$ between $x = -4$ and $x = 0$ (see Fig. 26·13).

$$A_{-4}^{0} = \int_{-4}^{0} \left(\frac{1}{2}x + 2\right) dx = \left[\frac{x^2}{4} + 2x\right]_{-4}^{0} = 0 - \left(\frac{16}{4} - 8\right)$$

$$= -(4 - 8) = -(-4) = +4$$

example 32 Find the area under the graph of $y = \frac{1}{2}x + 2$ between $x = -4$ and $x = +4$.

$$A_{-4}^{+4} = \int_{-4}^{+4} \left(\frac{1}{2}x + 2\right) dx$$

$$= \left[\frac{x^2}{4} + 2x\right]_{-4}^{+4} = \left(\frac{16}{4} + 8\right) - \left(\frac{16}{4} - 8\right) = (4 + 8) - (4 - 8)$$

$$= 12 - (-4) = 12 + 4 = 16$$

example 33 Find the area under the graph of $y = 3\sqrt{x}$ between $x = +9$ and $x = +36$.

$$A_9^{36} = \int_9^{36} 3x^{1/2}\, dx$$

$$= [2x^{3/2}]_9^{36} = (2 \times 216) - (2 \times 27)$$

$$= (432) - (54) = 378$$

Compare with Example 28.

fig. 26·13

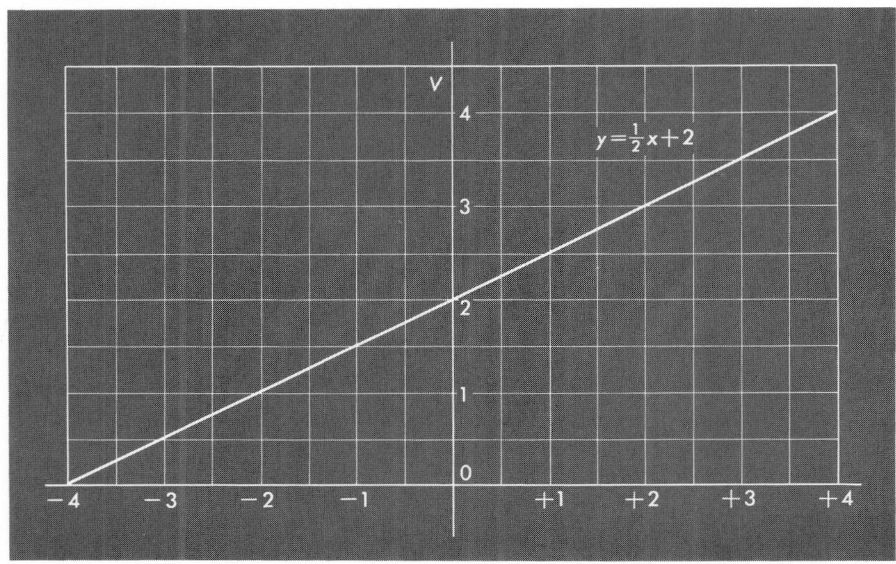

example 34 Find the area under the graph of $y = 6/x^2$ between $x = 2$ and $x = \infty$.

$$A_2{}^\infty = \int_2^\infty 6x^{-2}\,dx$$

$$= [-6x^{-1}]_2^\infty = \left[-\frac{6}{x}\right]_2^\infty = 0 - (-3) = +3$$

26·10 The mean value of a function

In Sec. 24·6 we discussed in an intuitive way what we mean by the *average* or *mean* ordinate of a graph. Figure 24·22 illustrates the graph of a function that is continuous on the closed interval with end points at a and b. We let $\bar{y}$ designate the average or mean ordinate of the graph between the limits a and b. We then defined $\bar{y}$ such that

$$\bar{y} = \frac{1}{b - a} \times \text{area under graph between } a \text{ and } b$$

Now that we have seen how to calculate the area under a graph, we may write

$$\bar{y} = \frac{1}{b - a}\int_a^b y\,dx \tag{81}$$

The above definition of an average ordinate is suggestive of a useful definition unrestricted by any graphical context.

If we have a function f which is continuous for $a \leq x \leq b$, we define the average value $\bar{y}$ of the function over this interval to be such that

$$\bar{y} = \frac{1}{b - a}\int_a^b f(x)\,dx \tag{82}$$

The practical applications of Eqs. (81) and (82) are many and varied. We shall point out some of them as we proceed through the rest of this chapter.

example 35 Find the average ordinate of the graph of the equation

$$y = 100 - x^2$$

between $x = 4$ and $x = 6$.

$$A_4{}^6 = \int_4^6 (100 - x^2)\,dx = \left[100x - \frac{x^3}{3}\right]_4^6 = (600 - 72) - (400 - 21.33)$$

$$= 528 - 378.67 = 149.33$$

$$\bar{y} = \frac{149.33}{6 - 4} = \frac{149.33}{2} = 74.67 \tag{83}$$

example 36 Find the average ordinate of the graph in Example 33.

The area under this graph within the prescribed limits is 378. The base interval is $36 - 9 = 27$. Therefore

$$\bar{y} = 378/27 = 14.00$$

EXERCISE 7

Find the average value of the functions defined in Probs. 1 through 6 below between the specified limits. Use the definite integral symbolism (also see Exercise 5).

1. $y = x^2/4$ between $x = 4$ and $x = 10$
2. $y = 6\sqrt{x}$ between $x = 4$ and $x = 9$
3. $y = 9 - x^2$ between $x = -3$ and $x = +3$
4. $y = x^2 - 4$ between $x = -2$ and $x = +2$
5. $y = 16/x^3$ between $x = 1$ and $x = 4$
6. $y = \sqrt{x + 9}$ between $x = 0$ and $x = 16$

7. Figure 26·14 shows a cantilever beam of length L ft loaded with a concentrated load of P lb at the free end. The equation of the curve of the beam with respect to the indicated axes is $EIy = (P/6)(3Lx^2 - x^3)$, where E and I are constants.

Figure 26·15 shows a similar cantilever beam of the same length and cross section but loaded with a uniform load of w lb per ft. The equation of the curve of the beam in this case is $EIy = (w/24)(6L^2x^2 - 4Lx^3 + x^4)$, where E and I are the same constants as before.

Suppose that the total load is the same in both cases so that $P = wL$ lb. Show that the *average ordinate* to the first curve for the span L ft is equal to the largest ordinate (the ordinate at $x = L$) to the second curve. Hence show that for any cantilever beam the *mean* deflection produced by a vertical load applied at the free end is equal to the deflection at the free end caused by the same load distributed uniformly over the length of the beam.

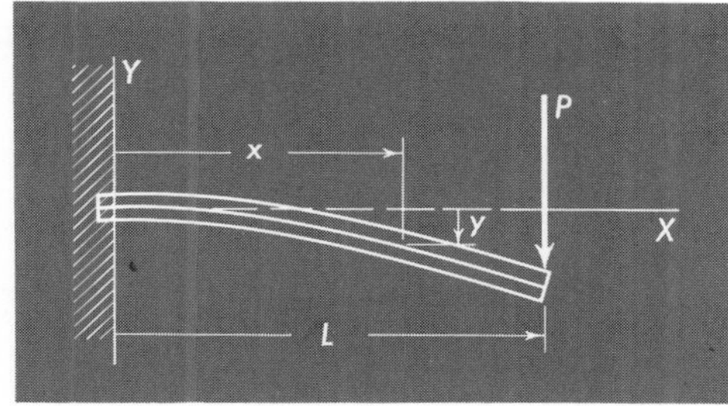

fig. 26·14

fig. 26·15

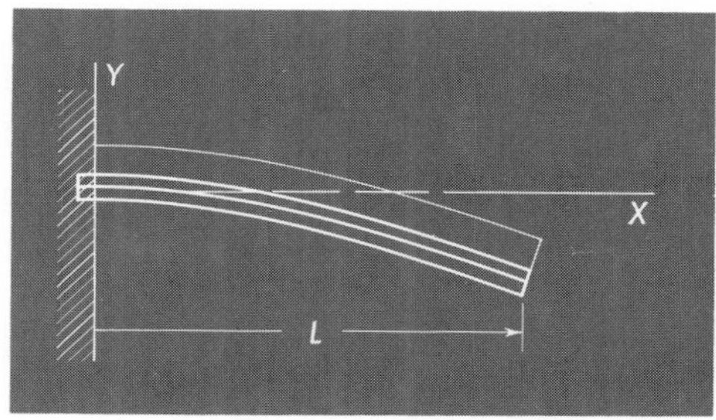

26·11 An area as the limit of a sum

In Sec. 24·9 and also in Secs. 26·8 and 26·9 we discussed, in some detail, methods of calculating the area of plane figures bounded by at least one curve.

It might appear that it is hardly worth while to go into this matter any more. However, by doing so we can develop techniques for many highly important problems having nothing to do with areas.

At this time the student should review Sec. 24·9, with particular emphasis on Eqs. (7) and (8).

To continue the present discussion, let the curve in Fig. 26·16 represent a function f such that $f(x) = y$, which is continuous and positive-valued over the domain $a \leq x \leq b$. We now divide this interval into n equal parts. Although it is not strictly necessary that they be equal, it is a convenience and does no harm. This division is accomplished by establishing partition points at

$$(a = x_0) < x_1 < x_2 < x_3 < x_{n-1} < (x_n = b)$$

Ordinates are erected at these points. The region under the graph between $x = a$ and $x = b$ is thus divided into strips of width $\Delta x = x_1 - x_0$, $\Delta x = x_2 - x_1$, $\Delta x = x_3 - x_2$, etc.

An approximation to the area of each strip can be obtained by multiplying Δx by some intermediate ordinate such as $y_1^*, y_2^*, y_3^*, y_n^*$, etc. This product, of course, gives the exact area of the corresponding rectangle (see Fig. 26·16).

Once again we remind the student that certain of the more sophisticated aspects of the present argument are omitted here. His geometric intuition should be quite sufficient, however.

The area under the graph between $x = a$ and $x = b$ can be approximated by

$$A_a{}^b \simeq y_1^*(\Delta x) + y_2^*(\Delta x) + y_3^*(\Delta x) + \cdots + y_n^*(\Delta x) \tag{84}$$

[Also see Eq. (7), Chap. 24.]

The right member of Eq. (84) is exactly the sum of the areas of the rectangles, where

$$\Delta x = \frac{b - a}{n}$$

y_1^* = any ordinate erected within 1st interval

y_2^* = any ordinate erected within 2d interval

y_3^* = any ordinate erected within 3d interval

y_n^* = any ordinate erected within nth interval

It should be intuitively evident that the area aP_0P_1b is the limit that the sum of the areas of these rectangles approaches as the number of

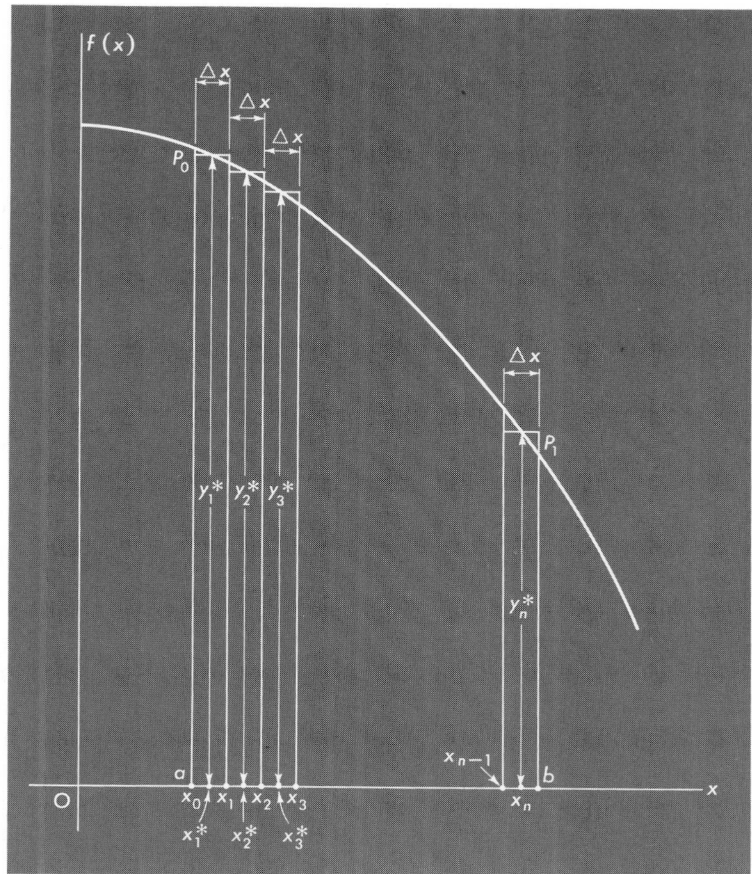

fig. 26·16

the rectangles increases. That is, we may write

$$A_a{}^b = \lim_{n\to\infty} [y_1^*(\Delta x) + y_2^*(\Delta x) + y_3^*(\Delta x) + \cdots + y_n^*(\Delta x)] \tag{85}$$

Equation (85) can be abbreviated to

$$A_a{}^b = \lim_{n\to\infty} \sum_1^n (y_k^*)\, \Delta x \tag{86}$$

[Compare with Eq. (8), Chap. 24.]

The symbol $\sum_1^n (y_k^*)\, \Delta x$ designates the sum whose typical (or kth) term is $(y_k^*)\, \Delta x$, where k may take on, in turn, any integral value between 1 and n.

If we replace $A_a{}^b$ in Eq. (86) by its equivalent from Eq. (79), we find

$$\int_a^b y\, dx = \lim_{n\to\infty} \sum_1^n (y_k^*)\, \Delta x \tag{87}$$

When we are dealing with areas, the quantity $(y_k^*)\ \Delta x$ denotes the approximate area of a typical strip whose height is y_k^* and whose width is Δx.

If $y = f(x)$, it is sometimes convenient to alter Eq. (87) to read

$$A_a{}^b = \lim_{n\to\infty} [f(x_1^*) + f(x_2^*) + f(x_3^*) + \cdots + f(x_n^*)]\ \Delta x \tag{88}$$

where $x_1^*, x_2^*, x_3^*, \cdots, x_n^*$ are points within the first, second, third, and nth subdivisions of the interval between $x = a$ and $x = b$. The width of each subdivision is Δx.

Equation (88) can be abbreviated to

$$A_a{}^b = \lim_{n\to\infty} \sum_1^n f(x_k^*)\ \Delta x \tag{89}$$

The symbol $\sum_1^n f(x_k^*)\ \Delta x$ designates the sum whose typical (or kth) term is $f(x_k^*)\ \Delta x$, where k may take on, in turn, any integral value between 1 and n.

If we replace $A_a{}^b$ in Eq. (89) by its equivalent from Eq. (78), we obtain

$$\int_a^b f(x)\ dx = \lim_{n\to\infty} \sum_1^n f(x_k^*)\ \Delta x \tag{90}$$

To avoid the use of relatively complex working drawings such as Fig. 26·16, indicating a large number of elemental areas, we often simplify a drawing such as Fig. 26·16 to one such as Fig. 26·17. Here we show only one elementary area, but the implication is clear that the area under the curve between $x = a$ and $x = b$ is the limit that the sum of a series of these elemental areas approaches as their number increases without limit.

It is quite common to indicate the area of an elemental strip as

$$dA = y\ dx \tag{91}$$

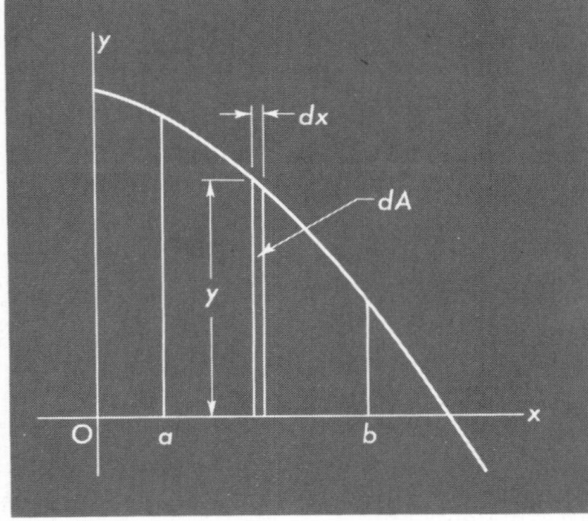

fig. 26·17

fig. 26·18

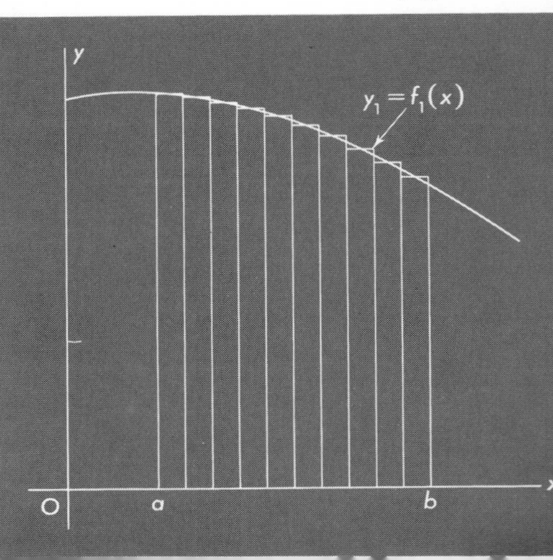

Then, without giving much attention to the details of the reasoning involved, we write

$$A_a{}^b = \int_a^b y\,dx \tag{92}$$

26·12 The area between curves

In Sec. 26·11 we discussed methods of finding the area of a particular kind of region in a coordinate plane (see Fig. 26·18). This region is bounded *above* by the graph of $y_1 = f_1(x)$, *below* by the x axis, on the *left* by the straight line $x = a$, and on the *right* by the straight line $x = b$.

Now let us investigate methods of finding the area of a somewhat different kind of region (see Fig. 26·19). Here we wish to find the area bounded *above* by the graph of the function f_1 for which $y_1 = f_1(x)$, *below* by the graph of the function f_2 for which $y_2 = f_2(x)$, on the *left* by the straight line $x = a$, and on the *right* by the line $x = b$.

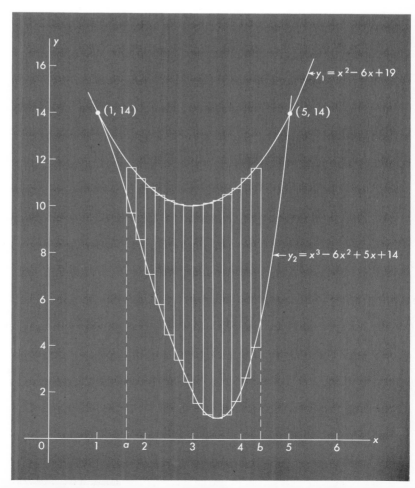

fig. 26·19

In this discussion we assume that both y_1 and y_2 are continuous over the interval $a \leq x \leq b$, and that over this interval, $y_1 \geq y_2$.

In Fig. 26·19 we shall divide the area between the curves in the interval from a to b into strips of width Δx. Then, following the same line of reasoning as was outlined in Sec. 26·11, we may develop Eq. (93), which is presented without further justification. Referred to Fig. 26·19,

$$A_a{}^b = \int_a^b (y_1 - y_2)\, dx \tag{93}$$

As an example, let us find the area between the curves of y_1 and y_2 from $x = 1$ to $x = 5$ (see Fig. 26·19). It can be verified by direct substitution that the points (1,14) and (5,14) are at the intersection of the two curves. Also observe for $1 \leq x \leq 5$ that $y_1 \geq y_2$.

In Fig. 26·19 we divide the interval from a to b into strips whose axes are parallel to the Y axis and whose width is Δx. Then, following Eq. (93), we may write

$$A_1{}^5 = \int_1^5 [(x^2 - 6x + 19) - (x^3 - 6x^2 + 5x + 14)]\, dx$$

$$A_1{}^5 = \int_1^5 (-x^3 + 7x^2 - 11x + 5)\, dx$$

$$A_1{}^5 = \left[-\frac{x^4}{4} + \frac{7x^3}{3} - \frac{11x^2}{2} + 5x\right]_1^5$$

$$A_1{}^5 = (-{}^{625}\!/\!_4 + {}^{875}\!/\!_3 - {}^{275}\!/\!_2 + 25) - (-{}^1\!/\!_4 + {}^7\!/\!_3 - {}^{11}\!/\!_2 + 5)$$

$$A_1{}^5 = 21\tfrac{1}{3}$$

Frequently we encounter a situation such as illustrated in Fig. 26·20. Here we wish to find the area bounded by the curve of the relation

$$y^2 - 8y + 16 = x$$

and the line $x = 4$. However, by writing this relation as

$$(y - 4)^2 = x$$

or

$$y - 4 = \pm\sqrt{x}$$

or

$$y = 4 \pm \sqrt{x}$$

we see that $y^2 - 8y + 16 = x$ expresses not *one* but *two functions* of x (see Sec. 6·2). Thus we may write

$$y_1 = f_1(x) = 4 + \sqrt{x}$$

for the portion of the curve from P to Q and

$$y_2 = f_2(x) = 4 - \sqrt{x}$$

for the portion of the curve from P to R.

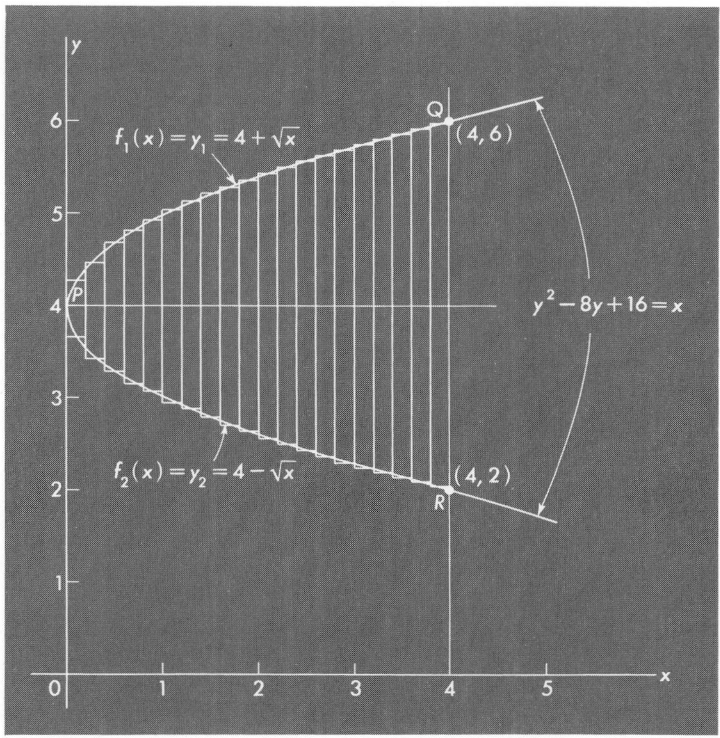

fig. 26·20

Now we can apply Eq. (93) which requires that y_1 and y_2 be *functions* of x and write

$$A_0^4 = \int_0^4 [(4 + \sqrt{x}) - (4 - \sqrt{x})]\,dx$$

$$A_0^4 = \int_0^4 (\sqrt{x} + \sqrt{x})\,dx = \int_0^4 2\sqrt{x}\,dx$$

$$A_0^4 = \int_0^4 2x^{1/2}\,dx = [\tfrac{4}{3}x^{3/2}]_0^4 = \tfrac{32}{3}$$

By changing our point of view somewhat, we can draw the elemental strips as shown in Fig. 26·21. Then we may consider y to be the independent variable and x to be the dependent variable. The width of each elemental strip is now Δy. The length of each elemental strip is $(4 - x)$. The area is given by

$$A_2^6 = \int_2^6 (4 - x)\,dy = \int_2^6 [4 - (y^2 - 8y + 16)]\,dy$$

$$A_2^6 = \int_2^6 (-y^2 + 8y - 12)\,dy = \left[-\frac{y^3}{3} + 4y^2 - 12y\right]_2^6$$

$$A_2^6 = (-72 + 144 - 72) - (-\tfrac{8}{3} + 16 - 24)$$

$$A_2^6 = (0) - (-\tfrac{8}{3} - 8) = \tfrac{32}{3}$$

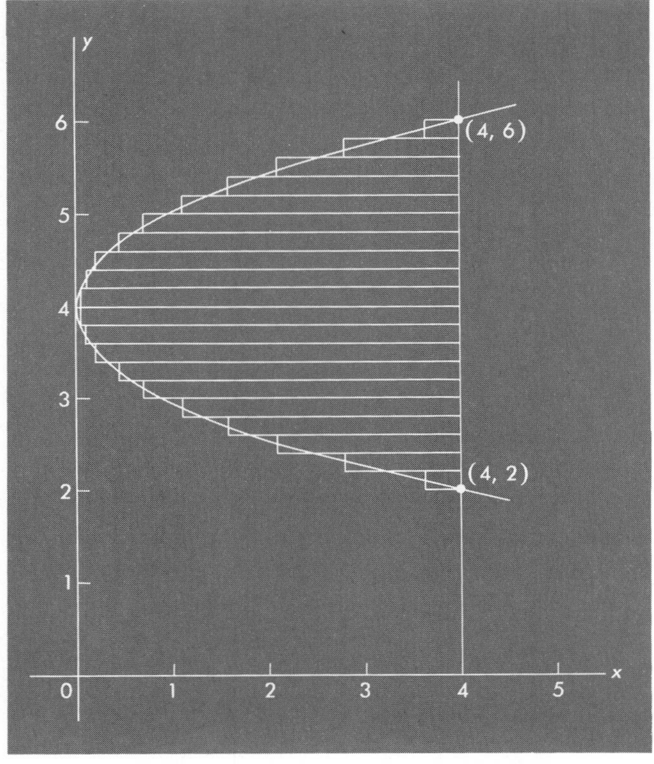

fig. 26·21

A somewhat more complicated situation is illustrated in Fig. 26·22. Here we wish to find the area between the graphs of

$$y^2 - 8y + 28 = 4x_2$$

and

$$y^2 - 8y + 16 = x_1$$

It can be verified by direct substitution that the points (4,6) and (4,2) are the intersections of the curves.

Observe that both

$$y^2 - 8y + 28 = 4x_2$$

and

$$y^2 - 8y + 16 = x_1$$

express two functions of x. However, as before, if we view x as the dependent variable and y as the independent variable, we find that x is a function of y for both curves. By drawing the axes of the elemental strips parallel to the axis we find, following Eq. (93), that

$$A_2{}^6 = \int_2^6 (x_2 - x_1)\,dy$$

$$= \int_2^6 \left[\left(\frac{y^2}{4} - 2y + 7\right) - \left(y^2 - 8y + 16\right)\right] dy$$

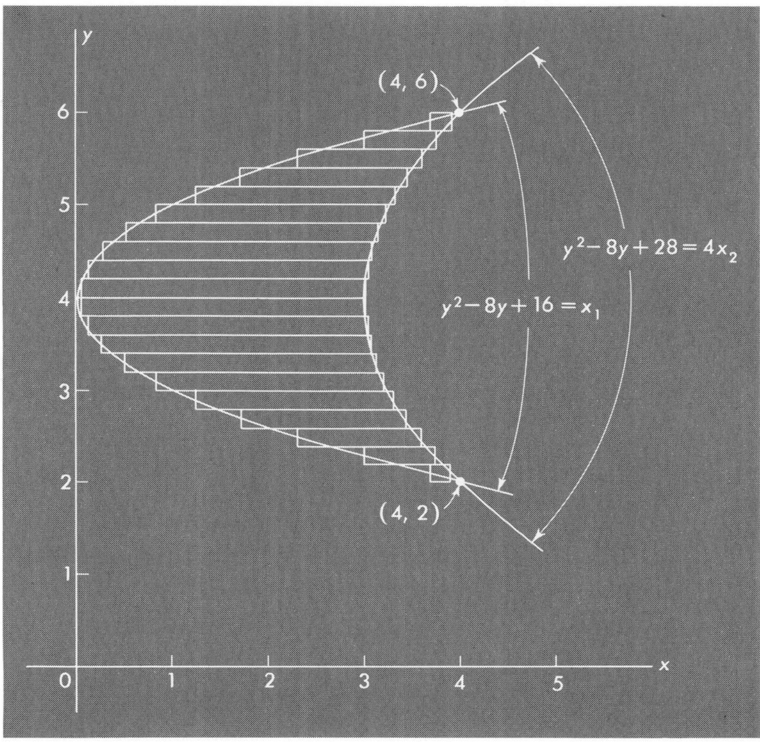

fig. 26·22

$$A_2{}^6 = \int_2^6 \left(-\frac{3y^2}{4} + 6y - 9\right) dy = \left[-\frac{y^3}{4} + 3y^2 - 9y\right]_2^6$$

$$A_2{}^6 = (-54 + 108 - 54) - (-2 + 12 - 18)$$

$$A_2{}^6 = 0 - (-8) = 8$$

Other areas with more complicated shapes can often be calculated similarly by decomposing them into a number of areas with simple shapes.

Suppose we wish to find the area between the graph of

$$y_1 = 3x - 10$$

and

$$y_2 = x^2 + 10x \qquad \text{(see Fig. 26·23)}$$

Here the coordinates of the points of intersection of both curves are not given. However, we may find these coordinates by solving the two given equations simultaneously. For example, in this case for an intersection to occur,

$$x^2 + 10x = 3x - 10$$

$$x^2 + 7x + 10 = 0$$

$$(x + 5)(x + 2) = 0$$

and

$$x = -5 \qquad \text{or} \qquad x = -2$$

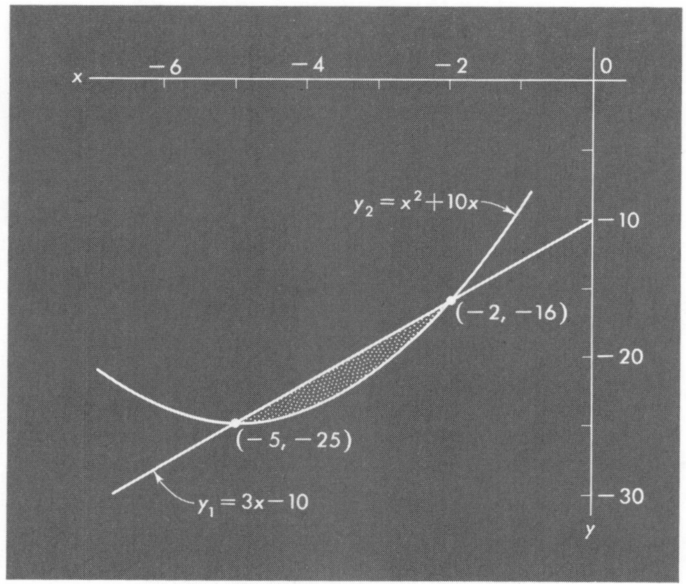

fig. 26·23

By substituting in

$$y = 3x - 10$$

we find that when $x = -5$,

$$y = -15 - 10 = -25$$

and when $x = -2$,

$$y = -6 - 10 = -16$$

The coordinates of the points of intersection are, therefore, $(-5, -25)$ and $(-2, -16)$ (see Fig. 26·23). Then

$$A_{-5}^{-2} = \int_{-5}^{-2} [(3x - 10) - (x^2 + 10x)]\, dx = \int_{-5}^{-2} (-x^2 - 7x - 10)\, dx$$

$$A_{-5}^{-2} = \left[-\frac{x^3}{3} - \frac{7x^2}{2} - 10x \right]_{-5}^{-2}$$

$$A_{-5}^{-2} = \left(\frac{8}{3} - 14 + 20\right) - \left(\frac{125}{3} - \frac{7 \times 25}{2} + 50\right)$$

$$A_{-5}^{-2} = \left(\frac{26}{3}\right) - \left(\frac{250 - 525 + 300}{6}\right)$$

$$A_{-5}^{-2} = (26/3) - (25/6) = 52/6 - 25/6 = 27/6 = 4\tfrac{1}{2}$$

EXERCISE 8

Find the area between the following graphs.

1. $y = \frac{1}{4}x^2$ and $y = 1.5x - 2$
2. $y = x^2 + 4x + 2$ and $y = 2x + 5$
3. $y = x^3 - 1$, $x = 2$, $y = -3$, and $x = 0$

4. $y = 18 - x^2$ and $y = x^2$
5. $y^2 = x$ and $y = x - 6$
6. $y = 9 - x^2$ and $y = 3 - x$
7. $y = x^2$ and $y = 6 - x$
8. $y = x^2 - 3x$ and $y = -x^2 + 7x$
9. $x = y^2 - 3y$ and $x = -y^2 + 7y$

26·13 Broader implications of the definite integral

Although it is quite true that we arrived at Eq. (88) by reasoning in terms of areas, this equation is not by any means limited to problems about areas.

If we are given a function f where $y = f(x)$ which is continuous for $a \leq x \leq b$, the definite integral

$$\int_a^b f(x)\,dx \tag{94}$$

is a number obtained as follows.

1. Divide the interval $a \leq x \leq b$ into n equal parts, each of width

$$\Delta x = \frac{b - a}{n}$$

As we mentioned before, these widths need not be equal, but it is convenient if they are.

2. Form the sum

$$[f(x_1^*) + f(x_2^*) + f(x_3^*) + \cdots + f(x_n^*)]\,\Delta x \tag{95}$$

where $x_1^*, x_2^*, x_3^*, \cdots, x_n^*$ are points (or numbers) within their respective intervals.

3. Take the limit of the above sum as n approaches ∞ to obtain

$$\int_a^b f(x)\,dx = \lim_{n\to\infty} \sum_1^n f(x_k^*)\,\Delta x \tag{96}$$

It is important to note that regardless of the context out of which this number $\int_a^b f(x)\,dx$ arose, still it is always possible to plot $y = f(x)$ in the xy plane. Then there will be a region in this plane whose area is measured by the same number.

In the work to follow we shall apply the arguments presented in this section to a variety of applications.

26·14 Volumes by integration

Figure 26·24*a* is a pictorial drawing of a solid such that the area As of every cross section perpendicular to the line X is the value of a continuous function of x. Then we may write

$$As = f(x) \tag{97}$$

where x is the distance of the cross section from point O measured along the line X. Figure 26·24b is a view in orthographic projection of the same solid.

We now divide the interval from a to b into n equal parts. Though it is not strictly necessary for our argument that they be equal, it is a convenience and does no harm. This division is accomplished by establishing partition points at

$$(a = x_0) < x_1 < x_2 < x_3 < \cdots < x_{n-1} < (x_n = b)$$

Planes are passed through each partition point perpendicular to the line X. The volume of the solid between $x = a$ and $x = b$ is thus divided into slices of width $\Delta x = x_1 - x_0$, $\Delta x = x_2 - x_1$, $\Delta x = x_3 - x_2$, etc.

fig. 26·24

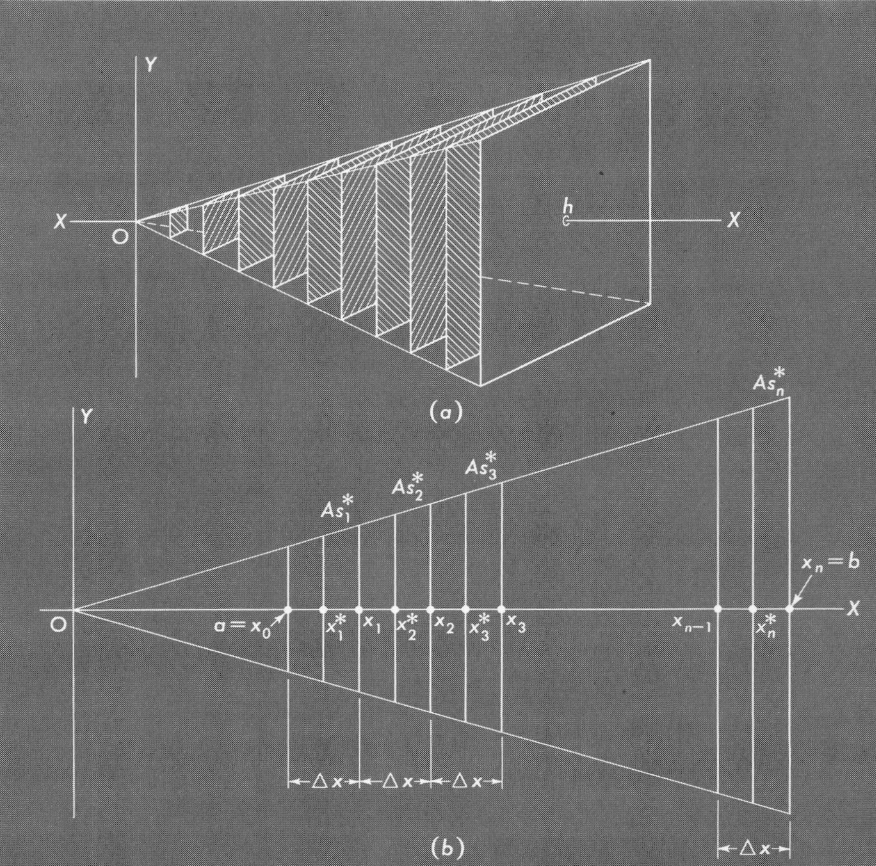

The volume of the solid between $x = a$ and $x = b$ can be approximated by

$$V_a{}^b \approx As_1^*(\Delta x) + As_2^*(\Delta x) + As_3^*(\Delta x) + \cdots + As_n^*(\Delta x) \tag{98}$$

where $\Delta x = \dfrac{b - a}{n}$

As_1^* = any cross-section area within 1st interval

As_2^* = any cross-section area within 2d interval

As_3^* = any cross-section area within 3d interval

As_n^* = any cross-section area within nth interval

It should be intuitively evident that the volume of the solid between $x = a$ and $x = b$ is the limit that the sum of the volumes of these slices approaches as the number of slices increases.

Therefore we may write

$$V_a{}^b = \lim_{n\to\infty} \sum_1^n (A_k^*)\, \Delta x \tag{99}$$

The symbol $\sum\limits_1^n (A_k^*)\, \Delta x$ designates the sum of a series of elemental volumes whose typical (or kth) elemental volume is $(A_k^*)\, \Delta x$, where k may take on in turn any integral value between 1 and n.

As we shall see presently, these elemental volumes need not be bounded on two sides by parallel planes. They may have other shapes.

Since we require that As be the value of some known and continuous function of x, we may write

$$V_a{}^b = \int_a^b (As)\, dx \tag{100}$$

To avoid the use of relatively complex working drawings such as Fig. 26·24a and Fig. 26·24b, indicating a large number of elemental volumes, we often simplify and work from a drawing such as Fig. 26·25. Here we indicate only one elemental volume, but the implication is clear that the volume of the solid between $x = a$ and $x = b$ is the limit that the sum of a series of these elemental volumes approaches as their number increases without limit.

It is quite common to indicate the typical elemental volume in some such form as

$$dV = As\, dx \tag{101}$$

Then if there is no need for going into the details of the theory involved, we may write immediately

$$V_a{}^b = \int_a^b As\, dx \tag{102}$$

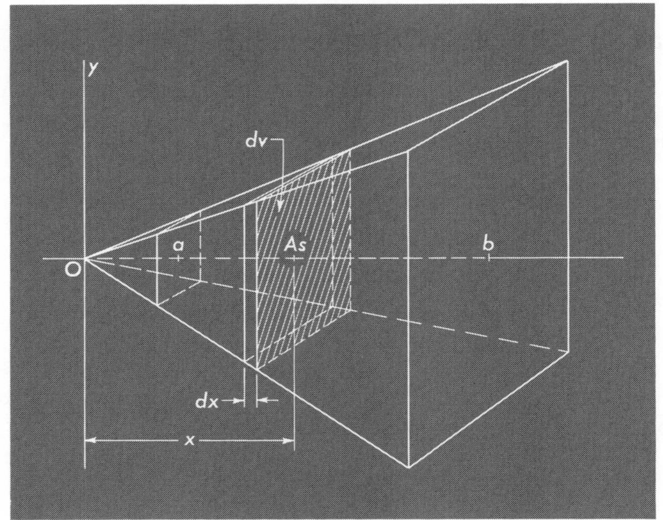

fig. 26·25

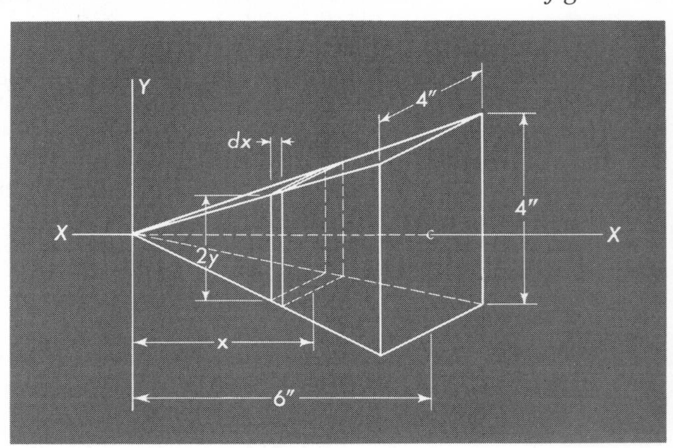

fig. 26·26

example 37 Find the volume of the square pyramid shown in Fig. 26·26.

Following Eq. (100)

$$V_0{}^6 = \int_0^6 A_s\,dx$$

In this case

$$A_s = (2y)^2$$

But by similarity

$$\frac{2y}{x} = \frac{4}{6}$$

and

$$2y = 4/6x = 2/3x$$

Therefore

$$A_s = 4/9x^2$$

and $$V_0{}^6 = \int_0^6 \frac{4}{9}x^2\,dx = \left[\frac{4x^3}{27}\right]_0^6 = \frac{(4)(6)^3}{27} = \frac{(4)(216)}{27} = 32$$

By elementary geometry

$$V = \tfrac{1}{3} \times \text{area of the base} \times \text{height} = \tfrac{1}{3}(4 \times 4) \times 6 = 32 \qquad \text{(check)}$$

In the following examples we shall find the volume of a hemisphere 10 in. in radius.

There are actually several different ways that this can be accomplished. All these ways involve dividing the hemisphere into certain elementary volumes and finding the limit which the total of these volumes approaches as the number of the volumes approaches infinity.

example 38 Find the volume of the hemisphere shown in Fig. 26·27.

We shall divide the hemisphere into circular slabs of equal thickness. One of these circular slabs is shown in the figure.

Following Eq. (100),

$$V_0{}^{10} = \int_0^{10} As\,dh$$

By inspection of the figure,

$$As = \pi r^2$$

Therefore, $$V_0{}^{10} = \int_0^{10} \pi r^2\,dh$$

But in this figure

$$r^2 = 10^2 - h^2 \qquad (103)$$

Therefore, from Eq. (103),

$$A_0{}^{10} = \int_0^{10} \pi(10^2 - h^2)\,dh = \int_0^{10} (100\pi - \pi h^2)\,dh$$

$$= \left[100\pi h - \frac{\pi h^3}{3}\right]_0^{10} = 1{,}000\pi - \frac{1{,}000\pi}{3} = \frac{2{,}000\pi}{3}$$

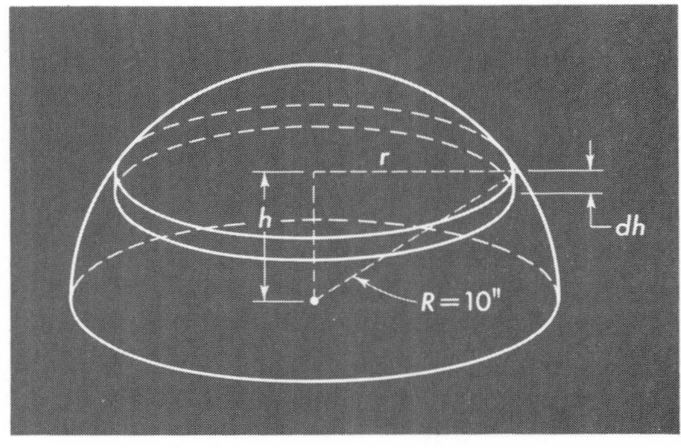

fig. 26·27

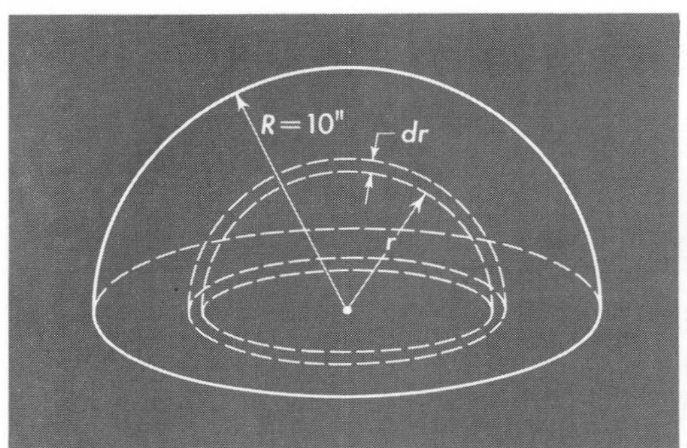

fig. 26·28

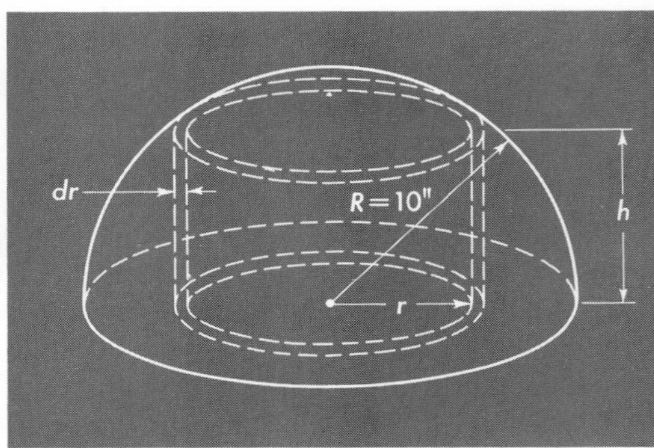

fig. 26·29

example 39 Find the volume of the hemisphere shown in Fig. 26·28.

We shall divide the hemisphere into hollow hemispherical shells. One of these shells is shown in the figure.

Following Eq. (100),

$$V_0{}^{10} = \int_0^{10} As\ dr$$

From the figure by inspection,

$$As = 2\pi r^2$$

Therefore,

$$V_0{}^{10} = \int_0^{10} 2\pi r^2\ dr = \left[\frac{2\pi r^3}{3}\right]_0^{10} = \frac{2\pi(1{,}000)}{3} = \frac{2{,}000\pi}{3}$$

example 40 Find the volume of the hemisphere shown in Fig. 26·29.

We shall divide the hemisphere into hollow tubes. One of these hollow tubes is shown in the figure.

Following Eq. (100),

$$V_0{}^{10} = \int_0^{10} As\ dh$$

From the figure by inspection,

$$As = 2\pi rh$$

But

$$h = \sqrt{100 - r^2}$$

Therefore,

$$V_0^{10} = \int_0^{10} 2\pi r\sqrt{100 - r^2}\, dr = \int_0^{10} 2\pi r(100 - r^2)^{1/2}\, dr$$

$$= 2\pi \int_0^{10} r(100 - r^2)^{1/2}\, dr = 2\pi[-\tfrac{1}{3}(100 - r^2)^{3/2}]_0^{10}$$

$$= -\frac{2\pi}{3}[-(100)^{3/2}] = \frac{2{,}000\pi}{3}$$

example 41 Find the volume of the wedge illustrated in Fig. 26·30.

We shall consider the wedge to be made up of a stack of horizontal sections of width w, length l, and thickness dh. Accordingly,

$$V_0^{10} = \int_0^{10} wl\, dh$$

Since w is at all times proportional to h and is 8 when $h = 10$, we may replace w by $0.8h$. l is a linear function of h, and since l is 9 when $h = 0$ and l is 14 when $h = 10$, it can be readily shown that $l = 9 + 0.5h$.

Therefore we may write

$$V_0^{10} = \int_0^{10} 0.8h(9 + 0.5h)\, dh$$

or

$$V_0^{10} = \int_0^{10} (7.2h + 0.4h^2)\, dh$$

and

$$V_0^{10} = [3.6h^2 + \tfrac{2}{15}h^3]_0^{10} = 360 + 133.3 = 493.3$$

Checking by the prismoidal formula, we obtain

$$V = \tfrac{1}{6}(10)[0 + 4(4 \times 11.5) + (8 \times 14)] = \tfrac{10}{6}(0 + 184 + 112) = 493.3$$

(See Prob. 91, page 104.)

fig. 26·30

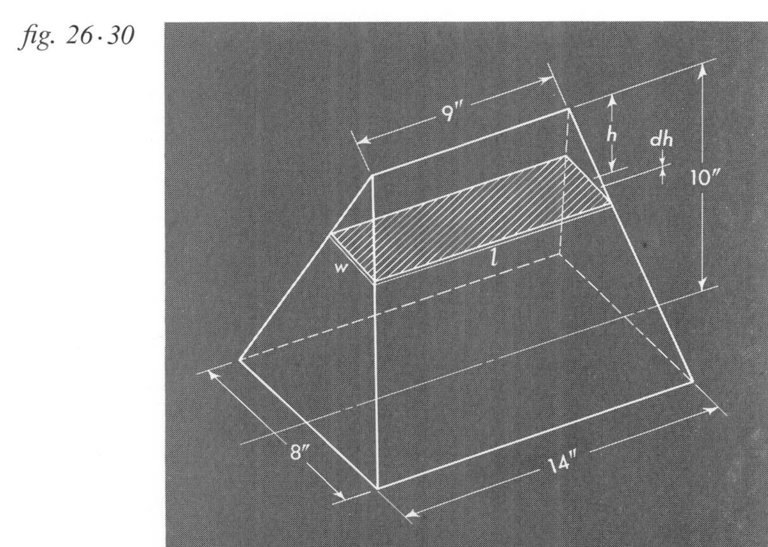

example 42 Find the volume of the wedge cut from the cylinder in Fig. 26·31.

If we divided the volume into many vertical right-triangular slabs of thickness dx, we obtain

$$V_0{}^5 = 2\int_0^5 \tfrac{1}{2}hy\,dx$$

(Note that we could just as logically have written

$$V_{-5}{}^5 = \int_{-5}^5 \tfrac{1}{2}hy\,dx$$

but the first method is shorter.)

In each triangular element $h = 3y$, or the area of the elemental section is

$$\tfrac{1}{2}hy = \tfrac{3}{2}y^2$$

But

$$y^2 = 25 - x^2$$

Therefore the area of the elemental section is

$$\text{Area} = \tfrac{3}{2}(25 - x^2)$$

Hence we may write

$$\begin{aligned} V_0{}^5 &= 2\int_0^5 \tfrac{3}{2}(25 - x^2)\,dx \\ &= 3\int_0^5 (25 - x^2)\,dx \\ &= 3\left[25x - \frac{x^3}{3}\right]_0^5 \end{aligned}$$

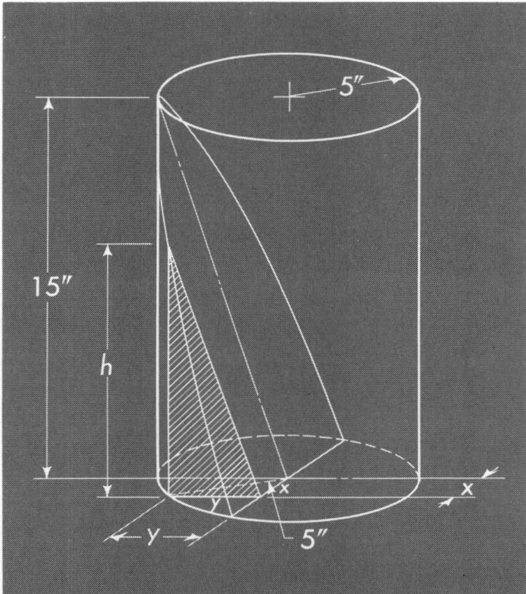

fig. 26·31

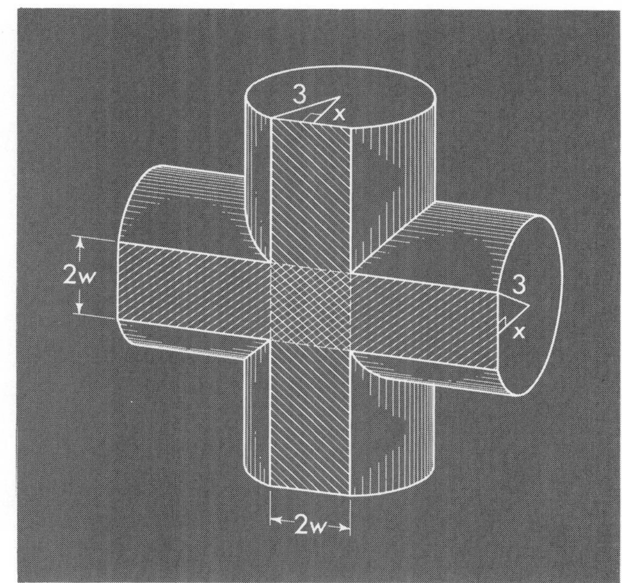

fig. 26·32

Therefore

$$V = 3(125 - {}^{125}\!/_3) = 250$$

example 43 Find the volume common to two cylinders (see Fig. 26·32), each of radius 3 in., whose axes intersect at right angles.

It will be seen that the volume of one of the elemental slabs making up the volume of intersection is

$$dv = (2w)^2\, dx$$

But

$$w = \sqrt{9 - x^2}$$

or

$$4w^2 = 36 - 4x^2$$

Hence

$$V = 2\int_0^3 (36 - 4x^2)\, dx = 2[36x - \tfrac{4}{3}x^3]_0^3 = 2\{[(36)(3) - \tfrac{4}{3}(3)^3] - 0\}$$

$$= 2(108 - 36) = 144 \text{ cu in.}$$

EXERCISE 9

1. Find, by integration, the volume of a sphere 20 in. in radius.
2. A plane is passed through the sphere in Prob. 1, 10 in. from the center. Find the smaller and the larger volumes cut off.
3. Water is poured from a cylindrical cup 5 in. in diameter and 5 in. high. Find the volume of water remaining when the surface of the water coincides with a diameter of the bottom of the cup.
4. A hemispherical tank 20 ft in diameter is filled with water to a depth of 4 ft. How many cubic feet of water are there in the tank?

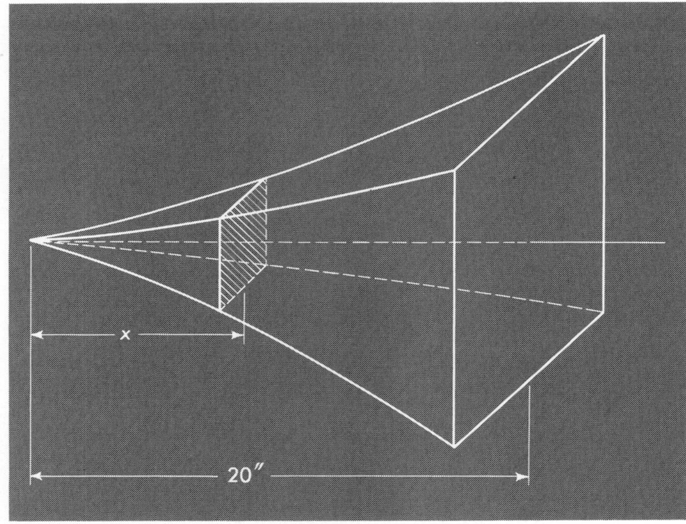

fig. 26·33

5. A cylindrical block of wood 10 in. in radius has a 20-in.-diameter hole bored in it such that the axis of the hole and the axis of the cylinder intersect at right angles. Find the volume of the material bored out.
6. Every cross section of the solid shown in Fig. 26·33 is a square whose sides are $0.2x^2$. Find the volume of the solid.
7. A metal sphere 10 in. in radius has a 12-in.-diameter hole bored in it. The axis of the hole passes through the center of the sphere. Find the volume of material removed.
8. Estimate the number of cubic yards of crushed rock necessary to make a roadbed of the dimensions shown in Fig. 26·34. The road is to be 1 mile long. Assume that any other material added merely fills up the voids. Also assume that the crown of the pavement is an arc of a parabola.

26·15 Volumes of revolution

There is a class of solids called *solids of revolution.* A solid of revolution is a solid having an axis of symmetry such that every section of the solid perpendicular to the axis of symmetry is a circle. In all solids of revolu-

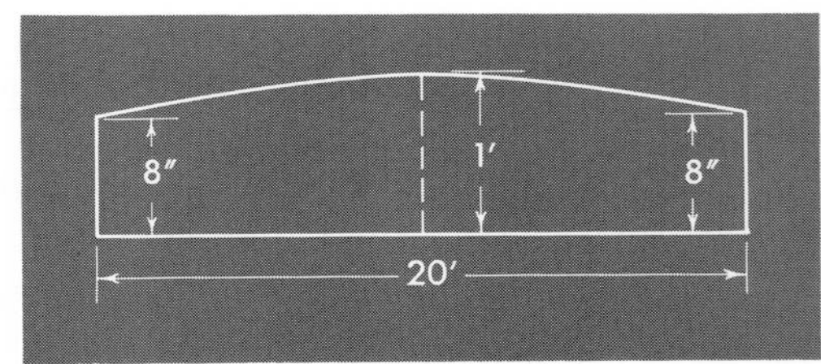

fig. 26·34

tion, then, the area of cross section A_s in Eq. (100) is a circle. Therefore, in this special case, Eq. (100) can be written

$$V_a{}^b = \int_a^b \pi r^2\, dx \tag{104}$$

where r = radius of circular cross section

Figure 26·35 is a solid of revolution since each section perpendicular to the X axis is a circle.

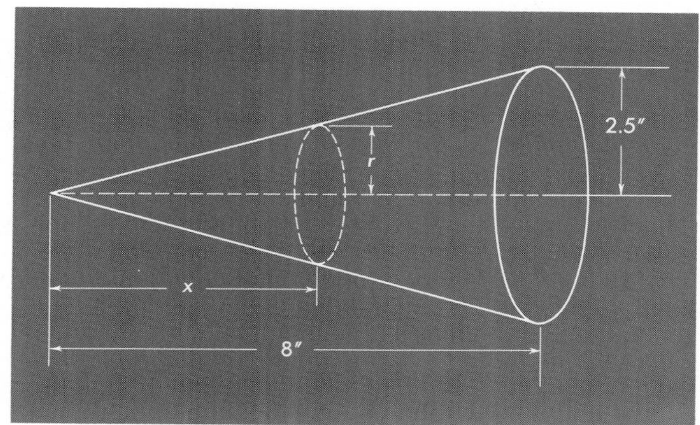

fig. 26·35

By similarity

$$\frac{r}{x} = \frac{2.5}{8}$$

$$r = \frac{2.5}{8}x$$

and

$$r^2 = \frac{6.25}{64}x^2$$

Equation (104) then becomes

$$V_0{}^8 = \int_0^8 \pi \frac{6.25}{64}x^2\, dx$$

$$= \left[\frac{6.25\pi}{3 \times 64}x^3\right]_0^8 = \frac{6.25 \times 8^3\pi}{3 \times 64} = \frac{3{,}200\pi}{192} = 52.36 \text{ cu in.}$$

example 44 Find the volume of revolution generated when the section of the curve $y = x^2$ between $x = 2$ and $x = 5$ is revolved about the X axis.

The cross-section area is

$$A_s = \pi y^2$$

But

$$y = x^2$$

Therefore

$$A_s = \pi x^4$$

and

$$V_2{}^5 = \int_2^5 \pi x^4\,dx = \left[\frac{\pi x^5}{5}\right]_2^5 = 625\pi - \frac{32x}{5} = 625\pi - 6.4\pi = 618.6\pi$$
$$= 1{,}943$$

example 45 Find the volume generated by revolving about the X axis the area bounded by the lines $y = x^3$, $x = 2$, $x = 4$, and $y = 0$.

$$A_s = \pi y^2$$

But $\quad y = x^3$

Therefore $\quad A_s = \pi x^6$

and

$$V_2{}^4 = \int_2^4 \pi x^6\,dx = \left[\frac{\pi x^7}{7}\right]_2^4 = \frac{16{,}384\pi}{7} - \frac{128\pi}{7} = \frac{16{,}256\pi}{7} = 7{,}295.7$$

EXERCISE 10

Find the volume generated by revolving about the X axis the area bounded by the following sets of curves:

1. $y = x^2, y = 0, x = 5$
2. $y = \sqrt{9 - x^2}, y = 0, x = 3$
3. $y = \sqrt{10x}, y = 0, x = 10$
4. $y = x, x = 2, x = 5, y = 0$
5. $y = \frac{12}{x}, x = 2, x = 6, y = 0$

26 · 16 Work

Before proceeding with this section, the student is advised to review the concept of work in any good general physics textbook.

Briefly, however, work is done only when a force is exerted on a body, causing it to move so that the force has a component along the line of motion.

When the body moves in a straight line and when the magnitude of the force component along this straight line remains constant, we have the elementary definition of work expressed as

$$W = Fx \qquad (105)$$

where F = component of force along line of motion
x = distance the body moves along line of motion (for the present at least we shall limit ourselves to positive distances)
W = work done on the body by applied force

If F is measured in pounds and x in feet, then work W is measured in foot-pounds. Work can also be measured in newton-meters, dyne-centimeters, etc., depending on the units in which F and x are measured.

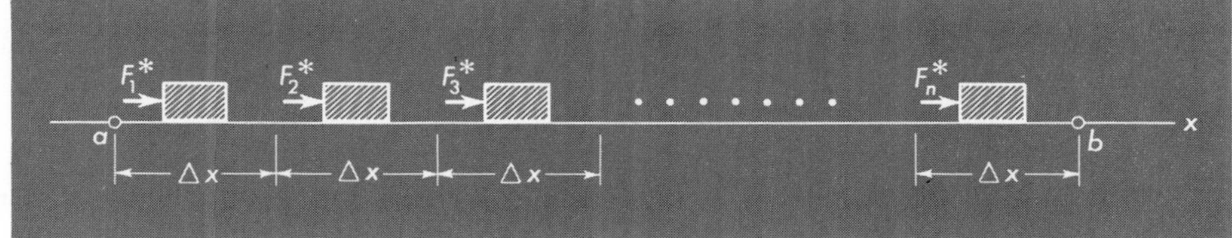

fig. 26·36

If the force component along the line of motion is not constant, then the arithmetical definition of work given in Eq. (105) no longer applies.

For example, see Fig. 26·36 in which we illustrate a variable force component F along a straight line, which we take to be the x axis. If this variable force component displaces the body from $x = a$ to $x = b$, we define the work done to be

$$W_a{}^b = \int_a^b F\,dx \tag{106}$$

Here, of course, we assume the force F to be the value of a continuous function of x.

Although the above equation is a definition and hence not subject to proof, there is a plausible motivation for choosing this particular definition.

To develop this motivation we shall proceed as follows:

1. Divide the interval $a \le x \le b$ into n equal parts, each of width

$$\Delta x = \frac{b - a}{n}$$

2. Form the sum

$$F_1^*(\Delta x) + F_2^*(\Delta x) + F_3^*(\Delta x) + \cdots + F_n^*(\Delta x) \tag{107}$$

or

$$[F_1^* + F_2^* + F_3^* + \cdots + F_n^*]\,\Delta x \tag{108}$$

where $F_1^*, F_2^*, F_3^*, \ldots, F_n^*$ are forces acting within their respective intervals. Therefore we conclude that $F_1^*(\Delta x), F_2^*(\Delta x), F_3^*(\Delta x), \ldots, F_n^*(\Delta x)$ represent the work done by $F_1^*, F_2^*, F_3^*, \ldots, F_n^*$ within their respective subintervals.

It seems intuitively evident that the work done between $x = a$ and $x = b$ is approximated by the sum of the work done in each of the successive subintervals. That is,

$$W_a{}^b \approx \sum_1^n F_k^*(\Delta x) \tag{109}$$

The symbol $\sum_1^n F_k^*(\Delta x)$ designates the sum whose typical (or kth) term is $F_k^*(\Delta x)$, where k may take on in turn any integral value between 1 and n.

Now by applying Eqs. (89) and (90) to Eq. (109), we obtain

$$W_a{}^b = \int_a^b F\,dx = \lim_{n\to\infty} \sum_1^n F^*(\Delta x) \tag{110}$$

example 46 Within certain limits, the force required to stretch a spring is proportional to the amount of stretch. The constant of proportionality is called the *modulus* of the spring.

A given spring having a normal length of 10 in. requires a force of 25 lb to stretch it ¼ in. Calculate the amount of work done in stretching it from 11 to 12 in.

By the statement of the problem

$$F = Kx$$

where x is the elongation in inches. We can evaluate the constant of proportionality from the conditions that $F = 25$ when $x = \frac{1}{4}$ in.

$$25 = \tfrac{1}{4}K$$

or

$$K = 100$$

and, in general,

$$F = 100x$$

From Eq. (106),

$$W_1{}^2 = \int_1^2 F\,dx = \int_1^2 (100x)\,dx = [50x^2]_1^2 = 50\cdot 4 - 50\cdot 1 = 150 \text{ in.-lb}$$

example 47 A reservoir filled with water is in the form of a right circular cone whose top diameter is 6 ft and whose height is 8 ft. Find the amount of work done in pumping the water over the top of the reservoir.

We approximate the conical volume of water by a set of elementary circular disks, each Δy thick. The kth (or typical) disk is shown in Fig. 26·37.

The work required to lift the kth elementary volume over the top of the reservoir is approximately

$$W_k^* = (\text{weight of } k\text{th disk})(8 - y_k^*)$$

The weight of the kth disk of water is

$$\text{Weight} = 62.5 \times \text{volume of } k\text{th disk in cu ft}$$
$$\text{Volume of } k\text{th disk} = \pi R_k^{*2}\,\Delta y$$

The weight of the kth disk is therefore

$$\text{Weight of } k\text{th disk} = 62.5\pi R_k^{*2}\,\Delta y$$
$$W_k^* = 62.5\pi R_k^{*2}(8 - y_k^*)\,\Delta y$$

By similar triangles

$$R_k^* = \tfrac{3}{8}y_k^*$$

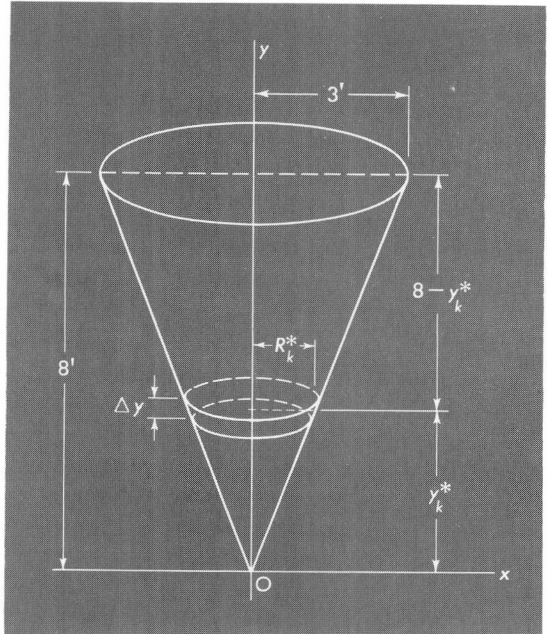

fig. 26·37

Therefore

$$W_k^* = \frac{9 \cdot 62.5 \cdot \pi}{64}(8 - y_k^*)y_k^{*2}\,\Delta y = \frac{9 \times 62.5 \times \pi}{64}(8y_k^{*2} - y_k^{*3})\,\Delta y$$

By following the same general line of reasoning as outlined in Sec. 26·11 we may write

$$W_0{}^8 = \int_0^8 \frac{9 \times 62.5 \times \pi}{64}(8y^2 - y^3)\,dy$$

$$= \frac{9 \times 62.5 \times \pi}{64}\left[\frac{8y^3}{3} - \frac{y^4}{4}\right]_0^8$$

$$= \frac{9 \times 62.5 \times \pi}{64}\left(\frac{8^4}{3} - \frac{8^4}{4}\right) = 3{,}000\pi$$

EXERCISE 11

1. A certain coil spring requires a force of 12 lb to stretch it ½ in. Find the work done in stretching it 3 in. beyond its free length.
2. The coil spring on a bumping post in a freight yard is compressed 1 in. by a force of 36,000 lb. Find the work done in compressing it ½ in.
3. The natural length of a coil spring is 10 in. The modulus of this spring is 24 lb per in. How much work is done in stretching it from a length of 11 in. to a length of 13 in.?
4. If 84 in.-lb of work is done on a spring whose initial elongation is 1 in. and whose modulus is 32 lb per in., find the final elongation.

5. The force used in driving a piston varies as follows: $F = 10/x^{1.5}$. Find the work done between $x = 20$ and $x = 50$.
6. A downward force is applied to a horizontal beam at its midpoint. If the deflection is proportional to the force and is ¼ in. when the force is 1,200 lb, find the work done as the force increases from 1,200 to 3,600 lb.
7. A cable 50 ft long and weighing 3 lb per ft supports a weight of 800 lb. Find the work done in winding this cable on a windlass until the weight has been lifted 50 ft.
8. A right circular cylindrical tank having a depth of 12 ft and a radius of 4 ft is one-third full of water. Find the work done in pumping the water to the top of this tank. (Weight of water equals 62.5 lb per cu ft.)
9. A right circular cylindrical tank is 18 ft deep and 8 ft in diameter. Find the work done in filling this tank if water is pumped in through the bottom of it from a depth of 16 ft below the bottom.
10. Calculate the work done in pumping out the water from a hemispherical reservoir whose radius is 10 ft, assuming that the reservoir is full of water at the time the pump starts work.
11. The inner surface of a tank has the form of a paraboloid of revolution whose axis is vertical. The depth of this tank and the diameter of the circular top are each 12 ft. If the tank is initially full of water, find the work done in pumping the water to the top of the tank.
12. A derrick lifts a shovel of sand through a vertical distance of 30 ft. The sand in the shovel weighs originally 400 lb and leaks out at a rate directly proportional to the square root of the distance traversed. If 320 lb of sand reaches the top, find the work done.
13. A volume of gas (V_1 cu in.) is enclosed in the tube shown in Fig. 26·38 under an absolute pressure of P_1 psi when the movable piston is at position h_1. A continuously increasing force F is applied to the piston until it comes to rest at h_2. Then the unit pressure is P_2 and the volume is V_2. Show that the work done in compressing this gas is

$$W = \int_{V_1}^{V_2} P\,dv$$

14. If in Prob. 13 the unit pressure P is given by $P = C/V^{\gamma}$, show that when the gas is compressed from P_1, V_1 to P_2, V_2, the work done on the gas is given by

$$W = \frac{P_2V_2 - P_1V_1}{1 - \gamma}$$

where C and γ are constants.

15. In the adiabatic compression of air the formula

$$PV^{1.4} = C$$

applies where P = pressure, V = volume, and C = a constant. If $V = 32$ cu ft when P is one atmosphere, find the work done in compressing 32 cu ft of air at one atmosphere to 5 cu ft (1 atm = 14.7 psi).

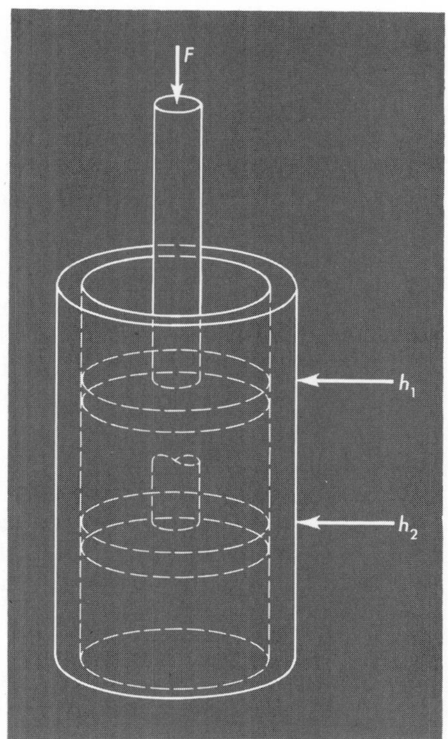

fig. 26·38

16. The earth's gravitational force on a given mass varies as $1/x^2$ where x is the distance of the mass from the center of the earth. The earth's radius is taken to be 4,000 miles, and the formula applies for distances greater than the radius of the earth. A certain amount of work will be needed to lift a given mass to an "infinite" distance from the surface of the earth. To what altitude above the surface of the earth would one-half of this work lift an object?

26·17 Fluid pressure

The student may find it advisable to review the matter of fluid pressure in a general physics textbook before proceeding with a study of this section. However, we shall present a brief review of the physical principles below.

We can confirm from experiment that for any incompressible fluid at constant temperature the fluid pressure at any point below the surface is directly proportional to the distance of the point below the surface of the fluid. The proportionality constant is the weight density of the fluid.

We may assume that variations in the acceleration of gravity are negligible. Thus

$$P = \rho h \tag{111}$$

where P = unit pressure
ρ = weight density of fluid
h = distance of point under consideration below surface of fluid

The quantities P, ρ, and h are, of course, measured in some compatible units. For example, P might be in pounds per square foot when ρ is measured in pounds per cubic foot and h is measured in feet.

Evidently from Eq. (111) the pressure varies with depth. Therefore the pressure on the vertical walls of a container enclosing a fluid is not constant but is greater near the bottom of the container and less near the surface of the fluid.

If the pressure were constant, the fluid force on a given area of side-wall would be given by Eq. (112) below. The student is reminded that F, as the symbol is used in Eq. (112), refers to the force caused by the weight of the fluid alone. The *total* force would include the effect of atmospheric pressure on the surface of the fluid.

$$F = P \times A \tag{112}$$

where F = force on area A due to fluid pressure
A = area on which force is exerted
P = unit pressure

However, this simple arithmetic formula is not adequate if we wish to calculate the total force that is exerted by a fluid on a given portion of a vertical wall which forms a part of the container.

example 48 Find the total fluid force exerted on one end of the trough indicated in Fig. 26·39 when it is full of water. Only the end view of the trough is shown in the figure.

fig. 26·39

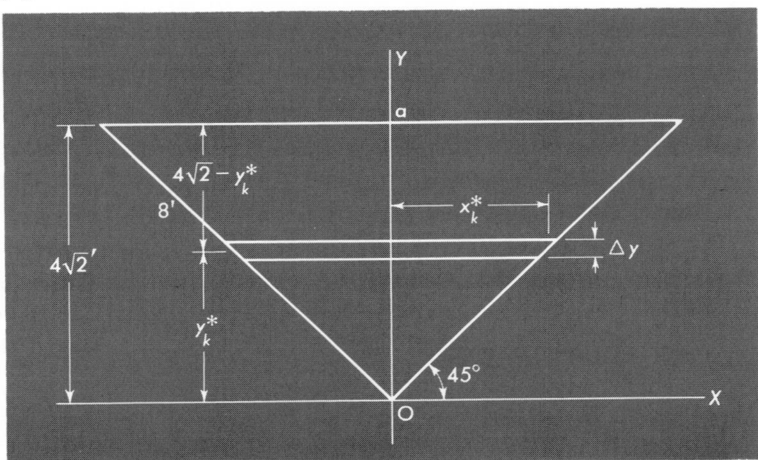

Following the same general line of approach as we have taken previously, we divide the interval $0 \le y \le 4\sqrt{2}$ into n equal parts, each Δy units in width, thus establishing n horizontal strips. A typical (or kth) strip is shown in the figure.

The total force exerted by the water on the kth strip is approximately

$$F_k^* \approx (4\sqrt{2} - y_k^*) \cdot 62.5 \cdot 2 \cdot x_k^* \, \Delta y$$

where 62.5 is the density of water in pounds per cubic foot.

By the geometry of the figure

$$y_k^* = x_k^*$$

Therefore

$$F_k^* \approx 125(4\sqrt{2}\, y_k^* - y_k^{*2}) \, \Delta y$$

or

$$F_0^{4\sqrt{2}} \approx \sum_1^n 125(4\sqrt{2}\, y_k^* - y_k^{*2}) \, \Delta y$$

Thus we are led to write

$$F_0^{4\sqrt{2}} = 125 \int_0^{4\sqrt{2}} (4\sqrt{2}\, y - y^2) \, dy = 125 \left[2\sqrt{2}\, y^2 - \frac{y^3}{3} \right]_0^{4\sqrt{2}}$$

$$= 125 \left(64\sqrt{2} - \frac{2 \cdot 64 \cdot \sqrt{2}}{3} \right) = 3{,}771 \text{ lb}$$

EXERCISE 12

1. The vertical end of a water trough is an isosceles triangle 5 ft across the top and 5 ft deep. Calculate the total force exerted on the end when this trough is full of water. (Water weighs 62.5 lb per cu ft.)
2. A horizontal cylindrical tank having a diameter of 8 ft is half full of oil weighing 60 lb per cu ft. Calculate the total force exerted on one end.
3. A rectangular gate in a vertical dam is 10 ft wide and 6 ft deep. Find the total force exerted against this gate when the water level is 8 ft above the top of the gate. Also find how much higher the water must rise in order to double the force against this gate.
4. A vertical cylindrical tank having a diameter of 30 ft and a height of 50 ft is full of water. Find the total force exerted against the curved surface of this tank.

EXERCISE 13

The following problems are intended to illustrate a few of the many and varied applications of the definite integral.

1. The potential energy stored in a rod because of a torque (twist) which has been applied to one end (the other end of the rod being fixed) and which twisted the bar through an angle of 30° is given by

$$\text{PE} = \int_0^{30\pi/180} \left(\frac{200\phi}{\pi} \right) d\phi$$

Evaluate.

2. Evaluate the following definite integral that appeared in a text on aeronautics:

$$\int_{r_0}^{r} \left(\frac{R}{r^2}\right)\left(\frac{G^2}{4\pi^2 r^2}\right) dr$$

where R, G, and r_0 are constants.

3. If a battery of E volts and zero internal resistance is connected to a long uncharged submarine cable of capacitance C farads and resistance R ohms (each per mile), the battery current t sec later is given by

$$i = E\left(\frac{C}{\pi R t}\right)^{1/2} \quad \text{amp}$$

(a) Sketch a graph of i as a function of t. To show the general shape of this curve, let $C = 2\pi \times 10^{-8}$, $R = 18$, and $E = 30$.

(b) Are the current i and the power $P = Ei$ undefined (momentarily infinite) when the battery is first connected?

(c) Determine the charge

$$Q = \int_0^T i\, dt$$

and the energy

$$W = \int_0^T P\, dt$$

taken from the battery up to the time T sec. Are these ever undefined (infinite)? Sketch each as a function of T.

REMARK: A mathematically "infinite" current is not physically possible, since no circuit can actually have zero resistance. However, the resistance can be so small that the momentary current is enormous compared with the normal current in the circuit and may be called "physically" infinite.

4. A sled is being pulled along level ice by a rope, which is inclined at an angle of 11° with the horizontal. The force pulling the sled varies thus with the time: $F = 24t - 0.9t^2$ (F in pounds and t in seconds). The change in momentum of the sled is defined to be the product of the force component in the direction of motion multiplied by the time interval during which this constant force acts. Find the change in momentum of the sled during the interval from $t = 1$ sec to $t = 5$ sec.

5. Integrate

$$A = 232 + \int_{176}^{t} (0.000{,}374t + 0.251)\, dt$$

6. The force ejecting a projectile from a gun changes with the time after firing according to the equation

$$F = \frac{4.35}{(0.05 + t)^4} \qquad \text{lb}$$

where t is in seconds. The total momentum given the projectile (momentum is defined as mass times velocity) during the 0.04 sec required for the projectile to pass through the bore of the gun is obtained by evaluating the definite integral

$$\int_{t_1}^{t_2} F\,dt = \int_0^{0.04} \frac{4.35\,dt}{(0.05 + t)^4}$$

Evaluate this definite integral.

7. The two following empirical formulas were found for the *specific heat* at constant pressure for hydrogen:

$$c_p = 3.45 - 0.0000551T + 0.0000000736T^2$$

$$c_p = 2.86 + 0.0000287T + \frac{10}{\sqrt{T}}$$

Compute

$$\int_{1,000}^{1,500} c_p\,dT$$

for the two approximate formulas and thus determine the total heat required to raise the temperature of 1 lb of hydrogen from 540 to 1040°F (T = absolute temperature = degrees Fahrenheit plus 460).

26·18 The integral of $ku^n \cdot du$ where $n = -1$

We recall from Sec. 25·15, particularly Eq. (96), that

$$\frac{d(\ln u)}{dx} = \frac{1}{u}\frac{du}{dx} = u^{-1}\frac{du}{dx}$$

The above equation leads directly to the integration formula

$$\int \frac{1}{u}\,du = \int u^{-1}\,du = \ln u + C \qquad \textbf{(113)}$$

where u is positive. This restriction was stated directly after Eq. (97) in Sec. 25·15.

If, in Eq. (113) above, u is negative, then $(-u)$ is positive, and

$$\int \frac{d(-u)}{-u} = \ln(-u) + C \qquad (113a)$$

Equations (113) and (113a) can be combined into a single formula:

$$\int \frac{du}{u} = \ln|u| + C \qquad u \neq 0 \qquad \textbf{(114)}$$

example 49 Find

$$\int \frac{9x^2\,dx}{1-2x^3} \tag{115}$$

If we let

$$u = 1 - 2x^3$$

then

$$du = -6x^2\,dx$$

and expression (115) does *not* contain *du exactly*. Therefore Eq. (114) does not apply directly. However, we may multiply and divide expression (115) by $-2/3$ without changing the value of (115) and obtain an equivalent expression,

$$-\frac{3}{2}\int \frac{-\frac{2}{3}\cdot 9x^2\,dx}{1-2x^3} = -\frac{3}{2}\int \frac{-6x^2\,dx}{1-2x^3}$$

for which Eq. (114) does apply directly and

$$\int \frac{9x^2\,dx}{1-2x^3} = -\frac{3}{2}\int \frac{-6x^2\,dx}{1-2x^3} = -\frac{3}{2}\ln(1-2x^3) + C$$

The equation for the graph shown in Fig. 24·25 is

$$F = \frac{10}{D}$$

The area under this graph is proportional to work w done by the force F in forcing the piston through the distance D. Therefore

$$w = \int \frac{10}{D}\,dD$$

Work done is

$$w = 10 \ln D + C$$

Now we wish to find the work accomplished when the piston moves from $D = 1$ to $D = 6$. When $D = 1$ the work in which we are interested is 0; therefore

$$0 = 10 \ln 1 + C$$

but

$$\ln 1 = 0$$

Therefore

$$C = 0$$

and

$$w = 10 \ln D$$

When $D = 6$,

$$w = 10 \ln 6$$
$$= 10 \times 1.792 = 17.92$$

EXERCISE 14

Find the following definite integrals.

1. $\int_0^9 \frac{dx}{x+3}$
2. $\int_3^5 \frac{s\,ds}{s^2-4}$
3. $\int_{-3}^0 \frac{8h^2\,dh}{1-4h^3}$
4. $\int_{0.1}^{0.5} \frac{(2t^2-4)\,dt}{6t-t^3}$

5. $\int_2^5 \frac{(\theta - 1)^2\, d\theta}{\theta^3 - 3\theta^2 + 3\theta}$

6. $\int_{2.5}^{3.2} \frac{(x - 1)\, dx}{x^2 - 2x}$

7. $\int_2^4 \frac{(t + 1)(t - 1)\, dt}{t^3 - 3t}$

8. $\int_0^2 - \frac{h\, dh}{3(9 - h^2)}$

9. The area under the curve of $y = s/(s^2 - 4)$ is 0.8 when the lower limit is 5. Find the upper limit.

10. Figure 24·25 was plotted from the equation $F = 10/D$. By integration, confirm the answer to Prob. 6, Exercise 7, Chap. 24.

11. Figure 26·40 shows the relation between pressure and volume in a cylinder, as the piston completes a full cycle. Determine the net work done by finding the shaded area.

Data:

A. $V = 1$ cu ft, $p = 14{,}400$ lb per cu ft, $C_1 = 14{,}400$
B. $V = 2$ cu ft, $p = 7{,}200$ lb per cu ft, $C_2 = 19{,}000$
C. $V = 6$ cu ft, $p = 1{,}545$ lb per cu ft, $C_3 = 9{,}270$
D. $V = 3$ cu ft, $p = 3{,}090$ lb per cu ft, $C_4 = 14{,}400$

fig. 26·40

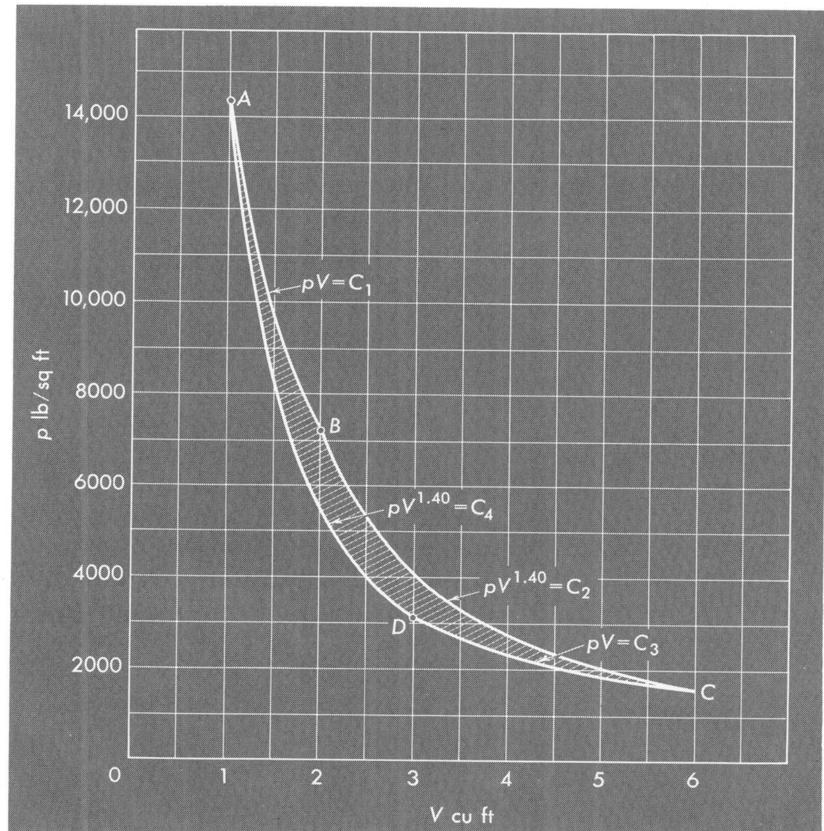

12. Show that

$$\int_a^b V^{-1}\,dV = \int_c^d V^{-1}\,dV$$

if $b/a = d/c$.

13. During a certain process in an engine, the pressure p lb per sq ft changes with the volume (V cu ft) according to the law

$$p = \left(\frac{3V^2}{5} + \frac{10}{V}\right)(144)$$

Determine the work done by evaluating

$$W = \int_{V_1}^{V_2} p\,dV$$

if the volume changes from $V_1 = 1$ cu ft to $V_2 = 3$ cu ft.

14. If the pressure (p lb per sq ft) changes with the volume (V cu ft) during a certain process in an engine according to the law $pV^n = C$, where C and n are constants, show that the work

$$W = \int_{V_1}^{V_2} p\,dV$$

is given by the two following equations:

(a) $$W = \frac{p_2V_2 - p_1V_1}{1-n} \qquad n \neq 1$$

(b) $$W = p_1V_1 \ln \frac{V_2}{V_1} \qquad n = 1$$

REMARK: The proofs of these two results are to be found in texts on thermodynamics, and the resulting equations are fundamental in that study.

15. A ship whose weight is 100 tons is traveling at the speed of 40 fps when the power is cut off. The acceleration at any time t sec later is given by

$$a = -\frac{1{,}600}{(t+50)^2} \qquad \text{ft/sec}^2$$

and this is valid for about 5 min. Determine the velocity and distance traveled (assuming that the ship moves along a straight path) as functions of the time t sec. What are their values at the time $t = 4$ min?

26·19 The integral of sin *u du* and cos *u du*

From Sec. 25·10 we note that if

$$y = k \sin u$$

then $$\frac{dy}{du} = k \cos u$$

or $$dy = k \cos u \, du$$

Consequently, $$\int k \cos u \, du = k \sin u + C \qquad \textbf{(116)}$$

Also from Sec. 25·10 we note that if

$$y = k \cos u$$

then $$\frac{dy}{du} = -k \sin u$$

or $$dy = -k \sin u \, du$$

Consequently, $$\int -k \sin u \, du = k \cos u + C$$

Also $$\int k \sin u \, du = -k \cos u + C \qquad \textbf{(117)}$$

example 50 Find

$$\int 6 \sin \left(2\theta + \frac{\pi}{2}\right) d\theta \qquad (118)$$

If we let

$$u = 2\theta + \frac{\pi}{2}$$

then $$du = 2 \, d\theta$$

and expression (118) does *not* contain *du exactly*. Therefore Eq. (117) does not apply directly. However, we may multiply and divide expression (117) by ⅓ without changing the value of this expression and obtain an equivalent expression,

$$3\int \frac{6}{3} \sin \left(2\theta + \frac{\pi}{2}\right) d\theta = 3\int 2 \sin \left(2\theta + \frac{\pi}{2}\right) d\theta$$

for which Eq. (117) does apply directly and

$$\int 6 \sin \left(2\theta + \frac{\pi}{2}\right) d\theta = 3\int 2 \sin \left(2\theta + \frac{\pi}{2}\right) d\theta = -3 \cos \left(2\theta + \frac{\pi}{2}\right) + C$$

example 51 Find

$$\int -\tfrac{1}{2} \cos 2\phi \, d\phi \qquad (119)$$

If we let

$$u = 2\phi$$

then $$du = 2 \, d\phi$$

and expression (119) does not contain *du* exactly. Therefore Eq. (116) does not apply directly. However, we may multiply and divide expression (119) by 4 without changing the value of this expression and obtain an equivalent expression

$$\frac{1}{4}\int -\frac{4}{2} \cos 2\phi \, d\phi = \frac{1}{4}\int -2 \cos 2\phi \, d\phi$$

for which Eq. (116) does apply directly and

$$\int -\frac{1}{2}\cos 2\phi \, d\phi = \frac{1}{4}\int -2\cos 2\phi \, d\phi = -\frac{1}{4}\sin 2\phi + C$$

EXERCISE 15

Integrate the following:

1. $\int 4\cos 2\theta \, d\theta$
2. $\int -\frac{\sin(\phi/2)}{8}\, d\phi$
3. $\int x\cos x^2 \, dx$
4. $\int 10\sin 2\theta \, d\theta$
5. $\int \cos(4-x)\, dx$
6. $\int \sin\left(\pi - \frac{\phi}{4}\right) d\phi$

One important application of the integral of a sine function occurs in the problem of finding the average ordinate of the sine wave over a half cycle. It will be recalled that we find the average ordinate of a curve by first finding the area under the curve and, second, by dividing that area by the abscissa distance between the limits chosen (see Sec. 26·10). We shall now proceed to find the average ordinate of the curve defined in the equation

$$y = \sin\phi \qquad 0 \le \phi \le \pi$$

The area under this curve over one-half the cycle is

$$A_0{}^\pi = \int_0^\pi \sin\phi \, d\phi = [-\cos\phi]_0^\pi \tag{120}$$

Evaluating (120) we write

$$\begin{aligned} A_0{}^\pi &= (-\cos\pi) - (-\cos 0) \\ &= [-(-1)] - [-(+1)] \end{aligned} \tag{121}$$

Therefore $\qquad A_0{}^\pi = (+1) + 1$

Thus the area under a sine curve over the interval between 0 and π radians is 2. The average height will be, therefore,

$$\text{Average height} = \frac{2}{\pi} = 0.6366 \tag{122}$$

The student should be careful to note that we are here finding the average ordinate of a sine curve, not the so-called effective ordinate of a sine curve. It would also be instructive to find the average ordinate of a sine curve over one entire cycle, that is, between the limits of 0 and 2π radians. Accordingly, let us alter Eq. (120) to find the area under a sine curve between the limits of 0 and 2π.

$$\begin{aligned} A_0{}^{2\pi} &= \int_0^{2\pi} \sin\phi \, d\phi = [-\cos\phi]_0^{2\pi} \\ &= (-\cos 2\pi) - (-\cos 0) \\ &= (-1) - (-1) = -1 + 1 = 0 \end{aligned} \tag{123}$$

Now let us find the *root-mean-square* value of a sine curve between $\phi = 0$ and $\phi = \pi$. The root-mean-square value of a sine curve is the square root of the average value of

$$y = \sin^2 \phi$$

between $\phi = 0$ and $\phi = \pi$.

The average value of this function is (see Sec. 26·10)

$$\bar{y} = \frac{A_0{}^{\pi}}{\pi}$$

but
$$A_0{}^{\pi} = \int_0^{\pi} \sin^2 \phi \, d\phi \tag{124}$$

We have as yet no formula by which we can integrate Eq. (124), but by Sec. 21·9 we can write the equivalent of Eq. (124) as

$$A_0{}^{\pi} = \int_0^{\pi} \left(\frac{1}{2} - \frac{\cos 2\phi}{2}\right) d\phi$$

Then
$$A_0{}^{\pi} = \int_0^{\pi} \frac{1}{2}\, d\phi - \int_0^{\pi} \frac{\cos 2\phi}{2}\, d\phi$$

From Example 51 above and Sec. 26·3 we may write

$$A_0{}^{\pi} = [\tfrac{1}{2}\phi]_0^{\pi} - [\tfrac{1}{4} \sin 2\phi]_0^{\pi}$$

Then
$$A_0{}^{\pi} = \left(\frac{\pi}{2} - 0\right) = \frac{\pi}{2}$$

The average ordinate of $y = \sin^2 \phi$ is therefore

$$\frac{\pi/2}{\pi} = \frac{1}{2}$$

However, the *effective* ordinate of a curve of sin u is, by definition, "the square root of the average ordinate of the curve of $\sin^2 \phi$"; that is, if $y = \sin \phi$,

$$y_{\text{eff}} = \sqrt{\frac{1}{2}} = \frac{\sqrt{2}}{2} = 0.707$$

The effective value of the function

$$y = k \sin \phi$$

is

$$y_{\text{eff}} = k\frac{\sqrt{2}}{2} = k \cdot 0.707 \tag{125}$$

EXERCISE 16

1. Find the area under the graph of each equation below between the specified limits. Also find the average height between these limits.

(a) $y = 4 \cos 2\theta$ between $\frac{\pi}{6}$ and $\frac{\pi}{4}$

(b) $y = -\frac{1}{8}\sin\frac{\phi}{2}$ between $\frac{\pi}{2}$ and $\frac{2\pi}{3}$

(c) $y = x\cos x^2$ between 0.2 and 0.5

(d) $y = 10\sin 2\phi$ between $\frac{\pi}{2}$ and $\frac{3\pi}{4}$

(e) $y = \cos(4 - x)$ between 4 and 5

(f) $y = \sin\left(\pi - \frac{\theta}{4}\right)$ between 4π and 5π

(g) $y = \frac{\sin\theta}{\cos^2\theta}$ between 0 and $\frac{\pi}{3}$

(h) $y = \frac{\cos x}{5\sin^3 x}$ between $\frac{\pi}{3}$ and $\frac{2\pi}{3}$

2. The equation for the linear speed of a point on the tread of an automobile tire traveling at a constant speed is

$$v = 32\pi \sin 8\pi t$$

where t is in seconds, and v is in feet per second. This is the equation from which Fig. 24·34 was plotted.
(a) Find the acceleration of the point when $t = 0.03$ (compare with Prob. 2, Exercise 9, Chap. 24).
(b) Find the time and value of the maximum speed (compare with Prob. 3, Exercise 9, Chap. 24).
(c) Find the speed of the car (compare with Prob. 4, Exercise 9, page 650).
(d) Find the outside diameter of the tire (compare with Prob. 5, Exercise 9, Chap. 24).
(e) Find the distance the point moves between $t = 0$ and $t = 1/8$ sec (compare with Prob. 6, Exercise 9, Chap. 24).

3. The voltage and current in an electric circuit are, respectively, given by

$$e = 25 \sin \omega t \text{ volts} \qquad i = 20 \sin\left(\omega t - \frac{\pi}{6}\right) \quad \text{amp}$$

(a) Determine the average power, defined as

$$\frac{1}{T}\int_0^T ei\,dt$$

where T is the period of both the voltage and the current (T is to be determined).
(b) Sketch the voltage and current waves from $t = 0$ to $t = 2\pi/\omega$. Sketch on the same graph the curve for instantaneous power, defined by $p = ei$. Then show the graphical meaning of the preceding definite integral.

4. The voltage in an electric circuit is given by

$$e = E \sin \omega t \text{ volts}$$

where E and ω are constants. You may assume, if you wish, that $\omega = 60$ cps $= 120\pi$ radians per sec.

(a) Determine the average voltage for the interval of time from $t = 0$ to $t = \pi/\omega$. Also determine the average voltage from $t = 0$ to $t = 2\pi/\omega$.

(b) Find the root-mean-square value of the voltage; that is, find the square root of the average value of the ordinate to the curve $y = E^2 \sin^2 \omega t$ from $t = 0$ to $t = 2\pi/\omega$.

(c) Use your result from (b) to determine to three significant figures the value of E so that the root-mean-square value will be 120 volts.

(d) Sketch graphs of $e = E \sin \omega t$ and $y = E^2 \sin^2 \omega t$, each for a complete period, and indicate the average ordinate for each curve for the complete period.

5. An alternating current is given by

$$i = I_1 \sin \omega t + I_3 \sin 3\omega t + \cdots + I_k \sin k\omega t \qquad \text{amp}$$

where k is an odd number. Determine formulas for (a) the average value of the current from $t = 0$ to $t = \pi/\omega$ sec, (b) the root-mean-square value of the current from $t = 0$ to $t = 2\pi/\omega$ sec.

6. An alternating voltage is given by

$$e = 100 \sin 100\pi t + 50 \sin 300\pi t + 10 \sin 500\pi t \text{ volts}$$

(a) Sketch a graph of the voltage wave for one complete period.

(b) Determine the average value of the voltage from (1) $t = 0$ to $t = 0.01$ sec, (2) $t = 0$ to $t = 0.02$ sec.

(c) Determine the root-mean-square value of the voltage over a complete period.

7. The voltage in the circuit discussed in Prob. 5 is given by

$$e = E_1 \sin \omega t + E_3 \sin 3\omega t + \cdots + E_k \sin k\omega t \text{ volts}$$

Determine the average power defined by

$$P = \frac{1}{T}\int_0^T ei\, dt$$

where $T = 2\pi/\omega$.

REMARK: Textbooks on alternating currents derive comparable formulas, but use equations for the voltage and current that involve both sine and cosine terms.

8. The instantaneous rate of heat production of a current i amp flowing in a constant resistance r ohms is i^2r watts. Determine the average rate of heat production over a cycle (one complete period) for the following periodic curves. Thus, determine the average ordinate to the curve $y = i^2r$ for a complete period.

(a) $i = I \sin 2\pi ft$, I is a constant.

(b) $i = I_1 \sin 2\pi ft + I_3 \sin 6\pi ft$, I_1 and I_3 are constants.

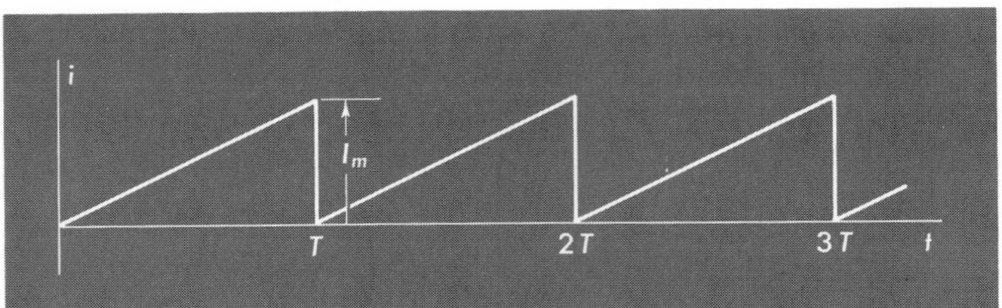

fig. 26·41

fig. 26·42

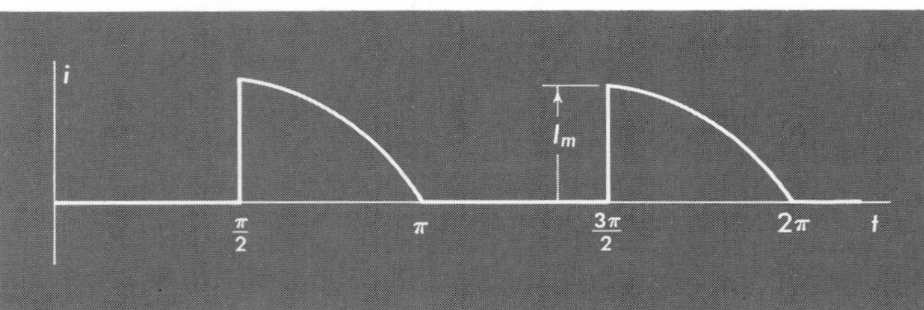

(c) $i = I_1 \sin \omega t + I_3 \sin (3\omega t - \theta)$, I_1, I_3, and θ are constants.
(d) Find the average ordinate to the curve $y = i^2r$ from Fig. 26·41.
(e) Do the same as in (d) for Fig. 26·42.

Portions of rectified sine waves (output of a controlled rectifier) are shown in Fig. 26·42.

REMARK: This heat production is the basis of the definition of the effective (root-mean-square) value of a periodically varying current; that is, $(I_{\text{effective}})^2(r)$ is the average rate of heat production over one cycle (one complete period).

9. The potential energy (PE) stored in a beam is given by

$$\text{PE} = \frac{EI}{2} \int_0^L \left(\frac{d^2y}{dx^2}\right)^2 dx$$

where E, I, and L are constants. Determine the potential energy stored in a cantilever beam (see Fig. 26·43) which has for its equation

$$y = y_0\left(1 - \cos\frac{\pi x}{2L}\right)$$

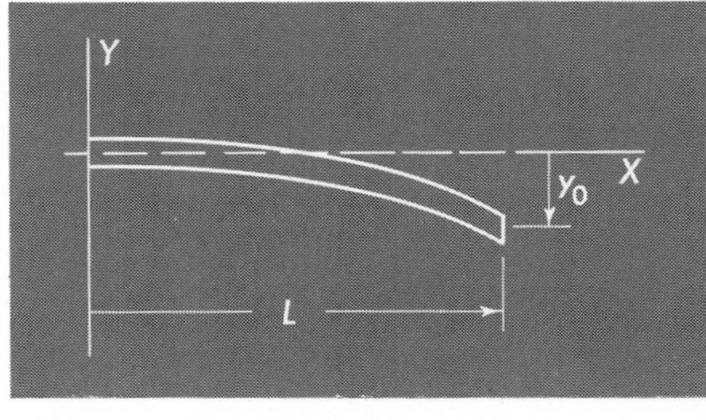

fig. 26·43

fig. 26·44

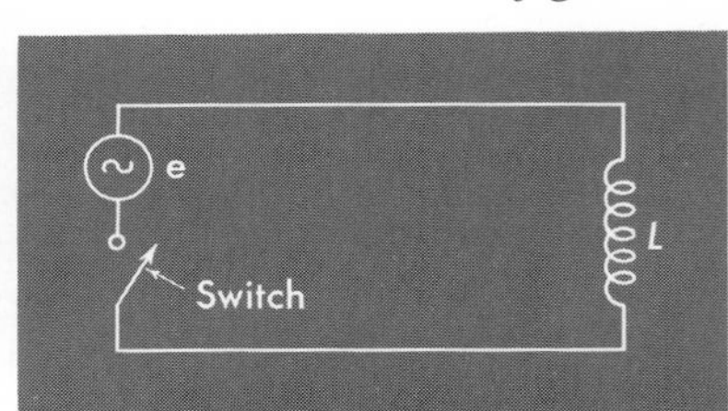

10. A circuit (see Fig. 26·44) consists of an inductance $L = 0.2$ henry connected to a generator with an electromotive force $e = 100 \sin \omega t$ volts ($\omega = 60$ cps $= 120\pi$ radians per sec). The switch is to be closed at the time $t = 0$; hence, when $t = 0$, the current $i = 0$ amp.

    Given $L(di/dt) = e = 100 \sin \omega t$, determine a formula for i in terms of the time t sec. Sketch the graph of i as a function of t for t from 0 to $\frac{1}{20}$ sec. Also determine the current flowing in the circuit when $t = \frac{1}{180}$ sec.

11. A bead of weight w lb slides without friction on the arc of a circle, which lies in a vertical plane. The radius of the arc is R ft. Starting with the expression for the work done by gravity as the bead moves from A to B (see Fig. 26·45)

$$W = \int_A^B w \cos \theta \, ds$$

where ds is an element of length of the circular wire, and θ is the angle which the tangent to this arc makes with the vertical, show that W is equal to the product of the weight w and the vertical distance between the points A and B.

What would be your result if the points A and B were joined by a straight line? By an arc of a parabola with vertex at A?

26·20 The integral of $ke^u \, du$

From Sec. 25·17 we note that if

$$y = ke^u$$

then
$$\frac{dy}{du} = ke^u$$

or
$$dy = ke^u \, du$$

fig. 26·45

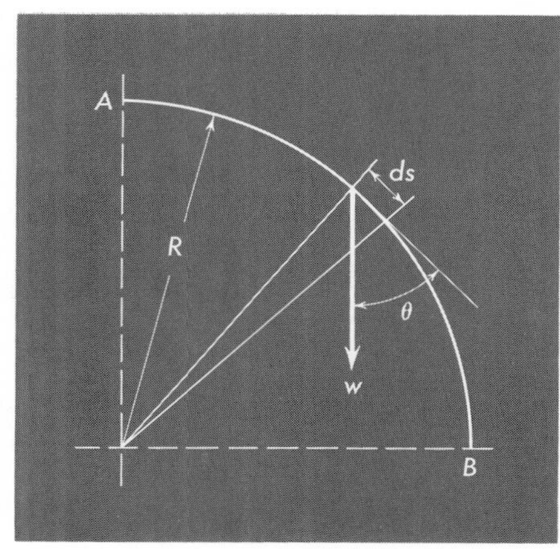

Consequently,

$$\int ke^u\,du = ke^u + C \tag{126}$$

For example, let us find

$$\int 10xe^{x^2}\,dx \tag{127}$$

If we let

$$u = x^2$$

then $$du = 2x\,dx$$

and expression (127) does not contain *du* exactly. Therefore Eq. (126) does not apply directly. However, we may multiply and divide expression (127) by ⅕ without changing the value of this expression and obtain an equivalent expression

$$5\int \tfrac{10}{5}xe^{x^2}\,dx = 5\int 2xe^{x^2}\,dx$$

for which Eq. (126) does apply directly and

$$\int 10xe^{x^2}\,dx = 5\int 2xe^{x^2}\,dx = 5e^{x^2} + C$$

EXERCISE 17

Integrate:

1. $\displaystyle\int e^{1-4x}\,dx$
2. $\displaystyle\int \frac{dx}{e^x}$
3. $\displaystyle\int e^{\pi x}\,dx$
4. $\displaystyle\int 6x^2e^{x^3}\,dx$
5. $\displaystyle\int \frac{e^{1/x}}{5x^2}\,dx$
6. $\displaystyle\int (e^{2x} + e^{-2x})^2\,dx$
7. $\displaystyle\int e^{3x+1}\,dx$
8. $\displaystyle\int xe^{x^2}\,dx$
9. $\displaystyle\int (e^x - e^{-2x})^2\,dx$
10. $\displaystyle\int (e^{2x} - e^{-2x})^2\,dx$
11. $\displaystyle\int \left(e^{3x} - \frac{1}{e}\right)^2 dx$
12. $\displaystyle\int \frac{e^x + 1}{e^{2x}}\,dx$
13. $\displaystyle\int (e^{2x} - e^{x/2})^2\,dx$
14. $\displaystyle\int \frac{x-1}{e^{x^2-2x}}\,dx$

15. Evaluate the following definite integral that was found in textbooks in chemical engineering and in technical journals for chemical engineering:

$$\int_0^1 y_n\,dw \text{ if } y_n = e^{ELw}(y_{n0} - Y_{n-1}) + Y_{n-1} \text{ and } E,\ L,\ y_{n0}$$

Y_{n-1} are constants.

16. In a circuit containing resistance and inductance in series, the power supplied to the magnetic field of the inductance is given by

$$P = \left(\frac{E^2}{R}\right)(e^{-Rt/L} - e^{-2Rt/L})$$

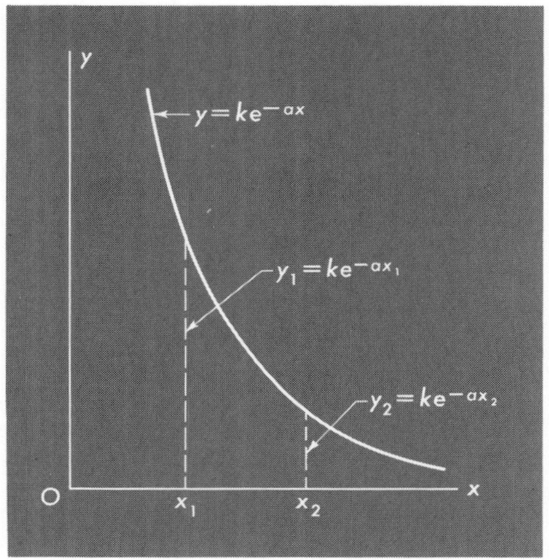

fig. 26·46

Show that the total energy stored in the magnetic field, a quantity defined by

$$W = \int_0^\infty P\,dt$$

has the value $W = LI^2/2$, where $I = E/R$.

17. If $h(x) = 2.995e^{-14.627x} + 2.18e^{-82.22x} + 1.006e^{-212x}$, obtain the equation for $\theta(x)$ if

$$1 - \theta(x) = 4\int_0^x h(x)\,dx$$

18. Figure 26·46 shows the graph of $y = ke^{-ax}$. Show that the average ordinate $\bar{y}$ is

$$\bar{y} = \frac{y_1 - y_2}{\ln(y_1/y_2)}$$

This relation is used in heat-exchanger problems to determine the average temperature difference, knowing the temperature differences at the beginning and the end of the exchanger.

19. Figure 24·24 was plotted from the equation

$$T = 50e^{-0.2t}$$

where T is the temperature difference between a warm body and its cooler surroundings. Find the average temperature difference during the first 10 min (see Prob. 18 above).

26·21 Integral tables

There are far too many types of integrals for the student to remember them all. Up to this point we have specifically discussed the following integration formulas where u is assumed to be the value of a differentiable function of x.

$$\int u^n \, du = \frac{u^{n+1}}{n+1} + C \qquad n \neq -1$$

$$\int e^u \, du = e^u + C$$

$$\int \frac{1}{u} \, du = \ln |u| + C$$

$$\int \sin u \, du = -\cos u + C$$

$$\int \cos u \, du = \sin u + C$$

The student may sometimes encounter integrals which do not match any of the above formulas. In such cases he can search a more extensive list of formulas found in a table of standard integrals such as:

Burington, R. & S.: "Handbook of Mathematical Tables and Formulas, 4th ed., McGraw-Hill Book Company, New York, 1964.

Hoag, Albert L., and Donald G. McNeese: "Engineering and Technical Handbook," Prentice-Hall, Inc., Englewood Cliffs, N.J., 1957.

"C.R.C. Standard Mathematical Tables," The Chemical Rubber Publishing Co., Cleveland, Ohio.

Peirce, B. O., and R. M. Foster: "A Short Table of Integrals," 4th ed., Ginn and Company, Boston, 1956.

For convenience, the expressions which are integrated are classified into types. In some cases, specific limitations are given. In addition, no formula is valid when zero occurs in the denominator or when an even root of a negative number is involved.

Many times the student will be unable to find in the table of integrals the precise form he wishes to integrate. Yet he may be able to alter the expression he wishes to integrate into an equivalent form which is in the integral table.

Some of the more common forms are illustrated in the following examples.

example 52 Find

$$\int \frac{5x \, dx}{3x - 2}$$

From a table of integrals we find the equation

$$\int \frac{x \, dx}{a + bx} = \frac{1}{b^2} [bx - a \ln (a + bx)] \tag{128}$$

(Note that the constant is usually omitted in the table of integrals.) We may alter the given expression to read

$$5 \int \frac{x \, dx}{-2 + 3x} \tag{129}$$

Note that expression (129) and the left-hand side of Eq. (128) are identical in form and that

$$a = -2 \qquad b = 3$$

Therefore we may write

$$5\int \frac{x\,dx}{-2 + 3x} = (5)(1/9)\,[3x - (-2)\ln(-2 + 3x)]$$
$$= 5/9\,[+3x + 2\ln(-2 + 3x)]$$

example 53 Find

$$\int_0^{2/3} \frac{dx}{4 + 9x^2} \tag{130}$$

From a table of integrals we find the equation

$$\int \frac{dx}{a + bx^2} = \frac{1}{\sqrt{ab}} \tan^{-1} \frac{x\sqrt{ab}}{a} \tag{131}$$

Note that expression (130) and the left-hand side of Eq. (131) are identical in form and that

$$a = 4 \qquad b = 9$$

Therefore we may write

$$\int_0^{2/3} \frac{dx}{4 + 9x^2} = \frac{1}{6}\left[\tan^{-1}\frac{6}{4}x\right]_0^{2/3}$$
$$= 1/6[\tan^{-1}(3/2 \times 2/3) - \tan^{-1}(3/2)(0)]$$
$$= \frac{1}{6}\left(\frac{\pi}{4} - 0\right) = \frac{\pi}{24}$$

example 54 Find

$$\int \frac{x\,dx}{2x^2 - 3x - 5} \tag{132}$$

From a table of integrals we find the equation

$$\int \frac{x\,dx}{X} = \frac{1}{2c}\ln X - \frac{b}{2c}\int \frac{dx}{X} \tag{133}$$

where $$X = a + bx + cx^2$$

Also, from a table of integrals we find the equation

$$\int \frac{dx}{X} = \frac{1}{\sqrt{-q}} \ln \frac{2cx + b - \sqrt{-q}}{2cx + b + \sqrt{-q}} \tag{134}$$

where $$X = a + bx + cx^2 \tag{135}$$

$$q = 4ac - b^2 \qquad b^2 > 4ac \tag{136}$$

Substituting Eq. (134) in Eq. (133) we obtain

$$\int \frac{x\,dx}{X} = \frac{1}{2c}\ln X - \frac{b}{2c}\left(\frac{1}{\sqrt{-q}}\ln\frac{2cx + b - \sqrt{-q}}{2cx + b + \sqrt{-q}}\right) \tag{137}$$

Note that expression (132) and the left-hand side of Eq. (137) are identical in form and that

$$\begin{aligned} X &= 2x^2 - 3x - 5 \\ a &= -5 \\ b &= -3 \\ c &= 2 \\ q &= 4ac - b^2 = -40 - 9 = -49 \end{aligned}$$

Substituting, we have

$$\int \frac{x\,dx}{2x^2 - 3x - 5} = \frac{1}{4}\ln(2x^2 - 3x - 5) + \frac{3}{4}\left(\frac{1}{7}\ln\frac{4x - 10}{4x + 4}\right)$$

example 55 Find

$$\int \sqrt{4 + \frac{9}{x^2}}\,dx \tag{138}$$

From a table of integrals we find the equation

$$\int \frac{\sqrt{x^2 + a^2}}{x}\,dx = \sqrt{x^2 + a^2} - a\ln\left(\frac{a + \sqrt{x^2 + a^2}}{x}\right) \tag{139}$$

We may alter expression (138) to read

$$\sqrt{\frac{4}{x^2}\left(x^2 + \frac{9}{4}\right)} = \frac{2\sqrt{x^2 + 9/4}}{x} \tag{140}$$

Note that the expression on the right-hand side of Eq. (140) and the expression on the left-hand side of Eq. (139) are identical in form and that $a^2 = 9/4$. Therefore

$$2\int \frac{\sqrt{x^2 + 9/4}}{x}\,dx = 2\left[\sqrt{x^2 + \frac{9}{4}} - \frac{3}{2}\ln\left(\frac{3/2 + \sqrt{x^2 + 9/4}}{x}\right)\right]$$

example 56 Find

$$\int_0^{1/2} \sqrt{1 - 4x^2}\,dx \tag{141}$$

From a table of integrals we find the equation

$$\int \sqrt{a^2 - x^2}\,dx = \frac{1}{2}\left(x\sqrt{a^2 - x^2} + a^2\sin^{-1}\frac{x}{a}\right) \tag{142}$$

We can alter the form of expression (141) to read

$$2\int_0^{1/2} \sqrt{1/4 - x^2}\,dx \tag{143}$$

Note that expression (143) and the left-hand side of Eq. (142) are identical in form and that $a^2 = \frac{1}{4}$. Therefore we may write

$$\int_0^{1/2} \sqrt{1 - 4x^2}\, dx = (2)(\tfrac{1}{2})[x\sqrt{\tfrac{1}{4} - x^2} + \tfrac{1}{4}\sin^{-1} 2x]$$

$$= \left(\frac{1}{2}\sqrt{0} + \frac{1}{4}\sin^{-1} 1\right) - \left(0\sqrt{\frac{1}{4}} + \frac{1}{4}\sin^{-1} 0\right)$$

$$= \frac{1}{4}\sin^{-1} 1 = \frac{\pi}{8}$$

example 57 Find, by integration, the area of a circle 10 in. in radius.

We shall first find the area of the quadrant shown in Fig. 26·47.

$$A = \int y\, dx$$

The limits between which we shall integrate are $x = 0$ and $x = 10$ in. Also, we see that

$$y = \sqrt{100 - x^2}$$

Therefore

$$A = \int_0^{10} \sqrt{100 - x^2}\, dx$$

Now by applying Eq. (142) we may write

$$A = \left[\frac{1}{2}\left(x\sqrt{100 - x^2} + 100 \sin^{-1}\frac{x}{10}\right)\right]_0^{10}$$

$$= \tfrac{1}{2}(10\sqrt{100 - 100} + 100 \sin^{-1} \tfrac{10}{10}) - \tfrac{1}{2}(0\sqrt{100 - 0} + 100 \sin^{-1} \tfrac{0}{10})$$

Note that

$$\sin^{-1} \tfrac{10}{10} = \sin^{-1} 1 = \frac{\pi}{2} \text{ radians}$$

$$A = \frac{1}{2}\left(100\frac{\pi}{2}\right) = 25\pi$$

The area of the entire circle is $4 \times 25\pi$, or 100π.

fig. 26·47

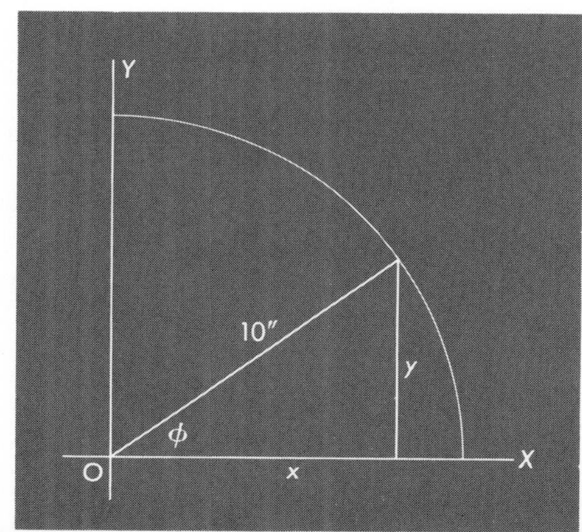

example 58 Find

$$\int_{\pi/4}^{\pi/2} x \sin^2 x \, dx \tag{144}$$

From a table of integrals we find the equation

$$\int x \sin^2 x \, dx = \frac{x^2}{4} - \frac{x \sin 2x}{4} - \frac{\cos 2x}{8}$$

Therefore we may write

$$\int_{\pi/4}^{\pi/2} x \sin^2 dx = \left[\frac{(\pi/2)^2}{4} - \frac{(\pi/2) \sin \pi}{4} - \frac{\cos \pi}{8}\right] - \left[\frac{(\pi/4)^2}{4} - \frac{(\pi/4) \sin (\pi/2)}{4} - \frac{\cos (\pi/2)}{8}\right]$$

$$= \left(\frac{\pi^2}{16} + \frac{1}{8}\right) - \left(\frac{\pi^2}{64} - \frac{\pi}{16}\right)$$

$$= \frac{3\pi^2}{64} + \frac{1}{8} + \frac{\pi}{16} = 0.784$$

example 59 Find

$$\int x^3 \ln x \, dx \tag{145}$$

From a table of integrals we find the equation

$$\int x^p \ln (ax) \, dx = \frac{x^{p+1}}{p+1} \ln (ax) - \frac{x^{p+1}}{(p+1)^2} \qquad p \neq -1 \tag{146}$$

Note that expression (145) and the left-hand side of Eq. (146) are identical in form, and

$$p = 3$$
$$a = 1$$

Therefore we may write

$$\int x^3 \ln x \, dx = \frac{x^4}{4} \ln x - \frac{x^4}{16}$$

example 60 Find

$$\int x^2 e^{3x} \, dx \tag{147}$$

From a table of integrals we find the equation

$$\int x^m e^{ax} \, dx = \frac{x^m e^{ax}}{a} - \frac{m}{a} \int x^{m-1} e^{ax} \, dx \tag{148}$$

Note that expression (147) and the left-hand side of Eq. (148) are identical in form and that

$$m = 2$$
$$a = 3$$

Also note that in this special case the quantity $(m - 1)$ in Eq. (148) is unity; therefore we may write

$$\int x^2e^{3x}\,dx = \frac{x^2e^{3x}}{3} - \frac{2}{3}\int xe^{3x}\,dx \tag{149}$$

Also from a table of integrals we find the equation

$$\int xe^{ax}\,dx = \frac{e^{ax}}{a^2}(ax - 1)$$

Therefore we may rewrite Eq. (148) as

$$\int x^2e^{3x}\,dx = \frac{x^2e^{3x}}{3} - \frac{2}{3}\left[\frac{e^{3x}}{9}(3x - 1)\right]$$

$$= \frac{e^{3x}}{27}(9x^2 - 6x + 2)$$

26·22 Simpson's rule

One of the primary uses of antidifferentiation in engineering and technology is to find a formula by which the numerical value of a definite integral may be calculated.

Unfortunately, the student will probably encounter functions for which he cannot find an antiderivative. However, if the given function is continuous over the interval from a to b, we know that its definite integral has a specific value.

In this section we shall discuss a method by which we can approximate

$$\int_a^b f(x)\,dx \qquad f(x) \geq 0$$

where $f(x)$ is continuous and $f(x) \geq 0$ for $a \leq x \leq b$.

As we have learned in the previous work, any definite integral $\int_a^b f(x)\,dx$ can be interpreted as an area. This sort of an integral can therefore be approximated by any method by which areas may be approximated. One such method is Simpson's rule, which we shall not derive.

Simpson's rule states that to find the approximate area under the graph of a function of the sort described above, we divide the area under the graph into an *even* number of strips of equal width by erecting an *odd number* of equally spaced ordinates. If we let h represent the distance between ordinates and designate the ordinates by $y_0, y_1, y_2, y_3, \ldots, y_n$, then the area under the graph is approximately

$$A \approx \frac{h}{3}(y_0 + 4y_1 + 2y_2 + 4y_3 + 2y_4 \cdots + 4y_{(n-1)} + y_n)$$

where y_0 is the ordinate erected at the lower limit of the area to be found and y_n is the ordinate erected at the upper limit of the area.

Thus we may write

$$\int_a^b y\,dx \approx \frac{h}{3}(y_0 + 4y_1 + 2y_2 + 4y_3 + 2y_4 + \cdots + 4y_{n-1} + y_n) \qquad \textbf{(150)}$$

where $a =$ lower limit of integration (left-hand limit)
$b =$ upper limit of integration (right-hand limit)
$y_0 =$ value of function when $x = a$
$y_n =$ value of function when $x = b$

example 61 Evaluate the definite integral

$$\int_2^{14} \frac{5x}{3x-2}\,dx$$

Following Eq. (150),

$$\int_2^{14} \frac{5x}{3x-2}\,dx \approx \frac{h}{3}(y_0 + 4y_1 + 2y_2 + 4y_3 + 2y_4 + \cdots + 4y_{n-1} + y_n)$$

where $h =$ distance between successive ordinates y_0, y_1, y_2, y_3, etc.
$y_0 =$ value of function

$$\frac{5x}{3x-2} \qquad \text{when } x = 2$$

and y_n is the value of the same function when $x = 14$.

It will be instructive to see how the answer varies depending on the number of strips used. While the student is cautioned against making too sweeping conclusions, the results should be highly suggestive.

We shall first use 2 strips; therefore $h = 6$.

x	$5x$	$3x - 2$	$\frac{5x}{3x-2}$
2	10	4	$2.5 \quad \times 1 = 2.50000 = y_0$
8	40	22	$1.81818 \times 4 = 7.27272 = 4y_1$
14	70	40	$1.750000 \times 1 = 1.75000 = y_2$
			11.52272

$$\int_2^{14} \frac{5x}{3x-2}\,dx \approx \frac{6}{3}(11.52272) = 23.045$$

Next we shall use 4 strips; therefore $h = 3$.

x	$5x$	$3x - 2$	$\frac{5x}{3x-2}$
2	10	4.0	$2.50000 \times 1 = 2.50000 = y_0$
5	25	13.0	$1.92307 \times 4 = 7.69228 = 4y_1$
8	40	22	$1.81818 \times 2 = 3.63636 = 2y_2$
11	55	31	$1.77419 \times 4 = 7.09676 = 4y_3$
14	70	40	$1.75000 \times 1 = 1.75000 = y_4$
			22.67540

$$\int_2^{14} \frac{5x}{3x-2}\,dx \approx \frac{3}{3}(22.67540) = 22.6754$$

Next we shall use 12 strips; therefore $h = 1$.

x	$5x$	$3x - 2$	$\dfrac{5x}{3x-2}$
2	10	4	$2.50000 \times 1 = 2.50000 = y_0$
3	15	7	$2.14286 \times 4 = 8.57144 = 4y_1$
4	20	10	$2.00000 \times 2 = 4.00000 = 2y_2$
5	25	13	$1.92307 \times 4 = 7.69228 = 4y_3$
6	30	16	$1.87500 \times 2 = 3.75000 = 2y_4$
7	35	19	$1.84211 \times 4 = 7.36844 = 4y_5$
8	40	22	$1.81818 \times 2 = 3.63636 = 2y_6$
9	45	25	$1.80000 \times 4 = 7.20000 = 4y_7$
10	50	28	$1.78571 \times 2 = 3.57142 = 2y_8$
11	55	31	$1.77419 \times 4 = 7.09676 = 4y_9$
12	60	34	$1.76471 \times 2 = 3.52942 = 2y_{10}$
13	65	37	$1.75676 \times 4 = 7.02704 = 4y_{11}$
14	70	40	$1.75000 \times 1 = 1.75000 = y_{12}$
			67.69316

$$\int_2^{14} \frac{5x}{3x-2}\,dx \approx \frac{1}{3}(67.69316) = 22.564$$

Next we shall use 24 strips; therefore $h = 0.5$.

x	$5x$	$3x - 2$	$\dfrac{5x}{3x-2}$
2.0	10.0	4.0	$2.50000 \times 1 = 2.50000 = y_0$
2.5	12.5	5.5	$2.27272 \times 4 = 9.09088 = 4y_1$
3.0	15.0	7.0	$2.14286 \times 2 = 4.28572 = 2y_2$
3.5	17.5	8.5	$2.05882 \times 4 = 8.23528 = 4y_3$
4.0	20.0	10.0	$2.00000 \times 2 = 4.00000 = 2y_4$
4.5	22.5	11.5	$1.95652 \times 4 = 7.82608 = 4y_5$
5.0	25.0	13.0	$1.92307 \times 2 = 3.84614 = 2y_6$
5.5	27.5	14.5	$1.89655 \times 4 = 7.58620 = 4y_7$
6.0	30.0	16.0	$1.87500 \times 2 = 3.75000 = 2y_8$
6.5	32.5	17.5	$1.85714 \times 4 = 7.42856 = 4y_9$
7.0	35.0	19.0	$1.84211 \times 2 = 3.68222 = 2y_{10}$
7.5	37.5	20.5	$1.82927 \times 4 = 7.31668 = 4y_{11}$
8.0	40.0	22.0	$1.81818 \times 2 = 3.63636 = 2y_{12}$
8.5	42.5	23.5	$1.80851 \times 4 = 7.23404 = 4y_{13}$
9.0	45.0	25.0	$1.80000 \times 2 = 3.60000 = 2y_{14}$
9.5	47.5	26.5	$1.79245 \times 4 = 7.16980 = 4y_{15}$
10.0	50.0	28.0	$1.78571 \times 2 = 3.57142 = 2y_{16}$
10.5	52.5	29.5	$1.77966 \times 4 = 7.11864 = 4y_{17}$
11.0	55.0	31.0	$1.77419 \times 2 = 3.54838 = 2y_{18}$
11.5	57.5	32.5	$1.76923 \times 4 = 7.07692 = 4y_{19}$
12.0	60.0	34.0	$1.76471 \times 2 = 3.52942 = 2y_{20}$
12.5	62.5	35.5	$1.76056 \times 4 = 7.04224 = 4y_{21}$
13.0	65.0	37.0	$1.75676 \times 2 = 3.51352 = 2y_{22}$
13.5	67.5	38.5	$1.75325 \times 4 = 7.01300 = 4y_{23}$
14.0	70.0	40.0	$1.75000 \times 1 = 1.75000 = y_{24}$
			135.34950

$$\int_2^{14} \frac{5x}{3x-2}\,dx \approx \frac{0.5}{3}(135.3495) = 22.5583$$

By reference to Example 52 we note that

$$\int_2^{14} \frac{5x}{3x-2}\,dx = \frac{5}{9}[3x + 2\ln(3x-2)]_2^{14}$$

$$= \frac{5}{9}\{[42 + 2\ln(42-2)] - [6 + 2\ln(6-2)]\}$$

$$= \frac{5}{9}(42 + 2\ln 40 - 6 - 2\ln 4)$$

$$= \frac{5}{9}(36 + 2\ln 10) = \frac{5}{9}(36 + 2 \times 2.30259) = 22.5584$$

example 62 Evaluate the definite integral

$$\int_{1.817}^{14.328} \frac{5x}{3x-2}\,dx$$

We could, of course, divide the region between $x = 1.817$ and $x = 14.328$ into strips, using, for example, 10 strips. However, in so doing we would be committed to using five- or six-digit abscissa distances. It will be much easier to consider three regions separately, as, for example, the region between $x = 1.817$ and $x = 2$, the region between $x = 2$ and $x = 14$, and finally the region between $x = 14$ and $x = 14.328$. Then we shall apply Simpson's rule to each region. The region between $x = 2$ and $x = 14$ has been evaluated in Example 61. We shall now evaluate the other two intervals by Simpson's rule.

Interval between $x = 1.817$ and $x = 2$

x	$5x$	$3x - 2$	$\frac{5x}{3x-2}$
1.817	9.085	3.451	$2.6326 \times 1 = 2.6326 = y_0$
1.9085	9.5425	3.7255	$2.5614 \times 4 = 10.2456 = 4y_1$
2.000	10.000	4.0000	$2.500 \times 1 = 2.5000 = y_2$
			15.3782

$$\text{Area} = \frac{0.0915}{3}(15.3782) = 0.4690$$

Interval between $x = 14$ and $x = 14.328$

14.000	70.000	40.000	$1.7500 \times 1 = 1.7500 = y_0$
14.164	70.820	40.492	$1.7490 \times 4 = 6.9960 = 4y_1$
14.328	71.640	40.984	$1.7480 \times 1 = 1.7480 = y_2$
			10.4940

$$\text{Area} = \frac{0.164}{3}(10.4940) = 0.574$$

The area between $x = 2$ and $x = 14$ was found in Example 61 to be 22.558.

$$\int_{1.817}^{14.328} \frac{5x}{3x-2}\,dx \approx 0.469 + 0.574 + 22.558 = 23.601$$

example 63 Evaluate the definite integral

$$\int_0^{2/3} \left(1 + \frac{e^x}{4}\right)^{1/2} dx$$

Following Eq. (150),

$$\int_0^{2/3} \left(1 + \frac{e^x}{4}\right)^{1/2} dx \approx \frac{h}{3}(y_0 + 4y_1 + 2y_2 + \cdots + 4y_{n-1} + y_n)$$

where h = distance between successive ordinates. We shall use 8 strips. The calculations are tabulated below.

x	e^x	$1 + \frac{e^x}{4}$	$\sqrt{1 + \frac{e^x}{4}}$
0	1.00000	1.25000	$1.11803 \times 1 = 1.11803 = y_0$
1/12	1.08690	1.27172	$1.12771 \times 4 = 4.51084 = 4y_1$
2/12	1.18136	1.29534	$1.13813 \times 2 = 2.27626 = 2y_2$
3/12	1.28402	1.32101	$1.14935 \times 4 = 4.59740 = 4y_3$
4/12	1.39561	1.34890	$1.16142 \times 2 = 2.32284 = 2y_4$
5/12	1.51690	1.37922	$1.17440 \times 4 = 4.69760 = 4y_5$
6/12	1.64872	1.41218	$1.18835 \times 2 = 2.37670 = 2y_6$
7/12	1.79200	1.44800	$1.20333 \times 4 = 4.81332 = 4y_7$
8/12	1.94773	1.48693	$1.21940 \times 1 = 1.21940 = y_8$
			27.93239

$$\int_0^{2/3} \left(1 + \frac{e^x}{4}\right)^{1/2} dx \approx \frac{1/12}{3}(27.93239) = 0.7759$$

EXERCISE 18

Evaluate the following definite integrals by such methods as the instructor directs.

1. $\int_5^8 x\sqrt{3x + 1}\, dx$
2. $\int_2^6 \frac{dx}{5x + 8x^3}$
3. $\int_{0.2}^{0.4} \frac{x\, dx}{3 - 4x}$
4. $\int_0^3 \frac{dx}{16 - x^2}$
5. $\int_2^5 \frac{x^2\, dx}{\sqrt{3x + 5}}$
6. $\int_{0.1}^{0.5} \frac{dx}{x^2(2 + 3x)}$
7. $\int_{-0.5}^{+0.5} \sqrt{\frac{1 + x}{1 - x}}\, dx$
8. $\int_0^5 \frac{dx}{\sqrt{x^2 + 3x + 1}}$
9. $\int_0^6 (100 - x^2)^{3/2}\, dx$
10. $\int_4^{10} \frac{x^3\, dx}{2x + 1}$
11. $\int_0^{1.6} \frac{(1 + x^2)\, dx}{\sqrt{4 - x^2}}$
12. $\int_0^{\pi/2} \sin^4 x\, dx$
13. $\int_0^7 3x(x + 1)^{-1/3}\, dx$
14. $\int_{\pi/6}^{\pi/3} \sin^2 \theta \cos^2 \theta\, d\theta$
15. $\int_0^2 x^2 e^{-x}\, dx$
16. $\int_0^8 e^{-x}\sqrt{3 - 2e^{-x}}\, dx$

17. $\int_1^3 \left(\frac{e^{2x}}{2x} + e^{2x} \ln x\right) dx$

18. $\int_{1.5}^{2.7} x^3 \ln x \, dx$

19. $\int_2^3 \frac{dx}{\ln x^2}$

20. $\int_1^8 (\ln x)^3 \, dx$

21. Evaluate the integral in Prob. 1 by substituting

$$x = z - \tfrac{1}{3}$$

22. Evaluate the integral in Prob. 10 (a) by dividing numerator by denominator obtaining four terms, (b) by substituting $(z - 1)/2$ for x.

23. In calculating the capacity of absorption towers in chemical engineering, it is necessary to evaluate certain definite integrals by approximate methods. Evaluate the following definite integrals by use of Simpson's rule using the given data (x_i is an empirical function of x; y_i is an empirical function of y):

$$\int_2^{12} \frac{dx}{x_i - x} \quad \int_{0.010}^{0.026} \frac{dy}{y - y_i} \quad \int_{0.010}^{0.026} \frac{(1 + y)(1 + y_i)}{y - y_i} dy$$

x	x_i	$\frac{1}{x_i - x}$	y	y_i	$\frac{1}{y - y_i}$
2	5.10	0.322	0.010	0.0008	108
3	5.55	0.392	0.012	0.0040	125
4	6.13	0.469	0.014	0.0082	172
5	6.70	0.587	0.016	0.0122	263
6	7.40	0.715	0.018	0.0156	416
7	8.15	0.869	0.020	0.0183	588
8	9.05	0.952	0.022	0.0203	588
9	10.10	0.909	0.024	0.0220	500
10	11.40	0.715	0.026	0.0233	370
11	13.25	0.444			
12	16.00	0.250			

24. The length of an indicator card is 3.6 in. The widths of the diagram at intervals 0.3 in. apart are 0, 0.40, 0.52, 0.63, 0.72, 0.93, 0.99, 1.00, 1.00, 1.00, 1.00, 0.97, 0. Determine the area of the indicator card by Simpson's rule and divide by the length of the card to obtain the mean effective pressure. Work this problem using 6 subdivisions and 12 subdivisions and compare your results.

25. A cylindrical tank is mounted with its axis horizontal. The tank is 15 ft in diameter and 40 ft long. How many gallons of liquid are there in the tank if the surface of the liquid is 5 ft from the bottom of the tank?

appendixes

A treatment of measured data

B computation aids and approximations

C interpolation

D solution of higher-degree equations

appendix A
treatment of measured data

A · 1 Measured data

Many of the data with which the average technical man works are obtained experimentally. There is a definite limit to their reliability. The *reliability* of a number may be expressed in terms of either precision or accuracy. *Precision* is gauged by the position of the last reliable digit relative to the decimal point, whereas *accuracy* is measured by the number of significant figures. *Significant figures* are those known to be reliable and include any zeros not merely used to locate the decimal point.

For instance, if the diameters of several wires had been measured with a micrometer and found to be 0.118, 0.056, 0.008, and 0.207 in., one might say that these diameters had been measured to a precision of 0.001 in. and to accuracies of three, two, one, and three figures, respectively.

The following statements apply to significant figures:

1. *All nonzero digits are significant.*
2. *Zero digits which lie between significant digits are significant.*
3. *Zero digits which lie to the right of both the decimal point and the last nonzero digit are significant.*
4. *Zeros at the beginning of a decimal fraction are not significant.*
5. *Zeros at the end of a whole number, if used only to locate the decimal point, are not significant. When one or more such zeros are known to be significant, the "tilde" (~) is written over the last significant zero to indicate this fact.*

example 1

Number	*Significant figures*	*Number of significant figures*
35.62	3,5,6,2	4
3,020	3,0,2	3
0.00046	4,6	2
0.000850	8,5,0	3
5.600	5,6,0,0	4
3.0080	3,0,0,8,0	5
12,6$\bar{0}$0	1,2,6,0	4
12,60$\bar{0}$	1,2,6,0,0	5
40,000	4	1

Should the definition of significant figures seem somewhat arbitrary, let us consider the computation of the volume of a rectangular sheet of metal. Suppose that the measured length, width, and thickness are 165.2, 5.07, and 0.0021 in., respectively, and that these measurements are correct to the last digit given. Let us now compare the effect on the volume of changing the last digit of each measurement by one. It will be seen that such a change introduces respective errors of about one-sixteenth of 1 per cent, one-fifth of 1 per cent, and 5 per cent. The length, then, is the most accurate, and the thickness the least accurate.

A·2 Rounding off numbers

Frequently a result will be rounded off because the last several digits either are in doubt or are not required in that particular computation. The operation of rounding off is governed by the following rule:

If the figures to be rejected represent less than half a unit in the last place to be retained, they are dropped. If they represent more than half a unit in the last place to be retained, the last retained digit is increased by one. If the rejected part is known to represent just half a unit in the last place to be retained, the last retained significant digit, if even, is left even or, if odd, is raised to the nearest even number.

example 2

Number	*Four figures*	*Rounded off to three figures*	*Two figures*
3.1416	3.142	3.14	3.1
14.815	14.82	14.8	15.
321.35	321.4	321	320
6,274.5	6,274	6,270	6,300
20,018	20,020	20,$\bar{0}$00	2$\bar{0}$,000
71,853	71,850	71,900*	72,000

* 71,853 is nearer to 71,900 than to 71,800.

In addition and subtraction the precision of the answer corresponds to the least precise of the quantities involved. *Perform the addition or subtraction and round off by eliminating any digits resulting from operations on broken columns on the right.*

example 3 Add:

$$\begin{array}{r} 175.6 \\ 2.126 \\ 13.04 \\ 0.0028 \\ \hline 190.7688 \end{array}$$

Since the last unbroken column on the right is that immediately after the decimal point, we round off to 190.8.

In multiplication and division the accuracy of the answer corresponds to the least accurate of the quantities involved. *Perform the multiplication or division and round off the answer to a number of significant figures equal to that in the least accurate quantity in the computation.*

example 4 Multiply:

$$3.14159 \times 47.82 = 150.2308338$$

Although the multiplicand has six significant figures, the multiplier has only four; therefore, we round off the product to four significant figures and get 150.2.

A·3 Scientific notation

In scientific work a very large or very small number is expressed as a number between 1 and 10 times an integral power of 10. Thus 2,580,000 would be written 2.58×10^6, and 0.0000258 would be written 2.58×10^{-5}. This is called scientific notation. The magnitude of the number is revealed by a glance at the exponent (see Table 10·4).

Several other advantages in this notation will become apparent. Space is saved, a particularly important point in tabulating data. The labor of counting figures to the right or left of the decimal point—a labor attended by risk of error—is eliminated. The accuracy with which a quantity is known is indicated by the number of figures to the right of the decimal point. For example, when we consider the number 72,000, we cannot tell whether there are two, three, four, or five significant figures. No uncertainty exists when we write 7.2×10^4, 7.20×10^4, 7.200×10^4, or 7.2000×10^4.

The ease of dealing with large and small quantities in this manner is illustrated by the following problem:

Simplify the expression

$$\frac{40\tilde{0},000 \times 8,\tilde{0}00,000 \times 0.0045}{60,0\tilde{0}0 \times 0.025 \times 10\tilde{0}} = \frac{4 \times 10^5 \times 8 \times 10^6 \times 4.5 \times 10^{-3}}{6 \times 10^4 \times 2.5 \times 10^{-2} \times 10^2}$$

$$= \frac{4 \times 8 \times 4.5}{6 \times 2.5} \times 10^{(5+6-3)-(4-2+2)} = 9.6 \times 10^4 = 96,000$$

There are two instances in which we depart from the rule of expressing a quantity as a number between 1 and 10 times a suitable power of 10.

If we were to extract the square root of 2.5×10^{-7}, we should write this as 25×10^{-8} in order to make the exponent of 10 divisible by the index of the root. The square root is readily seen to be 5×10^{-4}. Also, when quantities are to be added and subtracted, they must have the same exponents. Thus $4 \times 10^{-7} + 7 \times 10^{-5} = 4 \times 10^{-7} + 700 \times 10^{-7} = 704 \times 10^{-7} = 7.04 \times 10^{-5}$.

appendix B
computation aids and approximations

B · 1 Aids to computation

In this section we shall attempt to outline some of the more commonly useful short cuts in computation. With the exception of abbreviated multiplication and abbreviated division, these methods are in no sense approximations. They are intended to serve as a means of obtaining the correct answer at a saving of time and work.

Since most short cuts and approximations are soon forgotten unless constantly used, their treatment in this section is not intended to be complete, but should indicate what can be done as the need arises. The particular need of the student will depend upon his individual situation.

Division may be checked by multiplying the divisor by the integral part of the quotient and adding the resulting product to the remainder to get the original dividend.

B · 2 Abbreviated multiplication

This is a rapid method of obtaining a product if it is to contain no more significant figures than the multiplier or multiplicand.

Round off both multiplier and multiplicand to one more significant figure than desired in the product. Multiply the multiplicand by the left-hand digit in the multiplier. Round off the right-hand digit of the multiplicand, and multiply by the second digit from the left in the multiplier. Continue using successive digits of the multiplier and rounding off digits in the multiplicand. Keep the right-hand digits of the product in line, and determine the position of the decimal point by inspection.

example 1 Multiply 385.216 by 0.17278. The complete product, obtained in the usual way, is 66.55762048. Assume four significant figures are wanted in the product.

38522		
17278		
38522	(1 × 38522)	
26964	(7 × 3852)	
770	(2 × 385)	
273	(7 × 39)	
32	(8 × 4)	
66.561	or 66.56	(correct to four significant figures)

Somewhat greater accuracy can be obtained by attempting to compensate for discarded digits. For purposes of comparison we shall use the same product to illustrate this point.

38522		
17278		
38522	(1 × 38522)	
26965	(7 × 3852) + 1	(adding 1 to compensate for the discarded digit 2)
770	(2 × 385)	
270	(7 × 38) + 4	(adding 4 to compensate for the discarded digits 522)
31	(8 × 3) + 7	(adding 7 to compensate for the discarded digits 8,522)
66.558		

Multiplication may be checked by interchanging the multiplier and the multiplicand.

B · 3 Abbreviated division

This is a relatively fast method of obtaining a quotient containing a certain number of significant figures.

1. *The dividend and divisor are each rounded off to one more significant figure than is to be contained in the quotient. It may be necessary to retain still another digit in the dividend in order to make it larger than the divisor. Decimal points are disregarded during the operation, the position of the decimal point in the quotient being determined by inspection.*
2. *The first division is made using the entire divisor. Thereafter each successive division is made after rounding off successive digits from the right-hand side of the divisor.*

example 2 Divide 32,586.70143 by 481.60732, carrying out the division to five significant figures in the quotient. Division carried out in the usual manner gives an answer of 67.662388 to eight figures. In the abbreviated division the dividend and divisor are rounded off to seven and six figures, respectively.

```
                 6
481607/3258670
           2889642
   48161/ 369028/7
            337127
      4816/ 31901/6
             28896
        482/ 3005/6
              2892
          48/ 113/2
               96
```

ANS.: 67.662

B·4 Least common multiple

The least common multiple (LCM) of several numbers may be determined by arranging the numbers in a line and dividing by 2, or the lowest prime number which is contained in at least two of the original numbers. When division by the first prime is exhausted, we pass to the next higher prime number which is contained in two or more of the line of quotients. In any case where division is not even, the number is repeated. The process is continued until there are no longer two or more quotients divisible by a common prime. The least common multiple is the product of all the divisors on the left and quotients remaining in the bottom line.

To illustrate, find the LCM of 75, 50, 12, 42, and 105.

```
2/75; 50; 12; 42; 105
3/75; 25;  6; 21; 105
5/25; 25;  2;  7;  35
5/ 5;  5;  2;  7;   7
7/ 1;  1;  2;  7;   7
   1;  1;  2;  1;   1
```

The LCM $= 2 \times 3 \times 5 \times 5 \times 7 \times 2 = 2{,}100$.

B·5 Greatest common divisor

The greatest common divisor (GCD) of several numbers is obtained by using the process for LCM, except that the entire row must be divisible. The operation ends when the entire row is no longer divisible by a given prime. The product of the primes used as divisors is the GCD.

example 3 Find the GCD of 540, 756, and 72.

$$\begin{array}{r|lll} 2 & 540; & 756; & 72 \\ 2 & 270; & 378; & 36 \\ 3 & 135; & 189; & 18 \\ 3 & 45; & 63; & 6 \\ & 15; & 21; & 2 \end{array}$$

The GCD $= 2 \times 2 \times 3 \times 3 = 36$.

B · 6 Short methods of finding squares

Integers and mixed numbers may be squared easily by a process based on the algebraic identity

$$a^2 - b^2 = (a + b)(a - b)$$

Adding b^2 to both sides of the equation,

$$a^2 = (a + b)(a - b) + b^2$$

example 4 Find $(96)^2$.

Here $a = 96$, and a value of b is chosen such that either $a + b$ or $a - b$ becomes a round number facilitating the computation. In this case we choose $b = 4$. Then

$$(96)^2 = (96 + 4)(96 - 4) + 4^2 = (100)(92) + 16 = 9{,}216$$

example 5 Find $(53)^2$.

$a = 53$; take $b = 3$. Then

$$(53)^2 = (53 + 3)(53 - 3) + 3^2 = (56)(50) + 9 = 2{,}809$$

example 6 Find $(13\tfrac{1}{2})^2$.

$a = 13\tfrac{1}{2}$; take $b = \tfrac{1}{2}$. Then

$$(13\tfrac{1}{2})^2 = (13\tfrac{1}{2} + \tfrac{1}{2})(13\tfrac{1}{2} - \tfrac{1}{2}) + (\tfrac{1}{2})^2 = (14)(13) + \tfrac{1}{4} = 182\tfrac{1}{4}$$

This may be generalized into the following rule:

To square a mixed number ending in ½, multiply the next higher whole number by the next lower whole number and add ¼.

example 7 Find $(135)^2$.

$a = 135$; take $b = 5$. Then

$$\begin{aligned}(135)^2 &= (135 + 5)(135 - 5) + (5)^2 \\ &= (140)(130) + 25 = 18{,}225\end{aligned}$$

The procedure for the above calculation may be stated as follows:

To square a number ending in 5, multiply the number of tens appearing by the same number of tens plus one and annex 25 to the result.

example 8 Find $(7\frac{1}{4})^2$.

$a = 7\frac{1}{4}$; take $b = \frac{3}{4}$. Then

$$(7\tfrac{1}{4})^2 = (7\tfrac{1}{4} + \tfrac{3}{4})(7\tfrac{1}{4} - \tfrac{3}{4}) + (\tfrac{3}{4})^2$$
$$= (8)(6\tfrac{1}{2}) + \tfrac{9}{16} = 52\tfrac{9}{16}$$

example 9 Find $(8\frac{1}{3})^2$.

$a = 8\frac{1}{3}$; take $b = \frac{2}{3}$. Then

$$(8\tfrac{1}{3})^2 = (8\tfrac{1}{3} + \tfrac{2}{3})(8\tfrac{1}{3} - \tfrac{2}{3}) + (\tfrac{2}{3})^2$$
$$= (9)(7\tfrac{2}{3}) + \tfrac{4}{9} = 69\tfrac{4}{9}$$

B·7 Short cut in the use of the Pythagorean theorem

When the sides of a right triangle are given in the common binary system of linear measurement (for example, ½ in., ¼ in., ⅛ in., etc.), the work involved in the application of the Pythagorean theorem may be reduced by taking as a unit of length $1/n$, where n is the least common denominator.

example 10 Find the hypotenuse of a right triangle whose sides are $1\frac{5}{8}$ and $2\frac{3}{16}$ in.

Since 16 is the LCD, we shall take $\frac{1}{16}$ in. as the unit of length. Then

$$1\tfrac{5}{8} = 26 \text{ units}$$

and

$$2\tfrac{3}{16} = 35 \text{ units}$$

and

$$\sqrt{26^2 + 35^2} = 43.60 \text{ units}$$

$$\frac{43.60}{16} = 2.725 \text{ in.}$$

If the nearest $\frac{1}{64}$ in. is desired,

$$\frac{43.60}{16} = \frac{x}{64}$$

$$x = 174.4 \qquad \text{(call it 174)}$$

$$\tfrac{174}{64} = \tfrac{87}{32} = 2\tfrac{23}{32} \text{ in.}$$

The process of calculating square root may be shortened by obtaining the first half of the significant digits in the root by the usual means and the remaining digits in the root by abbreviated division.

example 11 Find $\sqrt{8813476.5625}$.

The answer, obtained in the usual way, is 2,968.75. By the short method,

```
                     2 9 6  .
                   √8813476.5625
                    4
                    481
    49 × 9    →     441
                     4034
   586 × 6    →      3516
  2 × 296 → 592/  5188/8
                     4736
                59/  452/7
                      413
                  6/  39/7
```

Approximate root = 2,968.77.

B·8 Averaging by averaging departures

If a series of numbers shows but little fluctuation, the average value may be readily obtained by averaging the departures from an arbitrarily chosen reference base.

example 12 Average the following set of numbers, assuming a reference base of 18.60.

	Departure
18.62	+2
18.65	+5
18.59	−1
18.60	0
18.64	+4
18.57	−3
18.56	−4
18.62	+2
	+5

$$\frac{0.05}{8} = +0.006$$

The average is 18.60 + 0.006, or 18.61.

B·9 Absolute and relative errors

The *absolute error* is the approximate value minus the true value of a number. It is positive or negative according to whether the approximate value is larger or smaller than the true value.

The *relative error* is the ratio of the absolute error to the exact value. Since the relative error is a ratio between two like quantities, it is an abstract number and is often expressed as a percentage.

example 13 The actual length of a metal bar is 11.52 in. The length as measured with a scale with a worn end is 11.56 in. Find the actual and relative errors.

The actual error is $11.56 - 11.52 = 0.04$ in.
The relative error is $(11.56 - 11.52)/11.52 = 0.00347 = 0.3$ per cent.

B · 10 Absolute error of a sum

The absolute error of a sum is the sum of the absolute errors of the numbers. By rounding off the numbers in such a way as to make the positive and negative absolute errors tend to compensate for each other, we reduce the absolute error of the sum.

example 14 Add 6.7295, 0.5436, 7.81752, 0.0058, 681.132, and 23.6836. The sum is to be correct to two decimal places.

```
  6.730 (raised)
  0.544 (raised)
  7.817 (lowered)
  0.006 (raised)
681.132
 23.683 (lowered)
-------
719.912
```

The sum correct to two decimal places is 719.91.

If we add several numbers of equal precision, the precision of the sum is decreased according to the number of quantities added. For example, if we add ten numbers, each correct to 0.01, the maximum possible error in each number is ± 0.005. The maximum possible error in the sum is ten times as large, or ± 0.05. Therefore the sum should be rounded to the nearest 0.1.

B · 11 Absolute error of a difference

The absolute error of the difference between two rounded numbers is equal to the algebraic difference between their absolute errors.

Again, rounding off should be done in such a way as to introduce compensating errors.

example 15 Subtract 13.85653 from 21.27238. The difference is to be correct to two decimal places.

```
21.272  (lowered)
13.856  (lowered)
------
 7.416  (call it 7.42)
```

It will be noted that in a subtraction the absolute error of the difference is sometimes greater, and the relative error of the difference often much greater, than that of the two original numbers.

In general, computation with rounded numbers should be performed to an accuracy or precision of at least one place better than that desired in the result.

B·12 Relative error of a product

The relative, or percentage, error of the product of two rounded numbers is approximately the algebraic sum of the relative errors of the multiplier and the multiplicand.

If one of these numbers is exact and the other approximate, the relative error in the product will be equal to the relative error in the approximate number.

example 16 Multiply the numbers 30.62584 and 8.23947, rounding off so that the product will not be in error by more than 0.01.

The product will evidently be about 250. $0.01/250 \approx 0.004$ per cent relative error. (The symbol $\approx$ represents "approximately equals.") If we round off 30.62584 to 30.625, the relative error is $-84/3{,}062{,}584$, or about -0.0028 per cent. If we round off 8.23947 to 8.240, the relative error is $53/823{,}947$, or about $+0.0064$ per cent. The relative error in the approximate product should, therefore, be about -0.0028 per cent + 0.0064 per cent, or slightly less than $+0.004$ per cent. This is verified by comparing the product of the original numbers, which is 252.3406899048, and the product of the rounded numbers, which is 252.35. This is within the allowable error. Note that slide-rule computation of relative errors is entirely adequate.

B·13 Relative error of a quotient

The relative error of the quotient of two rounded numbers is approximately the algebraic difference obtained by subtracting the relative error in the divisor from the relative error in the dividend.

example 17 Divide 574.62713 by 8.957241, obtaining a quotient correct to within 0.01 per cent.

In rounding off 574.62713 to 574.63, the relative error is $287/57{,}462{,}713 \approx +0.0005$ per cent. In rounding off 8.957241 to 8.957, the relative error is $-241/8{,}957{,}241 \approx -0.0027$ per cent. The relative error in the approximate quotient should be $+0.0005$ per cent $-$ $(-0.0027$ per cent), or slightly over $+0.003$ per cent. This is confirmed by comparing the division of the original numbers and that of the rounded numbers, the quotients (to six significant figures) being 64.1522 and 64.1543, respectively.

B·14 Relative error of a power

The relative error of a power of a rounded number is approximately the relative error of the number multiplied by the degree of the power.

example 18 Compute the value of $(5.761165)^3$, the result to be accurate within 0.01 per cent.

The allowable error in the original number should then not exceed 0.01/3, or 0.003 per cent. Round off 5.761165 to 5.761; the result is a relative error of $-165/5761165$, or -0.003 per cent, which is within the limit allowed. Checking, $(5.761165)^3 = 191.2189$, whereas $(5.761)^3 = 191.2025$, each being calculated to seven significant figures. The relative error is $(191.2025 - 191.2189)/191.2189 = -0.009$ per cent.

B·15 Relative error of a root

The relative error of a root of a rounded number is approximately the relative error of the rounded number divided by the index of the root.

example 19 Find the percentage error involved in taking $\sqrt{335.82}$ as equal to $\sqrt{336}$.

The relative error in the rounded number is 0.18/336, or 0.054 per cent. The relative error in the square root should approximate 0.054/2, or 0.27 per cent. Checking, $\sqrt{335.82} = 18.325$, whereas $\sqrt{336} = 18.330$, or a relative error of 0.027 per cent.

B·16 Approximations

Some of the more common approximations are given in Table B·1. The third column contains the term or terms which may be added to the first approximation to eliminate or reduce the error.

If any of the expressions in Group II is multiplied by a constant k, the approximation will also be multiplied by k.

example 20 $(4.014)^3 = 4^3(1.0035)^3 \simeq 64[1 + 3(0.0035)] \simeq 64.672$. The true value to five significant figures is 64.675.

table B·1

Expression*	First approximation	For closer approximation add	Notes
I $\sqrt{mn}$	$\frac{m+n}{2}$	$-\frac{(\sqrt{m}-\sqrt{n})^2}{2}$ †	The less the relative difference between *m* and *n*, the closer the approximation.
II $(1 \pm x)(1+y)$	$1 \pm x + y$	$\pm xy$†	*x*, *y*, and *z* must range between 1 and −1. The nearer they approach zero, the closer the approximation.
$(1 \pm x)(1-y)$	$1 \pm x - y$	$\mp xy$†	
$(1+x)(1+y)(1+z)$	$1+x+y+z$	$xy + xz + yz$	
$\frac{1+x}{1+y}$	$1 + x - y$	$y^2 - xy$	
$(1 \pm x)^m$	$1 \pm mx$	$\frac{m(m-1)x^2}{2}$	
$(1 \pm x)^2$	$1 \pm 2x$	x^2†	
$\sqrt[3]{1 \pm x}$	$1 \pm \frac{x}{3}$	$-\frac{x^2}{9}$	
$\frac{1}{1 \pm x}$	$1 \mp x$	x^2	
III $\sqrt{a^2 \pm b}$	$a \pm \frac{b}{2a}$	$-\frac{b^2}{8a^3}$	The smaller *b* is, relative to *a*, the closer the approximation.
$\sqrt{a^2 \pm b^2}$ $(b^2 < 2a)$	$a \pm \frac{b^2}{2a}$	$-\frac{b^4}{8a^3}$	
$\sqrt[3]{a^3 \pm b}$	$a \pm \frac{b}{3a^2}$	$-\frac{b^2}{9a^5}$	

* Each of these expressions may be substantiated by using the fundamental operations of algebra and the binomial theorem.

† Including this expression gives the exact value.

B·17 Derivation of some approximations

A number of very useful approximations exist, some of which have not had the attention they deserve. Possibly the word *approximation* itself suggests a rough answer. In too many cases the degree of "roughness" is left to the student's imagination. Actually, if we have a quantitative idea of the error involved, the correction can be computed by slide rule and added to the approximate answer to give a result correct to four and often five significant figures.

The approximations for the smallest angle of a right triangle and the sine of an angle lend themselves as a stopgap measure in the absence of a table of trigonometric functions.

The approximations for the length of an arc and the area of a segment, when the central angle is not given, are considerably shorter than the usual trigonometric solution.

It will be noted that three of the formulas appearing in the following derivations deal with the segment of a circle. These were chosen, not

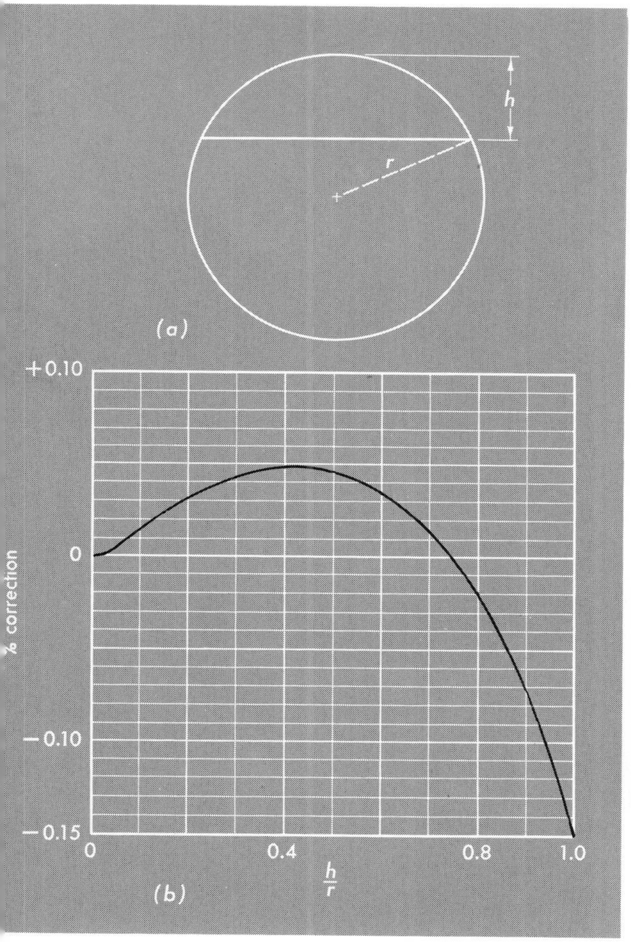

fig. B·1

fig. B·2

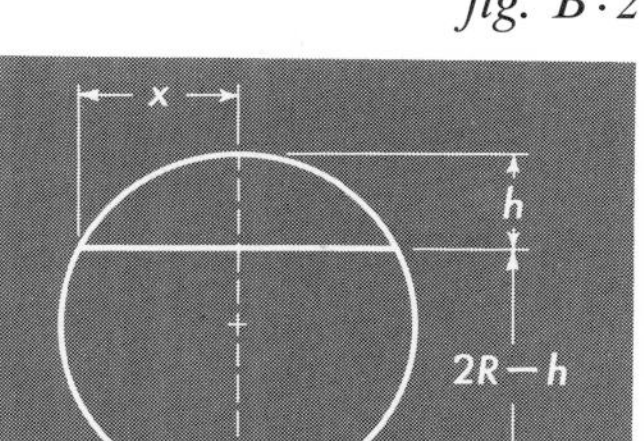

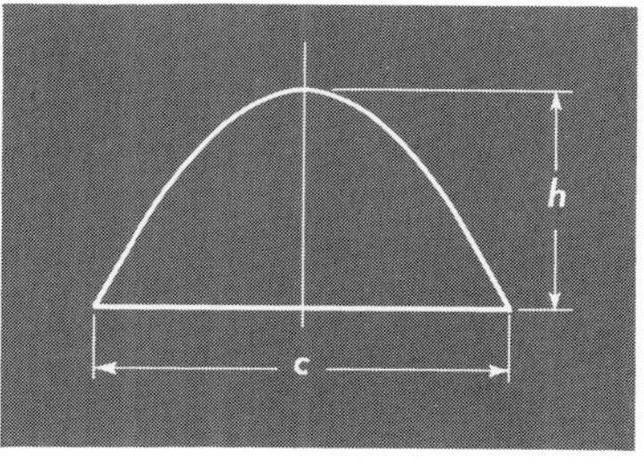

fig. B·3

to imply an overriding importance of the segment, but because they serve well to illustrate means by which some typical approximations are developed.

example 21 Find the area of a segment 3 in. high cut from a circle 20 in. in diameter. (This calculation arises in estimating the contents of a partially filled horizontal cylindrical tank.)

Using the formula (Fig. B·1*a*)

$$A \approx \frac{4}{3} h^2 \sqrt{\frac{2r}{h} - 0.608}$$

we find

$$A \approx \frac{4}{3}(3)^2 \sqrt{\frac{2(10)}{3} - 0.608}, \text{ or } 29.537$$

From the accompanying correction chart (Fig. B·1*b*) we see that for

$$\frac{h}{r} = \frac{3}{10} = 0.3$$

the correction is $+0.043$ per cent. By slide rule,

$$(0.00043)(29.5) = 0.0127$$
$$29.537 + 0.013 = 29.550$$

The value accurate to five figures obtained by the usual means is 29.550.

Let us analyze the equation

$$A \approx \frac{4}{3}h^2\sqrt{\frac{2r}{h} - 0.608} \tag{1}$$

With reference to Fig. B·2, the following equation applies to the circle:

$$x^2 = h(2r - h) \qquad \text{or} \qquad x = \sqrt{2rh - h^2}$$

If the segment in Fig. B·2 were assumed to be parabolic as in Fig. B·3, we could write

$$A \approx \frac{2}{3}h(2x) \approx \frac{4hx}{3}$$

or

$$A \approx \frac{4}{3}h\sqrt{2rh - h^2} \approx \frac{4}{3}h^2\sqrt{\frac{2r}{h} - 1}$$

But the area under a parabola is less than that of a circular segment of the same height and width. Therefore the expression $(2r/h) - 1$ is increased by trial until we obtain an overall expression representative of the segment. The optimum compromise value results when we write $(2r/h) - 0.608$.

example 22 Right triangle

$$\theta \approx \frac{172a}{b + 2c} \qquad (\theta = \text{smallest angle in degrees}) \tag{2}$$

Referring to Figs. B·4 and B·5 and the series expansions of the sine and cosine functions, we may write

$$\sin\theta = \frac{a}{c} = \theta - \frac{\theta^3}{3!} + \frac{\theta^5}{5!} \cdots \qquad \text{or} \qquad \frac{a}{c} = \theta - \frac{\theta^3}{6} + \frac{\theta^5}{120} \cdots \tag{3}$$

$$\cos\theta = \frac{b}{c} = 1 - \frac{\theta^2}{2!} + \frac{\theta^4}{4!} \cdots \qquad \text{or} \qquad \frac{b}{c} = 1 - \frac{\theta^2}{2} + \frac{\theta^4}{24} \cdots \tag{4}$$

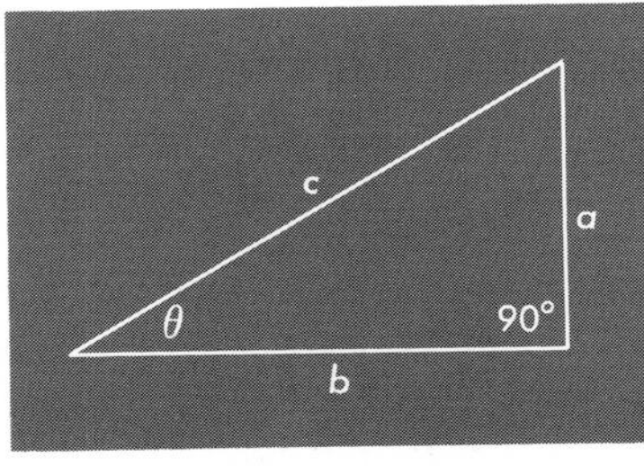

fig. B·4

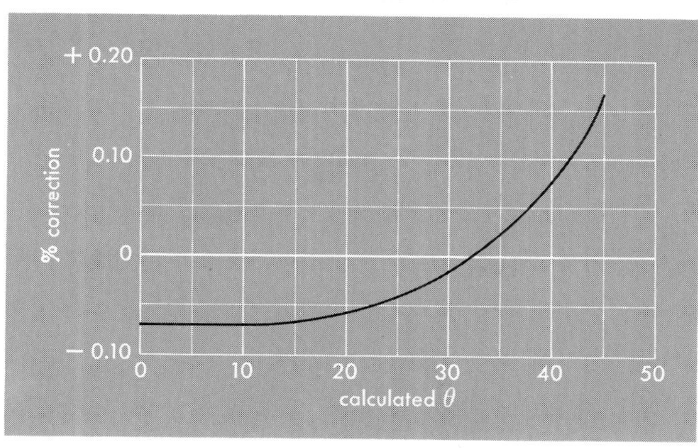

fig. B·5

Multiplying Eq. (3) by 3 $\quad \dfrac{3a}{c} = 3\theta - \dfrac{\theta^3}{2} + \dfrac{\theta^5}{40} \cdots \qquad (5)$

Multiplying Eq. (4) by θ $\quad \dfrac{b\theta}{c} = \theta - \dfrac{\theta^3}{2} + \dfrac{\theta^5}{24} \cdots \qquad (6)$

Subtracting $\quad \dfrac{3a}{c} - \dfrac{b\theta}{c} = 2\theta - \dfrac{\theta^5}{60}$ (negligible)

Therefore, $\quad \dfrac{3a}{c} \approx 2\theta + \dfrac{b\theta}{c} = \theta\left(2 + \dfrac{b}{c}\right)$

and $\quad \theta \approx \dfrac{3a}{c} \div \left(2 + \dfrac{b}{c}\right) = \dfrac{3a}{b + 2c}$ radians

or $\quad \dfrac{172a}{b + 2c}$ degrees (approximately)

23 Length of arc (Fig. B·6)

$$l \approx \frac{8b - c}{3} \qquad (7)$$

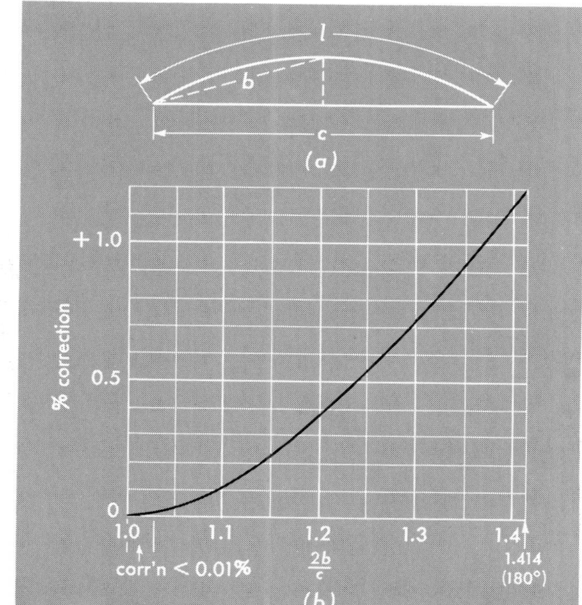

fig. B·6

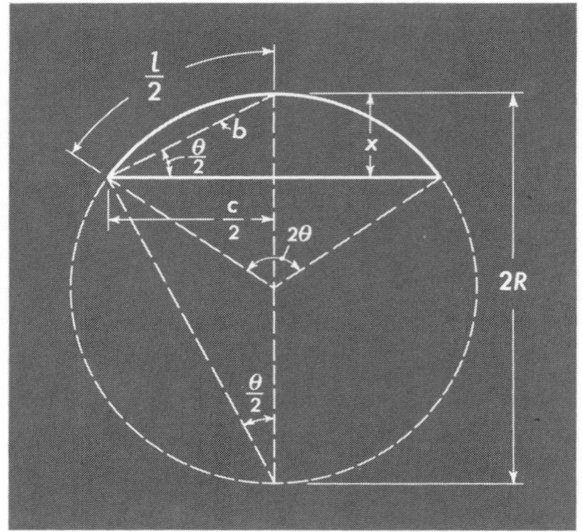

fig. B·7

By similar right triangles (see Fig. B·7)

$$\frac{2R}{b} = \frac{b}{x} = \frac{b}{\sqrt{b^2 - (c^2/4)}} \qquad \text{or} \qquad R = \frac{b^2}{\sqrt{4b^2 - c^2}} \tag{8}$$

Also $$l = 2\theta R \qquad (\theta \text{ in radians}) \tag{9}$$

From Fig. B·7 it is apparent that

$$\sin\frac{\theta}{2} = \frac{b}{2R} \qquad \text{or} \qquad \sin^{-1}\left(\frac{b}{2R}\right) = \frac{\theta}{2}$$

By the series for arcsine,

$$\sin^{-1}\left(\frac{b}{2R}\right) = \frac{\theta}{2} = \frac{b}{2R} + \frac{1}{6}\left(\frac{b}{2R}\right)^3 + \cdots$$

Then $$\theta \approx \frac{b}{R} + \frac{b^3}{24R^3} + \cdots \tag{10}$$

Substituting Eq. (10) in Eq. (9),

$$l \approx 2\left(\frac{b}{R} + \frac{b^3}{24R^3}\right)R \approx 2b + \frac{b^3}{12R^2} \approx 2b + \left(\frac{b^3}{12}\right)\left(\frac{1}{R^2}\right)$$

But $$\frac{1}{R^2} = \frac{4b^2 - c^2}{b^4} \qquad [\text{see Eq. (8)}]$$

Therefore

$$l \approx 2b + \left(\frac{b^3}{12}\right)\left(\frac{4b^2 - c^2}{b^4}\right) \approx 2b + \frac{4b^2 - c^2}{12b} \approx 2b - \frac{(c - 2b)(c + 2b)}{12b}$$

But since $c \approx 2b$, we may write

$$l \approx 2b - \frac{(c - 2b)(4b)}{12b}$$

Or $$l \approx 2b - \frac{c - 2b}{3} \approx \frac{8b - c}{3}$$

example 24 Area of segment

$$A \approx \frac{2}{3}hc + \frac{h^3}{2c} \tag{11}$$

This formula may be seen to be based on the formula $A = \frac{2}{3}hc$, which represents the area under a parabola (Fig. B·3).

Equation (11) is $A \approx \frac{2}{3}hc + h^3/2c$. This may be rearranged to read

$$A \approx hc\left[\frac{2}{3} + \frac{1}{2}\left(\frac{h}{c}\right)^2\right]$$

where h/c is a "form factor" or correction term—small when h is small relative to c.

example 25

$$A \approx \frac{r^2\theta^3}{12} \qquad (\theta \text{ radians}) \tag{12}$$

The area of the sector is

$$A = \frac{1}{2}r^2\theta \qquad (\text{Fig. B}\cdot 9) \tag{13}$$

The area of the triangle is

$$\frac{1}{2}r^2 \sin\theta = \frac{1}{2}r^2\left(\theta - \frac{\theta^3}{3!} + \frac{\theta^5}{5!} \cdots\right) \tag{14}$$

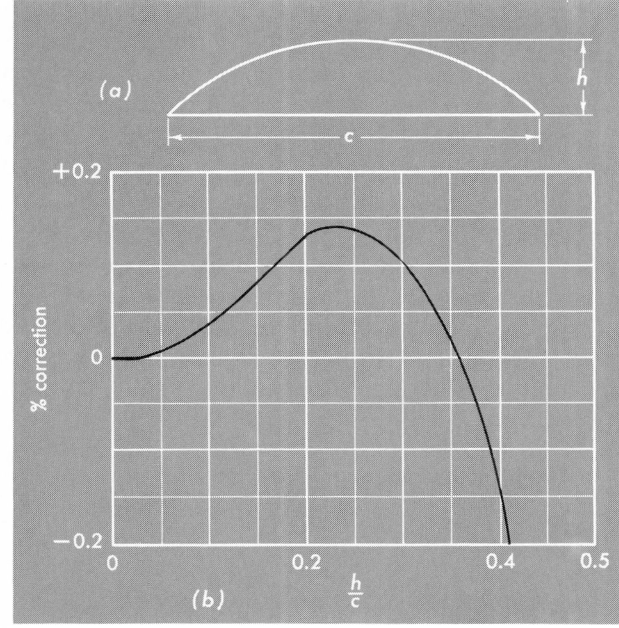

fig. B·8

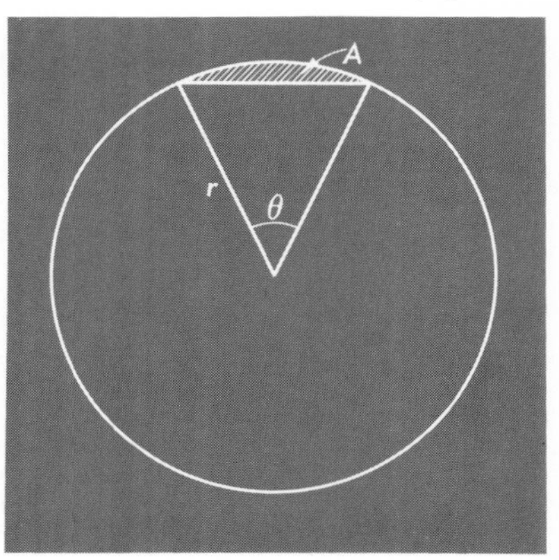

fig. B·9

Subtracting Eq. (14) from Eq. (13), we obtain for the segment

$$A = \frac{1}{2}r^2\theta - \frac{1}{2}r^2\left(\theta - \frac{\theta^3}{6} + \frac{\theta^5}{120}\cdots\right) = \frac{1}{2}r^2\theta - \frac{1}{2}r^2\theta + \frac{r^2\theta^3}{12} - \frac{r^2\theta^5}{240}\cdots$$

The area of the segment is then approximately

$$A = \frac{r^2\theta^3}{12} \qquad (\theta \text{ in radians})$$

$$A \approx 4.431 \times 10^{-7}r^2\theta^3 \qquad (\theta \text{ in degrees})$$

This is a good approximation when θ is small. Correction is roughly proportional to θ^2 and is about $+\frac{1}{2}$ per cent at $\theta = 0.3$ radian or 17°.

For a small angle the error inherent in calculating the very small difference between the area of a sector and the area of a triangle is avoided.

B·18 Iterative process for obtaining a square root

An iterative, or repetitive, process is based on assuming a value of the quantity to be found. The assumed value is tested against known information, which leads to a second and closer approximation. The second approximation is " fed back" into the process, giving us a third and still better approximation, and so on until the desired accuracy is obtained.

Specifically, in applying an iterative process to finding the square root of a number, we obtain from tables, slide rule, or mental estimate a reasonable first approximation for the square root. The number is divided by the first approximation, giving a quotient somewhat different from the divisor. Evidently the true square root must be between the values of the first trial divisor and the quotient; therefore the average of these quantities is taken for the second trial divisor. The process may be repeated (hence the term "iterative") until the desired accuracy is achieved. The process has the advantage of being self-correcting. An error, or a poor choice of the first trial divisor, will merely increase the number of iterations needed to obtain the desired answer. This method is very well adapted for use with a desk calculator.

In the next paragraph it will be shown that if the trial divisor and quotient agree to n significant figures, their average accurately represents the square root to at least $2n$ significant figures.

Assume $\sqrt{a^2}$ to be taken as equal to $a + b$ (our first trial divisor).

$$\frac{a^2}{a+b} = a - b + \frac{b^2}{a+b}$$

The average of the trial divisor and the quotient is

$$\frac{a + b + a - b + b^2/(a+b)}{2} = a + \frac{b^2}{2(a+b)}$$

If $b = a \times 10^{-n}$, the trial divisor will equal $a + a \times 10^{-n}$, and the quotient $\approx a - b \approx a - a \times 10^{-n}$. The relative difference between trial divisor and quotient (compared to a) is

$$\frac{(a + a \times 10^{-n}) - (a - a \times 10^{-n})}{a} = 2 \times 10^{-n} \tag{15}$$

Substituting $a \times 10^{-n}$ for b in the second approximation,

$$a + \frac{b^2}{2(a + b)} \approx a + \frac{b^2}{2a} \approx a + \frac{a^2 \times 10^{-2n}}{2a} \approx a + \frac{a \times 10^{-2n}}{2}$$

The error in the average relative to a is

$$\frac{(a \times 10^{-2n})/2}{a} = \frac{10^{-2n}}{2} \tag{16}$$

A comparison between Eqs. (15) and (16) shows conservatively twice as many digits in agreement in Eq. (16) as in Eq. (15).

example 26 Find $\sqrt{10}$ to eight decimal places.

Assume

$$\sqrt{10} = 3 \text{ (first trial divisor)} \qquad \frac{10}{3} = 3.33$$

$$\frac{3.33 + 3}{2} = 3.16 \text{ (second trial divisor)} \qquad \frac{10}{3.16} = 3.16456$$

$$\frac{3.16456 + 3.16}{2} = 3.16228 \text{ (third trial divisor)} \qquad \frac{10}{3.16228} = 3.1622753203$$

$$\frac{3.16228 + 3.1622753203}{2} = 3.1622776602$$

which we round off to 3.16227766, since only eight decimal places were required.

B·19 Use of ordinary graph paper as a means of calculation

There are a number of commonly occurring computations which are readily solved graphically by means of ordinary cross-section paper. In general, the degree of accuracy is less than that of the 10-in. slide rule. The chief advantage lies in the saving of time and effort. The proof of the validity of each of these graphical solutions will be left as an exercise for the student.

Sum and difference of reciprocals

Applications immediately apparent are work problems, parallel resistances, and focal length of lenses. To solve the equation $1/a + 1/b = 1/c$ for c, where a and b are given, draw a 45° line from the origin (see Fig.

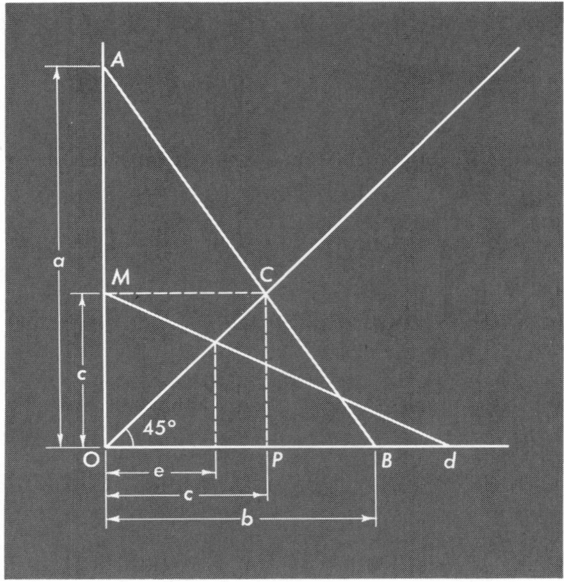

fig. B·10

B·10). Draw another line connecting A on one scale with B on the other. The location of the point of intersection of these two lines, which is C, may be referred to either axis.

With reference to Fig. B·10, it can be shown that right triangles AMC and CPB are similar, and that therefore we may write the equation

$$\frac{a-c}{c} = \frac{c}{b-c}$$

By applying a little elementary algebra the proof is easily completed.

If three or more reciprocals are to be added, as in the equation $1/a + 1/b + 1/d = 1/e$, the value of c as found above is connected with that of d on the opposite axis and the value e obtained. This process can be continued for the addition of any number of reciprocals.

The problem $1/a = 1/c - 1/b$ can, of course, be solved by reversing the process. (Connect the points B and C to find A.)

If the student finds much occasion to use this method, he would do well to have the 45° line already drawn and to locate point c by laying a straightedge over points a and b, rather than drawing an actual line on the paper.

Two-component mixtures

The solution of a typical problem will perhaps best explain the procedure.

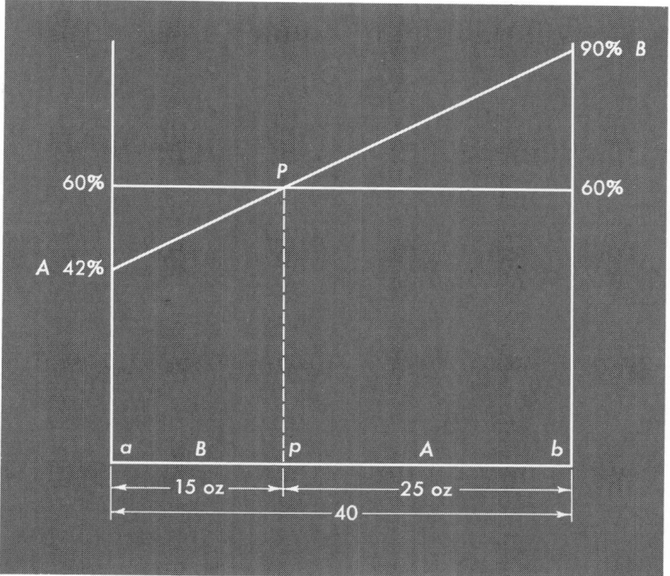

fig. B·11

Find how many ounces of alloy A containing 42 per cent silver and how many ounces of alloy B containing 90 per cent silver must be mixed to make 40 oz of an alloy containing 60 per cent silver.

Draw two vertical axes 40 units apart (Fig. B·11), locate the percentages 42 and 90, one on each axis, and connect with a straight line. Connect the point 60 per cent located on each axis with a horizontal line. The altitude Pp drawn from the intersection of these lines divides the base into sections bp and pa, indicating the amounts of A and B to be taken. Note that the percentage located on the left will correspond to the constituent on the right, and vice versa. In this example, 25 oz of 42 per cent alloy and 15 oz of 90 per cent alloy must be taken.

A consideration of the properties of similar triangles will suggest a simple arithmetical solution for such a problem; that is, weight of 42 per cent alloy $= [(90 - 60)/(90 - 42)]40 = 25$ oz.

It is suggested that the reader confirm the validity of this method by setting up a relationship between the similar right triangles in the figure.

It is evident that this same type of diagram could be used to determine the price per pound (60 cents) of an alloy formed by mixing 15 lb of 90-cent alloy and 25 lb of 42-cent alloy.

appendix C
interpolation

C · 1 Limitations on interpolation

A common type of table lists values of y corresponding to given values of x, y being a function of x. Reliability of an interpolated value of y may be limited by any of the following:

1. Number of significant figures in x. This is frequently unlimited, any limit present being imposed by an accuracy of measurement.
2. Precision of tabulated values of y.
3. Departure from linearity of the relationship between x and y.
4. Size of the interval within which interpolation is being calculated.

Examples of these factors are given below:

1. If values of y are *exact* and *linear,* the interpolated value may be calculated to as fine a degree as desired, subject only to the accuracy of x, if x is a measured quantity.

example 1

Miles	*Feet* (= 5,280 × *miles*)
3	15,840
3.4	?
4	21,120

Referring to Eq. (1), page 25, $\Delta x = 0.4$, $x_1 = 3$, $x_2 = 4$, $y_1 = 15{,}840$, and $y_2 = 21{,}120$. Therefore,

$$\Delta y = \left(\frac{0.4}{4 - 3}\right)(21{,}120 - 15{,}840) = 2{,}112$$

and our interpolated value of y is 15,840 + 2,112, or 17,952. However, this must be rounded off to 18,000 ft. The answer is limited to an accuracy of two significant figures solely because 3.4 miles, a measured quantity, is thus limited.

2. If values of y are *rounded* and *linear,* interpolation may be carried out either (a) to as many significant figures as there are in x, if x is a

measured quantity, or (*b*) to the precision of the tabulated values of y, whichever is less reliable.

example 2

Diameter	*Circumference* (= 3.1416 × *diameter*)
4	12.5664
4.74	?
5	15.7080

$$\Delta y = \left(\frac{0.74}{5 - 4}\right)(15.7080 - 12.5664) = 2.3248$$

Therefore, $y = 14.8912$, but we say that the circumference of a 4.74-in. circle is 14.9 in. The accuracy is limited by the three-figure accuracy in the diameter.

example 3

Diameter	*Circumference*
9	28.27
9.0852	?
10	31.42

The circumference of a 9.0852-in. circle is 28.54 in. Limit is set by the precision of 0.01 in circumferences.

Note that interpolation does not improve the precision of a value; i.e., 28.27 + (0.0852)(3.15) cannot be written 28.27 + 0.268, or 28.538 (see Example 3, page 837).

3. If values of y are *exact* and *nonlinear*, the extent of interpolation is limited to the less reliable of either (*a*) the accuracy of a measured value of x or (*b*) the precision corresponding to the position of the first digit in Δy showing variation. (Attainable precision may occasionally be one place better than this.)

example 4

x	$y(=x^2)$	Δy
71	5,041	
		143
72	5,184	
72.2	?	145
73	5,329	

The interpolated value of $(72.2)^2$ is 5,210, a limit of three significant figures of accuracy being set by the measured value 72.2.

example 5

x	$y(=x^3)$	Δy
11	1,331	
11.875	?	397
12	1,728	
		469
13	2,197	

The interpolated value of $(11.875)^3$ is 1,678, but since the calculated value is 1,674.56+, we are justified in writing only 1,670 or 1,680 as the answer. Δy shows a variation in the hundreds digit; accordingly a conservative calculation would be limited to the nearest 100, or 1,700.

4. If values of y are *rounded* and *nonlinear,* the controlling factor is the least reliable of the following: (*a*) accuracy of measurement of x; (*b*) precision of tabulated values of y; (*c*) precision depending upon the variation in Δy.

example 6

x	$y(=\sqrt{x})$	Δy	$\Delta^2 y$
37	6.0828		
37.6	?	0.0816	
38	6.1644		−0.0010
39	6.2450	0.0806	

$\Delta^2 y$ represents the second difference, or the "change in the change" in y.

The interpolated value of $\sqrt{37.6} = 6.13$. Note that if x had been given as 37.600, then, making the change in Δy the controlling factor, we might have written $\sqrt{37.600} = 6.132$. (It will be shown in Sec. C·2 that the maximum interpolation error $\leqq \frac{1}{8}\Delta^2 y$.)

example 7

x	$y(=\sqrt[3]{x})$	Δy	$\Delta^2 y$
55	3.803	0.023	
56	3.826		0
56.314	?	0.023	
57	3.849		

Since $\Delta^2 y = 0$, the controlling factor here is the precision of y (nearest thousandth); therefore we write $\sqrt[3]{56.314} = 3.833$.

example 8

x	$y\left(=\frac{1}{x}\right)$	Δy	$\Delta^2 y$
15	0.06667	0.00417	
16	0.06250		−0.00049
16.375	?	0.00368	
17	0.05882		

The interpolated value of $1/16.375 = 0.0611$ (precision is limited by the fact that $\frac{1}{8}(0.00049) = 0.00006$).

As an example of the effect of the width of the interval on the accuracy of interpolation, find the square of 5.283, the actual value of which is 27.910089.

Interpolation between 5 and 6 gives us $(5.283)^2 = 28$. Interpolation between 5.2 and 5.3 [looking up $(52)^2$ and $(53)^2$ and shifting the decimal point two places to the left] gives us 27.91.

Finally, by interpolation between 5.28 and 5.29 [looking up $(528)^2$ and $(529)^2$ and shifting the decimal point four places to the left], we obtain $(5.283)^2 = 27.9101$.

C·2 Second difference as a guide to interpolation

If we are concerned only with the limitations imposed by a nonlinear relationship, a helpful guide makes use of the value of the second difference $\Delta^2 y$. (We are assuming evenly spaced values of x.) The rule is: *The interpolation error does not, in general, exceed one-eighth of the second difference, that is,* $\epsilon \leqq \frac{1}{8}\Delta^2 y$.

The derivation of the expression for maximum error ϵ assumes a parabolic function $y = ax^2 + bx + c$. With reference to Fig. C·1, it can be shown that in the interval between x_o and $x_o + k$, the greatest departure from a straight line occurs at $x_o + (k/2)$.

Any three points not in the same straight line may be represented by a parabola. We shall designate these points as x_o, y_o; $x_o + k, y_1$; $x_o + 2k, y_2$. It follows that

$$y_o = ax_o^2 + bx_o + c \tag{1}$$

and

$$y_1 = a(x_o + k)^2 + b(x_o + k) + c = ax_o^2 + 2akx_o + ak^2 + bx_o + bk + c \tag{2}$$

Subtracting Eq. (1) from Eq. (2), we obtain

$$y_1 - y_o = \Delta_1 y = 2akx_o + ak^2 + bk \tag{3}$$

Also

$$y_2 = a(x_o + 2k)^2 + b(x_o + 2k) + c = ax_o^2 + 4akx_o + 4ak^2 + bx_o + 2bk + c \tag{4}$$

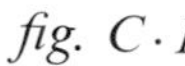
fig. C·1

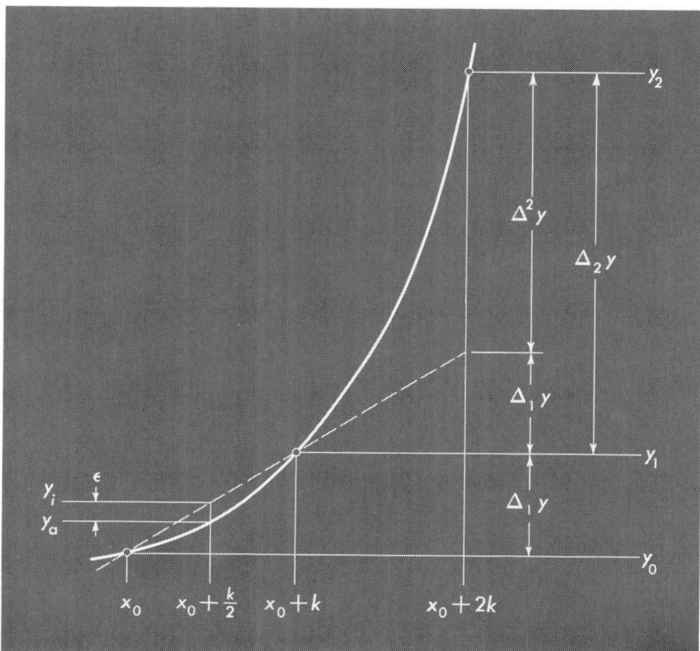

Subtracting Eq. (2) from Eq. (4), we obtain

$$y_2 - y_1 = \Delta_2 y = 2akx_o + 3ak^2 + bk \tag{5}$$

Subtracting Eq. (3) from Eq. (5), we have

$$\Delta_2 y - \Delta_1 y = \Delta^2 y = 2ak^2 \tag{6}$$

At $x_o + (k/2)$, the interpolated value of y is

$$y_i = \frac{1}{2}(y_1 + y_o) = ax_o^2 + akx_o + \frac{ak^2}{2} + bx_o + \frac{bk}{2} + c \tag{7}$$

Also at $x_o + (k/2)$, the actual value of y is

$$y_a = a\left(x_o + \frac{k}{2}\right)^2 + b\left(x_o + \frac{k}{2}\right) + c$$

This reduces to

$$y_a = ax_o^2 + akx_o + \frac{ak^2}{4} + bx_o + \frac{bk}{2} + c \tag{8}$$

Subtracting Eq. (8) from Eq. (7), we have $y_i - y_a = \epsilon = ak^2/4$. Since from Eq. (6) $\Delta^2 y = 2ak^2$, $\frac{1}{8}\Delta^2 y = ak^2/4$ and

$$\epsilon = \frac{1}{8}\Delta^2 y \tag{9}$$

More accurate interpolation may be performed through the use of the Gregory-Newton or the Lagrange formula which may be found in any standard numerical-analysis text and in many calculus texts.

example 9 Find $(2.5)^2$.

x	$y(=x^2)$	Δy	$\Delta^2 y$
1	1		
		3	
2	4		2
		5	
3	9		2
		7	
4	16		

According to our rule, the maximum error is $\frac{1}{8}\Delta^2 y = \frac{1}{8}(2) = 0.25$. This is confirmed by comparing the interpolated value, 6.5, and the true value, 6.25. Note that we have chosen the most unfavorable condition—the middle of an interval. If we had chosen to find $(2.1)^2$, the interpolated and true values, 4.5 and 4.41, respectively, would have been in better agreement.

example 10 Find $\sqrt[3]{1{,}085}$.

x	$y(=\sqrt[3]{x})$	Δy	$\Delta^2 y$
1,070	10.228091		
		31765	
1,080	10.259856		−196
		31569	
1,090	10.291425		−193
		31376	
1,100	10.322801		

If we take -194 as representative of $\Delta^2 y$, the maximum error is $\frac{1}{8}(-194) = -24$; that is, $\epsilon = -0.000024$.

Checking, we find

$$\begin{aligned} \text{Interpolated value of } \sqrt[3]{1085} &= 10.275641 \\ \text{Actual value of } \sqrt[3]{1085} &= 10.275664 \\ \text{Error} &= -0.000023 \end{aligned}$$

example 11 Find the reciprocal of 0.003125.

x	$y(=1/x)$	Δy	$\Delta^2 y$
0.00311	321.5434		
		-10306	
0.00312	320.5128		$+66$
		-10240	
0.00313	319.4888		$+65$
		-10175	
0.00314	318.4713		

$$\begin{aligned} \text{Interpolated value} &= 320.0008 \\ \text{Actual value} &= 320.0000 \\ \text{Error} &= 0.0008 \end{aligned}$$

[By our rule, the maximum error is $\frac{1}{8}(0.0066) = 0.0008$.]

appendix D
solution of higher-degree equations

Occasionally it may be necessary to solve an equation of the type $Ax^n + Bx^{n-1} + \cdots + Px + Q = 0$, where n is 3 or some higher integer. This may be done by extending the principles set forth on pages 263 and 275. [Newton's method (Sec. 25·26) which employs calculus is more direct.]

There we had occasion to state in effect that if $(x - a)(x - b) = 0$, then $x - a = 0$, $x - b = 0$, and the roots are $x = a$ and $x = b$. It can be shown that a polynomial expression of the type $Ax^n + Bx^{n-1} + \cdots + Px + Q = 0$ may be written as follows:

$$(x - a)(x - b)(x - c) \cdots = 0$$

When the expression is written in the factored form, it can also be shown that there are as many factors involving x (and therefore as many roots) as the degree of the equation.

The greater portion of our solution depends upon plotting the function. Plotting requires a tabulation of coordinate values—a process which can be greatly simplified by *synthetic substitution.*

To illustrate synthetic substitution, let us refer to the equation in Example 3 below. If we substitute any value a for x in the polynomial expression, we obtain

$$2a^3 - 17a^2 + 47a - 24$$

Rearranging,

$$a[a(2a - 17) + 47] - 24$$

It is evident that in this process we have multiplied 2 by a three times, -17 by a twice, and 47 by a once; -24 has not been affected.

example 1 Evaluate $2x^3 - 17x^2 + 47x - 24$ when $x = 3$.

The sequence of steps would be

$$\begin{aligned}(2)(3) &= 6\\ 6 - 17 &= -11\\ (-11)(3) &= -33\\ -33 + 47 &= 14\\ (14)(3) &= 42\\ 42 - 24 &= 18\end{aligned}$$

It can readily be shown that direct substitution of 3 for x in the usual way will lead to the same result.

When a is a less simple number, such as 2.087, synthetic substitution is easily performed on a calculating machine by setting the machine for a constant multiplier of 2.087 and performing the additions and subtractions mentally or on scrap paper.

We shall now illustrate how to evaluate to any desired degree of accuracy the real roots of a higher-degree equation in a single variable.

example 2 Find all the real roots of the equation

$$x^4 - 2x^3 - 14x^2 + 15x + 36 = 0$$

Since this is a fourth-degree equation, it may be expected to have four roots, of which some or all may be complex numbers. Using synthetic substitution, we obtain Table D·1.

table D·1

x	6	5	4	3	2	1	0	−1	−2	−3	−4	−5
y	486	136	0	−18	10	36	36	10	−18	0	136	486

Since, at each end of the table, y is receding from zero at an increasing rate, it is apparent that no points of interest will be outside of this range.

These data are plotted as Fig. D·1, which confirms the table in

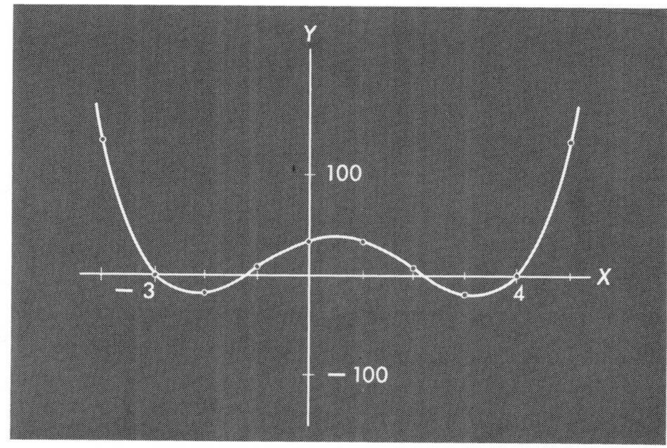

fig. D·1

indicating that two roots are $x_1 = 4$ and $x_2 = -3$. It follows that $x - (4)$ and $x - (-3)$, or $x - 4$ and $x + 3$, must be factors of the original expression.

If we divide the original equation through by $x - 4$ and by $x + 3$ (or by $x^2 - x - 12$), we shall obtain an equation of lower degree from which we can calculate the remaining factors. Accordingly, dividing the equation $x^4 - 2x^2 - 14x^2 + 15x + 36 = 0$ through by $x^2 - x - 12$, we obtain the equation

$$x^2 - x - 3 = 0$$

Solving by the quadratic formula,

$$x_3 = \frac{1 + \sqrt{13}}{2} = 2.303 \text{ (to three decimal places)}$$

$$x_4 = \frac{1 - \sqrt{13}}{2} = -1.303 \text{ (to three decimal places)}$$

Therefore all four roots are real; they are $+4$, -3, $+2.303$, and -1.303.

example 3 Compute to three decimal places the values of any real roots of the equation $2x^3 - 17x^2 + 47x - 24 = 0$.

Since this is a third-degree equation, we may expect to find three roots—not all of which will necessarily be real. Using synthetic substitution, we obtain Table D·2.

table D·2

x	-1	0	1	2	3	4	5
y	-99	-24	8	18	18	20	36

Plotting these data as Fig. D·2*a*, we note that there is only one real root. It apparently lies between 0.6 and 0.7.

If we compute the value of y when $x = 0.7$, we find $y = +1.26$. When $x = 0.6$, $y = -1.49$. Plotting these two points in Fig. D·2*b* and connecting by a straight line gives us an approximate root between 0.65 and 0.66. Repeating this process for $x = 0.65$ and $x = 0.66$, we obtain corresponding respective values for y of -0.083 and $+0.190$. These points and the connecting straight line are shown in Fig. D·2*c*. The indicated approximate root is 0.653, correct to the nearest thousandth.

The last two approximations might have been calculated by interpolating without graph paper. Figure D·2*b* corresponds to the computation

$$0.1\left(\frac{1.49}{1.49 + 1.26}\right) = 0.05$$

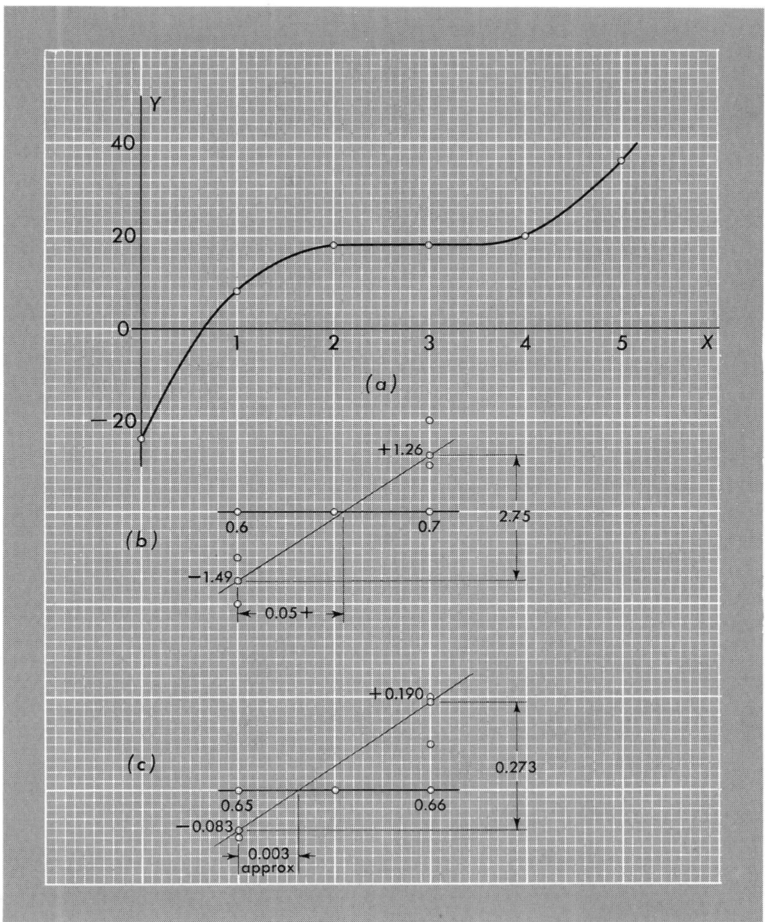

fig. D·2

and Fig. D·2*c* corresponds to the computation

$$0.01\left(\frac{0.083}{0.083 + 0.190}\right) = 0.003$$

Since 0.653 is the only x intercept, we conclude that the other two roots are complex numbers. These might have been found by dividing the equation $2x^3 - 17x^2 + 47x - 24 = 0$ by $x - 0.653$ and solving the resulting equation by the quadratic formula.

index

answers to odd-numbered problems

Chapter 1

EXERCISE 1 (*page 6*): **1a.** 1,270 **1c.** 1,872 **1e.** 341 **1g.** 792 **1h.** 207 **1j.** 153 **1l.** 432 **1n.** 875 **1o.** 138 **1q.** 243 **1s.** 476 **1u.** 96

EXERCISE 2 (*page 7*): **1.** 68.0 **3.** 29.7 **5.** 110,000 **7.** 887,000 **9.** 907,000 **11.** 416,000 **13.** 2,240 **15.** 1.16 **17.** 0.252 **19.** 2,100,000 **21.** 7,500

EXERCISE 3 (*page 8*): **1.** 0.360 **3.** 136 **5.** 14.6 **7.** 0.0440 **9.** 0.0267 **11.** 0.000497 **13.** 2.40

EXERCISE 4 (*page 9*): **1.** 1.6×10^2 **3.** 1.54×10^{-2} **5.** 1.216×10^2 **7.** 6.12×10^{-2} **9.** 3.1×10^{-3} **11.** 6.56×10^{-5}

EXERCISE 5 (*page 10*): **1.** 9.41 **3.** 5.43 **5.** 8.34 **7.** 11.9

EXERCISE 6 (*page 15*): **1.** 324 **3.** 36.6 **5.** 28,200 **7.** 0.01111 **9.** 268,000 **11.** 720,000,000 **13.** 0.136 **15.** 6.27 **17.** 1.677 **19.** 4.66 **21.** 0.0838 **23.** 0.915 **25.** 0.233 **27.** 214 **29.** 2,660 **31.** 343 **33.** 1,685 **35.** 0.00387 **37.** 12,470 **39.** 109,200,000 **41.** 480,000,000 **43.** 8.48 **45.** 0.191 **47.** 2.38 **49.** 42.4 **51.** 211 **53.** 7.79 **55.** 34.55

EXERCISE 7 (*page 17*): **1.** $d = 12.6$ miles; $C = 39.6$ miles; $A = 124.7$ sq miles **3.** $d = 156$ ft; $C = 490$ ft; $A = 19{,}100$ sq ft **5.** $r = 5.6$ yd; $C = 35.2$ yd; $A = 98.5$ sq yd **7.** $r = 7/16$ in.; $C = 2.75$ in.; $A = 0.602$ sq in. **9.** $r = 1.343$ in.; $d = 2.685$ in.; $A = 5.66$ sq in. **11.** $r = 1.785$ in.; $d = 3.57$ in.; $C = 11.22$ in.

EXERCISE 8 (*page 19*): **1.** 60.6 **3.** 663 **5.** 27.4 **7.** 16.65 **9.** 4,150 **11.** 2.53

EXERCISE 9 (*page 20*): **1.** 52.0865 **3.** 15.0047 **5.** 1.75183

EXERCISE 10 (*page 21*): **1.** 26, 19; 89, 65; 63, 46 **3.** 85, 41 **5.** 37, 42; 59, 67; 52, 59 **7.** 29, 38; 45, 59; 74, 97

Chapter 2

EXERCISE 1 (*page 28*):

	x^2	$\sqrt{x}$	x^3	$\sqrt[3]{x}$	$1/x$	πx	$\frac{1}{4}\pi x^2$
1.	944,780	31.177	9.1833×10^8	9.9058	0.0010288	3053.6	742,030
3.	94.478	3.1177	918.33	2.1341	0.10288	30.536	74.203

	x^2	$\sqrt{x}$	x^3	$\sqrt[3]{x}$	$1/x$	πx	$\frac{1}{4}\pi x^2$
5.	0.0094478	0.31177	9.1833×10^{-4}	0.45979	10.288	0.30536	0.0074203
7.	7.5625	1.6583	20.797	1.4010	0.36364	8.6394	5.9396
9.	0.39062	0.79057	0.24414	0.85499	1.6000	1.9635	0.30680
11.	61.035	2.7951	476.84	1.9843	0.12800	24.544	47.937
13.	0.0067514	0.28665	5.5474×10^{-4}	0.43474	12.170	0.25814	0.0053025

Chapter 3

EXERCISE 1 (*page 30*): **1.** 57°46′14″ **3.** $a = b = 132°32'$; $c = d = 47°28'$ **5.** 34° **7.** $a = 29°10'$; $b = 150°50'$ **9.** 5.59 in. **11.** 30°, 60°, 90°; 2:1 **13.** Side = 14 in.; Area = 84 sq in. **15.** Side = 13.31 in.; Area = 165 sq in. **17.** 114°7′ **19.** 8 3/16 in. **21.** 9.08 sq in. **23.** 90° **25.** 94° **27.** 45° **29.** 20.34 in. **31.** 9:16 **33.** 84.8 lb **35.** 10.39 in. **37.** 169 sq in. **39.** Volume = 4,920 cu in.; Surface = 1,127 sq in. **41.** 5.13 in.; 30° **43.** 0.996 A = 43,400 sq ft **45.** 25.9 ft; 11.1 ft **47.** 7.04 in. **49.** 183.2 A **51.** 7/9 **53.** 1.650 in. **55.** 61°30′ **57.** 86 gal **59.** 11 ft 8 in. **61.** 13 ft 8 in. **63.** 54.8 gpm **65.** 13.45 in. **67.** 11.196 s^2 **69.** 0.0016 in. **71.** 0.030 in. **73.** 4.8 **75.** 57½ hr **77.** 107.5 A **79.** 2,495 sq ft **81.** 1.03 in. **83.** 41°49′ **85.** 13°39′ **87.** 2.98 in. **89.** 23,560 ft **91.** 400 ft **93.** 21.69 sq ft **95.** 3.89 in. **97.** 49.34 sq ft **99.** 44.22 sq in. **101.** 50 gal, 9.0 in.; 100 gal, 14.8 in.; 150 gal, 20.0 in.; 200 gal, 25.2 in.; 250 gal, 31.0 in. **103.** 4.13 ft **105.** 27.9% **107.** 11,880 miles **109.** 7.2 miles

Chapter 4

EXERCISE 1 (*page 54*): **1a.** 13 **1c.** 14 **1e.** -14 **1g.** 4 **2a.** 3 **2c.** -6 **2e.** 8 **2g.** -22 **3a.** 4 **3c.** 5 **4a.** 40 **4c.** 48 **4e.** -24 **4g.** -36 **5a.** 4 **5c.** -5 **5e.** 4/3 **5g.** $-5/3$

EXERCISE 2 (*page 55*): **1.** $3a$ **3.** y^4 **5.** $4xy^2z^3$ **7.** w^4x^2 **9.** 7 **11.** 77 **13.** 20 **15.** 15 **17.** 49 **19.** 25 **21.** 9 **23.** 5 **25.** -8 **27.** 0 **29.** 900 **31.** $11x$ **33.** $13mn$ **35.** $6x + 9y$ **37.** $12m + 8p$ **39.** $4k^2 - 2km + 5m^2$ **41.** $9x - 2y - 3z$ **43.** $4x - y$ **45.** $12p$ **47.** $2k^2 - 2km - 3m^2$ **49.** $-x - 2y + 3z$ **51.** $-a^2 + a + 1$ **53.** $-6x^2 - 3xy + y^2$

EXERCISE 3 (*page 57*): **1.** x^6 **3.** y^7 **5.** a^{10} **7.** m^{15} **9.** $25x^6$ **11.** $64b^{24}$ **13.** x^3 **15.** y^5 **17.** $-b$

EXERCISE 4 (*page 59*): **1.** $5a + 3b$ **3.** $2x$ **5.** $4m - n$ **7.** $-6b - c$ **9.** $16ab - a^2b - 2ab^2$ **11a.** $5a + 2b - (4c - m + x)$ **11b.** $5a + 2b + (-4c + m - x)$ **13a.** $7mn + 3m^2 - 4n^2 - (8m - 5n - 2mn)$ **13b.** $7mn + 3m^2 - 4n^2 + (-8m + 5n + 2mn)$ **15a.** $9w^2 + 5y^3 - (2w^2y + 3wy^2 - w^3)$ **15b.** $9w^2 + 5y^3 + (-2w^2y - 3wy^2 + w^3)$

EXERCISE 5 (*page 60*): **1.** $32m^2nx$ **3.** $-36ab^2c^2d$ **5.** $a^3m^3x^3$ **7.** $-72a^5b^{11}c^9m^{11}$ **9.** $-18my + 15ty$ **11.** $30a^4b - 42a^3b^2 - 54a^2b^3$ **13.** $24a^3h^4k^4 - 66bh^2k^5$

EXERCISE 6 (*page 60*): **1.** $ac + bc + ad + bd$ **3.** $h^2 - k^2$ **5.** $6m^2 + mw - 35w^2$ **7.** $24x^2 - 78x - 39y - 6y^2$ **9.** $b^2 - x^2 - 2xy - y^2$ **11.** $n^3 - 8$ **13.** $x^5 + 3x^3 + 3x^2 + 1$

EXERCISE 7 (*page 61*): **1.** $17 - 120x$ **3.** $120x$

EXERCISE 8 (*page 61*): **1.** $2x + 2y$ **3.** $2c + 2y + 6x$ **5.** $xy - ab$ **7.** $cy - 12x^2$ **9.** $20x^2$ **11.** Surface = $2a^2 + ab - 2b^2$; Volume = $ab(a - b)$ **13.** $(D - d)/2$

EXERCISE 9 (*page 63*): **1.** $3c$ **3.** $-5c^2$ **5.** $4x^9$ **7.** $8xy^3/wz^2$ **9.** $3b - 4c$ **11.** $-2m + 3k$ **13.** $r + 2$ **15.** $5kr/3h + 5/2r - 7h/4r$

EXERCISE 10 (*page 65*): **1.** $a + 8$ **3.** $4m - 5w$ **5.** $2k^4 + 4k^2 + 8$ **7.** $h^4 - h^3 - h + 1$ **9.** $32x^5 + 16x^4 + 8x^3 + 4x^2 + 2x + 1$ **11.** $1/x - 1/x^2 + 1/x^3 - 1/x^4 + \cdots$

EXERCISE 11 (*page 67*): **1.** $20axy - 28bxy$ **3.** $6a^2b^2cx - 8ab^3cy + 14ab^2c^2z$ **5.** $x^2 - 9$ **7.** $64k^2 - 9m^2$ **9.** $81p^2q^2 - 49r^2$ **11.** $64 + 16n + n^2$ **13.** $16b^2 + 24b + 9$ **15.** $144a^2m^2 + 168amy + 49y^2$ **17.** $36 - 12m + m^2$ **19.** $25x^2 - 10x + 1$ **21.** $49t^2 - 126t + 81$ **23.** $25h^2 - 120hn + 144n^2$ **25.** $m^2 + 4m - 21$ **27.** $a^2 - 15a + 44$ **29.** $z^2 - 16z + 48$ **31.** $8c^2 + 18c - 5$ **33.** $30x^2 - 17x + 2$

EXERCISE 12 (*page 68*): **1.** $3(5x - 6y)$ **3.** $6(5ab - 7km)$ **5.** $a(a - c)$ **7.** $c(ab + bm + mx)$ **9.** $6x^2y(7a - 4bxy + 3cx^2)$ **11.** $5(2a^2x^2 - 3abxy + 4b^2y^2)$ **13.** No common factors

EXERCISE 13 (*page 69*): **1.** $(x + 2)(x - 2)$ **3.** $(6 + y)(6 - y)$ **5.** $(7m + 1)(7m - 1)$ **7.** $(5d + 8m)(5d - 8m)$ **9.** $(10yz + 7cd)(10yz - 7cd)$ **11.** $(4n^4 + 1)(2n^2 + 1)(2n^2 - 1)$ **13.** 49

EXERCISE 14 (*page 69*): **1.** $10x$ **3.** $14z$ **5.** $4a$ **7.** $30n$ **9.** $80bh$ **11.** 25 **13.** $49q^2$ **15.** $25x^2$

EXERCISE 15 (*page 69*): **1.** $(x - 2)^2$ **3.** $(6 - m)^2$ **5.** $(3 + 7z)^2$ **7.** $(8a - 5n)^2$ **9.** $(9m^2 - 4p)^2$

EXERCISE 16 (*page 69*): **1.** $(y + 3)(y + 4)$ **3.** $(m - 5)(m - 7)$ **5.** $(x + 3)(x + 16)$ **7.** $(h - 5)(h + 6)$ **9.** $(k^2 + 9)(k^2 - 8)$ **11.** $(x + 3y)(x + 18y)$ **13.** $(a + 1)(2a + 1)$ **15.** $(4m - 3)(m - 2)$ **17.** $(4b + 3)(2b + 3)$ **19.** $(9h - 10)(6h + 5)$

EXERCISE 17 (*page 70*): **1.** $3c(3a + 5b)$ **3.** $4(a + 5)(a - 5)$ **5.** $6(b - 2)(b - 1)$ **7.** $4(4k^2 + 9)$ **9.** $(9h - 25)(h - 1)$ **11.** $(9x^2 + 4)(3x + 2)(3x - 2)$ **13.** $2(2y - 3)(y - 6)$ **15.** $4(3t + 5)^2$ **17.** No factors **19.** $(ay + 2)(a^2y^2 - 2ay + 4)$ **21.** $(x + 2y + z)^2$ **23.** $(x + 1)^2(x - 1)$ **25.** $(3a - b)(x + y)$ **27.** $b(m - n)(m^2 + mn + n^2)$ **29.** $(5c + 3d - f)^2$ **31c.** 73, 55, 48; all triangles have integral sides

EXERCISE 18 (*page 72*): **1.** $-\frac{y}{5}$ **3.** $-\frac{x}{2}$ **5.** $\frac{3 - c}{4}$ **7.** $\frac{1 - a}{a + 1}$ **9.** $\frac{b + c}{a - c}$ **11.** $\frac{x - y}{(z - x)(y + z)}$ or $\frac{y - x}{(x - z)(y + z)}$ **13.** $\frac{(d - c)^3}{p + r}$

EXERCISE 19 (*page 72*): **1.** $\frac{y}{w + z}$ **3.** $\frac{m + n}{b - c}$ **5.** $\frac{1}{a + b}$ **7.** $\frac{2}{a - 2b}$ **9.** $\frac{3}{2a - 3b}$ **11.** $-\frac{a + 3}{3a}$ **13.** Not reducible **15.** $\frac{2(b - a)}{b + a}$ **17.** Not reducible **19.** $-\frac{(b - 2c)^2}{2b + c}$

EXERCISE 20 (*page 75*): **1.** $\frac{8x}{15}$ **3.** $\frac{x^2 + y^2 + z^2}{xyz}$ **5.** $\frac{109a - 39b}{72}$ **7.** $\frac{24bc - 6c^2 - 4a^2 - ab - 3b^2}{24abc}$ **9.** $\frac{m}{30}$ **11.** $\frac{a^2 - c^2}{a}$ **13.** $\frac{b^2 + 2b + 1}{b}$ **15.** $\frac{3a}{a^2 - b^2}$ **17.** $\frac{x - 3}{x - 6}$ **19.** $\frac{11}{c^2 - 9}$ **21.** $\frac{3c^2 - 2cd - 6d^2}{(c - d)^3}$

EXERCISE 21 (*page 76*): **1.** $\frac{3(a + b)}{4}$ **3.** $\frac{d(x^2 - x + 12)}{a(x^2 + x - 6)}$ **5.** 1 **7.** $\frac{3m}{2(n - m)}$ **9.** $\frac{2a}{3(a - 2)}$ **11.** $-\frac{8y}{9a}$ **13.** $\frac{21yz}{5x(2x - 3)}$ **15.** $\frac{3(a + 1)(5 - a)}{2}$ **17.** $x(a + bx)$ **19.** $\frac{1}{(c + dx)(a + bx)}$ **21.** $\frac{x^2}{(a + bx)^4}$

EXERCISE 22 (*page 78*): **1.** $\frac{y-x}{y+x}$ **3.** $\frac{c+d}{cd}$ **5.** -1 **7.** $q-1$ **9.** $\frac{1}{r-1}$ **11.** $2m^2-1$ **13.** x

EXERCISE 23 (*page 80*): **1.** 23 **3.** 75 T, 28 T

Chapter 5

EXERCISE 1 (*page 86*): **1.** 2 **3.** -2 **5.** ⅗ **7.** 4 **9.** 3 **11.** 4 **13.** ⅔ **15.** 1 **17.** 6 **19.** 8 **21.** -3 **23.** 0.7 **25.** 7 **27.** 4 **29.** 6 **31.** 7 **33.** 1 **35.** 13 **37.** -1 **39.** $\frac{t-r}{s}$ **41.** $\frac{a^2}{4}$ **43.** $\frac{m}{k}$ **45.** 3 **47.** $\frac{m+n}{2}$ **49.** $\frac{6}{a-b}$ **51.** $ac+bc$ **53.** $\frac{a}{b+c}$ **55.** $x=-\frac{a^2}{2b}$ **57.** $y=\frac{b+c}{2}$ **59.** $y=\frac{2r^2}{p-q-r}$ **61.** $x=-c-m$ **63.** $w=\frac{cd}{c+d}$ **65.** $z=\frac{n^2-p^2}{m}$

EXERCISE 2 (*page 88*): **1.** $\frac{WL}{Q}$ **3.** $E-IR$ **5.** $\frac{eR}{E-e}$ **7.** $\frac{Cb}{Kb+C}$ **9.** $\frac{\rho(d^2-L^2)}{2L}$ **11.** $T=\frac{2{,}097Q}{EI}$ **13.** $\frac{9}{5}C+32$ **15.** $\frac{HL}{0.4\pi N}$ **17.** $\frac{f(n+1)}{n}$ **19.** $\frac{1.299}{T-S}$ **21.** $\frac{r_1r_2}{r_1+r_2}$ **23.** $\frac{T_1h}{T_1h-(T_1-T)(h_0)}$ **25.** $\frac{6V-Bh-bh}{4h}$ **27.** $\frac{273(V_1-V_0)}{V_0}$

EXERCISE 4 (*page 92*): **1.** 88 ft/sec **3.** 7.22 g/cu cm **5.** g/(cm sec^2) **7.** g/(cm sec) **9.** g/(cm sec^2)

EXERCISE 6 (*page 95*): **1.** 23, 30 **3.** 5½, 16½ **5.** 23, 24, 25 **7.** 28⁄36 **9.** A, 44,199; B, 38,148 **11.** 14 **13.** 8⁄12 **15.** 114 **17.** 5-yr man $40; 10-yr man $80; 20-yr man $160 **19.** 4 in. **21.** 15 min **23.** 42 min **25.** 8⅓ in. from 3-lb weight **27.** Side = 5.86 ft; Area = 17.17 sq ft **29.** 72 ft **31.** 1,300 lb 18% tungsten steel; 1,700 lb 12% tungsten steel **33.** 6¼ in.; 7 in.; 7¾ in.; 8½ in.; 9¼ in. **35.** $1,115 **37.** 8.7 hr **39.** 15 men **41.** 24 ft **43.** $3.30 **45.** x = 5⅛ in.; y = 8⅛ in. **47.** 50 qt **49.** $R=30/(3+\pi)$ **51.** 23.7 miles **53.** 12.9 miles **55.** A, $6.16; B, $7.04 **57.** 11,750 ft **61.** A = 11.92 ft; B = 16.40 ft **63.** 5⅓ in. **65.** 7.3 in. **67.** 4.10 in. **69.** $w=(Ha-ka+kb)/H$ **71.** 0.852 ft/sec **73.** 63¾ yr **75.** 2.83 gal/day **77.** 77¾ yr **79.** $D=0.5863$ **81.** 142,857 **83.** a = 5¼ in.; b = 15¾ in.; c = 10½ in. **85.** 15,160 miles **87.** $0.24; Nov. 13 **89.** 68 in. **91.** V = ⅙$hw(4l+5L)$ **95.** 30

Chapter 6

EXERCISE 1 (*page 107*): **1.** -5 **3.** -5 **5.** 24 **7.** $-20/3$ **9.** $4(3a-4)/a(8-3a)$

EXERCISE 3 (*page 109*): **1.** Square **3.** Triangle **5.** Right triangle **7.** Right triangle

EXERCISE 5 (*page 113*): **1.** ⅓ **3.** $-$¾ **5.** 5⁄2 **7a.** $\sqrt{3}/3$ **7c.** $\sqrt{3}$ **7e.** -1

EXERCISE 6 (*page 115*): **1a.** $f(x_1)=94$; $f(x_1+\Delta x)=96$; $\Delta y/\Delta x=$ ⅓ **1c.** $f(x_1)=100$; $f(x_1+\Delta x)=105$; $\Delta y/\Delta x=$ ⅓ **2a.** $f(x_1)=7{,}400$; $f(x_1+\Delta x)=6{,}950$; $\Delta y/\Delta x=-150$ **2c.** $f(x_1)=5{,}000$; $f(x_1+\Delta x)=3{,}800$; $\Delta y/\Delta x=-150$

EXERCISE 7 (*page 121*): **1.** $x-2y=-8$ **3.** $2x-y=11$ **5.** $x-y=-4$ **7.** $x\sqrt{3}-y=5+2\sqrt{3}$ **9.** $y=7$ **11.** $y=-x+8$ **13.** $y=\frac{1}{3}x-4$

15. $y = \frac{1}{4}x + \frac{5}{2}$ **17.** $y = \frac{7}{5}x + \frac{14}{5}$ **19.** $y = \frac{3}{2}$ **21.** $x - 3y = -3$
23. $3x + 4y = -10$ **25.** $x + 4y = 3$ **27.** $y = 5$ **29.** $x - 2y = -4$
31. $2x + 3y = -18$ **33.** $3x - 4y = -24$ **35.** $2x + 3y = -30$

EXERCISE 8 (*page 124*): **1a.** $C = 0$ **1b.** $B = 0$ **1c.** $A = 0$ **1d.** $A = 24$ **1e.** $B = 2$ **3.** 6 **5.** 9 **7.** 5 **9.** $\sqrt{85} = 9.23$ **13.** (1.2,1.2) and (−6,6) **15.** $2x + 3y = 14$ **17.** $y = 3x - 19$

EXERCISE 9 (*page 127*): **1.** 48 **3.** 56 **5.** 55½ **9.** 56 **11.** 66½

EXERCISE 10 (*page 131*): **1.** $y = \frac{5}{2}x + 20$ **3.** $y = \frac{4}{5}x$ **5.** $y = \frac{8}{3}x - \frac{92}{3}$ **7.** $y = -\frac{24}{5}x - 60$

EXERCISE 11 (*page 134*): **1a.** $y = -1.5x + 80$; **1c.** $x = 62$ **2a.** $y = 0.08x - 4.2$; **2c.** $y = -1$ **3a.** $y = 0.628x + 13.3$; **3b.** $y = 47.8$ **5.** $w = 7.03d + 1.61$ (approx) **7.** $C = 20 + 0.1N$ (exact); \$20 overhead + \$0.10 per booklet **9.** $P = 26.62t - 1902$ (approx); $t = 0.0376P + 71.45$ **11.** $R_t = 53.6[1 + 0.00596(t - 20)]$ (exact); a = temp coef. of resistance

EXERCISE 12 (*page 140*): **1a.** 30 lb **1b.** 60 in.-lb **3.** 1840 ft-lb

EXERCISE 13 (*page 142*): **4.** 4.606 sec

Chapter 7

EXERCISE 1 (*page 144*): **1.** $x = 5; y = 3$ **3.** $x = -\frac{1}{2}; y = -4$ **5.** $x = -1; y = 2$ **7.** $x = \frac{7}{2}; y = 1$ **9.** Dependent **11.** $x = \frac{7}{3}; y = -\frac{1}{3}$ **13.** $x = \frac{1}{4}; y = -\frac{3}{5}$

EXERCISE 2 (*page 148*): **1.** $x = 4; y = 4$ **3.** $x = 6; y = 6$ **5.** $x = 5; y = 4$ **7.** $x = 6; y = -2$ **9.** $x = -3; y = 11$ **11.** $x = 9; y = 4$ **13.** $y = 5; z = \frac{7}{2}$ **15.** $x = 4; w = 3$ **17.** $x = 5; y = -2$ **19.** $x = -2; y = 4$ **21.** $x = 8; y = 3$ **23.** $x = \frac{1}{5}; w = \frac{2}{5}$ **25.** $x = \frac{16}{3}; y = \frac{20}{3}$ **27.** $w = 5; z = 1$ **29.** $x = 36.5; y = 7.06$

EXERCISE 3 (*page 151*): **1.** $x = c + d; y = c - 3d$ **3.** $x = 2a - b; y = a - 2b$ **5.** $x = \dfrac{3}{a}; y = \dfrac{1}{2b}$ **7.** $x = \dfrac{3c}{a}; y = \dfrac{4c}{b}$ **9.** $x = c; y = b$ **11.** $x = \dfrac{m+n}{2}; y = \dfrac{m-n}{2}$ **13.** $x = \frac{1}{5}; y = 1$ **15.** $x = 2; y = 3$ **17.** $x = \frac{1}{12}; y = \frac{1}{18}$

EXERCISE 4 (*page 153*): **1.** $x = 3; y = 4; z = 5$ **3.** $x = 7; y = 3; z = -2$ **5.** $x = -3; y = 5; z = 8$ **7.** $x = 6; y = 5; z = 4$ **9.** $x = \frac{2}{3}; y = \frac{3}{4}; z = -1$

EXERCISE 5 (*page 156*): **1.** 34, 19 **3.** Current, ¾ mph; boat, 6¾ mph **5.** 30 by 48 ft **7.** Man, 9 days; boy, 36 days **9.** A = 4½ in.; B = 9 in.; C = 8 in. **11.** $a = 0.0043$; $R_0 = 24.7$ **13.** 24.2 mph upgrade; 46.9 mph downgrade **15.** State tax = \$30,000; Federal tax = \$90,000 **17.** \$12 fixed charge; \$200 1st order; \$280 2d order; \$0.15 unit cost **19.** ½; ⅓ **21.** 100 lb **23.** A, 9.8 sec; B, 10.0 sec **25.** $a = 2$; $b = 3$; $c = 4$ **27.** $S(S^2 - 3P)$

EXERCISE 6 (*page 160*): **1.** −1 **3.** 32 **5.** $9a^2 - 20b^2$

EXERCISE 7 (*page 162*): **1.** Inconsistent **3.** Dependent **5.** $x = a/2; y = a/3$ **7.** $x = a - b; y = b - a$ **9.** $x = 4; y = -5$

EXERCISE 8 (*page 168*): **1.** −47 **3.** −48 **5.** −9 **7.** $15a$ **9.** $8a + 36b + 6c$ **11.** −812 **13.** −445

EXERCISE 9 (*page 170*): **1.** $x = 7; y = 5; z = 3$ **3.** $x = -4; y = \frac{3}{2}; z = 5$ **5.** $x = 3a + 2b + c; y = a + 2b + 3c; z = a + 3b + c$ **7.** $x = 5; y = 4; z = 3; w = 2$

EXERCISE 10 (*page 171*): **1a.** $I_1 = -0.638$; $I_2 = 6.68$ **1c.** $I_1 = -13.50$; $I_2 = 14.97$
2a. $I_1 = \dfrac{E_1 - I_2R_3}{R_1 + R_3}$; for negative I_1, $I_2R_3 > E_1$ **3.** $R_2 = 2$

EXERCISE 11 (*page 172*): **1a.** $I_1 = 1.474$; $I_2 = 1.068$; $I_3 = 0.0642$ **1c.** $I_1 = 0.165$; $I_2 = 0.101$; $I_3 = 0.0306$ **1e.** $I_1 = 2.252$; $I_2 = 1.492$; $I_3 = -0.0446$

EXERCISE 12 (*page 173*): **1.** 8 oz *A*, 8 oz *B*, 12 oz *C* **3.** 12.5 lb *A*, 28.6 lb *B*, 8.9 lb *C*
5. $W_2 = -2{,}191.5$; $W_3 = -3{,}331$; $W_4 = -2{,}606$; $W_5 = -1{,}548$
7. 1st group walks 4.91 miles; 2d group walks 3.57 miles; time for entire transfer = 1.87 hr

Chapter 8

EXERCISE 1 (*page 178*): **1.** x^6 **3.** b^{x+3} **5.** $3^5 = 243$ **7.** a^{5y} **9.** -16 **11.** $-8x^3$ **13.** $8x^3$
15. y^{12} **17.** a^{2n} **19.** a^{n^2} **21.** $25/9$ **23.** $32x^5/243$ **25.** $0.008x^3$ **27.** $a^{3n}b^6$
29. $4^n x^{2n} y^{n^2}$ **31.** x^5y^8 **33.** a^2 **35.** $1/y^4$ **37.** $1/a^4$ **39.** x/y **41.** $9/16$ **43.** y^{2n-2}/x^n
45. $2/3a^2$ **47.** c^n/a^n **49.** 64

EXERCISE 2 (*page 180*): **1.** $\sqrt[3]{-8} = -2$ **3.** $\sqrt[4]{81} = 3$ **5.** $\sqrt{1/25} = 1/5$ **7.** $\sqrt{49} = 7$ **9.** 5 **11.** 8
13. 3 **15.** 12 **17.** 2 **19.** -1 **21.** 0.2 **23.** 40 **25.** $-3/5$ **27.** $2ab^2c^3$ **29.** ax^2/c^3
31. $0.13x^8$

EXERCISE 3 (*page 183*): **1.** 2 **3.** $1/25$ **5.** $-1/27$ **7.** $27/8$ **9.** -2 **11.** 2.5 **13.** 81 **15.** $1/81$
17. 0.001 **19.** $1/2$ **21.** -32 **23.** $-1/2$ **25.** $x^{7/6}$ **27.** $4x^8$ **29.** $25x^3y^4$ **31.** $243a^2b^3$
33. $18y^2z^2/x^3$ **35.** w^4/x^2y **37.** $x - 2 + (1/x)$ **39.** $a - (9/a)$ **41.** $3/2$
43. $x = 5/4$; $y = 3/4$ **45.** $x^2y^2/(x^2 + xy + y^2)$ **47.** ab^{-3} **49.** $4^{-2}z^2$ **51.** $x^{1/6}y^{-1/2}$
53. $8a^{-9}b^3x^3y^{-6}$ **55.** $\sqrt{x}$ **57.** $1/\sqrt{a}$ **59.** $\sqrt[4]{x^3}\sqrt[4]{y}$ **61.** $1/\sqrt[3]{5x^2}$ **63.** $a^{3/2}$
65. $(x + y)^{1/4}$ **67.** $a^{1/2}bc^{3/2}$ **69.** $a^{2/3}/2x^2$

EXERCISE 4 (*page 186*): **1.** $2\sqrt{2}$ **3.** $2\sqrt{10}$ **5.** $15\sqrt{2}$ **7.** $12\sqrt{2}$ **9.** $2\sqrt[3]{3}$ **11.** $15\sqrt[3]{2}$
13. $-5\sqrt[3]{2}$ **15.** $10\sqrt[4]{6}$ **17.** $x^3\sqrt{x}$ **19.** $xy\sqrt{xy}$ **21.** $2xy^2\sqrt{3xy}$ **23.** $x\sqrt{a + b}$
25. $2\sqrt{m^2 - 4n^2}$ **27.** $a\sqrt[n]{a}$ **29.** $a\sqrt[n+1]{a^2}$ **31.** $a^2\sqrt[n+1]{a}$ **33.** $x^2y^2\sqrt[3]{y^a}$ **35.** $x^2y^2\sqrt[3]{x^2}$
37. $10\sqrt{53} = 72.80$ **39.** $5\sqrt{55} = 37.08$ **41.** $2\sqrt[3]{754} = 18.20$

EXERCISE 5 (*page 187*): **1.** $\frac{1}{2}\sqrt{2} = 0.7071$ **3.** $\frac{3}{2}\sqrt{2} = 2.121$ **5.** $\frac{2}{5}\sqrt{15} = 1.549$ **7.** $\frac{1}{2}\sqrt[3]{4} = 0.7937$
9. $2\sqrt[3]{4} = 3.175$ **11.** $2\sqrt[4]{3}$ **13.** $\frac{1}{3}\sqrt{6} = 0.8165$ **15.** $\frac{3}{5}\sqrt{15} = 2.324$
17. $\frac{1}{15}\sqrt[3]{180} = 0.3764$ **19.** $\dfrac{1}{x^2}\sqrt{x}$ **21.** $\dfrac{1}{a}\sqrt[3]{a}$ **23.** $\dfrac{1}{x}\sqrt[3]{x}$ **25.** $\dfrac{2a}{9c^2}\sqrt{6abc}$
27. $\dfrac{\sqrt{a^2 - b^2}}{a + b}$ **29.** $\dfrac{\sqrt[n]{x^{n-1}}}{x}$ **31.** $\dfrac{1}{a^{n+1}}\sqrt{a}$ **33.** $3/4$

EXERCISE 6 (*page 188*): **1.** $\sqrt{5}$ **3.** $\sqrt[3]{4}$ **5.** $\sqrt{xy}$ **7.** $yz\sqrt[3]{5x^2z}$ **9.** $\sqrt{x}$ **11.** $\frac{1}{2}\sqrt[3]{4}$
13. $\dfrac{1}{c}\sqrt[3]{c^2}$

EXERCISE 7 (*page 189*): **1.** $7\sqrt{2}$ **3.** $13\sqrt{3}$ **5.** $\frac{17}{2}\sqrt{2}$ **7.** $\frac{74}{7}\sqrt{7}$ **9.** $\sqrt{6}$ **11.** $-6\sqrt{7}$
13. $(1 + x + x^2)\sqrt{x}$ **15.** $\dfrac{2y}{x^2 - y^2}\sqrt{x^2 - y^2}$ **17.** $(a + b - 1)\sqrt{a + b}$
19. $\frac{11}{4}\sqrt{2} + \frac{5}{3}\sqrt{3}$ **21.** $\left(\dfrac{\sqrt{b}}{b} + \dfrac{2\sqrt{a}}{a} - 3b\right)\sqrt{a - 3b}$

EXERCISE 8 (*page 191*): **1.** $\sqrt{6} = 2.449$ **3.** $7\sqrt{2} = 9.899$ **5.** 66 **7.** $2a\sqrt{3b}$ **9.** $bc\sqrt{ad}$
11. $3\sqrt[3]{10} = 6.463$ **13.** $2\sqrt[6]{54}$ **15.** $2\sqrt[4]{2}$ **17.** 7 **19.** 7 **21.** $9 - 6\sqrt{2} = 0.515$

23. $5 + \sqrt{6} = 7.449$ **25.** $6\sqrt{10} + 20\sqrt{6} - 6 - 4\sqrt{15} = 46.47$ **27.** $\frac{1}{3}\sqrt{21} = 1.528$
29. $\frac{6}{5}\sqrt{5} = 2.683$ **31.** $\frac{1}{2z}\sqrt{6xz}$ **33.** $\sqrt[6]{24}$ **35.** $\sqrt[4]{3}$ **37.** $2(\sqrt{7} + 2) = 9.292$
39. $\frac{2(5 + \sqrt{7})}{3} = 5.097$ **41.** $\frac{3(2\sqrt{5} + \sqrt{6})}{2} = 10.38$ **43.** $\frac{15\sqrt{2} - 4\sqrt{5}}{37} = 0.3316$
45. $\frac{78 + 17\sqrt{15}}{33} = 4.359$ **47.** $\frac{x\sqrt{z} + z\sqrt{x}}{xz}$ **49.** $\left(\frac{x}{\sqrt{x^2 - a^2}}\right)^3$ **51.** $\frac{1}{\sqrt{x^2 + a^2}}$
53. $\frac{x}{\sqrt{ax + b}}$ **57.** $x = n - 2,\quad y = n - 1,\quad z = 2 - n$

EXERCISE 9 (*page 195*): **1.** -1 **3.** $-j$ **5.** $-j$

EXERCISE 10 (*page 197*): **1.** $2(-1 + j5)\sqrt{3}$ **3.** $(-4 + j9)\sqrt{2}$ **5.** $j7\sqrt{5}$ **7.** $j6 + (4 + j4)\sqrt{5}$
9. $-j2\sqrt{2}$ **11.** $-15xy^2$ **13.** $45ab$ **15.** $\sqrt{105}$ **17.** -40 **19.** -6 **21.** $-5 - 2\sqrt{6}$
23. $-j5\sqrt{6}$ **25.** $-\sqrt{30} + \sqrt{10} - 3\sqrt{2} + \sqrt{6}$
27. $j(6\sqrt{19} + \sqrt{627} + 6\sqrt{95} + \sqrt{3135} - 6\sqrt{10} - \sqrt{330} - 30\sqrt{2} - 5\sqrt{66})$ **29.** $\frac{7}{3}$
31. $j2\sqrt{5}$ **33.** $\frac{\sqrt{14}}{2}$ **35.** $\frac{\sqrt{2}}{2}$ **37.** $-\frac{j4\sqrt{5}}{5}$

EXERCISE 11 (*page 200*): **1.** $-1 + j31$ **3.** $-51 + j484$ **5.** -53 **7.** $4{,}282 - j1{,}475$
9. $11.0754 - j3.465$ **11.** 1 **13.** $-\frac{9}{20} + j\frac{3}{5}$ **15.** $\frac{1}{2} - \frac{j}{2}$ **17.** $\frac{2}{7} - \frac{j3\sqrt{5}}{7}$
19. $-\frac{1}{3} - j\frac{\sqrt{2}}{3}$ **21.** $-j\frac{\sqrt{10}}{2}$ **23.** $-\frac{3}{34} + j\frac{5}{34}$ **25.** $\frac{504}{157} + j\frac{332}{157}$
27. $0.931 + j0.361$ **29.** $-0.5572 + j5.563$

Chapter 9

EXERCISE 1 (*page 204*): **1.** $x^4 + 12x^3y + 54x^2y^2 + 108xy^3 + 81y^4$
3. $w^8 + 2w^6x + \frac{3}{2}w^4x^2 + \frac{1}{2}w^2x^3 + \frac{1}{16}x^4$
5. $1{,}024x^5 + 640x^3 + 160x + \frac{20}{x} + \frac{5}{4x^3} + \frac{1}{32x^5}$
7. $\frac{x^6}{y^6} + \frac{6x^5}{y^4z} + \frac{15x^4}{y^2z^2} + \frac{20x^3}{z^3} + \frac{15x^2y^2}{z^4} + \frac{6xy^4}{z^5} + \frac{y^6}{z^6}$
9. $(100)^3 - 3(100)^2(2) + 3(100)(2)^2 - (2)^3 = 941{,}192$

EXERCISE 2 (*page 205*): **1.** $84x^3y^6$ **3.** $1{,}512w^5z^3$ **5.** $-\frac{5x^7y^3}{18}$ **7.** $-34{,}560x^3y^3$ **9.** 90,720

EXERCISE 3 (*page 206*): **1.** $1 - y + y^2 - y^3 + \cdots$ **3.** $1 + \frac{x}{4} + \frac{5x^2}{32} + \frac{15x^3}{128} + \cdots$
5. $a + \frac{b}{3a^2} - \frac{b^2}{9a^5} + \frac{5b^3}{81a^8} - \cdots$ **7.** 7.0711 **9.** 1.2247 **11.** 3.9149 **13.** 2.0362
15. 8.5499 **17.** $K = 3.31 + \frac{7.45h}{H} + \frac{0.007}{H^{3/2}}$ **19.** $Q_g = \frac{Q}{2} + \frac{Q^2}{8W} + \cdots$

Chapter 10

EXERCISE 1 (*page 212*): **1a.** $\log_2 8 = 3$ **1b.** $\log_2 \frac{1}{64} = -6$ **1c.** $\log_7 \frac{1}{49} = -2$ **3a.** $\log_5 625 = 4$
3b. $\log_3 \frac{1}{27} = -3$ **3c.** $\log_{2/3} \frac{8}{27} = 3$ **5a.** $\log_3 \frac{1}{81} = -4$ **5b.** $\log_6 36 = 2$
5c. $\log_{1/5} 25 = -2$ **7a.** $\log_{16} 8 = \frac{3}{4}$ **7b.** $\log_{25} 5 = \frac{1}{2}$ **7c.** $\log_{27} 9 = \frac{2}{3}$
9a. $\log_{27} \frac{1}{3} = -\frac{1}{3}$ **9b.** $\log_{16} \frac{1}{32} = -\frac{5}{4}$ **9c.** $\log_{36} \frac{1}{216} = -\frac{3}{2}$

EXERCISE 2 (*page 212*): **1a.** 2 **1b.** 3 **1c.** 4 **3a.** $\frac{3}{2}$ **3b.** $\frac{4}{3}$ **3c.** $\frac{2}{3}$ **5a.** -3 **5b.** -3 **5c.** $-\frac{5}{2}$

EXERCISE 3 (*page 212*): **1a.** 8 **1b.** 25 **1c.** 81 **3a.** 100 **3b.** $\frac{1}{9}$ **3c.** 9 **5a.** 3 **5b.** 2 **5c.** 8 **7a.** 15 **7b.** any constant other than zero **7c.** 2 **9a.** $\frac{1}{27}$ **9b.** 0.1 **9c.** 8

EXERCISE 4 (*page 218*): **1d.** 8.61×10^3; 3.935 **1f.** 86,100; 8.61×10^4 **1h.** 0.861; 0.935 − 1 **1j.** 8.61×10^6; 6.935 **1l.** 0.00861; 8.61×10^{-3} **3a.** 0.549 − 2 **3b.** 0.549 − 1 **3c.** 3.902 **5a.** 354 **5b.** 79.8 **5c.** 0.0798 **7a.** 0.000354 **7b.** 7,980 **7c.** 0.00354

EXERCISE 5 (*page 220*): **1.** 5th to left of decimal point **3.** 2d to right of decimal point **5.** 10th to left of decimal point **7.** 6th to left of decimal point **9.** 14th to right of decimal point **11.** 9th to left of decimal point

EXERCISE 6 (*page 220*): **1.** 3.49178 **3.** 2.49136 **5.** 4.49360 **7.** 0.49859 **9.** 6.49136 **11.** 1.49136

EXERCISE 7 (*page 221*): **1.** 0.49443 − 3 **3.** 0.49748 − 1 **5.** 0.50065 − 2 **7.** 0.50120 − 1 **9.** 0.50379 − 6 **11.** 0.49206 − 2 **13.** 31.03 **15.** 3167 **17.** 0.0032 **19.** 32,040 **21.** 311,100 **23.** 31.63

EXERCISE 8 (*page 221*): **1a.** 3.09132 **1c.** 0.09132 − 2 **1e.** 2.60032 **3a.** 2.25455 **3c.** 0.03743 − 2 **3e.** 0.84911 − 4 **5a.** 0.008605 **5c.** 400,000 **5e.** 57,550

EXERCISE 9 (*page 225*): **1a.** 2.42843 **1c.** 1.32950 **1e.** 0.61802 **3a.** 4.07766 **3c.** 0.89962 − 4 **3e.** 8.07266 **5a.** 0.0010071 **5c.** 0.00079367 **5e.** 139,700

EXERCISE 10 (*page 226*): **1.** 228,380 **3.** 4.4216 **5.** 9.5530 **7.** 6,999,200,000 **9.** 8,157,900,000

EXERCISE 11 (*page 227*): **1.** −8.0425 **3.** 0.077289 **5.** 0.081484 **7.** 0.27963 **9.** 24,476 **11.** 0.018578

EXERCISE 12 (*page 228*): **1.** 1.3430×10^9 **3.** 4,096.4

EXERCISE 13 (*page 230*): **1a.** 2,753.3 **1b.** −1,655.5 **1c.** 0.17116 **3a.** 0.042008 **3b.** 0.018105 **3c.** 0.00024273 **5a.** 0.37876 **5b.** 69.553 **5c.** 16.150 **7a.** 2.3428 **7b.** 29.829 **7c.** 0.31216

EXERCISE 14 (*page 231*): **1a.** 9.9058 **1b.** 4.5979 **1c.** 2.1341 **3a.** 8.5711 **3b.** 5.5195 **3c.** 7.4326 **5.** 317.93 **7.** 2,354.0 **9.** 195.72 **11.** 0.40880 **13.** 0.74308 **15.** −3.2836 **17.** 0.16014

EXERCISE 15 (*page 232*): **1.** 6.6257 **3.** 6.9078 **5.** 1.2987

EXERCISE 18 (*page 236*): **1.** 6.2288 **3.** 1.2027 **5.** 20.939 **7.** $\frac{7}{4}$ **9.** 7.3365 **11.** $\frac{3}{2}$

EXERCISE 19 (*page 236*): **1.** 3.6%; 34,612 **3.** 77.8° **5.** 177.2 **7a.** 0.39 **7b.** 91.7 lb **7c.** 3.56 turns **9.** 0.315 ohm/1,000 ft **11.** 0.162 in. **13.** 3.18:1 **15.** 3.806 in. **17.** 1.55 **19.** 0.21 to 2.76 **21.** 24 *db* **23.** −10.8 **25.** 19.64 **27.** 39.9 **35.** 195°F **37.** 1.26 **39a.** 0.265 g/liter **39b.** 11 **41.** 3.00 **43.** 3,250 cir mils **45.** 47.3°F **47.** Approx 1:40 **49.** 0.623 lb/lb dry stock **51.** 4500°F **53.** 834,100 lb

Chapter 11

EXERCISE 1 (*page 253*): **1a.** 1.81482 **1c.** 0.67803 **1e.** 6.03309 **1g.** −4.44817 **2a.** 3.90661 **2c.** 8.18423 **3a.** 38.6 **3c.** 0.0496 **3e.** 79,500 **4a.** 59.6 **4c.** 0.001205 **4e.** 1973 **5a.** 44.70 **5c.** 0.2466 **5e.** 6.205 **5g.** 9.875 **6a.** 0.05734 **6c.** 77.95 **6e.** −0.07458

EXERCISE 2 (*page 254*): **1a.** $\log x = 1.32133$ **1c.** $\log x = 0.10041 - 1$ **1e.** $\log x = 0.25710 - 1$ **2a.** $\ln x = 5.0045$ **2c.** $\ln x = -2.8861$ **2e.** $\ln x = -2.9370$ **3a.** 20.95 **3c.** 0.1260 **3e.** 0.1808 **4a.** 1.7618 **4c.** 9.2103 **4e.** -5.2035

EXERCISE 3 (*page 255*): **2a.** $y = e^x$ **2c.** $y^a = e^x$ **3a.** $\ln z = w$ **3c.** $\ln (y/3) = -\frac{1}{2}$ (or $\ln y = 0.5986$) **4a.** 12.18 **4c.** 2.890 **5a.** $y = 5e^{0.47x}$ **5c.** $y = 3e^{3.465x}$ **6a.** $y = 0.63\,(14.88)^x$ **7a.** $(1/k) \ln (a/T)$ **7c.** $e^{-y/n}$ **8a.** 12 **8c.** 9 **9a.** $e^{3/2}$ **9c.** $2e$ **11.** 2.079 **13.** 1.099 **15.** 4.500 **17.** 1.386 **19.** $0.4343 - 1$ **21.** 19.03 **23.** $\frac{1}{7}$ **25.** 17

EXERCISE 4 (*page 256*): **1.** $i = \dfrac{E}{R} e^{-t/RC}$ **3.** 0.398 amp **5.** $i \approx 0$ **7a.** 0.114 amp **9.** 13.29 ft **11b.** 22.8 hr **13.** $i = 0.054$ **15.** $i \approx \dfrac{E}{R}$ **17.** 63.2% **19.** $v_1 = 1.71$ cu ft; $W = -4{,}840$ ft-lb

EXERCISE 5 (*page 259*): **1.** 1.2214 **3a.** 16.069 **3b.** 6,482 **5a.** 29.92 in. **5b.** 27.07 in. **5c.** 16.42 in. **6a.** 260.7 rpm at 5 min **6c.** 7.87 rpm at 15 min **7.** 15.83 g **8a.** 100.6° **9.** 49.2%

Chapter 12

EXERCISE 1 (*page 263*): **1.** $y = \pm 3$ **3.** $x = \pm 7$ **5.** $y = \pm 11$ **7.** $z = \pm 2\sqrt{2}$ **9.** $x = \pm\sqrt{30}$ **11.** $y = \pm 3a$ **13.** $w = a, 0$ **15.** $z = \pm(1/c)$ **17.** $x = \pm\frac{1}{4}$ **19.** $w = \pm(\sqrt{3}/6)$ **21.** $w = \pm 1\frac{1}{2}$ **23.** $x = \pm 12$ **25.** $y = \pm\frac{2}{7}$ **27.** $x = \pm(m/5)$ **29.** $z = \pm 4$ **31.** $x = \pm 6$ **33.** $w = \pm 6$

EXERCISE 2 (*page 266*): **1.** $x = 3, -1$ **3.** $x = 7, -8$ **5.** $x = 3, -8$ **7.** $x = 1, -\frac{2}{3}$ **9.** $x = 5, 3$

EXERCISE 3 (*page 266*): **1.** $x = 2, 2$ **3.** $x = 8, -9$ **5.** $x = -3, -4$ **7.** $x = 8, -6$ **9.** $x = 5, -8$ **11.** $x = -\frac{1}{2}, -1$ **13.** $x = \frac{3}{4}, -2$ **15.** $x = 8, 4$ **17.** $y = 3, 0$

EXERCISE 4 (*page 269*): **1.** $x = 1, -3$ **3.** $x = 1, -7$ **5.** $x = 2, -12$ **7.** $x = 13, -3$ **9.** $x = -b \pm a$ **11.** $x = 3b - 2a, -3b$ **13.** $x = 1, -\frac{5}{3}$ **15.** $y = 10 \pm j\sqrt{5}$ **17.** $w = 2 \pm 2\sqrt{3}$ **19.** $y = 7 \pm 2\sqrt{15}$ **21.** $x = -4 \pm 4\sqrt{3}$ **23.** $x = 7 \pm j\sqrt{10}$

EXERCISE 5 (*page 270*): **1.** $x = 12, 5$ **3.** $x = 15, -11$ **5.** $y = 1, -\frac{1}{6}$ **7.** $x = \dfrac{-1 \pm j\sqrt{3}}{2}$ **9.** $w = \dfrac{3 \pm j\sqrt{6}}{3}$ **11.** $x = \frac{3}{4}, -\frac{4}{9}$ **13.** $w = \dfrac{-5 \pm j\sqrt{3}}{2}$ **15.** $p = \dfrac{3 \pm j\sqrt{11}}{10}$

EXERCISE 6 (*page 273*): **1.** $x = \dfrac{2m}{5}, -\dfrac{m}{3}$ **3.** $w = c, -a - b$ **5.** $y = \dfrac{a - b}{b - c}, 1$ **7.** $z = \dfrac{h \pm \sqrt{h^2 + 60}}{6}$ **9.** $x = h + k, 0$

EXERCISE 7 (*page 276*): **1.** $y = 2, -\frac{1}{2}$ **3.** $z = 24, -1$ **5.** $y = m, n$ **7.** $d = \dfrac{-7 \pm \sqrt{5}}{22}$ **9.** $h = 6, \frac{25}{6}$ **11.** $c = 4 \pm j4\sqrt{3}$ **13.** $y = \dfrac{a}{3}, -\dfrac{a}{5}$ **15.** $x = -n \pm \sqrt{n^2 + \dfrac{A}{\pi}}$ **17.** $m = 12$ **19.** $x = \dfrac{b - c}{c - a}, 1$ **21.** $x = \pm 4a$ **23.** $x = \dfrac{h \pm jh\sqrt{35}}{18}$

EXERCISE 8 (*page 277*): **1.** 64, real, rational, unequal **3.** 0, real, rational, equal **5.** 49, real, rational, unequal **7.** 49, real, rational, unequal **9.** 0, real, rational, equal **11.** 201, real, irrational, unequal **13.** 289, real, rational, unequal

EXERCISE 9 (*page 278*): **1.** Min; 1, -16 **3.** Min; $-7/2$, $-25/4$ **5.** Max; 3, 1 **7.** Max; $7/12$, $1/24$ **9.** Max; $-1/2$, 16

EXERCISE 10 (*page 279*): **1.** $x = \pm 3, \pm 1$ **3.** $x = 1, 3, \dfrac{-3 \pm j3\sqrt{3}}{2}, \dfrac{-1 \pm j\sqrt{3}}{2}$ **5.** $x = 27, -1$ **7.** $x = -1/3, +1/2$

EXERCISE 11 (*page 280*): **1.** 14, 9 **3.** 13, 6 **5.** 8 **7.** 14, 16 **9.** 8 **11.** 1 sec, 6 sec **13.** 1½ by 5 in.; 2½ by 3 in. **15.** 36 ft **17.** 0.60 in. **19.** 4.23 in. **21.** 160 yd **23.** 15.1 ft **25.** 3.52 in. **27.** 5 in. **29.** 50 mph **31.** 29.1 sec **33.** 2.54 in. **35.** 82.0 ft **37.** 3.87 in. **39.** 242.4 g **41.** 4.606 sec **43.** Bus, 25 mph; train, 40 mph **45.** 20 ft; 21 ft; 29 ft **47.** 0.608 in. **49.** 305°C **51.** 13.29 mph; 9.21 mph **53.** 2.25 in.; 248.1 cu in. **55a.** 12.24 ft **55b.** 12.19 ft **57.** 0.0001 in. too high

EXERCISE 12 (*page 288*): **1.** 3 **3.** 18 **5.** No real roots **7.** 15 **9.** 7 **11.** 9 **13.** 2, $-11/3$ **15.** 2.69 in. **17.** 1.87 in. **19.** 11.38 in. **21a.** $y = \dfrac{4A^2t^2}{M^2} + \dfrac{4At\sqrt{h_1}}{M}$ **21b.** $y = 1.01 + 2.01\sqrt{h_1}$ ft

EXERCISE 13 (*page 291*): **1.** 8½, 8½ **3.** $V = 13\tfrac{1}{3}$ cu ft; $W = 560$ ft-lb **5.** 536 ft **7.** 12 in. each **9.** 50 cents admission; $1,250 receipts **11.** 150 fps, 12.5 kw **13.** 6,500; $42.25 **15.** $F = \dfrac{24 + 0.0032A - 0.00043A^2}{20}$ **17.** 2.81 in. diam circle; 2.79 in. side square

Chapter 13

EXERCISE 1 (*page 303*): **1.** x intercept $= -10$; y intercept $= 5$ **3.** (ellipse) x intercept $= \pm 6$; y intercept $= \pm 3$ **5.** (hyperbola) No intercepts **7.** No intercepts **9.** x intercept $= 2 \pm \sqrt{24}$; y intercept $= -5 \pm \sqrt{45}$

EXERCISE 2 (*page 306*): **1.** Both axes, origin **3.** y axis **5.** $y = \pm x$, origin **7.** $x = 4$ **9.** y axis, $y = -3$ **11.** Origin

EXERCISE 3 (*page 312*): **1.** Asymptotes $y = \pm x$, excluded regions $|x| > 4$, $|y| > 4$
3. Asymptotes $y = \pm x$, excluded regions $3 > y > -3$
5. Excluded regions 2d and 4th quad.
7. Asymptote x axis, excluded regions $y > 15$, $y < 0$
9. Asymptotes $y = 4$, $x = 1$; excluded regions $y > 4$, $x < 1$ and $y < 4$, $x > 1$

EXERCISE 4 (*page 318*): **11.** 7.16 ft

EXERCISE 6 (*page 326*): **1.** $x'y' = 2$ **3.** $y' = x'^2$ **5.** $x'y' = 8$ **7.** $y'^2 = 9x'$ **9.** $x'^2 + y'^2 = 36$ **11.** $3x'^2 + 3y'^2 = 25$ **13.** 18.3 ft **15a.** $f = 1{,}010{,}000$ **15b.** $f = 60.2$

EXERCISE 7 (*page 329*): **1.** $x = 3, -2/3$; $y = 2, -9$ **3.** $x = 1, 1$; $y = -4, -4$ **5.** $x = -5, -5$; $y = 4, 4$ **7.** $x = 1.9, -2.9$; $y = 3.1, -1.0$ **9.** $x = 3, -2, 1.8, -2.8$; $y = 3, -2, -2.8, 1.8$ **11.** Imaginary roots

EXERCISE 8 (*page 330*): **1.** $x = 4, -4$; $y = 12, -12$ **3.** $x = 10, -10$; $y = 8, -8$ **5.** $x = 3, -4$; $y = -4, 3$ **7.** $x = 7, -47/3$; $y = 3, 43/3$ **9.** $x = 2, -22/19$; $y = -4, 74/19$

EXERCISE 9 (*page 331*): **1.** $x = 1, -1, 1, -1$; $y = 3, 3, -3, -3$ **3.** $x = 2, 2, -2, -2$; $y = 0, 0, 0, 0$ **5.** $x = \sqrt{155/44}, -\sqrt{155/44}, \sqrt{155/44}, -\sqrt{155/44}$; $y = \sqrt{5/22}, \sqrt{5/22}, -\sqrt{5/22}, -\sqrt{5/22}$ **7.** $x = \tfrac{4}{7}\sqrt{21}, -\tfrac{4}{7}\sqrt{21}, \tfrac{4}{7}\sqrt{21}, -\tfrac{4}{7}\sqrt{21}$; $y = \tfrac{2}{7}\sqrt{91}, \tfrac{2}{7}\sqrt{91}, -\tfrac{2}{7}\sqrt{91}, -\tfrac{2}{7}\sqrt{91}$

EXERCISE 10 (*page 333*): **1.** $x = \frac{3}{13}\sqrt{13}, -\frac{3}{13}\sqrt{13}; y = \frac{10}{13}\sqrt{13}, -\frac{10}{13}\sqrt{13}$ **3.** $x = 7, -7, 6, -6;$ $y = 2, -2, 1, -1$ **5.** $x = 7, -7, \frac{j6}{5}\sqrt{3}, -\frac{j6}{5}\sqrt{3}; y = 2, -2, \frac{j14}{15}\sqrt{3}, -\frac{j14}{15}\sqrt{3}$
7. $x = 2, -2, \frac{4}{19}\sqrt{19}, -\frac{4}{19}\sqrt{19}; y = -5, 5, \frac{5}{19}\sqrt{19}, -\frac{5}{19}\sqrt{19}$ **9.** $K = \dfrac{D \pm \sqrt{D^2 - 4R^2}}{2R}$

Chapter 14

EXERCISE 1 (*page 335*): **1.** $y = x^2 - 2x - 8$ **3.** $y = -x^2 + 3x + 28$
5. $y = 0.172x^2 + 0.372x - 1.29$

EXERCISE 4 (*page 345*): **a.** $y = x^2$ **c.** $y = 0.2x^2$ **e.** $y = 0.5\sqrt{x}$ **g.** $y = 1/x$ **i.** $y = 2^x$
k. $y = 0.1(3)^x$ **m.** $y = 10(5)^{-x} = 10(0.2)^x$

EXERCISE 5 (*page 347*): **1a.** $a = 1.38; b = 1.05$ **1b.** $y = 1.05e^{0.322x}$ **3.** $a = 0.532; b = 168$
5. $C = 3.31; n = 1.48$ **7a.** $N = 20.2(0.243)^t$ **7b.** $N = 20.2e^{-1.415t}$
9. $E = 3.95(10)^{-2}t + 6.67(10)^{-6}t^2 - 5.07(10)^{-9}t^3$ **11.** $b = 5.52$
13. $p = 29.92(0.6825)^{h/10,000}$ **15.** $y = 37.4x^{-0.358}; y = 37.4; x = 0.188$
17. $y = 25x^{-0.398}$ **19.** $V = 1.2403[1 + 1.033(10)^{-3}t + 1.350(10)^{-6}t^2]$
21. $F = 1945(0.2165)^\theta$ **23.** $V = 141a^{-0.496}$ **25.** $P = 1.42(10)^5V^{-1.66}$
27b. 100% instantaneous depreciation rate (63.2% annual depreciation rate)
27d. 161% instantaneous depreciation rate (80% annual depreciation rate)
27f. 22.3% instantaneous depreciation rate (20% annual depreciation rate)

Chapter 15

EXERCISE 1 (*page 354*): **1.** 6:1 **3.** 1:9 **5.** 10:33 **7.** 10:3 **9.** 3:8 **11.** $3x{:}4a$ **13.** 4:3

EXERCISE 2 (*page 355*): **1.** 6 **3.** 21 **5.** $\dfrac{ac}{b}$ **7.** $\dfrac{bc}{a+b}$ **9.** $\dfrac{ad - bc}{a - b + c - d}$ **11.** ± 12
13. $\pm\frac{3}{4}$ **15.** $\pm 4abx$ **17.** $\pm 2(x + y)$ **19.** $\pm 6ab$

EXERCISE 3 (*page 359*): **1.** $W = kxy$ **3.** $V = \dfrac{kx^3}{d}$ **5.** $R = \dfrac{kw\sqrt{x}}{h^3}$ **7.** $N = \dfrac{7}{y}$ **9.** $V = \dfrac{4.8m}{t^2}$

EXERCISE 4 (*page 360*): **1.** $k = 2{,}520$ in.-lb; $V = 40$ cu in. **3.** $k = 1.8$ ft/sec^2; $V = 108$ fps
5. $k = 43{,}560$ sq ft/acre; $N = 1{,}440$ plants/acre **7.** $k = 1.63$ (no units); $V = 7.3$ fps
9. 56 **11.** $V = 819.2$

EXERCISE 5 (*page 361*): **1.** 54.5 lb **3.** 2 hr 59 min **5.** 318½ ft **7.** 6.30 in. **9.** 5.13 lb
11. Johnson, $185.08; Miller, $299.59; Spencer, $386.64; Weston, $412.36
13. 8.1% zinc oxide, 32.4% titanium dioxide, 13.5% lithopone
15. Double *m*, *x* multiplied by 2; double *f*, *x* multiplied by 1.414; double *w*, *x* divided by 2; double *a*, *x* decreased; double *b*, *x* decreased; double *k*, *x* increased **17.** 17½ cu yd cement, 35 cu yd sand, 52½ cu yd gravel
19. 4 min 46 sec **21a.** $v = (20/3)\sqrt{h}$ **23.** 23.9 miles **25.** 39 in. **27.** 13.8 hp
29a. 24½ rpm **29c.** 196 rpm **29e.** *A*, 60 teeth; *B*, 18 teeth **29g.** *A*, 96 teeth; *B*, 30 teeth **30a.** *D*, 420 rpm **30c.** *D*, 21 teeth **30e.** *A*, 48 teeth; *B*, 36 teeth; *C*, 48 teeth; *D*, 36 teeth **30g.** *A*, 36 teeth; *B*, 24 teeth; *C*, 48 teeth; *D*, 30 teeth; (Other selections may be equally valid in parts *e*, *g*.) **33.** 1 qt, 8.32 in.; 2 qt, 10.5 in.
35. 32.2 cents/lb **37.** 214,000 miles approx **39.** $-65°$F **43.** 0.014 in.

EXERCISE 6 (*page 369*): **1.** 26 **3.** 9 **5.** 7⅔ **7.** $-9x + 5y$ **9.** -112 **11.** $11a - 44b$ **13.** $5a + 15b$ **15.** $S = 372$; $a = -2$ **17.** $S = 385$; $d = -5$ **19.** $n = 12$; $l = -33$ **21.** $a = -4$; $l = 24$ **23.** $l = 15$; $d = 2$ **25.** 18 **27.** $-2\frac{1}{2}$ **29.** $\frac{17}{30}$ **31.** $x + y$ **33.** $\dfrac{y^2 + 1}{2y}$ **35.** 17, 20, 23, 26, 29, 32 **37.** -10, $-5\frac{1}{2}$, -1, $3\frac{1}{2}$, 8, $12\frac{1}{2}$, 17

EXERCISE 7 (*page 371*): **1.** \$1,115 **3.** 4,920 **5.** 12,400 **7.** \$1,524 **9a.** \$8,080 **9b.** \$74,800 **11.** 2, 8, 14 **13.** $S = 4{,}035$; $l = 236$; $n = 30$

EXERCISE 8 (*page 375*): **1.** 192 **3.** $\frac{1}{64}$ **5.** 104,976 **7.** $36\sqrt{2}$ **9.** 18; $r = \frac{3}{2}$ **11.** -19.2; $r = -\frac{5}{4}$ **13.** 5; $r = \frac{3}{2}$ **15.** -1, $\frac{1}{2}$ **17.** $\frac{2}{3}\sqrt{3}$, $\frac{1}{2}\sqrt{5}$ **19.** $47\frac{5}{8}$ **21.** $\frac{665}{288}$ **23.** 3,066 **25.** $S = 936$; $n = 4$ **27.** $S = 122$; $l = 162$ **29.** $n = 4$; $a = 13\frac{1}{2}$ **31.** $n = 6$; $r = -\frac{2}{3}$ **33.** 6 **35.** 20 **37.** -4 **39.** $\frac{3}{2}$ **41.** x^n **43.** -12, 36 **45.** ± 135, -45, ± 15 **47.** $\pm 10x^6$, $20x^8$, $\pm 40x^{10}$, $80x^{12}$, $\pm 160x^{14}$

EXERCISE 9 (*page 378*): **1.** 24 **3.** $62\frac{1}{2}$ **5.** $\frac{9}{20}$ **7.** $\dfrac{1}{1 - x}$ **9.** $\frac{2}{3}$ **11.** $\frac{3}{11}$ **13.** $\frac{5}{37}$ **15.** $\frac{9}{22}$

EXERCISE 10 (*page 379*): **1.** 18, 32 **3.** \$409.60 **5.** 1.05% **7.** 27.2°C **9.** 23.298 **11.** 68.6% **13.** 0.003% **15.** 36.4% **17.** 29.3% **19.** Four (1, 2, 4, 8)

Chapter 16

EXERCISE 1 (*page 387*): **1.** Possible **3.** Impossible **5.** Impossible **7.** Two possible triangles **9.** Possible **11.** Inconsistent

EXERCISE 5 (*page 392*): **1.** cos 70° **3.** sin 30° **5.** tan 73° **7.** sin 51.5° **9.** csc 65°

EXERCISE 6 (*page 393*):

	sin	*cos*	*tan*	*cot*	*sec*	*csc*
1.	0.35021	0.93667	0.37388	2.6746	1.0676	2.8555
3.	0.70690	0.70731	0.99942	1.0006	1.4138	1.4146
5.	0.43445	0.90070	0.48234	2.0732	1.1102	2.3018
7.	0.98619	0.16562	5.9545	0.16794	6.0379	1.0140
9.	0.00291	1.0000	0.00291	343.77	1.0000	343.78
11.	0.23203	0.97271	0.23854	4.1922	1.0281	4.3098
13.	0.82822	0.56040	1.4779	0.67663	1.7844	1.2074
15.	0.03054	0.99953	0.03055	32.730	1.0005	32.746

17. 10°24′ **19.** 48°57′ **21.** 44°03′ **23.** 21°16′ **25.** 3°06′ **27.** 50°29′ **29.** 55°35′ **31.** 48°03′ **33.** 25°05′ **35.** 11°10′ **37.** 67°25′ **39.** 50°08′ **41.** 41°06′ **43.** 29°15′ **45.** 5°10′

EXERCISE 7 (*page 398*): **1.** $a = 55.744$; $b = 76.072$; $B = 53°46'$ **3.** $a = 60.200$; $b = 117.47$; $A = 27°08'$ **5.** $a = 0.31011$; $b = 2.1698$; $B = 81°52'$ **7.** $a = 232.39$; $b = 92.168$; $B = 21°38'$ **9.** $a = 50.810$; $b = 39.389$; $A = 52°13'$ **11.** $b = 5{,}516.9$; $c = 40{,}998$; $B = 7°44'$ **13.** $b = 134.96$; $c = 143.04$; $B = 70°39'$ **15.** $b = 48.090$; $c = 50.103$; $B = 73°42'$ **17.** $b = 342.03$; $c = 463.29$; $A = 42°25'$ **19.** $a = 9{,}237.3$; $c = 12{,}302$; $B = 41°20'$ **21.** $A = 64°18'$; $B = 25°42'$; $c = 385.09$ **23.** $A = 69°25'$; $B = 20°35'$; $c = 71{,}707$ **25.** $A = 34°47'$; $B = 55°13'$; $c = 247.17$ **27.** $A = 18°10'$; $B = 71°50'$; $b = 2{,}556.9$ **29.** $A = 24°18'$; $B = 65°42'$; $b = 39{,}782$ **31.** $A = 21°20'$; $B = 68°40'$; $a = 4{,}082.8$ **33.** $A = 36°36'$; $B = 53°24'$; $a = 1{,}394.0$ **35.** $A = 16°49'$; $B = 73°11'$; $a = 297.70$

EXERCISE 8 (*page 401*):

	sin	*cos*	*tan*	*cot*	*sec*	*csc*
1.	0.04311	0.99907	0.04315	23.175	1.0009	23.196
3.	0.24678	0.96907	0.25466	3.9269	1.0319	4.0522
5.	0.64564	0.76365	0.84546	1.1827	1.3095	1.5489
7.	0.79646	0.60470	1.3172	0.75923	1.6538	1.2555
9.	0.98767	0.15653	6.3098	0.15848	6.3886	1.0125
11.	0.45795	0.88898	0.51514	1.9412	1.1249	2.1836
13.	0.95282	0.30354	3.1391	0.31856	3.2945	1.0495
15.	0.29674	0.95496	0.31073	3.2182	1.0472	3.3700

EXERCISE 9 (*page 401*): **1.** 6°04′06″ **3.** 35°04′20″ **5.** 46°35′24″ **7.** 12°01′10″ **9.** 88°37′48″ **11.** 40°59′27″ **13.** 24°54′20″ **15.** 46°16′30″ **17.** 86°23′12″ **19.** 32°52′07″ **21.** 87°30′45″ **23.** 51°24′30″ **25.** 64°44′48″ **27.** 6°08′51″ **29.** 46°17′30″

EXERCISE 10 (*page 402*): **1.** $a = 0.54882$; $b = 0.68148$; $B = 51°09'15''$ **3.** $a = 12.437$; $b = 9.1720$; $B = 36°24.5'$ **5.** $a = 2{,}517.9$; $b = 1{,}044.7$; $A = 67°27.9'$ **7.** $a = 6.3335$; $b = 8.5310$; $A = 36°35'26''$ **9.** $a = 6.8772$; $b = 12.194$; $A = 29°25'17''$ **11.** $b = 12{,}217$; $c = 12{,}281$; $B = 84°09'29''$ **13.** $b = 977.88$; $c = 1{,}389.3$; $B = 44°44.2'$ **15.** $b = 2{,}222.7$; $c = 2{,}334.5$; $B = 72°11.7'$ **17.** $a = 50.357$; $c = 757.90$; $A = 3°48.6'$ **19.** $a = 20.466$; $c = 55.313$; $B = 68°17'02''$ **21.** $A = 27°45'34''$; $B = 62°14'26''$; $c = 42.941$ **23.** $A = 14°30'38''$; $B = 75°29'22''$; $c = 18.517$ **25.** $A = 25°13'12''$; $B = 64°46'48''$; $c = 196.42$ **27.** $A = 18°49'13''$; $B = 71°10'47''$; $c = 1{,}357.5$ **29.** $A = 34°58'13''$; $B = 55°01'47''$; $c = 54.523$ **31.** $A = 20°33'36''$; $B = 69°26'24''$; $b = 391.92$ **33.** $A = 67°37'33''$; $B = 22°22'27''$; $b = 16.358$ **35.** $A = 55°45'08''$; $B = 34°14'52''$; $b = 639.64$ **37.** $A = 65°21'30''$; $B = 24°38'30''$; $a = 272.50$ **39.** $A = 42°21'28''$; $B = 47°38'32''$; $a = 12.577$ **41.** 6.3351 in. **43.** 0.9347 in. **45.** 1.0824 in. **47.** 1.9482 in. **49.** 36°30′40″

EXERCISE 11 (*page 405*): **1.** 10.719 in.; 2.3694 in. **3.** 47°09′24″; 73°44′22″ **5.** 0.828 in. above **7.** 66.002 sq in.

EXERCISE 12 (*page 407*): **1.** 4.95 in. **3.** 10.04 in. **5.** 6.93 in. **7.** 2.00 in.

EXERCISE 13 (*page 409*): **5.** 82.274 sq in. **7.** 3.000 sq in. **9.** π sq in.

EXERCISE 14 (*page 411*): **1.** $a = 89.488$; $b = 115.76$ **3.** $a = 47.868$; $b = 150.21$ **5.** $a = 0.65841$; $b = 1.2073$ **7.** $b = 0.42347$; $c = 15.364$ **9.** $a = 1{,}369{,}100$; $c = 1{,}369{,}200$ **11.** $A = 5°28'05''$; $b = 142.33$ **13.** $A = 30°07'41''$; $b = 9.3669$ **15.** $A = 38°39'08''$; $b = 0.45661$ **17.** $A = 84°47'01''$; $c = 96.028$ **19.** $A = 26°35'27''$; $c = 8.1702$

EXERCISE 15 (*page 415*): **1.** $A = 22°37'12''$; $B = 108°55'28''$; $C = 48°27'20''$ **3.** No solution **5.** $a = 17$; $c = 25$; $B = 25°03'27''$ **7.** $c = 73.000$; $A = 4°14'32''$; $B = 138°53'16''$ **9.** $c = 75$; $B = 8°47'50''$; $C = 118°04'21''$ **11.** $a = 28.441$; $B = 59°14'24''$; $A = 16°30'36''$

EXERCISE 22 (*page 427*): **1.** 13.748″ **3.** 1.06%; 41% **5.** $c = 60.033$ by both methods

Chapter 17

EXERCISE 1 (*page 433*): **1.** $\overrightarrow{AB}$, $\overrightarrow{GH}$ **3.** $\overrightarrow{AB}$, $\overrightarrow{GH}$, $\overrightarrow{KL}$, $\overrightarrow{EF}$, $\overrightarrow{IJ}$

EXERCISE 3 (*page 440*):

1. $|\sin 137°| = 0.68200$; $|\cos 137°| = 0.73135$; $|\tan 137°| = 0.93252$; $|\cot 137°| = 1.0724$; $|\sec 137°| = 1.3673$; $|\csc 137°| = 1.4663$ **3.** $|\sin 316°| = 0.69466$; $|\cos 316°| = 0.71934$; $|\tan 316°| = 0.96569$; $|\cot 316°| = 1.0355$; $|\sec 316°| = 1.3902$; $|\csc 316°| = 1.4396$

EXERCISE 4 (*page 443*):

	sin	*cos*	*tan*	*cot*	*sec*	*csc*
1.	0.64279	−0.76604	−0.83910	−1.1918	−1.3054	1.5557
3.	0.99540	−0.09585	−10.385	−0.09629	10.433	1.0046
5.	0.91708	−0.39870	−2.3001	−0.43475	−2.5081	1.0904
7.	0.08428	−0.99644	−0.08458	−11.823	−1.0036	11.865
9.	0.00568	−0.99998	−0.00568	−176.41	−1.0000	176.41

EXERCISE 5 (*page 443*): **1.** 6°04′06″; 173°55′54″ **3.** 35°04′20″; 144°55′40″ **5.** 46°35′24″; 133°24′36″ **7.** 12°01′10″; 347°58′50″ **9.** 88°37′48″; 271°22′12″ **11.** 139°00′27″; 319°00′27″ **13.** 155°05′40″; 335°05′40″ **15.** 46°16′30″; 226°16′30″ **17.** 93°36′48″; 273°36′48″ **19.** 147°07′53″; 327°07′53″ **21.** 87°30′45″; 272°29′15″ **23.** 51°24′30″; 308°35′30″ **25.** 64°44′48″; 295°15′12″ **27.** 6°08′51″; 173°51′09″ **29.** 226°17′30″; 313°42′30″

EXERCISE 6 (*page 446*): **1.** 30° **3.** 30° **5.** 120° **7.** 45° **9.** −30°

EXERCISE 7 (*page 448*): **1.** $r = 8.06$; $\phi = 29.74°$ **3.** $r = 10.66$; $\phi = 110.30°$ **5.** $r = 7.92$; $\phi = 349.80°$ **7.** $r = 6.00$; $\phi = 119.98°$ **9.** $r = 8.02$; $\phi = 79.95°$ **11.** $r = 8.54$; $\phi = 290.56°$ **13.** $r = 9.05$; $\phi = 20.04°$ **15.** $r = 12.93$; $\phi = 140.65°$ **17.** $x_1 = +3.84$, $\phi_1 = 320.21°$; $x_2 = -3.84$, $\phi_2 = 219.79°$ **19.** $y_1 = +4.31$, $\phi_1 = 151.38°$; $y_2 = -4.31$, $\phi_2 = 208.62°$ **21.** $x_1 = +10.32$, $\phi_1 = 339.78°$; $x_2 = -10.32$, $\phi_2 = 200.22°$ **23.** $x_1 = +9.44$, $\phi_1 = 19.27°$; $x_2 = -9.44$, $\phi_2 = 160.73°$

Chapter 18

EXERCISE 1 (*page 456*): **1.** 0.64279 **3.** 0.99540 **5.** 0.91708 **7.** 0.08428 **9.** 0.00568 **11.** 19°25′; 160°35′ **13.** 46°45′; 133°15′ **15.** 86°36′; 93°24′

EXERCISE 2 (*page 459*): **3.** $a/\sin A = b$ **5.** $A = 28°05'$; $C = 106°15'$; $B = 45°40'$ **7.** $a = 7.3205$; $b = 5.1764$ **9.** $a = 1{,}000$; $b = 1{,}732.05$; $h = 866.03$ **11a.** $b = 66.913$ **11b.** $b = 17.365$ **13.** $a = 1.2007$; $c = 1.9355$; $B = 53°31'$ **15.** $a = 2.8438$; $c = 1.7307$; $B = 130°13'$ **17.** $a = 1.3670$; $c = 6.0563$; $B = 122°46'$ **19.** $a = 1.1165$; $b = 11.795$; $C = 90°46'$ **21.** $b = 4.9509$; $c = 2.9099$; $A = 104°30'$ **23.** $a = 11.080$; $b = 32.048$; $C = 128°12'$ **25.** $a = 1.2045$; $B = 86°55'$; $A = 44°44'$; $A' = 38°34'$; $B' = 93°05'$; $a' = 1.0669$ **27.** $c = 6.3591$; $B = 67°46'$; $C = 54°37'$; $c' = 1.3745$; $B' = 112°14'$; $C' = 10°09'$ **29.** $c = 3.418$; $B = 71°58'$; $C = 46°40'$; $c' = 0.8644$; $B' = 108°02'$; $C' = 10°36'$ **31.** $b = 2.0267$; $B = 32°51'$; $C = 84°38'$; $b' = 1.4067$; $B' = 22°07'$; $C' = 95°22'$ **33.** $b = 2.7276$; $c = 4.3829$; $A = 59°12'$ **35.** $b = 20.678$; $c = 12.131$; $B = 87°44'31''$ **37.** $a = 56.356$; $b = 188.79$; $C = 10°13'15''$ **39.** $c = 30.238$; $A = 82°54'$; $C = 11°56'05''$ **41.** $a = 23.305$; $A = 42°20'10''$; $C = 28°26'34''$ **43.** $b = 10.002$; $A = 60°38'51''$; $B = 30°25'06''$ **45.** $b = 6.1150$; $c = 10.132$; $C = 65°51'09''$ **47.** $b = 43.227$; $c = 24.339$; $B = 130°19'$ **49.** $a = 13.398$; $c = 29.090$; $B = 111°36'58''$ **51.** $b = 7{,}363.2$; $c = 6{,}152.9$; $A = 56°54'48''$ **53.** $a = 61.048$; $c = 54.981$; $A = 107°26.7'$ **55.** $b = 1{,}964.2$; $c = 2{,}272.1$; $C = 122°45.7'$ **57.** $b = 413.14$; $c = 615.36$; $B = 30°45'51''$ **59.** $b = 96.050$; $c = 74.784$; $A = 113°50.8'$

EXERCISE 3 (*page 466*): **9.** 7.1414 **11.** 16.894 **13.** 10.890 **15.** 33.734 **17.** 13.416 **19.** $A = 46°23'49''$; $B = 104°15'00''$; $C = 29°21'09''$ **21.** $A = 61°55'39''$; $B = 81°12'10''$; $C = 36°52'11''$ **23.** $A = 34°02'53''$; $B = 44°24'54''$; $C = 101°32'13''$ **25.** $A = 44°24'54''$; $B = 57°07'18''$; $C = 78°27'47''$ **27.** $A = 42°32'13''$; $B = 56°18'45''$; $C = 81°09'00''$ **29.** $B = 15°35'00''$; $A = 29°03'21''$; $C = 135°21'37''$

EXERCISE 4 (*page 468*): **1.** $b = 36.828$; $A = 41°50'$; $C = 27°26'$ **3.** $a = 3.1646$; $B = 12°51'47''$; $C = 18°28'13''$ (a was calculated with seven-place tables) **5.** $a = 29.776$; $B = 38°02'07''$; $C = 132°21'53''$ **7.** $a = 0.33528$; $B = 78°26'$; $C = 96°10'$ **9.** $a = 1.8278$; $B = 137°32'$; $C = 33°10'$ **11.** $a = 25.000$; $B = 115°27'$; $C = 53°08'$ **13.** $a = 132.37$; $B = 15°37'11''$; $C = 151°41'59''$ (seven-place tables) **15.** $a = 43.633$; $B = 126°52'11''$; $C = 30°30'37''$

EXERCISE 5 (*page 470*): **1.** 56°15.0′ **3.** 84°19.6′ **5.** 12°59.7′

EXERCISE 6 (*page 470*): **1.** 4.5827 in. **3.** 10.819 in. **5.** 30.201 in. **7.** 4.0578 in.

EXERCISE 7 (*page 473*): **1.** 803.02 **3.** 1,200.1 **5.** 4,853.5 **7.** 206,940 **9.** 72,477 **11.** 75.103 **13.** 4,064,600 **15.** 3,912,400

EXERCISE 8 (*page 476*):

	Radians	*Degrees*	*Revolutions*
1.		143.24	0.39789
3.	17.453_r		2.7778
5.	$2{,}513.3_r$	144,000	
7.		72,000	200.00
9.	5.4977_r		0.87500

EXERCISE 9 (*page 477*): **1.** 64 in. **3.** 0.48_r **5.** 22.9 in.

EXERCISE 10 (*page 478*): **1.** 48_r **3.** $90/\pi$ rev **5.** 7500_r **7.** 3.33 radians/sec **9.** 314 sec

EXERCISE 11 (*page 479*): **1.** 45 ft/sec **3.** 0.00833 ft **5.** 9420 in./sec **7.** 214.9 deg/sec

Chapter 19

EXERCISE 1 (*page 485*): **1.** Error in departure = 0.08 ft; Error in latitude = 0.28 ft **3.** S 29°44′37″E; 909.90 ft **5.** Error in departure = 0.02 ft; Error in latitude = 0.19 ft **7.** $CJ = 711.85$ ft; $BK = 864.59$ ft (some variation permissible because of choice of method)

EXERCISE 2 (*page 488*): **1.** 198,200 sq ft **3.** 30,640,000 sq ft

EXERCISE 3 (*page 492*): **1a.** a straight line **1b.** slope = 0.00029 **1c.** 0.0174 **3.** 647.56 ft **5.** 133⅓ ft

EXERCISE 4 (*page 493*): **5.** 146.25 ft **9.** 636.10 ft **11.** $da = 5{,}038.2$ yd; $ac = 4{,}543.0$ yd; $bc = 3{,}673.5$ yd

EXERCISE 5 (*page 498*): **1.** 8°03′56″ **3.** 0.9806 in. **5.** 24°49′56″ **7.** 43°55′10″ **9.** 1.1516 in. **11.** 02°59′32″ **13.** 1.0776 in. **15.** 25°22′11″ **17.** 4.996 in. **19.** 122°10′25″ **21.** 5.8742 in. **23.** 2.000 in. **25.** $x = 0.321$ in.; $y = 1.476$ in.

EXERCISE 6 (*page 504*): **5.** 33°51′16″ **7.** 28°02′49″ **9.** 17°29′43″ **11.** 55°28′54″

Chapter 20

EXERCISE 1 (*page 512*):

	X projection	*Y projection*
1.	−3	−20
3.	−19	−16
5.	+10	−10
7.	+5	+3
9.	+8	+6

EXERCISE 2 (*page 516*):

	X projection	*Y projection*
1a.	+2.67	+1.362
1c.	−8.66	+5.00
1e.	0.00	+7.00
1g.	+13.12	+7.27
1i.	−14.14	−14.14
1k.	−1.532	−1.286
1m.	0.00	−3.00
1o.	+4.33	+2.50

	ρ	ϕ
2a.	6.71	63.43°
2c.	2.83	135.00°
2e.	7.81	309.81°
2g.	3.61	213.69°
2i.	1.00	315.00°
2k.	8.49	315°

EXERCISE 3 (*page 522*):

	X projection	*Y projection*
1a.	−100	−400
1c.	+200	−600

	Magnitude of vector sum	*Reference angle*
2a.	325 ft	133°
2c.	333 ft	221°
2e.	232 ft	329°

	X projection	*Y projection*	r	ϕ
3a.	+6.3	−2.8	6.89	336.04°
3c.	−3.2	+15.8	16.12	101.45°
3e.	+6.0	−3.0	6.71	333.44°

	X projection	*Y projection*	ρ	ϕ
4a.	−11.73	+19.20	22.5	121.42°
4c.	0.00	+4.00	4.00	90.00°
4e.	−22.9	−6.43	23.8	195.70°
4g.	+1.589	−6.07	6.28	284.67°
4i.	0.00	+40.00	40.00	90.00°

EXERCISE 4 (*page 526*):

	X projection	*Y projection*	ρ	ϕ
1a.	−5	+1	5.10	168.69°
1c.	−35	−5	35.4	188.13°
1e.	+58	−62	84.9	313.09°
2a.	21.2	1.213	21.2	3.27°
2c.	−31.4	15.13	34.9	154.28°
2e.	37.4	62.1	72.5	58.92°
2g.	−300	100	316	161.57°
2i.	65.8	−38.0	76.0	330.00°

EXERCISE 5 (*page 527*): Vector quantities: 1, 2, 3, 5, 7; Scalar quantities: 4, 6, 8

EXERCISE 6 (*page 532*): **1.** $R = 821.90$; $\phi = 5°35'33''$ **3.** 40°32′09″; 32°21′34″ **5.** $F_1 = 44.425$; $F_2 = 422.67$ **7.** F to submerge = 19.966; F horizontal = 15.045
9. Length BC = 31.855 ft; Force in BC = 740.81 lb; Force in AB = 976.73 lb

Chapter 21

EXERCISE 1 (*page 536*): **1.** $-\sin x$ **3.** 1 **5.** 1 **7.** $\cos A$ **9.** $1 - \cos A$ **11.** 1 **13.** $2\cos^2 x$ **15.** $\sin x$ **17.** $\csc M$ **19.** $-\cos x$ **21.** $\cos x$ **23.** $1 + \sin x$ **25.** $\sec K$ **27.** $\cos x$ **29.** $\sin x + \cos x$ **31.** $1 + \sin x$ **33.** $\dfrac{\sin x \cos x (\sin x + \cos x)}{\cos x - \sin x}$ **35.** $1 - \sin x$ **37.** $\dfrac{1 - \sin x}{\cos x}$ **39.** $\cot x$ **41.** $\sin x$ **43.** $\csc x$ **45.** $\sec x$ **47.** 1 **49.** $\cot^2 A$ **51.** $\sec^2 \theta$ **53.** $\cot \phi$ **55.** 1 **57.** $\cot x$

EXERCISE 2 (*page 539*): All odd-numbered problems are identities except problems 7, 23, 25, 29, 35, and 39.

EXERCISE 3 (*page 550*): All odd-numbered problems from problem 1 through problem 25 are identities except problems 1, 3, 5, and 11.
33. $p = 85 - 30\cos 240\pi t - 50\cos 480\pi t - 5\cos 720\pi t$
37d. $x = 0.98992L + 0.2L\cos\theta + 0.010102L\cos 2\theta - 0.0000258L\cos 4\theta$
37e. $x = r\cos\theta + L\left(1 - \dfrac{r^2}{2L^2}\sin^2\theta\right) = 0.99L + 0.2L\cos\theta + 0.01L\cos 2\theta$

EXERCISE 4 (*page 557*): **1.** 45°, 135° **3.** 60°, 300° **5.** 150°, 330° **7.** 0°, 45°, 180°, 225° **9.** 90°, 210°, 270°, 330° **11.** 90°, 210°, 270°, 330° **13.** 0°, 60°, 180°, 240° **15.** 0°, 90°, 270° **17.** 60°, 120° **19.** 0°, 180° **21.** 30°, 150°, 270° **23.** 45°, 225° **25.** No solution **27.** 78.46°, 281.54° **29.** 35.25°, 144.75°, 215.25°, 324.75° **31b.** $N = 2\cos^{-1}\dfrac{r + a}{r + b}$, $r = \dfrac{[b\cos(N/2)] - a}{1 - \cos(N/2)}$ **33.** $\theta = 35.43°$
37. 0°, 0°45′, 7°30′, 22°05′, 32°08′, 40°39′, 48°46′

Chapter 22

EXERCISE 1 (*page 562*): **1.** +0.868; +3.830; +1.710; −4.698; −4.330

EXERCISE 2 (*page 564*): **1a.** 8.55 **1b.** 25.00 **1c.** 19.15 **1d.** 0 **1e.** −12.50 **1f.** −25.00 **1g.** −21.65 **1h.** 0 **5.** 25.39 **7.** 45.6°; 134.4°; 225.6°; 314.4° **9.** 40° **11.** 20°; 140°; 80°; 40°

EXERCISE 3 (*page 571*):

	Amplitude	*Frequency*	*Period*	*Angular Velocity* *radians/sec*	*deg/sec*	*Phase Constant* *radians*	*deg*
6a.	23	50	0.02	100π	18,000	$\pi/6$	30
6c.	77	40	0.025	80π	14,400	$2\pi/7$	51.43
6e.	15	6×10^7	1.67×10^{-8}	$1.2\pi \times 10^8$	216×10^8	$-3\pi/5$	-108
6g.	200	1	1.00	2π	360	$-2\pi/5$	-72

7a. $y = 200 \sin (60\pi t - 5\pi/18)$ **7c.** $y = 5 \sin (2\pi \times 10^{12} t + \pi/2)$
7e. $y = 10 \sin (2{,}000\pi t - \pi/4)$ **7g.** $y = 20 \sin 50\pi t$ **7i.** $y = 100 \sin (100\pi t + \pi/2)$

EXERCISE 4 (*page 575*): **1.** Amplitude = 87; Phase angle = +29.35° **3.** Amplitude = 7; Phase angle = +34.06° **5.** Amplitude = 12; Phase angle = −28.95°

Chapter 23

EXERCISE 2 (*page 586*):

	Magnitude	*Reference angle*
1.	5.00	53.13°
3.	7.62	113.20°
5.	5.00	306.87°
7.	5.83	210.96°
9.	2.83	135.00°
11.	2.83	225.00°

EXERCISE 3 (*page 588*): **1.** $10.00\underline{/53.13^\circ}$ **3.** $7.21\underline{/33.69^\circ}$ **5.** $5.83\underline{/120.96^\circ}$ **7.** $11.70\underline{/19.98^\circ}$ **9.** $10.63\underline{/131.19^\circ}$ **11.** $8.06\underline{/209.74^\circ}$ **13.** $5.10\underline{/258.69^\circ}$ **15.** $16.55\underline{/244.98^\circ}$ **17.** $15.81\underline{/288.44^\circ}$ **19.** $8.02 + j13.25$ **21.** $10.62 + j24.8$ **23.** $10.13 + j11.84$ **25.** $2.02 + j2.37$ **27.** $37.1 - j17.31$ **29.** $-10.72 - j3.19$

EXERCISE 4 (*page 591*): **1.** $1 + j8$; $8.06\underline{/82.88^\circ}$ **3.** $-5 + j$; $5.10\underline{/168.69^\circ}$ **5.** $3 + j0$; $3\underline{/0^\circ}$ **7.** $-4.28 + j4.32$; $6.03\underline{/134.71^\circ}$ **9.** $7.59 - j11.75$; $13.99\underline{/302.86^\circ}$

EXERCISE 5 (*page 594*): **1.** $6\underline{/350.00^\circ}$ **3.** $20\underline{/70^\circ}$ **5.** $24\underline{/139.00^\circ}$ **7.** $26.2\underline{/139.64^\circ}$ **9.** $28.2\underline{/96.12^\circ}$

EXERCISE 6 (*page 597*): **1.** $3\underline{/60^\circ}$ **3.** $2.50\underline{/320^\circ}$ **5.** $5\underline{/170^\circ}$ **7.** $2.86\underline{/347.91^\circ}$ **9.** $1.414\underline{/202.38^\circ}$ **11.** $4.24\underline{/126.27^\circ}$ **13.** $6.87\underline{/29.90^\circ}$ **15.** $8.78\underline{/32.73^\circ}$ **17.** $17.19\underline{/219.90^\circ}$

EXERCISE 7 (*page 600*): **1.** $26.2\underline{/139.64^\circ}$ **3.** $28.2\underline{/96.11^\circ}$ **5.** $-29 + j29$ **7.** $11 - j27$ **9.** $-41 + j$ **11.** $29 - j3$ **13.** $41 - j$ **15.** $-29 + j3$ **17.** $29 - j29$ **19.** $-11 + j27$

EXERCISE 8 (*page 604*): **1a.** $0.151 - j0.472$; $0.495\underline{/287.74^\circ}$ **1c.** $2.08 - j0.615$; $2.17\underline{/343.50^\circ}$ **3.** $0 + j0.667$; $0.667\underline{/90^\circ}$ **5.** $1.154 - j1.769$; $2.11\underline{/303.11^\circ}$ **7.** $0.533 + j0.400$; $0.667\underline{/36.87^\circ}$ **9.** $-2.08 - j0.385$; $2.11\underline{/190.49^\circ}$ **11.** $-0.533 - j0.400$; $0.667\underline{/216.91^\circ}$ **13.** $2.08 + j0.385$; $2.11\underline{/10.49^\circ}$ **15.** $0 - j0.667$; $0.667\underline{/270.00^\circ}$ **17.** $-1.154 + j1.769$; $2.11\underline{/123.11^\circ}$

EXERCISE 9 (*page 604*): **1.** $7.50 - j1.50$ **3.** $4.62 - j1.837$ **5.** $2.93 + j1.886$ **7.** $33.4 - j10.83$

EXERCISE 10 (*page 607*): **1.** $125\underline{/60^\circ}$ **3.** $16\underline{/240^\circ}$ **5.** $625\underline{/0^\circ}$

EXERCISE 11 (*page 610*): **1.** $2\underline{/10^\circ}$; $2\underline{/130^\circ}$; $2\underline{/250^\circ}$ **3.** $2\underline{/0^\circ}$; $2\underline{/180^\circ}$ **5.** $3\underline{/70^\circ}$; $3\underline{/160^\circ}$; $3\underline{/250^\circ}$; $3\underline{/340^\circ}$

EXERCISE 12 (*page 612*): **1.** 1; -1 **3.** 1; $(0.309 + j0.951)$; $(-0.809 + j0.588)$; $(-0.809 - j0.588)$; $(0.309 - j0.951)$

EXERCISE 13 (*page 613*): **1.** 3; $\left(-\frac{3}{2} + j\frac{3\sqrt{3}}{2}\right)$; $\left(-\frac{3}{2} - j\frac{3\sqrt{3}}{2}\right)$ **3.** $\left(\frac{3}{2} + j\frac{3\sqrt{3}}{2}\right)$; $\left(-\frac{3}{2} + j\frac{3\sqrt{3}}{2}\right)$; $(-3 + j0)$; $\left(-\frac{3}{2} - j\frac{3\sqrt{3}}{2}\right)$; $\left(\frac{3}{2} - j\frac{3\sqrt{3}}{2}\right)$; $(3 + j0)$

EXERCISE 14 (*page 614*):

	Amplitude	*Frequency*	*Period*	*Phase constant*
1.	10	60	0.0167	+60°
3.	10	60	0.0167	+60°
5.	25	400	0.0025	0

Chapter 24

EXERCISE 1 (*page 626*): **1.** 0.74 **3.** 3⅓ **5.** -1.14 **7.** $x = 1, y = 2.5$ **9.** $\Delta y = +0.0005$ **11.** -0.022

EXERCISE 2 (*page 632*): **1a.** 60 in lb **1b.** 30 lb

EXERCISE 4 (*page 640*): **1.** 22.34

EXERCISE 5 (*page 640*): **1.** 78 sq ft **3.** 8.9 sq ft/ft; 0.112 ft/sq ft **5.** 5.9 sq ft/ft **7.** 6.7 sq ft/ft **9.** 8.9 sq ft/ft **11.** 7.6 sq ft/ft **13.** 4.7 ft **15.** 45 sq ft **17.** 800 cu ft

EXERCISE 6 (*page 642*): **1.** -1.35 deg/min **3.** -2.0 deg/min **5.** 3.5 min **7.** -3.9 deg/min **9.** -3.7 deg/min **11.** -6.0 deg/min **13.** $-12.4°$ **15.** $-0.045°$ **17.** 15.6° **19.** 20.6° **21.** -4.07 deg/min **23.** 0.01 min

EXERCISE 7 (*page 643*): **1.** $-⅝$ lb/ft **3.** -0.4 lb/ft **5.** $-⅔$ lb/ft; $-⅗$ ft/lb **9.** -2.5 lb/ft **11.** -0.0112 lb

EXERCISE 8 (*page 648*): **3.** 100.5 ft/sec **5.** 10 by 10 in. **7.** 125′

EXERCISE 9 (*page 650*): **1.** 2,040 ft/sec^2 **3.** 100.5 ft/sec at 0.0625 sec **5.** 2 ft

EXERCISE 11 (*page 651*): **7.** $-2{,}820$ ft/sec **9.** 437 sec **11.** 75 ft/sec^2 **13.** 66 sec, 4,380 ft/sec **15.** 206 sec **17a.** 3,270 ft/sec **17b.** 3,880 ft/sec **17c.** -24 ft/sec^2 **17d.** 75 ft/sec^2 **17e.** 61,400 ft

Chapter 25

EXERCISE 1 (*page 656*): **1.** $\frac{\Delta y}{\Delta x} = 15x^2 + 15x(\Delta x) + 5(\Delta x)^2$ **3.** $\frac{\Delta y}{\Delta x} = 14x + 7(\Delta x)$

5. $\frac{\Delta w}{\Delta u} = 2u + \Delta u - 3$ **7.** $\frac{\Delta w}{\Delta z} = \frac{2z^2 + 2z(\Delta z) + 1}{z(z + \Delta z)}$ **9.** $\frac{\Delta w}{\Delta x} = \frac{1}{\sqrt{x + \Delta x} + \sqrt{x}}$

11. $\frac{\Delta V}{\Delta R} = \frac{4}{3}\pi[3R^2 + 3R(\Delta R) + (\Delta R)^2]$

EXERCISE 2 (*page 661*): **1.** 0 **3.** +1.6 **5.** −6 **7.** +2 **9.** No single limit

EXERCISE 3 (*page 665*):

1. *Number of pamphlets*	*Total cost*	*Cost per pamphlet*
10	\$10.50	\$1.05
100	\$15.00	\$0.15
1,000	\$60.00	\$0.06
10,000	\$510.00	\$0.051
100,000	\$5,010.00	\$0.0501
1,000,000	\$50,010.00	\$0.05001

1c. \$0.05 **3.** $15x^2$ **5.** $3x^2 - 2$ **7.** $-3/u^2$ **9.** $3/(t+3)^2$

EXERCISE 4 (*page 671*): **1.** $y' = 6x$ **3.** $y' = 90x^8$ **5.** $y' = -\dfrac{6}{x^3}$ **7.** $y' = \dfrac{8\sqrt[3]{x^2}}{x}$ **9.** $y' = -\dfrac{14}{x^2}$ **11.** $y' = \dfrac{3\sqrt{x}}{x}$ **13.** $y' = \dfrac{4\sqrt{x}}{x^2}$ **15.** $y' = \dfrac{2.5\sqrt[4]{x}}{x}$ **17.** $y' = \dfrac{4a}{b}x^3$ **19.** $y' = -\dfrac{3\sqrt[4]{x}}{2x^2}$ **21.** $y' = \dfrac{-3\sqrt[4]{x}}{2\sqrt[4]{7}\,x^2}$ **23.** $y' = 0$ **27.** $5\sqrt{\pi}$ sq ft/ft; $\dfrac{1}{5\sqrt{\pi}}$ ft/sq ft **29.** $\dfrac{15\pi}{8}$ sq ft/ft **31.** $1\frac{5}{4}\sqrt{\pi}$ sq ft/ft **33.** $5\sqrt{\pi}$ sq ft/ft **35.** $3\pi/2$ sq ft/ft **37.** $a = 2.5\pi h - 25\pi$ **41.** −3.6 lb/ft **43.** −2.5 ft/lb **45.** $2\sqrt{5}$ lb

EXERCISE 5 (*page 677*): **1.** $2ax + b$ **3.** $12x - 13$ **5.** $\dfrac{15x-4}{6x^3}$ **7.** $\dfrac{n-1}{n\sqrt[n]{x}}$ **9.** $-\dfrac{12}{x^5}$ **11.** $-\dfrac{104}{x^5}$ **13.** $-\dfrac{3k}{x^4}$ **15.** $15x^4$ **17.** $2\pi x$ **19.** $\dfrac{3e - 2\pi x}{x^4}$ **21.** 16 ft-lb/sec **23.** 10.6 ft **25.** $a = 4$; $b = -2$

EXERCISE 6 (*page 681*): **1.** $8(3x+1)(3x^2+2x+5)^3$ **3.** $\dfrac{3-10x}{3(3x-5x^2)^{2/3}}$ **5.** $\dfrac{-7t}{2(6-7t^2)^{3/4}}$ **7.** $\dfrac{-3t}{(1-t^2)^{7/4}}$ **9.** $\dfrac{\sqrt{2}}{2t^{1/2}} + \dfrac{2}{3t^{2/3}}$ **11.** $\dfrac{8y}{3\sqrt[3]{1+y^2}}$ **13.** $\dfrac{12x^2}{(1-x^3)^2}$ **15.** $\dfrac{4t^2(3-t^2)}{(5t^3-t^5)^{4/5}}$ **17.** $\dfrac{dy}{dx} = -\dfrac{10}{(x+3)^2}, -\dfrac{10}{9} = -1.1$

EXERCISE 7 (*page 685*): **1.** $\dfrac{2x^2+3}{\sqrt{3+x^2}}$ **3.** $(x+5)(3x^2-7)^2(33x^3+135x^2-14)$ **5.** $-\dfrac{14(x+5)}{(x-2)^3}$ **7.** $-\dfrac{2x^4+x^2+5}{x^2(2x^2+5)^2}$ **9.** $-\dfrac{18}{(4x^2-9)^{3/2}}$

EXERCISE 8 (*page 693*): **1.** $x = -4$ (max), $x = +1$ (min) **3.** $x = 3$ (min), $x = -3$ (max) **5.** $x = -2$(min) **7.** $x = \frac{3}{2}$ (max), $x = -\frac{3}{2}$ (max) **11.** 5 in. **13.** $d = (5B/2A)^{1/7}$ **15c2.** 949 articles/day **17.** $\frac{5}{3}$ by $\frac{5}{3}$ in. **19.** 3 checks; 80 cents **21.** 38.65 ft **23.** $r = 3.325$ in.; $h = 6.651$ in. **25.** 1 to 1 **27.** 125′ **29.** $p_2/p_1 = (2/k+1)^{k/(k-1)}$; 0.528 **31.** 7.16 ft

EXERCISE 9 (*page 703*): **1.** $4x^3 \cos x^4$ **3.** $4(\sin^3 x)\cos x$ **5.** $-\frac{9}{2}\phi^{-1/4}\cos\phi^{3/4}$ **7.** $\dfrac{25\cos x}{2\sqrt{\sin x}}$ **9.** $-\dfrac{\sqrt{3}}{3}\phi^{-2/3}\sin\sqrt[3]{\phi}$ **11.** $\dfrac{6}{\phi^2}\sin\dfrac{2}{\phi}$ **13.** $-\left(1+\dfrac{1}{x^2}\right)\sin\left(x-\dfrac{1}{x}\right)$

15. $4 \tan^3 x \sec^2 x$ **17.** $\left(1 - \frac{1}{x^2}\right) \sec^2 \left(x + \frac{1}{x}\right)$ **19.** $-\frac{\csc^2 \sqrt{\theta}}{2\sqrt{\theta}}$

21. $\frac{25 \sin x \sqrt{\cos x}}{2 \cos^2 x}$ **23.** $\frac{3 \sin \sqrt{x}}{2\sqrt{x} \cos^2 \sqrt{x}}$ **25.** $-\frac{12 \cos (3\phi + 2)}{\sin^2 (3\phi + 2)}$ **27.** 19.6 lb

29a. The equation has physical meaning only between $t = 0$ and $t = \frac{1}{8}$ sec.
29b. One revolution takes ⅛ sec.

EXERCISE 10 (*page 708*): **1.** $\frac{3}{\sqrt{9 - x^2}}$ **3.** $-\frac{5x^4}{\sqrt{1 - x^{10}}}$ **5.** $\frac{2}{\sqrt{16y - 15 - 4y^2}}$

EXERCISE 11 (*page 709*): **1.** $1/x$ **3.** $5/x$ **5.** $3/x$ **7.** $150/x$

EXERCISE 12 (*page 711*): **1.** $\frac{2x}{x^2 + 2}$ **3.** $\frac{8x}{x^2 + 3}$ **5.** $\frac{1}{3x - 4}$ **7.** $\frac{0.8686x}{x^2 - 4}$ **9.** $\frac{0.4343x}{9 - x^2}$

11. $\frac{0.8686}{2x - 3}$ **13.** $\frac{6x^2}{x^3 - 8} [\ln (x^3 - 8)]$ **15.** $0.4343 \cot (\theta + \pi)$

EXERCISE 13 (*page 713*): **1.** $10xe^{5x^2}$ **3.** e^{x+8} **5.** $-\frac{e^{\sqrt{1-x}}}{2\sqrt{1 - x}}$ **7a.** -1.35 deg/min

7c. -2.0 deg/min **7e.** 3.47 min **7g.** -3.9 deg/min **7i.** -3.64 deg/min
7k. -6 deg/min **9a.** 200 amp/sec **9c.** 0.05 sec

EXERCISE 14 (*page 717*): **1.** $a^x \ln a$ **3.** $\frac{2^{\sqrt{x}-1}}{\sqrt{x}} \ln 2$ **11.** $x \cdot 3^x(2 + x \ln x)$ **15.** $-\frac{2(1 + x^3)}{(x^3 - 2)^2}$

17. $\frac{x^2(9 - 2x^5)}{(x^5 + 3)^2}$ **19.** $\frac{e^x(3 + x)}{(4 + x)^2}$ **21.** $\frac{e^{2x}(1 + 4x)}{2\sqrt{x}}$ **23.** $x^{\sin x}\left(\frac{\sin x}{x} + \ln x \cos x\right)$

3. $3 \cos 6\theta$ **5.** $\ln x - 2x + 1$

9. $10e^{3x^2} \tan x(3x \tan x + \sec^2 x)$

$\frac{3(2x^2 + 1) \sin^2 (7x^3 + 5)}{2\sqrt{2x^3 + 3x}}$

$\frac{\text{n} \sqrt{x} + \cos \sqrt{x}}{2x\sqrt{x}}$ **17.** $\frac{\cos x - 2 \sin x}{e^{2x}}$

$- (2x + 6)$ **23.** $\frac{x \sin 8x - 8x^2 - 24}{2\sqrt{x^2 + 3} \sin^2 4x}$

$- 9 \cos 3x$ **27.** $\frac{20 - 100x}{(x + 0.2)^3}$

$\frac{8x - 80}{+ 0.8)^2}$

$x)(\cos 5x)$ **5.** $\frac{1}{x^2(a + bx)}$ **7.** $\frac{x^3}{(x^2 + a^2)^{3/2}}$

$\sin x) + 2e^{2x}$ **13.** $-\frac{4}{(e^x - e^{-x})^2}$ **15.** $\frac{10}{(1 - x)^3}$

. $(16 - x^2)^{-3/2}$ **23.** $\frac{1}{x\sqrt{8x - 2x^2}}$ **25.** $\cos^2 x$

x

g **3.** 4; (−); decreasing **5.** 2.5; (−); decreasing
9. None (max); 3.85 (min)

EXERCISE 18 (*page 725*):

Problem	Max at:	Min at:	Point of inflection at:	Slope of primary curve at inflection point
1.	none	none	none	none
3.	$x = 0$	$x = +4$	$x = +2$	-12
5.	none	$x = 0.434$	none	none
7.	none	none	$x = +\sqrt[4]{3}$	$+3.51$
			$x = -\sqrt[4]{3}$	-3.51
9.	$x = 0$	$x = \pi/2$	$x = \pi/4$	-2
	$x = \pi$		$x = (3\pi)/4$	$+2$
11.	$\theta = \pi/2$	$\theta = 0$	$\theta = \pi/4$	$+3/4$
	$\theta = (3\pi)/2$	$\theta = \pi$	$\theta = 3\pi/4$	$-3/4$
		$\theta = 2\pi$	$\theta = 5\pi/4$	$+3/4$
			$\theta = 7\pi/4$	$-3/4$
13.	none	none	none	none
15.	none	$x = 1$	none	none
17.	$x = 1.47_r$	$x = 4.61_r$	2.94_r	-0.75
			6.08_r	$+0.52$

EXERCISE 19 (*page 725*): **1.** $v = 72 - 32t;\ a = -32$ **3.** $t = 4$ sec **5.** $t = 5.26$ in.; $s = 8.51$ in. **7.** 8.49 by 16.98 ft **9.** $V = wL/2 - wx$ **11.** 7.07 ft **13.** $\eta = \dfrac{E}{E + 2\sqrt{P_0R}}$ when $P_0 = I^2R$ **15.** 4.33 in. **17.** 66° approx

19d.

ωt	dx/dt exact	dx/dt approx	d^2x/dt^2 exact	d^2x/dt^2 approx
0	0	0	0.30	0.30
$\pi/4$	0.40406	0.40355	0.17730	0.17678
$\pi/2$	0.5	0.5	-0.0510	-0.0500
π	0	0	-0.20	-0.20

19e. Max force $= 0.30m$

EXERCISE 20 (*page 733*): **3.** $\dfrac{dy}{dx} = -\dfrac{5x}{3y}$ **5.** $\dfrac{dy}{dx} = \dfrac{15}{2y}$ **7.** $\dfrac{dy}{dx} = \dfrac{3x^2}{1 - 6y}$ **9.** $\dfrac{x^4(1 - y^5)}{y^4(x^5 - 1)}$

EXERCISE 21 (*page 734*): **1.** $-6\frac{2}{3}$ ft/min **3.** -4.734 ft/sec **5.** $dy/dt = -x$ **7.** $2.4kD^2$ **9.** -12.7 lbs/(sq ft)(sec)

EXERCISE 22 (*page 736*): **1.** 0.068″ **3.** 3.02 cu in. **7.** $dQ = 0.1b + 60c$ **11.** 0.056 ohms **13.** 0.263″

EXERCISE 23 (*page 740*): **1.** $\dfrac{dx}{x^2\sqrt{1 - 9/x^2}}$ **3.** $\sqrt{a + bx}\,dx$ **5.** $-\dfrac{x\,dx}{(a + bx)^3}$ **7.** $\dfrac{dx}{x^3\sqrt{x^2 - a^2}}$

9a. $dv = \dfrac{bv^3 - v^4}{pv^3 - av + ab}\,dp$

EXERCISE 24 (*page 743*): **1.** 1.562 **3.** 1.732 **5.** 1.924 **7.** 5.357 **9.** 1.338 **11.** 4.635 **13.** 2400° K **15.** 0.1758

Chapter 26

EXERCISE 1 (*page 750*): **9.** $\frac{x^4}{4} - 2x^3 + 250x^2 + 7x + C$ **11.** $\frac{5}{6}x^{3/2} + C$ **13.** $x^3 + x\sqrt{2} + C$ **15.** $-\frac{1}{4}x^{-4} + C$ **17.** $\pi x + \frac{7}{4}x^{12/7} + C$ **19.** $x^2 + C$ **21.** $\frac{1}{2}x^2 + C$ **23.** $-2x + C$ **25.** $\frac{3}{4}x^{4/3} + C$ **27.** $6\sqrt{x} + C$

EXERCISE 2 (*page 753*): **1.** $y = x^2 + 4$ **3.** $y = \frac{1}{2}x^2 + 12$ **5.** $y = -2x + 28$ **7.** $y = \frac{3}{4}x^{4/3} + 15.24$ **9.** $y = 6\sqrt{x} + 8$ **11.** $-0.49''$ **13.** The total energy is constant.

EXERCISE 3 (*page 755*): **1.** $-\frac{1}{5}(3 - t)^5 + C$ **3.** $-\frac{2}{3}(4 - m)^{3/2} + C$ **5.** $-\frac{1}{24}(3 - t^4)^6 + C$ **7.** $\sqrt{t^2 + 2t} + C$ **9.** $\frac{3}{4}(4x^2 - 9)^{5/2} + C$

EXERCISE 4 (*page 757*): **1.** 200 sec **3.** -51.6 ft/sec², 1.70 sec **5.** $s = 0.008t^3 - 0.4t^2 + 10t$

EXERCISE 5 (*page 764*): **1.** $h = -16t^2 + h_0$; $v = -32t$ **3.** $h = -16t^2 + 100t + 192$; $v = -32t + 100$ **5.** -149.6 in both cases **7.** 8 sec

EXERCISE 6 (*page 775*): **1.** 78 **3.** 36 **5.** 7.5 **7.** $65\frac{1}{3}$

EXERCISE 7 (*page 779*): **1.** $\bar{y} = 13$ **3.** $\bar{y} = 6$ **5.** $\bar{y} = 2.5$

EXERCISE 8 (*page 788*): **1.** $\frac{1}{3}$ **3.** 8 **5.** $20\frac{5}{6}$ **7.** $20\frac{5}{6}$ **9.** $41\frac{2}{3}$

EXERCISE 9 (*page 797*): **1.** $\frac{32{,}000\pi}{3}$ cu in. **3.** 20.8 cu in. **5.** $5{,}333\frac{1}{3}$ cu in. **7.** 2,044 cu in.

EXERCISE 10 (*page 800*): **1.** 625π **3.** 500π **5.** 48π

EXERCISE 11 (*page 803*): **1.** 108 in.-lb **3.** 96 in.-lb **5.** 1.64 ft-lb **7.** 43,750 ft-lb **9.** $450{,}000\pi$ ft-lb **11.** $54{,}000\pi$ ft-lb **15.** 186,500 ft-lb

EXERCISE 12 (*page 807*): **1.** 1,302 lb **3.** 41,250 lb; 11 ft higher **5.** 38,229 lb

EXERCISE 13 (*page 807*): **1.** 8.72 ft-lb **3c.** $Q = 2E\left(\frac{CT}{\pi R}\right)^{1/2}$; $W = EQ$ **5.** $A = 0.000187t^2 + 0.251t + 182$ **7.** 1,750 calories; 1,591 calories

EXERCISE 14 (*page 810*): **1.** 1.386 **3.** 3.128 **5.** 1.160 **7.** 1.086 **9.** 10.4 **11.** 3,550 ft-lb **13.** 2,330 ft-lb **15.** 13.5 ft/sec; 4,733 ft

EXERCISE 15 (*page 814*): **1.** $2 \sin 2\theta + C$ **3.** $\frac{1}{2} \sin x^2 + C$ **5.** $-\sin (4 - x) + C$

EXERCISE 16 (*page 815*): **1a.** 0.268; 1.023 **1c.** 0.1038; 0.346 **1e.** 0.841; 0.841 **1g.** 1; 0.955 **3.** 216.5 watts **5.** $\frac{2}{\pi}\left(I_1 + \frac{I_3}{3} + \frac{I_5}{5} + \cdots + \frac{I_k}{k}\right)$; $0.707(I_1^2 + I_3^2 + I_5^2 + \cdots + I_k^2)^{1/2}$ **7.** $\overline{P} = 0.5(E_1I_1 + E_3I_3 + E_5I_5 + \cdots + E_kI_k)$ **9.** $\frac{EI\pi^4 y_0^2}{64L^3}$

EXERCISE 17 (*page 820*): **1.** $-\frac{1}{4}e^{1-4x} + C$ **3.** $\frac{e^{\pi x}}{\pi} + C$ **5.** $-\frac{e^{1/x}}{5} + C$ **7.** $\frac{e^{3x+1}}{3} + C$
9. $\frac{e^{2x}}{2} + 2e^{-x} - \frac{e^{-4x}}{4} + C$ **11.** $\frac{e^{6x}}{6} - \frac{2e^{3x-1}}{3} + \frac{x}{e^2} + C$
13. $\frac{e^{4x}}{4} - \frac{4e^{5x/2}}{5} + e^x + C$ **15.** $\frac{y_{n0} - Y_{n-1}}{EL}(e^{EL} - 1) + Y_{n-1}$
17. $\theta(x) = 0.819e^{-14.627x} + 0.106e^{-82.22x} + 0.0190e^{-212x} + 0.0559$ **19.** 17.1°

EXERCISE 18 (*page 831*): **1.** 88.86 **3.** 0.03475 **5.** 9.620 **7.** 1.047 **9.** 4,981 **11.** 1.822 **13.** 42.30 **15.** 0.6467 **17.** 221.6 **19.** 0.5592 **21.** 88.86 **23.** 6.359; 5.823; 6.043 **25.** 3,822.9 lb